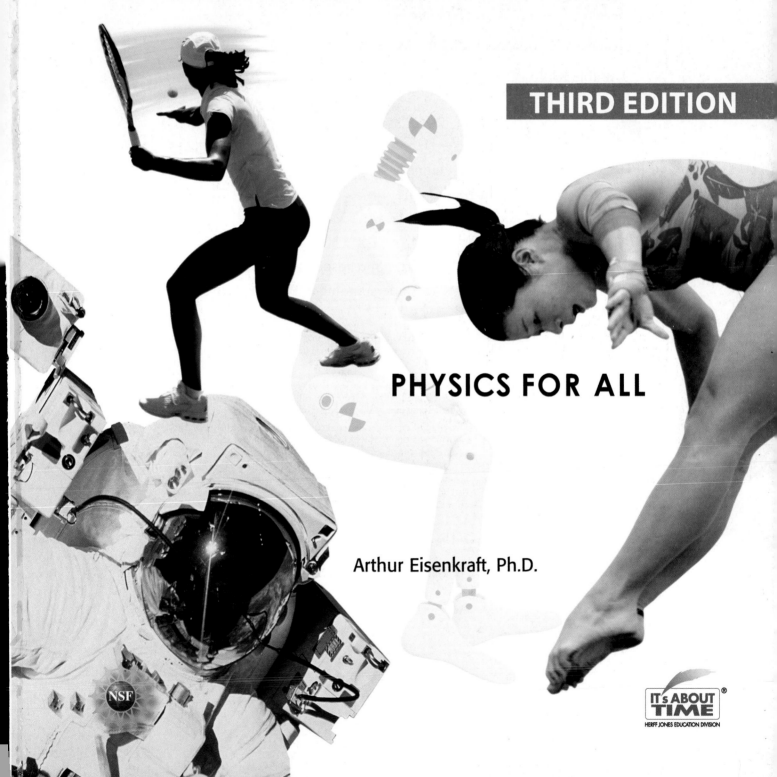

ACTIVE

PHYSICS®

A PROJECT-BASED INQUIRY APPROACH

THIRD EDITION

PHYSICS FOR ALL

Arthur Eisenkraft, Ph.D.

NSF

IT's ABOUT TIME®
HERFF JONES EDUCATION DIVISION

84 Business Park Drive, Armonk, NY 10504
Phone (914) 273-2233 Fax (914) 273-2227
www.its-about-time.com

Program Components

Student Edition

Teacher Edition – Three-Volume Set

Teacher's Resources – Blackline Masters

Durable Kits

Consumable Kits

Multimedia

— Student Edition Online

— Teacher's Edition Online

— Color Overheads and Blackline Masters CD

— Test Generator CD

— Content Videos and Excel Spreadsheets

— Constructing Physics Understanding (CPU) for *Active Physics*

Printed and bound in the United States of America.

ISBN 978-1-60720-000-0

1 2 3 4 5 VH 13 12 11 10 09

This project was supported, in part, by the
National Science Foundation under Grant No. 0352516.
Opinions expressed are those of the authors and not necessarily
those of the National Science Foundation.

Acknowledgments

Project Director

Dr. Arthur Eisenkraft has taught high school physics for over 28 years. He is currently the Distinguished Professor of Science Education at the University of Massachusetts, Boston, where he is also an Adjunct Professor of Physics and the Director of the Center of Science and Math In Context (COSMIC). Dr. Eisenkraft is the author of numerous science and educational publications and holds a patent for a Laser Vision Testing System, which tests visual acuity for spatial frequency.

Dr. Eisenkraft has been recognized with numerous awards, including: Presidential Award for Excellence in Science Teaching, 1986 from President Ronald Reagan; American Association of Physics Teachers (AAPT); Distinguished Service Citation for "excellent contributions to the teaching of physics," 1989; Science Teacher of the Year, Disney American Teacher Awards, 1991; Honorary Doctorate of Science, Rensselaer Polytechnic Institute, New York, 1993; AAPT Excellence in Pre-College Teaching Award, 1999; National Science Teachers Association (NSTA) Distinguished Service Award to Science Education, 2005 and recipient of the Robert A. Millikan Medal for "notable and creative contributions in physics education," 2009.

In 1999, Dr. Eisenkraft was elected to a three-year cycle as the President-Elect, President, and Retiring President of the NSTA, the world's largest organization of science teachers. He has served on numerous committees of the National Academy of Sciences, including the content committee that has helped author the National Science Education Standards, and in 2003 he was elected a fellow of the American Association for the Advancement of Science (AAAS). Dr. Eisenkraft has been involved with a number of projects and chaired many notable competitions, including the Toshiba/NSTA ExploraVisions Awards (1991 to present), which he co-created; the Toyota TAPESTRY Grants (1990 to 2005); and the Duracell/NSTA Scholarship Competition (1984 to 2000). In 1993, he served as Executive Director for the XXIV International Physics Olympiad after being Academic Director for the United States Team for six years.

Dr. Eisenkraft is a frequent presenter and keynote speaker at national conventions. He has published over 100 articles and presented over 200 papers and workshops. *Quantoons*, written with L. Kirkpatrick and featuring illustrations by Tomas Bunk, led to an art exhibition at the New York Hall of Science.

Dr. Eisenkraft has been featured in articles in *The New York Times, Education Week, Physics Today, Scientific American, The American Journal of Physics*, and *The Physics Teacher*. He has testified before the United States Congress, appeared on NBC's *The Today Show*, National Public Radio, and many other radio and television broadcasts, including serving as the science consultant to ESPN's *Sports Figures*.

Acknowledgments — Active Physics Team

Active Physics, Third Edition

was developed by a team of leading physicists, university educators, and classroom teachers with financial support from the National Science Foundation.

NSF Program Officer

Gerhard Salinger
National Science Foundation
Arlington, VA

Principal Investigators

Arthur Eisenkraft
University of Massachusetts
Boston, MA

Barbara Zahm
It's About Time
Herff Jones Education Division
Armonk, NY

Project Coordinator

Gary Hickernell
It's About Time
Herff Jones Education Division
Armonk, NY

Field Test Coordinator

George Amann
Rhinebeck, NY

Writers

Peter Collings
Swarthmore College
Swarthmore, PA

Ron DeFronzo
East Bay Educational Collaborative
Warren, RI

Robert Hilborn
University of Texas at Dallas
Richardson, TX

Ramon Lopez
University of Texas at Arlington
Arlington, TX

Dwight Neuenschwander
Southern Nazarene University
Bethany, OK

John Rowe
Cincinnati Public Schools
Cincinnati, OH

Sue Vincent
Turner Falls H.S.
Montague, NH

Bruce Williamson
Delaware Valley Friends School
Paoli, PA

Board of Advisors

Marilyn Decker
Boston Public Schools
Boston, MA

Michael Lach
Chicago Public Schools
Chicago, IL

Jim Nelson
AAPT
Gainesville, FL

John Roeder
The Calhoun School
New York, NY

Frederick Stein (deceased)
American Physical Society
Dillon, CO

Acknowledgments — Active Physics Team

James Stith
American Institute of Physics
Mitchellville, MD

Clara Tolbert
Urban Strategic Initiative (retired)
Philadelphia, PA

Consultants

George Amann
Rhinebeck, NY

Matthew Anthes-Washburn
East High School
Denver, CO

Scott Bartholomew
Parkway Academy of Technology
and Health
West Roxbury, MA

Pat Callahan
Catasauqua H.S.
Center Valley, PA

Gary Curts
Dublin Jerome H.S.
Dublin, OH

John Hubisz
North Carolina State University
Apex, NC

Elena Kaczorowski
Bedford H.S.
Bedford, NY

Ernest Kuehl
Lawrence H.S.
Cedarhurst, NY

John Koser
University of St. Thomas
St. Paul, MN

Desiree Phillips
Learning Specialist
Somerville, MA

Mary Quinlan
Radnor H.S.
Radnor, PA

Patricia Rourke
Educational Consultant
Alexandria, VA

Larry Weathers
The Bromfield School
Harvard, MA

Shari Weaver
Boston Public Schools
Dorchester, MA

David Wright
Tidewater Community College
Norfolk, VA

Evaluation Team

Frances Lawrenz
University of Minnesota
Minneapolis, MN

Nathan Wood
North Dakota State University
Fargo, ND

Safety Reviewer

George Amann
Rhinebeck, NY

Field Test Teachers

Andrea Anderson
Athens H.S.
The Plains, OH

Matthew Anthes-Washburn
East High School
Denver, CO

Joel Aquino
Splendora H.S.
Splendora, TX

Scott Bartholomew
Parkway Academy of Technology
and Health
West Roxbury, MA

Jeff Briggs
Commodore Perry H.S.
Hadley, PA

Pat Callahan
Delaware Valley H.S.
Frenchtown, NJ

Debra Cayea
Briarcliff H.S.
Briarcliff Manor, NY

Robin Chisholm
International School of Indiana
Indianapolis, IN

Kenneth Dugan
Deep Creek H.S.
Chesapeake, VA

Darrin Ellsworth
Fillmore C.H.S.
Harmony, MN

Pete Flores
Harlandale H.S.
San Antonio, TX

Jane Frye
Carter Co. H.S.
Ekalaka, MT

Tracey Greeley-Adams
Woodward Career Technical H.S.
Cincinnati, OH

Michelle Greenlee
Lauderdale County C.S.
Florence, AL

Stephanie Harmon
Rockcastle Co. H.S.
Mt. Vernon, KY

Karl Hendrickson
McGill-Toolen Catholic H.S.
Mobile, AL

LaTeise Jones
Bardstown H.S.
Bardstown, KY

Danielle Joslin
Fond du Lac H.S.
Fond du Lac, WI

Dolores Keeley
Forest Hills Eastern H.S.
Ada, MI

Mark Klawiter
Deerfield H.S.
Deerfield, WI

Jim Kyte
Urbandale H.S.
Urbandale, IA

Kathy Lucas
Casey County H.S.
Liberty, KY

Jennifer Lynch
Taft Middle School
Oklahoma City, OK

Keith Magni
Boston Community Leadership
Academy
Brighton, MA

Robert Malcolm
Greater Johnstown H.S.
Johnstown, PA

Janie Martin
Southwest H.S.
San Antonio, TX

Maryl McCrary
Thomas-Fay-Custer H.S.
Thomas, OK

Frederick Meshna
The Bromfield School
Harvard, MA

Kathy Naughton
West Delaware H.S.
Manchester, IA

Alan Nauretz
Shell Lake H.S.
Shell Lake, WI

Fred Nelson
Manhattan H.S.
Manhattan, KS

Vivian O'Brien
Plymouth Regional H.S.
Plymouth, NH

Steve Oszust
Gateway School for
Environmental Resource and
Technology
Stevenson H.S.
Bronx, NY

Jane Pollack
The Rayen School
Youngstown, OH

Marcia Powell
West Delaware H.S.
Manchester, IA

James Prosser
Fond du Lac H.S.
Fond du Lac, WI

Pamela Pulliam
Charleston Catholic H.S.
Charleston, WV

Randolph Reed
St. Albans H.S.
St. Albans, WV

Kristie Reighard
Bowling Green H.S.
Bowling Green, OH

Becky Reynolds
Sonoraville H.S.
Calhoun, GA

Milly Rixey
St. Margaret's School
Tappahannock, VA

Joan Salow
West Delaware H.S.
Manchester, IA

Judy Scheffler
Poth Jr. H.S.
Poth, TX

John Scholtz
Haverford H.S.
Havertown, PA

Paul Shafer
Mirta Ramirez Computer Science
Charter School
Chicago, IL

Katheryn Shannon
Highland West Jr. H.S.
Moore, OK

Sushma Sharma
School of Entrepreneurship at
Southshore
Chicago, IL

Chip Sheffield, Jr.
Robert E. Lee H.S.
Jacksonville, FL

Sandy Shutey
Butte H.S.
Butte, MT

Amy Stewart
Sonoraville H.S.
Calhoun, GA

Cheryl Schwartzwelder
Northpoint H.S. for Science,
Technology, and Industry
Pomfret, MD

Carla Taylor
Callisburg H.S.
Gainsville, TX

John Tracey
High Point Regional H.S.
Sussex, NJ

Jeff Voss
West Delaware H.S.
Manchester, IA

Elizabeth Walker
North Cobb H.S.
Kennesaw, GA

John Whitsett
Fond du Lac H.S.
Fond du Lac, WI

Donna Wolz
Cross County H.S.
Cherry Valley, AR

Daniel Wood
Tombstone H.S.
Tombstone, AZ

Active Physics, First and Second Editions

were developed in association with the American Association of Physics Teachers (AAPT) and the American Institute of Physics (AIP).

Primary and Contributing Authors

Richard Berg
Howard Brody
Chris Chiaverina
Ron DeFronzo
Ruta Demery
Carl Duzen
Jon L. Harkness
Ruth Howes
Douglas A. Johnson
Ernest Kuehl
Robert L. Lehrman
Salvatore Levy
Tom Liao
Charles Payne
Mary Quinlan
Harry Rheam
Bob Ritter
John Roeder
John J. Rusch
Patty Rourke
Ceanne Tzimopoulos
Larry Weathers
David Wright

Consultants

Peter Brancazio
Robert Capen
Carole Escobar
Earl Graf
Jack Hehn
Donald F. Kirwan
Gayle Kirwan
James La Porte
Charles Misner
Robert F. Neff
Ingrid Novodvorsky
John Robson
Mark Sanders
Brian Schwartz
Bruce Seiger
Clifford Swartz
Barbara Tinker
Robert E. Tinker

Joyce Weiskopf
Donna Willis

Safety Reviewer

Gregory Puskar

Equity Reviewer

Leo Edwards

Physics at Work

Alex Strauss
Mekea Hurwitz

First Printing Reviewer

John L. Hubisz

Unit Reviewers

Robert Adams
George A. Amann
Patrick Callahan
Beverly Cannon
Barbara Chauvin
Elizabeth Chesick
Chris Chiaverina
Andria Erzberger
Elizabeth Farrell Ramseyer
Mary Gromko
Thomas Guetzloff
Jon L. Harkness
Dawn Harman
James Hill
Bob Kearny
Claudia Khourey-Bowers
Steve Kliewer
Ernest Kuehl
Jane Nelson
Mary Quinlan
John Roeder
Patty Rourke
Gerhard Salinger
Irene Slater

Pilot Test Teachers

John Agosta
Donald Campbell
John Carlson
Veanna Crawford
Janie Edmonds
Eddie Edwards
Arthur Eisenkraft
Tom Ford
Bill Franklin
Roger Goerke
Tom Gordon

Ariel Hepp
John Herrman
Linda Hodges
Ernest Kuehl
Fran Leary
Harold Lefcourt
Cherie Lehman
Kathy Malone
Bill Metzler
Elizabeth Farrell Ramseyer
Daniel Repogle
Evelyn Restivo
Doug Rich
John Roeder
Tom Senior
John Thayer
Carol-Ann Tripp
Yvette Van Hise
Jan Haarvick
Sandra Walton
Larry Wood

Field Test Coordinator

Marilyn Decker

Field Test Workshop Staff

John Carlson
Marilyn Decker
Arthur Eisenkraft
Douglas Johnson
John Koser
Mary Quinlan
Elizabeth Farrell Ramseyer
John Roeder

Field Test Evaluators

Susan Baker-Cohen
Susan Cloutier
George Hein
Judith Kelley

Field Test Teachers

Rob Adams
Benjamin Allen
Robert Applebaum
Joe Arnett
Bix Baker
Debra Beightol
Patrick Callahan
George Coker
Janice Costabile
Stanley Crum

Russel Davison
Christine K. Deyo
Jim Doller
Jessica Downing
Douglas Fackelman
Rick Forrest
Mark Freeman
Jonathan Gillis
Karen Gruner
Larry Harrison
Alan Haught
Steven Iona
Phil Jowell
Deborah Knight
Thomas Kobilarcik
Sheila Kolb
Todd Lindsay
Malinda Mann
Steve Martin
Nancy McGrory
David Morton
Charles Muller
Fred Muller
Vivian O'Brien
Robin Parkinson
Donald Perry
Francis Poodry
John Potts
Doug Rich
John Roeder
Consuelo Rogers
Lee Rossmaessler
John Rowe
Rebecca Bonner Sanders
David Schilpp
Eric Shackelford
Robert Sorensen
Teresa Stalions
Roberta Tanner
Anthony Umelo
Judy Vondruska
Deborah Waldron
Ken Wester
Susan Willis

Contents

Contents

Contents

Active Physics

Dear Student Scientists,

Imagine meeting someone who never heard of your favorite movie or music group! Now imagine how enriched they would be if they could enjoy that movie or music the way you do.

Active Physics came about as a result of a similar frustration. The usual physics course is focused on so much math and so much reading that many students miss the beauty, the excitement, and the usefulness of physics. Many more students simply refuse to take the course. *Active Physics* began when a group of physicists and physics teachers wondered how to pass on their enjoyment of physics to high school students.

Physics should be experienced and make sense to you. Each chapter of *Active Physics* begins with a challenge—develop a sport that can be played on the Moon; design a roller coaster for a target audience; persuade your parents to lend you the family car; and so on. These are tough challenges, but you will learn the physics that will allow you to be successful at every one.

Part of your education is to learn to trust yourself and to question others. When someone tells you something, can they answer your questions: "How do you know?, Why should I believe you?, and Why should I care?" After *Active Physics*, when you describe why seat belts are important, or why sports can be played on the Moon, or why wind (or falling water) is able to generate electricity and someone asks, "How do you know?" your answer will be, "I know because I did an experiment."

Only a small number of high school students study physics. You are already a part of this select group. Physics awaits your discovery.
Enjoy the journey.

Arthur Eisenkraft

Welcome to Active Physics — Your Guide to Success

Physics is involved in every aspect of your life – from the way your body works to the things you like to do. *Active Physics* makes learning physics relevant, fun, and exciting! Here is how you are going to learn about physics in this book.

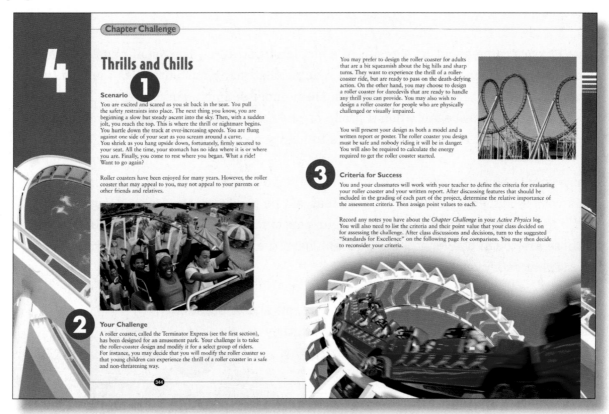

❶ Scenario

Each chapter begins with an event or situation that places physics in the context of a familiar everyday experience. Chances are that you can relate to each of these scenarios, but never thought about the physics involved! The topics involve things of interest to you and range from entertainment to driving and from sports to assisting people in developing nations.

❷ Your Challenge

Each chapter gives you a challenge that will be your group's responsibility for the next month or so. Physics knowledge, application, and synthesis will be necessary for the successful completion of this project. However, physics content alone is not sufficient for success. Each challenge will require imagination and creativity. Your group's challenge project will be unique and will reflect the interests and talents of the members of your group.

❸ Criteria for Success

Before you begin your *Chapter Challenge*, you will be part of an important decision-making process. You and your class will decide what constitutes an excellent project. Your teacher will help guide you through your decisions. The rubric you create will ensure that everybody knows what is required to meet the needs of the challenge and how many points each component will

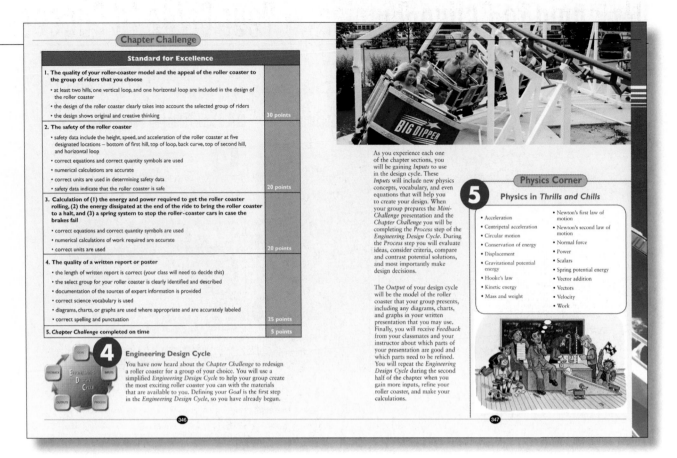

be worth. After you have developed a rubric, you can take a look at the *Standard for Excellence* chart that is provided. It is worthwhile to compare your rubric with this chart.

❹ Engineering Design Cycle

The *Chapter Challenge* is a problem that you need to solve. There are many different ways to solve problems. One sequence of steps that can be used to solve problems is called the *Engineering Design Cycle*. This cycle helps to remind you that when completing a project you have to be aware of the *Goals*. You then gather information (*Inputs*) and put this together through a design cycle. Once you have completed your work (*Output*), take a step back and provide *Feedback* for yourself and your group. You may also get feedback from other groups in your class. You are going to use a simplified *Engineering Design Cycle* as you address your challenge. You will apply it after getting halfway through the chapter.

The *Mini-Challenge* will prepare you for the requirements of the *Chapter Challenge*. It is a good way to step back and review the work done so far. At the end of the chapter, you get to use *Feedback* from the *Mini-Challenge* as well as new information to complete the *Chapter Challenge*.

❺ Physics Corner

As you enjoy learning the content necessary to develop a light and sound show, design and build an improved safety device for a car, or become a sports broadcaster, you and your teacher will be impressed by how much physics content you are learning. The *Physics Corner* previews all the physics concepts that the chapter will present. You will be actively involved and your teacher will help you keep track of all the physics concepts that you are learning.

Your Guide to Success

Section 4   Ohm's Law: Putting up a Resistance

6 What Do You See?

7 What Do You Think?

Lighting makes some rooms conducive to work and other rooms more relaxing.

- What determines the brightness of a light bulb?
- What determines how much current flows in a circuit?

Record your ideas about these questions in your *Active Physics* log. Be prepared to discuss your responses with your small group and the class.

8 Investigate

Imagine a "black box," a box that you cannot see inside. Inside the box is a resistor. In this *Investigate*, you will determine the contents of the black box electrically by measuring the voltage across and the current through the resistor inside.

1. In order to predict what is in the black box, you first will have to complete an investigation of three different resistors, a 5-Ω (ohm), a 10-Ω, and a 15-Ω resistor.

   You will need to set up a simple circuit with a resistor, a voltmeter, and an ammeter, as shown in the diagram on the next page. By varying the voltage of the battery, you can learn how the current of the circuit and the voltage across a resistor changes.

623

Active Physics

Learning Outcomes

In this section, you will

- **Calculate** the resistance of an unknown resistor given the voltage drop and current.
- **Construct** a series circuit.
- **Use** a voltmeter and ammeter in a series circuit accurately.
- **Express** the relationship between voltage and current for a resistor that obeys [Ohm's] law in a graph.

---

6 What Do You See?

A picture is worth a thousand words. At the beginning of each section, a cartoon is shown to get you thinking about physics. Discussing what you see in the cartoon will help you reflect on what you already know about the topics in the section. This is an important step in the learning process. Tomas Bunk, a well-known illustrator of *MAD* magazine, *Quantoons*, and *Garbage Pail Kids*, created the cartoons.

7 What Do You Think?

The *What Do You Think?* question gives you a chance to explore what you already know or think you know. This is sometimes called *eliciting prior understandings*. Your answers will help you become engaged and set the stage for the section. Don't worry about being "right" or "wrong." Answering the questions as well as you can is another important step in the learning process.

8 Investigate

Everyone learns better by doing rather than by watching. You can watch someone knitting a sweater for weeks, but you won't learn to knit if you never handle the knitting needles yourself. You can watch professional athletes play basketball, but you know that you won't ever play ball like they can, unless you practice, practice, and practice. Research says that you should explore a concept in a section before your teacher tries to explain it verbally. In *Active Physics*, the *Investigate* section is your opportunity to explore the world of physics.

9 Physics Talk

NEWTON'S FIRST LAW OF MOTION

Galileo's Law of Inertia

In the *Investigate*, you observed, measured, and compared the release height of a ball on one side of the track to the recovered height on the other side of the track. You found that they were not exactly equal, but they were close to being equal.

Galileo Galilei (1564–1642) was an Italian physicist, mathematician, astronomer, and philosopher. Galileo is sometimes called the father of modern science. He introduced experimental science to the world. Galileo performed an experiment similar to the one you just completed. He observed that a ball that rolled down one ramp seemed to seek the same height when it rolled up another ramp.

Galileo also did a "thought experiment" in which he imagined a ball made of extremely hard material set into motion on a horizontal, smooth surface, similar to the final track in your investigation. He concluded that the ball would continue its motion on the horizontal surface with constant speed along a straight line "to the horizon" (forever).

From this, and from his observation that an object at rest remains at rest unless something causes it to move, Galileo formed the law of **inertia**: Inertia is the natural tendency of an object to remain at rest or to remain moving with constant speed in a straight line.

Galileo changed the way in which people viewed motion. Early on, people thought that all moving objects would stop. After Galileo, people thought about how moving objects might continue to move forever unless a **force**, a push or a pull, stopped them. That idea is not easy to understand. Any time you have pushed an object to move it, you have seen it stop. Nobody ever observes an object moving forever. Even when the surface is very, very smooth, the sliding or rolling objects eventually stop. However, Galileo realized that objects do not stop "on their own" but stop because there is a frictional force working that you cannot see and that is the force that stops the object.

Newton's First Law of Motion

Like Galileo, Isaac Newton was a great thinker. He was born in England in 1642, the year of Galileo's death. Newton's achievements brought him a great deal of recognition. Poems were written that honored Newton. Science, government, and philosophy all changed because of Newton's insights about the physics of the world.

Newton used Galileo's law of inertia as the basis for developing his **(Newton's) first law of motion**: In the absence of an unbalanced force, an object at rest remains at rest, and an object already in motion remains in motion with constant speed in a straight-line path.

Galileo Galilei was a pioneer in the use of precise, quantitative experiments. He insisted on using mathematics to analyze the results of his experiments.

Physics Words

inertia: the natural tendency of an object to remain at rest or to remain moving with constant speed in a straight line.

force: a push or a pull.

Newton's first law of motion: in the absence of an unbalanced force, an object at rest remains at rest, and an object already in motion remains in motion with constant speed in a straight-line path.

134

Active Physics

Science Skills — These concepts are introduced on a need-to-know basis. Metric prefixes, SI units and symbols, dimensional analysis, and so on are explained when you need to use these skills.

Strategy: You can use the equation for acceleration.

Given: $\Delta v = 20$ m/s (20 m/s – 0 m/s)

$\Delta t = 10$ s (10 s – 0 s)

Solution: $a = \dfrac{\Delta v}{\Delta t}$

$= \dfrac{20 \ \frac{m}{s}}{10 \ s}$

$= 2 \ \dfrac{m/s}{s}$

The horse accelerated at a rate of two meters per second every second. That is, its speed changed at a rate of + 2 m/s for every second it was moving along the path.

Suppose the horse then came to a stop. In the language of physics, the horse is accelerating! Remember, acceleration is any change in speed or direction. The acceleration can be positive or negative.

Units for Acceleration

To calculate acceleration, you divide change in speed by change in time $\Delta v/\Delta t$. The units for acceleration are then, by definition, speed divided by time. The units for acceleration may be (m/s)/s or (km/h)/s.

When writing acceleration in meters per second per second, the final units are often simplified. For example, the following all mean the same thing.

$$1 \ \frac{m}{s} \cdot \frac{1}{s}, \ 1 \ \frac{m/s}{s}, \text{ or } 1 \ (m/s)/s = 1 \ \frac{m}{s^2} \text{ or } 1 \ m/s^2$$

The units are read as meter per second squared.

Checking Up

1. Describe the pattern of dots on a ticker tape for each of the following situations:
   a) constant speed
   b) positive acceleration
   c) negative acceleration

2. An athlete runs 400 m in 50 s. What is the runner's average speed?

3. What is the difference between instantaneous speed and average speed?

4. A vehicle accelerates from 0 km/h to 100 km/h in 10 s. What is its average acceleration?

151

Active Physics

Physics Words — Concepts are often more efficiently communicated when vocabulary is introduced. *Physics Words* highlights the important terms you want to know. They are also briefly explained for you to make reading and comprehension easier.

---

9 Physics Talk

The *Physics Talk* will help you make better sense of the investigation you have just completed. It will introduce you to the scientific way of explaining concepts. It will provide illustrations, charts, and mathematical equations to help guide your understanding. The *Physics Talk* is chock-full of physics content.

Checking Up — These questions are great tools for evaluating your understanding of the concepts that you have learned.

Your Guide to Success

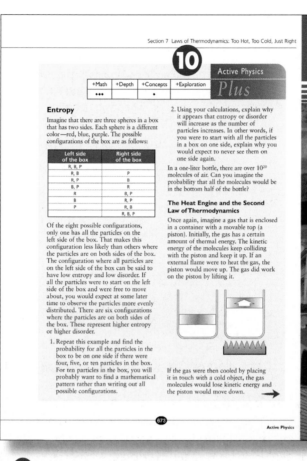

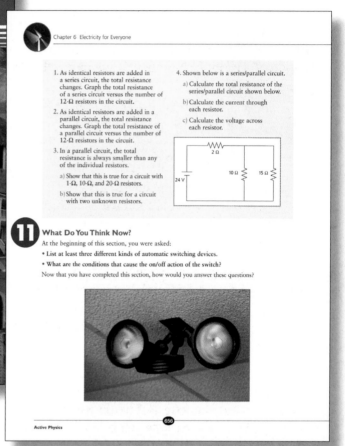

⑩ Active Physics Plus

Active Physics Plus is an opportunity to explore physics in additional ways. It may include more math, increased depth, additional concepts, or another investigation. *Active Physics Plus* can be considered optional topics for some students in some schools. For others, your teacher may require you to complete an *Active Physics Plus*. Your teacher is familiar with your state requirements and can guide you to appropriate personal challenges so that all students extend their knowledge and skills.

Each *Active Physics Plus* component will be noted with a grid, informing you which extension categories will be covered. The diamond notation (◆) indicates the level of intensity (three diamonds being the highest level).

⑪ What Do You Think Now?

At the beginning of each section, you were asked to think about one or two questions. At that point, you were not expected to come up with the "physics" answer. Now that you have completed the section, you will be asked to think about these questions again. Compare your initial answers to the answers you give at the end of the section.

⑫ Physics Essential Questions

As a student physicist, you join the physics community by recognizing and understanding the organizing principles of physics. You also need to focus on the essential questions of all scientific endeavors.

- What does it mean?
- How do you know?
- Why do you believe?
- Why should you care?

The first essential question is **What does it mean?** Answering this question will help you articulate one of the physics concepts that you investigated in each section.

The second essential question is **How do you know?** You will answer this question by describing the experimental evidence that you have gathered from your investigations. You "know" because you have done an experiment.

There are different facets of interpretation to the third essential question **Why do you believe?** One of the reasons you believe things in physics is because it connects with other physics content. Physics content is often grouped into a few large ways of seeing the world. Another reason you believe in the physics is because it fits with other Big Ideas of science. These Big Ideas are often referred to as organizing principles. The third reason you believe in the new physics content and concepts is because it is supported by experiments, data, math, or can be used to explain unrelated phenomena. The **Why do you believe?** question will help you better understand the nature of science, the philosophy of science, and the organizing principles of science. Rather than having an isolated chapter entitled "What Is Science," *Active Physics* has you confront the essence of physics throughout the course with each new topic and each new explanation.

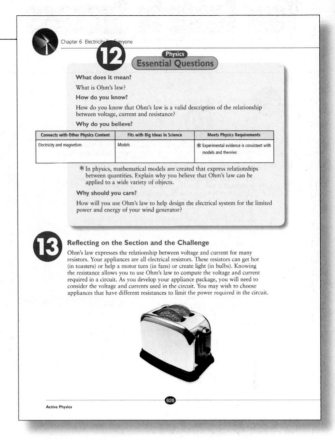

People learn better when the concepts being taught are relevant to their lives. The fourth essential question, **Why should you care?** asks you to explain how the present section relates to the *Chapter Challenge* and how you can use the content of the section in your group's project.

⑬ Reflecting on the Section and the Challenge

Research has shown that real learning takes place when people transfer their knowledge to a new domain. The physics content of each section is another puzzle piece that you can put in place to create your *Chapter Challenge* project. *Reflecting on the Section and the Challenge* provides guidance on how to transfer the knowledge and move forward on your project.

Your Guide to Success

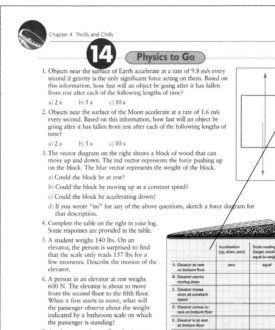

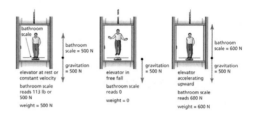

Preparing for the Chapter Challenge — This feature helps you organize and synthesize the knowledge you have mastered from the investigations in the chapter. It also serves as a guide to get another aspect of the *Chapter Challenge* completed.

⑭ Physics to Go

Often given as homework assignments, *Physics to Go* is another opportunity for you to elaborate on the physics content of the section. These are excellent study guide questions that help you to review and check your understanding.

⑮ Inquiring Further

Active Physics embraces inquiry as a way of learning. You are always involved in inquiry during the *Investigate* section. You have another opportunity for open inquiry when you are asked to inquire further. *Inquiring Further* often requires you to design your own experiment and, with teacher approval, to continue to enhance your learning. *Inquiring Further* also provides more challenging in-depth problems, questions, and exercises for extra credit.

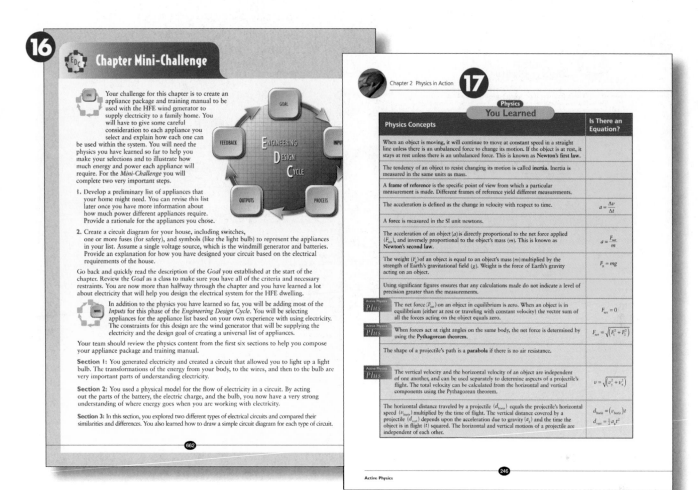

16 Chapter Mini-Challenge

When engineers design a product, they follow an *Engineering Design Cycle* with several distinct steps. The *Mini-Challenge* takes you through a first step of this cycle. As part of this process, the *Mini-Challenge* will encourage you to give your *Chapter Challenge* a first try. In this way, you are actually involved in the *Engineering Design Cycle* and not just reading about it. As you make your "product" for your *Chapter Challenge*, you will become increasingly aware of the many benefits of using the *Engineering Design Cycle*.

17 Physics You Learned

To complete your *Chapter Challenge*, you will need to use the physics principles you learned as you completed each section. For each chapter, you should review what you have learned and how you can use these concepts in your challenge. The *Physics You Learned* section lists many of the physics principles you investigated in the chapter. You can use this as a checklist to develop your own list. You may have heard it said that math is the language of nature. Physicists, in describing any phenomenon, ask themselves, "Is there an equation?" As student physicists, you will also need to ask this question. In *Physics You Learned*, you will be reminded of the equations used in this chapter.

Your Guide to Success

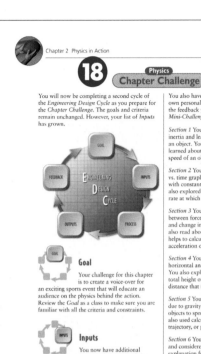

18 Physics Chapter Challenge

Business leaders want to hire people who know how to work effectively in groups and how to complete projects. The *Chapter Challenge* provides guidance on how to begin your work on the *Chapter Challenge* project, set deadlines, meet all the requirements, and combine the contributions of all members of the group. This section guides you without restricting you. Your group's creativity and imagination will be a major factor in your enjoyment and success. The best projects will reflect the diverse interests, backgrounds, and cultures of your group members. Once again, you will visit the *Engineering Design Cycle* as a way to help organize your work.

19 Physics Connections to Other Sciences

The fundamental ideas you have studied in this chapter are also basic to many other sciences that you will study in the future. Appreciating the connections among science disciplines helps scientists achieve a richer understanding of nature. Science research in the twenty-first century depends heavily upon the way these different disciplines interact, with disciplines such as biophysics and geophysics becoming major areas of study.

Physics At Work

Dr. Linda Shore

Director of the Teacher Institute at the Exploratorium; San Francisco, CA

Dr. Linda Shore was intrigued by science growing up, and thought that one day she could turn her intrigue into a career. "I grew up watching Carl Sagan's television show, *Cosmos: A Personal Voyage*, and remember being fascinated by his ability to translate science and make it exciting," said Shore.

She earned her masters degree in physics from San Francisco State University and her doctorate in Science Education at Boston University. When she returned to San Francisco in 1993, she joined the Exploratorium, an interactive science and art museum, founded in 1969 by famed physicist and educator Dr. Frank Oppenheimer.

Dr. Shore wants to dispel the myth that the Exploratorium is merely a science museum. "That is just the tip of the iceberg." The museum houses teacher-education programs, exhibits for sale and for rent, along with over 700 hands-on exhibits.

As the director of the Teacher Institute, Dr. Shore fills her days helping science teachers teach better, assisting with a Web cast or the design of an exhibit, and traveling to other museums to design teacher programs. "Every day is a little bit of a surprise," she said.

But Dr. Shore said that the biggest surprise about her job is how much it still teaches her about science. "My job is to translate science to the public, teachers, and students, which is similar to receiving interesting homework assignments; I never know what the questions are going to be."

Roger Barrett

Exhibit Designer; Science Museum of Minnesota, Minneapolis, MN

Roger Barrett has been an exhibit designer for five years at the Science Museum of Minnesota, known for its traveling exhibit program, its innovative interactive exhibits, and their Exhibits-for-Sale program.

Recent exhibits that Barrett has been involved in are Robots, Race, BioMusic, Water, the Science of Fear, and Nanotechnology. During the fabrication portion of the project, Barrett will work with a scientist or Curator to develop exhibit content. Barrett also is involved in choosing building materials, which is not an easy decision. "Durability is a factor, as well as aesthetics, cost, ease of construction and green materials," said Barrett.

Patricia Rayner

Physical Science Teacher and Inventor of the All American Atom; Bethel, CT

Patricia Rayner has been teaching science for over 25 years, but it was early on in her career when she discovered that students learn better through hands-on activities. It was then that she developed the "All American Atom" that allows students to learn about the atom by making a model of it.

"Model-making is very important," says Patricia. "You can feel it, touch it, and see it to understand it, and it uses the creative part of the brain." Her students use the kit she developed, which involves building a plastic, three-dimensional nucleus with atoms spinning inside.

897

Active Physics

Physics Practice Test

Before you try the Physics Practice Test, you may want to review sections 1-7, where you will find 29 Checking Up questions, 7 What Do You Think Now? questions, 28 Physics Essential Questions, 77 Physics to Go questions, and 11 Inquiring Further questions.

Content Review

1. A cart is rolling along a frictionless, horizontal surface. Which of the following describes the motion of the cart as it continues to roll along the surface?
   a) The cart will slow down as it runs out of the forward force.
   b) The cart will continue to roll with constant speed.
   c) The cart will continue to roll with constant speed only if it is rolling downhill.
   d) The cart will slow down as it uses up its speed.

2. Which object has the most inertia?
   a) a 0.001-kg bumblebee traveling at 2 m/s
   b) a 0.1-kg baseball traveling at 20 m/s
   c) a 5-kg bowling ball traveling at 3 m/s
   d) a 10-kg tricycle at rest

3. An athlete walks with a piece of ticker tape attached to herself with the tape timer running, and produces the tape shown below.

   beginning

   According to the tape, she was traveling with
   a) constant velocity.
   b) positive acceleration.
   c) negative acceleration.
   d) constant velocity, then negative acceleration.

4. A track coach with a meter stick and a stopwatch is trying to determine if a student is walking with constant speed. He should
   a) measure the walker's speed at regular intervals to see if it is always the same.
   b) measure the total distance the student travels and the total time to get the average speed.
   c) measure the beginning and ending speeds only to see if they are the same.
   d) use the meter stick to measure the student's stride length and time how long it takes to take one step.

5. If a cart is traveling with uniform negative acceleration, what conclusions can be drawn about the forces acting on the cart?
   a) The cart must be frictionless.
   b) The cart must be rolling downhill.
   c) The cart must have a net unbalanced force acting on it.
   d) No force is needed; the cart will naturally slow down.

6. A student wants to set up an experiment to determine the effect of a net force on an object's acceleration. To do this, she should
   a) vary the force acting on the object and the mass of the object at the same time.
   b) vary the mass of the object, but not the force acting on the object.
   c) vary the force acting on the object, but not the object's mass.
   d) keep both the force acting on the mass and the mass of the object constant as it rolls along a horizontal surface.

7. A 2-kg block is dropped from the roof of a tall building at the same time a 6-kg ball is thrown horizontally from the same height. Which statement best describes the motion of the block and the motion of the ball? (Disregard air resistance.)
   a) The 2-kg block hits the ground first because it has no horizontal velocity.
   b) The 6-kg ball hits the ground first because it has more mass.
   c) The 6-kg ball hits the ground first because it is round.
   d) The block and the ball hit the ground at the same time because they have the same vertical acceleration.

252

Active Physics

㉑ Physics at Work

The projects that you complete for the *Chapter Challenges* are often the actual jobs of real people. *Physics at Work* introduces you to people who use the physics of the chapter as part of their career. Reading about their lives may get you thinking about careers that interest you and help you make a difference in the world.

㉑ Physics Practice Test

You have been checking up on your own understanding of the physics concepts throughout each chapter. You have been asking yourself all sorts of questions as you complete the investigations and other parts of each section. High achievers learn to check for understanding and to recognize when they have to do a bit more work to fully understand something. The *Physics Practice Test* is a way in which you can find out how well you have learned the physics in this chapter. Before taking the *Physics Practice Test*, it makes sense to review each section's *Checking Up*, *Physics to Go*, *What Do You Think Now?*, and *Physics Essential Questions*. Reviewing the cartoons and illustrations of the investigations in the chapter may help you to remember all that you have learned.

How to Use Your Active Physics Log

Scientists must keep a record of all of their work. The scientist's notebook is a legal document that can be used as evidence in court to determine the time, description, and breadth of a discovery. As student scientists, you will be keeping an *Active Physics* log. This log or notebook will be a record of all that you learn and accomplish as well as a way to organize all your notes, lab investigations, homework, and conversations.

At the end of the first few months of school, what will your excellent student log look like? It will have each page numbered. The first few pages will be a table of Contents where you will list each chapter and each section of each chapter as you go along. The sections will all be in order (for example, *Section 1* will be followed by *Section 2*, which will be followed by *Section 3*, and so on). Your *Active Physics* log will have a complete record of all of your work including notes, lab procedures, data, graphs, and homework. For example, your teacher will be able to review your progress by turning to the table of Contents, finding the page for *Section 6* of a chapter and all the work for that section will be on those pages. Some of that work will be written in the log while other work will be glued into the log. It will be a log that brings you pride and respect.

How will you create such a log?

Scientists usually have a bound notebook. This insures that pages are not added to or removed from the log as can easily be done in a loose-leaf binder. Your first step in getting your bound or spiral notebook ready for use as a log is to number all the pages in the upper right-hand corner. The first page has a "1" and the back of the first page has a "2." It won't take long.

If your notebook has 150 pages, this will probably take between 150 and 300 seconds. That amounts to at most 5 minutes. If you get tired, you can number the first 50 pages now and number the rest later.

The second step is to write your name on the cover of the log and/or on the inside front cover. The third step is to write at the top of page 1, "Contents." You should begin your notes on page 5. This will allow you to use pages 1 to 4 as a table of contents for the entire book.

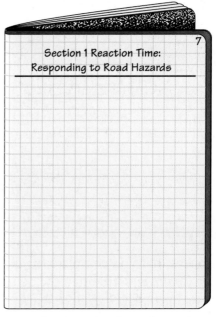

When you begin your first chapter, you should write at the top of page 5 the name of the chapter. For example, if you start with *Chapter 1*, you would write *"Chapter 1: Driving the Roads."* As you begin the chapter, you will record notes about the *Chapter Challenge*. When it is time to begin *Section 1*, you should begin a new page. Every time you start a new section, you should begin a new page.

Everything goes into this log. If you complete a homework that your teacher collects, the returned homework should be glued into the log. If your log has pages made of graph paper, you can make graphs directly in the log. If you use sheets of graph paper to make graphs, these sheets of paper will be glued into the log. If your teacher collects some homework, you must remember to skip a page or two to glue that homework into your log when it is returned. In this way, the homework assignments from *Section 4* will be with *Section 4*, even if it is not returned after you have begun *Section 5* or even *Section 6*. Because some of these items may be an entire page, you may fold them in half and glue them into the log sideways.

What do I do if I am absent from school?

Contents

Chapter 1: Driving the Roads

If you miss a day of school, you should find out from one of the members of your group how many pages should be left blank in your log for the work that took place while you were absent. When you do make up that work, you can place it in the appropriate place. This works whether your teacher asks you to make up the work or to get the notes and information from someone else on in your group.

Each time you complete a section, you create a link in the table of Contents. On the left side of the new line, you may write *Section 3*. On the right-hand side of the line, you record the page on which the beginning of all of the information for *Section 3* is located. Because you begin each section on a new page, this will make it easier to locate each section for a given chapter.

When you begin a new chapter, place the name of the chapter in your notebook and record the page reference for that chapter in the table of Contents. Skip a line between the end of one chapter and the beginning of a new chapter. The chapter title may also be written in capital letters or underlined in the table of contents to help with readability.

That should do it. The most difficult part will be remembering to skip pages for work that is to be returned or work that you will make up. Another difficult part will be keeping the table of Contents up to date. Try to remind yourself of these potential pitfalls.

If you have a question about your log or its format, ask your group members. If everyone seems confused, ask your teacher. With care and commitment, you will create a high-quality log.

Scientists keep logs. You, as a student scientist, will keep one as well.

Chapter Challenge

The challenge for this chapter is to demonstrate your knowledge of the physics of driving by making a presentation to a board of driving instructors. The instructors will evaluate your knowledge in both an oral and written presentation on the physics of braking distances, friction and curves, safe following distances, and yellow-light intersections.

Section Summaries	Physics Principles

Section 1 Reaction Time: Responding to Road Hazards

Using various reaction timers, students explore the time it takes them to react to a situation. This section introduces students to the process of first beginning with their own ideas and predictions, then implementing an investigation that results in both qualitative and quantitative data.

Reaction time

Section 2 Measurement: Errors, Accuracy, and Precision

Students count the number of strides it takes them to cover a selected distance in an area away from traffic. Students measure the length of their stride using a meter stick and calculate the entire distance by multiplying the total number of strides with the length of each stride. The measurements are then compared by each group. By comparing measurements students arrive at an understanding of error and the different kinds of errors present in a measurement.

Errors in measurement
Accuracy
Precision

Section 3 Average Speed: Following Distance and Models of Motion

Strobe or multiple-exposure photos of a moving vehicle are used to illustrate speed and acceleration. Students then use a motion detector to measure their walking speed and obtain a computer-generated graph of their motion. Information about speed and velocity is then connected to reaction distance with a discussion on tailgating.

Average speed
Instantaneous speed
Velocity
Reaction distance

Section 4 Graphing Motion: Distance, Velocity, and Acceleration

Students use sloped tracks to investigate the speed and distance an automobile travels before stopping. They then examine data on time and distance required to stop a vehicle moving at various speeds. This is connected to the total time required to react to a hazard, apply force to the brake, and slow the motion of the vehicle to a complete stop.

Acceleration
Positive acceleration
Negative acceleration
Vector quantity

Section 5 Negative Acceleration: Braking Your Automobile

The students investigate the relationship between an automobile's speed and the distance required to bring it to a stop. Students draw graphs to study the change in velocity with respect to time. The concept of negative acceleration is explored in this context.

Negative acceleration
Braking distance

Section 6 Using Models: Intersections with a Yellow Light

Using a spreadsheet model of an intersection, students explore how reaction time, speed, and stopping distance affect what they should do at a yellow light. This also introduces them to how transportation engineers use a computer simulation to model various factors affecting decisions about speed limits and traffic-light cycles. Students now have the opportunity to apply their understanding of reaction time, distance vs. velocity, and braking distance to identify the STOP, GO, and Dilemma Zones at intersections when they see a yellow light.

Speed
Negative acceleration
Distance vs. time relationships

Section 7 Centripetal Force: Driving on Curves

Students' perceptions and prior learning about the force needed to change the direction of a moving object are challenged in this section. After performing investigations, they reflect on the discrepancy between their perceptions and observed results. Students then read for more information on how forces change the direction of motion.

Force
Centripetal force
Centripetal acceleration

Chapter Challenge

The challenge for this section is to develop a 2–3 minute voice-over for a sports clip explaining the physics involved in the sport. The voice-over should be entertaining, as well as explain how a number of physics principles determine what is occurring during the sport. In addition, a written script will be submitted.

Section Summaries	Physics Principles
Section 1 Newton's First Law: A Running Start Students release a ball to roll down and then up the sides of a track. They first record its starting height and then the recovered height. From this, they are introduced to the concept of inertia.	Inertia and mass, Newton's first law of motion, Force, Velocity and speed, Acceleration, Frames of reference
Section 2 Constant Speed and Acceleration: Measuring Motion A timer and paper tape are used to record the motion of various objects. Distance, time, instantaneous and average velocities, and accelerations are calculated from the data.	Instantaneous speed Average speed Positive acceleration Negative acceleration
Section 3 Newton's Second Law: Push or Pull Students calibrate and use a simple force meter to explore the variables involved in the acceleration of an object. They then connect their observations and data to a study of Newton's second law of motion.	Newton's second law of motion Weight Free-body diagram Gravitational attraction between masses
Section 4 Projectile Motion: Launching Things into the Air Students explore the motion of objects that are projected in a gravitational field. Differences between objects being dropped, launched horizontally, and launched at an angle are explored in relation to the landing position of objects dropped straight down to those with projected motion.	Gravity, Independence of right-angle components, Trajectory of a projectile
Section 5 The Range of Projectiles: The Shot Put Students compare mathematical and physical models of projectile motion to that of a shot put. They apply this to describe the vertical and horizontal motion of the projected object and predict its trajectory.	Acceleration due to gravity, Range of a projectile, Mathematical versus physical models
Section 6 Newton's Third Law: Run and Jump Thinking about the direction in which they apply force to move in a desired way introduces students to the concept that every force has an equal and opposite force. They test this concept and then apply it to a variety of motions observed in sports.	Normal force Newton's third law Action-reaction pair forces Free-body diagrams Center of mass
Section 7 Frictional Forces: The Mu of the Shoe Students measure the amount of force necessary to slide athletic shoes on a variety of surfaces. From this and the weight of the shoe, they learn to calculate friction coefficients. They then consider the effect of friction on an athlete's performance.	Friction Coefficient of friction Normal force Weight
Section 8 Potential and Kinetic Energy: Energy in the Pole Vault Students use a penny launched from a ruler to model motion during the pole vault. They connect their observations to the concept of energy conservation.	Gravitational potential energy, Kinetic energy, Energy conversion, Law of conservation of energy, Work, Spring potential energy
Section 9 Conservation of Energy: Defy Gravity Students learn to measure hang time and analyze vertical jumps of athletes using slow-motion videos. This introduces the concept that work when jumping is force applied against gravity.	Gravitational potential energy, Kinetic energy, Energy conversions, Force and weight, Law of conservation of energy, Work, Spring potential energy

Chapter 3: Safety

Chapter Challenge

Your design team will develop a safety system for protecting automobile, airplane, bicycle, motorcycle, or train passengers during a collision. To illustrate this safety system, you will design and build a prototype safety system to protect an egg in a moving cart that undergoes a collision. This prototype will then be tested to see how effectively it protects the egg.

Section Summaries | Physics Principles

Section 1 Accidents
Students identify and evaluate safety features in automobiles. Students then consider what safety features they could use for various vehicles and for their design of a safety system.

Identifying criteria for building a safety feature

Section 2 Newton's First Law of Motion: Life and Death before and after Seat Belts
Students explain what occurs to passengers during a collision using Newton's first law. They read about the concept of pressure and apply this concept while designing and testing a seat belt to safely secure a clay passenger in a cart undergoing a collision.

Newton's first law
Pressure

Section 3 Energy and Work: Why Air Bags?
Students investigate and observe how spreading the force of an impact over a greater distance reduces the amount of damage done to an egg during a collision. They describe and explain their observations using the work-energy theorem.

Average velocity
Newton's second law
Work
Kinetic energy
Work-energy theorem

Section 4 Newton's Second Law of Motion: The Rear-End Collision
Students explore the effects of rear-end collisions on passengers, focusing on whiplash. They use Newton's laws to describe how whiplash occurs. They also describe, analyze, and explain situations involving collisions using Newton's first and second laws.

Newton's first law
Newton's second law

Section 5 Momentum: Concentrating on Collisions
After observing various collisions, students are introduced to the concept of momentum. Through measurements taken during various collisions they determine the mass of a cart. Students then calculate and consider the momentum of various objects.

Linear motion
Momentum

Section 6 Conservation of Momentum
Students investigate the law of conservation of momentum by measuring the masses and velocities of objects before and after collisions. Students then analyze various collisions by applying the law of conservation of momentum.

Newton's second law
Newton's third law
Momentum
Conservation of momentum

Section 7 Impulse and Changes in Momentum: Crumple Zone
Students design a device on the outside of a cart to absorb energy during a collision to assist in reducing the net force acting on passengers inside the vehicle. Students use probes to measure the velocity of the vehicle and the force acting on the vehicle during impact, and then describe the relationship between impulse ($F\Delta t$) and change in momentum ($m\Delta v$).

Newton's second law
Impulse
Momentum
Work-energy theorem

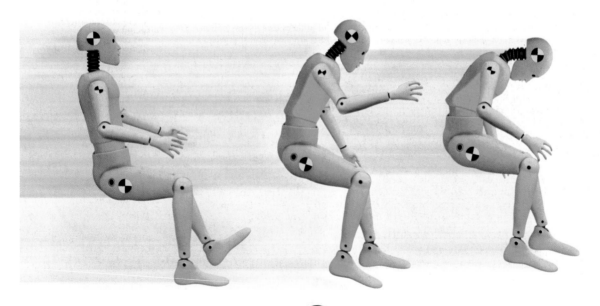

Chapter Challenge

The *Chapter Challenge* is to modify the design of a roller coaster to meet the needs of a specific group of riders who would not normally ride the roller coaster. The design should include calculations to insure the safety of the ride and the energy needed for the ride to operate. A written report and a class presentation of a model of the roller coaster are necessary to complete the assignment.

Section Summaries — Physics Principles

Section 1 Velocity and Acceleration: The Big Thrill

Students investigate methods of making mechanical drawings. Observing motion in class, they determine at which points changes that they associate with roller coasters occur. The velocity and acceleration of a steel ball are determined as it rolls along different tracks using a velocity meter.

Velocity
Acceleration
Acceleration due to gravity

Section 2 Gravitational Potential Energy and Kinetic Energy: What Goes Up and What Comes Down

Students discover what determines the speed of a ball as it rolls on an incline. This result is compared with the velocity of a pendulum swinging from different heights by graphing velocity squared versus height. Gravitational potential energy and kinetic energy are used to explain the similarity of results. Conservation of energy is explored in the transformation of energy forms.

Velocity versus distance
Gravitational potential energy
Kinetic energy
Law of conservation of energy

Section 3 Spring Potential Energy: More Energy

Students use a spring "pop-up" toy to investigate spring potential energy stored in a compressed spring. Using the concepts of kinetic and gravitational potential energy, they explore the law of conservation of mechanical energy that includes the energy stored when springs are compressed or stretched.

Stoichiometry
Gravitational potential energy
Kinetic energy
Spring potential energy
Law of conservation of energy

Section 4 Newton's Law of Universal Gravitation: The Ups and Downs of a Roller Coaster

Students investigate how the force of gravity varies with distance from the center of Earth using data for the acceleration due to gravity at various points. Using a graph, they determine the inverse square relationship between gravitational force and distance. The shape of Earth's gravitational field is noted. Newton's derivation of the gravitational force and the shape of celestial orbits are discussed.

Acceleration due to gravity
The force of gravity
Inverse square relationships
Earth's gravitational field

Section 5 Hooke's Law: Your "At Rest" Weight

Students explore the difference between mass and weight, and how the weight of an object depends upon the acceleration due to gravity. They determine how the stretch of a spring relates to the force applied to stretch or compress. By graphing their data, the students determine Hooke's law and calculate a spring constant. A spring is used to determine the size of an unknown mass. Equilibrium of forces is discussed.

Weight versus mass
Force due to springs
Hooke's law
Equilibrium and Newton's laws

Section 6 Forces Acting During Acceleration: Apparent Weight on a Roller Coaster

Students use a spring scale to investigate the net force required for an object to travel upward and downward, first at a constant velocity, then for upward and downward acceleration. Newton's second law for net forces is used to analyze a free-body diagram for objects undergoing accelerations. The apparent weight change in an elevator is related to its acceleration and the acting net force. Why the force of gravity accelerates all objects at the same rate is discussed.

Newton's second law
Free-body diagrams
Apparent weight
Acceleration due to gravity

Section 7 Circular Motion: Riding on the Curves

Students investigate centripetal force. They identify the direction of the centripetal force, acceleration, and velocity for objects moving in circles. The students investigate the relationship between centripetal force and the object's mass, speed, and the radius of the circle for both horizontal and vertical circles. The changing force required for a vertical circle is explored in depth in relation to Newton's second law.

Tangential velocity
Centripetal force
Centripetal acceleration
Apparent weight
Net force
Free-body diagrams
Normal force

Section 8 Work and Power: Getting to the Top

Students pull up a fixed height by various paths to demonstrate the independence of the path on the work being done. The definition of work is then developed from the students' data and then related to gravitational potential energy. Uncertainty in measurement and the development of scientific principles from data is discussed. The relationship between work and power is discussed, and the formula for power is introduced.

Work
Work and energy
Transformations
Power
Horsepower
Measuring uncertainty

Section 9 Force and Energy: Different Insights

Students develop concept maps on forces and energy relationships to organize their knowledge. The relationship between force and energy (work) is explored. Explicit examples of the principle of conservation of energy are explored for various points on the roller coaster. Analysis using energy considerations is explored, as well as situations where energy is insufficient information and force considerations are appropriate. The students do an exercise using vectors to locate the position of an object.

Gravitational potential energy
Spring potential energy
Kinetic energy
Work
Vectors and scalars
Vector addition
Forces

Section 10 Safety Is Required but Thrills Are Desired

Students investigate parameters that determine what limits are placed on their design. Students calculate centripetal force, apparent weight, normal force, and the net force acting on the roller coaster cars at various points to determine the forces acting on the coaster car.

Force, Newton's second law,
Centripetal force,
Centripetal acceleration,
Normal force, Apparent weight,
Net force

Chapter 5: Let Us Entertain You

Chapter Challenge

The *Chapter Challenge* is to design a sound and light show to entertain students your age. The sounds must come from musical instruments, human voices, or sound makers you build and the light from a laser or conventional lamps. An explanation of the physics principles involved in your show will also be required.

Section Summaries	Physics Principles
Section 1 Sounds in Vibrating Strings To connect vibrations and waves to sound, the students observe the vibration of a plucked string and investigate how the pitch varies with the length of the string. They then explore how the tension of the string affects the vibration rate and the pitch.	Sound and vibration Vibrations on strings Sound and tension Sound and string length Pitch and frequency
Section 2 Making Waves By making waves with coiled springs, students observe transverse and longitudinal waves, periodic wave pulses, and standing waves. The students investigate the relationship between wave speed and amplitude, the effect of a medium on wave speed, and when waves meet, wave addition (or the principle of superposition). Using standing waves, the students develop the relationship between wave speed, frequency, and velocity.	Periodic waves Wave pulse Transverse waves Longitudinal waves Standing waves Principle of superposition
Section 3 Sounds in Strings Revisited Students return to vibrating strings, interpreting what they observed in *Section 1* in terms of standing waves, wavelength, and the frequency of a vibrating string. The students then apply the wave equation to human motion, where speed equals stride length times frequency.	Wavelength Frequency Wave speed
Section 4 Sounds from Vibrating Air Drinking straws and test tubes partially filled with water are used to model wind instruments that use columns of vibrating air to produce sounds. The students investigate the relationship of pitch to the length of the vibrating column of air in longitudinal waves. Diffraction of waves is investigated as a method to transmit sound from the vibrating air column to its surroundings.	Longitudinal waves Frequency Wavelength Diffractiony Absolute zero
Section 5 Shadows In this section, students investigate how shadows are produced. The rectilinear nature of light rays is used to investigate how to produce the umbra and penumbra shadows of extended light sources.	Light travels in straight lines Shadows Umbra Penumbra
Section 6 Reflected Light Students explore how plane mirrors reflect light rays. First investigating how changing the angle of incidence affects the angle of reflection, the students use this to build up a model of how images are formed by plane mirrors.	Angle of incidence Angle of reflection Normal Virtual images Transverse waves
Section 7 Curved Mirrors Students explore how light rays reflect from convex and concave mirrors using a laser pointer. They investigate how a convex mirror is able to focus light, and how this property allows convex mirrors to focus light rays to produce real images. The relationship between the distance of the real image formed from the mirror, the object distance, and the mirrors' focal length is discovered. Virtual images formed by both the convex and concave mirror are also discussed.	Concave mirror Convex mirror Real image Virtual image Focal point Light rays
Section 8 Refraction of Light Using a laser pointer, the students send a ray of light through an acrylic block to explore how light refracts as it passes from one transparent medium to another. By measuring the angle of incidence and the angle of refraction, the students develop the concept of the index of refraction. As the angle of incidence approaches the critical angle, total internal reflection in a prism is explored.	Angle of incidence Angle of refraction Normal Index of refraction Snell's law Total internal reflection Critical angle
Section 9 Effect of Lenses on Light By shining light through a convex lens and locating the image formed at different positions of the light source, the students develop an understanding of how real images are formed by convex lenses. By projecting different sizes of images of the light source onto a surface, the students explore how images are formed and used in everyday equipment. Ray diagrams, as a method to predict image size and location are discussed, while *Active Physics Plus* further develops the lens equation.	Convex lens Real images Virtual images Ray diagrams Focal point Lens equation
Section 10 Color Students investigate colored shadows formed by multiple light sources using additive primary colors. By carefully tracing the light rays from different sources, the students investigate the colored shadows that are formed and how added light produces different colors. Subtractive primaries are also investigated.	Light rays Primary colors Color addition

Chapter 6: Electricity for Everyone

Chapter Challenge

The *Chapter Challenge* is to design an appliance package for a family that is powered by a wind-driven generator. The constraints are that no part of the package can draw more than 2400 W and the average daily consumption should not exceed 3 kWh. In addition, you will construct a training manual explaining the basic principles of electricity for the family, including a wiring diagram with the locations of outlets and switches.

Section Summaries	Physics Principles
Section 1 Generating Electricity With a simple hand generator, wires, and light bulbs, students investigate electric circuits and electrical energy. Using the hand generator introduces them to the concept that electricity is the result of converting one form of energy into another. The operation of a light bulb is also investigated.	Electricity Generator Closed circuit Energy sources
Section 2 Modeling Electricity: The Electron Shuffle Students develop a qualitative model of electricity, including how current flows in series and parallel circuits, and how electrical energy is delivered to devices by playing the part of electric charges as they move through a circuit.	Electric charge (coulomb), Electric energy, Electric current, Resistance, Series circuit, Circuit symbols
Section 3 Series and Parallel Circuits: Lighten Up The Electron Shuffle model is used again to investigate current, resistance, and how electrical energy behaves in a parallel circuit. Comparisons between series and parallel circuits are investigated. Fundamental charges are also discussed.	Series circuit Parallel circuit Electric energy Electric current Resistance Fundamental charges
Section 4 Ohm's Law: Putting Up a Resistance Students design an experiment to determine the resistance of an unknown resistor. Proper use of a voltmeter and ammeter are discussed, and the students set up a series circuit to determine the current for a series of voltages applied to the resistor. Graphing the relationship between voltage and current for a resistor demonstrates Ohm's law. The process is repeated for other resistors, and then for an unknown.	Voltage Current Resistance Voltmeter Ammeter Black box
Section 5 Electric Power: Load Limit Students create a simple fuse to see how fuses work. The teacher then connects a group of appliances to a power strip until a fuse in the circuit blows. The students then calculate the load limit of a household circuit and the watts required by appliances, comparing these to the limits given in the challenge. This also introduces the use of terms and equations for calculating power.	Voltage Current Power Power rating Load limit
Section 6 Current, Voltage, and Resistance in Parallel and Series Circuits: Who's in Control? Students assemble a parallel circuit to explore how switches control the flow of electricity through various sections of the circuit. They then use a voltmeter and ammeter to determine the voltage and current for the elements of a parallel circuit, as well as the circuit as a whole. Finally, they mathematically examine voltage, current flow, and total resistance in series and parallel circuits, while being introduced to circuit diagrams.	Switches Parallel circuit Series circuit Voltage equations Current equations Resistance equations Power equations Circuit analysis
Section 7 Laws of Thermodynamics: Too Hot, Too Cold, Just Right Students investigate the laws of heat transfer by mixing hot and cold water in different proportions. The concept of specific heat is developed as the students use hot metal to warm cold water. Conservation of energy is then discussed as the students calculate energy transfers between various materials. The difference between heat and temperature is emphasized while the laws of thermodynamics and entropy are discussed.	Heat transfer Temperature Specific heat Zeroth law of thermodynamics First law of thermodynamics Entropy Second law of thermodynamics Heat engines
Section 8 Energy Consumption: Cold Shower Electricity used by water heaters is the focus of this activity, which also reinforces concepts of energy transfer. Students investigate the amount of energy in joules needed to raise the temperature of water, and then calculate the efficiency of different water heaters. They also consider alternate solutions to the expectation of hot water in a home.	Heat transfer Electric energy Voltage Current Power, Efficiency
Section 9 Comparing Energy Consumption: More for Your Money Students conduct an experiment in which they determine and compare the power consumption and efficiency of three systems that could be used to heat water. They apply collected data to confirm their response to the challenge in which they recommend appliances for the universal home. Methods of heat transfer are discussed, including convection, conduction, and radiation.	Heat transfer Electric energy Power Efficiency Convection Conduction Radiation

Chapter Challenge

The *Chapter Challenge* is to design a toy that employs either a motor or a generator as a fun device to teach children about how generators and electric motors work. An instruction manual should be developed that explains how to assemble the toy and the basic physics principles of how and why it works.

Section Summaries	Physics Principles

Section 1 The Electricity and Magnetism Connection

Students explore the forces of magnetic attraction and repulsion as well as the magnetic properties of ferrous materials. They then plot the magnetic field of a bar magnet using a compass and iron filings. Students investigate the relationship between electricity and magnetism by using a compass to test for the magnetic field produced by a current-carrying wire. A method to predict the direction of the magnetic field around a current-carrying wire using the left hand is discussed.

Magnetic field
Magnet
Compass
Left-hand rule

Section 2 Electromagnets

Using a hand generator to power an electromagnet is the first step in a continuing investigation into the relationship between electricity and magnetism. Students test the strength and find the polarity of electromagnets made with different core materials and different currents.

Solenoid
Magnetic polarity
Core material

Section 3 Building an Electric Motor

Students construct and operate a DC motor. They also read about how a DC motor works, and how a commutator is necessary to operate a DC motor.

DC motor
Commutator
Force on a current-carrying conductor

Section 4 Detect and Induce Currents

Students construct a galvanometer by using the fact that a compass can detect the presence of a magnetic field. They will use a permanent magnet and a solenoid to create an induced current by manually alternating the motion of a magnet in a fashion similar to the process used by Faraday and Henry. Using the galvanometer to detect the induced current, they will explore the need for relative motion between magnetic fields and wires.

Galvanometer
Induced voltage
Lenz's law
Field lines

Section 5 AC and DC Currents

Producing an electric generator by rotating a coil of wire in a magnetic field is explored. Students learn the difference between how AC and DC currents are generated by considering both types of electric generators and analyzing the induced currents in their rotating coils. Students read about how a commutator changes AC electricity into DC electricity. Students also learn how to sketch output waveforms.

Electric generator
AC electricity
DC electricity
Commutator
Waveforms

Section 6 Electromagnetic Spectrum: Maxwell's Great Synthesis

Students start by classifying groups as a way to identify patterns. The students look at the relationships between electricity and magnetism they have studied and try to find a pattern. A discussion of the pattern discovered by Maxwell and his discovery that all electromagnetic waves travel at the speed of light is discussed. Several experiments that attempted to calculate the speed of light are also discussed. The students conclude by reading about the electromagnetic spectrum.

Maxwell's equations
Speed of light
Electromagnetic spectrum

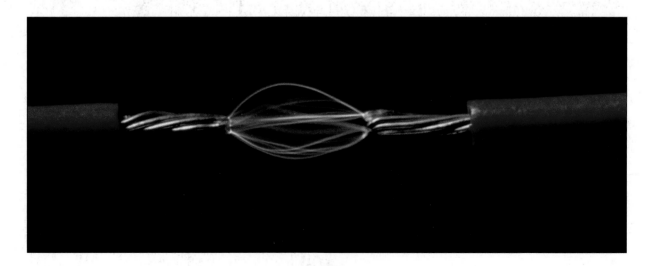

Chapter 8: Atoms on Display

Chapter Challenge

The *Chapter Challenge* is to develop a museum exhibit to acquaint visitors with aspects of the atom that they will see throughout the museum. An introductory and concluding poster about the exhibits, as well as written matter about the exhibit you designed, should be included.

Section Summaries

Physics Principles

Section 1 Static Electricity and Coulomb's Law: Opposites Attract

Using transparent cellophane tape, students investigate the static electricity of charged objects. Inductive electric forces are explored and the students read about conservation of charge and Coulomb's law to prepare them to understand the forces holding an atom together.

Electric fields
Charge
Conservation of charge
Coulomb's law
Grounding, Induction

Section 2 The Nature of Charge: Tiny and Indivisible

In a simulation of Millikan's oil-drop experiment, students use inquiry to find the number of coins enclosed in a film canister. They then learn how related techniques were used to determine that electric charge is quantized. The process of inference to obtain information about systems that cannot be directly measured is used.

Quantization of charge
Charge on the electron
Millikan experiment

Section 3 The Size of a Nucleus: How Big Is Small?

Using statistical measurements, students estimate the size of a penny. They then compare their statistical approach with direct measurement. Finally, they compare their experiment with Rutherford's experiment to determine the size of a nucleus in relation to an atom and the evidence we have to verify that knowledge.

Atomic models
Atomic nucleus
Atomic forces
Atom as mostly empty space

Section 4 Hydrogen Spectra and Bohr's Model of the Hydrogen Atom

Students investigate spectral lines by using a spectrometer to measure the wavelengths of light emitted by three gases. The unique spectra of atoms are discussed and the students then learn about the Bohr model of the atom. Using this model, they calculate the wavelengths of light emitted as electrons jump from one quantized orbit to another. The discovery of helium from its spectrum is discussed. In the *Active Physics Plus*, the formula for the energy of a photon is also discussed.

Bohr model
Quantized electron orbits
Atomic spectra
Electron energy levels
Balmer series

Section 5 Wave-Particle Model of Light: Two Models Are Better Than One!

The wave and particle nature of light is explored by investigating two-slit interference and the photoelectric effect. By drawing an analogy to standing waves on a string, a new interpretation of the Bohr orbit as standing waves of electrons is introduced, with a nonmathematical introduction of the Schrödinger wave equation. The dual wave and particle nature of electrons is also discussed.

Interference of waves
Photoelectric effect
Work function
Photon energy
Photon model of light
Schrödinger wave equation
DeBroglie waves

Section 6 The Strong Force: Inside the Nucleus

The proton-neutron model of the nucleus is introduced and explored. With a huge Coulomb repulsion pushing protons apart, the need for a strong attractive force in the nucleus is investigated. Students are then introduced to Feynman diagrams as a means of understanding how forces are transmitted.

Proton-neutron model
Strong force
Feynman diagram
Action at a distance
Virtual particles

Section 7 Radioactive Decay and the Nucleus

Students investigate the statistical properties of randomly tossing marked cubes. They then relate these results to the statistics of radioactive decay. The concept of half-life is introduced as a clock for measuring radioactive decay. Students are then introduced to complete nuclear equations for alpha, beta, and gamma decays.

Radioactive decay
Half-life
Atomic mass
Atomic number
Nuclear transmutation

Section 8 Energy Stored within the Nucleus

Students are introduced to Einstein's famous equation $E = mc^2$ and use it to calculate the energy liberated by the conversion of mass to energy. After calculating the mass defect of the nucleus, the equation is used to calculate nuclear binding energies.

Atomic mass unit
Conservation of mass energy
Nuclear mass defect
Nuclear binding energy
Particle-antiparticle annihilation

Section 9 Nuclear Fission and Fusion: Breaking Up Is Hard to Do

Students start by calculating the nuclear binding energy of various elements and then graph the binding energy per nucleon versus the element's atomic number. Students explore nuclear fission and fusion reactions. How a fission chain reaction works is also studied.

Binding energy per nucleon
Nuclear fission
Nuclear fusion

Chapter 9: Sports on the Moon

Chapter Challenge

The *Chapter Challenge* is to develop a proposal for NASA by either adapting or inventing a sport that can be played on the surface of the Moon with its reduced gravity. Writing a local newspaper article describing the championship match for your sport is also required.

Section Summaries	Physics Principles
Section 1 Identifying and Classifying: What Is a Sport? Students apply their knowledge of sports to identify attributes that define an activity as a sport. From this, they begin to consider how differences between Earth and the Moon can affect sports.	Pattern identification
Section 2 Acceleration Due to Gravity: Free Fall on the Moon Students compare the free fall of different objects. They then calculate acceleration with respect to gravity on the Moon using measurements obtained from a slow-motion video of an astronaut in space dropping objects.	Gravity Acceleration Distance covered by accelerating objects
Section 3 Mass, Weight, and Gravity Using a simulation that allows for the comparison of mass and weight between Earth and the Moon, students investigate the ratio of gravity on Earth to that on the Moon. After determining that an object's inertia does not change, the forces needed to overcome weight and inertia on the Moon are discussed.	Inertia Weight Universal law of gravitation Newton's second law
Section 4 Projectile Motion on the Moon Beginning with scale drawings, students calculate the distances that projected objects will travel on the Moon. These distances are then compared to projectiles launched on Earth with the same velocity to determine how sports that use projectiles would be changed on the Moon.	Projectile motion Gravity
Section 5 Gravity, Work, and Energy: Jumping on the Moon Students measure vertical distances when jumping and then analyze their motion in terms of work and conservation of energy. Applying what they know about gravity on the Moon, they predict vertical distances they could jump on the Moon.*	Work Gravitational potential energy Kinetic energy Conservation of energy
Section 6 Momentum and Gravity: Golf on the Moon Using a variety of balls, students measure the height each bounces when dropped and when projected by a collision. They use this data to infer a golf ball's speed when hit on Earth and on the Moon. The interaction of different golf clubs and golf balls with varying degrees of mass is also investigated.	Gravitational potential energy Kinetic energy
Section 7 Friction: Sliding on the Moon Students investigate the force necessary to overcome the friction between objects and the surfaces on which they move. They then relate this to gravity and predict the force needed to overcome the friction against a sliding motion made on the Moon.	Weight Friction Coefficient of friction Normal force Newton's second law
Section 8 Modeling Human Motion: Bounding on the Moon Using cylinders of different lengths and weights, students explore pendulum motion. They then compare the motion of the pendulums to the swinging motion of human legs when walking, finally predicting how walking on the Moon and on Earth is different.	Gravitational field strength Simple harmonic motion Period of a pendulum
Section 9 Air Resistance and Terminal Velocity: "Airy" Indoor Sports on the Moon Students start by investigating how mass and terminal velocity are related. They then use badminton shuttlecocks to investigate how air resistance affects motion. They then apply what they know about the ratio of gravity on Earth to that of the Moon to predict the air resistance to motion on the Moon.	Air resistance Terminal velocity

Chapter 1

DRIVING THE ROADS

Driving the Roads

Active Physics Driver's Manual

Active Physics is a research-based program. That means that what you will be doing in *Active Physics* and how you will be doing it is based on researching how students like you learn best.

In the first chapter, you will find notes that explain the various components of *Active Physics* and how they can help you actively engage in learning physics. Think of these notes as your driver's manual for navigating your way through *Active Physics*.

Stopping to think about the rules of the road and your driving habits can make you a better driver. Research shows that stopping to think about your learning can also make you a better learner.

Although some of these notes may seem like a lot of "teacher talk," as you work through each chapter, think about why you are doing each of the things you are asked to do. *The more you understand about how you learn, the better you will be at learning.*

Why is there a *Scenario*?

Welcome to *Active Physics*! You are about to begin an exciting year of discovering how useful, interesting, and fun physics can be. Each *Active Physics* chapter begins with a *Scenario*. The *Scenario* describes a realistic event or situation that you might have experienced or can imagine experiencing. The *Scenario* sets the stage for the *Chapter Challenge*, which follows.

Scenario

Imagine your parents just bought a new car and your favorite music group is in town. You ask your parents if you could use the new car to take a friend to the concert. What would your parents say? Would you have a conversation like the following?

"I don't care if it is your favorite music group. You are not ready to drive our car."

"But I've had my license for two whole months!"

"That test means nothing. You memorized a bunch of facts to get your license."

"Yes, and now I know all about the law."

"The traffic laws, maybe. But what about natural laws, like speed and stopping distances?"

"That's easy, the speed limits are all posted."

"The speed limit is the maximum speed you can go. You have to adjust your speed according to driving conditions."

"Okay, I'll do that. Then can I have the car?"

"No. I didn't say that. You don't know about reaction time and following distance. And what about curves; when should you slow down?"

"They have yellow signs to tell you what to do on the curves."

"You need to know more than that before you enter a curve. And what about a yellow light? What does it mean?"

"Step on it?"

"See what I mean, you're not ready to drive."

"It was a joke."

"Driving is no joke. What if you have an accident? What then? What if your friend in the car distracts you?"

"I don't plan on an accident; besides, I'll always wear my seat belt."

"No one plans on an accident—that's why they're called accidents!"

"But I have a valid driver's license."

"Yes, but you still have a lot more to learn."

"You just don't love me."

"I'm doing this *because* I love you."

Why is there a *Chapter Challenge*?

At this point, you are presented with what you and your group members will be required to do as a chapter project. The *Chapter Challenge* may be a problem you are expected to solve or a task you are expected to complete using the knowledge you gain in the chapter. When you first encounter the *Chapter Challenge,* you may find it overwhelming. However, all the physics content in the chapter will help you succeed at the challenge. Each section will provide you with another piece of the puzzle that, when put together, will answer the challenge.

The *Chapter Challenge* is the glue that holds the chapter together. In *Active Physics*, you will never be left wondering, "Why am I learning this?" You will need everything you learn in a chapter to complete the *Chapter Challenge*. You can think of the challenge as the job you need to do over the next few weeks.

Your Challenge

Automobile insurance for most teenage drivers is carried on their parents' policy. Your automobile insurance company says that, if new drivers can pass a course from a certified driving academy, your automobile insurance rates will be reduced. So, before your parents allow you to drive, you must pass a driving course. You find, upon checking with Active Driving Academy—the only driving school in your area—that they enroll students in groups. You are told that, as part of Active Driving Academy's requirements, your group must demonstrate some basic knowledge of the physics of driving. You must demonstrate this knowledge through a two-to three-minute presentation to academy instructors. At a minimum, the presentation must explain the following:

• the relationships among following distance, braking distance, and the total stopping distance, including the factors that affect each;

• how to decide what to do when the light turns yellow as you approach an intersection; and

• the connection among speed, friction, and radius of the curve when turning.

You will use graphs and charts on posters to enhance your presentation. Using a computer presentation program is permissible but not required. Your group must submit the written report of your presentation to assure academy instructors that you are properly prepared. In addition to the requirements of the driving school, before your parents allow you to drive their car, you must answer their questions about driving safety.

Why are there *Criteria for Success?*

To do well at any job, you need to know what the job expectations are. That applies in the classroom as well as in the workplace. It is essential to define and understand the *Criteria for Success*. Before you begin your job in each chapter, you and your class will discuss and list the criteria that you will be expected to meet. Next, you will determine the relative importance of the assessment criteria. Then, you can assign point values to each component. You will also need to clarify the details of the criteria. For example, you need to know how many physics principles are required to meet a standard of excellence (the best you can do).

Even though physics principles are necessary criteria in addressing the challenge, they are not enough. Each *Chapter Challenge* will also expect you to be imaginative and creative. Each completed project should be unique. It should be a reflection of the interests and talents of the members of your group.

Criteria for Success

For each part of the *Chapter Challenge*, imagine what criteria are required for an excellent presentation and written report. For example, should an excellent presentation have charts or graphs? If you think so, is one chart or graph enough? As a class, list these criteria first. Then read the suggestions given in the *Standard for Excellence* table on the next page and compare them to your class list. By listing your criteria first, you will gain a greater understanding of the challenge. You will also have a chance to revisit the criteria at the end of the chapter before the presentation is due.

Record any notes you have about the *Chapter Challenge* in your *Active Physics* log. You will also need to list the criteria and their point value that your class decided on for assessing the challenge.

Standard for Excellence

1. The use of physics principles and terms in the presentation and written report • physics concepts from the chapter are integrated in the appropriate places (including the relationship between following distance, braking distance, and the total stopping distance; yellow-light analysis; and the connection between speed, friction, and radius of the curve when turning) • physics terminology and equations are correct and used where appropriate • correct estimates of the magnitude of physical quantities are used (such as reaction time, following distance, speed, acceleration)	**50 points**
2. The quality of the presentation • knowledge of traffic laws and the basic operation of an automobile • easy to follow and understand • appropriate amount of explanation of charts and graphs • duration of presentation between two and three minutes • all members of the team participate	**20 points**
3. The quality of the written report • number of pages within determined amount (you and your class will reach consensus on this) • proper use of graphs and charts for your presentation • the use of correct science vocabulary • correct spelling, punctuation, and grammar • appropriate use of equations and correct units of measurement	**20 points**
4. Challenge completed on time	**10 points**

Why is there an *Active Physics* log?

As a student scientist, everything that you think and do should be recorded in your *Active Physics* log. You may be beginning the year with this chapter. Write the name and number of the chapter, *Chapter 1: Driving the Roads*, at the top of page 5 in your log. Remember to keep the first four pages for your *Table of Contents*. If you have not already set up your log, refer to how to create your *Active Physics* log in the introduction of this book.

Variable	Change		Predicted effect of change on GO Zone	Actual effect of change on GO Zone
t_y	yellow-light time	increase t_y		
		decrease t_y		
t_r	response time	increase t_r		
		decrease t_r		
v	speed limit	increase v		
		decrease v		
a	deceleration rate	increase a		
		decrease a		
w	width of intersection	increase w		
		decrease w		

Why is there an *Engineering Design Cycle?*

The *Chapter Challenge* is a problem that you need to solve. There are many different ways to solve problems. One sequence of steps that can be used to solve problems is called the *Engineering Design Cycle.* You are going to use a simplified *Engineering Design Cycle* as you address your challenge. There are five basic steps to a simplified engineering design.

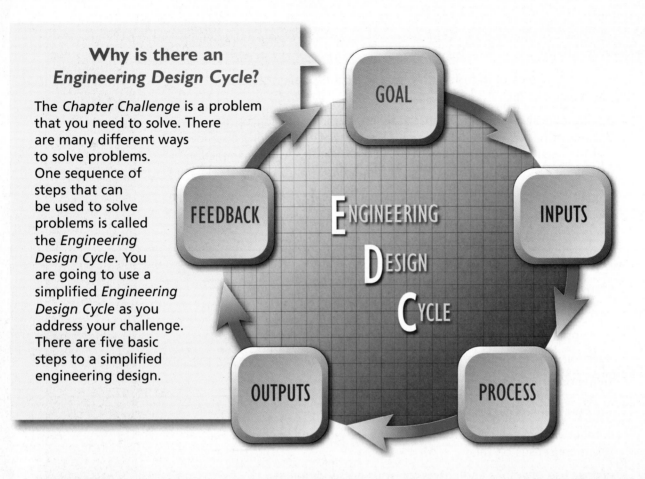

Simplified Engineering Design Cycle	
GOAL	• define the problem • identify available resources • draft potential solutions • list constraints to possible actions
INPUTS	• complete the investigations in each section • learn new physics concepts and vocabulary
PROCESS	• evaluate work to date • compare and contrast methods and ideas • examine possible trade-offs to help reach goals and maximize efforts • create a model from your information • design experiments to test ideas and the suitability of the model
OUTPUTS	• present *Mini-Challenge* and intermediary steps or products • present *Chapter Challenge* based on feedback to *Mini-Challenge*
FEEDBACK	• obtain response from target audience leading to modification of the goal • identify additional constraints, requiring restarting the input and process stages

You have now heard about your *Chapter Challenge*. You need to give a presentation and write a report that demonstrates your basic knowledge of the physics of driving. You will use a simplified *Engineering Design Cycle* to help your group put together the presentation. Establishing a clear *Goal* is the first step in this process. You have defined the problem you need to solve, identified the *Criteria for Success*, and thought about some of the constraints that you will need to face. You may also already be thinking of some possible ways of giving your presentation. You are well on your way to establishing your *Goal*.

As you experience each one of the chapter sections, you will be gaining *Inputs* to use in the design cycle. These *Inputs* will include new physics concepts, vocabulary, and even equations that will help you with your presentation.

The first *Outputs* of your design cycle will be a short presentation to the driving-academy instructors, along with posters displaying graphs and charts. After several sections, you will work on part of your presentation. Finally, you will receive *Feedback* from your classmates and your instructor about which parts of your presentation are good and which parts need to be refined. You will then repeat the *Engineering Design Cycle* during the second half of the chapter when you gain more *Inputs* and refine your presentation.

The 7E Instructional Model

Active Physics uses a 7E instructional model. The steps (phases) are

• Elicit • Engage • Explore • Explain • Elaborate • Extend • Evaluate

Look for these phases as you work through the first section of this chapter.

Why is there a *Physics Corner*?

The *Physics Corner* lists all the physics principles that the chapter will present. You will learn the physics concepts and master the skills necessary to complete the investigations and the challenge, through active involvement and by engaging your creativity. It will be important for you to understand all the physics principles you are learning, because you will need to apply them at the end of the chapter to complete the *Chapter Challenge*. The *Physics Corner*, along with your teacher, will help you keep track of all the physics concepts you will learn in the chapter.

Physics Corner

Physics in *Driving the Roads*

• Acceleration
• Accuracy in measurement
• Average speed
• Centripetal acceleration
• Centripetal force
• Circular motion
• Distance and time
• Doppler effect
• Friction
• Instantaneous speed
• Momentum
• Positive and negative acceleration
• Precision in measurement
• Reaction time
• Velocity

Section 1

Reaction Time: Responding to Road Hazards

Learning Outcomes

In this section, you will

- **Measure** reaction time using one of two different methods.
- **Compare** the different methods of measuring reaction time.
- **Compare** the reaction times of your classmates.
- **Investigate** how distractions affect reaction time.

What Do You See?

Why is there a *What Do You See?* and *What Do You Think?*

The *What Do You See?* and *What Do You Think?* are the **Elicit** and **Engage** phases of learning. You have already spent a number of years at school learning about many different subjects. You watch television, read, or listen to others talk. You have your own ideas about how things work and about what makes things happen. It is very important for you to think about what you already know or what you think you know. That is what you will use to build your understanding. You need to compare what you think you know to what you are learning in the classroom to build a new understanding. The **Elicit** phase of learning is thinking about what you already know.

The **Engage** phase is meant to capture your attention. The *What Do You See?* picture in each section has been drawn by Tomas Bunk. Tomas Bunk is not a physicist but a well-recognized cartoonist. He uses his artistic talent and enjoys drawing humorous illustrations that show real physics concepts in a very personal way. When you look at the illustrations, what do you see? What do you not understand about what is happening in the illustration that you would like to learn more about? How much fun and how personal can you make your encounter with physics?

When you think about the *What Do You Think?* questions, what interests you and what other questions come to your mind that you would like answered? The **Engage** phase of the instructional model is designed to get you interested in what you will be learning.

What Do You Think?

Many deaths that occur on the highway result from the inability of a driver to respond in time to a hazard on the road. The driver could not react quickly enough to avoid being involved in a collision.

- **What factors affect the time you need to react to an emergency situation while driving?**

Begin a new page in your *Active Physics* log. Write *Section 1 Reaction Time* at the top of the new page. Also record the section and page number in your *Table of Contents*. Record your ideas about this question in your log.

Why is there an *Investigate*?

The *Investigate* is the **Explore** phase of the 7E instructional model. Confucius, a Chinese philosopher, said, "I hear and I forget. I see and I remember. I do and I understand." The best way to learn is by doing. In *Active Physics,* whenever possible, you will explore a concept by doing an investigation.

One purpose of the investigation is to "level the playing field" and ensure that everybody has a common experience through which to discuss physics. For example, some students have been in a motor-vehicle accident, while others have not. It would not be sensible for everybody to experience an accident. However, it is possible to provide a classroom experience that everybody can discuss and not limit the discussion to only those students who have been in an accident.

The investigation also provides you with a real dialog with nature. In *Active Physics*, you will not be limited to having to believe what somebody wrote in a book. You will have an opportunity to observe, record data, isolate variables, design and plan experiments, create graphs, interpret results, develop hypotheses, and organize your findings. Sometimes, the entire class will participate in a demonstration.

All scientists value inquiry. The **Explore** phase is part of an inquiry approach to learning. In *Active Physics*, you are not physics students, you are student physicists.

Scientists often record their results in lab books. When you see this symbol ✎, you should record the information required for the *Investigate* in your *Active Physics* log.

Investigate

In this *Investigate*, you will measure reaction time using one of two methods. You will then compare the methods to decide which is the best method of measurement. You will also compare the reaction times of the members of your class, both with and without distractions.

1. To stop an automobile, you must first decide you want to stop. Then you must move your foot from the gas pedal to the brake pedal. The time required to decide to stop and move your foot to the brake is called your *reaction time*. Reaction time includes the time for you to react and the time for you to complete an action.

   Begin by finding how long it takes to move your right foot between imaginary gas and brake pedals.

   ✎ a) Estimate how long it takes to move your foot between the imaginary pedals. Record your estimate. (A way in which to estimate time is to count "one one-thousand, two one-thousand, three one-thousand.") Try counting like this until you reach "ten one-thousand" while your partner uses a stopwatch or clock to measure 10 s (seconds). Slow or quicken your counting pace so that it comes close to ten seconds when you finish counting "ten one-thousand." If the time to move your foot from one pedal to the other is less than one second, you can estimate how much time elapsed by how far you got in your counting of one one-thousand [for example, one (¼ s) one- (¼ s) thou- (¼ s) sand (¼ s)].

2. The first step in stopping an automobile occurs even before you move your foot to the brake pedal. It takes time to see or hear something that tells you to move your foot.

Test your reaction time by having a classmate stand behind you and clap. When you hear the sound, move your foot between the imaginary pedals.

a) Estimate how long it took you to react to the sound of the clap. Record your estimate. Your partner can begin counting "one one-thousand" as soon as he or she claps.

Now you will use one of the following methods to measure the time it takes you to react to something you see. Your teacher will assign you one of the following methods.

Method A: Starting and Stopping Stopwatches

1. Obtain two stopwatches. One student starts both stopwatches at the same time, and gives one stopwatch to his/her lab partner. When the first student stops his/her stopwatch, the lab partner stops his/her stopwatch, too. The difference between the times on each stopwatch is the reaction time.

a) Record your reaction time in your *Active Physics* log.

b) Repeat at least three times. Calculate and record your average reaction time.

Method B: Catching a Ruler

1. Obtain a metric ruler. Hold the metric ruler at the top, between thumb and index finger, with the zero centimeter at the bottom. Your lab partner places his/her thumb and index finger at the lower end of the ruler, but does not touch it. Drop the ruler. Your partner must stop the ruler from falling by catching it between his/her thumb and index finger.

a) The position of your lab partner's fingers on the ruler marks the distance the ruler fell while his/her nervous system was reacting. Record the distance in your log.

b) Repeat at least three times. Calculate and record your average reaction distance.

c) The graph below shows the relationship between the distance the ruler fell and the time it took to catch it. Use the graph to find and record your reaction time.

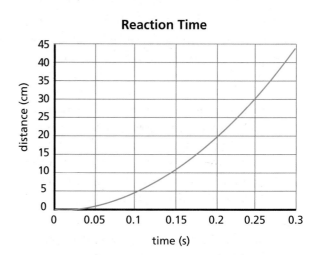

Reaction Time

Comparing Methods of Measuring Reaction Time

1. Compare your group's average reaction-time measurements with the average reaction-time measurements of other groups using the other method.

   a) Explain why they were not all the same.

   b) Which method do you think most accurately measures reaction time? Explain why.

2. Compare your reaction-time measurements with those of your group and other groups that used the same method.

   a) Record the results for the fastest, slowest, and average reaction times.

   b) Do you think reaction times vary for people of the same age? Discuss this with your group and then record your answer.

Reaction Time with Distractions

1. Before your partner clapped or dropped the ruler, you already knew what you were supposed to do upon receiving that signal. Suppose you had to make a decision after the clap or the ruler drop. Repeat the ruler-catching experiment while being distracted by a decision you have to make.

   The student dropping the ruler now says either "red" at the moment the ruler is dropped, which means you should catch the ruler, or "green" which means you should let the ruler drop. You will have to calculate the average of five reaction times. If you catch the ruler when "green" is called, then you have to do all the trials over. (This is to ensure that you react to the color as well as the ruler dropping.)

   a) How does your reaction time with needing to make a decision compare to your reaction time without needing to make a decision?

   b) How could you apply the difference in reaction time when you need to make a decision to a situation while driving an automobile?

2. Suppose you are talking on a cell phone or changing a CD while driving. How do these distractions affect your reaction time? To find out, repeat the ruler drop with one hand (using the "red" and "green" cues), while at the same time you do one of the following:

   • pretend to change a CD with your other hand.

   • simulate dialing a phone number by entering the phone number on your calculator.

   a) Compare your average reaction time with the distraction to your average reaction time without the distraction.

   b) In your *Active Physics* log, make a list of 10 activities that could distract you from driving safely.

Active Physics

Why are there *Physics Words?*

It is easier and more effective to communicate concepts when the appropriate vocabulary is used. In science, a single word is often used to precisely describe a complex idea. *Physics Words* highlight the important terms that you need to know and use. In the *Physics Talk*, these words appear in a **bold-face type** the first time they are used. Sometimes it will be necessary for these words to be used in the *Investigate* first. You will recognize these words because they are printed in *italics* (a slanted type). The best way to learn new vocabulary is to practice using the words frequently and correctly. It is not useful to memorize a lot of terms and definitions.

Why is there a *Physics Talk?*

The *Physics Talk* is the **Explain** phase of the 7E instructional model. Reading the *Physics Talk* and discussing it with other students and your teacher will help you make better sense of the concepts you just explored in the investigation. In the *Physics Talk*, the results of your investigation are explained in terms of scientific models, laws, and theories. You will also be introduced to scientific vocabulary after the concepts are explained. The *Physics Words* highlight the vocabulary you need to know. You will find that using this vocabulary makes it easier to discuss the concepts with your class and answer the *Checking Up* questions. These questions will help you check that you have understood the explanation.

In *Active Physics*, you always **Explore** before you **Explain**. This ensures that you have some experience (**Explore**) with what is being described and discussed (**Explain**). You can think of this as ABC (Activity Before Concept). You will also be introduced to science vocabulary after you understand the concept. This is what scientists do and how student scientists should learn. You can think of this as CBV (Concept Before Vocabulary).

The *Physics Talk* may also include the **Elaborate** phase of the 7E instructional model. After you are able to explain the physics of the investigation, you will be introduced to additional related physics principles that you will understand based on what you learned in the *Investigate*.

Physics Talk

AVOIDING COLLISIONS

Reaction Time and Distractions

Physics Words

reaction time: the time it takes to respond to a situation.

The time taken to respond to a situation is called **reaction time.** Your reaction time while driving can be a matter of life and death. How fast you respond to an emergency could help you avoid an accident. In the *Investigate*, you estimated your reaction time. You found your quickest or best reaction time. You knew something was going to happen, you were ready to respond, and you knew how you were supposed to respond. Then you measured the time of your reaction. You also measured reaction time while you were being distracted in some way.

You probably found you had a slower reaction time when you were distracted. In both situations, your reaction was probably quicker than your reaction time would be while driving, because you knew that you were expected to respond and how you would respond (for example, by catching the ruler, or stopping a stopwatch).

While driving, people are often distracted by conversations, music, or things happening along the road. As you discovered in the *Investigate*, distractions slowed your reaction time. If a decision has to be made suddenly, the slower reaction time may increase the chances of being involved in a collision.

Some distractions cannot be avoided. If you sneeze, your eyes automatically close for a moment and there is nothing you can do about it. However, drivers often consciously decide to take their eyes off the road to look at a passenger in the automobile. Some drivers' reaction time becomes even longer due to eating, changing a CD, or talking on their cell phone while driving.

Other Factors Affecting Reaction Time

Every state in the United States has a law prohibiting driving a vehicle while under the influence of alcohol or drugs. Alcohol and drugs can significantly slow a person's reaction time. Drugs that affect reaction time are not necessarily just illegal drugs. Some medications that are legally prescribed by a doctor instruct the user not to drive after taking the medicine.

There are many other factors that can affect reaction time. Psychologists (scientists who study the human mind) have found that age, gender, practice, fatigue, exercise, attentiveness, and even personality are some of the factors that can increase reaction time. The relationships among these factors and reaction time are complex. You may wish to research some of these relationships further.

Checking Up

1. How do distractions affect reaction time?

2. Why is driving under the influence of alcohol or drugs illegal?

3. Name three factors in addition to distractions and drugs or alcohol that can affect reaction time.

Why is there an *Active Physics Plus*?

In *Oliver Twist*, a book written by Charles Dickens, the young boy, Oliver, at breakfast declares, "Please sir, I want some more." *Active Physics Plus* is for those students who want more.

Active Physics Plus is more. But you may be wondering, "More what?" The *Active Physics Plus* will be more of one of the following four types of extensions.

Extension 1: More mathematics. Some students appreciate and enjoy the fact that physics content can be expressed efficiently and effectively through mathematics. This type of *Active Physics Plus* extension will provide guidance in how math can help elaborate a topic and add to its understanding.

Extension 2: More depth. Some topics can be elaborated by looking at the content in more depth or by relating it to other topics that have been studied.

Extension 3: More concepts. Sometimes a related concept can be introduced after learning the concept in a particular section.

Extension 4: More exploration. Further investigation of the section concept can include taking additional measurements or performing related investigations.

The *Active Physics Plus* includes the **Elaborate** phase of the 7E instructional model. After you are able to explain the physics of the investigation, you will be introduced to additional physics through the extensions.

Each *Active Physics Plus* component will be noted with a grid, informing you which extension categories will be covered. For example, *Active Physics Plus* for a section may include both a math and a concept extension. The grid at the beginning of the *Active Physics Plus* would look like the following:

+Math	+Depth	+Concepts	+Exploration
◆◆		◆	

The diamond notation (◆) indicates the level of intensity, with three diamonds ◆◆◆ signifying an intensive extension. In the example shown above, the depth of the concepts presented is moderate and the math required is more intensive.

Active Physics Plus can be considered optional topics for some students in some schools. For others, your teacher may require you to complete an *Active Physics Plus*. Your teacher is familiar with your state requirements and can guide you to appropriate personal challenges so that all students stretch themselves. Your teacher may also ask you to work as individuals or as teams on the *Active Physics Plus*.

If your teacher decides to skip the *Active Physics Plus*, you can still be sure that you will be able to complete the *Chapter Challenge* and follow the sequence of the sections. *Active Physics Plus* is supplemental and not a required component.

+Math	+Depth	+Concepts	+Exploration
◆			◆

Calculating Reaction Time

You were able to find your reaction time by dropping a ruler and using a graph that relates the distance a ruler falls to the time it took to catch the ruler. The reaction-time graph was constructed using the following equation:

$$d = \frac{1}{2}at^2$$

where *d* is the distance the ruler falls (measured in centimeters),

a is the acceleration due to gravity on Earth (980 cm/s²), and

t is the time of fall (in seconds).

1. Use a computer spreadsheet and graphing program.

   a) Make data for this equation where the time varies from 0 s to 0.6 s in 0.02-s increments.

Time (s)	Distance (cm)
0.00	
0.02	
0.04	
0.06	

   b) Graph this data with time on the *x*-axis and the distance on the *y*-axis.

   c) Compare this graph with the one in the investigation.

   To find the time of the fall, the equation can be rewritten as follows:

   $$t = \sqrt{\frac{2d}{a}}$$

2. By measuring the distance of fall for the ruler, you can use a calculator to determine the reaction time.

a) Calculate the reaction time if the ruler is caught at the 6.0-cm mark, and the 7.5-cm mark.

b) Calculate the reaction time as you repeat the experiment, dropping the ruler and catching it in the following ways:

   - with the thumb and index finger of your right hand
   - with the thumb and index finger of your left hand
   - with the index and middle finger.

c) Compare the right-hand reaction time with the left-hand reaction time.

d) Compare the reaction time of catching the ruler with the thumb and index finger to the reaction time of catching the ruler with the index and middle finger.

3. Use the equation to construct a reaction-time ruler with the distance measurement converted to time. You can now read response times directly on the ruler.

4. Do different groups of people have better or worse response times than others? Consider groups such as athletes that need good hand-eye coordination, taxi drivers, video-game players, and so on. Design and carry out an investigation to collect data that will help you find an answer. Include in your plan the number of subjects, how you will test them, and how you will organize and interpret the data collected. Use the response-time ruler to take your measurements. With the approval of your teacher, carry out your investigation. Record your findings and report them to the class.

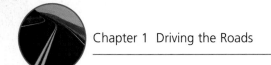

Why is there a *What Do You Think Now?*

At the beginning of each section, you are asked to think about one or two questions. At that point, you are not expected to necessarily come up with a correct physics answer, but you are expected to think about what you know. Now that you have completed the investigation, you have learned the physics you need to know to answer the questions. Think about the questions again.

Compare your answers now to the answers you gave initially. Comparing what you think now with what you thought before is a way of "observing your thinking." Remember, research shows that stopping to think about your learning makes you a better learner.

What Do You Think Now?

At the beginning of the section, you were asked the following:

- **What factors affect the time you need to react to an emergency situation while driving?**

How would you answer this question now? Revisit your initial ideas on reaction time, and explain why reaction time is so crucial to avoiding automobile accidents. Explain how distractions can increase the possibility of having an accident in reference to reaction time.

Why are there *Physics Essential Questions?*

As a student physicist, you need to focus on the *Physics Essential Questions* that unite all science endeavors.

- *What does it mean?* (What is the physics content that you are learning?)

- *How do you know?* (What evidence do you have that supports the content?)

- *Why do you believe?* (What are the organizing principles of physics? How is the physics of this section the same as the physics outside this classroom? How does the physics of this section relate to other areas of physics?)

- *Why should you care?* (How is what you learned relevant to your life and/or the *Chapter Challenge?*)

As a student physicist, you are also part of the science community that understands that what you are learning can be placed into the larger context of physics knowledge and organizing principles.

The *Physics Essential Questions* are another **Elaborate** phase of the 7E instructional model. Here you review the physics from this section and put it in a larger context. You will discover how physics is meaningful to you by asking and answering these four essential questions:

- The *What does it mean?* question requires you to describe the content of the section.

- To answer the *How do you know?* question, you can describe the experimental evidence that you gathered from your investigations. You "know" because you did an investigation or saw a demonstration.

- The *Why do you believe?* question will help you better understand the nature of science, the philosophy of science, and the organizing principles of science. Rather than having a separate chapter called "What is Science?" in *Active Physics* you confront the essence of physics throughout the course with each new topic and each new explanation.

- The *Why should you care?* question asks you to explain how the physics in this section relates to your life and/or the *Chapter Challenge*.

Physics
Essential Questions

What does it mean?

What is reaction time?

How do you know?

How did you measure reaction time in this section? What was the range of reaction times obtained by other students in your class?

Why do you believe?

Connects with Other Physics Content	Fits with Big Ideas in Science	Meets Physics Requirements
Forces and motion	✱ Change and constancy	Makes mathematical sense

✱ Physics concepts are often concerned with how things change over time. Describe how reaction time is a measure of change over time.

Why should you care?

What relevance does reaction time have to driving safely?

Why is there a *Reflecting on the Section and the Challenge?*

This part of the section is the **Extend** phase of the 7E instructional model. It gives you an opportunity to practice transferring what you learned in a section to another situation. In the case of *Active Physics*, you will need to apply your knowledge to complete the *Chapter Challenge*. Each section of a chapter is like another piece of the puzzle that completes the challenge. Transfer of knowledge is an important element in learning. This component presents a connection between each section and the chapter. It will guide you to producing a better *Chapter Challenge*.

Reflecting on the Section and the Challenge

In a Virginia study reported in 2003, researchers found that traffic, or roadside incidents, caused the largest number of accidents. Rubbernecking was responsible for most of the accidents reported (16%) followed by driver fatigue (12%), looking at scenery or landmarks (10%), passenger or child distractions (9%), adjusting the radio, tape, or CD player (7%), and cell phone use (5%).

The amount of time you need to react to a situation has a direct impact on your driving ability. It takes time to notice a situation and more time to respond. A person who requires more time to respond to what they see or hear is more likely to have an accident than someone who responds in a shorter period of time. One part of your *Chapter Challenge* is to explain the effect of reaction time on driving.

Why is there a *Physics to Go*?

The *Physics to Go* is another opportunity for you to **Elaborate** on the physics content in the section. It also provides an additional chance to **Extend** your knowledge. Often, you will be assigned *Physics to Go* questions as homework. They are excellent study-guide questions that help you to review and to check your understanding.

The *Physics to Go* is also a part of the **Evaluate** phase. This is one place where you evaluate your learning. However, it is not the only place. You were also evaluating your learning when you asked yourself "What do I see?" and "What do I think?" and "What do I think now?" You also evaluated your learning during the *Investigate* (**Explore**) and the *Physics Talk* (**Explain**). One difference between beginning and expert learners is that expert learners are more aware of their understanding through a constant evaluation of what they know and do not know.

Physics to Go

1. Test the reaction time of some of your friends and family with the metric ruler by following Method B in the *Investigate*. Obtain results from at least three people of various ages.

2. How did the reaction times you obtained in *Question 1* compare with those you obtained in class? What do you think explains the difference, if any?

3. Cut out a 6 cm × 15 cm rectangle from a sheet of paper. This is about the size of a dollar bill. Fold the paper in half lengthwise. Have your lab partner try to catch the paper between his/her index finger and middle finger.

   a) Explain why it is so difficult to catch the paper. Repeat the paper test, letting people catch it with their thumb and index finger.

   b) Explain why catching the paper with thumb and index finger may have been easier than catching it with index finger and middle finger. Try to include measurements in your answer, such as length of the paper, time for the paper to fall, and average reaction time.

   c) Is there a large range of values for the reaction time? Explain your answer.

   d) How would your reaction time change after repeating the same task several times? Why?

4. Does a race car driver need a faster reaction time than someone driving in a school zone? Explain your answer, giving examples of the dangers each driver encounters.

5. What does alcohol, changing radio stations, or talking on a cell phone do to your reaction time?

6. What are the consequences of driving if one's reaction time is slow rather than quick?

7. Even though teenagers often have good reaction times, why is auto insurance more expensive for teenage drivers than it is for older, more experienced drivers?

Why is there a *Preparing for the Chapter Challenge*?

This feature serves as a guide to get part of the *Chapter Challenge* completed. As you complete each section or a couple of sections of a chapter, you need to take time to organize the knowledge that you are learning and to try to apply it to the challenge. The *Preparing for the Chapter Challenge* is another **Extend** phase of the 7E instructional model.

8. *Preparing for the Chapter Challenge*

Apply what you learned from this section to describe how knowing your own reaction time can help you be a safer driver. You will use this information to meet the *Chapter Challenge*.

Why is there an *Inquiring Further*?

Active Physics uses inquiry as a way of learning. Inquiry lets you think like a scientist. It is the process by which you ask questions, design investigations, gather evidence, formulate answers, and share your answers. You are involved in inquiry during each section of a chapter. However, *Inquiring Further* gives you an additional opportunity to do inquiry on your own. Sometimes you will be asked to design an experiment and with the approval of your teacher, carry out your experiment. Other times, the *Inquiring Further* will ask you to answer questions that require additional sources of information, or to solve more challenging, in-depth problems.

Inquiring Further

1. **Reaction time of different groups of people**

   Do some groups of people have faster or slower reaction times than those of students in your class? Consider groups such as basketball players, video-game players, taxi drivers, older adults, and young children. Plan and carry out an investigation to collect data that will help you find an answer to the question.

2. **Red light–green light reaction timer**

Design and build a device with a red light and a green light. If the red light turns on, you must press one button and measure the reaction time. If the green light turns on, you must press a second button and measure the reaction time. Have your teacher approve your design before proceeding. How do reaction times to this decision-making task compare with the reaction times measured earlier?

Why is there a 7E instructional model?

At the beginning of this section, you were introduced to the 7E instructional model. You were also asked to think about why you are asked to do certain things in *Active Physics*. Review the components of this section, and think about what instructional-model phase is addressed by each component.

Phases of the 7E Instructional Model	Where is it in the section?
Elicit	*What Do You See?* *What Do You Think?*
Engage	*What Do You See?* *What Do You Think?*
Explore	*Investigate*
Explain	*Physics Talk* *Physics Words*
Elaborate	*Physics Talk* *What Do You Think Now?* *Checking Up* *Physics Essential Questions* *Physics to Go*
Extend	*Reflecting on the Section and the Challenge* *Preparing for the Chapter Challenge* *Inquiring Further*
Evaluate	*Formative evaluation — You evaluate your own understanding and the teacher can evaluate your understanding during all components of the chapter. Additional evaluations may include:* Lab reports, *Checking Up*, Quizzes, *What Do You Think Now?*, *Physics Essential Questions*, *Physics to Go.*

Section 2

Measurement: Errors, Accuracy, and Precision

What Do You See?

Learning Outcomes

In this section, you will

- **Calibrate** the length of a stride.
- **Measure** a distance by pacing it off and by using a meter stick.
- **Identify** sources of error in measurement.
- **Evaluate** estimates of measurements as reasonable or unreasonable.

What Do You Think?

When driving a vehicle, you often mentally measure distances and times. When investigating vehicle collisions, police officers take actual measurements at the scene. For example, the length of skid marks help officers to calculate the speed at which a vehicle was traveling.

- Two students measure the length of the same object. One reports a length of 3 m, the other reports a length of 10 m. Has one of them made a mistake?

- If the students reported measurements of 3 m and 3.01 m, do you think one of them has made a mistake?

Record your ideas about these questions in your *Active Physics* log. Explain your reasoning. Be prepared to discuss your responses with your small group and the class.

Remember to begin a new page in your *Active Physics* log each time you begin a new section. Write *Section 2 Measurement* at the top of the new page. Also record the section and page number in your *Table of Contents*.

Investigate

In this *Investigate*, you will measure a given distance by various techniques. You will have to determine which technique is best and why it is the best. You will also use estimation to decide if certain measurements are reasonable or not.

1. Your teacher and class will select and agree on a cleared distance along the floor of the cafeteria, corridor, or path around the classroom.

2. Each group will have a member pace off the distance. That is, count the number of strides it takes you to cover the marked-off distance.

   a) Record the number of strides in your log.

3. Have a group member measure the length of your stride using a meter stick. By finding the length of your stride, you are making a calibration, or a scale for a measuring instrument.

   a) Record your measurement in your log.

4. Use the number of strides you took in *Step 2* and the length of your stride to compute the distance in meters.

   a) Record your calculations.

5. List the results of the measurements made by all the groups on the board.

   a) Do all the measurements agree? By how much do the results vary?

   b) Why do you think there are differences among the measurements made by different groups? List as many reasons for the differences in measurements as you can.

   c) Suggest a way of improving your measurements. If all groups try your method, how will the range of measurements change this time?

6. Measure the selected distance with a single meter stick. You will have to move the meter stick over and over.

   a) Record your measurement in your log.

7. List the results of the measurements made by all the groups on the board.

   a) Do all the measurements agree? By how much do the results vary?

   b) Why do you think there are differences among the measurements made by different groups? List as many reasons for the differences in measurements as you can.

   c) Suggest a way of improving your measurements. If all groups try your method, what will the range of measurements be this time?

   d) What do you think would happen if each group were given a very long tape measure? List possible values the different teams may get. Do you think each group would get the exact same value?

   e) Can you develop a system that will produce measurements, all of which agree exactly, or will there always be some difference in measurements? Justify your answers.

8. A difference in measurement close to a certain accepted value is called an error. Physicists identify two kinds of errors in measurement. An error that can be corrected by calculation is called a *systematic error*. For example, if you measured the length of an object starting at the 1 cm mark on a ruler instead of at the end of the ruler, you could correct your measurement by subtracting 1 cm from the final reading on the ruler.

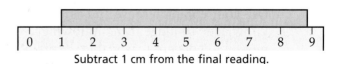
Subtract 1 cm from the final reading.

An error that cannot be corrected by calculation is called a *random error*. No measurement is perfect. When you measure something, you make an approximation close to a certain accepted value. Random errors exist in any measurement. But you can estimate the amount of uncertainty in measurements that random errors introduce. Scientists provide an estimate of the size of the random errors in their data.

Make an approximation.

a) When measuring the hallway or class, did you have any systematic errors?

b) Estimate the size of your random errors using each technique.

9. Sometimes a precise measurement is not needed. A good estimate will do. What is a good estimate?

Example:

• Suppose one of your friends estimates that a single-serving drink container holds 5 kg (weighing about 11 lb) of liquid.

This is not a good estimate. It is unreasonable. A mass of 5 kg, or a weight of 11 lb, is about the weight of a bowling ball or a turkey. A single-serving drink weighs much less than this.

Use your common sense and prior knowledge to judge if the following measurements are reasonable. Explain your answers.

a) A college football player has a mass of 100 kg (weighing about 220 lb).

b) A high-school basketball player is 4 m (13 ft) tall.

c) Your teacher works 1440 min every day.

d) A poodle has a mass of 60 kg (about 132 lb).

e) Your classroom has a volume of 150 m^3 (about 5300 ft^3).

f) The distance across the school grounds is 1 km (about 0.6 mi).

g) On a rural road, while driving 50 mi/h (about 80 km/h), you encounter a tractor moving very slowly. You are about ¼ mi (0.4 km) away when you see that another automobile is coming toward you. Is it safe to pass the tractor?

h) While driving your pickup truck on a rural road, you approach a narrow bridge and see you will reach it at the same time as a dump truck that is coming from the opposite direction. What must you estimate in order to decide whether to stop and wait for the dump truck to cross the bridge first, or to go ahead and squeeze by the dump truck while on the bridge?

Active Physics

i) You are driving a motor home with bicycles standing upright in a bicycle rack mounted on the roof. A sign before the entrance to a tunnel states that the maximum height is 21 ft (6.4 m). Will your automobile make it safely through the tunnel?

Physics Talk

ERRORS IN MEASUREMENT

Random Errors

There is no exact measurement. In the *Investigate*, when you used your stride length as the measuring tool, the distance of the hallway was different for many of the groups. If you tried to improve the measurement by using a meter stick, you found that there were still differences in the measurement. Even if you had used a tape measure, there would still have been differences in your measurements.

Physicists know that all measuring tools produce **random errors**, or errors that cannot be corrected by calculating. It is the responsibility of the student scientist to record all the values of a measurement and recognize that the data will include random errors. Every time you measure the length of your desk, you might find that the measurement is different from a previous value by 0.1 cm. This difference could be in either direction (± 0.1 cm). You can use a more precise ruler and that may decrease this random error or uncertainty to only 0.05 cm (± 0.05 cm). However, the uncertainty can never be completely eliminated.

Physics Words

random error: an error that cannot be corrected by calculation.

Both the measuring tool and the person doing the measuring are responsible for the uncertainty. A meter stick that has only the centimeters noted would have a greater uncertainty than a meter stick that has the millimeters noted. A meter stick that has millimeters noted may still have a large uncertainty if the person using it is not very careful in aligning the meter stick with the length being measured.

➡

In your measurement of the distance, you found different distributions of measurement. If you made histograms as shown below, of the length of a hallway using your stride (left figure), the meter stick (middle figure) or a tape measure (right figure), you can get a sense of the uncertainty in each type of measurement. The middle value is probably the "best guess" for the length of the room, but there will always be an uncertainty surrounding that value, as shown by the spread to the left and right of the middle value.

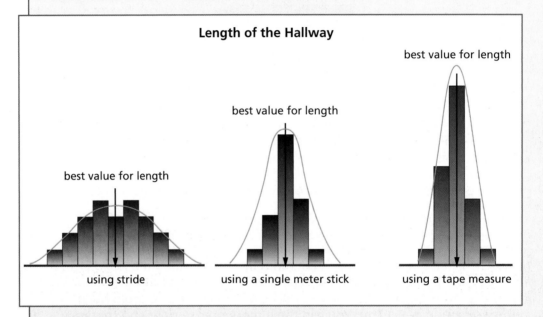

Length of the Hallway

best value for length

best value for length

best value for length

using stride

using a single meter stick

using a tape measure

Physics Words

systematic error: an error produced by using the wrong tool or using the tool incorrectly for measurement and can be corrected by calculation.

accuracy: an indication of how close a series of measurements are to an accepted value.

precision: an indication of the frequency with which a measurement produces the same results.

Systematic Errors

There are also **systematic errors**. If you mistake a yardstick for a meter stick and report your measurement as 4 m, when in fact it is 4 yd, that is a systematic error. Every measurement you record with that yardstick will have this error. Systematic errors can be avoided or can be corrected by calculating.

Accuracy and Precision

In shooting arrows at a target, you can have **accuracy** and **precision** by getting all the arrows in the bull's-eye (left figure). You can have precision, but not accuracy by having all the arrows miss the bull's-eye by the same amount (middle figure). You can also have accuracy, but without precision by having all the arrows surrounding the bull's-eye spread out over the area (right figure). Notice that here the average position is the bull's-eye (accuracy), but not one of the arrows actually hit the bull's eye (precision).

Measurements can also vary with accuracy and/or precision just as the arrows in the target.

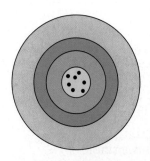
accurate and precise

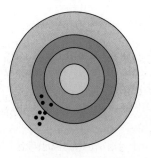
precise not accurate

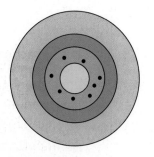
accurate but not precise

People do not always need the same level of precision in their measurements. One decision you must make is how precise a measurement you want. For example, in motor racing, horse racing, or Olympic skiing, time has to be measured to the thousandths or tens-of-thousandths of a second. But when a painter estimates the time required to paint a customer's house, she or he may only need to know the time within a few hours. As you increase the need for precision, the measurement becomes more difficult (and often, more expensive to make).

SI System

In *Active Physics*, you will be using the International System of Units. The units are known as SI units, abbreviated from *Le Système International d'Unités*. This is the system of units that is used by scientists. The system is based on the metric system. All units are related by some multiple of ten. There are seven base units that can be combined to measure all scientific properties. The base units that you will use in *Active Physics* are shown in the table.

Quantity	Unit	Symbol
length	meter	m
mass	kilogram	kg
time	second	s
temperature	kelvin	K
current	ampere	A

You will also be using other units that are a combination of these base units. You will be introduced to these units when you need to use them. The best way to learn units is to use them frequently and correctly. It is not helpful to memorize lots of units.

Active Physics

In this section, you measured the length of a distance in meters. The meter (m) is the base unit of length. Other units that you will use for measuring and describing length are the kilometer (km), centimeter (cm), and millimeter (mm). These three units are made up of the base unit meter and a prefix.

An important feature of the metric system is that there is a single set of prefixes that relates larger and smaller units. All the prefixes are related by some power (multiple) of ten.

Prefix	Symbol	Multiple of ten by which base unit is multiplied	Example
kilo	k	$10^3 = 1000$	1 km = 1000 m 1 m = 0.001 km
centi	c	$10^{-2} = 0.01$	1 cm = 0.01 m 1 m = 100 cm
milli	m	$10^{-3} = 0.001$	1 mm = 0.001 m 1 m = 1000 mm

Driving the Roads and United States Units of Measurement

The United States does not use the metric system for everyday measurements. Distances along the road are measured in feet, yards, or miles. Speed limits are posted in miles per hour rather than kilometers per hour, as they are in many other countries.

Below are some conversion factors for length in United States measurements.

12 inches (in.) = 1 foot (ft)

3 feet = 1 yard (yd)

5280 feet (1760 yd) = 1 United States statute mile (mi)

In this chapter, *Driving the Roads,* United States measurements will be used to express distances and speeds with respect to driving and traffic. In the classroom, you will use SI units for measuring.

When obeying speed-limit signs, it is important to know what units of measurement are being used.

Checking Up

1. Explain the difference between systematic and random errors.

2. Explain why there will always be uncertainty in measurement.

3. What would the positions of arrows on a target need to be to illustrate measurements that are neither accurate nor precise?

Active Physics

Plus

+Math	+Depth	+Concepts	+Exploration
◆	◆		

Precise Measurements and Olympic Records

The events in the Olympic Games depend on precise measurements of distances and times to determine who will receive a gold medal. If one skier has a time that is ³/₁₀₀₀ of a second better than another skier, this can be the difference between a gold and silver medal. In running and swimming, the athletes compete side by side and whoever is first wins the gold. However, the record times are compared from one Olympics to the next. If a swimmer in one Olympics beats the old record from 4 or 8 years earlier by only ¹/₁₀₀₀ of a second, the swimmer has the new world record. But did that swimmer really swim faster than the prior record holder? Not necessarily. By following a discussion including measurements and uncertainty, you will find that the new world record holder may actually be slower than the old record holder if the time difference was only ¹/₁₀₀₀ of a second.

Every four years, the Summer Olympics are held in a different city, and a new swimming pool must be built. The length of the swimming pool must be 50 m. You know from your investigation that every measurement has an uncertainty associated with it. When a pool is built for the Summer Olympic Games, do you think that pool's length could vary by 1 m? If so, the pool could be 49 m or 51 m in length. This is a huge difference. You can be sure that they build the pools to be closer to 50 m than 49 m.

1. What is the range of lengths for 50-m pools that have an uncertainty of ± 10 cm? ±1 cm? ± 1 mm? (For example, if the uncertainty of the pool were ± 1 m, the range of lengths would be 49–51 m.)

Suppose an Olympic pool is accurate to ± 1 cm. In one Olympics, the pool could be 49.99 m, while in another Olympics it could be 50.01 m. This does not seem to be a big difference and it seems like an accurate 50-m pool. It means that in one Olympic Games in one city, the swimmers may actually swim 50.01 m while in another Olympics in another city, the swimmers may actually swim only 49.99 m.

2. How much extra time does it take to swim 50.01 m than 49.99 m (a difference of 2 cm)? Assume a good swimmer can swim 50 m in 25 s.

The 1500-m race requires a swimmer to swim 30 lengths of the pool. If the pool in one Olympic Games is 50.01 m and in another Olympics the pool is only 49.99 m, then one swimmer will be swimming an extra 2 cm for every lap. In one Olympics, the swimmer may be swimming a total of 60 cm more than the other swimmer.

3. Estimate how long it takes to swim 60 cm. Assume a good time for the 1500-m race is 15 min.

4. In watching the Olympic Games, you hear that someone just broke the record for the 1500-m swim by 1/1000 of a second.

29

Active Physics

Explain how it is possible that this person (the new record holder) may actually be slower than the previous record holder. (Can it be that the new record holder is swimming in a shorter 50 m pool than the prior record holder?)

Comparing records for the 1500-m swim from one Olympics to the next depends on the length of the pools that the swimmers race in. The length of each pool cannot be exactly 50 m.

5. Write a letter to the Olympic commission addressing this issue. Include in your letter a solution to this problem that you have discovered. Including calculations of what would happen if the pools were built with an accuracy of 0.5 cm or 1 mm would make your letter more persuasive. You may also want to include something about the additional cost of making a 50-m pool this much more accurate.

What Do You Think Now?

At the beginning of this section, you were asked to think about the following:

- Two students measure the length of the same object. One reports a length of 3 m, the other reports a length of 10 m. Has one of them made a mistake?

- If the students reported measurements of 3 m and 3.01 m, do you think one of them has made a mistake?

How would you answer these questions now? Review what you have learned about random errors in measurement. How can you reduce random errors?

Physics
Essential Questions

What does it mean?

Suppose your friend mistakes a yardstick for a meter stick and measures the length of an intersection in your neighborhood. Is this error random or systematic? Which of these types of errors affect precision or accuracy?

How do you know?

Suppose you want to buy some gold jewelry. The jeweler tells you that the jewelry contains exactly 1 oz of gold. How do you know that the jeweler cannot be sure that it is exactly 1 oz?

Why do you believe?

Connects with Other Physics Content	Fits with Big Ideas in Science	Meets Physics Requirements
All physics includes measurements	Change and constancy	✳ Experimental evidence is consistent with models and theories

✳ All physics knowledge is based on experimentation. All experiments require measurements. How can you trust experiments if all measurements have uncertainties?

Why should you care?

What are the consequences of not estimating stopping distances accurately, or the width of a space between your vehicle and other vehicles while driving?

Reflecting on the Section and the Challenge

A measurement is never exact. When you make a measurement, you estimate that measurement. All measurements have systematic and random errors. An example of a systematic error might be using a measuring tape that stretches a little bit when it is pulled tightly. But if you know the amount of stretch, then you can correct the measurement using calculations. In contrast, random errors are part of any measurement process because you can only approximate a mark on a meter stick or the time on a stopwatch, with an accuracy to the closest decimal place. You can try to minimize random errors, but you cannot eliminate them entirely.

When a speed limit is 60 mph (about 100 km/h), you may find that sometimes you drive at 58 mph while other times you drive at 62 mph. These differences are random errors as you try to hold the speed constant. If a police officer stops you because you were driving at 75 mph (about 120 km/h) in a 30 mph zone, you will not be able to convince her that this was just an uncertainty in your measurement. Uncertainties in speeds may be something that you wish to include in your presentation or report.

Physics to Go

1. Get a meter stick and centimeter ruler. Find the length of five different-sized objects, such as a door, a tabletop, a large book, a pencil, and a stamp.

   a) Which measuring tool is best for measuring each object?

   b) Estimate the uncertainty in each measurement.

2. Count the number of strides it takes to walk around your classroom and estimate the length of each stride. Calculate the size of the room by multiplying the number of strides taken by the estimated length of each stride. Estimate your accuracy. Then check your accuracy with a meter stick.

3. Give an estimated value of something that you and your friend would agree on. Then, give an estimated value of something that you and your friend would not agree on.

4. An oil tanker is said to hold five million barrels of oil. In your estimate, how accurate is the measurement? Suppose each barrel of oil is worth $100. What is the possible uncertainty in value of the oil tanker's oil?

5. Choose five food products. How accurate are the measurements on labels?

6. Are the following estimates reasonable? Explain your answers.

   a) A 2-L bottle of soft drink is enough to serve 12 people at a meeting.

   b) A mid-sized automobile with a full tank of gas can travel from Boston to New York City without having to refuel.

7. If you are off by 1 m in measuring the width of a room, is that as much as an error as being off by 1 m in measuring the distance between your home and your school?

8. You are driving on a highway that posts a 65 mph (105 km/h) speed limit. The speedometer is accurate within 5 mph (8 km/h).

   a) What speed should you drive as shown on the speedometer to guarantee that you will not exceed the speed limit?

   b) What could a passenger in the vehicle do while you are driving to estimate how accurate the speedometer is? (Hint: The road has mile markers, and the passenger has a wristwatch that shows seconds.)

9. *Preparing for the Chapter Challenge*

   Many accidents are caused by speeding. To limit the number of collisions, police officers give speeding tickets to drivers. If the speed limit were 30 mph (50 km/h) in a residential neighborhood, a person may get a ticket for driving at 40 mph (65 km/h). Legally, they could also get a ticket for traveling at 31 mph (51 km/h). Given the uncertainties in measurements (the driver has to keep the gas pedal "just right"), you may wish to mention how these uncertainties are a part of safe driving. You may wish to explain why driving 31 mph in a 30 mph zone does or does not warrant a ticket. If you do not think that 31 mph deserves a ticket, you will need to explain what speed should get a ticket and why.

Inquiring Further

1. Measurement and national standards

The National Institute of Standards and Technology (NIST) is the nation's measurement laboratory. It provides companies and other organizations with references to use to check the accuracy of their equipment.

What type of certainty in measurement would you expect if you were buying vegetables by the pound, gas by the gallon, or carpeting by the yard? Investigate what types of measurement standards are regulated by the government. Report to your class the certainty of the measurements that are used in industry and the marketplace.

2. Random error and number of measurements

People who study the statistics of measurement have shown that, if you make N independent measurements of the same object, then the size of the random error decreases as:

$$\sqrt{\frac{1}{N}}$$

Plot histograms, graphs that measure frequency distribution, of the measurement of desks in the classroom and see if the size of the random error decreases as you measure more and more identical desks.

Section 3

Average Speed: Following Distance and Models of Motion

What Do You See?

Learning Outcomes

In this section, you will

- **Define** and contrast average speed and instantaneous speed.
- **Use** strobe photos, graphs, and an equation to describe speed.
- **Use** a motion detector to measure speed.
- **Construct** graphs of your motion.
- **Interpret** distance-time graphs.
- **Calculate** speed, distance, and time using the equation for average speed.

What Do You Think?

In a rear-end collision, usually the driver who strikes a vehicle from behind is legally at fault.

- **What is a safe following distance between your automobile and the vehicle in front of you?**

- **How do you decide what a safe following distance is?**

Record your ideas about these questions in your *Active Physics* log. Be prepared to discuss your responses with your small group and the class.

Investigate

In this *Investigate*, you will use strobe photos to observe constant motion at different speeds. You will then use a motion detector to measure velocity and to generate graphs of motion.

1. A "strobe photo" is a combination of photographs taken at regular time intervals. A single picture can then show the position of the object over equal time intervals.

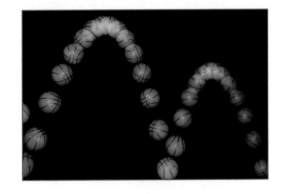

The diagram below shows what a strobe photo of an automobile traveling at 30 mph (about 50 km/h) would look like. The position of the car is shown at the end of every minute.

a) Make a sketch of the diagram in your log. (You can use rectangles to show the automobiles.)

2. Think about the difference between the motion of an automobile traveling at 30 mph (50 km/h) and one traveling at 45 mph (75 km/h).

a) Draw a sketch of a strobe photo, similar to the one above, of an automobile traveling at 45 mph (75 km/h).

b) Is the automobile the same distance apart between successive photos? Were your images farther apart or closer together than they were at 30 mph (50 km/h)? How far does each car go in one minute?

c) Draw a sketch of an automobile traveling at 60 mph (100 km/h). Describe how you decided how far apart to place the automobiles.

3. The following diagrams show an automobile traveling at different speeds. *Speed* is the distance traveled in a given amount of time.

A

B

C

a) In which diagram is the automobile traveling the slowest? In which diagram is the automobile traveling the fastest? Explain how you made your choice.

b) Is each automobile traveling at a constant speed? How can you tell?

4. A motion detector is a device that measures the position of an object over a time interval. It can be connected to a computer or calculator-based lab equipment to produce a graph of the motion.

Safety is always important in the laboratory. Appropriate warnings concerning possible safety hazards are included where applicable. You need to be aware of all possible dangers, listen carefully to your teacher's instructions, and behave accordingly.

⚠ Make sure the path of motion is clear of any hazards.

Use the motion-detector setup to obtain the following graphs to print or sketch in your log. Put the time on the horizontal axis (*x*-axis) and the object's location on the vertical axis (*y*-axis).

a) Sketch the graph of a person walking toward the motion detector at a normal steady speed.

Active Physics

b) Sketch the graph of a person walking away from the motion detector at a normal speed.

c) Sketch the graph of a person walking away from the motion detector then toward it at a very slow speed.

d) Sketch the graph of a person walking in both directions at a fast speed.

e) Describe the similarities and differences among the graphs. Explain how the direction and speed that the person walked contributed to these similarities and differences.

5. Predict what the graph will look like if you walk toward the motion detector at a slow speed and away from it at a fast speed.

a) Sketch a graph of your prediction.

b) Test your prediction. How accurate was your prediction?

6. Do two more trials using the motion detector. In trial 1, walk slowly away from the detector. In trial 2, walk quickly away from the detector.

a) Sketch the lines from the two trials on the same labeled axes. Be sure to record the endpoints for each line.

b) Suppose someone forgot to label the two lines. How can you determine which graph goes with which line?

7. In physics, the total distance traveled by an object during a given time is the *average speed* of the object.

a) From your graph, determine the total distance you walked in each trial.

b) How long did it take you to walk each distance?

c) Divide the distance you walked (your change in position) (*d*) by the time it took for each trial (*t*).

This calculation gives you your average speed in meters per second (m/s).

$$v_{av} = \frac{d}{t}$$

d) How could you go about predicting your position after walking for twice the time in trial 2? When you extrapolate data, you make an assumption about the walker. What is the assumption? (Extrapolate means to estimate a value outside the known data points.)

8. An automobile is traveling at 60 ft/s (about 40 mph or 65 km/h).

a) If the reaction time is 0.5 s, how far does the automobile travel in this time?

b) How much farther will the automobile travel if the driver is distracted by talking on a cell phone or unwrapping a sandwich, so that the reaction time increases to 1.5 s?

c) Answer the questions in *Steps 8.a*) and *8.b*) for an automobile moving at 50 ft/s (about 35 mph or 56 km/h).

d) Repeat the calculation for *Step 8.c*) for 70 ft/s (about 48 mph or 77 km/h).

e) Imagine a driver in an automobile in traffic moving at 40 ft/s (about 28 mph or 45 km/h). The driver ahead has collided with another vehicle and has stopped suddenly. How far behind the preceding automobile should a driver be to avoid hitting it, if the reaction time is 0.5 s?

f) An automobile is traveling at 60 ft/s (about 40 mph or 65 km/h). How many automobile lengths does it travel per second? A typical automobile is 15 ft (about 5 m long).

Physics Talk

UNDERSTANDING MOTION

As part of your *Chapter Challenge*, you need to describe the motion of a motor vehicle while you are driving. You are expected to explain what factors affect following distance, braking distance, and the total stopping distance. One factor that affects all of these is **speed**. Speed is the distance traveled per unit time. In the *Investigate*, you represented **constant speed** (speed that does not change over a period of time) by using strobe photographs, distance-time graphs generated by a motion detector, and an equation.

Model I: Describing Motion and Speed Using Strobe Photos

As you discovered in the *Investigate*, there are many different ways to describe motion. One way to show motion is with the use of strobe photos. A strobe photo is a multiple-exposure photo in which a moving object is photographed at regular time intervals. You used diagrams of strobe photos in the *Investigate* to represent different speeds.

The illustrations below show constant motion at a slow speed (top) and constant motion at a fast speed (bottom).

You saw that when an object is moving at a slow speed, the distance between the objects is less than when the object is moving at a fast speed. This makes sense, because at a slow speed, the object travels a shorter distance during the same time than at a fast speed.

Physics Words

speed: the distance traveled per unit time; speed is a scalar quantity, it has no direction.

constant speed: speed that does not change over a period of time.

average speed: the total distance traveled divided by the time it took to travel that distance.

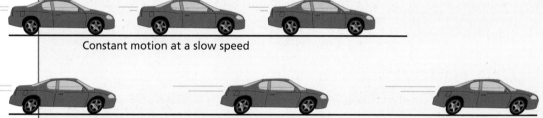

Constant motion at a slow speed

Constant motion at a fast speed

Model II: Describing Motion and Speed Using an Equation

In the *Investigate*, you also used an equation to describe speed. The **average speed** of a vehicle is the ratio of the total distance traveled to the total elapsed time.

$$\text{Average speed} = \frac{\text{distance traveled}}{\text{time elapsed}}$$

Is There an Equation?

Physicists try as much as possible to describe things they observe mathematically. They use equations to express relationships. Equations are precise and give you a lot of information with few words. Equations can also help you make numerical predictions of what will change under new circumstances. Student physicists, like you, often ask, "Is there an equation?" Whenever possible, *Active Physics* will provide you with an equation you can use. The equations that you use are summarized for you at the end of each chapter.

This equation can be written using quantity symbols.

$$v_{av} = \frac{\Delta d}{\Delta t}$$

where v_{av} is average speed,

Δd is change in position or total distance traveled,

Δt is change in time or elapsed time.

The Greek letter *delta*, "Δ," is often used in science to mean "a change in." In this section, you will be dealing only with situations in which you are given total distance traveled and elapsed time.

Symbols for Physical Quantities

Symbols for SI units are unique and precise. There is only one symbol for each SI unit. For example, "m" stands for meter and "s" stands for second. The same SI symbol is used in every language.

When writing equations in science, there is also a need for other symbols. Symbols are needed for quantities such as distance, time, or speed. These symbols are not a part of SI. They are also not always unique. For example, V can stand for volume or voltage. As much as possible, scientists try to use standard symbols for quantities. However the SI symbol V only stands for volts.

When writing equations, you should use the same symbols used in *Active Physics*. To distinguish the two types of symbols in printed materials, sloping *(italic)* type is used for quantity symbols and upright (roman) type is used for SI symbols.

Sample Problem 1

If you drive a distance of 400 mi (about 640 km) in 8 h, what is your average speed?

Strategy: You can use the equation for average speed. $v_{av} = \frac{\Delta d}{\Delta t}$

Given: $\Delta d = 400$ mi

$\Delta t = 8$ h

Solution: $v_{av} = \frac{\Delta d}{\Delta t}$

$= \frac{400 \text{ mi}}{8 \text{ h}}$

$= 50 \frac{\text{mi}}{\text{h}}$

Your average speed is 50 mi/h.

The average speed of 50 mi/h (80 km/h) does not tell your fastest speed or your slowest speed. It only tells you that over a period of time, 8 h, you traveled a given distance, 400 mi (80 km).

Before your vehicle started moving, the speed was 0 mi/h. When you stopped your vehicle at the end of the trip, your speed was again 0 mi/h. During the trip you probably slowed down and sped up as you drove along. You may have stopped for a meal. The speedometer reading at any moment during the trip is your **instantaneous speed**, which is the speed at a given moment. Instantaneous speed is the speed measured during an instant.

Using the Equation for Speed to Find Other Quantities

Equations are a powerful mathematical tool. Using the equation for average speed, you are not limited to just solving for speed. If you know the average speed and the time it took you to travel that speed, you can find the distance you traveled in that time. You can also find the time traveled if you know the distance traveled and the average speed.

$$\text{Average speed} = \frac{\text{distance traveled}}{\text{time elapsed}}$$

Using algebra, it follows that

$$\text{Distance} = \text{average speed} \times \text{time}$$

$$\text{Time} = \frac{\text{distance}}{\text{average speed}}$$

Using quantity symbols these equations can be written as

$$v_{av} = \frac{\Delta d}{\Delta t}$$

$$\Delta d = v_{av} \times \Delta t$$

$$\Delta t = \frac{\Delta d}{v_{av}}$$

You can use the following helpful circle to do your calculations:

By covering up the variable you wish to find, you can see the equation.

To find average speed (v_{av}), cover up the (v_{av}) and you see $\frac{\Delta d}{\Delta t}$.

To find distance (Δd), cover up (Δd) and you see $v_{av} \times \Delta t$.

To find time (Δt), cover up (Δt) and you see $\frac{\Delta d}{v_{av}}$.

It is important to note that there is one equation for average speed, but you can write it in three equivalent ways.

➡

Physics Words

instantaneous speed: the speed at a given moment.

39

Active Physics

Sample Problem 2

You are traveling at 35 mph (about 50 ft/s) and your reaction time is 0.2 s. Calculate the distance you travel during your reaction time.

Strategy: You can rewrite the equation for average speed to solve for distance traveled.

$$\Delta d = v_{av} \times \Delta t$$

Remember that ft/s means $\dfrac{ft}{s}$.

Given: $\Delta t = 0.2$ s

$v_{av} = 50$ ft/s

Solution: $\Delta d = v_{av} \times \Delta t$

$$\Delta d = 50\,\frac{ft}{\cancel{s}} \times 0.2\,\cancel{s}$$

$$= 10\ ft$$

Calculations and Units

In physics, when you do calculations, it is very important to pay close attention to the units in your answer. Notice how in the previous calculation the units for seconds (s) in the top and bottom of the equation cancel out, leaving feet (ft), the unit for distance that you need for your answer. Checking to see if the units make sense is a tool that physicists use to ensure that their calculations make sense and that they have not made a mistake.

Sample Problem 3

In an automobile collision, it was determined that a car traveled 150 ft before the brakes were applied.

a) If the car had been traveling at the speed limit of 40 mph (60 ft/s), what was the driver's reaction-time (time it took to apply the brakes)?

b) Witnesses say that the driver appeared to be under the influence of alcohol. Does your reaction-time data support the witnesses' testimony?

Strategy:

a) You can rewrite the equation for average speed to solve for time elapsed.

$$\Delta t = \frac{\Delta d}{v_{av}}$$

Given: $\Delta d = 150$ ft

$v_{av} = 60$ ft/s or $60 \dfrac{\text{ft}}{\text{s}}$

Solution: $\Delta t = \dfrac{\Delta d}{v_{av}}$

$$\Delta t = \dfrac{150 \text{ ft}}{60 \dfrac{\text{ft}}{\text{s}}}$$

$$= 2.5 \text{ s}$$

Note, mathematically, $\dfrac{\text{ft}}{\dfrac{\text{ft}}{\text{s}}} = \text{ft} \times \dfrac{\text{s}}{\text{ft}} = \text{s}$

b) Reaction time with distractions was measured in *Section 1*. The reaction time of 2.5 s seems very slow. The driver has the reaction time of someone who could be under the influence of alcohol.

Speed and Velocity

> In *Active Physics*, you will often explore the same topic several times. Being exposed to the same topic at different times and in different situations helps you learn and understand the topic better. The difference between speed and velocity will be explored at different times in this book. Velocity will also be explored in greater depth in later chapters.

A term you often hear used when talking about speed is velocity. **Velocity** is speed in a given direction. Velocity always includes both speed and direction.

Model III: Describing Motion and Speed Using a Distance-Time Graph

You investigated how to represent motion with strobe photos and with a mathematical equation. A third way to represent motion is with graphs. Graphs are a visual way to represent data. The graph at right shows an automobile traveling at a constant speed of 50 mi/h.

Notice that time is on the *x*-axis and distance is on the *y*-axis. By reading the coordinates on the graph, you can see that the automobile reached the 50 mi position at the end of 1 h; the 100 mi position at the end of 2 h; and the 150 mi position at the end of 3 h.

Physics Words

velocity: the speed in a given direction.

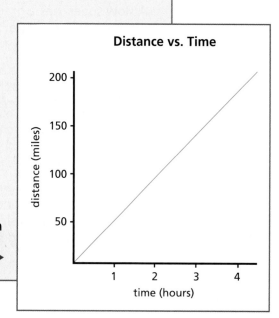

Distance vs. Time

Active Physics

Chapter 1 Driving the Roads

It is quite unrealistic to assume that an automobile could keep this speed of 50 mph for a full 3 h. If it did, however, you can see that the distance-time graph forms a straight line. Anytime an object moves at a constant speed, the distance-time graph is a straight line.

In the *Investigate*, you used a motion detector to generate graphs to represent your motion. You can determine the general motion of a person (a vehicle or any object) by reviewing a distance-time graph. Look at the following graphs. All graphs have the same time and distance scales.

Graph A: A person is at rest. As time increases, there is no change in the position of the person. The person is standing still.

Graph B: A person is traveling at a slow speed. As time increases, there is a small change in the position.

Graph C: A person is traveling at a fast speed. As time increases, there is a greater change in the position.

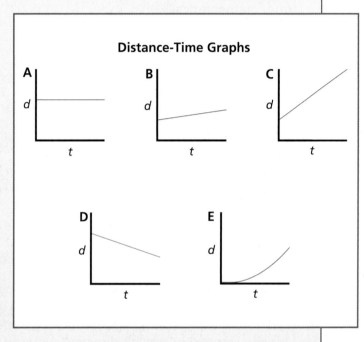

Distance-Time Graphs

Notice that the slope of the graph indicates the speed of the person. A slow speed has a gradual slope. A fast speed has a steep slope. No motion has zero slope. The graph of a person at rest is a horizontal line with a slope of zero—representing a speed of zero.

Graph D: A person is traveling in the opposite direction of the person in the previous graphs. As time passes, the change in position is in the opposite direction.

Graph E: A person is changing speed. As time passes, the change in position is increasing for each second. Notice that a changing speed is a curve on a distance-time graph.

In the *Investigate*, you noticed that walking toward the motion detector produced a slope in one direction. Walking away from the motion detector produced a slope in the opposite direction. The slope was zero, or close to zero, when standing still.

42

Active Physics

Speed and the Slope of a Distance-Time Graph

You compared speeds by looking at the slope of lines on distance-time graphs. You can also use the slopes of distance-time graphs to obtain a quantitative (number) value for speed. The slope of a line is the rise (change along the *y* dimension) divided by the run (change along the *x* dimension). If you look at a distance-time graph, the rise is the distance covered and the run is time taken. Distance divided by time is the equation you used to calculate speed.

$$\text{slope} = \frac{\text{rise}}{\text{run}} \qquad v_{av} = \frac{\Delta d}{\Delta t}$$

The measure of the slope of a *d* vs. *t* graph is equal to the speed of the object.

More about the SI System: Units for Measuring Speed and Velocity

In *Active Physics*, speed and velocity (speed in the direction of motion) in the classroom is measured in meters per second (m/s). Notice that the unit for speed or velocity is made up of a combination of two of the SI base units, meters (m) and seconds (s). These are called derived SI units.

Other units can also be used for speed. For example, highway speeds could be measured in kilometers per hour (km/h). The movement of Earth's crust could be measured in centimeters per year (cm/yr).

Kilometers and Miles

Highway signs and speed limits in the United States of America are given in miles per hour (mi/h or mph). Almost every other country in the world uses kilometers to measure long distances. A kilometer is a little less than two-thirds of a mile (1.0 km ≈ 0.6 mi). Kilometers per hour (km/h) is used to measure highway driving speed. For shorter distances, such as stopping distances and experiments in a science class, speed is measured in meters per second, m/s.

You will use miles per hour when working with driving speeds, but meters per second for data you collect in class. It is important to be able to understand and compare measurements.

There are mathematical conversions that can help you convert from miles per hour to kilometers per hour and meters per second. To help you relate the speed with which you are comfortable to the data you collect in class, the chart at the right gives approximate comparisons. It shows standard speed limits for the United States and Canada.

Speed-Limit Conversion Table			
United States (Imperial)		Canada (Metric)	
mph	ft/s	km/h	m/s
20	29	30	8
30	44	50	14
50	73	80	22
70	102	100	28

Speed and the Doppler Effect

Driving safely is everybody's responsibility. Part of safe driving is obeying the speed limit. All roads have a speed limit. This speed limit is posted for some roads but not for all. As a driver, you must know the speed limit of roads without a posting. Most people are aware that going too fast is dangerous. An accident at a high speed results in much greater damage than at slower speeds. However, traveling too slowly can also be dangerous and can result in accidents.

You can find out if you are speeding by reading the speedometer in the car. You can also calculate the speed by using posted mile markers on some roads. If you measure the time it takes your vehicle to travel between two mile-markers, you can find the speed of the vehicle by using the equation for average speed, $v = \dfrac{\Delta d}{\Delta t}$.

You can also get a sense of the speed of a passing vehicle by listening carefully to the sound of the engine and the tires on the road. Sound travels in waves. The shorter the wavelength, the higher the pitch (frequency). The longer the wavelength, the lower the pitch. As you stand on the side of a street, you can hear the change in pitch of a vehicle as it moves past you. In auto racing, the shift in pitch is quite noticeable. As the race car approaches, you hear a high pitch, and as the car departs, you hear a low pitch. The change in pitch of the sound is indicative of the speed of the car. The driver of the vehicle would not notice any change in pitch, because the driver is traveling along with the source of the sound.

Physics Words

Doppler effect: the change in the pitch, or frequency of a sound (or the frequency of a wave) for an observer that is moving relative to the source of the sound (or source of the wave).

The change in pitch is called the **Doppler effect**. It is named in honor of Christian Doppler, an Austrian physicist and mathematician, who was one of the first to analyze this phenomenon. He noticed that the pitch (frequency) of a train whistle was higher as the train approached and lower as the train departed.

To help you understand why this effect occurs, look at the diagrams on the following page of a stationary source of sound and a moving source. In the first diagram, the sound source is stationary. A person standing at position X and one standing at position Y would hear the same frequency of sound. In the second diagram, the sound source is moving to the right. As the sound waves approach position Y, they are closer together than if the source were stationary. A person at this position would hear a higher frequency sound. The source is moving away from position X. As the sound waves approach that position, they are farther apart. A person standing at X would hear a lower frequency sound. You will learn more about sound waves in a later chapter.

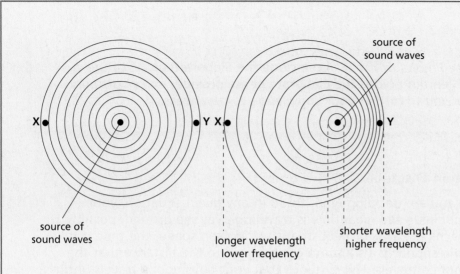

source of sound waves

source of sound waves

longer wavelength lower frequency

shorter wavelength higher frequency

Is there an equation for the Doppler effect? The equation relating the increased frequency and the speed of the train is given by

$$f = \frac{f_0 \cdot s}{s - v}$$

where f is the observed frequency when the train is moving;

   f_0 is the frequency when the train is at rest;

   v is the speed of the train; and

   s is the speed of sound, about 340 m/s.

Using the Doppler effect for sound waves is not an effective way of measuring a precise speed of a moving vehicle. Police use radar guns that use the Doppler effect for microwaves. The police radar sends out microwaves of a certain frequency. These microwaves reflect off the vehicle. If the vehicle is stationary, the reflected microwaves have the same frequency as the emitted microwaves.

If the vehicle is moving toward the radar gun, the reflected microwaves have a higher frequency. If the vehicle is moving away from the radar gun, the reflected microwaves have a lower frequency. The emitted frequency and the reflected frequency are compared electronically and the radar gun determines the speed.

The Doppler effect is also used to measure the speed of galaxies at huge distances from Earth. The frequency of the light from the galaxies is shifted to lower frequencies. Astronomers interpret this to mean that the galaxies are moving away from Earth. By calculating the speed of many galaxies, astronomers form theories about the birth and structure of the universe.

The *Physics Talk* may also include the **Elaborate** phase of the 7E learning cycle. The **Elaborate** phase provides an opportunity for you to further your knowledge to new areas.

Reaction Distance

While you are deciding what to do in any given situation, your automobile in the meantime is traveling over the ground, possibly approaching traffic or pedestrians. At a given speed, the time it takes you to respond to a situation corresponds to the distance that the automobile travels. This distance that your automobile travels until you respond is known as the **reaction distance**.

In *Sample Problem 2*, you saw that for a reaction time of 0.2 s, your automobile would move 10 ft if the automobile were traveling at 35 mph (about 50 ft/s). A longer reaction time increases the distance you travel before you even begin to brake or turn. The longer your reaction time, the greater the distance the automobile moves before you begin stopping, swerving, or taking other appropriate action. Your reaction time therefore has a direct effect on the distance your vehicle travels and the possibility of being involved in an accident.

Physics Words

reaction distance: the distance that a vehicle travels in the time it takes the driver to react.

Checking Up

1. Explain how the average speed of a vehicle is different from instantaneous speed.

2. How are the speed and velocity of an object different?

3. If the distance-time graph shows a straight, inclined line, what does the line represent?

4. How does reaction time affect reaction distance?

+Math	+Depth	+Concepts	+Exploration
◆	◆		

Active Physics
Plus

More About Average Speed

An automobile travels the first half of an 80.0 mi trip at 20.0 mi/h and the second half of the trip at 40.0 mi/h. What is the average speed for the entire trip?

A first guess may be 30.0 mi/h because this is the average of the two speeds. However, this is not correct. To find the average speed, you must use the definition of average speed. Average speed is equal to the total distance traveled divided by the total time.

In this problem, you can set up a table like the one below to help you find the average speed.

	Distance	Time
1st half of the trip at 20 mi/h	40.0 mi	2.0 h
2nd half of the trip at 40 mi/h	40.0 mi	1.0 h
Total trip	80.0 mi	3.0 h (1.0 h + 2.0 h)

The average speed of the entire trip is the total distance covered divided by the total time taken.

$$v_{av} = \frac{\Delta d}{\Delta t}$$
$$= \frac{80.0 \text{ mi}}{3.0 \text{ h}}$$
$$= 27 \text{ mi/h}$$

Does this answer make sense? Why should the average speed be 27 mi/h instead of 30 mi/h?

To better understand this situation, look at a more extreme case. Imagine an automobile that travels 100 mi. The first 50 mi, the automobile travels at 1 mi/h. The first 50 mi will take 50 h (more than two days of driving). During the last 50 mi, the automobile travels at 50 mi/h. The last half of the trip only requires 1 h. The average speed would not be 25.5 mi/h (the average of 1 mi/h and 50 mi/h). The average would be very close to 1 mi/h because this driver drove at only 1 mi/h for many hours and only got a chance to drive at 50 mi/h for 1 h. Average speed is about distance and time.

1. Draw a distance versus time graph for both situations described above (the 80 mi trip and the 100 mi trip).

2. Draw a strobe sketch for both situations described above (the 80 mi trip and the 100 mi trip).

3. Suppose someone travels 50 mi at 50 mi/h, then travels 50 mi at 25 mi/h, then travels 50 mi at 10 mi/h.

   a) Estimate their average speed.

   b) Calculate the average speed. How close was it to your estimate?

4. If you travel the first half of a trip at 20 mi/h, how fast must you travel the second half of the trip so that your average speed will be 40 mi/h?

47

What Do You Think Now?

At the beginning of this section, you were asked the following:

- **What is a safe following distance between your automobile and the vehicle in front of you?**

- **How do you decide what a safe following distance is?**

How would you answer these questions now? Now that you know how speed is related to distance and time, why is it important to pay attention to speed while driving? How does speed impact the distance covered when the driver is trying to avoid a rear-end collision?

Physics
Essential Questions

What does it mean?
What does it mean to say that the speed of a vehicle is 40 mi/h?

How do you know?
How would you go about measuring the speed of a vehicle? What measurements would you have to take? What calculations would you have to perform?

Why do you believe?

Connects with Other Physics Content	Fits with Big Ideas in Science	Meets Physics Requirements
Forces and motion	✳ Models	Experimental evidence is consistent with models and theories

✳ Physicists use models to better understand the world. Speed can be modeled with a strobe photo, an equation, or a graph. How can all three models represent a car moving at 20 m/s?

Why should you care?
Safe driving includes an understanding of speed, reaction time, and reaction distance. Some collisions are difficult to avoid, but any collision would be less severe, if the speed of the vehicles were less. Many highway accidents occur because of tailgating—the practice of leaving very little room between your automobile and the automobile in front of you. Explain how the reaction distance depends on your reaction time and your speed.

Reflecting on the Section and the Challenge

When you drive an automobile, you are controlling its velocity. You change the automobile's velocity by changing its speed (stepping on the gas pedal or brake pedal), and/or by changing its direction of motion (by turning the steering wheel). As you drive, you are continuously monitoring the automobile's velocity (speed and direction). You adjust both speed and direction as necessary.

Based on all the information you have just read, you now have ways to symbolically represent motion. You can use a strobe sketch or a distance–time graph. Also, you can calculate the reaction distance by knowing the speed of the automobile and the driver's reaction time.

You should be able to make a good argument against tailgating as a result of learning about reaction distance as part of the *Chapter Challenge*. Tailgating is when a driver leaves little space between his or her automobile and the automobile in front. You also should be able to make a good argument against excessive speed in any driving situation, especially when approaching an intersection or places where there may be pedestrians.

Physics to Go

1. Describe the motion of each automobile below. The diagrams of strobe photos were taken every 3 s (seconds).

   a)

   b)

2. Sketch diagrams of strobe photos of the following:

   a) An automobile starting from rest and reaching a final constant speed.

   b) An automobile traveling at a constant speed then coming to a stop.

3. A race car driver travels at 350 ft/s (that's almost 250 mph) for 20 s. How far has the driver traveled during this time?

4. A salesperson drives the 215 mi from New York City to Washington, DC, in 4.5 h.

   a) What was her average speed?

   b) Do you know how fast she was going when she passed through Baltimore? Explain your answer.

5. If you planned to bike to a park that was five miles away, what average speed would you have to maintain to arrive in about 15 min? (Hint: To compute your speed in miles per hour, consider this: What fraction of an hour is 15 min?)

6. For each graph below, describe the motion of the automobile. The vertical axes are labeled with the distance the automobile traveled, denoted *d*.

a)
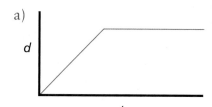

b)
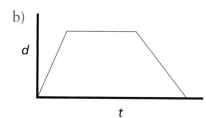

c)
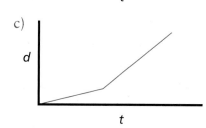

d)
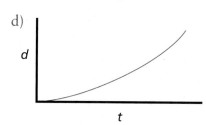

7. Use your average reaction time from *Section 1* to answer the following:

a) How far does your automobile travel in meters during your reaction time if you are moving at 55 mi/h (25 m/s)?

b) How far does your automobile travel during your reaction time if you are moving at 35 mi/h (16 m/s)? How does the distance compare with the distance at 55 mi/h?

c) Suppose you are very tired and your reaction time is doubled. How far would you travel at 55 mi/h during your reaction time?

8. According to traffic experts, the following distance between your automobile and the vehicle in front of you should be three seconds. As the vehicle in front of you passes a fixed point, say to yourself "one thousand one, one thousand two, one thousand three." Your automobile should not reach that point before you complete the phrase.

a) A second is a unit of time. How can traffic experts be sure this is a safe following distance?

b) Will three seconds following "distance" be equally as safe on an interstate highway as on a rural road? Explain your answer.

9. A sneeze requires you to close your eyes for one third of a second.

a) If you are driving at 70 mi/h (100 ft/s), how far will you travel with your eyes closed during a sneeze?

b) Is this longer than the length of your classroom?

10. Imagine you are driving your automobile at 60 mi/h (88 ft/s) moving in a straight line and your reaction time is 0.5 s.

   a) How far does your automobile travel in this time?

   b) How many automobile spaces is this for an automobile that is 15 ft long?

   c) Answer *Questions a)* and *b)* when you travel 30 mi/h.

   d) Answer *Questions a)* and *b)* when you travel 90 mi/h. What fraction of a football field is this distance?

   e) If talking on the cell phone while driving at this speed doubles your reaction time, how do these distance numbers change at 30 mi/h, 60 mi/h, and 90 mi/h?

11. Consider an automobile traveling at 60 mi/h. Sketch a graph showing distance traveled versus reaction time, with reaction times of 0.25 s, 0.50 s, 0.75 s, and 1.00 s.

12. *Preparing for the Chapter Challenge*

   Apply what you learned in this section to write a convincing argument that describes why tailgating (following an automobile too closely) is dangerous. Include the factors you would use to decide how following too closely counts as tailgating.

Inquiring Further

1. **Calculating speed over a longer distance**

   Measure a distance of about 100 m. You can use a football field or get a long tape measure or trundle wheel to measure a similar distance. You also need a watch capable of measuring seconds. Determine your average speed traveling that distance for each of the following:

   a) a slow walk

   b) a fast walk

   c) running

   d) another method of your choice

2. **Other models for motion**

   In this section, you learned three models that physicists use to describe motion—the strobe photo, the mathematical equation, and the motion graph. Painters, writers, poets, and photographers have also found ways to describe motion. Many people have heard the description of Superman's speed— "faster than a speeding bullet." Investigate and record descriptions of motion by people in the arts. How do artists and writers depict motion? How does one compare the physicist's model with that of the artist?

Section 4

Graphing Motion: Distance, Velocity, and Acceleration

What Do You See?

Learning Outcomes

In this section, you will

- **Measure** a change in velocity (acceleration) of a cart on a ramp using a motion detector.

- **Construct** graphs of the motion of a cart on a ramp.

- **Define** acceleration using words and an equation.

- **Calculate** speed, distance, and time using the equation for acceleration.

- **Interpret** distance-time and velocity-time graphs for different types of motion.

What Do You Think?

Some automobiles can accelerate from 0 to 60 mph (about 100 km/h) in 5 s. Other vehicles can take up to 10 s or more to reach the same speed.

- **An automobile and a bus are stopped at a traffic light. What are some differences and similarities of the motion of these two vehicles as each goes from a stop to the speed limit of 30 mph?**

Record your ideas about this question in your *Active Physics* log. Be prepared to discuss your responses with your small group and the class.

Investigate

In this *Investigate*, you will use a motion detector to explore motion. You will produce distance-time and velocity-time graphs for a cart as it moves down and up an inclined ramp. You will also use the defining equation to calculate acceleration.

1. Set a motion detector at the top of a ramp along with a cart. Before collecting the data, you will make several predictions.

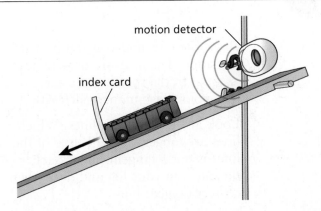

motion detector

index card

a) Predict how the distance the cart travels will change with respect to time. Will it go the first half of the distance in the same amount of time as the last half of the distance?

b) Below are four different distance-time (*d-t*) graphs. In one of them, the cart does not move. In the other three, the more time that elapses, the further the cart has gone. One graph shows that the cart travels at a constant speed. In another, the cart travels faster at the beginning. In another one, the cart travels fastest at the end.

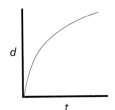

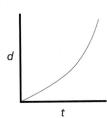

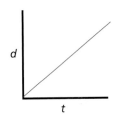

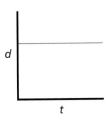

Identify which graph corresponds to which motion. (Hint: Compare the distance traveled in the first few seconds of the trip with the distance traveled in the last few seconds of the trip.)

c) Predict what you think a distance-time graph will look like when your cart is released from the top of the ramp. Sketch your predicted graph in your log along with an explanation.

2. Release the cart and collect the distance-time data. You may need to try this several times to make sure the motion detector collects consistent results.

a) Sketch the *d-t* graph from the calculator or computer in your log.

b) Compare your predictions in *Step 1.c)* to what really happened. Explain any differences you find.

c) In *Section 3*, you found that the slope of a distance-time graph represents the speed. If your graph is a curve rather than a straight line, you can still find the slope at a single point on the curve. To do this, choose the point where you want to measure the slope. Then place a ruler so that it intersects the curve at points to the right and left of the point. Slide the ruler so that it finally intersects the curve at a single point. It is now a *tangent line*. A tangent line is a straight line that touches a curve at only one point.

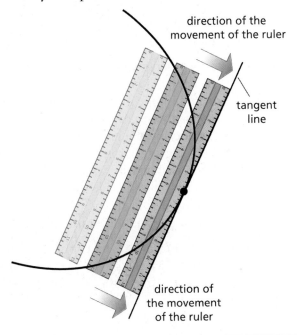

direction of the movement of the ruler

tangent line

direction of the movement of the ruler

Active Physics

Draw the line, and you can measure the slope. The measure of that slope is equal to the speed of the cart at that point (instantaneous speed).

Look at the following lines. Which lines are tangent lines? If one of the lines is not a tangent line, sketch the curve in your log and draw the correct tangent line.

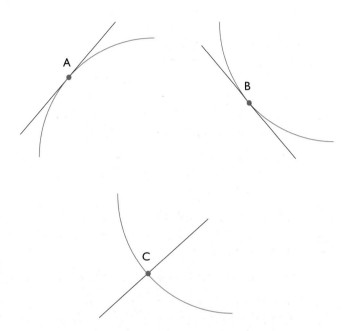

🖎 d) Returning to your distance-time graph, what happens to the slope of the d-t graph as time increases? What does this tell you about the velocity?

🖎 e) As you have seen, the motion of the cart can be modeled with a distance-time graph. It could also be modeled with a velocity-time graph. A velocity-time graph shows how the velocity changes as time elapses. Predict what you think a velocity-time (v-t) graph will look like for the cart moving down the incline. Sketch it in your log along with an explanation.

3. Replace the cart at the top of the ramp as in *Step 1*. Release the cart and collect the velocity-time data. You may need to try this several times to make sure the motion detector collects accurate data.

🖎 a) Sketch the v-t graph from the calculator or computer into your log. Use the "TRACE" function to label three to four data points along each line. These data points will assist you in making some calculations.

🖎 b) Compare your predictions in *Step 2.e)* to what really happened. Explain any differences you find. Why does the graph start at 0, 0?

🖎 c) As time increases, what happens to the slope of the v-t graph? Why does this happen?

🖎 d) The slope of the v-t graph is the *acceleration* of the cart. Acceleration is defined as the change in velocity with respect to a change in time and is expressed as follows:

$$\text{Acceleration} = \frac{\text{change in velocity}}{\text{change in time}}$$

This relationship can be written as an equation using symbols

$$a = \frac{\Delta v}{\Delta t}$$

where *a* is acceleration,
    Δv is change in velocity,
    Δt is change in time or elapsed time.

Velocity represents both speed and direction. There is an acceleration:
- if there is a change in speed over a given time,
- if there is a change in direction over a given time, or
- if there is both a change in speed and a change in direction.

Since the cart going down the ramp has no change in direction, you can think of the acceleration as a change in speed with respect to time.

What happens to the acceleration of the cart as it travels down the ramp?

✎ e) Use pairs of data points from your graph to calculate the acceleration.

4. Prepare to run another trial. This time, move the cart to the bottom of the ramp. Practice giving the cart a push until it nearly reaches the top of the ramp. You can ignore the data for the downward motion. Before taking data, predict the following:

✎ a) What do you think the *d-t* graph will look like? Sketch it in your log along with an explanation.

✎ b) What do you think the *v-t* graph will look like? Sketch it in your log along with an explanation.

5. Give the cart a push and collect the data. Be sure to stop the cart on the way up if it looks like it will hit the motion detector.

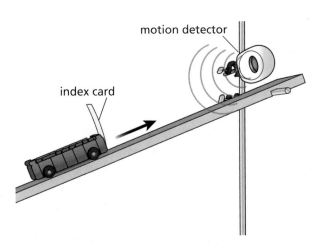

motion detector

index card

✎ a) Sketch both the *d-t* and *v-t* graphs from the calculator or computer. Use the "TRACE" function to label three to four data points along each line.

✎ b) Compare your predictions in *Steps* 4.*a*) and b) to what really happened. Explain any differences you find.

✎ c) What happens to the slope of the *d-t* graph? Why does this happen?

✎ d) What happens to the slope of the *v-t* graph? Why does this happen?

✎ e) Use pairs of data points from your graph to calculate the acceleration.

6. Prepare to run another trial. This time, move the detector and the cart to the bottom of the ramp, pointing them both toward the top of the ramp. Practice giving the cart a push until it nearly reaches the top of the ramp. Be sure to catch the cart on the way down before it strikes the motion detector. You can ignore the data for the downward motion. Before taking data, predict the following:

✎ a) What do you think the *d-t* graph will look like? Sketch it in your log along with an explanation.

✎ b) What do you think the *v-t* graph will look like? Sketch it in your log along with an explanation.

7. Give the cart a push and collect the data.

✎ a) Sketch both the *d-t* and *v-t* graphs from the calculator or computer. Use the "TRACE" function to label three to four data points along each line.

✎ b) Compare your predictions in *Steps* 6.*a*) and b) to what really happened. Explain any differences you find.

✎ c) What happens to the slope of the *d-t* graph? Why does this happen?

✎ d) What happens to the slope of the *v-t* graph? Why does this happen?

✎ e) Use pairs of data points from your graph to calculate the acceleration.

8. On the next page, you are provided with four graphs. Describe a motion of a cart on an incline that could produce each of these graphs. Include where the motion detector would have to be placed to produce the graph.

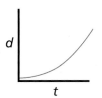

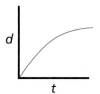

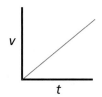

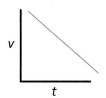

$$\left(60\,\frac{\text{mi}}{\text{h}}\right)\left(\frac{1\,\text{h}}{60\,\text{min}}\right)\left(\frac{1\,\text{min}}{60\,\text{s}}\right)\left(\frac{5280\,\text{ft}}{1\,\text{mi}}\right)=88\,\frac{\text{ft}}{\text{s}}$$

You should notice that to convert 60 mi/h to 88 ft/s, the 60 mi/hr was multiplied by fractions that always equaled 1 (for example, 1 h and 60 min are the same value of time). Multiplying by ¹⁄₁ keeps the value the same.

The following table was constructed on a spreadsheet. You can use the conversions in this table to give you a sense of the different units and to help you answer some of the questions in this chapter.

9. You will now take a closer look at acceleration in a straight line. Look at the automobile data provided at the end of this chapter on pages 116-117. The tables contain a lot of information including fuel economy, passenger accommodations, acceleration, and braking. In this section, you will be concerned with acceleration.

   a) Record in your log where the acceleration information is located on the automobile table.

10. The speed on the table provided by automobile manufacturers is given in miles per hour (mi/h or mph), but the distances are recorded in feet and the time in seconds. To analyze this data more easily, it is helpful to record the speed in feet per second (ft/s). The table at right converts miles per hour to feet per second. Note that there are 60 min in 1 h and 60 s in 1 min. You should also note that there are 5280 ft in 1 mi. When you convert 60 mi/h to 88 ft/s, the conversion looks like the following:

$$\left(60\,\frac{\text{mi}}{\text{h}}\right)\left(\frac{1\,\text{h}}{60\,\text{min}}\right)\left(\frac{1\,\text{min}}{60\,\text{s}}\right)\left(\frac{5280\,\text{ft}}{1\,\text{mi}}\right)=88\,\frac{\text{ft}}{\text{s}}$$

If you deal with the units in the same way that you deal with the numbers, you will see that the miles cancel miles, hours cancel hours, and minutes cancel minutes.

	A	B	C	D
1	**Common Speed Conversions**			
2	**United States**		**Canada**	
3	mph	ft/s	m/s	km/h
4	0	0	0	0
5	10	15	5	16
6	20	29	9	32
7	30	44	13	49
8	40	59	18	65
9	50	73	23	81
10	60	88	27	97
11	70	103	31	113
12	80	117	36	130
13	90	132	41	146
14	100	147	45	162

11. The sports car's acceleration data from the table at the end of the chapter is shown below with miles per hour changed to feet per second.

Acceleration Data of a Sports Car in Feet per Second	
Final speed (ft/s)	**Total time (s)**
0	0.0
44	2.0
59	2.9
73	4.2
88	5.2
103	6.6
117	8.7
132	10.9
147	13.3

🔖 a) Sketch a graph of speed vs. total time and label it "Velocity-Time Graph." Put the time on the x-axis (horizontal) and the speed on the y-axis (vertical). Plot your points from the table using feet per second (ft/s) units for velocity.

🔖 b) During which time interval is the velocity changing the most?

🔖 c) During which time interval is the velocity changing the least?

🔖 d) Acceleration is defined as the change in velocity for each time interval. Where is acceleration the greatest? Where is acceleration the least?

12. You can now calculate the acceleration for each time interval.

The acceleration is equal to the change in velocity (final speed − initial speed) divided by the change in time.

$$a = \frac{\Delta v}{\Delta t}$$

$$= \frac{v_f - v_i}{\Delta t}$$

Where a is acceleration,

Δv is change in velocity,

v_f is final velocity,

v_i is initial velocity,

Δt is change in time or elapsed time.

The first acceleration calculation is shown below.

$$a = \frac{\Delta v}{\Delta t}$$

$$= \frac{v_f - v_i}{\Delta t}$$

$$= \frac{44 \text{ ft/s} - 0 \text{ ft/s}}{2 \text{ s}}$$

$$= \frac{22 \text{ ft/s}}{s}$$

The acceleration is equal to 22 feet per second every second. This is a change in speed (22 ft/s) with respect to time (1 s). This can also be written in the following ways:

22 ft/s every s

22 ft/s per s

22 (ft/s) per s

22 ft/s² (feet per second squared)

The last way is the easiest to say, but the first way is the easiest to understand.

If the automobile moved at a constant acceleration of 22 ft/s every second, you would see a constant increase in the speed every second, from 0 ft/s to 22 ft/s, then to 44 ft/s, and then to 66 ft/s. A constant acceleration is what happened to the cart on the ramp. However, this increase is not what usually happens to an automobile. An automobile does not move at a constant acceleration.

🔖 a) You can calculate the acceleration for the next time interval by calculating the acceleration of the sports car from 44 ft/s to 59 ft/s. This change in speed required 0.9 s. Complete this calculation. Did you get the value in the table of 16 ft/s every second?

Calculating Acceleration of a Sports Car in Feet per Second Squared

Initial Speed (ft/s)	Final Speed (ft/s)	Change in time (s)	Acceleration (ft/s every second)
0	44	2.0	22
44	59	0.9	16
59	73	1.3	
73	88	1.0	
88	103		
103	117		
117	132		
132	147		

b) Work with your group members to complete the Calculating Acceleration of a Sports Car in Feet per Second Squared table in your log.

c) Compare the table with the velocity-time graph you sketched in *Step 11.a)*.

Recall that the slope of the velocity-time graph is equal to the acceleration. Where does the table indicate the greatest acceleration took place? Where does the graph have the steepest slope?

Physics Talk

CHANGING SPEED

Acceleration

When things change speed, it is usually noticeable. The motion of a falling object is a common example of something changing speed. Galileo Galilei, an Italian scientist, was the first person to apply mathematics to the study of the change in the speed of a falling object. To describe the change quantitatively, he needed to make measurements. In the *Investigate*, you used a motion detector to make measurements of **acceleration**. Since Galileo lived in the 1600s, he did not even have access to clocks and had to devise original ways to measure time with accuracy and precision. One technique he used involved a water clock. In a water clock, water flows through a funnel into a bowl. The more time that elapses, the more water is collected.

Physics Words

acceleration: the change in velocity with respect to a change in time.

To help him explore falling objects, he first investigated balls rolling down an incline. He thought that a ball rolling down an incline was like watching a falling object in "slow motion."

Through his experimentation with balls rolling down inclines, Galileo found that if he looked at the change in speed with respect to the change in time, the value remained the same as the ball descended the ramp. He then defined this as acceleration. The definition of acceleration as change in velocity with respect to time is still in use today.

In this section, you observed, just as Galileo did with rolling balls, that a cart traveling down an inclined plane has a constant acceleration. The velocity of the cart changes at a regular rate and is represented by a straight line on the velocity vs. time graph.

Acceleration Is a Vector Quantity

Acceleration means "how fast the velocity changes." You will recall that the word velocity means "how fast an object is going (speed) and in what direction." Velocity, therefore, is a **vector** quantity. A vector quantity is a quantity that has both magnitude (size) and direction. A bus and an automobile can each accelerate by changing speed from 0 to 60 mph (about 100 km/h) and from 60 to 0 mph when braking, and both can change velocity by driving around curves. But the automobile can produce these velocity changes in much less time. The automobile can exhibit greater acceleration than the bus.

The distinction between speed and velocity becomes important when changes in direction can occur. For example, when driving on curves, you can have changes in the direction, and thus a change in velocity, even while maintaining a steady speed. For example, a person driving around a curve at a steady speed of 15 m/s is accelerating. There is no change in speed, but there is a change in direction.

So the ways to change your automobile's velocity are

• to speed up (increasing the speed, or magnitude of velocity),

• to slow down (decreasing the speed, or magnitude of velocity), or

• turn (change the direction of velocity).

And, of course, you can change speed and direction simultaneously, as when you drive on mountain roads with curves.

All of these motions involve accelerations, because the velocity changes as time elapses. In this section, acceleration for an automobile moving along a straight line (no curves or turns) is discussed. You will investigate changing directions later in this chapter. For now, consider motion in a straight line.

In one part of the *Investigate*, you observed a cart going up a ramp. In this case, the final velocity (at the top of the incline) was less than the initial velocity. This is a **negative acceleration**. You may have heard the word deceleration used to describe something that is slowing down. However, in physics, that term is not used. The vocabulary used to describe a change in velocity with respect to time is **positive acceleration** and negative acceleration. The precision of these terms avoids confusion that may arise when the common word, deceleration, is used.

Physics Words

vector: a quantity that has both magnitude and direction.

negative acceleration: a decrease in velocity with respect to time. The object can slow down (20 m/s to 10 m/s) or speed up (-20 m/s to -30 m/s).

positive acceleration: an increase in velocity with respect to time. The object can speed up (20 m/s to 30 m/s) or slow down (-20 m/s to -10 m/s).

Active Physics

You will investigate negative acceleration further in *Section 5*. For motion in a straight line, positive acceleration means that the velocity of the object is increasing over time. Negative acceleration means that the velocity of the object is decreasing over time, if the object is moving in a straight line.

Vector and Scalar Quantities

A quantity that involves both direction and size (magnitude) is called a vector quantity. A quantity that has size, but not direction, is called a scalar quantity. Speed is a scalar quantity. It only indicates the change in position over a period of time in a straight line. Velocity is a vector quantity. It can indicate a change in position over a period of time and the direction.

Describing Accelerated Motion Using Strobe Pictures

Recall that you used three different models to describe motion: strobe pictures, graphs, and equations. Each gives the same information, but in different forms. You will use the same models to describe acceleration.

Because the speed is always changing during constant acceleration, the strobe illustration below shows the automobiles moving greater distances during each second of travel.

Describing Acceleration Using an Equation

In the *Investigate*, you used an equation to describe acceleration. You calculated acceleration by finding the change in velocity with respect to time.

$$\text{Acceleration} = \frac{\text{change in velocity}}{\text{change in time}}$$

This relationship can be written as an equation using symbols.

$$a = \frac{\Delta v}{\Delta t}$$

where a is acceleration,
Δv is change in velocity,
Δt is change in time or elapsed time.

Units for Measuring Acceleration

To calculate acceleration, you divide change in velocity by change in time $\frac{\Delta v}{\Delta t}$. The units for acceleration are then, by definition, velocity divided by time. Recall from the previous section, the units for velocity can be m/s or km/h. Assume that the time interval is measured in seconds. The units for acceleration would then be (m/s)/s or (km/h)/s. The change in velocity is given in meters per second every second, or kilometers per hour every second.

When writing the units for acceleration, the final units are often simplified. For example, the following all mean the same thing. The simplified units are read as meters per second squared.

$$\frac{m/s}{s}, \text{ or } (m/s)/s = \frac{m}{s^2} \text{ or } m/s^2$$

In the *Investigate*, you calculated acceleration in feet per second every second, or feet per second squared (ft/s^2).

Using the Equation for Acceleration to Find Other Quantities

The defining equation for acceleration shows the relationship between acceleration, velocity, and time. If you know two of these, you can find the third.

$$\text{Acceleration} = \frac{\text{change in velocity}}{\text{change in time}}$$

Using algebra, it follows that

$$\text{Change in velocity} = \text{acceleration} \times \text{time}$$

$$\text{Time} = \frac{\text{change in velocity}}{\text{acceleration}}$$

Using symbols, these equations can be written as

$$a = \frac{\Delta v}{\Delta t}$$

$$\Delta v = a \times \Delta t$$

$$\Delta t = \frac{\Delta v}{a}$$

61

As you did with the equations for speed in the previous section, you may find it helpful to use a circle, like the following:

By covering up the variable you wish to find, you can see the equation. To find change in velocity (Δv), cover up the Δv, and you see $a \times \Delta t$.

To find acceleration (a), cover up the a, and you see $\frac{\Delta v}{\Delta t}$.

To find time (Δt), cover up the Δt and you see $\frac{\Delta v}{a}$.

There is only one definition of acceleration. Algebra allows you to write it in different forms.

Sample Problem

At the start of a race, a toy car increases speed from 0 m/s to 5.0 m/s as the clock runs from 0 s to 2.0 s. Find the acceleration of the toy car.

Strategy: Use the definition of acceleration as the change in velocity over a change in time.

Given:

Final velocity $(v_f) =$ 5.0 m/s

Initial velocity $(v_i) =$ 0 m/s

Final time (t_f) = 2.0 s

Initial time (t_i) = 0 s

Solution:

$$a = \frac{\Delta v}{\Delta t}$$

$$= \frac{v_f - v_i}{t_f - t_i}$$

$$= \frac{5.0 \text{ m/s} - 0 \text{ m/s}}{2.0 \text{ s} - 0 \text{ s}}$$

$$= \frac{5.0 \text{ m/s}}{2.0 \text{ s}}$$

$$= 2.5 \text{ m/s}^2$$

The acceleration is 2.5 m/s every second, and can be written and stated in three equivalent ways:

- 2.5 meters per second every second, or
- 2.5 (m/s)/s (meters per second per second), or
- 2.5 m/s^2 (meters per second squared).

Describing Acceleration Using Graphs

A third way to represent acceleration is with graphs. If distance is represented on the *y*-axis and the time is represented on the *x*-axis, then the graph showing constant acceleration is a curve. The slope of the **tangent line** to the curve at any point gives the instantaneous speed at that point. One such tangent is shown on the graph below. If you imagine tangents at different points, you can see that the slopes of the tangents increase as time increases. Thus, the speed is increasing during this time. An increasing speed during a time interval is an acceleration.

If the velocity is represented on the *y*-axis and the time is represented on the *x*-axis, then the slope of the graph will be equal to the change in velocity with respect to time. The acceleration is equal to the value of the slope of the velocity-time graph. Notice that the slope has the same value at all points. You can conclude that since the slope of the *v-t* graph is constant, the acceleration is constant.

Describing Types of Motion Using Graphs

You can determine the general motion of an automobile by reviewing the distance vs. time graph, the corresponding velocity vs. time graph, and the corresponding acceleration vs. time graph. Each column in the table on the following page provides a way to describe the motion of an automobile.

Note: When interpreting graphs, you must always check to see if the *y*-axis represents distance, velocity, or acceleration. A horizontal line on a graph has very different meanings if the graph is a *d-t* graph, a *v-t* graph, or an *a-t* graph.

Use the Comparing Motion Graphs table on the next page to determine the general motion of an automobile. All of the three graphs in a column represent the same motion of the same car. One column gives the information in terms of changes in distance, another represents velocity, and the third acceleration over time.

Physics Words

tangent line: a straight line that touches a curve in only one point.

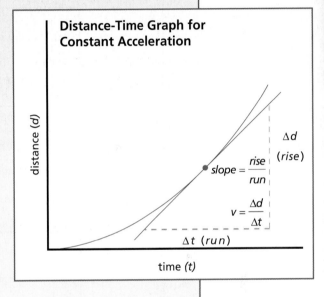

Distance-Time Graph for Constant Acceleration

$$slope = \frac{rise}{run}$$

$$v = \frac{\Delta d}{\Delta t}$$

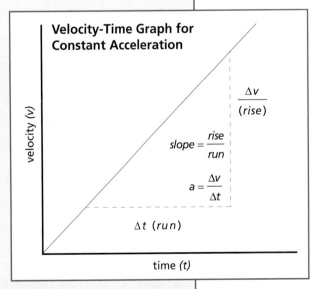

Velocity-Time Graph for Constant Acceleration

$$slope = \frac{rise}{run}$$

$$a = \frac{\Delta v}{\Delta t}$$

Active Physics

Comparing Motion Graphs

	Automobile at rest	Automobile with constant velocity	Automobile with constant acceleration
d-t graph	Distance (position) does not change.	Distance (position) changes at a constant rate.	Distance (position) changes at a non-constant rate (the *d-t* graph is a curve, not a straight line).
	distance (d) vs. time (t) — horizontal line	distance (d) vs. time (t) — straight increasing line	distance (d) vs. time (t) — upward curve
v-t graph	Velocity is always 0 because the position does not change.	The change in distance vs. time is constant and therefore the velocity is constant rate.	The speed is increasing as can be seen by the increasing slope of the distance vs. time graph.
	velocity (v) vs. time (t) — flat at zero	velocity (v) vs. time (t) — horizontal line	velocity (v) vs. time (t) — straight increasing line
a-t graph	Acceleration is always 0 because velocity does not change.	There is a constant velocity. With no change in velocity, there is 0 acceleration.	The velocity is changing at a constant rate. The automobile is moving at a constant acceleration.
	acceleration (a) vs. time (t) — flat at zero	acceleration (a) vs. time (t) — flat at zero	acceleration (a) vs. time (t) — horizontal line above zero

Checking Up

1. Give the defining equation for acceleration in words, and by using symbols.

2. What is an SI unit for measuring acceleration? Use words and unit symbols to describe the unit.

3. What is the difference between a vector and a scalar quantity?

4. Sketch a distance-time graph for
   a) constant velocity
   b) constant acceleration

5. What does the slope of a velocity-time graph represent?

Active Physics

+Math	+Depth	+Concepts	+Exploration
◆◆◆		◆◆	

Active Physics

Plus

Determining Distance Using the Acceleration Equation

The definition of acceleration provides the relationship between velocity, acceleration, and time. If you know the acceleration, you can determine the change in velocity after a given time has elapsed by using the following equation:

$$\Delta v = a\Delta t$$

If an automobile has a constant acceleration, you can also determine the distance traveled after a given time has elapsed.

Knowing the initial and final velocity, you can now determine the average velocity (v). For a constant acceleration, the average velocity is determined the same way the average of any two numbers is determined.

$$\bar{v} = \frac{v_f + v_i}{2}$$

Once you know the average velocity, you can use the definition of average velocity to determine the distance traveled.

Using some algebra, you can also determine the distance traveled in one step with a newly derived equation.

$$d = \bar{v}t$$

You can now determine how an object's position and velocity depend on the elapsed time from the definition of velocity and acceleration.

$$d = \bar{v}t$$

$$d = \left(\frac{v_f + v_i}{2}\right)t$$

Since $v_f - v_i = at$

then $v_f = v_i + at$

$$d = \left(\frac{(v_i + at) + v_i}{2}\right)t$$

$$d = \left(\frac{(at) + 2v_i}{2}\right)t$$

$$d = \frac{1}{2}at^2 + v_i t$$

Sample Problem

An automobile accelerates from rest at 5.0 m/s every second (5.0 m/s²). How far does it travel after 3.0 s?

Given:

Initial velocity $\left(v_i\right)$ = 0 m/s

Acceleration $\left(a\right)$ = 5.0 m/s²

Time $\left(\Delta t\right)$ = 3.0 s

Strategy 1:

Find the final velocity using the definition of acceleration; then find the average velocity; and then use the relationship between distance, average velocity, and time.

Solution:

$$v_f = at + v_i$$

$$v_f = \left(5.0 \frac{m}{s^2}\right)(3.0 \, s) + 0$$

$$v_f = 15 \text{ m/s}$$

Active Physics

Knowing that the final velocity is 15 m/s and the initial velocity equals 0, you can calculate the average velocity.

$$\bar{v} = \frac{v_f + v_i}{2}$$

$$= \frac{15 \text{ m/s} + 0 \text{ m/s}}{2}$$

$$= 7.5 \text{ m/s}$$

Using the definition of average velocity, the distance can be computed:

$$d = \bar{v}t$$

$$= 7.5\,\frac{m}{s} \times 3.0\,s$$

$$= 22.5 \text{ m}$$

Strategy 2:

Because acceleration, time, and initial velocity are provided, use the derived relationship of distance, acceleration, and time. There is no need to find the final velocity.

Solution:

$$d = \frac{1}{2}at^2 + v_i t$$

$$= \frac{1}{2}\left(5\frac{m}{s^2}\right)(3\,s)(3\,s) + 0$$

$$= 22.5 \text{ m}$$

What Do You Think Now?

At the beginning of this section, you were asked the following:

- **An automobile and a bus are stopped at a traffic light. What are some differences and similarities of the motion of these two vehicles as each goes from a stop to the speed limit of 30 mph?**

How would you answer this question now? Now that you have investigated change in velocity over time, compare and contrast the motion of the vehicles using the term acceleration. Sketch a velocity-time graph for each vehicle.

Physics
Essential Questions

What does it mean?

One race car has a greater acceleration than a second race car. But the second race car can reach a higher top speed than the first. How is this possible?

How do you know?

As you enter the highway, your automobile goes from rest to the speed limit. What measurements would you have to take to calculate the acceleration of your automobile as it enters the highway?

Why do you believe?

Connects with Other Physics Content	Fits with Big Ideas in Science	Meets Physics Requirements
Forces and motion	✳ Models	Experimental evidence is consistent with models and theories

✳ Physicists use models to better understand the world. How can a distance vs. time graph, a velocity vs. time graph and an acceleration vs. time graph all represent a car moving with a constant acceleration?

Why should you care?

Safe driving saves lives. How can your understanding of velocity and acceleration help you to become a safer driver? In the unfortunate possibility that you are in an accident, how could *d-t*, *v-t*, and *a-t* motion graphs help you explain why the accident was not your fault?

Reflecting on the Section and the Challenge

Driving is all about accelerations. Automobiles accelerate when they speed up, slow down, or make a turn. Drivers depend on negative accelerations to avoid accidents when they apply the brakes. Speeding up too quickly can also lead to accidents.

You now know how to calculate accelerations and to determine accelerations from a velocity-time graph. You may want to use these calculations and/or graphs in your description of safe driving, or perhaps in your presentation.

Active Physics

Physics to Go

1. Can a situation exist in which an object has zero acceleration and nonzero velocity? Explain your answer.

2. Can a situation exist in which an object has zero velocity and nonzero acceleration, even for an instant? Explain your answer.

3. If two automobiles have the same acceleration, do they have the same velocity? Why or why not?

4. If two automobiles have the same velocity, do they have the same acceleration? Why or why not?

5. Can an accelerating automobile be overtaken by an automobile moving with constant velocity?

6. Is it correct to refer to speed-limit signs instead of velocity-limit signs? Why or why not? What units are assumed for speed-limit signs in the United States?

7. Suppose an automobile were accelerating at 2 mi/h every 5 s and could keep accelerating for 2 min at that rate.

   a) How fast would it be going at t = 2 min?

   b) How far would it be from the starting line?

8. At an international auto race, a race car leaves the pit after a refueling stop and accelerates uniformly to a speed of 75 m/s in 9 s to rejoin the race.

   a) What is the race car's acceleration during this time?

   b) What was the race car's average speed during the acceleration?

   c) How far does the race car go during the time it is accelerating?

   d) A second race car leaves after its pit stop and accelerates to 75 m/s in 8 s. Compared to the first race car, what is this race car's acceleration, average speed during the acceleration, and distance traveled?

9. During a softball game, a player running from second base to third base reaches a speed of 4.5 m/s before she starts to slide into third base. When she reaches third base 1.3 s after beginning her slide, her speed is reduced to 0.6 m/s.

   a) What is the player's acceleration during the slide?

   b) What was the distance of her slide?

   c) If she had slid for only 1.1 s, how fast would she have been moving when she reached third base? (Assume she had the same acceleration as before.)

   d) Which of these two trials would get her from second base to third base faster?

10. Suppose an astronaut on an airless planet is trying to determine the acceleration of an object that is falling toward the ground. She has a motion detector in place that records the graph to the right for the falling object until just before it strikes the ground.

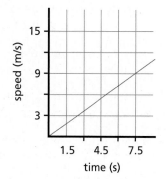

a) From the graph, approximately what was the top speed recorded by the astronaut for the falling object?

b) What is the acceleration of gravity on this planet?

c) If the astronaut had dropped the object from a greater height, what would happen to the object's acceleration as it falls and the object's final velocity before striking the ground?

11. A boy riding a bike with a speed of 5 m/s across level ground comes to a small hill with a constant slope and lets the bike coast up the hill. All graphs have time on the x-axis.

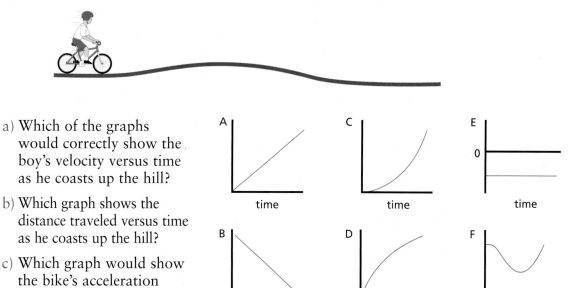

a) Which of the graphs would correctly show the boy's velocity versus time as he coasts up the hill?

b) Which graph shows the distance traveled versus time as he coasts up the hill?

c) Which graph would show the bike's acceleration as it coasts uphill?

d) Which graph shows after reaching the top of the hill, the speed of the boy as he coasts down the hill on the bike?

e) Which graph could show the boy's speed versus time graph as the boy coasts up the hill and then down the hill?

f) Starting from the top of the hill, which graph could correctly show the boy's distance vs. time as he goes down the hill?

Active Physics

12. An automobile magazine runs a performance test on a new model car, and records the graph of distance versus time as the car goes around a track. During which segment or segments of the graph is the car

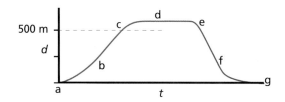

    a) traveling with constant speed?

    b) increasing speed?

    c) at rest?

    d) decreasing speed?

    e) How far did the car travel during the total test?

    f) According to the graph, where was the car when the test was completed?

13. A jet taking off from an aircraft carrier goes from 0 to 250 mi/hr in 30 s.

    a) What is the jet's acceleration?

    b) If after take-off, the jet continues to accelerate at the same rate for another 15 s, how fast will it be going at that time?

    c) How much time does it take for the jet to reach 500 mi/hr?

    d) How much distance would it take for that same jet to reach 500 mi/hr?

14. Whenever air resistance can be neglected or eliminated, an object in free-fall near Earth's surface accelerates vertically downward at 9.8 m/s^2 due to Earth's gravity. This acceleration is also called 1 g.

    a) If the object falls for 100 m, how fast is it traveling?

    b) How much time is required for it to fall this 100 m?

    c) If the object falls for 10 s, how fast is it traveling?

    d) How far has it fallen in this 10 s?

    e) How would your answers to these questions change for an object falling above the Moon, where the acceleration is about ⅙ g (1.6 m/s^2)?

15. In 1954, in a study of human endurance prior to the manned space program, Colonel John Paul Stapp rode a rocket-powered sled that was boosted to a speed of 632 mi/hr (1017 km/h). The sled and he were then decelerated to a stop in 1.4 s.

    a) What was the acceleration of this stop?

    b) What is this acceleration in terms of g's?

    c) In what distance did the speed of the sled travel as its speed changed from 1017 km/hr to 0?

16. **Active Physics** *Plus* An automobile accelerates from rest at 4.0 m/s every second (4.0 m/s^2).

   a) How far does it travel after 1.0 s?

   b) How far does it travel after 2.0 s?

   c) How far does it travel after 3.0 s?

   d) How far does it travel after 4.0 s?

   e) Complete a *d-t* graph for this automobile.

   f) Complete a *v-t* graph for this automobile.

   g) How does the motion of this automobile compare with the motion of a real automobile (as you investigated previously)?

17. *Preparing for the Chapter Challenge*

   On highways, you can pass slower-moving vehicles by moving into the left lane and driving past them. You can then return to the right lane, all the while traveling at the speed limit. On a rural road, you must do this by entering the oncoming traffic lane. This can be very dangerous. To pass the vehicle safely and quickly, you may have to accelerate until you get back into your lane. You can describe the motion of both vehicles by creating graphs with two lines on each one—one depicting your vehicle and the other depicting the slower-moving vehicle. Describe how you can safely pass a slower-moving vehicle using *d-t*, *v-t*, and *a-t* graphs to convince the driving academy that you understand safe driving.

Inquiring Further

Speed conversions

Using a spreadsheet program, complete a table like the one below that converts mph to ft/s to m/s to km/hr.

	A	B	C	D
	mi/hr	ft/s	m/s	km/h
1				
2	0			
3	5			
4	10			
5	15			
6	20			
7	25			
8	30			
9	35			
10	40			
11	45			
12	50			

Why is there a *Mini-Challenge?*

You are using a simplified *Engineering Design Cycle* to help you address the *Chapter Challenge.* At the beginning of the chapter, you established your *Goal.* At that time, you also identified the criteria and constraints that you have. You then completed several sections of the chapter. The physics content that you learned about in each section provides the *Inputs* that you can use to address the challenge. As you work through each section, you are also involved in the *Process* phase. You have the opportunity of evaluating the different ideas that you and your team have for how to use and incorporate the physics content into the final product.

Now is the time for the *Outputs* and *Feedback* phases of the *Engineering Design Cycle.* It is time to present the intermediary phases or intermediary products that you have designed. When engineers design products, they usually do not create the best or most successful product on the first try. They often go through many iterations (repetitions) before they have a final product. In *Active Physics*, you will only have one opportunity to present your intermediary product. You will present it in the *Chapter Mini-Challenge.* The presentation is the *Outputs.*

An extremely important phase is the *Feedback.* Other teams will have an opportunity to provide you with formal or informal *Feedback.* You will find out if your product meets the criteria, if you have used the physics concepts correctly, and if your product is entertaining, exciting, useful, or creative. You will also have an opportunity to provide feedback to yourself. You will have a chance to reflect on what went well and what can be improved.

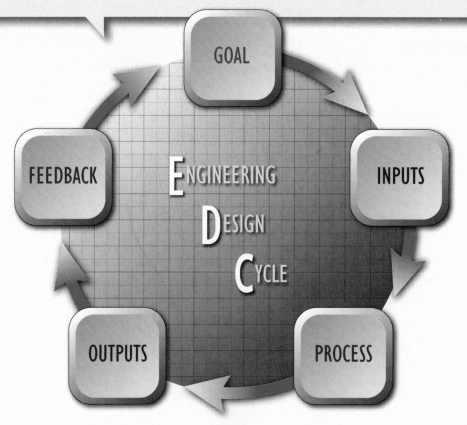

Your challenge for this chapter is to create a two-to three-minute group presentation that will convince the Active Driving Academy that you have learned enough about the physics of safe driving to be eligible for graduation. Your group needs to apply the physics concepts you have studied in this chapter to develop that presentation. Your presentation must, at the minimum, include:

- **the relationship between following distance, braking distance, and the total stopping distance, including the factors that affect each;**

- **how to decide what to do when the light turns yellow as you approach an intersection; and**

- **the connection between speed, friction, and radius of the curve when turning.**

Your *Mini-Challenge* for this chapter is a one-to two-minute presentation to the class. The *Mini-Challenge* will help you learn about what you should or should not include in your *Chapter Challenge* presentation. You will not be able to address all of the requirements at this time, but you should do your best to fully address the topics that you have already studied. Anything you create for the *Mini-Challenge* can be used to complete your final *Chapter Challenge*.

Look back at the *Goal* you wrote at the beginning of the chapter. Rewrite your *Goal* so that you are clear on what you will prepare for the *Mini-Challenge*. Review the *Goal* as a class to make sure you have all of the criteria and the necessary constraints.

 For the *Inputs* phase of the *Engineering Design Cycle*, you have completed four sections and learned some of the physics content that can be used in your presentation. Your group should review the physics content from these sections to help you begin your safe-driving presentation.

Section 1 You used different methods to measure reaction time and compared the reaction time of different members of your class. You also investigated how distractions affect reaction time.

Section 2 You used a stride and a meter stick to measure distance. You identified the sources of error in measurement and read about units of measurement used in science classrooms and when driving the roads in the United States.

Section 3 You defined average and instantaneous speed and used strobe pictures, graphs, and equations to represent motion. You also used the equation for average speed to calculate speed, distance, and time. You read about how speed can affect following distance when driving on the roads.

Section 4 You learned how changes in speed, direction or acceleration are related to time and distance for a moving vehicle. You also interpreted distance-time and velocity-time graphs for different types of motion.

In addition to the information you learned in the first four sections, your group might also like to look for some statistics about safe stopping distances, safe following distances, and safe braking distances as they relate to vehicle accidents. This information would help make your physics information more impressive to the presentation audience.

The *Process* phase is when you decide what information you have that will help you meet the criteria of the *Goal*. This *Mini-Challenge* requires a thorough evaluation of the physics you have learned so far to help you determine how each piece influences the aspects of time and distance as they relate to driving. You can perform a *Resource Analysis* by creating a list of what you learned in the first four sections of the chapter. For each one, decide if:

- it can be used to help you measure or determine a safe following distance;

- it can be used to help find a braking distance, and

- it can be used to find a stopping distance.

By categorizing the information you already have learned, you can focus your energy on addressing the parts of the challenge that you are prepared to answer at this point.

Your *Resource Analysis* has revealed which of the topics in the first four sections will be helpful for answering each part of the challenge presentation. Your group might assign individuals or teams of two to work on specific answers for your presentation and then put all of the individual answers together to present later. Each person or team will now know which chapter section or sections they can use to help him/her address their part of the presentation.

During your *Resource Analysis* you can also make a list of missing information you still need to complete the *Chapter Challenge*. This list will help you complete the final sections of the chapter and frame your answers to the *Physics Essential Questions*.

The *Outputs* of your *Engineering Design Cycle* is a two-minute presentation. Remember, everyone is working with the same requirements and constraints. You only need to do a good job of meeting the *Goal* requirements to do well.

Presenting your information to the class are your design-cycle *Outputs*. You should have a presentation that addresses factors for safe following distances, safe braking distances, and safe stopping distances. Remember to use graphs or charts from the investigations to help illustrate your explanations. Remember to leave enough time for your group to rehearse or at least agree on who will present which information.

Finally, you will receive *Feedback* from your classmates that will tell you what you have done well according to the criteria from the *Goal*. They might also tell you some things you can improve to get a good grade on the final presentation. To give good *Feedback*, it is important to consider each point of the requirements and the constraints to see how well each different design satisfies them. Your statements should say which parts were satisfied and which, if any, were not. This is an objective process and should focus on the products, not on the engineers who produced them.

This *Feedback* will become an *Input* for your final design in the *Chapter Challenge*. You will have enough time to make corrections and improvements, so you will want to pay attention to the valuable information they provide. Remember to correct any parts of your explanations that you received critical feedback on. You may have also learned something from watching presentations that you want to add to your group's presentation. It will be easier and faster to improve your answers now rather than waiting until the chapter is complete to go back and correct any mistakes. Then, store all of your information in a safe place so that it will be ready to use in the *Chapter Challenge*!

Section 5   Negative Acceleration: Braking Your Automobile

What Do You See?

Learning Outcomes

In this section, you will

• **Plan** and carry out an experiment to relate braking distance to initial speed.

• **Determine** braking distance.

• **Examine** accelerated motion.

What Do You Think?

In recent years, more than 80 percent of speed-related traffic deaths happened on secondary highways (such as two-lane, rural roads). Imagine you are driving at the speed limit on a secondary highway, and you suddenly see an animal crossing the road ahead of you. Suppose you cannot swerve to miss the animal because of trees on each side of the road.

• **What factors must you consider to determine if you will be able to stop in the distance between you and the animal to avoid hitting it?**

Record your ideas about this question in your *Active Physics* log. Be prepared to discuss your response with your small group and the class.

Investigate

In this *Investigate*, you will plan and carry out an experiment to determine the relationship between the initial speed and the braking distance of an automobile.

1. Knowing how far your automobile will travel after you have stepped on the brake pedal is important. One factor that may have an impact on braking distance is the initial speed of the automobile.

The initial speed is the speed at which you begin to apply the brakes. Braking distance is the distance required to bring the vehicle to rest once the brakes are applied. In your investigation, the initial speed will be the speed at the point at which you begin your measurement of braking distance. You will collect data to study the relationship between initial speed and braking distance.

a) What would a graph of braking distance vs. initial speed look like? Sketch a graph that shows what you think the data would show. (Place the initial speed on the *x*-axis and the braking distance on the *y*-axis.) While sketching the graph, imagine what would happen to the braking distance for a slow-moving vehicle, a faster-moving vehicle, and a very fast-moving vehicle.

b) Provide an explanation for the way you sketched the graph.

2. Your teacher will provide your group with equipment similar to the equipment shown in the illustration below. Discuss with your group how you could use the equipment to study the relationship between initial speed and braking distance.

To plan your experiment, consider the following:

- How will you vary the initial speed of the cart (that is, the velocity the cart has at the bottom of the hill when the brakes are applied)?

- The cart does not really have brakes applied by a driver, but the cart will stop on its own. Friction plays the role of brakes in the cart.

- How will you determine the initial speed of the cart just before it begins braking?

- How will you measure the braking distance? (What tool should you use? Should you measure from the front or the back of the cart? How accurate will you make your measurements?)

- How many different initial speeds will your group need to examine to find a pattern?

- How many trials should you perform at each initial speed?

- What will each group member be responsible for?

- How will you organize your data?

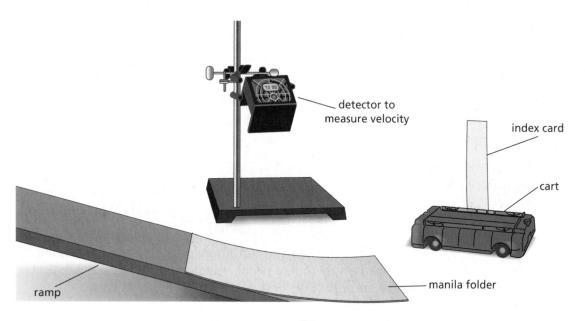

detector to measure velocity

index card

cart

ramp

manila folder

3. After discussing these questions in your group, develop a plan for what your group will do. Your teacher may ask you to either draw a flowchart or an outline showing the steps you will take.

4. Set up your equipment and perform your experiment.

 a) Record both numerical data and observations in your *Active Physics* log.

> ⚠ Place the ramp on the floor in a way that does not obstruct people's ability to walk around the classroom. Do not block the emergency exit.
>
> If you are setting up the ramp on the table, provide some means to contain the cart and prevent it from falling off the table.

5. Use the data you collected to complete the following:

 a) Draw a graph showing how the braking distance depends on the initial speed. Place the initial speed on the horizontal axis and the braking distance on the vertical axis.

 b) How does the braking distance change with initial speed?

 c) How does your graph compare to the graph you sketched in *Step 1.a)*?

 d) Compare your graph with those of other groups. What are some similarities and some differences?

 e) Does looking at the other groups' graphs make you feel more confident or less confident about your data? Explain your answer.

6. Select two values of initial speed from your graph, with one value approximately twice the value of the other. Note the braking distance which corresponds to each initial speed.

 a) What is the effect of doubling the initial speed on the distance traveled during braking?

7. Select two values of initial speed from your graph, with one value approximately three times as fast as the other. Note the braking distance which corresponds to each initial speed.

 a) What is the effect of tripling the initial speed on the distance traveled during braking?

 b) Predict how going four times faster will affect the braking distance.

8. Use the data on the sports car provided at the end of this chapter on pages 116-117 to answer the following:

 a) Where is the braking data located?

 b) The braking distance is shown for two speeds. The ratio of the two speeds is 80 mi/hr : 60 mi/hr. This ratio is $80/60 = 1.33$. This is an increase of 133 percent. Do you expect the ratio of the braking distances to also be in the ratio of $80/60 = 1.33$? What is the ratio of the braking distances? How does it compare with the ratio of the two speeds?

 c) How does this data correspond to what you found in your experiment?

Active Physics

Physics Talk

SPEED AND BRAKING DISTANCE

Negative Acceleration and Positive Acceleration

From your investigations in this section and the previous section, you observed that acceleration of an object is determined by how fast the velocity of the object changes with respect to time.

This is represented mathematically with the following equation:

$$\text{Acceleration} = \frac{\text{change in velocity}}{\text{change in time}}$$

$$a = \frac{\Delta v}{\Delta t}$$

The symbol Δ stands for "change in." This equation can also be written in the following way:

$$a = \frac{v_f - v_i}{\Delta t}$$

where a is acceleration,
v_i is initial velocity and
v_f is final velocity.

The cart in your experiment undergoes a **negative acceleration**, because the final velocity v_f is zero when it stops, which is less than its initial velocity v_i. For an object stopping, $v_f = 0$. Therefore,

$$a = \frac{0 - v_i}{\Delta t}$$

$$= \frac{-v_i}{\Delta t}$$

Physics Words

negative acceleration: a change in the velocity with respect to time of an object by decreasing speed in the positive direction or increasing speed in the negative direction.

Recall that you read that sometimes people use the term acceleration to describe speeding up, and they use deceleration to describe something slowing down. In order to be clear about meanings in physics, the terms positive acceleration and negative acceleration are used. Positive represents one direction and negative represents the opposite direction. Furthermore, an object could have a negative acceleration by decreasing its speed in the positive direction or increasing its speed in the negative direction.

Imagine you are driving an automobile to pick up a friend to go to the movies. You know the street your friend lives on and the house number. You slowly drive down the street but accidentally pass your friend's house. Realizing your mistake, you slow down and stop. When you are moving forward (a positive speed), but slowing down, the automobile has an acceleration backward (a negative acceleration).

After the automobile has stopped, you check to see if it is safe, and then start to back up (with the automobile still pointing forward). When you start to increase your speed in the opposite direction you are moving backward (a negative speed), and your acceleration is also backward (a negative acceleration) until you are traveling with constant speed in reverse.

As you slow down again to stop when you are approaching the correct house, you are still moving backward (a negative speed), but you now have a forward (positive) acceleration to bring the automobile to a stop.

Finally, your friend gets into the automobile, and you now pull away going forward with a forward (positive) acceleration until you are driving with a forward (positive) constant speed to the movies.

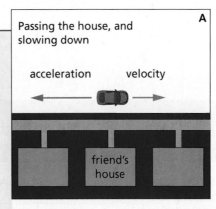

A

Passing the house, and slowing down

acceleration   velocity

friend's house

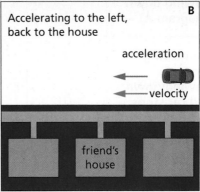

B

Accelerating to the left, back to the house

acceleration

velocity

friend's house

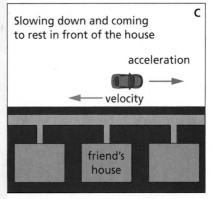

C

Slowing down and coming to rest in front of the house

acceleration

velocity

friend's house

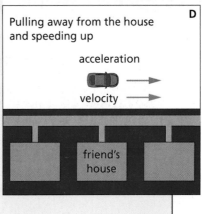

D

Pulling away from the house and speeding up

acceleration

velocity

friend's house

Active Physics

Motion of Car	Time (s)	Velocity of car (ft/s)	Acceleration of car (ft/s²)	Positive or Negative
Car moving forward and slowing down (Diagram A)	0	+6	$\dfrac{v_f - v_i}{\Delta t} = \dfrac{(+4)-(+6)}{1}$ $= -2$	negative acceleration
	1	+4		
Car moving forward, slowing down and car stops	2	+2	$\dfrac{v_f - v_i}{\Delta t} = \dfrac{(0)-(+2)}{1}$ $= -2$	negative acceleration
	3	0		
Car moving backward and speeding up (Diagram B)	4	-2	$\dfrac{v_f - v_i}{\Delta t} = \dfrac{(-4)-(-2)}{1}$ $= -2$	negative acceleration
	5	-4		
Car moving backward and slowing down (Diagram C)	6	-6	$\dfrac{v_f - v_i}{\Delta t} = \dfrac{(-4)-(-6)}{1}$ $= +2$	positive acceleration
	7	-4		
Car moving backward and stopping	8	-2	$\dfrac{v_f - v_i}{\Delta t} = \dfrac{(0)-(-2)}{1}$ $= +2$	positive acceleration
	9	0		
Car moving forward and speeding up (Diagram D)	9	0	$\dfrac{v_f - v_i}{\Delta t} = \dfrac{(+2)-(0)}{1}$ $= +2$	positive acceleration
	10	2		

In this example, you can see that a negative acceleration can sometimes decrease the speed of an automobile $(t = 0$ to $t = 3)$ or increase the speed of an automobile $(t = 4$ to $t = 5)$, but it always decreases the velocity of the automobile by exactly 2 ft/s every second $(\text{from} + 6 \text{ to} + 4 \text{ to} + 2 \text{ to } 0 \text{ to} - 2 \text{ to} - 4)$.

Calculating Braking Distance

Using the definition of velocity and acceleration, you can derive an equation for the braking distance when a vehicle comes to rest. The equation is shown below:

$$v_f^2 = 2ad + v_i^2$$

v_f is the final velocity of the car.

v_i is the initial velocity of the vehicle. Notice that it must be squared. This is the same as multiplying it by itself, $v_i^2 = v_i \times v_i$.

a is the acceleration. It is a negative acceleration.

d is the braking distance.

Because the final velocity of a vehicle is zero after the car comes to a stop, you may put a zero in for the final velocity, and of course zero times zero is still zero.

$$0 = 2ad + v_i^2$$

or

$$v_i^2 = -2ad$$

You can use the helpful circle to solve for any of the variables in this equation as well.

Of all the equations in your first year of physics, this one may have the greatest impact on your safety. Understanding this equation may one day even help to save your life! From this equation, you can see that if you double the initial velocity, then the braking distance d will have to quadruple. If you triple the initial velocity, then the braking distance d will be nine times as great.

You probably found in the *Investigate* that doubling the speed increased the distance traveled while the vehicle was braking by about a factor of four and that tripling the speed increased the braking distance by about a factor of nine. Look at the data for the sports car. The speed increased by 1.33 while the braking distance increased by approximately 1.33 × 1.33 = 1.77. Experiments completed with a great deal of care, ensuring that the braking acceleration is constant between trials, find that this relationship is true.

Active Physics

(The v^2 relationship is derived assuming constant acceleration, which is *approximately* true for real automobiles in everyday stopping situations. The $v^2 = -2ad$ equation models reality very closely, and is therefore useful for describing braking.)

How can knowledge of the v^2 relationship save many lives? If you were to decrease your speed to one third your original speed, you would need only one ninth of the braking distance. If you double the speed you do not require double the distance for the car's brakes to stop the car, but four times the distance. Decreasing your speed can save lives because of the significant effect the slower speed has on braking distance.

You have seen how equations can model the motion of an automobile braking. An automobile with a negative acceleration can also be described using graphs of distance vs. time, velocity vs. time, and acceleration vs. time as shown below.

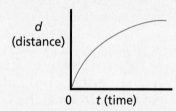
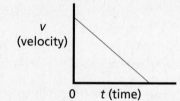

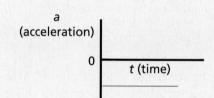

Checking Up

1. If a vehicle is traveling at constant velocity and then comes to a sudden stop, has it undergone negative acceleration or positive acceleration? Explain your answer.

2. Explain how you know that increasing the velocity of an automobile increases the braking distance.

3. Why is the term negative acceleration used instead of deceleration?

In the velocity vs. time graph, you can see that the velocity is decreasing as the automobile comes to rest. Notice that "at rest" is equivalent to a velocity equal to 0. You should also notice that the slope of the graph is constant. This implies that the acceleration is constant since the slope of the v-t graph is equal to the acceleration. Finally, notice that the slope is negative (sloping downward) which implies that the acceleration is negative.

In the acceleration vs. time graph, you can see that the acceleration is constant and negative.

In the distance vs. time graph, you can see how the change in distance for a given time changes as the speed changes. Notice that the slope at the beginning times is very steep, corresponding to a large velocity. Toward the end, the slope becomes 0, corresponding to the car stopping. (Thus, the graph is a curve.)

Active Physics

+Math	+Depth	+Concepts	+Exploration
♦♦♦	♦♦	♦♦	

Active Physics

Plus

Motion Equations

Five motion equations can describe all the relations among position, velocity, and constant acceleration. The equations are all derived from the definitions of velocity and acceleration.

$$d = \bar{v}t$$
$$v_f = at + v_i$$
$$\bar{v} = \frac{v_f + v_i}{2}$$
$$d = \frac{1}{2}at^2 + v_i t$$
$$v_f^2 = 2ad + v_i^2$$

The first equation is a restatement of the definition of average velocity. (The v with a bar over the top is a shorthand way of writing $v_{average}$.) The second equation is a restatement of the definition of acceleration. The third equation is for average velocity when there is constant acceleration. The fourth equation helps to determine distance traveled if you know the acceleration and time without the need for first finding the final velocity. The fifth equation relates the stopping distance to the acceleration and velocities without the need for calculating the time.

The fifth equation can be derived from the other four equations using algebra. Assume that the initial velocity equals zero to ease the mathematics.

You may want to try to derive the equation with acceleration not being zero, using the same approach.

These are the variables in the motion equations: d, t, a, v_f, v_i and $v_{average}$.

$$v_f = at + v_i$$

Assuming $v_i = 0$,

$$v_f = at$$

Square each side

$$v_f^2 = a^2 t^2$$
$$v_f^2 = 2a\left(\frac{1}{2}at^2\right)$$
$$v_f^2 = 2ad$$

If the acceleration is constant and you are able to find or are given any three of these variables, you can use the motion equations to solve for the other two variables and completely describe the motion of the object. The object can be an automobile, an animal, a galaxy, or a cell. The motion equations describe them all.

Sample Problem 1

A softball pitcher accelerates a ball from rest to a speed of 25 m/s over a distance of 1.8 m. What is the ball's acceleration?

Strategy:

Using the fifth equation of motion, derived from the other four equations using algebra, and knowing v_i, v_f, and d, you can solve for acceleration.

Given:

$$v_i = 0$$
$$v_f = 25 \text{ m/s}$$
$$d = 1.8 \text{ m}$$

Solution:

Knowing that $v_f^2 = 2ad + v_f^2$, and that $v_i = 0$, the equation becomes $v_f^2 = 2ad$.

Active Physics

$$v_f^2 = 2ad$$

$$a = \frac{v_f^2}{2d}$$

$$= \frac{(25\,\text{m/s})^2}{2(1.8\ \text{m})}$$

$$= \frac{25^2(\text{m/s})(\text{m/s})}{2(1.8\ \text{m})}$$

$$= 173.6\ \text{m/s}^2 \text{ or } 170\ \text{m/s}^2$$

Therefore, the acceleration of the softball is $170\,\text{m/s}^2$.

Sample Problem 2

During an auto race, a car with a speed of 75 m/s accelerates past another car at a rate of 3.0 m/s² for 4.0 s. How far does the car travel during this time?

Strategy:

Knowing the car's initial velocity, time, and acceleration you can use the fourth equation

$$d = \frac{1}{2}at^2 + v_i t \text{ to determine}$$

distance traveled without the need for first finding the final velocity.

Given: $v_i = 75\,\text{m/s}$

$$a = 3.0\,\text{m/s}$$

$$t = 4.0$$

Solution:

Using $d = \frac{1}{2}at^2 + v_i t$ and solving for d gives

$$d = \frac{1}{2}at^2 + v_i t$$

$$d = \frac{1}{2}(3.0\,\frac{\text{m}}{\text{s}^2})(4.0\ \text{s})^2 + (75\,\frac{\text{m}}{\text{s}})(4.0\ \text{s})$$

$$d = 324\ \text{m or } 320\ \text{m}$$

Therefore, the car travels 320 m, or almost one quarter of a mi.

1. When a jet lands on an aircraft carrier, its speed goes from 90.0 m/s to zero in 1.5 s as it is stopped by a cable running across the aircraft carrier's deck.

   a) If the direction the jet is traveling is positive, was the jet's acceleration positive or negative?

   b) What is the jet's acceleration during the stopping process?

   c) If the jet undergoes a constant acceleration while stopping, what is the jet's average speed?

   d) How far does the jet travel along the carrier's deck while it is being brought to a stop?

2. A race is held between a sports car and a motorcycle. The sports car can accelerate at 5.0 m/s² and the motorcycle can accelerate at 8.0 m/s². The two vehicles start the race at the same time and accelerate from rest.

   a) After 5.0 s, how fast is the sports car going?

   b) After 6.0 s, what distance will the motorcycle have gone?

   c) To make the race fair, the sports car starts 50.0 m ahead of the motorcycle. If the course is 200.0 m long, which vehicle wins the race? (Hint: The vehicle that covers its distance in the least time wins.)

3. A student on a skateboard pushes off from the top of a small hill with a speed of 2.0 m/s, and then goes down the hill with a constant acceleration of 0.5 m/s².

   a) After traveling a distance 12.0 m, how fast is the student going?

   b) How much time does it take the student to move a distance of 21.0 m while accelerating at this rate?

Graphing Models

You have been using graphs to better understand motion. You have seen that there is a relationship among corresponding *d-t*, *v-t* and *a-t* graphs.

The slope of a *d-t* graph of an automobile is equal to the velocity of the automobile.

The slope of a *v-t* graph of an automobile is equal to the acceleration of the automobile.

Given a *d-t* graph, you can use this information to determine the *v-t* graph and the *a-t* graph as you have seen earlier.

The velocity vs. time graph can also tell you about the distance traveled.

In the following two velocity vs. time graphs, the shaded areas under the velocity vs. time graphs are equal to the distance traveled. This can be proven in the following way.

In the first velocity vs. time graph, the average velocity is constant, because the velocity does not change. With no change in velocity, the acceleration must be zero. The shaded area under the graph is equal to the distance traveled. The shaded area under the graph is the area of a rectangle (*A* = height × base). This area is (average velocity) × (time), which is the definition of distance traveled.

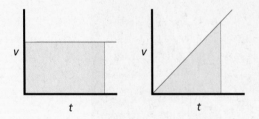

Velocity vs. Time

The second graph shows a constant acceleration. The area under the second graph is identical to the area of a triangle. The area of a triangle is ½ height × base. The base is the time. The height is the final velocity. One half the height is the average of the final velocity and the initial velocity of 0.

$$\frac{1}{2}\ \text{height} \times \text{base} = \frac{1}{2}\ (\text{final velocity}) \times (\text{time})$$

$$= (\text{average velocity}) \times (\text{time})$$

$$\frac{1}{2}\ h \times b = \frac{1}{2}\ (v_f) \times (t)$$

$$= (v_{average}) \times (t)$$

Once again, from the definition of average velocity (average velocity = distance/time), there is a way to calculate the distance traveled.

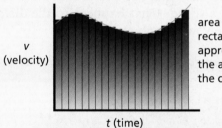

area of rectangles is approximately the area under the curve

The area under a velocity vs. time graph is always equal to the distance traveled. For non-constant accelerations, the velocity vs. time graph is a curve. You can see in the diagram above how you can break a curve into a series of tiny rectangles that approximates the curve. The total area under the curve is approximately equal to the total area of all the rectangles. This is the beginning of your introduction to calculus—an advanced mathematics invented by Sir Isaac Newton, an English physicist and mathematician, to better understand physics.

85

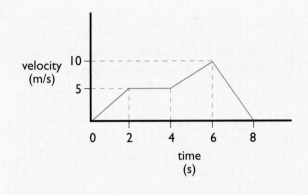

For the velocity vs. time graph shown:

1. Describe the motion from $t = 0$ to $t = 8$ s.

2. Calculate the acceleration of the object for each 2 s.

3. Calculate the distance traveled for each 2 s. (Hint: For $t = 4$ to $t = 6$, the area under the curve is a trapezoid made up of both a rectangle and a triangle.)

4. Calculate the total distance traveled.

What Do You Think Now?

At the beginning of this section, you were asked the following:

- **What factors must you consider to determine if you will be able to stop in the distance between you and the animal to avoid hitting it?**

How would you answer this question now? After studying the equations of motion, how do you think velocity affects the time it takes to suddenly stop an automobile? According to the equation for braking distance, if you double an automobile's speed, what happens to the distance needed for a vehicle's brakes to bring the vehicle to a stop?

Essential Questions

What does it mean?

An automobile safety manual states that the braking distance increases with the square of the velocity of the vehicle. What does this mean? Why is this related to safe driving?

How do you know?

What evidence do you have that tripling the speed of an automobile will increase the braking distance by a factor of $3 \times 3 = 9$?

Why do you believe?

Connects with Other Physics Content	Fits with Big Ideas in Science	Meets Physics Requirements
Forces and motion	Models	✱ Good, clear, explanation, no more complex than necessary

✱ Physics tries to use a few simply related principles to describe phenomena. Describing many different things requires a precision in language. In everyday language, you may use the words acceleration and deceleration. In physics, you use only the word acceleration. Describe the difference between positive and negative acceleration.

Why should you care?

Safe driving saves lives. How does knowing about the relationship between speed and braking distance help you to become a safe driver?

Reflecting on the Section and the Challenge

Safe driving requires the ability to stop safely. Some people think that if you triple your speed, the automobile will require triple the braking distance. You now know that it will take more than triple the braking distance – it is closer to nine times the braking distance!

You should be able to explain the importance of braking distance as it relates to speed. You should understand why slowing down is beneficial in terms of braking distance and what will happen to the required braking distance if you decrease your speed by one third.

You should always reduce your speed when driving through a school zone or a parking lot of a crowded supermarket. Slowing down decreases your braking distance and will protect unaware pedestrians.

In your *Chapter Challenge*, you can now demonstrate your understanding of the relationship of speed to braking distance to the Active Driving Academy.

Physics to Go

1. A student measured the braking distance of her automobile and recorded the data in the table. Plot the data on a graph and describe the relationship that exists between initial speed and braking distance.

Initial speed	Braking distance
5 m/s	4 m
10 m/s	15 m
15 m/s	35 m
20 m/s	62 m
25 m/s	98 m
30 m/s	140 m

2. Below is a graph of the braking distances in relation to initial speed for two automobiles. Compare qualitatively (without using numbers) the braking distances when each automobile is going at a slow speed and then again at a higher speed. Which automobile is safer? Why? How did you determine what "safer" means in this question?

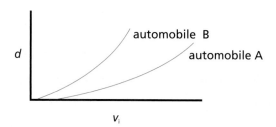

3. An automobile is able to stop in 20 m when traveling at 30 mi/hr. How much distance will it require to stop when traveling at the following:
   a) 15 mi/hr? (half of 30 mi/hr)   b) 60 mi/hr? (twice 30 mi/hr)
   c) 45 mi/hr? (three times 15 mi/hr)   d) 75 mi/hr? (five times 15 mi/hr)

4. An automobile traveling at 10 m/s requires a braking distance of 30 m. If the driver requires 0.9 s reaction time, what additional distance will the automobile travel before stopping? What is the total stopping distance, including both the reaction distance and the braking distance?

5. Consult the information for the sports car at the end of this chapter. This shows the stopping distance. How far would you expect this automobile to travel until coming to rest when brakes are applied at a speed of 30 mi/hr?

6. Use the information for the sedan at the end of this chapter. Find the braking distances for 50 mi/hr and 25 mi/hr. Draw a graph using the different braking distances. Plot the speeds on the horizontal axis and the braking distances on the vertical axis.

7. Does the braking information for the sedan include the driver's reaction time? If it does not, then how much distance is added to the total braking distance, supposing that the driver has a ½ s reaction time? Who should let the consumer know about the ½ s reaction time— the information sheet or a driver training manual?

8. Apply what you learned in this section to write a statement explaining the factors that affect stopping distance. The total stopping distance includes the distance you travel during your reaction time, plus the braking distance. What do you now know about stopping that will make you a safer driver?

9. In a perfect experiment, your data would show that the braking distance is proportional to the square of the velocity. Real data is not perfect. Describe two possible sources of error and explain how they could have impacted your results.

10. How could you revise this experiment to study better/worse braking situations? Predict how your graph might change.

11. *Preparing for the Chapter Challenge*

    Apply what you have learned in this section to write a convincing argument against excessive speed when approaching an intersection, a traffic light, crosswalk, school zone, or any other driving situation that may require sudden braking on your part. Excessive speed means you cannot stop in the available distance if necessary. What are the consequences of approaching these situations with excessive speed?

Inquiring Further

Reconstructing an accident

Collect newspaper clippings or summarize television news reports of traffic accidents in your city or town that involved automobiles and/or motorcycles. Become an accident investigator and imagine rewinding the events leading into the accident.

- What advice might you have given to the driver(s) involved about speed, reaction time, and braking distances, that would have enabled them to avoid the accident?

- In writing, comment on whether the accident might have been prevented simply by slowing down, or whether there were other contributing factors as well (such as icy roads). If there were other factors, would they be additional reasons for reducing speed?

Section 6

Using Models: Intersections with a Yellow Light

What Do You See?

Learning Outcomes

In this section, you will

- **Investigate** the factors that affect the STOP and GO Zones at intersections with traffic lights.

- **Investigate** the factors that result in an Overlap Zone or a Dilemma Zone at intersections with traffic lights.

- **Use** a computer simulation to mathematically model the situations that can occur at an intersection with traffic lights.

What Do You Think?

Some traffic lights stay yellow for three seconds. Others stay yellow for six seconds.

- **If all traffic lights stayed yellow the same amount of time, how would this affect drivers' decisions at intersections?**

- **How could an intersection with a traffic light be dangerous?**

Record your ideas about these questions in your *Active Physics* log. Be prepared to discuss your responses with your small group and the class.

Investigate

In this *Investigate*, you will use a computer simulation to model the factors that affect the STOP and GO Zones at an intersection with a yellow light. You will then investigate what happens at an intersection when the STOP and GO Zones do not overlap.

Part A: Variables Affecting STOP and GO Zones at Intersections with Traffic Lights

1. Watch the video of an intersection, carefully noting what happens when the light turns yellow.

a) Are there vehicles that you think should have stopped?

b) Were there vehicles that stopped, but you think should have continued through the intersection?

2. Watch the video a second time. This time pay attention to the position of the vehicles at the moment the light turns yellow.

a) Can you identify a "cutoff" point for a vehicle to make it through the intersection before the light turns red?

3. The diagram below shows the position of three automobiles at the moment a light turns yellow. Assume all three automobiles are moving with the same speed. Automobile A is able to make it through the intersection before the light turns red. It is in the GO Zone. Automobile C may not be able to make it through during the yellow light. The light may turn red before automobile C gets to the intersection.

a) Will automobile B be able to make it through during the yellow light?

b) Is automobile B in the GO Zone? Explain your answer.

c) Would any automobile closer to the intersection than automobile A be in the GO Zone?

d) Is automobile C in the GO Zone? What might happen if automobile C decides to continue?

4. In the following diagram of an intersection, automobile D is able to come to a safe stop when the light turns red because it is in the STOP Zone. In this zone, automobiles can stop safely before they reach the intersection. Automobile F is closer to the intersection than automobile D. If the driver of automobile F tries to stop the automobile, he or she may not be able to stop in such a short distance. Again, assume that all the automobiles have the same initial speed.

a) Is automobile E in the STOP Zone? Explain your answer.

91

STOP Zone   **GO Zone**

Vehicles in this zone can stop safely before the light turns red.

Vehicles in this zone cannot stop safely. They must go completely through the intersection.

b) Is automobile F in the STOP Zone? Explain your answer. What might happen if automobile F decides to stop?

c) Sketch the STOP Zone and GO Zone in your log for the intersections in the diagrams. Place automobiles A, B, C, D, E, and F in the appropriate zones.

5. In order to study the yellow-light problem, transportation engineers use a computer simulation to model how various factors affect the GO Zone and the STOP Zone. In the yellow-light model shown at the right, there are five input variables that can affect the two output variables.

Yellow-Light Model

INPUT		OUTPUT
yellow-light time (t_y)............		
driver response time (t_r)........		GO Zone
speed of vehicle (v)...............		
negative acceleration (a).......		STOP Zone
width of intersection (w).......		

a) In your log, list the five variables shown in the model.

b) You will first study how the variables affect the GO Zone. Copy the table at the right into your log.

c) Predict how increasing or ldecreasing each variable affects the size of the GO Zone.

Variable	Change		Predicted effect of change on GO Zone	Actual effect of change on GO Zone
t_y	yellow-light time	increase t_y		
		decrease t_y		
t_r	response time	increase t_r		
		decrease t_r		
v	speed limit	increase v		
		decrease v		
a	negative acceleration	increase a		
		decrease a		
w	width of intersection	increase w		
		decrease w		

92

Remember to consider one variable at a time. The other four variables will stay constant. For example, if the time the light is yellow increases from 3 s to 3.5 s, how will the boundaries and size of the GO Zone change? Will the zone increase or decrease? Record your predictions.

6. Look at the copies of the following spreadsheets.

	A	B	C	D	E	F	G
1	INPUT VARIABLES					OUTPUT	
2		3	seconds			meters	GO Zone
3	yellow-light time (t_y)	1	seconds	YELLOW	53	meters	STOP Zone
4	human-response time (t_r)	20	m/s	LIGHT	60		
5	speed of vehicle (v)	5	m/s/s	MODEL			
6	negative acceleration rate (a)	7	meters				
7	width of intersection (w)						
8							
9							

	A	B	C	D	E	F	G
1	INPUT VARIABLES					OUTPUT	
2							
3	yellow-light time (t_y)	3.5	seconds				
4	human-response time (t_r)	1	seconds	YELLOW	63	meters	GO Zone
5	speed of vehicle (v)	20	m/s	LIGHT	60	meters	STOP Zone
6	negative acceleration rate (a)	5	m/s/s	MODEL			
7	width of intersection (w)	7	meters				
8							
9							

a) What is the distance of the GO Zone if the yellow-light time is 3 s?

b) What happens to the GO Zone when the yellow-light time is increased to 3.5 s?

c) Would increasing the yellow-light time allow you to get through the intersection from a further distance away? Explain your answer in your log.

d) Record the effect of changing the yellow-light time in your log.

7. Use a computer spreadsheet program to obtain quantitative data (numbers you can use to test your predictions). Remember to change only one variable at a time. For each variable you investigate, record the following:

a) Did the effect of the change of the variable make sense to you? Explain your answer.

b) Record the effect of changing each variable in your *Active Physics* log. How did the actual effect compare with your predictions in *Step 5.c)*?

Active Physics

	E	F	G
		OUTPUT	
	= (B5*B3)-B7	meters	GO Zone
	= (B5*B4)+(B5^2)/(2*B6)	meters	STOP Zone

✎ c) Look for a pattern in your results and try to determine how the GO Zone is calculated by the spreadsheet. Click on the cell that gives the GO Zone value. Look at the formula bar and convert this notation to an equation. Record this equation in your log.

✎ d) Discuss with your group and explain why the yellow-light time, speed, and the width of the intersection appear in the equation for the GO Zone. Record this information in your log.

✎ e) Why do the reaction time and negative acceleration not appear in the equation? Why do these two variables have no effect on the GO Zone?

8. Now you will investigate how changing each variable will affect the STOP Zone.

✎ a) Record your predictions in a chart similar to the one you used for the GO Zone.

✎ b) Use the spreadsheet investigation to find the actual effect of each variable on the STOP Zone. Record the effect in your chart.

✎ c) Compare your prediction with the actual effect. Do your results make sense to you? Explain your answer.

9. Look for patterns in your results and try to determine how the STOP Zone is calculated by the spreadsheet.

✎ a) Click on the cell that gives the STOP Zone value. Look at the formula bar and convert this notation to an equation. Record this equation in your log.

✎ b) Discuss the relationship with your group and explain why the yellow-light time and the width of the intersection do not appear in the equation for the STOP Zone.

✎ c) Why do the reaction time, velocity, and negative acceleration appear in the equation? Why do the other two variables have no effect on the STOP Zone?

Part B: Yellow-Light Dilemma

1. Imagine that you are at intersection I shown in the diagram below.

a) Would you go or stop if the light turned yellow when you were driving in automobile A? Automobile B? Automobile C? Automobile D?

Intersection I

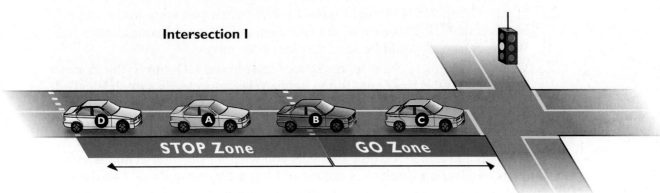

2. Imagine that you are at intersection II.

a) Would you go or stop if the light turned yellow when you were driving in automobile E? Automobile F? Automobile G? Automobile H?

Intersection II

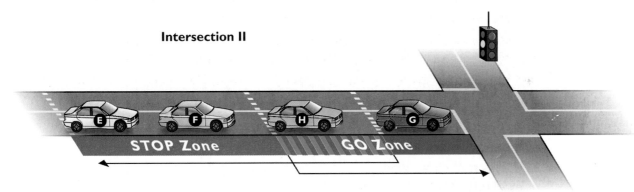

3. Imagine you are at intersection III.

a) Would you go or stop if the light turned yellow when you were driving in automobile J? Automobile K? Automobile L? Automobile M?

Intersection III

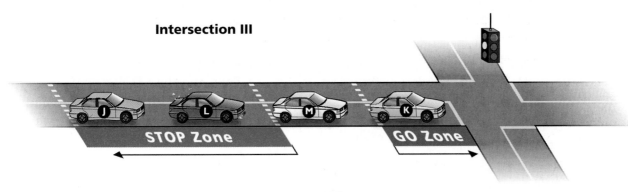

4. Compare the GO Zone and the STOP Zone for intersections I, II, and III.

🖊 a) How are the intersections different?

🖊 b) In intersection II, if the light turned yellow when you were between the GO Zone and the STOP Zone, what would your choices be? Which choice(s) would be safe? Explain your answer.

🖊 c) In intersection III, if the light turned yellow when you were in the space between the STOP Zone and the GO Zone, what would your choices be? Which choice(s) would be safe? Explain your answer.

🖊 d) When both choices are safe, the space between the GO and STOP Zones is called the Overlap Zone. When neither choice is clearly safe, it is called the Dilemma Zone. Intersections with a Dilemma Zone are not safe. Which intersection has an Overlap Zone and which has a Dilemma Zone?

5. Use a computer spreadsheet program, similar to the one you used in *Part A*. There is an additional outcome that tells you whether the intersection is safe and has an Overlap Zone or is unsafe and has a Dilemma Zone. Use the spreadsheet to determine ways in which an unsafe intersection can be made into a safe intersection. Which variables, when adjusted incorrectly, could make the intersection unsafe?

	A	B	C	D	E	F	G
1	INPUT VARIABLES					OUTPUT	
2							
3	yellow-light time (t_y)	3.7	seconds				
4	human-response time (t_r)	1.2	seconds	YELLOW	64	meters	GO Zone
5	speed of vehicle (v)	20	m/s	LIGHT	64	meters	STOP Zone
6	negative acceleration rate (a)	5	m/s/s	MODEL	0	meters	Overlap Zone
7	width of intersection (w)	10	meters				Safe
8							
9							
10							
11	yellow-light time (t_y)	3.7	seconds				
12	human-response time (t_r)	1.2	seconds	YELLOW	101	meters	GO Zone
13	speed of vehicle (v)	30	m/s	LIGHT	126	meters	STOP Zone
14	negative acceleration rate (a)	5	m/s/s	MODEL	-25	meters	UNSAFE
15	width of intersection (w)	10	meters				
16							

🖊 a) How does the spreadsheet determine whether the intersection is safe? What is the relationship between the GO Zone and the STOP Zone at an unsafe intersection?

🖊 b) Use the sample spreadsheet shown above. Is there an Overlap or Dilemma Zone at 20 m/s (45 mi/hr)?

c) What happens to the GO Zone and the STOP Zone when the speed is increased to 30 m/s (65 mi/hr)? Is there still an Overlap Zone or Dilemma Zone?

d) Now lower the speed to 10 m/s (20 mi/hr). Is the intersection safer now? Explain your answer.

6. Continue your investigation by resetting the speed to its original value of 20 m/s. Adjust the yellow-light time and determine its effect on the Dilemma and Overlap Zones.

a) Record the results of this investigation in your log. (Include the changes you make to the variable as well as their effect on the zones.)

7. What effect do reaction time, negative acceleration, and width of the intersection have on the safety of the intersection? Does changing any of these variables create a Dilemma Zone? Conduct investigations with your spreadsheet.

a) Record the results in your log. (Include the changes you make to the variable as well as their effect on the zones.)

8. More than one variable change can eliminate a Dilemma Zone and replace it with an Overlap Zone.

a) Of the five variables, explain the ease or difficulty in changing each one to make the intersection safer. For example, why might you suggest changing the yellow-light time rather than changing the width of the intersection?

9. The yellow-light problem is based on a simple model and only provides approximate calculations. It does not include other factors such as whether the road is flat or the length of the automobile.

a) How does the length of the automobile affect the model? Which outputs are affected by the length of the automobile?

Physics Talk

MODELS

The arrival of spring, the movements of birds flying in the air, and the power of a storm have been observed by humans for thousands of years. Some creative people have tried to communicate what they have experienced through music, dance, painting, and sculpture. Invisible things like love, suspicion, and suspense have also been portrayed by creative artists.

Physicists often rely on mathematical models to better understand the world. It is one of the reasons, you keep being asked, "Is there an equation?" A mathematical equation does not need to have anything to do with the real world. For example, the equation $x + y = 10$ tells you that the two numbers x and y must add up to 10. It does not have to relate to any real objects. The physics equation $d = vt$ tells you mathematically that there is a relationship between a distance traveled (d) and an object's velocity (v).

Yellow-Light Model

You began this section by thinking about what happens as vehicles approach a yellow light. Do the vehicles continue to go through the intersection or do they stop? Some of the vehicles are traveling faster than others. Some of the intersections are larger than others. Some of the yellow lights stay yellow for a briefer time than others. There are many possible situations when a vehicle approaches a yellow light. Physicists can make sense of these by creating a mathematical model for the yellow-light problem.

The first part of model-building was to recognize that the intersection with a yellow light could be modeled with a GO Zone and a STOP Zone. You then used this model to describe whether vehicles could safely proceed through an intersection when the light turns yellow.

Yellow-Light Model

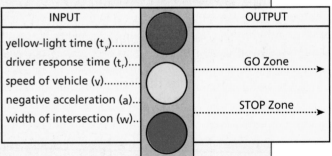

INPUT		OUTPUT
yellow-light time (t_y).........		
driver response time (t_r)....		GO Zone
speed of vehicle (v)..........		
negative acceleration (a)..		STOP Zone
width of intersection (w)..		

The GO Zone

The GO Zone includes all positions where the automobile can safely proceed through the intersection when the light turns yellow. Each position depends on the automobile's speed, the length of time of the yellow light, and the width of the intersection. You investigated why these variables are important and how they each affect the GO Zone.

The equation for calculating the GO Zone is $GZ = vt_y - w$

where vt_y is the distance the automobile travels while the light is yellow, and

w is the width of the intersection.

• The GO Zone increases if the yellow-light time increases. This makes sense because the automobile has a few more seconds to make it safely through the intersection.

- The GO Zone decreases if the width of the intersection increases because the vehicle has to travel a greater distance to safely go through the intersection at the same speed.

- The GO Zone increases with an increase in speed because the vehicle can travel a greater distance during the time that the light is yellow.

- The braking acceleration does not affect the GO Zone because vehicles trying to go through the intersection do not use the brakes.

- The driver's reaction time is also not important because a driver who is going to continue through the intersection does not have to decide to use the brakes and move from the gas to the brake.

The STOP Zone

The STOP Zone includes all positions where the car can safely stop before reaching the intersection. Each position depends on the vehicle's speed, the braking acceleration, and the driver's reaction time. You investigated why these variables are important and how they each affect the STOP Zone.

The equation for calculating the STOP Zone is $SZ = vt_r + \dfrac{v^2}{2a}$

where vt_r is the distance the vehicle travels as the driver decides to stop (the reaction distance), and

$\dfrac{v^2}{2a}$ is the braking distance.

- The STOP Zone decreases if the speed decreases. A slower-moving vehicle can be closer to the intersection and still stop safely.

- The STOP Zone decreases if the braking acceleration increases. Better brakes means that a vehicle can stop in a shorter distance.

- The STOP Zone decreases if the human reaction time decreases. The faster someone can react and move the foot from the gas to the brake, the smaller the distance required to stop.

- The width of the intersection does not affect the STOP Zone. Because vehicles in the STOP Zone do not enter the intersection, the size of the intersection does not matter.

- The yellow-light time does not affect the STOP Zone. Because you are stopping your vehicle, it does not matter how long the light stays yellow.

Overlap Zone and Dilemma Zone

A properly designed yellow-light intersection must be safe for drivers when they are obeying the posted speed limits. For this reason, the STOP and GO Zones are adjusted so that a driver can either safely stop the vehicle before the intersection when the light turns yellow, or safely proceed through the intersection before the light turns red. The STOP and GO Zones must form an Overlap Zone. In the Overlap Zone, when the light turns yellow, the driver of the vehicle has the choice of either stopping or going through the intersection safely before the light turns red.

→

In a poorly designed intersection, a Dilemma Zone may exist. The Dilemma Zone is a space between the STOP and GO Zones. In this region, a driver traveling the speed limit cannot safely stop before the intersection or pass through the intersection completely before the light turns red. The driver is faced with the dilemma of choosing between two dangerous options. Fortunately, traffic engineers rarely make errors such as this.

Limitations of the Yellow-Light Model

You began using a simple input/output table based on the model. You input the values for the speed of the vehicle, the width of the intersection, the yellow-light time, the braking acceleration, and the reaction time. The model then provided the output values for the GO Zone and the STOP Zone. You then explored how the model calculated these values. The physics equations of motion were used to determine the values for the GO Zone and the STOP Zone.

The GO Zone and STOP Zone model lets you analyze an intersection much more precisely than merely watching the motion of cars. Most drivers do not know about the GO Zone and the STOP Zone. They have a sense of what to do when the light turns yellow, but have not developed a model in the way that you have. This model helps traffic engineers to determine if an intersection is safe or if it can be made safer by lowering the speed limit or lengthening the yellow-light time.

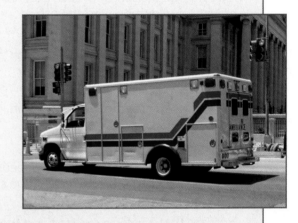

All models have limitations. The GO Zone and STOP Zone models that you developed do not take into account the length of the vehicle. You can expand the model by including this variable. The model does not include the colors of the vehicles. A person viewing an intersection may notice that an ambulance is responding to an emergency or a series of vehicles are part of a procession. This information may help explain the motion of the vehicles. The GO Zone and STOP Zone model does not take either of these situations into account. The colors of the vehicles is not an important factor in determining the GO and STOP Zones. You should always ask yourself where the model is useful and where the model is limited. You should also remind yourself that the model is not the same as the actual event. For example, the equations for the GO Zone and STOP Zone are not the same as vehicles approaching a yellow light.

In this section, you worked with a traffic model. In much of physics, you will be working with models that attempt to describe nature. There will be models that describe how forces affect motion, how light behaves and how something called energy can neither be created nor destroyed. The laws of physics are mathematical models that try to accurately predict what will occur and try to give you a glimpse into how nature works.

Checking Up

1. In this section, the spreadsheet is referred to as a model. What makes it a model?

2. In your own words, describe what is meant by the GO Zone.

3. In your own words, describe what is meant by the STOP Zone.

4. Describe what is meant by the Overlap Zone.

5. Describe what is meant by the Dilemma Zone.

Active Physics

+Math	+Depth	+Concepts	+Exploration
◆◆	◆◆	◆	

Active Physics

Plus

Speed and the Yellow-Light Model

As a driver, you have control over the speed of your automobile. How does that speed affect the GO and STOP Zones for a yellow light?

1. Predict how increases or decreases in speed will affect the GO Zone and STOP Zone.

2. Using a spreadsheet program or a graphing calculator, graph the relationship of the GO Zone vs. different speeds.

3. Graph the relationship of the STOP Zone vs. different speeds.

4. Using a graphing calculator or a spreadsheet program, graph the STOP Zone and the GO Zone vs. speed on the same set of axes. Try different values for the other variables from your earlier work.

5. Indicate the Overlap or Dilemma Zones on your graph.

6. In the *Investigate*, you analyzed how decreasing the speed of the automobile can eliminate the Dilemma Zone. Your graph may indicate that there is a new Dilemma Zone at very low speeds. Explain how this can be.

7. In the *Scenario* for this chapter, the teenager jokes that a yellow light means "step on it." Would accelerating help you get through a yellow light? Calculate how much it may help.

8. Revise the spreadsheet model to test your answer to the question above. How would an acceleration of your automobile affect the GO Zone? Try to use realistic values of the acceleration and the time you have to accelerate. If you do increase your speed and find yourself in the intersection when the light has turned red, an accident at the faster speed will be much more severe. Assuming you are traveling at the speed limit, calculate how far above the speed limit you may be going to try to "beat the light."

What Do You Think Now?

At the beginning of this section, you were asked the following:

• **If all traffic lights stayed yellow the same amount of time, how would this affect drivers' decisions at intersections?**

• **How could an intersection with a traffic light be dangerous?**

Now that you have investigated the effects of factors on a GO Zone and STOP Zone, what do you think would be the effect of having all lights stay yellow for the same length of time? Explain what could make an intersection with a traffic light dangerous and what can be done to correct the situation. Include the term Dilemma Zone in your explanation.

Active Physics

Physics
Essential Questions

What does it mean?

What factors determine the size of the GO Zone, the STOP Zone, and whether an intersection has a Dilemma Zone?

How do you know?

What measurements can you make to test your understanding of the GO, STOP, Overlap, and Dilemma Zones? In this section, you used equations and calculations on a computer model (spreadsheet) to determine these zones. How could you verify the conclusions from your spreadsheet to determine the zones?

Why do you believe?

Connects with Other Physics Content	Fits with Big Ideas in Science	Meets Physics Requirements
Forces and motion	✳ Models	Makes mathematical sense

✳ Physics uses mathematical models to describe physical situations. How do the GO Zone and STOP Zone models help you to improve your understanding of traffic at a yellow-light intersection?

Why should you care?

How can understanding the physics behind the GO, STOP, Overlap, and Dilemma Zones make you a better, more aware, and more informed driver?

Reflecting on the Section and the Challenge

In earlier sections, you learned that an automobile travels a certain distance while you are moving at a constant velocity and deciding whether to stop. You also learned that your automobile travels a certain distance after the brakes have been applied.

In this section, you learned that deciding what to do when you see a yellow light is not a simple decision. It requires a judgment of the distance to the intersection, the width of the intersection, and how much time it will take you to get there at the speed you are traveling. You also need some sense of how well your brakes work and how quickly you can respond. Finally, you need to know the time that the light is yellow before turning red.

You also know that it is important for traffic engineers to make sure that an intersection has an Overlap Zone and not a Dilemma Zone between the STOP and GO Zones.

You now know which factors affect the zones at an intersection. You know any intersection can be made safer by lowering the speed limit or by lengthening the yellow-light time. You also know how these zones may change if your reaction time is slower or if your negative acceleration is being affected by bad weather or road conditions. Part of the *Chapter Challenge* is to explain these factors and how they affect your reaction time based on your investigations and conclusions.

Physics to Go

1. An *Active Physics* student group is studying an intersection. The width of the intersection is measured by pacing and is found to be approximately 15-m wide. The yellow-light time for the intersection is 4 s. The speed limit on this road is 30 mi/hr (approximately 15 m/s). The speed of an automobile decreases by 5 m/s every second during negative acceleration. Assume that the people who are driving the automobiles have a reaction time of 1 s.

   a) Calculate the GO Zone using the math equation on the computer spreadsheet. Use a calculator. To guide you, the first two steps are provided for you.

   GO Zone = (velocity × yellow-light time) − width of intersection

   $GZ = vt_y - w$

   $GZ = (15 \text{ m/s})(4 \text{ s}) - 15 \text{ m}$

   $GZ =$

   b) Calculate the STOP Zone using the math equation on the computer spreadsheet. Use a calculator to help you.

   STOP Zone = (velocity × reaction time) + velocity^2/(2 × negative acceleration)

   $SZ = vt_r + \dfrac{v^2}{2a}$

   c) Make a sketch of the intersection and label both the GO Zone and the STOP Zone. Include the dimensions of the intersection and each zone.

2. Some people disregard the 30 mi/hr speed limit (15 m/s) and travel at 60 mi/hr (30 m/s) on the road described in *Question 1*.

   a) Use the spreadsheet or calculator to calculate STOP and GO Zones at 60 mi/hr. Sketch the intersection marking both zones. Explain the danger of driving at this speed.

   b) How would a decrease in the speed limit to 20 mi/hr (about 10 m/s) affect the STOP and GO Zones in *Question 1*? Use the spreadsheet or calculator to calculate both, then sketch the intersection, marking both zones.

3. A person is listening to loud music while driving. Explain why the increase in reaction time caused by the music does not affect the GO Zone. Explain how it affects the STOP Zone.

4. An automobile has worn tires and bad brakes. How will this affect the GO Zone and the STOP Zone at a yellow light?

5. Sometimes, when a light turns red at an intersection, the light for the traffic on the cross street does not turn green for a couple of seconds. What is the reason for this delay?

6. In the 1960s, the traffic engineers in a city experimented with a traffic light that featured a clock. As you approached an intersection with a green light, in the space for the yellow light there was a countdown: …, 5, 4, 3, 2, 1, 0. When the clock reached "0" the light turned yellow.

This experiment was never implemented, and not even the city where this experiment was done uses the countdown to the yellow light today. Why do you think the traffic engineers decided this countdown was not a good idea? How does such a countdown affect the STOP and GO Zones of the oncoming traffic?

7. With the grid below, compute the GO and STOP Zones for each intersection. Also, determine if each intersection is safe and describe how you know it is safe.

Intersection	A	B	C	D	E
Yellow-light time	3.0 s	4.0 s	3.0 s	3.0 s	3.5 s
Reaction time	1.2 s	1.2 s	1.0 s	1.8 s	1.2 s
Speed of automobile	20 m/s	20 m/s	20 m/s	20 m/s	15 m/s
Acceleration	−7 m/s^2	−7 m/s^2	−7 m/s^2	−7 m/s^2	−7 m/s^2
Width of intersection	12 m	8 m	12 m	12 m	12 m

8. Do you think it would be a good idea to paint lines at all intersections showing the boundaries of the STOP and GO Zones? Explain your answer.

9. *Preparing for the Chapter Challenge*

Write a pretend letter to your parents, asking to borrow their car. You must try to convince them based on what you have learned in this section about intersections. Be sure to explain what you have learned about the STOP, GO, Overlap and Dilemma Zones.

Inquiring Further

Study a real intersection

Now that you know how the length of the yellow-light time and other factors affect the safety of a traffic intersection, you are ready to study an actual intersection.

a) Choose a traffic intersection in your neighborhood and measure the yellow-light time.

b) Obtain the width of the intersection from a local police officer or from the municipal government.

c) Assume that the driver's reaction time is 1.0 s and the negative acceleration is 5 m/s every second. Run the spreadsheet program with this data and find the STOP and GO Zones. You may also use a calculator and the appropriate equations.

d) Draw a sketch of the intersection and include the GO Zone and the STOP Zone.

e) From your data, does a Dilemma Zone or an Overlap Zone exist? Is the intersection safe?

Section 7

Centripetal Force: Driving on Curves

What Do You See?

Learning Outcomes

In this section, you will

- **Recognize** the need for a centripetal force when rounding a curve.

- **Predict** the effect of an inadequate centripetal force.

- **Relate** speed to centripetal force.

What Do You Think?

You are driving along a road at the posted speed limit of 50 mph (80 km/h). A road sign warns that you are approaching a curve and tells you to slow down to 25 mi/hr (40 km/h).

- **Why is the sign indicating to slow down?**

- **How is the amount you should slow down determined?**

Record your ideas about these questions in your *Active Physics* log. Be prepared to discuss your responses with your small group and the class.

Investigate

In this *Investigate*, you will model some of the problems a driver faces when driving around curves. You will investigate how speed and the tightness of a curve can affect what happens to a vehicle on a curve.

1. Driving around a curve produces some unique problems. Physics lets you model some of these problems.

   a) Imagine that you have a toy car at the end of a string, and it is moving in a circle. If you let go of the string, which way would the car travel? The diagrams on the following page show several possibilities.

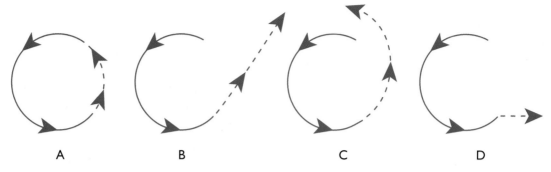

| A | B | C | D |

In which direction do you think the car will travel? Write your choice and how you made your decision in your log.

2. The best way to check your answer is to try out the model. That is what it means to do science. Tie a motorized toy car to one end of a string. If you do this on a table, the string should be a little less than half the width of your table. (You can use a longer string if you do this on the floor.) With a finger, hold the other end of the string fixed to the tabletop. Turn on the car's motor, so that the car travels in a circle with your finger at the center, as shown in the diagram.

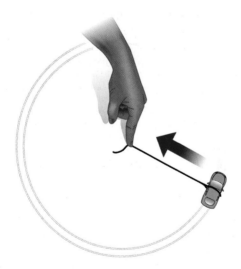

a) The string makes the car travel in a circle. In which direction does the string pull on the car? This pull is referred to as a *force* in physics. Understanding forces is a topic that you will return to many times in this course and every future physics course.

b) Now release the string. Which way does the car travel when it is released?

3. As you know, there is no string attached to a real automobile when it makes a turn, but there must be a force (like the force of the string) that keeps it moving in a circular path. The pull or force toward the center of a circular curve is the friction between the tires and the road. On an icy road, there is very little friction and the automobile cannot move in a curve and continues in a straight line. You can learn more about friction and how to measure friction in another chapter.

a) Draw a diagram of an automobile traveling north and making a right turn. On your diagram, draw the direction of the frictional force that keeps the car moving in a circular curve.

4. To further investigate the factors that determine whether an automobile will stay on the road as it goes around a curve, you will do a second investigation. Place a block of wood near the edge of a turntable (or revolving tray).

a) Record the distance from the block to the center of the turntable. This is the radius of the curve.

5. Spin the turntable. As it spins, the block is held on the spinning surface by friction. (In other words, the block is prevented from sliding off the turntable by friction. If the friction suddenly disappeared while the block was rotating, it would be similar to letting go of the string of the motorized toy car.) This friction between the block and the surface of the turntable

is not identical to the friction that holds an automobile on the road, but it is similar to the friction between the surface of the road and an automobile's tires.

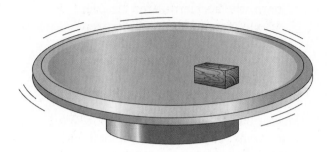

6. Gradually increase the rotational speed of the turntable until the block just begins to slide. To repeat the experiment after the block slides, place it back on the turntable at the original distance from the center. Now practice until you find the fastest speed that allows the block to stay in place.

a) Measure and record the time required for 10 revolutions.

b) Record the number of revolutions per minute made by the block when the friction is strong enough to keep the block going in a circle.

c) How much time goes by during one revolution?

d) How fast (revolutions per second) is the turntable turning when friction can no longer hold the block in place?

7. To calculate the speed of the block, divide the distance traveled by the time needed to go that distance.

When an object moves in a circle, the distance traveled in one revolution is the circumference (distance around the outside) of a circle.

Circumference = $2\pi \times$ radius of circle

$$C = 2\pi r$$

a) What was the speed of the block when it stayed on the turntable?

b) What was the block's speed when it slid off the turntable? Record your results in a table in your log.

Note: You may not be able to find the exact speed at which the block leaves the turntable. You can find a maximum speed at which the block stays in place. You can call this a safe speed. Any speed lower than the safe speed will also be safe. You can also find the minimum speed at which the block is not able to stay on the turntable. You can call this an unsafe speed. Any speed higher than this will also be unsafe.

8. Tape some sandpaper or place a rubber mat on top of the turntable. Place the block on the sandpaper or the mat. Repeat the entire investigation. Keep the distance between the block and the turntable's center the same as it was previously.

a) Record all the necessary data.

b) Calculate the greatest speed at which the block can stay on the sandpaper or rubber mat.

c) Compare the maximum safe speed with the sandpaper or mat to the maximum safe speed without it. How does the surface affect the maximum speed?

9. In addition to the speed and the road surface, you also need to look at the curvature of the road (how tight the turn happens to be). Curves come in many shapes. The arc of a circle is a good approximation for at least a segment of any curve. The arc of a large circle (a circle with a large radius) can represent a gentle curve. The arc of a small circle (a circle with a small radius) can represent a tight curve.

a) Investigate the effect of the amount of curve by placing the block at various distances from the center of the turntable.

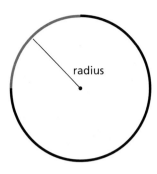

b) At each radius, find the maximum safe speed of the block. Record your data and results in your table.

c) As the radius of the turntable decreases (becomes tighter) what happens to the maximum speed?

10. Get an accelerometer from your teacher. An accelerometer is a device used to measure accelerations.

a) For example, a necklace hanging from the rearview mirror of an automobile acts as a simple accelerometer. How can something such as a hanging necklace tell you if the automobile is accelerating, even if you are not looking out the windows for other clues?

b) Hold an accelerometer in your hands and observe it as you either sit on a rotating stool or spin around while standing. What is the direction of the acceleration indicated by the accelerometer? (For a "cork" accelerometer, you can find out how the cork indicates acceleration by holding it and noting its behavior as you accelerate forward.)

c) In your log, make a sketch that simulates a snapshot photo taken from a horizontal position as the accelerometer was moving along a circular path. Show the circular path, the accelerometer "frozen" at one instant, the cork "frozen" in a leaning position, and an arrow to represent the velocity of the accelerometer at the instant represented by your sketch.

11. Start a ball rolling across the floor. While it is rolling, catch up with the ball and use a rolled-up newspaper or magazine to push the ball sideways or perpendicular to the motion of the ball with a fixed amount of force. Carefully follow alongside the ball and keep adjusting the direction of push so that it is always perpendicular to the motion of the ball.

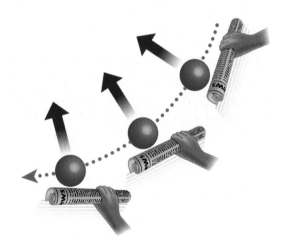

a) Make a top-view sketch in your log that shows:

- A line that represents the straight-line path of the ball before you began pushing sideways on it.

- A dashed line to represent the straight-line path on which the ball would have continued moving if you had not pushed it sideways.

- A line of appropriate shape to show the path taken by the ball as you pushed perpendicular to the direction of the ball's motion with a constant amount of force.

b) When you pushed the ball perpendicular or sideways to its motion, did you cause the ball to move faster or slower? Explain your answer.

c) Assuming that friction could be eliminated to allow the ball to continue moving at constant speed, describe what you would need to do to keep the ball moving on a circular path.

d) If you stop pushing the ball, how does the ball move? Try it, and make a sketch in your log of what happens.

12. Repeat *Step 11* when the ball is moving faster, and continue using the rolled-up newspaper to keep the ball moving in the same-sized circle.

a) How is the force you need to exert on the faster ball different from the force exerted in *Step 11*?

13. Repeat *Step 12* when the ball is moving at the same speed but in a smaller circle.

a) How is the force you need to exert to keep the ball moving in a smaller circle different from the force exerted in *Step 12*?

b) Compare driving around a curve on dry pavement to driving around the same curve when it is covered with ice.

Physics Talk

CIRCULAR MOTION

Centripetal Force

In the *Investigate*, you observed a toy car moving in a circle. The car required the **force** of the string to keep it moving in a circle. When you let go of the string, the car traveled in a straight line. There was no longer a force on the car to keep it moving in a circle. This motion can be explained using Newton's laws, which you will study in more detail in other chapters.

Physics Words

force: a push or a pull.

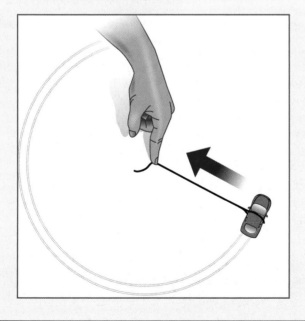

Active Physics

Newton's first law of motion states that an object in motion will stay in motion at a constant speed and travel in a straight line unless a force acts on it. When you let go of the string, the car traveled in a straight line, since no force was acting on it. Any time you observe something moving along a curved path, you should recognize that there has to be a force acting on the object.

The force of the string keeps the toy car moving in a circle. This force of the string is always toward the center of the circle. In a similar way, the force of friction between the block and the turntable kept the block moving in a circle. This force of friction is also always toward the center of the circle.

When an automobile makes a turn, it is traveling along part of a circle. There is a force of friction between the tires and the road that keeps the automobile moving in the circle.

Eliminate this friction, which is what happens on an icy road, and the automobile will move in a straight line and will not be able to turn (regardless of what you do with the steering wheel). This force of friction is toward the center of the circular curve.

Physics Words

centripetal force:
a force directed toward the center to keep an object in a circular path.

centripetal acceleration:
a change in the direction of the velocity with respect to time.

Checking Up

1. What is the direction of the force that keeps an object moving in a circle?

2. What is the name of the force that keeps an object moving in a circle?

3. Name the force that keeps an automobile moving in a circular path on a road.

4. Explain how the velocity of an object can change even if the speed is not changing.

5. Describe three situations in which acceleration can take place.

6. What is the force that keeps Earth moving in a circle around the Sun?

The force that keeps an object moving in a circular path is called a **centripetal force.** The centripetal force can be the tension in the string, the friction between the block of wood and surface of the turntable, or the friction between an automobile and the road. For Earth moving in a circle around the Sun, the centripetal force is gravity. (You will learn more about the forces of friction and gravity in later chapters.) For a baseball bat moving in a circle during a swing, the centripetal force is the force of the muscles in the batter's arms.

As the toy car moves in a circle, its speed remains the same. It does not appear to go faster or slower. Its velocity does change because the direction is changing. The car is changing its direction. For a moment it is moving east, then it is moving south, then it is moving west, then north, and then east again as it starts its next revolution. Changes in velocity with respect to time are called *accelerations.* In the previous sections, you associated accelerations with changes in speed as a vehicle speeded up or slowed down.

A vehicle that is changing directions is also accelerating. The acceleration associated with an automobile changing directions is referred to as **centripetal acceleration.**

Acceleration is the change in velocity with respect to time. Velocity can change when an object speeds up, slows down, or changes direction.

Active Physics

+Math	+Depth	+Concepts	+Exploration
◆	◆		

Active Physics

Plus

Calculating Centripetal Acceleration and Centripetal Force

You learned that the force of the string on the toy car or the force of friction between the tires and the road cause an automobile to move in a circle. The direction of the force is toward the center of this circle. The size of the force depends on the mass of the automobile, the speed of the automobile, and the radius of the curve. You can use the following equations to calculate the centripetal force and the corresponding centripetal acceleration.

$$a = \frac{v^2}{r}$$

$$F = \frac{mv^2}{r}$$

where a is acceleration
F is force
v is velocity
m is mass
r is the radius of the curve

Sample Problem

Calculate the centripetal acceleration and centripetal force of a 1000-kg automobile traveling at 27 m/s (60 mi/h) that turns on an unbanked curve having a radius of 100 m.

Strategy: Because the automobile is moving along a circular path, the centripetal acceleration must be directed toward the center of the curve. The magnitude can be found because the speed and radius are given.

Given:
Mass $(m) = 1000$ kg

Speed $(v) = 27$ m/s

Radius of curve $(r) = 100$ m

Solution:
This acceleration changes the direction of the velocity of the automobile.

$$a = \frac{v^2}{r}$$
$$= \frac{(27 \text{ m/s})^2}{100 \text{ m}}$$
$$= \frac{729 \text{ m}^2/\text{s}^2}{100 \text{ m}}$$
$$= 7.29 \text{ m/s}^2 \text{ or } 7.3 \text{ m/s}^2$$

The speed of the automobile remains the same.

Because the automobile is moving along a circular path, the centripetal force must be exerted toward the center of the curve. The magnitude can be found because the mass, speed, and radius are all given.

$$F = \frac{mv^2}{r}$$
$$= \frac{1000 \text{ kg} \times (27 \text{ m/s})^2}{100.0 \text{ m}}$$
$$= \frac{1000 \text{ kg} \times 729 \text{ m}^2/\text{s}^2}{100 \text{ m}}$$
$$= 7290 \text{ kg} \cdot \text{m/s}^2 = 7300 \text{ N}$$

If the centripetal force, which in this case is the force of friction, cannot cause sufficient acceleration, the automobile will not follow the curve and will skid in the direction of its velocity at the instant the tires break loose. Your experiment with the block sliding off the turntable demonstrated this. For a given v and a given r, the centripetal force must be enough to provide the acceleration $\frac{v^2}{r}$.

Active Physics

For a given road surface, there is a maximum frictional force that can provide this centripetal force. Hence, there is a maximum $\frac{v^2}{r}$ that a road surface can provide. If your speed is too fast, or the curve too sharp, then the maximum $\frac{v^2}{r}$ will be exceeded, and off the road you go – perhaps to disaster...

A curve with a radius of 40 m has a warning sign that limits the speed to 30 mi/h (14 m/s). Assume that an automobile has a mass of 1000 kg.

a) What is the frictional force of an automobile that is driving the speed limit?

b) How much additional frictional force does the automobile need if the driver decides to exceed the speed limit and travel at 20 m/s?

c) If the frictional force were reduced by half due to wet leaves and water on the road, what speed would you recommend for drivers?

What Do You Think Now?

At the beginning of this section, you were asked the following:

You are driving along a road at the posted speed limit of 50 mi/hr (80 km/h). A road sign warns that you are approaching a curve and tells you to slow down to 25 mi/hr (40 km/h).

• **Why is the sign indicating to slow down?**

• **How is the amount you should slow down determined?**

After having investigated the effect of speed on centripetal force, why should you slow down? Use the results of your investigations to support your answer.

Essential Questions

What does it mean?

What is a centripetal force? Draw a sketch of an automobile making a turn. Show the direction of the velocity and the direction of the centripetal force.

How do you know?

What evidence do you have that circular motion requires a force toward the center of the circle?

Why do you believe?

Connects with Other Physics Content	Fits with Big Ideas in Science	Meets Physics Requirements
Forces and motion	Change and constancy	✱ Good, clear, explanation, no more complex than necessary

✱ In physics, a few simply stated principles explain a large variety of phenomena. How can an automobile be accelerating if it does not speed up or slow down?

Why should you care?

What are the consequences of exceeding the physical speed limit imposed by the road-tire interface and the radius of the curve?

Reflecting on the Section and the Challenge

In this section, you learned that friction between the road and the tires helps keep an automobile on the road when it goes around a curve. More friction allows you to move faster and still stay on the road.

A tight turn requires more friction or a slower speed than a wider turn. Because you cannot change or control the friction between the road and tires (other than keeping good tires in good condition), a slower speed will keep the automobile on the road.

Part of your challenge requires you to explain why it is necessary to drive at a slower speed around a curve than on a straight section of the road. You also may want to explain what happens if the road conditions change, if the friction is reduced because the tires are worn out, or if the curve in the road is very tight.

Physics to Go

1. A person at the equator travels once around the circumference of Earth in 24 h. The radius of Earth is 6400 km. How fast is the person going? Compute the speed in kilometers per hour (km/h) and in meters per second (m/s). Recall that 1 km is equal to 1000 m.

2. Earth travels in a circular motion around the Sun. The radius of Earth's motion is about 1.5×10^8 km. What is the speed of Earth around the Sun? Compute the speed in km/h and m/s.

3. A fan turns at a rate of 60 revolutions per second. If the tip of the blade is 15 cm from the center, how fast is the tip moving?

4. Friction can hold an automobile on the road when it is traveling at 20 m/s and the radius of the turn is 15 m. What happens if:

   a) the curve is tighter?

   b) the road surface becomes slippery?

   c) both the curve is tighter and the road is slippery?

5. Think about other examples in which objects travel in curved paths, such as the clothes in a spin dryer, or the Moon traveling around Earth. For each example, explain what produces the force that is constantly being applied to the object toward the center of the curve.

6. Sketch a graph that shows the radial distance and the maximum speed at which the block remains on a turntable for one type of surface.

7. Explain the following statement: "The driver may turn the wheels but it is the road that turns the automobile."

8. **Active Physics Plus** A jet pilot in level flight at a constant speed of 270 m/s (600 mi/hr) rolls the airplane on its side and executes a tight circular turn that has a radius of 1000 m. What is the pilot's centripetal acceleration? Draw a sketch of the acceleration's direction relative to the ground.

9. Below you will find alternate explanations of the same event given by a person who was not wearing a seat belt when an automobile went around a sharp curve.

   "I was sitting near the middle of the front seat when the automobile turned sharply to the left. A force made my body slide across the seat toward the right, outward from the center of the curve, and then my right shoulder slammed against the door on the passenger side of the automobile."

   "I was sitting near the middle of the front seat when the automobile turned sharply to the left. My body kept going in a straight line while, at the same time due to insufficient friction, the seat slid to the left beneath me, until the door on the passenger side of the automobile had moved far enough to the left to exert a centripetal force against my right shoulder."

   Are both explanations correct? Explain your answer in terms of both explanations.

10. Race cars can make turns at 150 mi/hr. What forces act on a race car as it moves along a circular path at constant speed on a flat, horizontal surface?

11. Why are highway curves that have radii that decrease as you go into them especially dangerous? In other words, curves that start out as gentle turns but become tighter and tighter as you get into them.

12. In the United States, vehicles drive on the right-hand side of a two-lane road. If the curve bends to the right and you lose traction in the turn, would you end up in the ditch on your side of the road, or into the lane of oncoming traffic? What if the curve bends to the left?

13. *Preparing for the Chapter Challenge*

    Write a few sentences telling your parents that you know how to apply the physics from this section to drive safely around curves. You should include information about why you need to slow down around curves in rainy or icy weather.

Inquiring Further

1. **Banking a curve**

   Design an investigation to determine the effect of banking a curve on the speed at which the curve can be safely negotiated. After your teacher approves your procedure, conduct your investigation.

2. **Mass and speed on a curve**

   Design an investigation to determine if the mass of an automobile has an effect on the safe speed around a curve. After your teacher approves your procedure, conduct your investigation.

TOURING SEDAN

0-60 mph	7.2 s
0-¼ mi	15.4 s
Top speed	est 143 mph
Skidpad	0.83 g
Slalom	61.9 mph
Brake rating	excellent

TEST CONDITIONS

Temperature	70°F
Wind	calm
Elevation	1010 ft

ENGINE

Type	aluminum bloc and heads, **V-6**
Valvetrain	dohc 4 valve/cyl
Displacement	155 cu in./2544 cc
Bore × stroke	3.24 × 3.11 in./ 82.4 × 79.0 mm
Compression ratio	10.0:1
Horsepower (SAE)	**195 bhp @ 6625 rpm**
Bhp/liter	76.7
Torque	**165 lb-ft @ 5625 rpm**
Maximum engine speed	6750
Fuel injection	elect. sequential port
Fuel	prem unleaded, 91 pump oct

CHASSIS & BODY

Layout	**front engine/front drive**
Body/frame	unit steel
Brakes	
Front	**10.9-in. vented discs**
Rear	**9.9-in. vented discs**
Assist type	vacuum; ABS
Total swept area	366 sq in.
Wheels	cast alloy, **16 × 6½**
Tires	steel-belted touring, **P205/55ZR-16**
Steering	**rack & pinion** power assist
Overall ratio	14.5:1
Turns, lock to lock	2.7
Turning circle	38.4 ft
Suspension	
Front	**struts**, lower A-arms, coil springs, tube shocks, anti-roll bar
Rear	**struts**, trailing links, dual lower lateral links, coil springs, tube shocks, anti-roll bar

DRIVE TRAIN

Transmission	**5-sp manual**

Gear	Ratio	Overall ratio	(Rpm) Mph
1st	3.42:1	13.89:1	(6750) 34
2nd	2.14:1	8.69:1	(6750) 55
3rd	1.45:1	5.89:1	(6750) 81
4th	1.03:1	4.18:1	(6750) 114
5th	0.77:1	3.13:1	(6750) 143

Final drive ratio	4.06:1
Engine rpm @ 60 mph in 5th	2650

GENERAL DATA

Curb weight	**3055 lb**
Test weight	3180 lb
Weight dist (with driver), f/r, %	63/37
Wheelbase	106.5 in.
Track, f/r	59.2 in./58.5 in.
Length	**183.9 in.**
Width	**69.1 in.**
Height	**54.5 in.**
Ground clearance	8/2 in.
Trunk space	18.0 + 7.0 cu ft

MAINTENANCE

Oil/filter	5000 mi/5000 mi
Tuneup	100,000 mi
Basic warranty	36 mo/36,000 mi

ACCOMMODATIONS

Seating capacity	**5**
Head room, f/r	39.0 in./35.0 in.
Seat width, f/r	2 × 20.5 in./50.0 in.
Front-seat leg room	43.0 in.
Rear-seat leg room	25.0 in.
Seatback adjustment	85 deg
Seat travel	8.5 in.

INTERIOR NOISE

Idle in neutral	54 dBA
Maximum in 1st gear	78 dBA
Constant 50 mph	66 dBA
70 mph	71 dBA

INSTRUMENTATION

160-mph speedometer, 8000-rpm tach, coolant temp, fuel level

ACCELERATION

Time to speed	Seconds
0-35 mph	2.5
0-40 mph	3.8
0-50 mph	5.2
0-60 mph	7.2
0-70 mph	9.3
0-80 mph	11.6
0-90 mph	14.8
0-100 mph	18.8
Time to distance	
0-100 ft	3.3
0-500 ft	8.4
0-1320 ft (¼ mi)	15.4 @ 91.5 mph

FUEL ECONOMY

Normal driving	20.0 mpg
EPA city/highway	20/29 mpg
Cruise range	270 miles
Fuel capacity	14.5 gal

BRAKING

Minimum stopping distance	
From 60 mph	135 ft
From 80 mph	228 ft
Control	excellent
Pedal effort for 0.5 g stop	na
Fade, effort after six 0.5 g stops from 60 mph	na
Brake feel	excellent
Overall brake rating	excellent

HANDLING

Lateral accel (200-ft skidpad)	0.83 g
Balance	moderate understeer
Speed thru 700-ft slalom	61.9 mph
Balance	mild understeer
Lateral seat support	very good

Subjective ratings consists of excellent, very good, good, average, poor; na means information is not available

Active Physics

SPORTS CAR

0-60 mph	5.2 s
0-¼ mi	13.8 s
Top speed	est 165 mph
Skidpad	na
Slalom	62.5 mph
Brake rating	excellent

TEST CONDITIONS

Temperature	86°F
Wind	calm
Elevation	est 700 ft

ENGINE

Type	aluminum bloc and heads, **V-8**
Valvetrain	ohv 2 valve/cyl
Displacement	346 cu in./5666 cc
Bore × stroke	3.90 × 3.62 in./99.0 × 92.0 mm
Compression ratio	10.0:1
Horsepower (SAE)	**345 bhp @ 5600 rpm**
Bhp/liter	60.9
Torque	**350 lb-ft @ 4400 rpm**
Maximum engine speed	6000
Fuel injection	elect. sequential port
Fuel	prem unleaded, 91 pump oct

CHASSIS & BODY

Layout	**front engine/rear drive**
Body/frame	fiberglass/steel unit frame

Brakes

Front	**12.8-in. vented discs**
Rear	**12.0-in. vented discs**
Assist type	vacuum; ABS
Total swept area	433 sq in.
Swept area/ton	257 sq in.
Wheels	cast magnesium; **17 × 8½ f**
	18 × 9½ r
Tires	steel-belted sports;
	P245/45ZR-17 f, P275/40ZR-18 R
Steering	**rack & pinion**
	variable power assist
Overall ratio	16.1:1
Turns, lock to lock	2.7
Turning circle	38.5 ft

Suspension

Front	**upper & lower A-arms,** Transverse composite monoleaf spring, tube shocks, anti-roll bar
Rear	**upper & lower A-arms,** toe links, transverse composite monoleaf spring, tube shocks, anti-roll bar

DRIVE TRAIN

Transmission				**6-sp manual**
Gear	Ratio	Overall ratio	(Rpm)	Mph
1st	2.66:1	9.10:1	(6000)	52
2nd	1.78:1	6.09:1	(6000)	77
3rd	1.30:1	4.45:1	(6000)	105
4th	1.00:1	3.42:1	(6000)	137
5th	0.74:1	2.53:1	est (5365)	165
6th	0.50:1	1.71:1	est (3625)	165
Final drive ratio				3.42:1
Engine rpm @ 60 mph in 6th				1320

GENERAL DATA

Curb weight	**est 3240 lb**
Test weight	**est 3380 lb**
Weight dist (with driver), f/r, %	51/49
Wheelbase	104.5 in.
Track, f/r	62.0 in./62.0 in.
Length	**179.7 in.**
Width	**73.6 in.**
Height	**47.7 in.**
Ground clearance	3/7 in.
Trunk space	13. 5 cu ft (top up)/ 10.8 cu ft (top down)

MAINTENANCE

Oil/filter change	7500 mi/7500 mi
Tuneup	100,000 mi
Basic warranty	36 mo/36,000 mi

ACCOMMODATIONS

Seating capacity	**2**
Head room, f/r	36.5 in.
Seat width	2 × 18.0 in.
Leg room	43.5 in.
Seatback adjustment	45 deg
Seat travel	8.0 in.

INTERIOR NOISE

Idle in neutral	61 dBA
Maximum in 1st gear	78 dBA
Constant 50 mph	73 dBA
70 mph	76 dBA

INSTRUMENTATION

200-mph speedometer, 7500-rpm tach, coolant temp, fuel level, volts, oil press.

ACCELERATION

Time to speed	Seconds
0-30 mph	2.0
0-40 mph	2.9
0-50 mph	4.2
0-60 mph	5.2
0-70 mph	6.6
0-80 mph	8.7
0-90 mph	10.9
0-100 mph	13.3
Time to distance	
0-100 ft	3.0
0-500 ft	7.5
0-1320 ft (¼ mi):	13.8 @ 102.1 mph

FUEL ECONOMY

Normal driving	est 18.5 mpg
EPA city/highway	18/28 mpg
Cruise range	270 miles
Fuel capacity	19.1 gal

BRAKING

Minimum stopping distance	
From 60 mph	118 ft
From 80 mph	209 ft
Control	excellent
Pedal effort for 0.5 g stop	na
Fade, effort after six 0.5 g stops from 60 mph	na
Brake feel	excellent
Overall brake rating	excellent

HANDLING

Lateral accel (200-ft skidpad)	na
Balance	na
Speed thru 700-ft slalom	62.5 mph
Balance	moderate understeer
Lateral seat support	excellent

Subjective ratings consists of excellent, very good, good, average, poor; na means information is not available

Physics You Learned

Physics Concepts	Is There an Equation?
When driving it takes a certain amount of time, called **reaction time**, to recognize a hazard, decide what to do, and initiate an action such as applying the brakes. During this time, the vehicle is still moving, and the distance traveled is the reaction distance.	
All instruments must be adjusted to read correctly in a process called calibration. This process compares the instrument to a standard to determine its accuracy.	
No measurement is exact (accurate to an infinite number of decimal places). Measurements are often repeated many times to average out uncertainties. Sources of uncertainty include **systematic errors** due to improper calibration, and **random errors**.	
Accuracy refers to the ability of measurements to give an average value close to the accepted standard. **Precision** refers to the ability to repeat a measurement to almost the same value regardless of its accuracy.	
Scientists use the SI system of measurements. Units are related to their sub-units in multiples of ten.	
Average speed is the distance traveled, Δd, in a given interval of time, Δt. By definition, average speed is distance traveled divided by time taken.	$v_{av} = \dfrac{\Delta d}{\Delta t}$
The equation of average speed can be used to find the time needed for an object to travel a certain distance or the distance traveled during a period of time.	$\Delta d = v_{av} \times \Delta t$ $\Delta t = \dfrac{\Delta d}{v_{av}}$
The slope of a distance vs. time graph at any point is the object's instantaneous speed. If the object is traveling with constant speed, the graph is a straight line with a constant slope. If the graph is not a straight line, the slope may be found by drawing a tangent to the curve at a point.	
When a source of sound is moving toward or away from an observer, the frequency of the sound detected by the observer is shifted. This shift is referred to as the **Doppler effect**.	$f = \dfrac{f_0 s}{(s - v)}$
Acceleration is a change in an object's velocity, Δv, with respect to time, Δt. By definition, acceleration is the change in an object's velocity divided by the interval of time. Acceleration can be positive or negative.	$a = \dfrac{\Delta v}{\Delta t}$
An object's change in velocity with respect to time, or the time that is required for an object to change its velocity, can be found using the definition of acceleration.	$\Delta v = a \times \Delta t$ $\Delta t = \dfrac{\Delta v}{a}$
The slope of a velocity vs. time graph at any point is the object's acceleration at that time. If the slope of the velocity vs. time graph is constant, the object is traveling with constant acceleration.	

118

When an object is moving, the direction of the movement is as important as the size (magnitude). Quantities that have both size and direction, such as velocity and acceleration, are **vectors**. Those that have only size and no direction, such as mass, are known as **scalars**.		
The equations of motion can be used to predict whether a vehicle is in the STOP, GO, Dilemma, or Overlap Zone when approaching a yellow light.		
Active Physics *Plus*	The average velocity (v_{av}) of a constantly accelerating object is equal to the quantity initial velocity (v_i) plus the final velocity (v_f) divided by 2. The average velocity is the average of the initial and final velocities for an accelerating object.	$v_{av} = \dfrac{(v_i + v_f)}{2}$
Active Physics *Plus*	The distance covered by an accelerating object (d) is equal to the object's initial velocity (v_i) times the time of travel (t) plus one half of the object's acceleration (a) times the square of the travel time (t^2). The distance traveled by an accelerating object depends upon both its initial velocity and its acceleration.	$d = v_i t + \dfrac{1}{2} a t^2$
The distance covered by an object that is undergoing uniform, negative acceleration when coming to rest depends upon the initial velocity squared.		$v_i^2 = 2ad$
The stopping distance for an automobile (d) is equal to the square of the initial velocity $(v_i)^2$ divided by twice the acceleration provided by the brakes (a). The distance covered by an object that is undergoing uniform, negative acceleration when coming to rest depends upon the square of the initial velocity.		$d = \dfrac{v_i^2}{2a}$
Active Physics *Plus*	The square of the final velocity (v_f^2) of an accelerating object is equal to the square of the initial velocity (v_i^2) plus twice the acceleration times distance traveled while accelerating. When an object accelerates, the final velocity of the object depends upon the initial velocity, the object's acceleration, and the distance traveled during the acceleration.	$v_f^2 = v_i^2 + 2ad$
When an automobile goes around a curve, a centripetal force is needed to cause the direction of the automobile to change so that it can make the turn safely. The force is directed toward the center of the circle.		
Active Physics *Plus*	The centripetal acceleration (a_c) of an object traveling in a circle at constant speed equals the square of the object's speed (v^2) divided by the radius of the circle (r).	$a_c = \dfrac{v^2}{r}$
Active Physics *Plus*	The centripetal force (F_c) on an object traveling in a circular path with constant speed equals the mass of the object (m) multiplied by the square of the object's speed (v^2) divided by the radius (r) of the circle.	$F_c = \dfrac{mv^2}{r}$

Physics
Chapter Challenge

You will now be completing a second cycle of the *Engineering Design Cycle* as you prepare for the *Chapter Challenge*. The goals and criteria remain unchanged. However, your list of *Inputs* has grown.

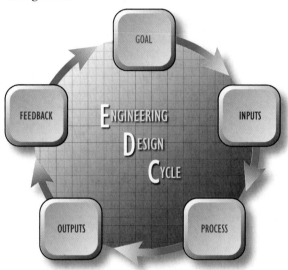

Goal

Your challenge for this chapter is to create a group presentation that will convince the Active Driving Academy that you have learned enough about the physics of safe driving to be eligible for graduation. Review the *Goal* as a class to make sure you are familiar with all the criteria and constraints.

Inputs

You now have additional physics information to help you address the safe-driving topics. You have completed all the sections of this chapter and learned the physics content you need to complete your challenge. This is part of the *Inputs* phase of the *Engineering Design Cycle*. Your group needs to apply these physics concepts to build your presentation. You also have additional *Inputs* of the feedback you received following your *Mini-Challenge* presentation.

Section 1 You used different methods to measure reaction time and compared the reaction time of different members of your class. You also investigated how distractions affect reaction times.

Section 2 You used a stride and a meter stick to measure distance. You identified the sources of error in measurement and read about units of measurement used in science classrooms and when driving the roads in the United States.

Section 3 You defined average and instantaneous speed and used strobe pictures, graphs, and equations to represent motion. You also used the equation for average speed to calculate speed, distance, and time. You read about how speed can affect following distance when driving on the roads.

Section 4 You learned how changes in speed or direction, called accelerations, are related to time and distance for a moving vehicle. You also interpreted distance-time and velocity-time graphs for different types of motion.

Section 5 You designed an experiment to investigate negative acceleration and stopping distance. You used friction as your brakes and measured the stopping distance for different starting speeds to compare speeds and stopping distances.

Section 6 You used models to examine vehicles approaching intersections with yellow lights. You used diagrams and computer models to help isolate locations where drivers are in a safe GO Zone, a safe STOP Zone, a safe Overlap Zone, or an unsafe Dilemma Zone. You also used the computer model to examine which factors influenced the locations of these zones.

Section 7 You explored the force necessary to make a moving object travel in a circle. You also explored the role that friction plays in creating that force for moving vehicles traveling through turns with different radii (sharp or gentle turns).

120

Process

In the *Process* phase you need to decide what information you have that you will use to meet the *Goal*. Decide on the format for your presentation. Will your group compare and contrast different driving scenarios and their safe distances, or will you simply address each of the distances individually? You may also have your own excellent idea for organizing your answers. Creativity is encouraged and will help your presentation be memorable to the judges of the Active Driving Academy. Just make sure that every member of your group is included and knows how she or he can contribute to your presentation.

Consider charts, graphs, and diagrams for your presentation. Your presentation could certainly include charts, graphs, and diagrams to illustrate your ideas. Remember to make any materials that you include neat and readable in the presentation format your group will use. Colors and large text can help make your point clearer.

This chapter made extensive use of models in *Section 6* for considering the complex analysis of the yellow light. A similar model would allow you to compare and contrast safe distances for following, braking, and stopping under different driving scenarios. A model for safe driving in curves could also help you compare the different factors that ensure safety for the passengers there. Your group could use models to find and present answers for each of the three safe driving considerations in the challenge. A model will provide a fixed reference point from which you can consider individual changes like a faster speed, more time to react, a sharper curve, and so on. When you describe the result for each change in the model, you enable the audience to easily compare the result to the results for a previous set of design conditions. Models can be very useful for learning and presenting information.

Address each of the three safe-driving topics. Refer back to the goal and constraints for the presentation regularly to make sure you are answering each part. If your class has a grading rubric for the challenge, use that to guide your work so that you don't forget to include any important information.

Outputs

Presenting your information to the class are your design-cycle *Outputs*. You should try to create a very convincing presentation. After all, your freedom is on the line! A combination of good analysis, creativity, well-managed development, and engaging presentation skills will be required to create a successful product.

Feedback

Your classmates will give you *Feedback* on the accuracy and the overall appeal of your presentation based on the criteria of the design challenge. This *Feedback* will likely become part of your grade but could also be useful for additional design iterations. No design is perfect, because there is always room for optimization or improvement, no matter how slight. From your experience with the *Mini-Challenge* you should see how you could continuously rotate through the design cycle to refine almost any idea.

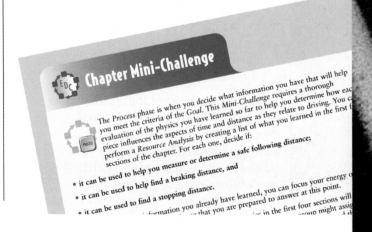

Chapter Mini-Challenge

The *Process* phase is when you decide what information you have that will help you meet the criteria of the *Goal*. This *Mini-Challenge* requires a thorough evaluation of the physics you have learned so far to help you determine how eac piece influences the aspects of time and distance as they relate to driving. You c perform a *Resource Analysis* by creating a list of what you learned in the first f sections of the chapter. For each one, decide if:

- it can be used to help you measure or determine a safe following distance;
- it can be used to help find a braking distance, and
- it can be used to find a stopping distance.

...formation you already have learned, you can focus your energy o ... that you are prepared to answer at this point. ... in the first four sections will ... oup might assi

Physics

Connections to Other Sciences

The fundamental ideas you have studied in this chapter are also basic to many other sciences that you will study in the future. Appreciating the connections among science disciplines helps scientists achieve a richer understanding of nature. Science research in the twenty-first century depends heavily upon the way these different disciplines interact, with areas such as biophysics and geophysics becoming major areas of study.

Here are some examples of how the concepts you studied in this chapter relate to other sciences.

Response Time

Biology An animal's response time may be critical for its survival. A bird that responds too slowly to a hawk, or a fly that fails to evade a frog's tongue, will not survive long.

Chemistry The time it takes a chemical to respond to light, and then bond with other chemicals, is one of the criteria for determining film speed for cameras.

Earth Science The response of the polar ice caps due to global warming may take hundreds of years to become completely visible.

Circular Motion

Biology Many birds will soar in circles on thermals—rising columns of warm air. The birds bank their wings to provide a centripetal force toward the center of the thermal and the lifting force of the rising air.

Chemistry Magnetic fields cause charged molecular fragments to travel in a circle. The larger the circle, the more massive the charged fragments must be, giving chemists an idea of what the composition of these parts may be.

Earth Science Most of the weather systems on Earth are examples of large masses of air that circle around a central position due to the Coriolis force that is experienced by air masses moving on a rotating Earth. This force is part of the reason for Earth's global winds and ocean currents.

Speed and Velocity

Biology The speeds obtainable by living organisms vary, from that of a diving peregrine falcon (almost 200 mph or 322 km/h) to that of a slime mold (1 mm/hr or 0.04 in./hr).

Chemistry The high speed gained by molecules in a chemical explosion is responsible for the damage they do.

Earth Science The speed of advance of a glacier may be as much as several feet per day.

Acceleration

Biology The fastest land animal, the cheetah, is able to accelerate from rest to a speed of 60 mph in only 3 seconds, or almost 9 m/s^2 (30 ft/s^2)!

Chemistry Electrons are accelerated to a very high speed and collide with molecules in a device known as a mass spectrometer, which is used in forensics for solving crimes.

Earth Science An earthquake may accelerate the floor of the ocean upward for a very short time, causing a tsunami that is capable of damaging large sections of a coastline.

Doppler Effect

Biology The velocity measurement of blood flow in arteries and veins, based on the Doppler effect, is an effective tool for diagnosis of vascular problems.

Chemistry The random motion of atoms of a gas due to their kinetic energy results in a shift in the frequency of the light emitted by the atoms due to the Doppler effect. Thus, the light emitted by a gas has a wider range of frequencies than that of a single atom.

Earth Science The expansion rate of the universe is determined by astronomers who use the Doppler effect to calculate the speed of moving galaxies.

Active Physics

Christine Lopez

New York State Trooper; Poughkeepsie, NY

On average, Christine Lopez spends 12 hours a day in a car. No, she is not a chauffeur or a professional race car driver. For the past 14 years, Lopez has been a New York State Trooper in Troop K headquarters, which covers Columbia, Dutchess, Putnam and Westchester counties.

Lopez said that State Troopers are responsible for assisting the public in a variety of circumstances, including motor vehicle accidents, burglaries, assaults and larcenies. Lopez said that since a State Trooper's job involves long hours in a vehicle, their risk of being involved in a collision is heightened. "Law enforcement officers are ten times more likely than the average driver to be involved in a collision," said Lopez. "Troopers may be exempt from vehicle and traffic laws while responding to emergencies, but they are bound by the same laws of nature as the average driver."

In 2007 alone, Troop K dealt with 3933 accidents. According to Lopez, 814, or 22 percent of those accidents involved drivers between the ages of 16 and 19. The majority of those accidents were caused by unsafe speed, following too closely, and driver inattentiveness/distraction. "All drivers should adhere to the three-second rule for following distance," said Lopez. "By allowing three seconds between your vehicle and the vehicle in front of you, you will have ample braking distance to allow you to make a complete stop."

Lopez also believes that reaction time plays a crucial role in preventing accidents. "The average reaction time is 1.6 seconds. This varies from individual to individual depending on age, illness, fatigue, and alcohol consumption. A drunk driver will take longer to perceive hazards and will have a slower reaction time," said Lopez.

Dr. Jose Holquin-Veras

Professor, Rensselaer Polytechnic Institute; Troy, NY

Dr. Jose Holquin-Veras is a Professor of Civil and Environmental Engineering at Rensselaer Polytechnic Institute (RPI). Veras believes that an understanding of physics is essential in solving problems and designing roads. "I design traffic signals to deal with the Dilemma Zone, and use braking distance to take reaction time into account." According to Veras, in order to avoid a Dilemma Zone, traffic engineers must use physics to ensure that a yellow light is long enough for a driver to stop or go through the light.

Alyson Coyle

Instructor, Transportation Safety Institute; Oklahoma City, OK

Alyson Coyle is an instructor with the Transportation Safety Institute. Coyle's division is responsible for developing training programs for the National Highway Traffic Safety Administration (NHTSA). Coyle informs participants about everything that happens in a crash, including how seat belts and child safety seats protect occupants. "The best part of my job is helping to save lives every day. According to NHTSA, more than 62,000 lives have been saved by seat belts in the past ten years," said Coyle.

Physics
Practice Test

Before you try the Physics Practice Test, *you may want to review sections 1-7, where you will find* **29 Checking Up** *questions,* **11 What Do You Think Now?** *questions,* **28 Physics Essential Questions,** **79 Physics to Go** *questions, and* **11 Inquiring Further** *questions.*

Content Review

1. Many driving experts recommend that novice drivers do not drive with groups of friends in their automobile. The major reason the experts suggest this is because friends may
   a) suggest that the driver exceed the speed limit, increasing risk.
   b) want to drink alcohol in the automobile.
   c) be a distraction that would increase driver reaction time.
   d) urge the driver to go through a yellow light when in the STOP Zone.

2. In a class demonstration, a teacher drops a dollar bill held between the fingers of a student to test how quickly the student can respond by catching the bill. The reason the bill is so difficult to catch is because
   a) the dollar bill is thrown downward.
   b) student's reaction time is too long.
   c) the dollar bill is affected by air resistance.
   d) student's fingers are affected by air resistance.

3. Middle-aged drivers often have better safety records than younger drivers. The most likely reason for this is that middle-aged drivers
   a) have quicker reaction times than teenagers.
   b) are never distracted while driving.
   c) will avoid streets with stoplights to avoid Dilemma Zones.
   d) rely on experience to avoid situations where a short reaction time is important for safety.

4. A friend measures the length of the school soccer field to be sure that it is the correct size. Which measuring device will most likely help your friend get the most accurate answer?
   a) A 50-m tape measure accurate to the nearest cm.
   b) A meter stick accurate to the nearest cm.
   c) A meter stick accurate to the nearest mm.
   d) A 30-cm ruler accurate to the nearest mm.

5. A friend claims that he can measure exactly how much water is in a one-gallon jug after taking a drink from it. You disagree with your friend. Which of the following reason(s) would a scientist give for agreeing with you?

   I. All measurements contain random errors.
   II. All measurements are at best an estimate of the true value.
   III. A perfect measurement requires a very expensive instrument, which your friend cannot afford.

   a) I only   c) II only
   b) I, II, III   d) I and II only

6. At a stock car race, you want to check the posted speed for the leading driver in the race. You time how long it takes the driver to make three laps around the track with your stopwatch. What else do you need to know to calculate the race car's average speed for this time?
   a) the length of the track
   b) how many cars the driver passed
   c) the size of the car's wheels
   d) the time that the race began

7. The distance vs. time graph for an automobile is shown below. Which reason below might best explain the automobile's change in motion at point X?

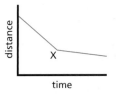

   a) the automobile sped up
   b) the automobile slowed down
   c) the road became less steep
   d) the road was no longer straight

8. Some students decide to take a bike ride. For the first two hours they travel at a speed of 15 mi/hr, they then stop for lunch for an hour. The students then ride for another hour at 10 mi/hr. What was their average speed for the trip?

   a) 10 mi/hr   c) 13.3 mi/hr

   b) 12.5 mi/hr   d) 15 mi/hr

9. The graph below shows the velocity of an automobile vs. time as the automobile accelerates on a road. An automobile that has a greater acceleration would have a velocity vs. time graph that has

   a) a higher velocity at $t = 0$.
   b) a lower velocity at $t = 0$.
   c) a greater slope.
   d) a longer line.

10. A police officer accelerates from rest to catch a speeding motorcycle traveling with constant velocity on a highway. To catch up to the speeder, the police car must
   a) have an acceleration less than the speeding motorcycle.
   b) match the speeding motorcycle's velocity.
   c) match the police car's acceleration to the speeding motorcycle.
   d) have a velocity greater than the speeding motorcycle.

11. The velocity vs. time graph for two automobiles is shown below. At time (t), the automobiles have the same

   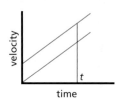

   a) velocity.
   b) acceleration.
   c) velocity and acceleration.
   d) velocity, acceleration, and distance traveled

12. Two identical automobiles are approaching a yellow light. The first automobile has a speed 30 mi/hr, and the second automobile has a speed 42 mi/hr. Compared to the 30 mi/hr automobile, the stopping distance of the 42 mi/hr automobile will be

   a) the same   c) double

   b) 1.4 times longer   d) 4 times longer

13. Which of the following has no effect on the stopping distance of an automobile approaching a yellow light?
   a) the driver's reaction time
   b) the automobile's velocity
   c) the condition of the automobile's brakes
   d) the time the light remains yellow

14. A student is holding an accelerometer made of a ball hanging from a piece of string in her hand. The student is then spun around in a rotating chair as shown. The direction of the hanging string when the chair is rotating indicates

   a) the centripetal force is away from the student.
   b) the centripetal acceleration is toward the student.
   c) the direction of rotation of the chair.
   d) the force needed to overcome the friction of the chair.

15. Which of the following objects cannot be used to accelerate an automobile?
   a) the gas pedal
   b) the brake pedal
   c) the steering wheel
   d) the rearview mirror

Practice Test *(continued)*

Critical Thinking

16. Your teacher tells you to design an experiment to find the acceleration of a ball rolling down an inclined plane.
    a) What measuring instruments will you need?
    b) What measurements will you take to determine the ball's acceleration?
    c) Show how you will use this data to calculate the ball's acceleration.

17. A ball is rolling across a horizontal table at a constant speed from left to right, then rolls up a ramp where it comes to rest.
    a) Draw a strobe photograph of the ball's motion as it is rolling across the table. Label the first point A and each successive point, B, C, D, and so on.
    b) Draw a velocity vs. time and a distance vs. time graph for the ball as it rolls across the table.
    c) Draw a strobe photograph of the ball's motion as it rolls up the ramp. Label the first point on the ramp 1 and each successive point, 2, 3, 4, and so on.
    d) Draw a velocity vs. time and a distance vs. time graph for the ball as it rolls up the ramp.

18. An automobile is traveling along a smooth, dry road, when the driver suddenly sees a small child run into the street.
    a) If the brakes are applied to the maximum force, what factors other than the condition of the automobile determine how far it takes the automobile to stop?
    b) How would changing each of the factors change the stopping distance?
    c) Which factor would increase the stopping distance the most if it was doubled?

19. Compute the GO Zones and STOP Zones for the intersection described below.
    a) yellow-light time   4.0 s
       reaction time   1.2 s
       speed of automobile   25 m/s
       acceleration -7 m/s^2
       width of intersection   12 m
    b) Determine if the intersection is safe and describe how you know if it is safe or not.

20. You are driving in an automobile going around a curve at constant speed as shown in the diagram below.

    a) On the diagram, draw the direction of the automobile's acceleration at the position shown.
    b) On the diagram, show the direction of the net force on the automobile at the position shown.
    c) Explain why a passenger in the automobile feels as if he is being pushed outward from the center of the circle.

Active Physics

Plus

21. A race car accelerates from 50 m/s to 75 m/s over a distance of 400 m. What is the race car's acceleration?

22. An automobile with a mass of 1200 kg is rounding a curve with a radius of 200 meters. If the maximum force of friction the road can provide to the automobile's tires is 2400 newtons, what is the maximum speed at which the automobile can safely take the turn?

23. The graph below shows the acceleration vs. time graph for a jet taking off from the catapult of an aircraft carrier. Draw the graph for the jet's velocity vs. time graph.

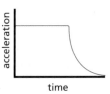

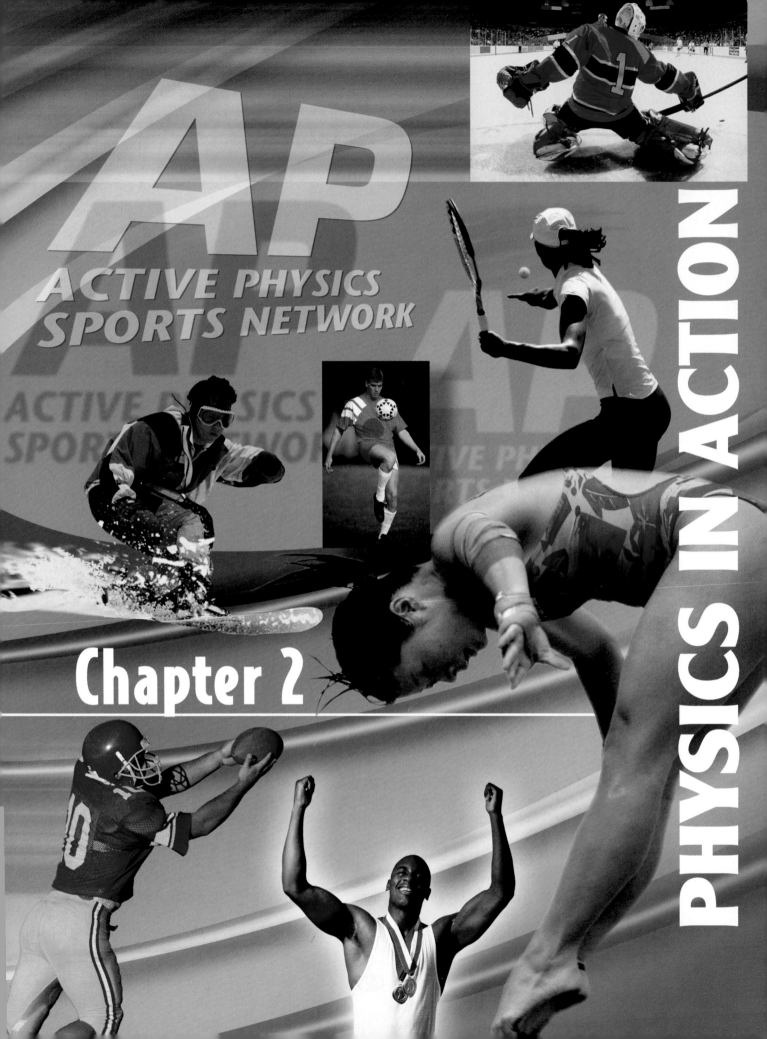

AP

ACTIVE PHYSICS SPORTS NETWORK

Chapter 2

PHYSICS IN ACTION

Physics in Action

Scenario

Have you ever imagined being a TV sports analyst and having millions of people listen to you describe a football or baseball game? Perhaps you would like to provide the commentary for a sport in the Summer Olympics or an analysis of a figure-skating performance on television?

What qualifications are needed to have a career in sportscasting? Should you major in communication in college or be a retired professional athlete to do this job? Could a physics course be a key to becoming a sports analyst? Perhaps a student with physics knowledge can bring to the TV viewer a different perspective that might provide a new outlook on sporting events.

Your Challenge

A public broadcasting service has decided that it wants to televise a variety of sporting events and wants these programs to be educational as well as entertaining. To test out this idea, you are to provide the voice-over narration for a sports video. The narration will need to explain the physics of the action appearing on the screen. You will do a "science commentary" on a short (two to three minutes) sports video or a series of sports videos that add up to two to three minutes.

The public broadcasting service wants people to understand that the laws of physics deal not only with the things that happen in the laboratory, but also with everyday events in the real world.
Your task is not to give a play-by-play description of the sporting event or give the rules of the game, but rather to go a step beyond.

You are to educate the audience by describing to them the rules of nature that govern the event. This approach will give the viewer (and you) a different perspective on both sports and physics.

You can think of this narration as a tryout for a broadcasting job. In this tryout, a traditional sports broadcaster will give the play-by-play and then turn the microphone over to you to give the physics of sports overview. You can provide the narration live, dub it onto the video soundtrack, or record an audio version. You will also need to submit a written script of the narration.

Criteria for Success

What criteria should be used to evaluate a voice-over narration or script of a sporting event? Since the intention is to provide an interesting analysis of the physics of sports, the voice-over should include the use of physics terms and physics principles. However, remember that physics principles are not enough. Your voice-over narration will also need to be entertaining.

Work with your class to develop a set of criteria for a successful voice-over narration. When you have decided what is required, compare your list with the list on the following page.

Standard for Excellence

1. The use of physics terms and principles in the narration • number of physics principles used • physics concepts from the chapter integrated in the appropriate places • physics terminology and equations used where appropriate • correct estimates of the magnitude of physical quantities used • additional research, beyond the basic concepts presented in the chapter	**50 points**
2. The quality of the oral narration • knowledge of the sport • entertainment value with respect to humor, excitement, and/or drama • ease of following and understanding • appropriate amount of narration • duration of narration between two and three minutes	**25 points**
3. The quality of the written script of the narration • use of correct science vocabulary • consistent sentence structure • correct spelling, punctuation, and grammar • appropriate use of science symbols for units of measurement	**20 points**
4. Challenge completed on time	**5 points**

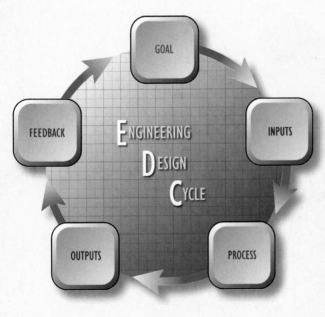

Engineering Design Cycle

The *Chapter Challenge* is to create an educational and entertaining sports voice-over. Now that you have read all of the criteria, you will use a simplified *Engineering Design Cycle* to help your group complete this design challenge. Clearly defining the *Goal* is the first step in the *Engineering Design Cycle*.

Although many people may be in the broadcast booth, a voice-over narration becomes the product of one person—the commentator or the scriptwriter. Although you will be working in cooperative groups during the chapter, each person will be responsible for a part of the voice-over or script for a sporting event. As a team you may share different aspects of the job, but the output of work per person should be the same.

As you experience each one of the chapter sections, you will be gaining *Inputs* to use in the design cycle. These *Inputs* will include new physics concepts, vocabulary, and even equations that will help you to educate your sports audience. When your group prepares the *Mini-Challenge* presentation and the *Chapter Challenge*, you will be completing the *Process* step of the *Engineering Design Cycle*. During the *Process* step you will evaluate ideas, consider criteria, compare and contrast potential sports footage, and most importantly, make decisions about what physics principles you will include in your script.

The *Output* of your design cycle will be the sports commentary that your group presents to the class. Finally, you will receive *Feedback* from your classmates and your instructor about what parts of your presentation are good and which parts need to be refined.

Physics Corner

Physics in *Physics in Action*

- Acceleration
- Center of mass
- Coefficient of sliding friction
- Constant speed
- Frames of reference
- Frictional force
- Galileo's law of inertia
- Gravitational potential energy
- Gravity
- Law of conservation of energy
- Law of conservation of momentum
- Momentum = mass × velocity

- Newton's first law of motion
- Newton's second law of motion
- Newton's third law of motion
- Normal force
- Potential and kinetic energy
- Principle of inertia
- Projectile motion
- Relationship of mass and force to acceleration
- Unit of force–newton
- Velocity
- Work

Section 1

Newton's First Law: A Running Start

What Do You See?

Learning Outcomes

In this section, you will

- **Describe** Galileo's law of inertia.

- **Apply** Newton's first law of motion.

- **Recognize** inertial mass as a physical property of matter.

- **Use** examples to demonstrate that speed is always relative to some other object.

- **Explain** that the speed of an object depends on the reference frame from which it is being observed.

What Do You Think?

Every sport includes moving objects or people or both. That is what makes sports entertaining.

- How do figure skaters keep moving across the ice at high speeds for long times while seeming to expend no effort?

- Why does a soccer ball continue to roll across the field after it has been kicked?

Record your ideas about these questions in your *Active Physics* log. Be prepared to discuss your responses with your group and the class.

Investigate

In this *Investigate*, you will use a track and a ball to explore the question, "When a ball is released to roll down a track and up the opposite side of the track, how does the vertical height that the ball reaches on the opposite side of the track relate to the vertical height from which the ball is released?"

1. Make a track that has the same slope on both sides, as shown in the diagram on the next page. Your teacher will suggest how high the ends of the track sections should be.

132

The slope should be quite steep. For a 1-m track, the ends should be elevated 30 cm.

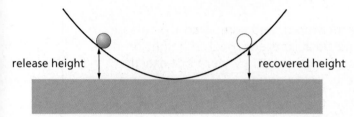

release height   recovered height

🖎 a) Place the ball on the left-hand section of the track. Measure and record the vertical height (not the distance along the track) from which the ball will be released. This should be about halfway up the track. This is the starting height.

🖎 b) Release the ball and mark where it reaches the highest point on the opposite track. This is the recovered height. Measure and record the vertical height of this mark. Concentrate on comparing the vertical height of the ball's release position to the vertical height of the position where the ball stops before rolling back.

2. Change the recovered-height section of track so that its slope is less steep, but its end is still as high as the height from which you release the ball. The track should be arranged approximately as shown in the next diagram, with a medium steep up-slope.

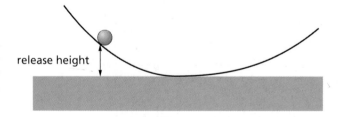

release height

🖎 a) Predict where the ball will reach its highest position on the recovered-height section of the track if it is released from the same place as before.

Mark your prediction on the recovered-height section of the track and explain your thoughts about this prediction in your log.

3. Now try it for real. Mark on the track where the ball reaches its highest point.

🖎 a) How close was your prediction to the actual outcome? Why do you think your prediction was "close" or "way off"?

🖎 b) Measure the vertical height where the ball stopped. Write a sentence that fully describes the movement of the ball in terms of its starting and recovered vertical heights.

4. Repeat *Steps 2* and *3* when the recovered-height section of the track has an even less steep slope.

🖎 a) First record your prediction.

🖎 b) Compare your prediction with the actual outcome.

5. Imagine what would happen if you changed the right-hand section of the track so that it would be horizontal (zero slope), as shown below.

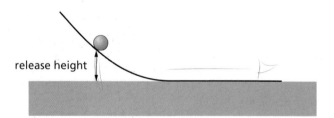

release height

🖎 a) No matter how far along the horizontal track the ball rolls, would it ever recover its starting height?

🖎 b) How far do you think the ball would roll?

🖎 c) What would keep the ball rolling on a horizontal track, like the one shown in the diagram above?

133

Physics Talk

NEWTON'S FIRST LAW OF MOTION

Galileo's Law of Inertia

In the *Investigate*, you observed, measured, and compared the release height of a ball on one side of the track to the recovered height on the other side of the track. You found that they were not exactly equal, but they were close to being equal.

Galileo Galilei (1564–1642) was an Italian physicist, mathematician, astronomer, and philosopher. Galileo is sometimes called the father of modern science. He introduced experimental science to the world. Galileo performed an experiment similar to the one you just completed. He observed that a ball that rolled down one ramp seemed to seek the same height when it rolled up another ramp.

Galileo also did a "thought experiment" in which he imagined a ball made of extremely hard material set into motion on a horizontal, smooth surface, similar to the final track in your investigation. He concluded that the ball would continue its motion on the horizontal surface with constant speed along a straight line "to the horizon" (forever).

From this, and from his observation that an object at rest remains at rest unless something causes it to move, Galileo formed the law of **inertia**: Inertia is the natural tendency of an object to remain at rest or to remain moving with constant speed in a straight line.

Galileo Galilei was a pioneer in the use of precise, quantitative experiments. He insisted on using mathematics to analyze the results of his experiments.

Galileo changed the way in which people viewed motion. Early on, people thought that all moving objects would stop. After Galileo, people thought about how moving objects might continue to move forever unless a **force**, a push or a pull, stopped them. That idea is not easy to understand. Any time you have pushed an object to move it, you have seen it stop. Nobody ever observes an object moving forever. Even when the surface is very, very smooth, the sliding or rolling objects eventually stop. However, Galileo realized that objects do not stop "on their own" but stop because there is a frictional force working that you cannot see and that is the force that stops the object.

Newton's First Law of Motion

Like Galileo, Isaac Newton was a great thinker. He was born in England in 1642, the year of Galileo's death. Newton's achievements brought him a great deal of recognition. Poems were written that honored Newton. Science, government, and philosophy all changed because of Newton's insights about the physics of the world.

Newton used Galileo's law of inertia as the basis for developing his **(Newton's) first law of motion**: In the absence of an unbalanced force, an object at rest remains at rest, and an object already in motion remains in motion with constant speed in a straight-line path.

Physics Words

inertia: the natural tendency of an object to remain at rest or to remain moving with constant speed in a straight line.

force: a push or a pull.

Newton's first law of motion: in the absence of an unbalanced force, an object at rest remains at rest, and an object already in motion remains in motion with constant speed in a straight-line path.

Newton also explained that an object's **mass** is a measure of its inertia, or tendency to resist a change in motion. Given different masses moving at the same speed, the one with the greatest mass has the greatest inertia. The tendency of an object at rest to remain at rest appears to be common sense and few people think otherwise. The tendency of an object that is moving to continue moving (forever) unless acted upon by an unbalanced force is very different from what common sense would tell you. The evidence from the investigation you conducted should help to convince you that objects in motion stay in motion unless a force acts upon them. You will have to remind yourself of this many, many times since most people's intuition is that moving objects do not remain in motion, but tend to stop.

Physics Words

mass: the amount of matter in an object.

Here is an example of how Newton's first law of motion works: An empty grocery cart has a mass of 10 kg and a cart full of groceries has a mass of 30 kg. The cart with the greater mass has greater inertia.

To test your understanding of Newton's first law of motion, decide which of the following carts has the greatest inertia:

a) 1 kg moving at 5 m/s   b) 2 kg moving at 3 m/s

c) 3 kg moving at 1 m/s   d) 4 kg moving at 1 m/s

The correct response is d) because the 4-kg cart has the most inertia. The speed is not important in determining inertia.

Isaac Newton credited Galileo and others for their contributions to his thinking. He is quoted as saying, "If I have seen farther than others, it is because I have stood on the shoulders of giants."

SI System: The Kilogram

In this section, you read that inertia is related to mass. The kilogram is the base unit of mass. This particular base unit is a bit unusual. It is the only base unit that has a prefix. The prefix, kilo (k) placed in front of gram (g) stands for one thousand (10^3). The kilogram is equal to one thousand grams (1 kg = 1000 g).

It might be useful for you to relate the SI units that you will be using in *Active Physics* to the units that you use every day. A two-pound brick has a mass of about one kilogram.

In one of the most important science books of all time, *Principia*, Isaac Newton wrote his first law of motion. It is interesting both historically and in terms of understanding physics to read Newton's first law in his own words:

Active Physics

"Every body perseveres in its state of rest, or of uniform motion in a right line, unless it is compelled to change that state by forces impressed thereon."

In Newton's time, "right line" meant "straight line."

Running Starts

You saw how Newton's first law of motion applies to a ball rolling down one track and up another track. Think about how Newton's first law of motion applies to sporting events.

"Running starts" take place in many sporting activities. In sports, where the objective is to maximize the speed of an object or the distance traveled in air, the prior motion of a running start is very important.

For example, in the javelin throw, an athlete is running holding a javelin. At the instance of release, the speed of the javelin is the same as the speed of the hand that is throwing the javelin. Newton's first law of motion tells you that when the athlete releases the javelin, the javelin will continue at the same speed. If the athlete then applies additional force to move the elbow and the shoulder of the arm carrying the javelin forward, the speed of the javelin will be the sum of these speeds.

The hand has a forward speed relative to the elbow, the elbow has a forward speed relative to the shoulder (because the arm is rotating around the elbow and shoulder joints), and the shoulder has a forward speed relative to the ground because the body is rotating and the body is also running forward.

The **speed** of the javelin is the sum of each of the above speeds. If the thrower is not running forward very fast, then the running speed does not add very much to the javelin's speed relative to the ground.

You can write a velocity equation to show the speeds involved. The letter *v* stands for velocity.

$$v_{javelin} = v_{hand} + v_{elbow} + v_{shoulder} + v_{body}$$

The term velocity is used in physics more than the term speed. **Velocity** is speed in a given direction. The two terms, speed and velocity, have slightly different meanings, but at this point, you can use them interchangeably.

Motion captures everyone's attention in sports. Sometimes speeds are constant. These motions are examples of Newton's first law: Objects in motion (at constant speed) stay in motion (at constant speed) unless a force acts on them. When a force acts, the speeds change. This change in speed during a specific time is referred to as **acceleration**. Acceleration occurs during starting, stopping, and changing direction.

Physics Words

speed: the change in distance per unit of time.

velocity: speed in a given direction.

acceleration: the change in velocity per unit of time.

Acceleration is definitely an exciting component of many sports. You will be learning about acceleration in other sections of this chapter. However, ordinary, straight-line motion is just as important in sports, but it is easily overlooked.

Speed and Velocity

In *Active Physics*, you will often explore the same topic several times. Being exposed to the same topic at different times and in different situations helps you learn and understand the topic better. The difference between speed and velocity will be explored frequently in this book.

Frames of Reference

In this section, you investigated Newton's first law. In the absence of external forces, an object at rest remains at rest and an object in motion remains in motion. If you were challenged to throw a ball as far as possible, you would now be sure to ask if you could have a running start. If you run with a ball prior to throwing it, the ball gets your speed before you even try to release it.

If you can run at 5 m/s (meters per second), then the ball will get the additional speed of 5 m/s when you throw it. When you do throw the ball, the ball's speed is the sum of your speed before releasing the ball, 5 m/s, and the speed of the release relative to your body.

It may be easier to understand this if you think of a toy cannon that could be placed on a skateboard. The toy cannon always shoots a small ball forward at 7 m/s. This can be checked with multiple trials. The toy cannon is then attached to the skateboard. A release mechanism is set up so that the cannon continues to shoot the ball forward at 7 m/s when the skateboard is held at rest. Now imagine that the skateboard is moved along at a constant speed of 3 m/s. If the cannon releases the ball while the skateboard is being moved at 3 m/s, the ball's speed is now measured to be 10 m/s. From where did the additional speed come? The ball's speed is the sum of the ball's speed from the cannon plus the speed of the skateboard (7 m/s + 3 m/s = 10 m/s).

You may be wondering if the ball is really moving at 7 m/s or 10 m/s. Both values are correct — it depends on your **frame of reference**. The ball is moving at 7 m/s relative to the skateboard. The ball is moving at 10 m/s relative to the ground.

Physics Words

frame of reference: a vantage point with respect to which position and motion may be described.

Imagine that you are on a train that is stopped at the platform. You begin to walk toward the front of the train at 1 m/s. Everyone in the train will agree that you are moving at 1 m/s toward the front of the train. This is your speed relative to the train. Everyone looking into the train from the platform will also agree that you are moving at 1 m/s toward the front of the train. This is your speed relative to the platform.

Imagine that you are on the same train, but now the train is moving past the platform at 8 m/s. You begin to walk toward the front of the train at 1 m/s. Everyone in the train will agree that you are moving at 1 m/s toward the front of the train. This is your speed relative to the train. Everyone looking into the train from the platform will say that you are moving at 9 m/s (1 m/s + 8 m/s) in the direction the train is moving. This is your speed relative to the platform.

Whenever you describe speed, you must always ask, "Relative to what?" Often, when the speed is relative to the ground, this is not specifically stated and you are expected to assume this fact. If your frame of reference is the ground, then it all seems quite obvious. Frame of reference is a vantage point with respect to which position and motion may be described.

Checking Up

1. What is inertia?

2. Describe Newton's first law of motion.

3. What needs to act on an object to stop it from moving at a constant speed?

4. In the real world, a rolling ball does not roll forever. What stops the motion of the ball?

5. Given two different-size masses moving at the same speed, which mass will have the greater inertia?

6. You throw a ball in a moving train. Why is it important to establish a frame of reference when describing the speed of the ball?

If your frame of reference is the moving train, then more thought is required to figure out the speeds measured by people on the train and by people on the platform.

In sports, where you want to provide the greatest speed to a baseball, lacrosse ball, football, or a tennis ball, that speed could be increased if you were able to get on a moving platform. That being against the rules, an athlete will try to get the body moving with a running start, if allowed. If the running start is not permitted, the athlete tries to move every part of his or her body to get the greatest speed.

+Math	+Depth	+Concepts	+Exploration
◆◆◆			

Active Physics

Plus

Part A: Calculating Velocity for Different Frames of References

You read that when describing speed or velocity it is important to give a frame of reference. You can calculate the velocity relative to a particular frame of reference mathematically by using positive and negative numbers.

Sample Problem 1

A sailboat has a constant velocity of 8.0 m/s east. This is a velocity because it has both a speed and a direction. Someone on the boat prepares to toss a rock into the water.

a) Before being tossed, what is the speed of the rock with respect to the boat?

b) Before being tossed, what is the speed of the rock with respect to the shore?

c) If the rock is tossed with a velocity of 6.0 m/s east, what is the rock's velocity with respect to the shore?

d) If the rock is tossed with a velocity of 6.0 m/s west, what is the rock's velocity with respect to the shore?

Strategy: Before determining a velocity, it is important to check the frame of reference. The rock's velocity with respect to the boat is different from the velocity with respect to the shore.

The direction the rock is thrown also affects the final answer. Let the direction east be a positive value. Use a negative sign to indicate the direction west.

Given:

v_b (velocity of the boat) = 8.0 m/s east

v_r (velocity of the rock) = 6.0 m/s
(direction varies)

Solution:

a) With respect to the boat, the rock's velocity is 0 m/s. The rock is moving at the same speed as the boat, but you would not notice this velocity if you were in the boat's frame of reference.

b) With respect to the shore, the rock's velocity is 8.0 m/s east. The rock is on the boat, which is traveling at 8.0 m/s east. Relative to the shore, the boat and everything on it act as a single unit traveling at the same velocity.

c) The relative velocity is the sum of the velocity values. Since each is directed east, the value of each velocity is positive.

$$v = v_b + v_r$$
$$= 8.0 \text{ m/s east} + 6.0 \text{ m/s east}$$
$$= 8.0 \text{ m/s} + 6.0 \text{ m/s}$$
$$= 14.0 \text{ m/s east}$$

Active Physics

With respect to the shore, the rock's velocity is now 14.0 m/s east.

    d) Since the direction of the rock is the opposite to the direction of the boat, the velocity of the rock has a negative value compared to the velocity of the boat. The relative velocity is the sum of the positive and negative velocities.

$$v = v_b + v_r$$
$$= 8.0 \text{ m/s east} + (6.0 \text{ m/s west})$$
$$= 8.0 \text{ m/s east} + (-6.0 \text{ m/s east})$$
$$= 2.0 \text{ m/s east}$$

With respect to the shore, the rock's velocity is now 2.0 m/s east.

Sample Problem 2

A quarterback on a football team is getting ready to throw a pass. If he is moving backward at 1.5 m/s and he throws the ball forward at 10.0 m/s relative to his body, what is the velocity of the ball relative to the ground?

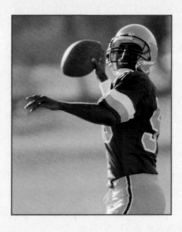

Strategy: Use a negative sign to indicate the backward direction. Add the two velocities to find the velocity relative to the ground.

Given:

v_q (velocity of the quarterback) $= -1.5$ m/s

v_f (velocity of the football) $= 10.0$ m/s

Solution:

Add the velocities.

$$v = v_f + v_q$$
$$= 10.0 \text{ m/s} + (-1.5 \text{ m/s})$$
$$= 8.5 \text{ m/s}$$

The ball is moving forward at 8.5 m/s relative to the ground.

Part B: Calculating Recovered Distance along the Ramp

In the investigation, you predicted and then observed the distance the ball rolled up and along the right-hand slope. Assume that you are using a "perfect ball and ramp" that allows the recovered height to be exactly equal to the starting height. Now that you have completed the investigation, you know that the recovered height is the same as the starting height (in a "perfect" situation). Therefore, you can calculate the distance along the ramp that the ball will roll.

1. Imagine that the ball starts from a point on the left-hand slope with a vertical height of 10 cm. How far up the right-hand slope (measured along the slope) will the ball roll if the angle of the right-hand slope is set at the following angles:

    a) 45°   b) 30°   c) 20°

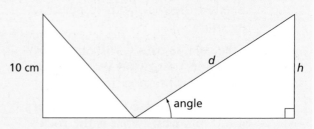

To answer these questions, look at a diagram of the setup above. You can use the right-hand slope and the height of the track to form a right-angled triangle. The hypotenuse of the right-angled triangle is the distance up the ramp the ball rolls (d) and the opposite side is the height of the ball when it stops rolling (h). If you know the angle and you know the height at which the ball was released, you can find the distance along the ramp using a scale diagram. Try this for the three angles given.

You can also use trigonometry to solve this problem by using the value of the sine of the angle of the ramp. The sine of the angle of the right-hand ramp is equal to h/d (opposite/hypotenuse).

The value of the sine of the angle can be found using the "sin" button on your calculator (make sure your calculator is in "degree mode"). Then you may use that value in h/d and solve for d.

2. Use a calculator to check the accuracy of the values of d you obtained using scale diagrams.

3. Use a calculator to find how far up the right-hand slope (measured along the slope) the ball will roll if the angle of the right-hand slope is:

   a) 10°

   b) 1°

   c) 0.1°

   d) 0.01°

4. How in a "perfect frictionless world" would the calculations you did above help you explain Newton's first law of motion?

What Do You Think Now?

At the beginning of this section, you were asked the following:

- How do figure skaters keep moving across the ice at high speeds for long times while seeming to expend no effort?

- Why does a soccer ball continue to roll across the field after it has been kicked?

The ice skater effortlessly gliding across the ice at high speed and the soccer ball moving across the field are like the ball rolling along the horizontal portion of your track. What determines their horizontal speed and why do they keep moving without someone doing anything to keep them moving?

Essential Questions

What does it mean?

Even the greatest thinkers may not know why objects have inertia, but your investigations show that they do have inertia. Observation is the basis for all physical concepts. What does it mean when you say that an object with mass has inertia whether it is moving or stationary?

How do you know?

How do you know that the rolling ball you examined in your experiment would keep rolling forever unless some force acted on it? Why is the steady, straight-line motion of an object not "explained" but is simply stated as the way the world works in Newton's first law of motion?

Why do you believe?

Connects with Other Physics Content	Fits with Big Ideas in Science	Meets Physics Requirements
Force and motion	Change and constancy	✳ Experimental evidence is consistent with models and theories

✳ In physics, ideal situations are often used to illustrate concepts. Nobody has ever arranged for a rolling ball to roll forever, so why do you believe that it would? Provide examples in which an object might keep moving in a straight line with a constant speed even longer than a rolling ball might.

Why should you care?

In your sports voice-over, you will want to use Newton's first law. Give an example in a sport where an object in motion remains in motion, or where an object at rest remains at rest.

Reflecting on the Section and the Challenge

"Immovable objects," such as defensive linemen in football, illustrate the tendency of highly massive objects to remain at rest and can be observed in many sports. Running starts can also be observed in many sports. Many observers may not realize the important role that inertia plays in preserving the speed already established when an athlete engages in activities such as jumping, throwing, or skating from a running start. For the challenge, you should have no problem finding a great variety of video segments that illustrate Newton's first law.

The segment that you select for your challenge might illustrate:

• That "an object at rest remains at rest."

• That the more massive an object, the more difficult it is to get it to start moving or to stop moving.

- How an object will tend to stay in motion until an external force stops it.
- How relative motion depends on the speeds of the player and the ball and the reference frame in which it is measured.

Physics to Go

1. You push a ball to start it rolling along a "perfectly frictionless" surface.

   a) How far will the ball roll?

   b) Explain your answer for a) using Newton's first law of motion.

2. A ball is released from a vertical height of 20 cm. It rolls down a "perfectly frictionless" ramp and up a similar ramp. What vertical height on the second ramp will the ball reach before it starts to roll back down?

3. Do you think it is possible to arrange conditions in the "real world" to have an object move, unassisted, in a straight line at constant speed forever? Explain why or why not.

4. Use what you have learned in this section to describe the motion of a hockey puck between the instant the puck leaves a player's stick and the instant it hits something. (No "slap shot" allowed; the puck must remain in contact with the ice.)

5. **Active Physics Plus** You are riding your bike and steadily pulling your little brother in his red wagon while someone standing still watches you and your little brother go by. He has a ball, and he throws the ball forward at a velocity of 2.5 m/s relative to his body while you are pulling the wagon at a velocity of 4.5 m/s. At what speed does the person who is standing nearby see the ball go by?

6. **Active Physics Plus** A track and field athlete is running forward with a javelin at a velocity of 4.2 m/s. If he throws the javelin at a velocity relative to him of 10.3 m/s, what is the velocity of the javelin relative to the ground?

7. **Active Physics Plus** You are riding in a train. Since the train car is almost empty, you and your friend are pushing a low-friction cart back and forth between the front and rear of the car. The train is moving at a speed of 5.6 m/s. Suppose you push the cart toward each other at 2.4 m/s.

   a) What is the velocity of the cart relative to the ground when the cart is moving toward the front of the car?

   b) What is the velocity of the cart relative to the tracks when it is moving toward the rear of the car?

   c) What if you and your friend push the cart perpendicular to the aisle as the train moves forward? This is a more complicated situation. What is the cart's velocity relative to the ground?

8. **Active Physics** **Plus** While riding a horse, a competitor shoots an arrow horizontally toward a target. The speed of the arrow relative to the ground as it reaches the target is 85 m/s. If the horse was traveling at 18 m/s, at what speed did the arrow leave the bow? (Assume the horse and arrow are traveling in the same direction.)

9. **Active Physics** **Plus** A ball is released on a ramp at a vertical height of 15 cm. Calculate how far up a second ramp (measured along the slope) the ball will roll if the angle of the second ramp is:

   a) 45°   b) 20°   c) 15°   d) 5°

10. *Preparing for the Chapter Challenge*

   a) Provide three examples of Newton's first law in sporting events. Describe the sporting event and which object when at rest stays at rest, or when in motion stays in motion.

   b) Describe these same three examples in the manner of a sportscaster.

Inquiring Further

1. Curling and Newton's first law

Find out about a sport called curling. It is an Olympic competition that involves some of the oldest Olympians. How can this sport be used to illustrate Newton's first law of motion?

2. Sliding into base

Why do baseball players often slide into second base and third base, but they almost never slide into first base after hitting the ball? (Hint: The answer depends on both the rules of baseball and the laws of physics.)

Section 2

Constant Speed and Acceleration: Measuring Motion

Learning Outcomes

In this section, you will

- **Give** examples of distance, time, speed, and acceleration.
- **Differentiate** between instantaneous speed and average speed.
- **Recognize** when motion is accelerated.
- **Calculate** average speed and acceleration.

What Do You Think?

Some major-league pitchers can throw a baseball 100 mi/h, about 45 m/s. The ball reaches home plate in less than half a second. In that time, the batter must decide whether or not to swing at the pitch. If the batter decides to swing, he then must be able to react quickly enough to the pitch. It is no surprise that so few athletes are capable of competing in the major leagues.

- **In your own words, explain the meaning of 100 mi/h and 45 m/s.**

Record your response in your *Active Physics* log. Be prepared to discuss your response with your group and the class.

Investigate

In this *Investigate*, you will use a measuring device called a ticker timer to explore the concepts of constant speed and acceleration.

1. A ticker timer makes a dot on a paper tape every ¹⁄₆₀ of a second. As you pull the tape through the ticker timer, a dot will be made on the tape every ¹⁄₆₀ of a second. You can use the ticker timer to determine how fast something is moving.

Active Physics

Imagine that the end of the tape is attached to your body. Predict what you think the distance between the dots will look like in each of the following situations. Use phrases such as close together, far apart, or evenly/not evenly spaced to describe the distances between the dots.

a) You move at a constant speed.

b) You move at a faster constant speed.

c) You move at a slower constant speed.

d) Predict how you think the distance between the dots will change if you walk at a constant speed, and then walk faster and faster.

2. Your teacher will show your group how to set up the timer. Give the end of a 2-m long piece of the tape to a group member. Let the student begin to pull the tape at a constant speed and then immediately start the timer.

3. The timer makes dots that are separated by equal amounts of time. Call the time interval from one dot to the next a "tick." (A tick is $\frac{1}{60}$ s.) Take the tape from the timer and draw lines across the tape to separate it into segments of 6-tick intervals each. (Count 6 spaces not 6 dots.)

tape with six spaces between vertical lines

4. Number the segments you marked off on the tape. Start by numbering the segment closest to the end your group member held with a "1."

5. Cut the tape along the lines you drew in *Step 3* to make segments.

6. Paste the segments in order and side-by-side on another piece of paper to make a bar graph. Each segment of paper (bar on the graph) is the distance covered by the student during $\frac{1}{10}$ of a second ($6 \times \frac{1}{60}$ s).

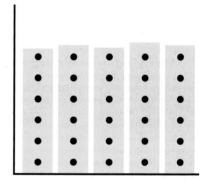

a) One student in the group should paste the piece of paper with the segments into his or her log. The other students should record sketches of the pasted segments in their logs.

7. Interpret the graph you made. The speed is the distance traveled on the tape divided by the time it took the tape to travel that distance. If the speed was constant, all the segments should be approximately equal in length.

146

a) Explain why you would expect all the segments to be about equal in length if the speed was constant.

b) Was the speed constant? How could you tell? If the speed was not constant, try again.

8. Use a new 2-m long section of tape. This time, ask the student pulling the tape to start at a slow speed and gradually increase his or her speed. Recall from the previous section, that a change in speed over a given time is called acceleration. Again, mark the tape into segments of 6-tick intervals and number the segments. Cut the segments apart and paste them in order, side-by-side, on a second sheet of paper. The length of each segment (bar on the graph) is the distance covered by the student during $1/10$ of a second.

a) One student in the group should paste the piece of paper with the segments into his or her log. The other students should record sketches of the pasted segments in their logs.

b) What does the length of the paper segments (bars on the graph) tell you about the student's speed during each time interval?

c) Is there a trend in the lengths of the paper segments of your graph?

9. Remember that the student pulling the tape started at slow speed (short strip) and then gradually speeded up (increasing the length of subsequent strips). The difference in the length of each successive strip measures the change in the student's speed during that $1/10$ of a second. A change in speed is called *acceleration*. Acceleration measures how much an object's speed changes in a given time interval.

a) In your log, measure the acceleration for each time interval on your graph by measuring the difference in length of each strip compared to the previous strip. Do not worry about exact time intervals yet. Use the differences in strip lengths to represent acceleration.

b) Did the student pulling the tape move with a constant acceleration? Was the change in the length of the strips constant?

10. Use another new section of tape. This time, ask the student pulling the tape to start moving at high speed and steadily slow down. Again, mark and cut the tape into 6-tick segments and make a paper-tape bar graph.

a) One student in the group should paste the piece of paper with the segments into his or her log. The other students should record sketches of the pasted segments in their logs.

b) How do you expect the pattern on the graph when decreasing speed to be different from the pattern on the graph when increasing speed?

c) Measure the acceleration for each $1/10$ of a second (equal to 6 ticks) by using the difference in strip lengths to represent the change in speed. Did the student travel with a constant acceleration?

11. Compare the graphs for increasing and decreasing speed. Physicists often consider the acceleration with increasing speed positive and the acceleration with decreasing speed negative.

a) Describe the tape of a person who speeds up and then slows down using this +/- acceleration convention.

Physics Talk

MEASURING MOTION

Constant Speed and Acceleration Using a Ticker Timer

Physics Words

acceleration: a change in the velocity of an object over time.

In the *Investigate*, you explored constant speed and **acceleration** using a ticker timer. By observing the lengths of paper tape that passed through the timer during equal time intervals ($6 \times \frac{1}{60}$ s or $\frac{1}{10}$ s), you were able to come to conclusions about the speed the person pulling the tape was traveling. You were also able to tell whether the person was moving at a constant speed or accelerating.

You found that at a constant speed, the distances between the ticks were equal in length. (You also probably found it difficult to move at a constant speed.) When you traveled at a slow, constant speed, the distances between the ticks were shorter than when you traveled at a fast, constant speed. At a fast, constant speed, you covered a greater distance during a given time interval than when you traveled at a slow, constant speed.

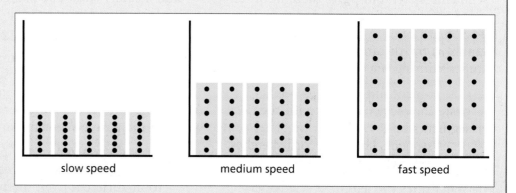

slow speed   medium speed   fast speed

By looking at the ticker tape you were also able to tell if someone was accelerating. When the person was accelerating, the distances between the dots on the tape were not equal. For positive acceleration, when the person was gradually increasing speed, the distances between the dots gradually got longer. For negative acceleration, when the person was gradually decreasing speed, the distances between the dots gradually got shorter. Sometimes, the word deceleration is used in everyday language to describe negative acceleration. Physicists prefer negative acceleration.

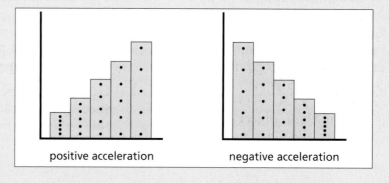

positive acceleration   negative acceleration

Calculating Speed

One way to measure motion is to calculate speed. Speed is a ratio of distance traveled to time taken. The unit for speed is always written as a distance per unit of time. **Average speed** is the distance traveled divided by the time taken to travel that distance.

$$\text{Average speed} = \frac{\text{distance traveled}}{\text{time elapsed}}$$

This can be written using symbols.

$$v_{av} = \frac{\Delta d}{\Delta t}$$

where v_{av} is average speed,

    Δd is change in distance or total distance,

    Δt is change in time or time elapsed.

The Greek letter *delta*, "Δ," is often used in science to mean "a change in."

Sample Problem 1

If you drive 140 km in 2 h (hours), calculate your average speed.

Strategy: You can use the equation for average speed.

Given:

$\Delta d = 140$ km

$\Delta t = 2$ h

Solution:

$$v_{av} = \frac{\Delta d}{\Delta t}$$

$$= \frac{140 \text{ km}}{2 \text{ h}}$$

$$= 70 \text{ km/h}$$

Your average speed is 70 km/h.

To travel at the average speed of 70 km/h, you might drive 70 km/h throughout the trip. But common sense tells you that your speed changes during a road trip. Before the vehicle starts moving forward, its speed is 0 km/h. At the end of the trip, you slow the vehicle to 0 km/h. And during the trip you probably slow down and speed up as you drive. The speedometer reading at any moment during the trip is your **instantaneous speed**, which is the speed at that moment.

Calculating Acceleration

When an object changes its speed, it is accelerating. Acceleration is the change of the speed divided by time. Acceleration is also a change in the direction of motion, but this will be discussed later.

To calculate acceleration in one direction caused by speeding up or slowing down, you divide the change in speed by the time interval during which the change took place.

$$\text{Acceleration} = \frac{\text{change in speed}}{\text{time interval}}$$

$$a = \frac{\Delta v}{\Delta t}$$

where a is acceleration,
Δv is change in speed,
Δt is change in time or time elapsed.

Sample Problem 2

A horse is stopped on a straight path. It begins moving forward and reaches a full gallop along the path in 10 s. The horse gallops at a speed of 20 m/s. What was the horse's acceleration?

Strategy: You can use the equation for acceleration.

Given: $\Delta v = 20$ m/s (20 m/s – 0 m/s)

$\Delta t = 10$ s (10 s – 0 s)

Solution: $a = \dfrac{\Delta v}{\Delta t}$

$= \dfrac{20\,\frac{m}{s}}{10\,s}$

$= 2\,\dfrac{m/s}{s}$

The horse accelerated at a rate of two meters per second every second. That is, its speed changed at a rate of + 2 m/s for every second it was moving along the path.

Suppose the horse then came to a stop. In the language of physics, the horse is accelerating! Remember, acceleration is any change in speed or direction. The acceleration can be positive or negative.

Units for Acceleration

To calculate acceleration, you divide change in speed by change in time $\Delta v/\Delta t$. The units for acceleration are then, by definition, speed divided by time. The units for acceleration may be (m/s)/s or (km/h)/s.

When writing acceleration in meters per second per second, the final units are often simplified. For example, the following all mean the same thing.

$$1\,\dfrac{\frac{m}{s}}{s},\ 1\,\dfrac{m/s}{s},\ \text{or } 1\ (m/s)/s = 1\,\dfrac{m}{s^2}\ \text{or } 1\ m/s^2$$

The units are read as meter per second squared.

Checking Up

1. Describe the pattern of dots on a ticker tape for each of the following situations:

   a) constant speed

   b) positive acceleration

   c) negative acceleration

2. An athlete runs 400 m in 50 s. What is the runner's average speed?

3. What is the difference between instantaneous speed and average speed?

4. A vehicle accelerates from 0 km/h to 100 km/h in 10 s. What is its average acceleration?

Active Physics

+Math	+Depth	+Concepts	+Exploration
◆	◆		

Large Accelerations at Slow Velocity

Because acceleration is the change in velocity during an interval of time divided by the duration of the time interval, it is possible to have large accelerations even though the velocity is never high. Imagine dropping a steel ball on a steel plate. Suppose the ball is traveling at 0.50 m/s, a fairly slow velocity, when it hits the steel plate.

1. Now imagine that the ball bounces off the steel plate, reversing its velocity to a value of −0.50 m/s in a very short time interval, say 0.01 s. What is its acceleration while in contact with the steel plate? Remember to take into account the fact that the direction of the velocity is opposite at the beginning and end of the time interval.

2. Suppose the collision is "cushioned" by putting some rubber on the steel plate. When the steel ball strikes the rubber with a velocity of 0.5 m/s, it deforms the rubber and bounces back. But this time the ball is in contact with the rubber for 0.20 s. What is the acceleration while the ball is in contact with the rubber?

3. Assume the acceleration of the ball is constant while in contact with the rubber (this is not usually true), what is the acceleration at the following three times?

   a) Just after the ball makes contact with the rubber on its way downward.

   b) At the point where the velocity of the ball changes from being downward to being upward (it has zero velocity at this point).

   c) Just before the ball stops making contact with the rubber on its way upward.

What Do You Think Now?

At the beginning of this section, you were asked the following:

• **In your own words, explain the meaning of 100 mi/h and 45 m/s.**

How would you explain it now in terms of distance traveled and elapsed time?

Physics
Essential Questions

What does it mean?

The discipline of physics is based on observation of the physical world and one of the most important aspects of the physical world is that it changes. Motion is one of the characteristics of change in the physical world and concepts such as speed and acceleration allow you to observe and describe motion. Explain what speed and acceleration mean.

How do you know?

The concepts of physics are acceptable only if they describe the physical world well. How did you know that the speed of the person pulling the ticker tape was constant?

Why do you believe?

Connects with Other Physics Content	Fits with Big Ideas in Science	Meets Physics Requirements
Force and motion	Change and constancy	✳ Good, clear, explanation, no more complex than necessary

✳ In physics, the goal is to develop concepts that are useful for as wide a range of the physical world as possible. In this section, you found that the concepts of speed and acceleration were useful in describing your motion as you walked in one direction. Why do you believe that these same concepts are useful in describing the motion of such different objects as a baseball, a subatomic particle, or a spacecraft?

Why should you care?

If physics is to be a successful science, you must be able to transfer what is learned in one realm of the physical world to another realm. In developing your sports-video voice-over narration, you are going to shift from walking in the classroom to a sports situation. Give an example from a sport in which the concepts of speed and acceleration as developed in this section help to describe what is happening in the sport.

Reflecting on the Section and the Challenge

Newton's laws involve motion, and to measure motion, you can measure speed. In this section, you learned how to measure speed. You also learned that a change in speed with respect to time is called acceleration. You are likely to use the concepts of speed and acceleration in your sports voice-over narration. Think about what these concepts mean and imagine several sports situations where they would be crucial to a sportscaster's commentary.

Your sports segment may include a player or a ball moving at constant speed. You may wish to explain how you recognize this as constant speed. It may also include players or objects changing speeds. You can describe this change in speed as either a positive or a negative acceleration.

Active Physics

Physics to Go

1. In your own words, compare average speed and instantaneous speed.

2. Calculate the average speed in each of the following situations.

   a) A horse runs 1 km in 15 s.

   b) A skier travels 84 m in 6 s.

   c) You walk 9.6 km in 2 h.

   d) A car travels 400 km in 4.5 h.

3. In which of the following cases is acceleration occurring?
   If acceleration is occurring, indicate if it is positive or negative.

   a) A runner falls down.

   b) A runner takes off from a starting block.

   c) You walk down a straight hall at a steady speed.

   d) A soccer ball is caught by the goalie.

   e) A bowling ball rolls along the gutter at a constant speed.

   f) A parachutist falls at constant speed.

4. You have measured speed in terms of the lengths of paper tape. A quick
   and portable way of representing the paper-tape graphs you made is by
   drawing graphs of the data. The four graphs labeled A—D are histograms.
   Each bar on the histogram represents a piece of the cut paper tape.

   a) Which graph(s) represent(s) a student moving with a constant increase in speed?

   b) Which graph(s) represent(s) a student moving with a constant speed?

   c) Which graph indicates the greatest change in speed each second?

   d) Which graph(s) represent(s) the motion of a student whose speed
      first increased but later decreased?

   e) The acceleration of an object is defined as the change in speed of the object
      per second. What is the acceleration of the student in A? In B? In C? In D?

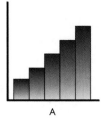
A

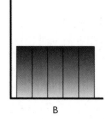
B

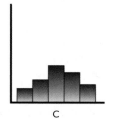
C

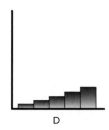
D

5. An object's motion was recorded on a ticker-timer tape. The length of each 6-tick segment of tape represents the distance traveled during that 0.1 s interval and is given in the table. Complete the table in your *Active Physics* log by calculating the average speed for each 0.1 s interval (distance traveled divided by elapsed time).

Total elapsed time (s)	Length of 6-tick segment (cm)	Average speed (cm/s)
0.1	0.7	
0.2	2.1	
0.3	3.5	
0.4	4.9	
0.5	6.3	
0.6	7.7	
0.7	9.1	
0.8	10.5	
0.9	11.9	
1.0	13.3	
1.1	14.7	
1.2	16.2	

6. A vehicle traveling at 45 km/h comes to a stop in 9 s. (Hint: When a vehicle comes to a stop, its speed is 0 km/h.)

   a) How fast did the vehicle accelerate?

   b) Does the acceleration have a positive value or a negative value?

7. Describe the motion of the object that made each of the following ticker tapes:

   a)

   b)

   c)

   d)

8. A family drives 100 mi in 2 h. What is their average speed?

9. A person drives to work at an average speed of 15 m/s. Does this mean that the person's instantaneous speed was always 15 m/s? Explain.

10. A sprinter (someone who runs short distances very fast) starts from rest and then accelerates to her top speed. If she were pulling on a ticker tape, sketch what the tape might look like.

11. A sports car accelerates at 4 m/s every second. Calculate the speed of the car after each of the first 5 s.

12. The average speed of a bicycle is 6 m/s. If a world-class sprinter can run 100 m in 10 s, can the sprinter move faster than the cyclist?

13. One track event is the 4 × 100-m relay in which each athlete runs 100 m and passes a baton (stick) to the next runner who then runs 100 m, and so on for a total of four runners. The runners receiving the baton can start moving before they receive the baton. They must have the baton in their hand when they begin their 100-m run. The average speed of the 400-m relay is less than the average speed for a 100-m sprint. In the 100-m sprint, the runner begins from a stopped position in starting blocks. Use what you know about acceleration, average speed, and running starts to explain how this is possible.

14. *Preparing for the Chapter Challenge*
Describe a situation during a sports event that might produce ticker-tape patterns similar to the ones you produced in the *Investigate*.

a) constant motion at an average speed

b) constant motion at a fast speed

c) constant motion at a slow speed

d) positive acceleration

e) negative acceleration

Section 3

Newton's Second Law: Push or Pull

What Do You See?

What Do You Think?

Venus Williams is a record holder for one of the fastest serves in the world by a female tennis player. The speed of the serve was almost 208 km/h (129 mi/h). To serve a tennis ball at that speed requires skill, timing, and force.

• **What is a force?**

• **How will the same amount of force affect a tennis ball and a bowling ball differently?**

Record your ideas about these questions in your *Active Physics* log. Be prepared to discuss your responses with your small group and the class.

Investigate

In this *Investigate*, you will use a flexible ruler to continuously push a cart (or a can or plastic bottle) across a table, floor, or open space.

1. Hold one end of the ruler against the table. Push on the other end of the ruler with your finger. Notice that a small force produces a small bend in the ruler and that a large force produces a large bend. You have created a force meter (an instrument that you can use to measure force).

Learning Outcomes

In this section, you will

• **Identify** the forces acting on an object.

• **Determine** when the forces on an object are either balanced or unbalanced.

• **Compare** amounts of acceleration semi-quantitatively.

• **Apply** Newton's second law of motion.

• **Apply** the definition of the newton as a unit of force.

• **Describe** weight as the force due to gravity on an object.

2. Use the ruler to push the cart continuously with only a slight bend in the ruler (a small force) as shown above. Make sure you do not push the cart in spurts. The push (force) must be applied as a continuous motion so the ruler keeps the same amount of bend. You will need to keep up with the cart as it moves and to keep the same amount of bend in the ruler. It may be useful to have another member of your group watch to make sure the ruler keeps the same amount of bend throughout the duration of the push. You may need to practice a few times to be able to do this.

a) Describe the motion of the cart.

3. This time, push the cart continuously with a large amount of bend in the ruler (a large force) as shown above.

Remember, you need to keep up with the cart as you continually push it to keep the large amount of bend in the ruler.

a) Describe the motion of the cart.

b) How was the motion of the object similar with a push from a ruler with a small bend and from a ruler with a large bend?

c) How was the motion of the object different with a push from a ruler with a small bend and from a ruler with a large bend?

d) Remember that acceleration is a measure of the change in speed with respect to time. Write a statement that describes the relationship between the force applied to the cart and the resulting acceleration of the cart.

Begin your statement with: "The greater the constant force pushing on an object, the…"

4. Select an object that has a smaller mass than the cart, can, or bottle. Use the ruler to push the object with a large, steady force (a large bend in the ruler).

a) Record a description of the object (especially its mass) and the motion of the object.

5. Now use the same large amount of force to push objects of greater and greater mass.

a) Record the results for each object in a data table in your log.

b) Complete the statement below that describes the relationship of the mass of an object and its acceleration and write the entire completed statement in your log: "When equal amounts of a constant force are used to push objects having different masses, the more massive object…"

6. You conducted two different experiments. You first varied the amount of force on a single object. You then used the same force to push on objects of different mass. By conducting two different experiments, you were able to analyze the effects of changing either the mass or the force.

a) If you had conducted only one experiment in which you pushed on a large object with a small force and then pushed on a small object with a large force, what conclusions would you have drawn?

7. You noticed earlier that a small bend of the ruler corresponded to a small force and a large bend to a large force.

You can now check this relationship more precisely. Carefully clamp the flexible ruler to the end of a table.

8. Place one coin on the top surface of the ruler near the outside end. Observe what happens to the ruler.

a) Record your observations.

9. Repeat by placing two, three, and four coins on the ruler.

a) What happens to the ruler each time you add a coin?

b) How many pennies represent a small force? How many pennies represent a large force?

c) What force is causing the ruler to bend?

Qualitative and Quantitative Observations

An observation is information that you get through your senses. When you describe the qualities of objects, events, or processes, the observations are qualitative. If you say that something smells spicy, tastes sweet, or feels sticky, you are making qualitative observations.

Observations that are based on measurements or counting are quantitative, because they deal with quantities. The temperature of a sauce cooking on the stove is a quantitative measurement.

In this *Investigate*, you made semi-quantitative observations. The first measurements that you made of the bend of the ruler were small and large. These are semi-quantitative observations. You then calibrated the bend and compared the bend to the number of pennies required to make the ruler bend. The number of pennies that correspond to a small force and a large force are quantitative measurements.

Physics Talk

NEWTON'S SECOND LAW OF MOTION

Evidence for Newton's Second Law of Motion

In the *Investigate*, you observed that it was difficult to push on an object with a constant force because the object would move faster and faster. This observation that a constant force produces an acceleration is very important in physics.

You also found that if you pushed on a more massive object with the same force, it did not accelerate as much. This observation that the acceleration decreases with an increase in mass is also very important.

Based on observations from investigations similar to yours, Isaac Newton wrote his **(Newton's) second law of motion**: The acceleration of an object is directly proportional to the unbalanced force acting on it and is inversely proportional to the object's mass. The direction of the acceleration is the same as the direction of the unbalanced force.

You saw the evidence for Newton's second law in the *Investigate*. When you pushed an object with a small force, the object had a small acceleration. The speed of the object increased, but not very quickly. When you pushed the object with a large force the object had a large acceleration. Newton's second law states this: "The acceleration of an object is directly proportional to the unbalanced force acting on it." This is a mathematical way of saying that the larger force produces a larger acceleration. As the force gets larger, the acceleration gets larger — a direct proportion. In this *Investigate*, the force was a push.

You also found that the same force on a small mass produced a larger acceleration than it did on a large mass. Newton's second law states this, "The acceleration of an object is... inversely proportional to the object's mass." This is a mathematical way of saying that the larger the mass, the smaller the acceleration. As the mass gets larger, the acceleration gets smaller — an inverse proportion. To achieve a big acceleration, you need to apply a large force to a small mass.

In one of the most important science books of all time, *Principia*, Isaac Newton wrote his second law of motion. It is interesting both historically and in terms of understanding physics to read Newton's second law in his own words:

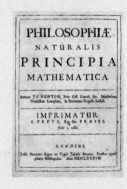

"The change in motion is proportional to the motive force impressed; and is made in the direction of the right line in which that force is impressed."

Physics Words

Newton's second law of motion: the acceleration of an object is directly proportional to the unbalanced force acting on it and inversely proportional to the object's mass. The direction of the acceleration is the same as the direction of the unbalanced force.

An Equation for Newton's Second Law of Motion

Newton's second law can be written as an equation:

$$\text{Acceleration} = \frac{\text{force}}{\text{mass}}$$

$$a = \frac{F}{m}$$

where a is acceleration expressed in meters per second squared (m/s²),

F is force expressed in newtons (N), and

m is mass expressed in kilograms (kg).

With a bit of algebra, Newton's second law can be arranged so that it is easier to find the unknown quantity of F, m, or a.

$$a = \frac{F}{m} \qquad F = ma \qquad m = \frac{F}{a}$$

Some students like to use a helpful circle:

If you want to find:

• force, F, cover it up and you see m next to a (or $F = m \times a$).

• acceleration, a, cover it up and you see F over m (or $a = F \div m$).

• mass, m, cover it up and you see F over a (or $m = F \div a$).

Newton: A Derived SI Unit with a Special Name

When you measured speed and acceleration, you used derived units with compound names. You measured speed in meters per second (symbol, m/s) and acceleration in meters per second per second, or meters per second squared (symbol, (m/s)/s or m/s²). These are derived units. They are made up of one or more base SI units.

In the equation for Newton's second law, force is expressed in newtons (symbol, N). What is a newton? A newton is a derived SI unit with a special name. A newton is the force required to make one kilogram of mass accelerate at one meter per second squared.

With this definition, the unit newton can be written in its equivalent form: $1 \, \text{kg} \cdot \text{m/s}^2$.

$$1 \, \text{N} = 1 \, \text{kg} \cdot \text{m/s}^2$$

Knowing the equivalent form for a newton will be important when using Newton's second law to do calculations to find mass and acceleration. Mathematically, the dot represents multiplication.

$$1 \, \text{kg} \cdot \text{m/s}^2 \text{ means } 1 \, \text{kg} \times \frac{\text{m}}{\text{s}^2} \text{ or } 1 \, \text{kg} \times \frac{\text{m}}{\text{s} \times \text{s}}$$

Where There's Acceleration, There Must Be an Unbalanced Force

There are lots of different everyday forces. There is the force of the bent ruler in this investigation. There is also the force of a spring, the force of a rubber band, the force of a magnet, the force of your hand, the force of a bat hitting a ball, the force of friction, the buoyant force of water, and many more. Newton's second law tells you that accelerations are caused by unbalanced forces. It does not matter what kind of force it is or how it originates. If you observe an acceleration (a change in velocity), then there must be an unbalanced force causing the acceleration. When you apply a force to an object that has a small mass, the acceleration may be quite large. If the object has a large mass, the acceleration will be smaller for the same force. Occasionally, the mass is so large that you cannot measure the acceleration because it is so small.

If you push on a small cart with the largest force you can, the cart will accelerate a great deal. If you push on a car with that same force, the acceleration will be much smaller. If you were to push on a truck, the acceleration would be too small to measure. Can you convince someone that a push on a truck accelerates the truck? Why should you believe something that you cannot measure? If you were to assume that the truck does not accelerate when you push on it, then you would have to believe that Newton's second law stops working when the mass gets too big. If that were so, you would want to determine how big is "too big." When you conduct such experiments, you find that the acceleration gets less and less as the mass gets larger and larger. Eventually, the acceleration gets so small that it is difficult to measure. Your inability to measure it does not mean that it is zero. It just means that it is smaller than your best measurement. In this way, you can assume that Newton's second law is always valid.

Calculations Using Newton's Second Law of Motion

Since Newton's second law relates force, mass, and acceleration, you can use the equations for Newton's second law to solve a variety of problems.

Sample Problem I

As the result of a serve, a tennis ball (m_t = 58 g) accelerates at 430 m/s² for the very brief time it is in contact with the racket.

a) What force is responsible for this acceleration?

b) Could an identical force accelerate a 5.0-kg bowling ball at the same rate?

Strategy: Newton's second law states that the acceleration of an object is directly proportional to the applied force and inversely proportional to the mass ($F = ma$).

Given:

a = 430 m/s²

m_t = 58 g = 0.058 kg

m_b = 5.0 kg

Solution:

a) $F = m_t a$

$\quad$ = (0.058 kg) (430 m/s²)

$\quad$ = 24.94 kg • m/s² or 25 kg • m/s²

$\quad$ = 25 N

Recall that 1 N = 1 kg • m/s²

b) Since the mass of the bowling ball has a much greater mass than the tennis ball, an identical force will result in a smaller acceleration. (You can calculate the acceleration.)

$$a = \frac{F}{m_b}$$

$$= \frac{25\ N}{5.0\ kg}$$

$$= \frac{25\ \cancel{kg} \cdot m/s^2}{5.0\ \cancel{kg}}$$

$$= 0.5\ m/s^2$$

This is much smaller than the acceleration of the tennis ball.

Calculations and Units

In physics, when you do calculations, it is very important to pay close attention to the units in your answer. Notice how in the calculation above you can write the unit N as kg • m/s². Then the units kg in the top and bottom of the equation cancel out, leaving m/s², the unit for acceleration that you need for your answer.

Active Physics

Sample Problem 2

A tennis racket hits a sand-filled tennis ball with a force of 4.0 N. While the 275-g ball is in contact with the racket, what is its acceleration? (Notice that here "g" stands for grams of mass. You have to really pay attention in physics!)

Strategy: Newton's second law relates the force acting on an object, the mass of the object, and the acceleration given to it by the force. Use the form of the equation that solves for acceleration. The force unit, the newton, is defined as the amount of force needed to give a mass of 1.0 kg an acceleration of 1.0 m/s². Therefore, you will need to change the grams to kilograms.

Given:

$F = 4.0$ N

$m = 275$ g

Remember: 1000 g equals 1 kg

Solution:

$$m = (275 \text{ g})\left(\frac{1 \text{ kg}}{1000 \text{ g}}\right)$$

$$m = 0.275 \text{ kg}$$

$$a = \frac{F}{m}$$

$$= \frac{4.0 \text{ N}}{0.275 \text{ kg}}$$

$$= \frac{4.0 \text{ kg} \cdot \text{m/s}^2}{0.275 \text{ kg}}$$

$$= 14.5 \text{ m/s}^2$$

Using Measurements in Calculations

When you perform calculations using measurements, you need to express the result of your calculations in a way that makes sense of the precision of the measurements you used. You must look at the number of significant figures (or digits) in the number. The number of significant figures represents how carefully, and with what level of accuracy or precision, the measurement was taken. A calculation will never add significant figures. If one value from measurements has two significant figures and all your other values were from more precise measurements and had four significant figures, your calculation using these values can have no more than two significant figures.

Determining the Number of Significant Figures in a Measurement

There are guidelines that you can use to determine the number of significant figures in a measurement.

All nonzero numbers are considered to be significant figures. In the measurement 152.5 m, all the digits are significant. The measurement has four significant figures.

Zeros may or may not be significant, depending on their place in a number.

• A zero between nonzero digits is a significant figure. In the measurement 308 g, the zero is significant. The measurement has three significant figures.

• A zero at the end of a decimal number is considered significant. In the measurement 1.50 N, the zero is significant. The measurement has three significant figures.

• A zero at the beginning of a decimal number is not significant. In the measurement 0.023 kg, the zeros are not significant. The measurement has two significant figures.

• In a large number without a decimal point, the zeros are not significant. In the measurement 2000 kg, the zeros are not significant. The measurement has one significant figure.

Significant Figures in Calculations

There are also guidelines that you can use when making your calculations.

Adding and Subtracting

When adding or subtracting, the final result should have the same number of decimal places as the measurement with the fewest decimal places.

Multiplying and Dividing

When multiplying or dividing, the result should have no more significant digits than the factor having the fewest number of significant digits.

Gravity, Mass, Weight, and Newton's Second Law

In the *Investigate*, you observed another type of force — the force of gravity. As you added coins to the ruler attached to the end of the table, the ruler began to bend. Earlier, you saw the ruler bend when you applied a force from your arm to push the cart. You know that if you observe the ruler bending there must be a force acting. When you drop a ball, you notice that it accelerates to the floor. Newton's second law informs you that if there is an acceleration, there must be an unbalanced force acting.

In both cases, you cannot see the force, but you know it is there from the observations you make. In the case of the force bending the ruler, this is the force due to gravity.

You know that if you apply a force of 1.0 N to a 1.0-kg mass, the mass will accelerate at a rate of 1.0 m/s². That means that if you observe a 1.0-kg mass accelerate at 1.0 m/s², there must be a 1.0 N force acting on it.

If you drop a 1.0-kg mass on Earth, you will observe that the mass accelerates toward Earth at 9.8 m/s². That means that there must be a force of 9.8 N acting downward on the mass. This is the force of gravity acting on the mass. You will have an opportunity to measure the acceleration due to gravity yourself in a later section.

Physics Words

weight: the vertical, downward force exerted on a mass as a result of gravity.

If you put a backpack on your back, you can feel the force you must exert so that the pack does not fall to the ground due to the force of gravity. This force of gravity on the backpack is also called its weight. **Weight** is the force of gravity acting on an object, and it depends on the mass of the object and the acceleration due to gravity.

Using Newton's second law, you can calculate the weight of an object.

$$F_{gravity} = ma_{gravity}$$
$$w = mg$$

where w is the weight (by definition, the force of gravity),

> m is the mass in kilograms, and

> g is the acceleration due to gravity (9.8 m/s²)

Active Physics

Balanced and Unbalanced Forces

In the *Investigate*, you observed that when one force acts on an object, the object accelerates. When two forces act at the same time, the direction as well as the magnitude of the forces determine the motion of the object. If the forces are in the same direction, then the sum of the forces or net force will cause a larger acceleration than either force alone. If two forces are in opposite directions, then the net force could be zero and there would be zero acceleration. A free-body diagram is usually drawn to help determine the net force. A **free-body diagram** is a diagram used to show the relative size and direction of all forces acting on an object.

When you hold an object in your hand, it does not move or accelerate downward. However, there is still a force of gravity on it. The object does not accelerate because there is the force of your hand pushing up on the object. The free-body diagram is shown to the right.

The blue arrow corresponds to the force of gravity. The red arrow corresponds to the force of your hand. Since the two forces are equal in magnitude, there is a net force of zero newtons and there is zero acceleration.

If the object were placed on a table, the free-body diagram would be identical. Later in this chapter, you will read about how a table can push on objects.

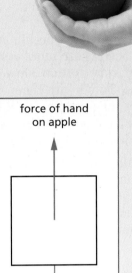

force of hand
on apple

force of gravity
on apple

Sometimes the force you apply is immediately balanced by a frictional force or a force of air resistance so that there is no acceleration. A vehicle moving down the highway at a constant speed of 100 km/h (about 60 mi/h) has a force of the road on the tires moving it forward. The force of air resistance is applied against the vehicle. A free-body diagram showing these forces would look like this:

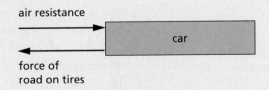

air resistance

car

force of
road on tires

The two forces must be equal and opposite because the vehicle is not accelerating. You know it is not accelerating because the description states that the vehicle is moving at a constant speed in a given direction. No change in speed or direction implies no acceleration.

Physics Words

free-body diagram: a diagram showing the forces acting on an object.

Checking Up

1. Describe Newton's second law of motion in your own words.

2. For a constant force, what effect does increasing an object's mass have on its acceleration?

3. An object weighs 30 N. How would you explain this statement according to what you know about mass and acceleration due to gravity?

4. If you went to a planet with a higher acceleration due to gravity, what would happen to your weight? What would happen to your mass?

+Math	+Depth	+Concepts	+Exploration
◆◆	◆		

Active Physics

Plus

Adding Vectors

Many of the numbers you use every day are scalars. Scalars are numbers defining quantities that do not have any specific direction associated with them. They only have sizes or magnitudes. Some examples of scalars include temperature, prices, time, mass, lengths, and widths.

Unlike a scalar quantity, a vector is a quantity that has both magnitude and direction. The velocity of an object is a vector. Its magnitude is the speed of the object and its direction is the direction the object is moving.

Force is also a vector because you can measure how big it is (its magnitude) and its direction. Acceleration is also a vector. Newton's second law reminds you that the force and the acceleration must be in the same direction. Mass is not a vector — it has no direction associated with it, so it is a scalar. Weight, however, is a force and does have direction associated with it. All forces are vectors. The direction of the weight vector is down (toward the center of Earth).

Often, more than one force acts on an object. If the two forces are in the same direction, the sum of the forces is simply the algebraic addition of the two forces. A 30-N force by one person and a force of 40 N by a second person (pushing in the same direction) on the same desk provide a 70-N force on the desk. If the two forces are in opposite directions, then you give one of the forces a negative value and one a positive value to show that they act opposite to each other. Then you add them algebraically.

If one student pushes on a desk to the right with a force of 30 N and a second student pushes on the same desk to the left with a force of 40 N, the net force on the desk (also called the total force or the unbalanced force) will be 10 N to the left. Mathematically, you would state that $30 \text{ N} + (- 40 \text{ N}) = - 10 \text{ N}$ where the negative sign denotes "to the left." Choosing left as the negative direction is an arbitrary choice.

Occasionally, the two forces acting on an object are at right angles. For instance, one student may be kicking a soccer ball with a force of 30 N ahead toward the goal, while the second student kicks the same soccer ball with a force of 40 N toward the sideline. To find the net force on the ball and the direction the ball accelerates, you must use vector addition. You can do this by using a vector diagram or the Pythagorean theorem.

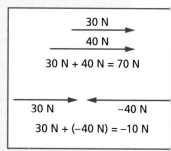

In the actual situation shown on the next page, the two force vectors are shown as arrows acting on the soccer ball. The magnitudes of the vectors are drawn to scale. If you were to draw this using the scale that 10 N = 1.0 cm, then the 30-N force would be 3.0 cm long and the 40-N force would be 4.0 cm long. To add the vectors, slide them so that the tip of the 30-N vector can be placed next to the tail of the 40-N vector (tip to tail method).

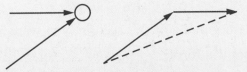

The sum of the two vectors is then drawn from the tail of the 30-N vector to the tip of the 40-N vector as shown in the vector diagram below. This resultant vector is measured and is found to be 5.0 cm, which is equivalent to 50 N. The angle is measured with a protractor and is found to be 53°.

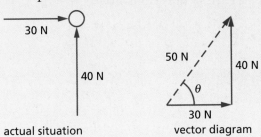

actual situation   vector diagram

A second method of finding the resultant vector is to recognize that the 30-N and 40-N force vectors form a right triangle. The resultant is the hypotenuse of this triangle. Its length can be found using the Pythagorean theorem.

$$a^2 + b^2 = c^2$$
$$(30 \text{ N})^2 + (40 \text{ N})^2 = c^2$$
$$900 \text{ N}^2 + 1600 \text{ N}^2 = c^2$$
$$2500 \text{ N}^2 = c^2$$
$$c = \sqrt{2500 \text{ N}^2}$$
$$c = 50 \text{ N}$$

The angle can be found by using the tangent function.

$$\tan \theta = \frac{\text{opposite}}{\text{adjacent}} = \frac{40 \text{ N}}{30 \text{ N}} = 1.33$$
$$\theta = 53°$$

Adding vector forces that are not perpendicular is a bit more difficult mathematically, but you can use scale drawings to make vector diagrams. Two other players are kicking a soccer ball in the directions shown in the top right diagram. The resultant vector force can be determined using the tip-to-tail approach.

The two arrows in the left diagram correspond to the actual situation in which two players kick the ball at different angles. The vector diagram at the right shows the two vectors being added "tip to tail." The resultant vector (shown as a dotted line) represents the net force and is the direction of the acceleration of the soccer ball.

1. One player applies a force of 125 N north on a soccer ball. Another player pushes with a force of 125 N west on the ball. What is the magnitude and direction of the resultant force?

2. Three hockey players are fighting for a loose puck. Hockey player A exerts a force of 40 N due north on the puck, while player B exerts a force of 70 N due south. Player C exerts a force of 40 N due west. The forces are shown in the diagram below.

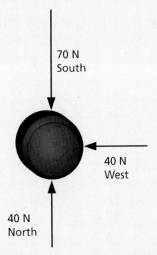

70 N
South

40 N
West

40 N
North

a) What is the resultant force exerted by players A and B on the hockey puck?

b) What is the resultant force of all three players on the hockey puck?

c) What is the direction of the net force on the puck?

169

What Do You Think Now?

At the beginning of this section, you were asked the following:

• What is a force?

• How will the same amount of force affect a tennis ball and a bowling ball differently?

In the *Investigate*, you changed the force with which you pushed a mass, and the size of the mass you pushed. How would you answer these questions now?

Physics
Essential Questions

What does it mean?

What does it mean when Newton's second law states that acceleration and mass are inversely proportional?

How do you know?

What part of your investigation shows you that stronger forces cause larger accelerations?

Why do you believe?

Connects with Other Physics Content	Fits with Big Ideas in Science	Meets Physics Requirements
Force and motion	✳ Change and constancy	Good, clear, explanation, no more complex than necessary

✳ Newton's second law is used to describe and explain motion of large objects and small objects. It helps you better understand the motion of people in sports, cells in the body, colliding atoms, and planets in the Solar System. Entire physics courses in college are based on Newton's second law. Why do you believe that if you push on a truck, the truck has a tiny acceleration?

Why should you care?

All sports involve motion. All accelerated motion involves unbalanced forces. If you identify an acceleration of a person or an object in your sports video, you can discuss the forces that cause that acceleration. What is one way that this idea will come up in your voice-over challenge?

Reflecting on the Section and the Challenge

What you learned in this activity really increases the possibilities for interpreting sports events in terms of physics, particularly when events have motions along straight paths. Now you can explain why accelerations occur in terms of the masses and forces involved. You know that unbalanced forces are the only things that produce accelerations. Therefore, if you see an acceleration occur, you know to look for unbalanced forces. In soccer and baseball, the ball accelerates. In soccer, the force to increase its speed or change the direction of the ball is the player's foot or head. In baseball, one force is the bat hitting the ball. In football, one player tries to accelerate another player by pushing on him. If the player being pushed is small, the acceleration can be quite large. If the player being pushed is quite massive, the acceleration is much smaller. You can apply Newton's second law to the sport you will describe.

You can also discuss the weight of players and objects in the sports by recognizing that weight is a force that is equal to the mass of the object multiplied by g, acceleration due to gravity, which is 9.8 m/s² on Earth.

Physics to Go

1. Copy the following table in your log. Use Newton's second law of motion to calculate the missing values in the table. Be sure to include the unit of measurement for each missing item (examples: kg, N, m/s²).

Newton's second law:	F	=	m	×	a
sprinter beginning 100-m dash	?		70 kg		5 m/s²
long jumper in flight	800 N		?		10 m/s²
shot-put ball in flight	70 N		7 kg		?
ski jumper going downhill before jumping	400 N		?		5 m/s²
hockey player "shaving ice" while stopping	−1500 N		100 kg		?
running back being tackled	?		100 kg		−30 m/s²

2. The following items refer to the table in *Question 1*.

   a) In which cases in the table does the acceleration match g (the acceleration due to gravity, 9.8 m/s²)? Are the matches to g coincidences or not? Explain your answer.

   b) The force on the hockey player stopping is given in the table as a negative value. Should the player's acceleration also be negative? What do you think it means for a force or an acceleration to be negative?

   c) The acceleration of the running back being tackled also is given as negative. Should the unbalanced force acting on the running back also be negative? Explain your answer.

171

3. What is the acceleration of a 0.30-kg volleyball when a player uses a force of 42 N to spike the ball?

4. What force would be needed to accelerate a 0.040-kg golf ball at 20.0 m/s²?

5. Most people can throw a baseball farther than a bowling ball, and most people would find it less painful to catch a flying baseball than a bowling ball flying at the same speed as the baseball. Explain these two situations in terms of

   a) Newton's first law of motion.

   b) Newton's second law of motion.

6. Calculate the weight of a new fast-food sandwich that has a mass of 0.1 kg (approximately the mass of a quarter pound). Think of a clever name for the sandwich that would incorporate its weight in newtons.

7. In the United States, people measure body weight in pounds. Imagine a person weighs 150 lb.

   a) Convert the person's weight in pounds to the international unit of force, newtons. To do so, use the following conversion equation:
   Weight in newtons = (weight in pounds) (4.38 newtons per pound)

   b) Use the person's body weight, in newtons, and the equation

$$\text{Weight} = mg$$

   to calculate the person's body mass (m), in kilograms.

8. If you were doing the voice-over for a tug-of-war competition, how would you explain what was happening? Write a few sentences as if you were the science narrator of that athletic event.

9. You throw a ball. When the ball is many meters away from you, is the force of your hand still acting on the ball? When does the force of your hand stop acting on the ball?

10. Carlo and Sara push on a desk in the same direction. Sara pushes with a force of 50 N, and Carlo pushes with a force of 40 N. What is the unbalanced force acting on the desk? The unbalanced force on an object is sometimes called the total force, or net force, on an object.

11. A vehicle is stuck in the mud. Four adults each push on the back of the vehicle with a force of 200 N. What is the combined force, due to all four adults, on the vehicle?

12. A baseball player throws a ball. While the 700.0-g ball is in the pitcher's hand, there is a force of 125 N on it. What is the acceleration of the ball?

13. **Active Physics**
    Plus
    During a football game, two players try to tackle another player. One player applies a force of 50.0 N to the east. A second player applies a force of 120.0 N to the north. What is the resultant force applied to the player being tackled? (Since force is a vector, you must give both the magnitude and direction of the force.)

14. **Active Physics Plus** In auto racing, a crash occurs. A red car hits a blue car from the front with a force of 4000 N. A yellow car also hits the blue car from the side with a force of 5000 N. What is the resultant force on the blue car? (Since force is a vector, you must give both the magnitude and direction of the force.)

15. The acceleration due to gravity at the surface of Earth is approximately 9.8 m/s^2. What force does the gravitational attraction of Earth exert on a 12.8-kg object, such as a toolbox loaded with tools?

16. **Active Physics Plus** A force of 30.0 N acts on an object. At right angles to this force, another force of 40.0 N acts on the same object.

a) What is the net force on the object?

b) What acceleration would this object have if it is a 5.6-kg wagon?

17. **Active Physics Plus** Bob exerts a 30.0-N force to the left on a box ($m = 100.0$ kg). Carol exerts a 20.0-N force on the same box, perpendicular to Bob's force.

a) What is the net force on the box?

b) Determine the acceleration of the box.

c) At what rate would the box accelerate if both forces were to the left instead of perpendicular to each other?

18. ***Preparing for the Chapter Challenge***
Using a sport of your choice, write a script for a voice-over that deals with accelerated motion and forces.

Inquiring Further

Gaining and losing weight

The acceleration due to gravity is different at the surface of the Moon and the other planets in the Solar System. Where would you choose to "live" if you wanted to lose weight? What would be the weight of a 150-lb person on the Moon and on each of the planets?

Section 4

Projectile Motion: Launching Things into the Air

What Do You See?

Learning Outcomes

In this section, you will

- **Apply** the terms free fall, projectile, trajectory, and range.

- **Provide** evidence concerning projectiles launched horizontally from the same height at different launch speeds (including zero launch speed).

- **Explain** the relationship between the vertical and horizontal components of a projectile's motion.

- **Recognize** the factors that affect the range of a projectile.

- **Infer** the shape of a projectile's trajectory.

What Do You Think?

Some track and field events involve launching things into the air, such as a shot put, a javelin, or even one's body in the case of the long jump. In golf, football, tennis, and baseball, balls move through the air as well.

- **What determines how far an object thrown into the air travels before landing?**

Record your ideas about this question in your *Active Physics* log. Be prepared to discuss your response with your small group and the class.

Investigate

Part A: Observe Two Coins Dropping

In this part of the *Investigate*, you will observe two coins as they fall from a table. One coin will be dropped from the table, and the other will be projected from the table.

1. Hold two coins the same distance above the floor. Drop them at the same time. Listen to the sound they make as they strike the floor.

   a) Do they hit the floor at the same time?

2. Place one coin at the edge of a table with about half of the coin hanging over the edge. Place another coin flat on the table. Use your fingers to "flick" this coin across the tabletop to strike the first coin. Aim "off center" so that the coin at the edge of the table drops straight down and the projected coin leaves the edge of the table with some horizontal speed.

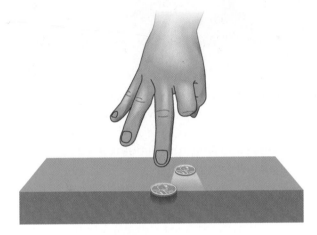

Your teacher may also decide to use a "coin launcher" for this experiment as shown in the diagram below.

Repeat the event as many times as needed to record your answer to the following question in your log.

a) Do the coins hit the floor at the same or different times? (Hearing is the key to observation here, although you may wish to rely on sight as well.)

3. Vary the speed of the projected coin.

a) Does the speed of the projected coin affect whether the two coins hit the floor at the same time? Explain your answer.

b) Does the speed of the projected coin change how far it lands horizontally from the coin that fell straight down? Explain your answer.

c) Draw a single sketch that includes both the path of the coin that is falling and the coin that is projected. Imagine where each coin is at four identical points in time and note these predicted locations on your sketch. Label these times A, B, C, D.

4. Use a box, chair, or a stack of books to change the height from which you project the coins.

a) Do the coins hit the floor at the same or different times?

b) How does changing the height affect how far the projected coin travels horizontally as it falls?

Part B: Vertical and Horizontal Motion of a Projectile

In this part of the *Investigate*, the class will observe a student throwing a ball into the air while sitting in a moving chair.

Active Physics

1. To illustrate an object that has both vertical and horizontal motion at the same time, your teacher will supervise a class activity in which one student sits on a chair that is moving at constant speed. While the chair is moving, the student on the chair will throw a ball straight up into the air and try to catch it when it comes down. The class will stand in a line beside the path of the chair to observe the event, prepared to mark the vertical position of the ball as it passes them.

a) In your log, write your prediction of what you think will happen.

2. This activity can be done in several ways. It is ideal if the chair's path can be parallel to the chalkboard. Another option is to take a large roll of paper and tape the paper to a wall parallel to the path of the chair on the opposite side from the observing students. The bottom horizontal side of the board or paper should be at the height the student in the chair launches and catches the ball. Each student observing the event draws a vertical line on the board or paper marking their position beside the path. As the event takes place, each observing student keeps track of the height of the ball

as it passes the line representing their position. After the event, each student puts a mark on the board or paper corresponding to the point where the ball passed the line.

a) Write in your log what you observed about the ball's trajectory (shape of the ball's path) and the ball's approximate range (horizontal distance) for trials in which you varied the speed of the chair and the launching speed of the ball. Remember, to see the effect of both the ball's trajectory and approximate range, be sure to only change one variable at a time during your trials.

b) According to your observations, what factors affect the range of the ball?

Physics Talk

PROJECTILES AND TRAJECTORIES

By observing two falling coins and by tossing a ball in a moving chair, you gained evidence of two very important aspects of how thrown objects move. Since the javelin, the baseball, the football, and even a high jumper are objects thrown in the air, the two observations of **projectile** motions are crucial to your voice overdub of sporting events.

The horizontally thrown coin and the dropped coin hit the ground at the same time when there is little or no air resistance. (This does not work for a falling feather.) Under careful observations, you find that this is always true — the horizontal motion of the coin does not affect its downward motion. If you were to take a picture of the coin every tenth of a second, you would observe the two coins as shown in the diagram.

Both coins fall the same amount in each tenth of a second. The vertical motions of the coin falling directly down to the floor near the table and the coin landing further away from the table are identical. The projected coin kept moving to the right, but its vertical motion was identical to the dropped coin.

"Believing is Seeing"

The *Investigate* you completed may not have convinced you that the two coins hit the ground at the same time. Intuition tells you that the dropped coin should hit first. In this case, intuition is wrong. The two coins do hit at the same time. If you believe strongly that the dropped coin hits first, you fool yourself into seeing that. The phrase "seeing is believing" should actually be "believing is seeing." If you believe that the dropped coin hits first, you will see it hit first even though it hits at the same time. To defend your intuition, you may even state that the dropped coin hit a tiny, tiny bit before the coin landing further away. There have been high-speed photos taken that show they hit at the same time. There are computer simulations that you can find on the Internet that also try to help people accept this "hard to accept" truth about motion.

The projected coin has a constant speed to the right, when there is no air resistance. The vertical motion does not affect this constant horizontal speed. The falling coin has no speed to the right, in a perfect fall.

Physics Words

projectile: an object traveling through the air or other medium.

Active Physics

Any hit or thrown ball travels horizontally and vertically. The horizontal velocity remains the same (if there is no air resistance). The vertical velocity is constantly changing. As it rises, the ball slows down. As it falls, the ball speeds up. The change in velocity of the ball is always 9.8 m/s every second or 9.8 m/s². For ease of discussion and problem solving, it is sometimes convenient to round this number to be 10 m/s every second or 10 m/s². Since the acceleration is always down to Earth, use –10 m/s² as the value. Think of any velocity in the "up" direction as + and any velocity in the down direction as –.

If an object is thrown straight up at 40 m/s, its velocity decreases by 10 m/s every second. Its speed at the end of each second is shown in the top diagram.

It comes to rest at the top of the path because its velocity is 0 m/s. Its acceleration will still be –10 m/s² because its speed is still changing by –10 m/s every second. Its new speed is –10 m/s one second after it begins its fall.

The horizontal speed of the object will remain constant since no force acts on the ball horizontally.

These two motions can be combined to allow you to mathematically predict the motion of a thrown object. If you space the horizontal position of the ball at equal distances as it rises and falls, you can represent the motion of the ball.

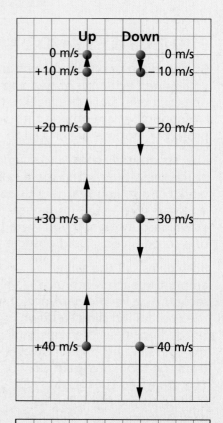

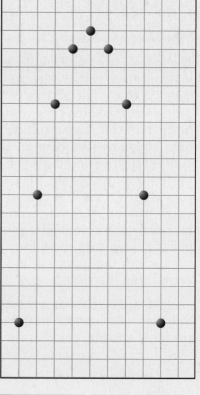

Checking Up

1. If a pen and a ruler are dropped together from the same height, will they reach the ground at the same time? Explain your answer.

2. When an object falls vertically down, does its velocity remain the same? Explain your answer.

3. If a ball is thrown upward, what is the ball's velocity at its point of highest rise? What is the ball's acceleration?

Active Physics

Plus

+Math	+Depth	+Concepts	+Exploration
◆			

Vector Components

In the investigation you just completed, the projected coin left the table horizontally. At any point in its motion, the projected coin is moving down and to the right. You can draw its velocity at any time. This velocity has two parts. One part describes the horizontal motion and the second part describes the vertical motion.

A short time after leaving the table, the projected coin has a small vertical speed and a constant horizontal speed.

You can add these parts as vectors. To add these two velocity vectors, use the "tip-to-tail" method. By sliding one vector over (maintaining its length and direction), the resultant is then drawn from the tail of the first vector to the tip of the second vector.

When you look at the coin's velocity some time later, you notice that the coin is moving faster in the vertical direction but continues horizontally at the same speed. If you have the values for the speeds of the vertical and horizontal motions of the coin, you can add the vectors to determine what happens to the total (or resultant) vector.

The resultant velocity or total velocity (often simply called the coin's velocity) has become larger and its direction has changed. The coin's resultant or total velocity is pointing in a more vertical direction.

If you measure the velocity at any one point in the path, you could also use that resultant or total velocity vector to find its horizontal and vertical "components." The components of a vector are themselves vectors, namely, the vectors along two perpendicular axes that add up to the vector. First, you draw the total or resultant velocity vector to the correct size and pointing in the correct direction. Second, you draw horizontal and vertical axes from the tail of the vector. Third, you draw lines from the tip of the vector to each axis, making sure the lines are parallel to the other axis. By doing this, you can obtain the horizontal and vertical components of the velocity (the vectors that add together to produce the total or resultant velocity vector).

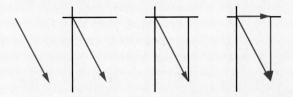

If you were to construct numerous velocity vectors along the path of the object, you would notice two things. First, the horizontal velocity components are always equal. Second, the vertical velocity components increase as time goes on.

Sample Problem

a) A football is thrown at 20.0 m/s at an angle of 30° with respect to the horizontal. What is its horizontal velocity (often called the *x*-component of its velocity)?

b) If the football were thrown at 20.0 m/s at an angle of 60°, what is its horizontal velocity?

c) How far does each football travel in the horizontal direction in 3.0 s?

Strategy: You can solve the first two parts by drawing vector diagrams to scale and finding the *x*-components. In *c)*, you can find how far each football traveled by using the relationship for steady motion:

Distance = (velocity) × (time)

$$d = vt$$

Solution:

a) The first vector must be 20 units long at an angle of 30°. (The scale is 1 unit = 1 m/s.) Use a protractor to draw the angle accurately.

Measuring the *x*-component and using the scale, you find the *x*-component is 17.3 m/s.

b) The second vector is also 20 units long at an angle of 60°.

Measuring the *x*-component and using the scale, you find the *x*-component is 10 m/s.

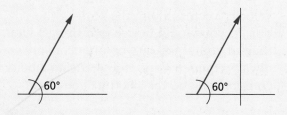

c) The first trajectory has a horizontal velocity component of 17.3 m/s for 3.0 s. Its distance is:

$$d = vt$$
$$= (17.3 \text{ m/s})(3.0 \text{ s})$$
$$= (17.3 \times 3.0)\left(\frac{\text{m}}{\cancel{s}} \times \cancel{s}\right)$$
$$= 51.9 \text{ m or } 52 \text{ m}$$

The second trajectory has a horizontal velocity of 10 m/s. Its distance is:

$$d = vt$$
$$= (10 \text{ m/s})(3.0 \text{ s})$$
$$= 10 \times 3.0 \left(\frac{\text{m}}{\cancel{s}} \times \cancel{s}\right)$$
$$= 30 \text{ m}$$

1. A football is kicked with a vertical velocity of 30 m/s and a horizontal velocity of 10 m/s.

   a) Calculate the vertical and horizontal velocities for each second that the football is in the air.

   b) Draw a diagram showing the vertical and horizontal positions of the ball after each second.

2. A batted baseball leaves the bat with a velocity of 50 m/s at an angle of 30° from the horizontal.

   a) If the ball leaves the bat at time equal to zero, what are the horizontal and vertical components of the velocity at time equal to zero?

   b) What are the horizontal and vertical components of the velocity at time equal to 1 s?

   c) What are the horizontal and vertical components of the velocity at time equal to 5 s?

   d) What is the magnitude and direction of the velocity at time equal to 5 s?

What Do You Think Now?

At the beginning of the section, you were asked the following:

• **What determines how far an object thrown into the air travels before landing?**

From the observations you made in the *Investigate* section, what do you now think determines how far an object travels after it is thrown?

Physics
Essential Questions

What does it mean?

A very important principle of physics is that motion in the horizontal direction and motion in the vertical direction are independent of each other. What does it mean to say that the horizontal motion of a projectile is independent of the vertical motion of the same projectile?

How do you know?

What evidence do you have to convince yourself that the horizontal and vertical motions of a projectile are independent of each other?

Why do you believe?

Connects with Other Physics Content	Fits with Big Ideas in Science	Meets Physics Requirements
Force and motion	Models	✳ Experimental evidence is consistent with models and theories

✳ Physics attempts to explain as much as possible with a single concept. Both the motion of a projectile and a swimmer crossing a river can be understood if their horizontal and vertical motions are considered independently. Give a reason why you believe that all motion can be examined in this way.

Why should you care?

Many sports involve projectiles. Think of a sport where a projectile is involved and describe how the independence of its horizontal and vertical motions explains its trajectory.

Reflecting on the Section and the Challenge

In *Part A* of this *Investigate* (two falling coins), you observed that the time required for a coin to fall is independent of its horizontal speed. If two long jumpers rise to the same height, they will then remain in the air for identical times.

In *Part B* of the *Investigate* (the rolling chair), you saw that the faster the chair is moving, the farther the ball will travel horizontally. If a long jumper is able to increase horizontal speed, then the jumper will travel farther.

Most sports have objects or people "flying through the air." You can describe how projectile motion relates to a sport you might choose for the challenge.

Physics to Go

1. Draw a sketch of two coins leaving the table. Show where each coin is at the end of each tenth of a second. Remember to emphasize that they both hit the ground at the same time.

2. Repeat the sketch of the two coins leaving the table, but this time have one of the coins moving at a very high speed.

3. It is said that a bullet shot horizontally and a bullet dropped will both hit the ground at the same time if air resistance is neglected. Draw sketches of this (the bullet is like a very, very fast-moving coin).

4. Survey your friends and family members to find out which they think will hit the ground first, a bullet that is dropped, or a horizontally-shot bullet (neglecting air resistance).

   Explain why you think people may believe that the two coins hit the ground at the same time, but that they have a more difficult time believing the same fact about bullets.

5. Use evidence from your observations of the two coins in this section to prove that a 100 mi/h pitch thrown horizontally by a major league player will hit the ground in the same amount of time as a 10 mi/h pitch thrown horizontally from the same height by a child.

6. Use evidence from your observations of the ball and chair in this section to show the truth of the statement, "A projectile's horizontal motion has no effect on its vertical motion, and vice versa."

7. Look at the diagram of an arrow being shot horizontally from a bow and another arrow dropped from the same height. Arrow A is shot horizontally at a speed of 50 m/s. A second arrow, B is dropped from the same height and at the same instant as arrow A is released. Neglecting air friction, how does the time A takes to strike the horizontal plane (ground) compare to the time B takes to strike the horizontal plane?

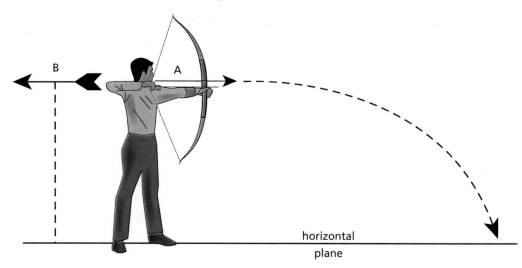

horizontal
plane

Use a protractor for *Questions 8 – 10.*

8. A swimmer jumps into a river and swims directly for the opposite shore at 2.0 km/h as shown in the diagram. The current in the river is 3.0 km/h and flows from left to right in the diagram. What is the swimmer's velocity relative to the shore?

opposite shore

current 3.0 km/h

9. **Active Physics Plus** A football is thrown at 15 m/s at an angle of 37° in the horizontal direction.

a) What is its velocity in the horizontal direction?

b) How far in the horizontal direction has the football traveled in 2.0 s?

10. **Active Physics Plus** A shot put is released at 12 m/s at an angle of 45° in a horizontal direction.

a) What is its velocity in the horizontal direction?

b) How far in the horizontal direction has the shot put traveled in 0.5 s?

11. *Preparing for the Chapter Challenge*
Write a script for a sports telecast that describes the motion of a baseball while it is pitched and then hit into the outfield.

Inquiring Further

Investigating more *x*- and *y*-components of motion

Ask another student to roll a marble slowly across the table in front of you. As the marble rolls by, apply a momentary force to it with a small object such as a block of wood. Make sure the force you apply is directly away from you and perpendicular to the initial velocity of the marble. If you define the *x*-direction to be along the initial velocity of the marble, then you can define the *y*-direction as the direction of the force you are applying. Investigate whether you can change the *x*-component of the marble's velocity by applying a force in the *y*-direction. Relate your observation to what you have learned about projectile motion.

Active Physics

Section 5

The Range of Projectiles: The Shot Put

What Do You See?

Learning Outcomes

In this section, you will

- **Measure** the acceleration due to gravity.

- **Calculate** the speed attained by an object that has fallen freely from rest.

- **Identify** the relationship between the average speed of an object that has fallen freely from rest and the final speed attained by the object.

- **Calculate** the distance traveled by an object that has fallen freely from rest.

- **Use** mathematical models of free fall and uniform speed to construct a physical model of the trajectory of a projectile.

- **Use** the motion of a real projectile to test a physical model of projectile motion.

- **Use** a physical model of projectile motion to infer the effects of launch speed and launch angle on the range of a projectile.

What Do You Think?

A world record in the men's shot put of 23.12 m was set by Randy Barnes of the United States in 1990. In the women's javelin throw, Osleidys Menendez of Cuba broke the world record at 71.70 m in 2005.

- **Describe the trajectories of projectiles launched from the ground at various angles.**

- **Describe how a greater launch speed of a projectile might change the range when the launch angle is the same.**

Record your ideas in your *Active Physics* log. Be prepared to discuss your responses with your small group and the class.

Investigate

In this *Investigate*, you will measure the acceleration due to gravity. You will then use a mathematical model to construct a physical model of the trajectory of a projectile. Finally, you will use a real projectile to test the physical model.

1. Your teacher will provide you with a method of measuring the acceleration caused by Earth's gravity for objects in a condition of free fall.

One simple recommended method uses a "picket fence" and a photogate timer attached to a computer. The picket fence is dropped and the computer measures the time between black slats of the fence. The computer then displays the acceleration due to gravity.

A second method uses a ticker-tape timer and a mass. The mass is attached to the ticker tape then dropped and the ticker tape is analyzed. One pair of successive dots allows you to calculate the velocity at the time those two dots were made. Another pair of successive dots allows you to calculate the velocity at the time those two dots were made. The acceleration can then be calculated by finding the change in velocity during the time between the first pair of dots and the second pair of dots. To increase the precision of the calculation, many pairs of dots can be used and an average acceleration can be found.

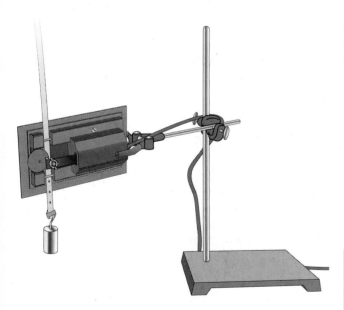

a) In your log, describe the procedure, data, calculations, and the value of the acceleration of gravity obtained. As you have learned, the acceleration due to gravity comes up often and has its own symbol, g.

2. After calculating the acceleration due to gravity (or using the value of $g = 10$ m/s^2), you can use this knowledge to analyze the path of a projectile.

a) In your log, make a table similar to the following:

Time of fall (s)	Final speed (m/s)	Average speed (m/s)	Distance (m)
0.0	0	0.0	
0.1	1	0.5	
0.2	2		
0.3			
0.4			
0.5			

(Some data for a falling object has already been calculated and entered in the table to help you get started.)

b) In the table, calculate and record the speed of a falling object at the end of each 0.10 s of its fall for a total of 0.5 s. To simplify the calculations, use a rounded off value for g of 10 m/s^2. The first three values are provided in the second column. Complete the table using the example below as a guide.

Example:

What you know: $g = 10$ m/s^2

Speed $=$ acceleration $\times$ time

Speed at the end of 0.2 s $= (10$ m/s$^2) \times (0.2$ s$)$

Speed $= 2$ m/s

c) When speeds are changing at a constant rate, then the average speed during a time interval is the average of the speeds at the beginning and the end of the time interval. Calculate and record the average speed for each time interval in the table. The falling object's speed has increased uniformly from zero to the final speed. In each time interval, the average speed will be the average of zero and the final speed reached at the end of each 0.10 s of falling. This average speed will come out to one half of the final speed.

Example:

Average speed =

$$\frac{\text{zero + speed at the end of time interval}}{2}$$

Average speed during 0.2 s of fall =

$$\frac{(0 \text{ m/s} + 2 \text{ m/s})}{2}$$

$$= 1 \text{ m/s}$$

Complete the third column of the chart.

d) Calculate and record the distance the object has fallen at the end of each 0.10 s of its fall. To do this, use the familiar equation:

Distance = average speed × time.

Example:

The average speed during 0.2 s of falling is 1 m/s.

Distance = average speed × time

$$= (1 \text{ m/s}) \times (0.2 \text{ s})$$

$$= 0.2 \text{ m}$$

---

3. The table you have completed is a mathematical model of an object falling freely from rest. Now you will change the mathematical model into a physical model. Your teacher will assign your group a particular row in the data table providing information about the falling object.

Assemble two identical string and mass assemblies, as shown in the diagram, with an assembly length equal to the distance of fall assigned to your group.

4. Label the mass showing your group's name and the time of fall.

5. Your teacher will place a horizontal row of pins or tape labeled 0.0 s, 0.1 s, 0.2 s, and so on, along the top edge of a chalkboard in your classroom. The times noted on the labels correspond to the instants for which you calculated distances of fall in the table. The horizontal spacing of the pins is a model of the positions an object would have every 0.10 s if it traveled along the horizontal row of pins at a constant speed.

a) Calculate the horizontal speed by dividing the distance traveled during each 0.1-s time interval by 0.1 s. (Dividing a number by 0.1 is equivalent to multiplying the number by 10.) Show your calculation and the result in your log.

6. Hang one of your string and mass assemblies from the pin corresponding to the time assigned to your group. Place a small mark on the chalkboard at the bottom end of the string and mass assembly.

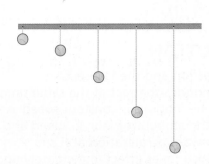

7. A volunteer from the class should draw a smooth curve connecting the marks on the chalkboard. This curve corresponds to the path of an object thrown horizontally. Another volunteer should try to match the path, the trajectory, by throwing a tennis ball horizontally from your starting point (time = 0.0 s). To match the trajectory, the ball will need to be thrown horizontally at the speed calculated in *Step 5.a*). This may require a few practice tries.

🖎 a) Write your observations in your log.

8. Create the other half of the trajectory by hanging your other mass assembly at the corresponding position to the left of the 0.0 pin. Hang the string and mass assemblies, mark the chalkboard, and connect the points to create the other half of an "arch-shaped" model of a trajectory. The goal is to put the two halves together to produce a single trajectory for an object thrown into the air.

9. If this curve represents the path of a ball, then you should be able to get a thrown ball's path to match this curve. A volunteer should try to throw a ball to match this trajectory. Have another person prepared to catch the ball.

🖎 a) What conditions seem to be necessary to match the trajectory? Write your observations in your log.

🖎 b) When a volunteer is able to match the trajectory, the class should agree upon and give the volunteer instructions to test, one at a time, the effects of launch speed and launch angle on the range of the projectile. Write your observations in your log.

10. Your teacher will show you a "portable" version of the row of pins used in *Step 5*.

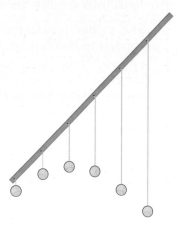

11. Rest the end of the stick corresponding to 0.0 s on the tray at the bottom of the chalkboard while inclining the stick at an angle of 30°.

🖎 a) Is the path indicated by the bottom ends of the string and mass assemblies a "true" trajectory? Have a volunteer try to match it. Record your observations.

🖎 b) Repeat for angles of 45°, 60°, and other angles of interest. Record your observations (it may be necessary to rest the lower end of the model on the floor to prevent the upper end from hitting the ceiling of the room).

🖎 c) What was your observation?

🖎 d) Incline the stick to 90° (straight up). Do this outdoors if the ceiling is not high enough. What is being modeled in this case? Record your thoughts.

Physics Talk

MODELING PROJECTILE MOTION

The *Investigate* you completed in this section and the last section demonstrate that a projectile has two motions that act at the same time and do not affect one another. One of the motions is constant speed along a straight line, corresponding to the amount of launch speed and its direction. The second motion is downward acceleration at 9.8 m/s² caused by Earth's gravitational force, which takes effect immediately upon launch. The trajectory of a projectile becomes simple to understand when these two simultaneous motions are kept in mind.

This section also demonstrates the main thing that scientists do: create models to help understand how things in nature work. In this section, you saw how two kinds of models, a mathematical model (the table of times, speeds, and distances during falling) and a physical model (the evenly spaced strings of calculated lengths) correspond to reality when a ball is thrown. For a scientific model to be accepted, the model must match reality in nature. By that requirement, the models used in this section were good ones.

Trajectories of projectiles can be modeled using a computer or graphing calculator. These tools allow you to manipulate variables such as launch angle, launch speed, launch height, and range to enhance your ability to simulate, explore, and understand projectile motion. You can find projectile motion simulations on the Internet.

If you ignore air resistance, the path of all trajectories are parabolas (bowl-shaped curves). If you throw a ball, it follows a parabolic path. You demonstrated this as your ball toss matched the parabola that you calculated and modeled with the hanging masses.

The diagram below shows plots of trajectories launched at many different angles (10°, 20°, 30°, 45°, 60°, 70°, 80°), but always with the same initial speed.

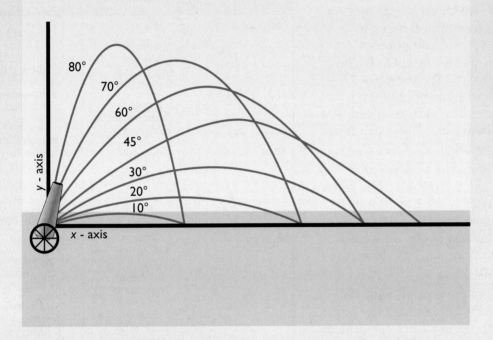

Notice the following:

• All balls travel in parabolas.

• The 45° launch angle produces the greatest range (largest distance).

• The distance traveled at pairs of angles (30° and 60°, 20° and 70°, 10° and 80°) are identical.

• Small angles have greater horizontal velocities but are in the air a short time. Large angles have smaller horizontal velocities but are in the air a long time.

In the real world of sports, the air resistance makes trajectories more complex. Baseballs and golf balls do not follow true parabolic paths. Baseballs can curve if the pitcher puts a certain type of spin on the ball. The temperature of the air also affects the distance a ball will travel.

Checking Up

1. What are the two types of motion that help you understand the trajectory of a projectile?

2. What is the fundamental requirement a scientist must meet when proposing a model of some natural phenomenon?

3. For projectiles launched at various angles, summarize how the height and range of projectiles vary as the angle of launch is increased from 10° to 80°.

+Math	+Depth	+Concepts	+Exploration
◆			

Active Physics

Plus

Analyzing Two-Dimensional Motion Mathematically

You now have a means to analyze two-dimensional motion mathematically. The analysis of two-dimensional motion begins with the recognition that the horizontal and vertical components are independent of one another, as you discovered in this and the previous section. The horizontal speed always remains the same. The vertical speed of a falling object always increases with time as the object descends.

During a long jump the athlete runs and then travels in a parabola. The faster she runs, the faster is her horizontal velocity. She must jump in the air to get height so she can stay in the air longer. She does this without slowing down the horizontal velocity.

If a jumper leaves the ground with the same total velocity but changes the angle, the longest jump occurs when the athlete leaves the ground at an angle of 45°.

Let's see if this makes sense. If the athlete jumps straight up, she maximizes her time in the air but has no horizontal velocity. She will be in the air a long time, but won't go anywhere horizontally. If the athlete jumps straight out at a very small angle, she has a large horizontal component, but is not in the air very long. If she leaves the ground at 45° she is in the air for quite some time and still has a large horizontal velocity. This angle of 45° gives the maximum range.

In physics, you can use mathematical equations to describe the world with accuracy and precision.

Here is a table that describes the horizontal and vertical motion of a trajectory.

	Horizontal Component	Vertical Component
Position	$x = v_x t$ where x is the horizontal displacement v_x is the horizontal component of the velocity t is the time	$y = \frac{1}{2}at^2$ where y is the vertical displacement traveled a is the acceleration due to gravity ($a = 9.8$ m/s² on Earth) t is the time
Velocity	The horizontal velocity is constant. There is no net force in the horizontal direction. With no force, there is no acceleration.	$v_y = at$ where v_y is the vertical velocity a is the acceleration due to gravity ($a = 9.8$ m/s² on Earth) t is the time
Acceleration	No acceleration in the x-direction.	Acceleration due to gravity in the y-direction = 9.8 m/s²

Sample Problem

You can analyze a long jumper with the mathematics that you have practiced in this section. Suppose the height that the long jumper achieves is 1.6 m with a horizontal velocity of 6.0 m/s. How far does the jumper move horizontally?

Strategy: Begin by thinking about what will happen if the long jumper jumps horizontally from a ledge with a height of 1.6 m with a horizontal velocity of 6.0 m/s. Where will she land? Jumping from the ledge is identical to the second half of her jump from the maximum height of 1.6 m to the ground.

Solve for the vertical motion and then solve for the horizontal motion.

Step 1: Use the vertical-motion information to determine the time in the air for the second half of the trip. Her vertical fall is 1.6 m irrespective of the horizontal velocity. It is identical to her falling straight down.

If she fell straight down from 1.6 m or jumped horizontally from 1.6 m, her vertical motion would be identical.

You were able to find the vertical distance traveled by first finding the average speed and then multiplying that average speed by the time.

If the vertical speed at the start is zero, the vertical distance traveled can be found in one step by using the equation,

$$y = \frac{1}{2}at^2$$

where *a* is the acceleration due to gravity (9.8 m/s² on Earth).

The value of 9.8 m/s² is often rounded up to be 10 m/s².

Using the equation $y = \frac{1}{2}at^2$ you can find the time she is in the air.

Given:
$$y = 1.6 \text{ m}$$

Solution:
$$y = \frac{1}{2}at^2$$

You can use your calculator to find a value for *t*, such that:

$$1.6 \text{ m} = \frac{1}{2}at^2$$

or you can practice your algebra skills and rearrange the equation to solve for time.

$$t = \sqrt{\frac{2y}{a}}$$
$$= \sqrt{\frac{2(1.6\text{m})}{9.8 \text{ m/s}^2}}$$
$$= 0.57 \text{ s or } 0.6 \text{ s}$$

Strategy:

Step 2: If she has a horizontal velocity of 6.0 m/s and she is in the air for 0.6 s, where will she land? Her horizontal motion can be found by recognizing that distance equals velocity times time.

Active Physics

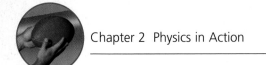

Solution:

$$x = v_x t$$
$$= (6.0 \text{ m/s})(0.6 \text{ s})$$
$$= 3.6 \text{ m}$$

The jumper moves horizontally 3.6 m on the way down for the second half of the trip.

Strategy:

Step 3: If a long jumper achieves a height of 1.6 m and has a horizontal velocity of 6.0 m/s for the second half of the trip, then her horizontal distance is twice the value of the distance for the entire trip, since she moves horizontally on the way up as well. (Remember modeling the other part of the motion in the *Investigate*.)

Solution: x_{total} = 2(3.6 m)
$$= 7.2 \text{ m}$$

1. Calculate how far horizontally a long jumper travels if she achieves a height of 1.7 m and a horizontal velocity of 7.0 m/s.

You can solve lots of problems by analyzing half of the motion like this. You can calculate the path of a football or baseball or golf ball. The calculations will not apply to real-life situations as well as you might expect because of the effects of air resistance.

The path of a golf ball should be a parabola. Air resistance changes the shape. A baseball should also travel in a parabola, but when the pitcher puts a certain type of spin on it, the air resistance allows it to curve and therefore change the calculated path of our model.

2. Calculate how far a ball will travel horizontally if the ball reaches a high of 1.5 m above the ground and is thrown at a horizontal velocity of 45.0 m/s. Assume that the ball is caught at the same height it is thrown and that there is no air resistance.

What Do You Think Now?

At the beginning of this section, you were asked the following:

• **Describe the trajectories of projectiles launched from the ground at various angles.**

• **Describe how a greater launch speed of a projectile might change the range when the launch angle is the same.**

You can use evidence from the mathematical model and the physical model of this section to describe the path of the object and to describe how the angle of the trajectory determines the distance the object travels.

Physics
Essential Questions

What does it mean?

It is said that any thrown object travels in a parabola. Describe three different paths and explain how they each can be a parabola.

How do you know?

What evidence do you have that the mathematics correctly predicted the path that a thrown object would take?

Why do you believe?

Connects with Other Physics Content	Fits with Big Ideas in Science	Meets Physics Requirements
Force and motion	✳ Models	Experimental evidence is consistent with models and theories

✳ The use of models is a physicist's way of making sense of the world. Did the mathematical model and the physical model in your investigation adequately describe the path of a trajectory?

Why should you care?

Many sports have objects moving in the air. Baseballs, footballs, and soccer balls all travel in parabolas. Divers and high jumpers also travel in parabolas. As a diver's body twists and turns in the air, how could a television broadcaster show that the path is a parabola?

Reflecting on the Section and the Challenge

The information learned about projectile motion in this section applies not only to the shot put, but to any sporting event that involves throwing things into the air (including the self-launching of a human body, as in the hurdles, long jump, or high jump). It has been reported that one Olympian who competed in the shot put increased his range in that event by nearly 4 m, based on suggestions made by a physicist. You are now a physicist specializing in projectile motion. Imagine what you might say in your voice-over when covering the long jump event or describing a home run ball or a punt in football. You may want to comment on how the vertical motion and horizontal motion are independent of one another. You may wish to mention that the angle will help determine the range of the ball, with 45° producing the longest range. You will certainly want to mention that the curved path of the ball is a parabola. In the real world of sports, the air resistance makes trajectories more complex. Baseballs and golf balls do not follow true parabolic paths. Baseballs can curve if the pitcher puts a certain type of spin on the ball. The temperature of the air affects the distance a ball will travel. Although the details of these are complex to analyze, you may wish to mention them in your voice-over.

Active Physics

Physics to Go

1. If the launching and landing heights for a projectile are equal, what angle produces the greatest range? Why?

2. Compared to a launch angle of 45°, what happens to the amount of time a projectile is in the air if the launch angle is

   a) greater than 45°?

   b) less than 45°?

3. For a constant launch speed, what angle produces the same range as a launch angle of

   a) 30°?

   b) 15°?

4. Analyses of performances of long jumpers has shown that the typical launch angle is about 18°, far less than the angle needed to produce maximum range. Why do you think this occurs?

5. You might be familiar with Carl Lewis as a medal-winning sprinter. But he is also an Olympic gold medalist in the long jump. Why do you think he was successful in both events?

6. The diagram below shows a ball thrown toward the east and upward at an angle of 30° to the horizontal. Point X represents the ball's highest point.

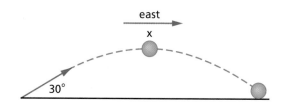

   a) What is the direction of the ball's acceleration at point X? (Ignore friction.)

   b) What is the direction of the ball's velocity at point X?

7. **Active Physics** *Plus*   A diver jumps horizontally off a cliff with an initial velocity of 5.0 m/s. The diver strikes the water 3.0 s later.

   a) What is the vertical speed of the diver upon reaching the surface of the water?

   b) What is the horizontal speed of the diver 1.0 s after the diver jumps?

   c) How far from the base of the cliff will the diver strike the water?

8. The diagram of the baseball player shows a baseball being hit with a bat. Angle θ represents the angle between the horizontal and the ball's initial direction of motion. Which value of θ would result in the ball traveling the longest horizontal distance if air resistance is neglected?

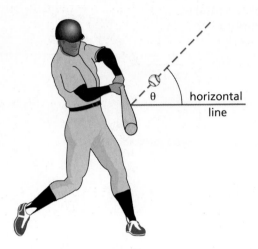

9. Four balls, each with mass (m) and initial velocity (v), are thrown at different angles by a baseball player. Neglecting air friction, which angular direction produces the greatest projectile height?

10. **Active Physics** *Plus* The diagram below shows a ball projected horizontally with an initial velocity of 20.0 m/s east, off a cliff 100-m high.

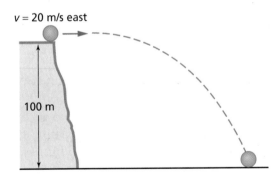

a) During the flight of the ball, what is the direction of its acceleration?

b) How many seconds does the ball take to reach the ground?

c) How far from the base of the cliff does the ball land?

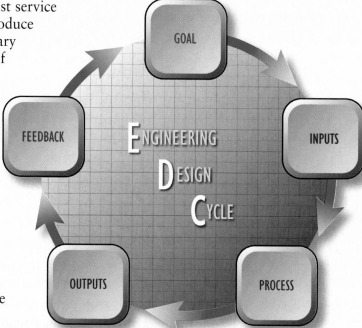

GOAL Your challenge for this chapter is to create a sports voice-over for the public broadcast service that will engage viewers and introduce physics concepts. Your commentary should be two or three minutes of engaging information that will educate the viewer on the laws of nature governing the sport they are watching.

For your initial design you will need the following:

- A sport that contains physics concepts you have studied

- The physics concepts you have studied linked to the sport

- Appropriate use of physics equations and terminology

- Proper units and approximate values for the magnitude of concepts relating to the sport

- Two to three minutes of live voice-over or recorded voice-over

- A written script of the narration

You still have more to learn before you can complete the challenge but this is a good time to give the *Chapter Challenge* a first try. It will give you a good sense of what the challenge entails and how you and other teams are going to approach your "broadcasting job." Your *Mini-Challenge* for this chapter is to develop and present a one-minute voice-over narration to explain the physics behind the sport that you will be broadcasting. At this point you have a handful of physics topics to choose from and the entire world of sports to apply them to.

Go back and quickly review the *Goal* you established at the start of your chapter. This *Mini-Challenge* offers a unique opportunity because it allows you to complete a full trial-run of the *Chapter Challenge* with the physics information you have learned so far. As you learn additional physics information in the remaining sections you can add that to your *Mini-Challenge* voice-over or you could create an entire second voice-over, even choosing a different sport if you want to.

 INPUTS In the *Engineering Design Cycle*, you are adding a critical *Input* by choosing the sport and the specific sports action that you will be describing. You also have the new physics knowledge you have gained from *Sections 1-5* in this chapter which you should review to help you compose your sports voice-over.

Section 1: You investigated Galileo's principle of inertia and learned about the mass of an object and how mass is related to the concept of inertia. You also read about Newton's first law and reference frames for measuring the speed of an object.

Section 2: You measured speed by making speed vs. time graphs using a ticker timer for objects with constant speeds and objects with changing speeds. You also explored the concept of acceleration, or the rate that speed is increasing or decreasing.

Section 3: You investigated the relationship between forces and the changes of speed and acceleration of an object. You also used Newton's second law to calculate the unbalanced force, mass, or acceleration for an object when any two of those quantities can be measured.

Section 4: You used models to learn about the horizontal and vertical motion of a projectile. You learned how the horizontal speed and total height of a projectile will affect the horizontal distance it will travel.

Section 5: You measured acceleration due to gravity and discovered how it causes all objects to speed up as they fall toward Earth. You also used calculations and models to describe the trajectory, or path, of a projectile.

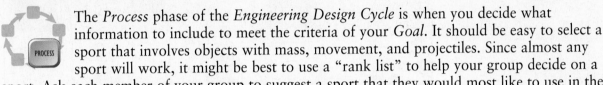

The *Process* phase of the *Engineering Design Cycle* is when you decide what information to include to meet the criteria of your *Goal*. It should be easy to select a sport that involves objects with mass, movement, and projectiles. Since almost any sport will work, it might be best to use a "rank list" to help your group decide on a sport. Ask each member of your group to suggest a sport that they would most like to use in the voice-over and list the sports chosen on a small scrap of paper. Each student will then rank the sports in the order in which they would prefer to work on them. One student will then tally the ranking for each sport and the sport with the lowest total is selected. Once your sport is selected you will need a bit of action, something that will be exciting for the audience to hear about.

Presenting your information to the class is your *Output* of the *Engineering Design Cycle*. Your voice-over should describe actual game play and include as many of the physics topics as you can in your one-minute narration. Don't forget that you are also responsible for turning in a written script for your narration. Use your creativity when choosing a character for your voice-over. Sports fans often have a favorite announcer known for his or her distinct voice or personality. The "character" you choose to portray is part of the entertainment value of your presentation.

Your classmates will give you *Feedback* on the accuracy and the overall appeal of your presentation based on the criteria of the *Mini-Challenge*. This feedback will become an *Input* for your final design in the *Chapter Challenge*. You will have enough time to make corrections and improvements, so you will want to pay attention to the valuable information they provide.

Remember to correct any parts of your script that were identified as not correct by your audience. Then, store all of your information in a safe place so that it will be ready to use in the *Chapter Challenge*.

Take another look at your sports action play. Look for pieces of sports action that you did not have a comment for or you felt you could not address completely. Additional information in the remaining sections may help you describe that action. You will study additional physics topics that apply to the general motions in sports, so it is likely you will be able to give a better description later in the chapter.

Your group may also decide that the sport you chose was not as good of a fit as you might have liked. You are welcome to pick a new sport now that you have a better idea of which sports work well with your challenge. You may also find that a different sport fits better with the physics from the remaining chapter sections.

Section 6

Newton's Third Law: Run and Jump

What Do You See?

Learning Outcomes

In this section, you will

- **Provide** evidence that forces come in pairs, with each force acting on a different object.

- **Use** Newton's third law to analyze physical situations.

- **Describe** how Newton's third law explains much of the motion in your everyday life.

What Do You Think?

The high-jump record is 2.45 m (about 8 ft) for men and 2.09 m (about 6 ft) for women.

- **Pretend that you have just met somebody who has never jumped before. What instructions could you provide to get the person to jump up (that is, which way do you apply the force when you push with your feet)?**

Record your ideas about this question in your *Active Physics* log. Be prepared to discuss your responses with your small group and the class.

Investigate

In *Part A* of this *Investigate*, you will observe what happens when an object pushes or pulls on another object. In *Part B*, you will observe how a meter stick applies an upward force on a mass.

Part A: Push, Push Back and Pull, Pull Back

1. Carefully stand or sit on a skateboard or sit on a wheeled chair near a wall. (Your teacher may have one person demonstrate this part of the activity for safety reasons.) By touching only the wall, not the floor, cause yourself to move away from the wall to "coast" across the floor.

Use words and diagrams to record answers to the following questions in your log:

a) When is your motion accelerated? (Recall that acceleration is the change in velocity over time.) For what distance does the accelerated motion last? In what direction do you accelerate?

b) When is your motion at constant speed? If you ignore the effects of friction, how far should you travel? (Remember Galileo's principle of inertia and Newton's first law when answering this question.)

c) Newton's second law, $F = ma$, says that a force must be acting when acceleration occurs. What is the source of the force, the push or pull, that causes you to accelerate in this case? Identify the object that pushes on your mass (body plus skateboard) to cause the acceleration. Also identify the direction of the push that causes you to accelerate.

d) Obviously, you do some pushing, too. On what object do you push? In what direction?

e) How do you think, on the basis of both amount and direction, the following two forces compare?

 • The force exerted by you on the wall.

 • The force exerted by the wall on you.

2. Once again, as a class demonstration, two students can stand on skateboards. With extreme caution, the students should push on each other's palms.

a) Describe the motion of student A.

b) What force caused the motion of student A?

c) Describe the motion of student B.

d) What force caused the motion of student B?

3. Do a "thought experiment" about the forces involved when you are running or walking on a horizontal surface. Use words and sketches to answer the following questions in your log:

a) Since you move forward, not backward, there must be a force in the forward direction that causes you to accelerate. Identify where the forward force comes from, and compare its amount and direction to the backward force exerted by your shoe with each step.

b) Would it be possible to start walking or running on an extremely slippery surface (like an ice-skating rink) when wearing ordinary shoes? Discuss why or why not in terms of forces.

4. You and a member of your group will now see if you can apply unequal forces on each other. Clip two spring scales together. Each of you will pull on one scale. Try to pull so that one of you pulls with twice the force of the other. Do not pull on the scales so hard that they read a measurement above the highest value. You will have applied unequal forces if you can make one scale read twice the value of the other scale.

a) Record your results in your log.

b) In a diagram, draw the force exerted by you on your partner and the force exerted by your partner on you.

Active Physics

Part B: Observing a Meter Stick Push Back

1. When you hold up a book, you apply an upward force and gravity applies a downward force of equal strength. As a result, the book has no acceleration. A *free-body diagram* (a diagram showing the forces acting on an object) to illustrate this is shown below. When a book sits on a table, gravity applies a downward force and the table supplies an upward force of equal strength. The free-body diagram illustrating the force of gravity on a book lying on a table is similar to the one of the hand holding up a book.

3. Place a washer or coin in the center of the meter stick.

   a) In your log, record what happens.

4. Remove the washer and replace it with a 100-g mass (weight of 100-g mass = 1.0 N). Continue to place a few more 1.0 N weights on the center of the meter stick. Note what happens as you place each weight on the stick.

   a) Measure the deflection of the meter stick for each 1.0 N of weight and record the values for these deflections.

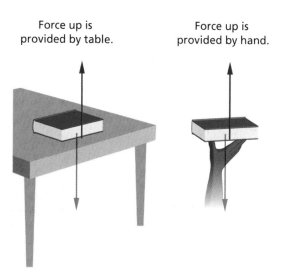

Force up is provided by table.

Force up is provided by hand.

Force down is provided by gravity.

Force down is provided by gravity.

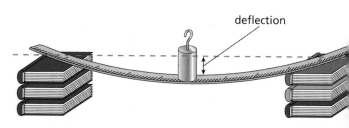

deflection

Walls, tables, and floors are extremely stiff, making it difficult to understand how they can produce forces. In this part of the *Investigate*, you will use something much less stiff, like a meter stick, to uncover how inanimate objects produce forces.

2. Set up a meter stick with a few books for support as shown.

   b) How does the deflection of the meter stick compare to the weight it is supporting? In your log, sketch a graph to show this relationship.

   c) Remove the weights one at a time, noticing the change in deflection. Once all the weights have been removed, place the washer or coin back in the center of the meter stick. Do you think that the meter stick is deflecting? Write a concluding statement concerning the washer and the deflection of the meter stick.

   d) Draw the forces acting on the 100-g mass when it is at rest on the meter stick. (This is a free-body diagram.)

Physics Talk

NEWTON'S THIRD LAW OF MOTION

Pushing and Pulling Back

In earlier sections, you learned that an acceleration is always accompanied by an unbalanced force, and the acceleration and the force are in the same direction. This is expressed in Newton's second law.

In *Part A* of the *Investigate*, when the student on the skateboard pushed against a wall, the student moved away from the wall. What was the force pushing the student in that direction? The leg movement was toward the wall, but the student moved away from the wall. It seems as if the wall pushed on the student. This push or force is equal and opposite to the force of the student on the wall. It is particularly difficult to believe that a wall can push. It is clear however, that if there were no wall, the student would not be able to push horizontally and move away.

When two students on skateboards pushed on each other, both students moved in opposite directions. Student A accelerated because of the force of student B on student A. At the same time, student A was also pushing on student B. This caused student B to accelerate in the opposite direction.

When you walked across the room, your foot applied a force to the ground. This force was backward, but you moved forward. The floor must have been responsible for the force that pushed you forward since you accelerated forward. The force of you on the floor was equal in strength and opposite in direction to the force of the floor on you.

When you and your partner pulled on the spring scales, you found that the forces were always identical, no matter how much one of you tried to pull twice as hard as the other.

All of these are instances of **Newton's third law of motion**. It states:

For every applied force, there is an equal and opposite force. The two forces always act on different objects.

- The student pushed (applied a force) on the wall. The wall pushed on the student.

- Student A on the skateboard pushed on student B. Student B pushed on student A.

- You pushed on the floor backward. The floor pushed on you forward.

- You pulled on the spring scale. The spring scale pulled on you. As you observed, the forces were always equal and in the opposite direction.

Physics Words

Newton's third law of motion: forces come in pairs; the force of object A on object B is equal in strength and opposite in direction to the force of object B on object A.

Active Physics

Newton's third law states that forces always come in equal and opposite pairs. If you push on the wall, the wall pushes on you with the same force. If you press your finger against the table, the table presses against your finger with the same force. You cannot touch someone without someone touching you back. The equal and opposite pairs of forces in Newton's third law always act on different objects. When you and your partner pulled on the spring scales, the forces were equal and you could not do anything to make the forces unequal. One spring scale pulled on your partner's finger and the other spring scale pulled on your finger. The two equal forces acted on different objects. The two forces that were applied can be shown in a diagram.

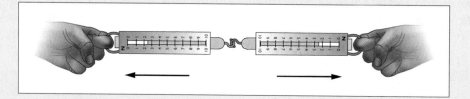

Inanimate Objects Can Push Back

The belief that a wall or a floor can apply a force is troublesome. How does a floor push, and how does it push with different amounts of force on different objects? In *Part B* of the *Investigate*, the masses on the meter stick provided evidence of how an inanimate object can apply a force. When a large mass was placed on the meter stick, you noticed a bend in the meter stick. This bend provides a force. The force of the meter stick on the mass in the upward direction was exactly equal to the force of gravity on the mass in the downward direction. The mass was therefore able to stay at rest. A smaller mass on the meter stick required a smaller force and the meter stick bent a bit less. The washer required a very small force, and the meter stick bent such a small amount that it may not have been observable.

A force diagram of the forces on the mass can be drawn. Recall that a diagram that shows the forces acting on an object is also called a **free-body diagram**.

When you stand on the floor, your mass is pulling you down. You would fall if the floor were not applying an equal force up on you. The floor provides that force by bending just a bit. If you stand in the center of a trampoline, the bend is quite noticeable; however, floors made of wood or concrete provide less of a bend.

Physics Words

free-body diagram: a diagram showing the forces acting on an object.

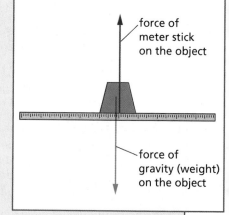

force of meter stick on the object

force of gravity (weight) on the object

How to Draw a Free-Body Diagram

A free-body diagram is a diagram used to show the relative strength and the direction of all the forces acting on an object in a given situation. In a free-body diagram, each force is represented by an arrow. The direction of the arrow is the direction of the force. The size of the arrow is the strength of the force. Each arrow is labeled to show the type of force acting. Often, the actual object is drawn as a box. The weight of the object can be represented by an arrow emerging from the **center of mass**. This is the point at which all the mass of an object is considered to be concentrated. The other forces can be represented by arrows emerging from the contact point (such as the table on the book).

Physics Words

center of mass: the point at which all the mass of an object is considered to be concentrated.

Identifying the Opposite and Equal Forces of Newton's Third Law

Do not confuse *Part A* with *Part B* of the *Investigate*. In *Part A*, you found evidence for Newton's third law, which states that forces always come in pairs. These forces always act on different objects. You pushed on the wall and the wall pushed on you. Your weight applied a force to the floor and the floor pushed up on you. You pulled your partner's finger with the spring scale and your partner pulled your finger with the spring scale.

In *Part B*, you found evidence that an inanimate object can apply a force by bending. When the 100-g mass did not move as it rested on the meter stick, you drew two forces acting on the mass. The force of gravity pulled down on the mass. The meter stick pushed up with an equal force on the mass. These two forces are not the equal and opposite forces of Newton's third law. They are two forces on the same object, not equal and opposite forces acting on different objects.

You can combine your knowledge from *Parts A and B* of the *Investigate* to get the full picture. When the mass sits on the meter stick, there are two pairs of forces.

First pair of forces of Newton's third law: The meter stick pushes up on the mass and the mass pushes down on the meter stick. (Do not worry about the force on the meter stick here.)

Second pair of forces of Newton's third law: Earth pulls down on the mass with a force of gravity and the mass pulls up on Earth with an equal force of gravity. (Do not worry about the force on Earth here.)

In this situation, the focus is only on the mass. The two forces on the mass are the force of gravity pulling downward, and the force of the meter stick pushing upward. Each of these has an equal and opposite force on a different object and that is not a concern because attention is restricted only to the mass.

➤

Active Physics

Drawing Free-Body Diagrams

When you drew the force diagram (free-body diagram) of the forces on the mass, you only showed the forces on the mass and you did not show the force on the meter stick or the force on Earth.

When you drew the forces on the 100-g mass resting on the meter stick, you drew them from a point located in the center of the 100-g mass. The force of gravity acts on every little part that makes up the 100-g mass, and if you add all these forces on different parts together, it equals the weight of the 100-g mass (Weight $= mg = (100 \text{ g})(10 \text{ m/s}^2) = 1.0$ N). So instead of many forces on different parts of the 100-g mass, you can consider a single force equal to the weight acting on the 100-g mass. But on what part of the 100-g mass should this single force act? The proper point is called the center of mass of the 100-g mass.

How Newton Described the Third Law of Motion

Newton's third law of motion can be stated in three equivalent ways:

• For every force applied to object A by another object B, there is an equal and opposite force applied to object B by object A.

• If you push or pull on something, that something pushes or pulls back on you with an equal amount of force in the opposite direction. This is an inescapable fact — it happens every time.

• Forces always come in pairs.

In one of the most important science books of all time, *Principia*, Isaac Newton wrote his third law of motion. It is interesting both historically and in terms of understanding physics to read Newton's third law in his own words:

"To every action there is always opposed an equal reaction: or, the mutual actions of two bodies upon each other are always equal, and directed to contrary parts."

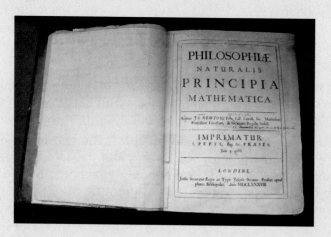

In reading a passage written so long ago, you should be aware that slightly different meanings may be associated with some words. For example, your definition of the word "reaction" is probably something that happens after whatever causes it. Newton did not mean this.

The equal and opposite reaction happens instantaneously with the action that causes it. There is no delay. It is not a reaction, in today's use of the word, but an equal and opposite force that occurs at exactly the same time.

Challenging Newton's Third Law

After learning Newton's third law, students are often traditionally challenged to explain how a horse can pull a cart or how a person can pull a chair across the room. The argument goes like this: "If I pull on the chair then the chair pulls on me with an equal force. Therefore, the two forces cancel and nothing should move. Newton's third law must be wrong."

This would actually be true if the person and chair were on very slippery ice and there was no traction. However, on the ground, there are additional forces as shown in the diagram below.

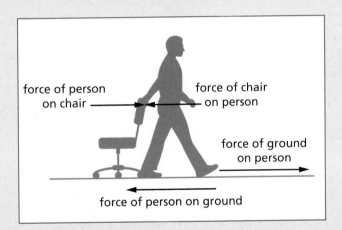

force of person on chair — force of chair on person

force of ground on person

force of person on ground

Assume that the chair is on wheels, as in this *Investigate*. The person pulling the chair applies a force to the ground. By Newton's third law, the ground pulls on the person. These two forces are equal and opposite. That force moves the person forward as the person pulls on the chair.

The person pulls on the chair with a small force. The chair pulls back on the person with an equal small force. Because there is only one force on the chair, the chair moves forward. There are two forces on the person — the force of the ground and the force of the chair. These are not equal. The force on the ground is larger than the force on the chair, thus, moving the person forward.

Checking Up

1. Describe Newton's third law of motion.

2. Earth pulls down a mass with a force of gravity. What is the equal and opposite force acting in this situation?

3. What does a free-body diagram illustrate?

Active Physics

+Math	+Depth	+Concepts	+Exploration
	◆		

Active Physics

Plus

Analyzing Forces Using Free-Body Diagrams

1. Imagine two books sitting at rest on top of each other on a table. The top book has a mass of 2 kg, the book under the top book has a mass of 3 kg, and the table has a mass of 20 kg. Clearly there is a force of gravity (weight) on all three objects. In addition, because some of the objects are in contact with other objects, there may be forces by one object on another object.

a) Draw a free-body diagram for each object. On each diagram, draw arrows representing the force of gravity and any other forces on the object by another object (including the floor).

b) What is the acceleration of each of the objects?

c) What is the force of gravity on each object?

d) What is the force on each object by the other objects?

2. A person is pulling a frictionless 10-kg wagon with a 100-N force. The 10-kg wagon is attached to a frictionless 4-kg wagon.

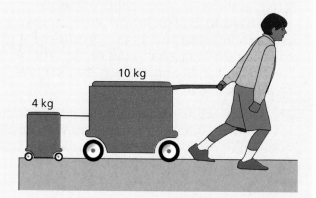

a) Draw a free-body diagram for each object. On each diagram, draw arrows representing the force of gravity and any other forces on the object by another object.

b) What is the acceleration of each of the objects?

c) What is the force of tension in each string?

d) What is the force on each object by the other objects?

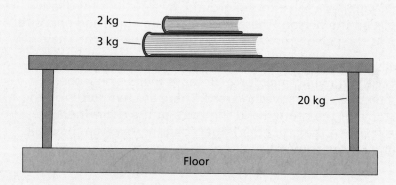

What Do You Think Now?

At the beginning of this section, you were asked the question

- Pretend that you have just met somebody who has never jumped before. What instructions could you provide to get the person to jump up (that is, which way do you apply the force when you push with your feet)?

When you jump, in what direction do you push on the floor? When you push on the floor, what direction does the floor push on you? What happens to the floor that results in an upward force on you? Use your investigations of Newton's third law to justify your answers.

Physics
Essential Questions

What does it mean?

In a video clip, a player catches a football. In another video clip, a soccer ball is caught by the goalie. Newton's third law states that there are equal and opposite forces in each video. Identify the forces of Newton's third law for each of these situations.

How do you know?

Two children pull on spring scales and neither child moves. What evidence do you have that the forces of the students are equal and opposite?

Why do you believe?

Connects with Other Physics Content	Fits with Big Ideas in Science	Meets Physics Requirements
Force and motion	Models	* Experimental evidence is consistent with models and theories

* In relying on observation to come up with explanations, physics often includes ideas that do not seem plausible to someone who has not thought about it. Why do you believe that a table bends when you put a plate on it?

Why should you care?

In sports, forces are exerted by both animate and inanimate objects. In your sports voice-over, you will need to comment on one or both of these situations. Give an example from the sport you have selected in which a force is exerted by an inanimate object.

Active Physics

Reflecting on the Section and the Challenge

According to Newton's third law, each time an athlete acts to exert a force on something, an equal and opposite force acting on the athlete happens in return. There will probably be countless examples of this in your video production. When you kick a soccer ball, the soccer ball exerts a force on your foot. When you push backward on the ground, the ground pushes forward on you (and you accelerate). When a boxer's fist exerts a force on the other boxer's body, the body of the other boxer exerts an equal force on the first boxer's fist. You can now use the same sports video sequence of a sport to describe how it illustrates all three of Newton's laws of motion.

Physics to Go

1. When an athlete is preparing to throw a shot put, does the ball exert a force on the athlete's hand equal and opposite to the force the hand exerts on the ball? Explain your answer.

2. When you sit on a chair, the seat of the chair pushes up on your body with a force equal and opposite to your weight. How does the chair "know" exactly how hard to push up on you—are chairs intelligent? Is there any "deflection" going on?

3. You have weighed yourself by stepping on a scale many times. How do you think a simple bathroom scale works?

4. For a hit in baseball, compare the force exerted by the bat on the ball to the force exerted by the ball on the bat. Why do bats sometimes break?

5. Compare the amount of force experienced by each football player when a big linebacker tackles a small running back.

6. Identify the forces active when a hockey player "hits the boards" at the side of the rink at high speed.

7. Newton's second law, $F = ma$, suggests that when catching a baseball in your hand, a great amount of force is required to stop a high-speed baseball in a very short time interval. The great amount of force is needed to provide the great amount of acceleration required (in this case negative acceleration). Use Newton's third law to explain why baseball players prefer to wear gloves for catching high-speed baseballs. Use a pair of forces in your explanation.

8. *Preparing for the Chapter Challenge*

   a) Write a sentence or two explaining the physics of an imaginary sports clip using Newton's third law. How can you make this description more exciting so that it can be used as part of your sports voice-over?

   b) Describe how deflection of the ground can produce a force. What would make this description more exciting and therefore a valuable part of your sports voice-over?

Inquiring Further

Forces acting on you in an elevator

Ask the manager of a building that has an elevator for permission to use the elevator for a physics experiment. Your teacher may be able to help you make the necessary arrangements.

Stand on a bathroom scale in the elevator and record the force indicated by the scale while the elevator is:

- At rest.
- Beginning to move upward (upward acceleration).
- Appearing to move upward at constant speed.
- Beginning to stop while moving upward (downward acceleration).
- Beginning to move downward (downward acceleration).
- Appearing to move downward at constant speed.
- Beginning to stop while moving downward (upward acceleration).

For each of the above conditions of the elevator's motion, Earth's downward force of gravity is the same. If you are accelerating upward, the floor must be pushing up on you with a force larger than the force due to gravity.

a) Make free-body force diagrams that show the vertical forces acting on your body when standing on a scale in the elevator.

b) Use Newton's laws of motion to explain how the forces acting on your body are responsible for the kind of motion (at rest, constant speed, positive and negative acceleration) that your body experiences.

Section 7

Frictional Forces: The Mu of the Shoe

What Do You See?

Learning Outcomes

In this section, you will

• **Apply** the definition of the coefficient of sliding friction, μ.

• **Measure** the coefficient of sliding friction between the soles of athletic shoes and a variety of surfaces.

• **Calculate** the effects of frictional forces on the motion of objects.

What Do You Think?

A shoe store may sell as many as 100 different kinds of sport shoes.

• **Why do some sports require special shoes?**

• **Why would different features of a shoe be useful for different sports?**

Record your ideas about these questions in your *Active Physics* log. Be prepared to discuss your responses with your small group and the class.

Investigate

In this *Investigate*, you will examine how difficult it is to pull a shoe across a surface.

1. Take an athletic shoe. Use a spring scale to measure the weight of the shoe, in newtons.

   a) Record a description of the shoe (such as its brand) and the shoe's weight, in your log.

   b) List some things (which scientists call "variables") that may affect the force required to pull the shoe.

2. Design an experiment that would allow you to determine how one of the variables you listed affects the force required to pull the shoe. Include in your design:

- What you will be able to conclude as a result of your experiment.

- What data you will record.

- What tools you will use to measure your data.

- How you will analyze your data.

a) Record your procedure in your log.

Your teacher may ask you to continue with your experimental design or, because of equipment or safety concerns, ask you to proceed with the experiment as described below.

3. Your teacher may ask you to use blocks of wood instead of shoes for greater precision in your results. However, wooden shoes are not recommended for sports. Place the shoe on a horizontal surface (either rough or smooth) designated by your teacher. Attach the spring scale to the shoe as shown below (low down at the toe or heel or hooked onto the front lace loop) so that the spring scale can be used to slide the shoe across the surface while, at the same time, the scale can be read. Be sure to keep the spring scale parallel to the surface.

a) Record a description of the surface in your log.

b) Measure and record the amount of force, in newtons, needed to keep the shoe sliding on the surface at a slow, constant speed. Be careful to pull horizontally so that you do not tend to lift the shoe or pull downward on the shoe. Do not measure the force needed to start the shoe moving. Measure the force needed to keep it sliding at a slow, constant speed. How will you determine if the shoe is moving with a constant speed?

When the shoe is being pulled across the surface, there are four forces acting on it. The first is the horizontal force you apply and is measured by the spring scale. But since the shoe moves at a slow, constant speed, it is not accelerating horizontally. There must be a second force on the shoe of equal strength and in the opposite direction to the force you apply. This second horizontal force is the force due to *friction* between the shoe and the surface. The third force is the downward force of gravity on the shoe, which is equal to the weight of the shoe. But since the shoe is not accelerating downward, there must be a fourth force on the shoe. This is the force of the table on the shoe; this force is equal in strength and in the opposite direction to the shoe's weight. Since this force is directed perpendicularly to the surface, it is often called the *normal force*, since the word "normal" sometimes means "perpendicular to."

The *coefficient of sliding friction*, symbolized by the Greek letter μ (mu), is calculated using the following equation:

$$\mu = \frac{\text{force of friction}}{\text{perpendicular force exerted by the surface on the object}}$$

Example:

Brand X athletic shoe has a weight of 5.0 N. If 1.5 N of applied horizontal force is required to cause the shoe to slide with constant speed on a smooth concrete floor, what is the coefficient of sliding friction?

The force of friction is equal to the applied horizontal force because there was no acceleration. The perpendicular force exerted by the surface on the shoe must be equal to the force exerted by the shoe on the surface (which is the weight of the shoe). In this case, that would be the same as the weight of the shoe.

$$\mu \text{ on concrete} = \frac{1.5 \, \text{N}}{5.0 \, \text{N}} = 0.30$$

c) Use the data you have gathered to calculate μ, the coefficient of sliding friction for this particular kind of shoe on the particular kind of surface used. Show your calculations in your log.

4. Add something to the shoe to approximately double its weight. Pull the shoe with a spring scale.

a) Record the force to pull the heavier shoe.

b) Calculate μ for the heavier shoe, showing your work in your log.

c) Taking into account possible errors of measurement, does the weight of the shoe seem to affect μ? Use data to answer the question in your log.

d) How do you think the weight of an athlete wearing the shoe would affect μ? Why?

5. Place the shoe on the second surface designated by your teacher. Repeat the procedure.

a) Make a sketch (free-body diagram) to show the forces acting on the shoe.

b) Calculate μ for this new surface and the shoe.

c) How does the value of μ for this surface compare to the value of μ for the first surface used? Suggest reasons for any difference in μ.

d) Would it make any difference if you used the empty shoe or the weighted shoe to calculate μ in this step? Explain your answer.

Physics Talk

FRICTION

Analyzing the Forces Acting on the Shoe

In this *Investigate*, you pulled the shoe at a constant velocity. Newton's second law informs you that motion with a constant velocity happens only when there is no net force on the shoe. So all the forces on the shoe must add up to zero.

You applied a horizontal pulling force and measured the value of the force with the spring scale. The shoe moved at a slow, constant speed. It was not accelerating horizontally. Therefore, there must be a second force on the shoe of equal strength and in the opposite direction to the force you applied. This second force was the force due to **friction** between the shoe and the surface. The pulling force you applied was equal to the frictional force, and since the two forces were in opposite directions, the net or

Physics Words

friction: a force that resists relative motion between two bodies in contact.

total force due to them was zero. Note that you actually measured the pulling force but used its value as the value for the frictional force. This is perfectly fine, since the two forces are equal in strength.

In the *Investigate*, the shoe did not move in the vertical direction. Newton's second law informs you that the vertical forces on the shoe must add up to zero. The downward force of gravity on the shoe (weight) must be equal to the upward force applied to the shoe by the surface. Since this force is directed perpendicularly to the surface, it is often called the **normal force**, since the word "normal" sometimes means "perpendicular to." This force is equal in strength and in the opposite direction to the shoe's weight. Note that you measured the weight of the shoe, but used its value as the value for the normal force. Again, this is perfectly fine, since the two forces are equal in strength.

A free-body diagram can help you see the relationships among the four forces when the shoe moves with a constant speed.

Physics Words

normal force: the force acting perpendicularly or at right angles to a surface.

coefficient of sliding friction: a dimensionless quantity symbolized by the Greek letter μ; its value depends on the properties of the two surfaces in contact and is used to calculate the force of friction.

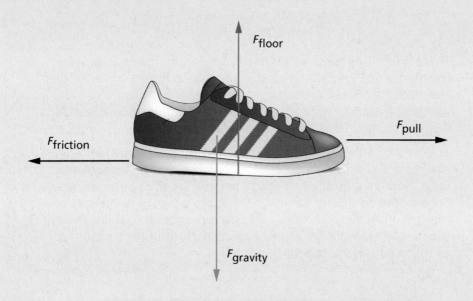

Coefficient of Sliding Friction, μ

The **coefficient of sliding friction**, symbolized by μ, is defined as the ratio of two forces:

$$\mu = \frac{\text{force of friction}}{\text{perpendicular force exerted by the surface on the object (normal force)}} = \frac{F_f}{F_N}$$

The force of friction is equal to the force required to slide the object on the surface with a constant speed.

Active Physics

Note the following about the coefficient of sliding friction:

- μ does not have any units because it is a force divided by a force; it has no unit of measurement.

- μ usually is expressed in decimal form, such as 0.85 for rubber on dry concrete (0.60 on wet concrete).

- μ is valid only for the pair of surfaces in contact when the value is measured; any significant change in either of the surfaces (such as the kind of material, surface texture, moisture, or lubrication on a surface, etc.) may cause the value of μ to change.

- The situation in this section was chosen deliberately so that the "perpendicular force exerted by the surface on the object" was exactly equal to the weight. If the surface were tilted, or if the pulling force were angled upward or downward, then the force exerted by the surface on the object would be more difficult to determine.

The Greek Alphabet

There are not enough letters in the English alphabet to provide the number of symbols needed in physics, so letters from another alphabet, the Greek alphabet, are also used as symbols. The Greek alphabet has been used for centuries to write the Greek language. It is one of the oldest alphabets in use today.

The letters of the Greek alphabet are often used in physics and mathematics. The letter μ (pronounced like "mew" and rhymes with "you") traditionally is used in physics as the symbol for the "coefficient of sliding friction." There are other Greek letters you may use in *Active Physics* or other physics courses that are shown below. For example, you have already used the Greek letter "Δ" to represent "a change in."

Checking Up

1. Why can you say that the force of friction is equal to the force reading on the spring scale when pulling an athletic shoe across a surface with a constant speed?

2. Why does the coefficient of friction have no units?

3. What determines the coefficient of friction?

Active Physics

+Math	+Depth	+Concepts	+Exploration
◆◆		◆	

Active Physics

Plus

Static Friction

As you worked on this *Investigate*, you might have noticed that it takes a larger force to get an object sliding across a surface than to keep it sliding once it has started to move. In that section, only sliding friction is discussed. When the object is not sliding, friction still acts between the surface and the object, but the force of friction now assumes the appropriate value between zero and a maximum so that the object remains at rest.

Imagine the athletic shoe at rest and you are not pulling on it. Now start to pull very gently. You are clearly applying a force to the shoe, but since the shoe is still at rest, the force of static friction must be equal and opposite to the force you are applying. Now pull on it a bit harder. If the shoe does not move, then the frictional force has also increased, so it is still equal and opposite to the force you are applying. Notice that the static frictional force can take on various values. This is unlike the sliding frictional force that always has a definite value for a given situation. If you keep increasing your pull on the shoe, the static frictional force also keeps increasing, until it reaches its maximum value given by $F_x = \mu_s F_N$. As soon as the force you are applying is greater than the maximum static frictional force possible, the shoe breaks loose and accelerates. Because this force is greater than the sliding frictional force ($\mu_s > \mu$), you have to decrease the force you exert on the shoe in order for it to slide with a constant velocity. This is something that you may have noticed.

1. A block sitting on an incline makes an angle of 30° with the horizontal. The block has a mass of 1.5 kg.

   a) Sketch the block. Draw three arrows representing the forces on the block (weight pointing downward, perpendicular force [also known as the normal force] of the incline on the block, and the force of static friction pointing parallel to the incline opposite to the direction the block may slide).

   b) Draw a set of axes with one axis parallel to the incline and one axis perpendicular to the incline. Notice that two of the forces fall along these axes.

   c) Draw the two components of the weight along these axes. Use a scale diagram or trigonometry (sines and cosines) to find the values of these components.

   d) Because the block is at rest (not accelerating), all the forces must add up to zero. Use this fact to find the normal force and the force of static friction.

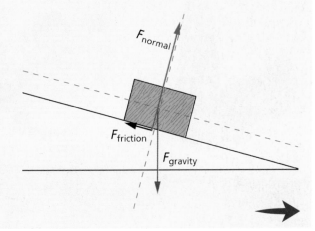

Active Physics

2. Imagine that you can vary the angle of the incline in the previous problem. As you increase the angle, at first, the block just stays where it is. However, at some angle θ, the block begins to slide down the incline. Let the mass of the block be m so you can work only with symbols. The coefficient of friction is equal to the tangent of this angle.

$$\mu = \tan \theta$$

(Tangent is a trigonometry function that you can find on many calculators.)

a) Find the frictional force by pulling a block at a constant speed across a horizontal table. Calculate μ.

b) Find the μ by tilting the table so that once started, the block can move with a constant speed. Measure the angle of the tilt, and calculate $\tan \theta$.

c) Compare the values in *a)* and *b)*.

What Do You Think Now?

At the beginning of this section, you were asked the following:

• **Why do some sports require special shoes?**

• **Why would different features of a shoe be useful for different sports?**

Record your ideas about these questions now. Use the concept of sliding friction to answer the questions this time.

Physics
Essential Questions

What does it mean?

An athlete may complain that the field is slippery. How can you describe the same situation using the terms friction, coefficient of sliding friction, forces, and the symbol μ?

How do you know?

A running shoe is pulled along the ground at a constant speed. How do you know that a frictional force was equal to the pulling force?

Why do you believe?

Connects with Other Physics Content	Fits with Big Ideas in Science	Meets Physics Requirements
Force and motion	Change and constancy	* Experimental evidence is consistent with models and theories

* Physicists often believe in invisible forces. Friction is invisible; it happens without you seeing it. A sliding object slows down and stops. If you did not believe in friction, could Newton's first and second laws explain this motion?

Why should you care?

Friction, or the lack of enough friction, is critical to sports. Describe two parts of your sport where friction is critical and what you are going to say about it in your voice-over.

Reflecting on the Section and the Challenge

Many athletes seem more concerned about their shoes than other items of equipment, and for good reason. Small differences in the shoes (or skates or skis) can affect performance. Athletic shoes have become a major industry because people in all "walks" of life have discovered that athletic shoes are great just about anywhere. Now that you have studied friction, you know about a major aspect of what makes shoes function well. You are prepared to do physics commentary on athletic footwear and other effects of friction in sports when the need exists to be "sure-footed." Your sports commentary may discuss the μ of the shoe, the change in friction when a playing surface gets wet, and the need for friction when running. You may also wish to discuss the use of cleats on certain surfaces or the friction of tires on the road in stock car races. No matter which sport you choose, friction will play an important role.

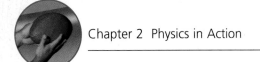

Physics to Go

1. Think of a sport and changing weather conditions that would cause an athlete to want to increase friction to have better footing. Name the sport, describe the change in conditions, and explain what the athlete might do to increase friction between the shoes and the surface of the ground.

2. Think of a sport in which athletes desire to have frictional forces as small as possible and describe what the athletes do to reduce friction.

3. If a basketball player's shoes provide an amount of friction that is "just right" when she plays on her home court, can she be sure the same shoes will provide the same amount of friction when playing on another court? What details about the other court would she need to know to answer this question?

4. Tennis is played on clay, grass and hard surfaces. Please explain why you think tennis players have or don't have different shoes for each surface.

5. A cross-country skier who weighs 600 N has chosen ski wax that provides $\mu = 0.03$. What is the minimum amount of horizontal force, perhaps from a tailwind, that would keep the skier coasting at constant speed across level snow?

6. A vehicle having a mass of 1000 kg had an accident on a wet, but level, concrete road under foggy conditions. The tires were measured to have $\mu = 0.55$ on wet concrete. The driver locked the brakes, skidded for 6 seconds, and then hit the guardrail causing a very small dent because the vehicle stopped just as it touched the guardrail. The driver claimed to be driving 65 miles per hour (29 m/s). You have been hired as an investigator to determine if the driver is telling the truth.

    a) What is the weight of the vehicle?

    b) The frictional force produces the negative acceleration (often called deceleration) that reduces the velocity of the vehicle from its initial unknown speed to zero. Find the value of the frictional force.

    c) Use the frictional force to calculate the acceleration (remember that it is a negative number).

    d) Using the acceleration and the time over which acceleration occurred, calculate the change in speed that the acceleration would produce.

    e) Use the change in speed to find the original speed of the vehicle when the brakes were applied. Write a statement of your findings, including your opinion of the driver's claim.

7. In some sports, the air or water have limiting effects on motion similar to sliding friction. Do you think that the forces of "air resistance" and "water resistance" remain constant or do they change when speeds change? Use examples from your own experience with these forms of resistance as a basis for your answer.

8. If there is a maximum frictional force between your shoe and the track, does that set a limit on how fast you can start (accelerate) in a sprint? Does that mean you cannot have more than a certain acceleration even if you have incredibly strong leg muscles? What is done to solve this problem?

9. How might an athletic shoe company use the results of your experiment to "sell" a shoe? Write copy for such an advertisement.

10. Explain why friction is important to running. Why are cleats used in football, soccer, and other sports?

11. *Preparing for the Chapter Challenge*
Choose a sport and describe an event in which friction with the ground or the air plays a significant role. Create a voice-over or script that uses physics to explain the action.

Inquiring Further

Frictional force and the weight of a player

You found that for a given coefficient of sliding friction, the frictional force increased with the weight of the shoe. Of course, if a person is wearing the shoe, it is the weight of the person that determines the frictional force (assuming the person has only one foot on the surface). This means that the heavier the athlete, the greater the frictional force. Does this imply that the heavier a person is, the greater his or her acceleration can be?

a) Calculate the force of sliding friction for a 50-kg person using a shoe with a μ of 0.6.

b) Calculate the acceleration of the 50-kg person due to the force of sliding friction.

c) Calculate the force of sliding friction for a 90-kg person using a shoe with a μ of 0.6.

d) Calculate the acceleration of the 90-kg person due to the force of sliding friction.

e) Can the heavier person achieve a greater acceleration using the same shoes?

Section 8

Potential and Kinetic Energy: Energy in the Pole Vault

Learning Outcomes

In this section, you will

- **Apply** equations for kinetic energy, gravitational potential energy, and elastic potential energy.

- **Recognize** that restoring forces are active when objects are deformed.

- **Apply** the equation for the force necessary to compress or stretch a spring.

- **Measure** the transformations among the different forms of energy.

- **Conduct** simulations of the transformations of energy involved in the pole vault.

What Do You See?

What Do You Think?

You would need a fence more than 6.0 m (about 20 ft) high to keep the world champion pole vaulter out of your yard.

- If champion pole vaulters can clear a 6.0-m high bar with a 5.5-m long pole, why can't they vault over a 12.0-m high bar with a pole 11.0 m long?

- What factors (variables) do you think limit the height a pole vaulter has been able to attain?

Record your ideas about these questions in your *Active Physics* log. Be prepared to discuss your responses with your small group and the class.

Investigate

Pole vaulters rely on the energy stored in their flexible poles to soar to remarkable heights. In this section, you will design an experiment that simulates the factors that determine the amount of energy stored in a pole vaulter's pole by launching a penny with a flexible ruler.

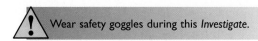

Wear safety goggles during this *Investigate*.

1. Hold one end of a ruler on the table and press down on the other end. Try to get a penny (or some other small mass) to travel close to the height of the ceiling without hitting the ceiling.

   a) Record your technique for blasting the penny high in the air.

   b) What factors about the ruler and how it is positioned determine the height the penny achieves?

2. Design an experiment to test one of the variables and its effect on the height of the penny.

   Include in your design:

   • What you will be able to conclude as a result of your experiment.

   • What data you will record.

   • What tools you will use to make your measurements.

   • How you will analyze your data.

   Your teacher may ask you to continue with your experimental design or, because of equipment or safety concerns, may ask you to proceed with the experiment as described below.

3. Carefully clamp a ruler in a vertical position so that the clamp is near the bottom end of the ruler. The top end should extend a few centimeters above the edge of a tabletop.

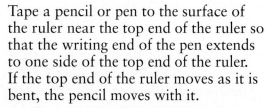

Tape a pencil or pen to the surface of the ruler near the top end of the ruler so that the writing end of the pen extends to one side of the top end of the ruler. If the top end of the ruler moves as it is bent, the pencil moves with it.

4. Set up a ramp as shown in the bottom left diagram. Three different starting points on a ramp will be used to roll a ball across the tabletop at three different speeds. Each time the ball rolls, it will strike the ruler near the top end, causing the ruler to bend. A marking surface held in contact with the tip of the pencil or pen will be used to measure the deflection.

5. Roll the ball from three different starting points on the ramp to achieve a low, medium, and high speed. In each case, measure the amount of deflection of the end of the ruler as indicated by the length of the pencil mark.

   a) Record the amount of deflection in each case.

   b) If the rolling ball represents the running vaulter and the ruler represents the pole in this model of the pole vault, how does the amount of bend in the pole depend on the vaulter's running speed? Record your data and response in your log.

6. Carefully clamp a ruler flat-side down to a tabletop so that two-thirds of the ruler's length extends over the edge of the table as shown below.

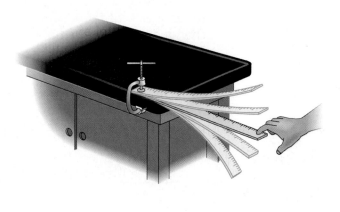

Active Physics

7. Place a penny on the top surface of the ruler at the outside end.

8. Bend the clamped ruler downward. Use a second ruler to measure a 2-cm downward deflection from the unbent position of the ruler. Prepare to measure the maximum height to which the penny flies upward. Use the position of the penny when the ruler is relaxed as the "zero" vertical position of the penny. Release the ruler, launching the penny.

  a) Record in your log the height that the penny travels.

9. Repeat *Step 8* for ruler deflections of 4 cm and 6 cm.

  a) In each case, record the maximum height of the "vaulted" penny.

  b) How is the height that the penny reaches related to the amount of deflection of the ruler?

  c) If the ruler represents the pole in this model of the pole vault, and the penny is the pole vaulter, how does the amount of bend in the pole affect the height that the pole vaulter can attain? Record your response in your log.

Physics Talk

LAW OF CONSERVATION OF ENERGY

When a force acts on an object, the speed and position of the object may change. In many cases, the speed and position of the object change in a way that makes it possible for the speed and position to change back to their original values. Throwing a ball vertically into the air is a good example of this. A force acting on the ball gives it an upward speed. That speed then decreases as the ball travels upward and is acted upon by a gravitational force. When the ball reaches the very top of its trajectory, its vertical position has increased and its vertical speed has decreased to zero. But you know that as time continues, the ball will fall, returning to its original position and increasing its speed to its original value right after the force was applied. This idea that a force can change the position and speed of an object in a way that allows the position and speed to change back prompted scientists studying motion to wonder: was there some quantity that was not changed in these situations?

Physics Words

kinetic energy: energy associated with motion.

gravitational potential energy: the energy an object possesses because of its vertical position from Earth.

To identify what was not changed in these situations, scientists came up with the concept of energy. Energy comes in various forms. Two very important forms of energy are **kinetic energy** (energy associated with motion) and **gravitational potential energy** (energy associated with position). When forces act on objects, energy changes from one form

Active Physics

to another, but the sum of the kinetic and **potential energy** (the total energy) remains constant. That is why it is often possible for the objects to reverse the transformation of one form of energy to the other and return to their past positions and speeds. The concept that the total energy remains constant is referred to as the **law of conservation of energy**.

Energy and Work

While a ball is rising or falling, the sum of the gravitational potential energy and the kinetic energy remains constant. For the ball to start to rise, a force had to be applied to the ball over a distance. In the case of throwing a ball up in the air, the force acting on the ball is the force of your hand acting over a distance in an upward direction. For the ball to stop, another force had to be applied to the ball over another distance. In this case, it is gravitational force acting in a downward direction as the ball rises over a distance into the air. Whenever a force is applied to an object over a distance (in the same direction or opposite direction of the force), **work** is done. Work is a precisely defined physics quantity that equals the force multiplied by the distance. Whenever work is done, the energy of an object changes. Therefore, one very appropriate way to think about energy is to consider it "stored work."

Conservation of Energy in the Pole Vault

The coin in the investigation is a good example of work and conservation of energy. You applied a force to the ruler to bend it a certain distance. This was the work done on the ruler to add energy. After that, the ruler had **elastic potential energy**. When you released the ruler, that energy was transferred to the coin as the ruler applied a force to the coin over a certain distance. The coin now had kinetic energy. It traveled up in the air and the kinetic energy became gravitational potential energy as the coin rose. At its peak, the coin stopped momentarily. It now had no kinetic energy, but did have gravitational potential energy. As the coin began to fall, it gained kinetic energy as it lost gravitational potential energy. At all points during the rise and fall, the sum of the kinetic energy and gravitational energy of the coin was constant.

The pole vault is another wonderful example of the law of conservation of energy. The forms of energy are changed, or transformed, from one to another during a vault, but, in principle, the total amount of energy in the system of the vaulter and the pole remains constant.

Physics Words

potential energy: energy associated with position.

law of conservation of energy: energy cannot be created or destroyed; it can be transformed from one form to another, but the total amount of energy remains constant.

work: the product of the displacement and the force in the direction of the displacement.

elastic potential energy (also called spring potential energy): the energy of a spring due to its compression or stretch.

Active Physics

Food energy provides muscular energy for the vaulter to run, gaining an amount of kinetic energy. Some of the vaulter's kinetic energy is used to catapult the vaulter with an initial speed upward and the remaining kinetic energy is converted into an amount of elastic potential energy as the vaulter does work on the pole as it bends. As the bent pole straightens, its elastic potential energy is transferred to the vaulter to increase the vaulter's gravitational potential energy as the vaulter's height increases.

Richard Feynman's Explanation of the Conservation of Energy

In making measurements of the ruler's deflection and the height of the coin, you were investigating conservation of energy — one of the most important principles of science. Richard Feynman, an American physics giant of the twentieth century, provides a story that may help you to understand energy conservation.

In his story, a child plays with 28 blocks. Every day the child's mother counts the blocks and always finds the total to be 28. On one occasion, she only finds 27 blocks, but then realizes that one block is hidden in a box. On another day, she finds only 25 blocks, but can see that the water in a pail is higher than expected. By measuring the height difference, and knowing something about the original height of the water and the volume of a block, she determines that 3 blocks are below the surface of the water. Feynman equates counting the blocks with measuring the total energy. There were 28 blocks and there will always be 28 blocks. If there are 28 units of energy, then there will always be 28 units of energy.

Is There an Equation?

Physicists always ask if there is an equation that can help them understand and explain the model of observed events.

Work:

You can calculate the work done using the following equation.

$$W = F \cdot d$$

where F is the force applied in newtons (N) and
$\quad$ d is the distance in meters (m) over which the force was applied.

The following equations can be used to calculate the different forms of energy.

Elastic (spring) potential energy:

$$EPE = \frac{1}{2}kx^2$$

where k is the spring constant in newtons per meter (N/m) and
$\quad$ x is the amount of bending in meters (m).

Gravitational potential energy:

$$GPE = mgh$$

where m is the mass of the object in kilograms (kg),
$\quad$ g is the acceleration due to gravity in meters
$\quad\quad$ per second squared (m/s²), and
$\quad$ h is the height in meters (m) through which the object is lifted.

Kinetic energy:

$$KE = \frac{1}{2}mv^2$$

where m is the mass in kilograms (kg) of the moving object and
$\quad$ v is the speed in meters per second (m/s) of the object.

SI Units of Work or Energy

The unit of work or energy is called the joule (J). From the formula for work, you can see that $1\ J = 1\ N \cdot m$. From the formulas for gravitational potential energy and kinetic energy you can see that $1\ J = 1\ kg \cdot m^2/s^2$, which makes sense since $1\ N = 1\ kg \cdot m/s^2$. Work and energy are scalar quantities. They have no direction.

When solving problems involving work and energy units, it is important to remember that the following are all the same unit.

$$J = 1\ N \cdot m = 1\ \frac{kg \cdot m^2}{s^2}$$

You may sometimes see $1\ kg \cdot m^2/s^2$ written as $1\ kg \cdot m^2 \cdot s^{-2}$. They are the same unit.

Active Physics

Sample Problem 1

A weightlifter uses a force of 325 N to lift a set of weights 2.00 m off the ground. How much work did the weightlifter do?

Strategy: You can use the following equation for calculating work:

$$W = F \cdot d$$

Given:

$$F = 325 \text{ N}$$
$$d = 2.00 \text{ m}$$

Solution:

$$W = F \bullet d$$
$$= 325 \text{ N} \times 2.00 \text{ m}$$
$$= 650 \text{ N} \bullet \text{m or } 650 \text{ J}$$

Work done by the weightlifter is 650 J.

Sample Problem 2

How much energy is stored in a pole with a spring constant of 15 N/m if it is deflected 1.6 m?

Strategy: You can use the following equation for calculating elastic potential energy:

$$EPE = \frac{1}{2}kx^2$$

Given:

$$k = 15 \text{ N/m}$$
$$x = 1.6$$

Solution:

$$EPE = \frac{1}{2}kx^2$$
$$= \frac{1}{2} \bullet 15 \ \frac{\text{N}}{\text{m}} \bullet (1.6 \text{ m})^2$$
$$= 19.2 \text{ N} \bullet \text{m or } 19 \text{ J}$$

Elastic potential energy in the pole is 19 J.

Sample Problem 3

One of the highest pop flies ever recorded in baseball was about 172 m. What is the gravitational potential energy of a baseball with a mass of 145 g that is hit that high into the air? Use the value of 9.8 m/s^2 for the acceleration due to gravity.

Strategy: You can use the following equation for calculating gravitational potential energy:

$$GPE = mgh$$

Given:

$$m = 145 \text{ g or } 0.145 \text{ kg}$$
$$h = 172 \text{ m}$$
$$g = 9.8 \text{ m/s}$$

Solution:

$$GPE = mgh$$
$$= 0.145 \text{ kg} \times 9.8 \text{ m/s}^2 \times 172 \text{ m}$$
$$= 244 \text{ kg} \cdot \text{m}^2/\text{s}^2 \text{ or } 244 \text{ J}$$

The gravitational potential energy of the baseball is 244 J.

Sample Problem 4

A football player has a mass of 100.0 kg and runs at a speed of 6.0 m/s. What is his kinetic energy?

Strategy: You can use the equation for calculating kinetic energy.

$$KE = \frac{1}{2}mv^2$$

Given:

$$m = 100.0 \text{ kg}$$
$$v = 6.0 \text{ m/s}$$

Solution:

$$KE = \frac{1}{2}mv^2$$
$$= \frac{1}{2} \times 100 \text{ kg} \times \left(6\,\frac{m}{s}\right)^2$$
$$= \frac{1}{2} \times 100 \text{ kg} \times 6\,\frac{m}{s} \times 6\,\frac{m}{s}$$
$$= 1800 \text{ kg} \cdot \text{m}^2/\text{s}^2 \text{ or } 1800 \text{ J}$$

The kinetic energy of the football player is 1800 J.

Checking Up

1. What is required for the energy of an object to change?

2. From where does the penny that is launched into the air get its energy?

3. From where does the pole vaulter get the energy needed to bend the pole and then rise over the bar?

4. What are the units for work, kinetic energy, gravitational potential energy, and spring potential energy?

+Math	+Depth	+Concepts	+Exploration
◆ ◆			

Active Physics

Plus

Energy Is "Stored Work"

The energy equations you have been using can be related to the work that increases the energy of an object. Work has a very special meaning in physics. Work is done on an object when a force is applied over a certain distance. The distance must be in the same direction as the force. This can be written as:

$$W = F \cdot d$$

Work done on a spring gives the spring elastic or spring potential energy. When the spring is released, that spring potential energy can move an object.

Imagine applying a force to stretch a spring. Some springs are easy to stretch and others require a large force to stretch. The difficulty of stretching a spring is defined by a number for each spring, called the spring constant k. The force required to stretch a spring with spring constant k, a distance x, is given by the equation $F = kx$. A larger stretch requires a larger force.

The average force will be halfway between the zero force (to start the stretch) and the final force for the last bit of stretch. The final force is kx. The initial force is 0. The average force is:

$$F_{avg} = \frac{kx + 0}{2} = \frac{1}{2}kx$$

The total stretch of the spring is x. The work done is:

$$W = F \cdot d = \left(\frac{1}{2}kx\right)x = \frac{1}{2}kx^2$$

which is the expression for the elastic potential energy that was given to you earlier. Now you know where it comes from!

You can also calculate the work done to lift an object of mass m up through a distance h. In order for you to move the object vertically, you must apply an upward force that is just equal to its weight. You don't want to apply a force greater than this, because then there will be an upward unbalanced force that will cause acceleration, increase the speed of the mass, and give it kinetic energy.

$$W = F \cdot d = mgh$$

This is the expression for the gravitational potential energy given earlier.

You can also calculate the work done in accelerating an object from an initial velocity v_i to a final velocity v_f with a constant force. All you need to remember is that the acceleration, a, is equal to the change in velocity, $v_f - v_i$, divided by the time t, and that the distance traveled d is equal to the average velocity, $(v_f + v_i)/2$, times the time t.

$$W = F \cdot d$$

Since $F = ma$, then

$$W = mad$$

$$= m\left[\left(\frac{v_f - v_i}{t}\right)\right]\left[\left(\frac{v_f + v_i}{2}\right)\right]t$$

$$= \frac{1}{2}mv_f^2 - \frac{1}{2}mv_i^2$$

which is the expression for the change in kinetic energy you saw earlier.

Although the energy equations were stated first, notice that they result from the idea that whenever work is done, energies change. The energy equations simply reflect the amount of work done. This is where the statement "energy is stored work" originates.

Sample Problem 1

Your teacher gives you a pop-up toy. When you push down on it, it sticks to the desk for a moment and then pops into the air.

a) If the toy has a mass of 100.0 g and leaps 1.20 m off the table, how much potential energy does it have at its point of maximum height? (Use $g = 9.80$ m/s².)

Strategy:

The toy at its peak has a type of energy that depends on its position in Earth's gravitational field. So you need to use the formula for gravitational potential energy.

Given:

$$m = 100.0 \text{ g or } 0.100 \text{ kg}$$
$$h = 1.20 \text{ m}$$

Solution:

$$GPE = mgh$$

$$= (0.100 \text{ kg})(9.8 \tfrac{\text{m}}{\text{s}^2})(1.20\text{m})$$

$$= 1.18 \text{ kg} \cdot \text{m}^2/\text{s}^2 \text{ or } 1.18 \text{ J}$$

b) When the toy jumps off the desk, with what speed does it leave?

Strategy: At the point where it jumps off the desk, the toy has its maximum amount of kinetic energy. This is what becomes the potential energy at the peak of its trajectory.

Because energy is conserved, these two values will be equal—kinetic energy at the bottom equals the potential energy at the peak.

Given:

$$GPE = 1.18 \text{ J}$$

Solution:

$$GPE = KE$$

$$KE = \frac{1}{2}mv^2$$

Since you know that the *KE* must be equal to 1.18 J and you know the mass is 0.100 kg, you can use your calculator to find a value for v such that $\frac{1}{2}mv^2 = 1.18$ J.

Alternatively, you can practice your algebra skills and find the value directly.

You can use algebra to rearrange the equation to solve for v.

$$v = \sqrt{\dfrac{KE}{\tfrac{1}{2}\text{m}}}$$

$$= \sqrt{\dfrac{1.18\text{J}}{\tfrac{1}{2}(0.100 \text{ kg})}}$$

$$= 4.90 \text{ m/s}$$

c) If you push the toy down 2.0 cm to make it stick to the desk, what is the spring constant of the spring in the toy?

Strategy: The kinetic energy to make the toy leap off the desk came from doing work on the spring and storing it as elastic potential energy. Using the conservation of energy, this energy was then transformed into kinetic energy.

Given:

$$x = 2.0 \text{ cm} = 0.020 \text{ m}$$

Solution:

$$EPE = 1.18 \text{ J}$$

You can use your calculator to find a value for k, such that:

$$\frac{1}{2}kx^2 = 1.18 \text{ J}$$

or you can use algebra again to rearrange the equation to solve for k.

$$k = \frac{1.18 \text{ N} \cdot \text{m}}{\frac{1}{2}(0.020 \text{ m})(0.020 \text{ m})} (1 \text{ J} = 1 \text{ N} \cdot \text{m})$$

$$= 5900 \frac{\text{N}}{\text{m}}$$

d) What force was needed to compress the spring the 2.00 cm?

Strategy: Now that you know the compression and the spring constant, it is possible to find the amount of force required to press down on the spring.

Given:

$$k = 5900 \text{ N/m}$$

$$x = 0.0200 \text{ m}$$

Solution:

$$F = kx$$

$$= \left(5900 \frac{\text{N}}{\text{m}}\right)(0.0200 \text{ m})$$

$$= 118 \text{ N or } 120 \text{ N}$$

Sample Problem 2

At what height, above the ground, could a tennis ball ($m = 57$ g) be dropped to give it the same kinetic energy it has when traveling at 45 m/s? (Neglect air resistance.)

Strategy: Assume that you are looking for the vertical position that will yield a speed of 45 m/s the instant before the ball touches the ground. The problem can be solved in one step using conservation of energy.

Given:

$$m = 57 \text{ g} = 0.057 \text{ kg}$$

$$v = 45 \text{ m/s}$$

$$g = 9.8 \text{ m/s}^2$$

Solution:

$$GPE = KE$$

$$mgh = \frac{1}{2}mv^2$$

Notice that you do not have to take into account the mass of the ball.

$$h = \frac{v^2}{2g}$$

$$= \frac{\left(45 \dfrac{\text{m}}{\text{s}}\right)^2}{2\left(9.8 \dfrac{\text{m}}{\text{s}^2}\right)}$$

$$= \frac{2025 \dfrac{\text{m}^2}{\text{s}^2}}{19.6 \dfrac{\text{m}}{\text{s}^2}}$$

$$= 103.3 \text{ m or } 100 \text{ m}$$

When the ball is traveling at 45 m/s, it has a kinetic energy of 58 J. You can calculate this:

$$KE = \frac{1}{2}mv^2 = \frac{1}{2}(0.57 \text{ kg})(45 \text{ m/s})^2 = 58 \text{ J}$$

If the tennis ball were positioned at a location 103 m above Earth, the gravitational potential energy of the ball would also equal 58 J.

$$GPE = mgh = (0.57 \text{ kg})(9.8 \text{ m/s}^2)(103 \text{ m})$$

$$= 58 \text{ J}$$

What Do You Think Now?

At the beginning of this section, you were asked the following

- If champion pole vaulters can clear a 6.0-m high bar with a 5.5-m long pole, why can't they vault over a 12.0-m high bar with a pole 11.0 m long?

- What factors (variables) do you think limit the height a pole vaulter has been able to attain?

Use energy conservation to explain how to determine why there is a limit to the height pole vaulters have been able to attain.

Physics
Essential Questions

What does it mean?

In attempting to understand the physical world, physics often discovers quantities that remain unchanged while other quantities change. What does it mean when you say energy is conserved during the pole-vault event?

How do you know?

Conservation of energy is an important concept in physics because it is observed to be the case over and over again in the physical world. What did you observe in this activity that made the concept of conservation of energy plausible?

Why do you believe?

Connects with Other Physics Content	Fits with Big Ideas in Science	Meets Physics Requirements
Force and motion	✱ Conservation laws	Good, clear, explanation, no more complex than necessary

✱ In physics, organizing principles like the conservation of energy are used to explain a wide range of phenomena. Although you may never have seen a rugby match, why do you believe that you can use conservation of energy to describe the event?

Why should you care?

Conservation of energy is such an important concept of physics because it is important in so many situations. It is going to be important in your sports voice-over. Give an example in which your commentary is going to discuss conservation of energy.

Reflecting on the Section and the Challenge

In this section, you were told that throughout the event of pole vaulting, energy changes from one form to another, but the total amount of energy in the system at all instants remains the same. (A small amount of energy may be transformed into internal energy by making a dent in the end of the pit that stops the pole or by raising the temperature of the pole as it bends.) Therefore, a sportscaster covering the pole vault event has many opportunities to explain what is happening in terms of the law of conservation of energy.

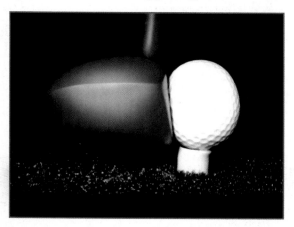

As a sportscaster, you can also describe the law of conservation of energy as it applies to a baseball rising in the air. In soccer, when you kick the ball, you do work on the ball and compress it. This elastic potential energy becomes kinetic energy. If the ball rises, some of that kinetic energy becomes gravitational potential energy. From a physics perspective, the behavior of a golf ball or a tennis ball is identical. High-speed photographs can show the compression of the balls. Since conservation of energy is one of the organizing principles of all science, you may want to include this in your voice-over.

Physics to Go

1. Describe the energy transformations in the shot put.

2. Describe the energy transformations in golf.

3. Assume that a vaulter is able to carry a vaulting pole while running as fast as Carl Lewis in his world record 100-m dash (around 12 m/s). Also assume that all of the vaulter's kinetic energy is transformed into gravitational potential energy. What vaulting height could that person attain?
   (Hint: Use the equation $\frac{1}{2}mv^2 = mgh$.)

4. Why does the length of the pole alone not determine the limit of vaulting height?

5. The temperature of some poles increases slightly as they flex. Use the law of conservation of energy to explain how this would affect performance.

6. The women's pole vault world record as of spring 1997 was 4.55 m, set by Emma George. What do you estimate was Emma's speed prior to planting the pole? Use conservation of energy for your prediction.

7. Sergei Bubka held the world record for the pole vault as of spring 1997 at 6.14 m. How did Sergei's speed compare with Emma George's speed? (See *Question 6*.)

8. A 2.0-kg rock is dropped off a 100-m high cliff.

a) Using energy considerations only, calculate the speed the rock is going when it gets to the bottom of the cliff.

b) Can you do this calculation if you do not know the mass of the rock? What does this imply for the speeds of falling objects when friction is not considered?

9. **Active Physics** *Plus* A bow is strung with a bowstring that has a spring constant, k, of 1500 N/m.

a) If you pull the bowstring back 25 cm, how much work have you done on it?

b) If the string is pushing against an arrow that has a mass of 0.10 kg, how fast is the arrow going when it leaves the bow?

10. **Active Physics** *Plus* An exercise spring has a spring constant of 315 N/m.

a) How much work is required to stretch the spring 30 cm?

b) What force is needed to stretch the spring 30 cm?

11. A toy car ($m = 0.04$ kg) is released from rest and slides down a frictionless track 1 m high. At the bottom of the track it slides along a horizontal portion until it hits a spring ($k = 18$ N/m). The spring is attached to an immovable object. What is the maximum compression of the spring?

12. The unit for energy is the joule. It is also the unit of work. One joule is the work done by a force of one newton over a distance of one meter ($1 \text{ J} = 1 \text{ N} \cdot 1 \text{ m}$).

a) Using $F = ma$, show that $1 \text{ N} = 1 \text{ kg} \cdot 1 \text{ m/s}^2$.

b) Using $GPE = mgh$, show that GPE is measured in joules.

c) Using $KE = \dfrac{1}{2}mv^2$, show that KE is measured in joules.

d) Using $EPE = \dfrac{1}{2}kx^2$ and $GPE = \dfrac{1}{2}kx^2$, show that EPE is measured in joules.

   (The spring constant k has units of N/m, as you can see from the equation $F = kx$.)

13. A high diver jumps off the diving board, travels up and then down twirling her body. Explain high diving in terms of energy transformations among EPE, GPE, and KE.

14. A volleyball player is setting the ball by hitting it directly up with her hands. Describe the energy transformations in the volleyball play.

15. A long fly ball in baseball can be described in terms of energy transformations. Can you make your descriptions entertaining so that it can be used in a sports announcer's voice-over?

16. *Preparing for the Chapter Challenge*
Describe how the law of conservation of energy applies to the sport you are going to describe in your voice-over. Include a specific example you might be able to use in your voice-over.

Section 9   Conservation of Energy: Defy Gravity

What Do You See?

Learning Outcomes

In this section, you will

- **Measure** changes in height of the body's center of mass during a vertical jump.

- **Calculate** changes in the gravitational potential energy of the body's center of mass during a vertical jump.

- **Apply** the definition of work.

- **Recognize** how work is related to energy.

- **Apply** the joule as a unit of work and energy using equivalent forms of the joule.

- **Describe** the concepts of work and conservation of energy to the analysis of a vertical jump, including weight, force, height, and time of flight.

What Do You Think?

No athlete can escape the pull of gravity.

- **Does the "hang time" of some athletes defy the pull of gravity?**

- **Does a world-class figure skater defy gravity to remain in the air long enough to do a triple axel?**

Record your ideas about these questions in your *Active Physics* log. Be prepared to discuss your responses with your small group and the class.

Investigate

In this *Investigate,* you will trace the energy conversions that take place as you jump vertically.

1. Your teacher will show you a slow-motion video of a world-class figure skater doing a triple axel jump. The image of the skater will appear to "jerk," because a video camera completes one "frame," or one complete picture every $\frac{1}{30}$ s. When the video is played at normal speed, you perceive the action as continuous. Played at slow motion, the individual frames can be detected and counted. The time interval between frames is $\frac{1}{30}$ s.

✎ a) As a class, count and record in your log the number of frames during which the skater is in the air.

✎ b) Calculate the skater's time in the air or "hang time." (Show your calculation in your log.)
Time in air (s) = (No. of frames) (¹⁄₃₀ s)

✎ c) Did the skater "hang" in the air during any part of the jump, appearing to "defy gravity"? If necessary, view the slow-motion sequence again to make the observations necessary to answer this question in your log. If your observations indicate that hanging did occur, be sure to indicate the exact frames during which it happened.

2. Your teacher will show you a similar slow-motion video of a basketball player whose hang time is believed by many fans to defy gravity.

✎ a) Using the same method as above for the skater, show in your log the data and calculations used to determine the player's hang time during the "slam dunk."

✎ b) Did the player hang? Cite evidence from the video in your answer.

3. How much force and energy do you use to do a vertical jump? You use body muscles to "launch" your body into the air, and, it is primarily your leg muscles that provide the force. First, analyze only the part of jumping that happens before your feet leave the ground. Find your body mass, in kilograms, and your body weight, in newtons, for later calculations. Remember, a mass of 1 kg

has a weight of about 10 N. If you do not wish to use data for your own body, you may use the data for another person or one of your favorite athletes. If you know your body weight in pounds, you can find your mass in kilograms:

• First convert your weight in pounds to newtons.
Weight (N) = Weight (lb) (4.38 N/lb)

• Use your body weight, in newtons, and the equation Weight = mg to calculate your body mass (m), in kilograms.

4. Every object has a point called the center of mass. This point is special because when a force is exerted on the object, the center of mass moves as if all the mass of the object were located there. Your center of mass is in the middle of your body near your waist. Place a patch of tape on either the right or left side of your clothing (above one hip) at waist level. Crouch as if you are ready to make a vertical jump. While crouched, have an assistant measure the vertical distance, in meters, from the floor to the level of your body's center of mass (C of M).

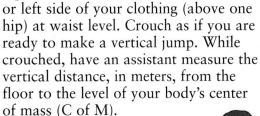
center of mass

✎ a) In your log, record the distance, in meters, from the floor to your C of M in the "ready position."

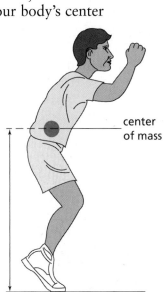
center of mass

5. Straighten your body and rise to your tiptoes as if you are ready to leave the floor to launch your body into a vertical jump, but don't jump yet.

Hold this launch position while an assistant measures the vertical distance from the floor to the level of your center of mass.

✎ a) In your log, record the distance, in meters, from the floor to your C of M in the "launch position."

✎ b) By subtraction, calculate and record the vertical height through which you use your leg muscles to provide the force to lift your center of mass from the "ready position" to the "launch position."

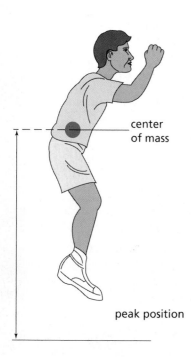

center of mass

peak position

6. Now it's time to jump! Have a group member ready to observe and measure the vertical height from the floor to the level of your center of mass at the peak of your jump. When your group member is ready to observe, jump straight up as high as you can. (Can you hang at the peak of your jump for a while to make it easier for your group member to observe the position of your center of mass? Try it, and see if your group member thinks you are successful.)

✎ a) In your log, record the distance from the floor to your C of M at the "peak position."

✎ b) By subtraction, calculate and record the vertical height through which your center of mass moved during the jump from the launch position to the peak position.

7. The jump can be analyzed at the three positions. In the ready position, you have only elastic potential energy (EPE). In the peak position, you have only gravitational potential energy (GPE). In the launch position, you have some GPE and some kinetic energy (KE).

✎ a) The best place to start to analyze your jump is the peak position. At this point in your jump, all the elastic potential energy you started with in the ready position has been transformed to gravitational potential energy. Use the equation $GPE = mgh$ where h is the distance between your peak position and your ready position. Calculate your gravitational potential energy at the peak position (in joules) and write it in your log.

✎ b) The next step is to realize that when you are in the ready position, all your energy is in the form of elastic potential energy. Therefore, the law of conservation of energy tells you that the amount of elastic potential energy in the ready position must equal the amount of gravitational potential energy in the peak position. Write this amount of energy in your log as your elastic potential energy (EPE).

✎ c) When you are in the launch position, the elastic potential energy you had in the ready position has been transformed into both gravitational potential energy and kinetic energy. Use the equation, $GPE = mgh$, where h is the distance between the ready position and the launch position.

Calculate your gravitational potential energy in the launch position. The law of conservation of energy tells you that the rest of the elastic potential energy in the ready position must be kinetic energy, so subtract the gravitational potential energy at the launch position from the elastic potential energy at the ready position to find the kinetic energy at the launch position.

Write both numbers in the proper places in your log. Compute the total energy at the launch position.

✎ d) The conservation of energy states that the total energy in the three positions should be equal. Create a chart that compares the sum of *GPE*, and *EPE*, and *KE* at the ready position, the launch position, and the peak position.

8. An ultrasonic ranging device coupled to a computer or graphing calculator, which can be used to monitor position, speed, acceleration, and time for moving objects, may be available at your school. If so, it can be used to monitor a person doing a vertical jump. This would provide interesting information to compare to the data and analysis that you have already done.

Physics Talk

CONSERVATION OF ENERGY

In this *Investigate*, you jumped and measured your vertical leap. You went through a chain of energy conversions where the total energy remained the same, in the absence of air resistance. You began by lifting your body from the crouched "ready position" to the "launch position." The work that you did was equal to the product of the applied force and the distance. The work done must have lifted you from the ready position to the launch position (an increase in gravitational potential energy) and also provided you with the speed to continue moving up (an increase in kinetic energy). After you left the ground, your body's gravitational potential energy continued to increase, and the kinetic energy decreased. Finally, you reached the "peak position" of your jump, where all of the energy became gravitational potential energy. On the way down, that gravitational potential energy began to decrease and the kinetic energy began to increase.

When you are in the ready position, you have elastic potential energy. If you were a spring, the elastic potential energy would be present due to compression of the material making up the spring. In your case, the potential energy you are going to use is present due to chemical reactions waiting to happen in your muscles. As you move toward the launch position, you have exchanged your elastic potential energy for an increase in

Energy→ Position↓	Elastic potential energy	Gravitational potential energy = mgh	Kinetic energy $= \frac{1}{2}mv^2$
ready position	maximum	0	0
launch position	0	some	maximum
peak position	0	maximum	0

gravitational potential energy and an increase in kinetic energy. As you rise in the air, you lose the kinetic energy and gain more gravitational potential energy. You can show this in a table.

The energy of the three positions must be equal. In this first table, the sum of the energies in each row must be equal.

→

Active Physics

The launch position has both gravitational potential energy and kinetic energy. Assume the total energy at each position is 410 J.

In the ready position, all 410 J is elastic potential energy. In the peak position, all 410 J is gravitational potential energy. In the launch position, the total energy is still 410 J but 150 J is gravitational potential energy and 260 J is kinetic energy.

Consider someone the same size, who can jump much higher. Since that person can jump much higher, the peak position is greater, and therefore the gravitational potential energy of the jumper is greater. In the example shown to the right, the gravitational potential energy is 600 J. Notice that this means the elastic potential energy of the jumper's legs must be 600 J. And when the jumper is in the launch position, the total energy (potential plus kinetic) is also 600 J.

Energy→ Position↓	Elastic potential energy	Gravitational potential energy = mgh	Kinetic energy $= \frac{1}{2}mv^2$
ready position	410 J	0	0
launch position	0	150 J	260 J
peak position	0	410 J	0

Energy→ Position↓	Elastic potential energy	Gravitational potential energy = mgh	Kinetic energy $= \frac{1}{2}mv^2$
ready position	600 J	0	0
launch position	0	150 J	450 J
peak position	0	600 J	0

A third person of the same size is not able to jump as high. What numbers should be placed in blank areas to preserve the principle of conservation of energy? Total energy must be conserved. Therefore, in the launch position the kinetic energy of the jumper must be 50 J. In the peak position, all the energy is gravitational potential energy and must be 200 J.

Energy→ Position↓	Elastic potential energy	Gravitational potential energy = mgh	Kinetic energy $= \frac{1}{2}mv^2$
ready position	200 J	0	0
launch position	0	150 J	
peak position	0		0

The conservation of energy is a unifying principle in all science. It is worthwhile to practice solving problems that will help you to see the variety of ways in which energy conservation appears.

A similar example to jumping from a hard floor into the air is jumping on a trampoline (or your bed, when you were younger). If you were to jump on the trampoline, the potential energy from the height you are jumping would provide kinetic energy when you landed on the trampoline. As you continued down, you would continue to have kinetic energy because you would still be losing gravitational potential energy. However, the trampoline bends and/or the springs holding the trampoline stretch. Either way, the trampoline or springs gain elastic potential energy at the expense of your kinetic energy and changes into gravitational potential energy.

Energy→ Position↓	Elastic potential energy	Gravitational potential energy = mgh	Kinetic energy $= \frac{1}{2}mv^2$
High in the air position	0	2300 J	0
Landing on the trampoline position	0	500 J	1800 J
Lowest point on the trampoline position	2300 J	0	0

The conservation of energy is one of the great discoveries of science. You can describe the type of energy in words (elastic potential energy, gravitational potential energy, and kinetic energy). There is also sound energy, light energy, chemical energy, electrical energy, nuclear energy, and the internal energy that reveals itself through temperature. These words, however, do not give the complete picture. Each type of energy can be measured and calculated. In a system not exchanging energy with objects external to it, the total of all the energies at any one time must equal the total of all the energies at any other time. That is what is meant by the conservation of energy.

If you choose to look at one object in the system, that one object can gain energy. For example, in the collision between a player's foot and a soccer ball, the soccer ball can gain kinetic energy and move faster. Whatever energy the ball gained, you can be sure that the foot lost an equal amount of energy. The ball gained energy, the foot lost energy, and the "ball and foot" total energy remained the same. The ball gained energy because work (force on the ball over a distance in the same direction) was done on it. The foot lost energy because negative work (force on the foot over a distance in opposite directions) was done on it. The total system of "ball and foot" neither gained nor lost energy.

Physics provides you with the means to calculate energies. You may wish to practice some of these calculations now. Never lose sight of the fact that you can calculate the energies because the sum of all of the energies remains the same.

Active Physics

Sample Problem

A trainer lifts a 5.0-kg equipment bag from the floor to the shelf of a locker. The locker shelf is 1.6 m off the floor.

a) How much force will be required to lift the bag off the floor?

b) How much work will be done in lifting the bag to the shelf?

c) How much potential energy does the bag have as it sits on the shelf?

d) If the bag falls off the shelf, how fast will it be going when it hits the floor?

Strategy: This problem has several parts. It may look complicated, but if you follow it step-by-step, it should not be difficult to solve.

Given:

$$m = 5.0 \text{ kg}$$

$$h = 1.6 \text{ m}$$

$$a = 9.8 \text{ m/s}^2$$

Strategy:

a) Why does it take a force to lift the bag? It takes a force because the trainer must act against the pull of the gravitational field of Earth. This force is called weight, and you can solve for it using Newton's second law.

Solution:

$$F = ma = w$$
$$= (5.0 \text{ kg})(9.8 \text{ m/s}^2)$$
$$= 49 \text{ kg} \cdot \text{m/s}^2 \text{ or } 49 \text{ N}$$

A force of 49 N is required to lift the bag.

Strategy:

b) The information you need to find the work done on an object is the force exerted on it and the distance it travels. The distance was given and you calculated the force needed. Use the equation for work.

Solution:

$$W = F \cdot d$$
$$= (49 \text{ N})(1.6 \text{ m})$$
$$= 78.4 \text{ N} \cdot \text{m or } 78 \text{ J}$$

The work done lifting the bag is 78 J.

Strategy:

c) The amount of potential energy depends on the mass of the object, the acceleration due to gravity, and the height of the object above what is designated as zero height (in this case, the floor). You have all the needed pieces of information, so you can apply the equation for potential energy.

Solution:

$$GPE = mgh$$
$$= (5.0 \text{ kg})(9.8 \text{ m/s}^2)(1.6 \text{ m})$$
$$= 78.4 \text{ kg} \bullet \text{m}^2/\text{s}^2 \text{ or } 78 \text{ J}$$

Should you be surprised that this is the same answer as *Part b)*? No, because you are familiar with energy conservation. You know that the work is what gave the bag the potential energy it has. So, in the absence of work that may be converted to internal energy because of friction, which you did not have in this case, the work equals the potential energy.

Strategy:

d) The bag has some potential energy. When it falls off the shelf, the potential energy becomes kinetic energy as it falls. Just before it strikes the ground in its fall, it has zero potential energy and all kinetic energy. You calculated the potential energy. Conservation of energy tells you that the kinetic energy will be equal to the potential energy. You know the mass of the bag so you can calculate the velocity with the kinetic energy formula.

Solution:

$$KE = \frac{1}{2}mv^2$$

You can use your calculator to find a value for *v*, such that:

$$78 \text{ J} = \frac{1}{2}mv^2$$

or you can practice your algebra and solve for *v*

$$v^2 = \frac{KE}{\frac{1}{2}m}$$
$$= \frac{78 \text{ J}}{\frac{1}{2}(5.0 \text{ kg})}$$
$$= 31 \text{ m}^2/\text{s}^2$$
$$v = \sqrt{31 \text{ m}^2/\text{s}^2}$$
$$= 5.6 \text{ m/s}$$

The bag will be traveling 5.6 m/s when it hits the ground.

Checking Up

1. Where does the energy come from that allows the jumper to move from the ready position to the launch position?

2. In the launch position, what types of energy will the student have? What types of energy will the student have at the peak of the jump?

3. What are three other types of energy beside potential and kinetic?

Active Physics

Plus

+Math	+Depth	+Concepts	+Exploration
◆	◆		

Kinetic Energy as a Scalar Quantity

One of the fascinating aspects of kinetic energy is that it is a scalar quantity. It makes no difference what direction an object is going. All objects with the same mass and speed have the same amount of kinetic energy, regardless of the directions of their motions. Objects moving on frictionless tracks frequently change directions. In computing the kinetic energy, this makes no difference. Just use speed to find kinetic energy and don't worry about direction.

1. A roller coaster is poised at the top of a hill 50 m high.

   a) How fast will it be going when it goes over the top of the next hill on the track that is only 30 m high?

   b) From a practical point of view, why is it advantageous that this ride is mass independent?

2. A water balloon (m = 300 g) is launched horizontally from a platform 2 m above the ground with a slingshot. The slingshot (k = 60 N/m) is stretched 40 cm before launch. How far from the platform will the balloon strike the ground?

3. In a motorcycle jumping exhibition, a rider zooms down an incline starting 25 m off the ground at rest. At the bottom of the incline the track slopes upward and ends 5 m above the ground, at which point the motorcycle is airborne. The mass of the motorcycle and rider is 200 kg. While on the track, the motorcycle receives 200,000 J of energy from the engine and loses 50,000 J to friction. To what height above the ground does the motorcycle ascend when airborne if its horizontal velocity at the highest point while airborne is 40 m/s?

What Do You Think Now?

At the beginning of this section, you were asked

- **Does the "hang time" of some athletes defy the pull of gravity?**

- **Does a world-class figure skater defy gravity to remain in the air long enough to do a triple axel?**

How would you answer these questions now that you have closely analyzed a jump? Do world-class athletes defy gravity in any way during a slam dunk or a triple axel?

Physics
Essential Questions

What does it mean?

How can a jump be described as an example of the conservation of energy?

How do you know?

Conservation of energy is not merely a description of *GPE*, *EPE*, and *KE*. Each of these energies can be calculated. How did you calculate the total energy of your jump?

Why do you believe?

Connects with Other Physics Content	Fits with Big Ideas in Science	Meets Physics Requirements
Force and motion	✳ Conservation laws	Good, clear, explanation, no more complex than necessary

✳ The conservation of energy is a major organizing principle of all science. This theory is one of the great achievements of science. When someone throws a baseball straight up, the ball gains kinetic energy, *KE*, which gets converted into gravitational potential energy, *GPE*. How can you say that energy is conserved if the ball began with no energy and then gained *KE* and *GPE*?

Why should you care?

Physics says that objects on the surface of Earth cannot "defy gravity." Therefore, this must be true for all sports events. Give an example from your sport in which it is clear that the motion of a person or object is exactly what physics says it has to be.

Reflecting on the Section and the Challenge

Work, the force applied by an athlete to cause an object to move (the athlete's own body can be the object in some cases), multiplied by the distance the object moves while the athlete is applying the force explains many things in sports. For example, the vertical speed of any jumper's takeoff (which determines height and "hang time") is determined by the amount of work done against gravity by the jumper's muscles before takeoff. You will be able to find many other examples of work in action in sports videos, and now you will be able to explain them. In creating a description of a sporting event, you may decide to describe the work done and then move to a description of the energy transformations — how kinetic energy may become gravitational potential energy.

Physics to Go

1. Calculate the work a male figure skater does when lifting a 50-kg female skating partner's body a vertical distance of 1 m in a pairs competition, if she does nothing to propel herself upward and just lets him lift her.

2. Describe the energy transformations during a bobsled run, beginning with team members pushing to start the sled and ending when the brake is applied to stop the sled after crossing the finish line. Include both work and energy in your answer and ignore friction.

3. Suppose that a person who saw the video of the basketball player used in the *Investigate* said, "He really can hang in the air. I've seen him do it. Maybe he was just having a 'bad hang day' when the video was taken, or maybe the speed of the recording or playback was not accurate." How might you and the person go about seeing if the person's statements are correct?

4. If someone claims that a law of physics can be defied or violated, should they be required to provide observable evidence, or should someone else need to prove that the claim is not true? Who do you think should have the burden of proof? Discuss this issue within your group and write your own personal opinion in your log.

5. Identify and discuss two ways in which an athlete can increase his or her maximum vertical jump height.

6. Calculate the amount of work, in joules, done when a:

   a) 1.0-N weight is lifted a vertical distance of 1.0 m.

   b) 1.0-N weight is lifted a vertical distance of 10 m.

   c) 10-N weight is lifted a vertical distance of 1.0 m.

   d) 0.10-N weight is lifted a vertical distance of 100 m.

   e) 100-N weight is lifted a distance of 0.10 m.

7. List how much gravitational potential energy, in joules, each of the weights in *Question* 6 above would have after being lifted.

8. List how much kinetic energy, in joules, each of the weights in *Questions* 6 and 7 would have at the instant before striking the ground if dropped.

9. How much work is done on a go-cart if you push it with a force of 50.0 N parallel to its path and move it a distance of 43 m, ignoring any friction that may exist?

10. What is the kinetic energy of a 62-kg cyclist if she is moving on her bicycle at 8.2 m/s?

11. A net force of 30.00 N acts on a 5.00-kg wagon that is initially at rest.

    a) What is the acceleration of the wagon?

    b) If the wagon travels 18.75 m, what is the work done on the wagon?

Active Physics

12. Assume you do 40,000 J of work by applying a force of 3200 N to a 1200-kg car (ignore friction).

    a) How far does the car move during the time you are doing work on it?

    b) What is the acceleration of the car?

13. A baseball (m = 150.0 g) is traveling at 40.0 m/s. How much work must be done to stop the ball?

14. A boat exerts a force of 417 N pulling a water skier (m = 64.0 kg) from rest. The skier's speed becomes 15.0 m/s. Over what distance was this force exerted?

15. Create a chart showing the *GPE*, *EPE*, and *KE* and their sum at different positions for a pole vault (running, full bend of the pole while on the ground, peak height, landing, and collapsing on the cushion).

16. Create a chart showing the *GPE*, *EPE*, and *KE* and their sum at different positions for a person on a trampoline (at peak height, upon landing on the trampoline, and at lowest point of the trampoline).

17. Create a chart showing the *GPE*, *EPE*, and *KE* and their sum at different positions for a skier at the top, middle, and bottom of a slope.

18. ***Preparing for the Chapter Challenge***
    Use the law of conservation of energy to prepare an exciting voice-over for one part of the action in the video you have selected to use.

Physics You Learned

Physics Concepts	Is There an Equation?
When an object is moving, it will continue to move at constant speed in a straight line unless there is an unbalanced force to change its motion. If the object is at rest, it stays at rest unless there is an unbalanced force. This is known as **Newton's first law**.	
The tendency of an object to resist changing its motion is called **inertia**. Inertia is measured in the same units as mass.	
A **frame of reference** is the specific point of view from which a particular measurement is made. Different frames of reference yield different measurements.	
The acceleration is defined as the change in velocity with respect to time.	$a = \dfrac{\Delta v}{\Delta t}$
A **force** is measured in the SI unit newtons.	
The acceleration of an object (a) is directly proportional to the net force applied (F_{net}), and inversely proportional to the object's mass (m). This is known as **Newton's second law**.	$a = \dfrac{F_{net}}{m}$
The weight (F_g) of an object is equal to an object's mass (m) multiplied by the strength of Earth's gravitational field (g). Weight is the force of Earth's gravity acting on an object.	$F_g = mg$
Using significant figures ensures that any calculations made do not indicate a level of precision greater than the measurements.	
Active Physics Plus The net force (F_{net}) on an object in equilibrium is zero. When an object is in equilibrium (either at rest or traveling with constant velocity) the vector sum of all the forces acting on the object equals zero.	$F_{net} = 0$
Active Physics Plus When forces act at right angles on the same body, the net force is determined by using the **Pythagorean theorem**.	$F_{net} = \sqrt{\left(F_1^2 + F_2^2\right)}$
The shape of a projectile's path is a **parabola** if there is no air resistance.	
Active Physics Plus The vertical velocity and the horizontal velocity of an object are independent of one another, and can be used separately to determine aspects of a projectile's flight. The total velocity can be calculated from the horizontal and vertical components using the Pythagorean theorem.	$v = \sqrt{\left(v_y^2 + v_x^2\right)}$
The horizontal distance traveled by a projectile (d_{horiz}) equals the projectile's horizontal speed (v_{horiz}) multiplied by the time of flight. The vertical distance covered by a projectile (d_{vert}) depends upon the acceleration due to gravity (a_g) and the time the object is in flight (t) squared. The horizontal and vertical motions of a projectile are independent of each other.	$d_{horiz} = \left(v_{horiz}\right)t$ $d_{vert} = \frac{1}{2}a_g t^2$

Active Physics

The maximum range of a projectile returning to the same height as the launch point occurs when it is launched at 45° degrees to the horizontal.	
Active Physics Plus When an object is projected at an angle to the horizontal, the motion may be analyzed after the velocity is broken into vertical and horizontal components.	
Forces come in pairs. Whenever a force is exerted on a mass b $(F_{a \text{ on } b})$, the mass b exerts an equal force in the opposite direction on the mass a $(-F_{b \text{ on } a})$. This is known as **Newton's third law.**	$(F_{a \text{ on } b} = -F_{b \text{ on } a})$
The normal force is a force that acts perpendicular to a surface.	
A **free-body diagram** is a sketch of all the forces acting on an object.	
The force of friction (F_f) equals the coefficient of friction (μ) multiplied by the normal force (F_N). Friction is a force acting between two bodies in contact that resists the relative motion of those bodies. It always acts parallel to the surfaces in contact.	$F_f = \mu F_N$
The coefficient of friction (μ) is a dimensionless constant.	
Active Physics Plus The coefficient of static friction (μ_s) on an inclined plane equals the tangent of the angle the plane makes with the horizontal $(\tan\theta)$.	$\mu_s = \tan\theta$
An object's **kinetic energy** (KE) is proportional to the object's mass (m) multiplied by its velocity squared (v^2). Kinetic energy is an object's energy of motion.	$KE = \frac{1}{2}mv^2$
Gravitational potential energy (GPE) is proportional to an object's mass (m) multiplied by its vertical height above Earth (Δh) and the acceleration due to gravity (g). Gravitational potential energy is energy due to an object's vertical position above Earth's surface.	$GPE = mg\Delta h$
Elastic potential energy (EPE) is proportional to the spring constant of the material (k) multiplied by the material's change in length (x) squared. Elastic potential energy is energy stored in a material due to its compression or stretch.	$EPE = \frac{1}{2}kx^2$
Active Physics Plus Work (W) done on an object can increase its kinetic energy (ΔKE). When work is done on an object moving on a horizontal surface, the kinetic energy of the object increases.	$W = \Delta KE$ $= \left(\frac{1}{2}mv_f^2 - \frac{1}{2}mv_i^2\right)$
Work (W) is the product of the force exerted on an object (F), and the displacement in the direction of the force (d). Work done on an object increases its energy and may change an object's kinetic or potential energy.	$W = Fd$
The **law of conservation of energy** states that energy may change its forms, but not its amount. The total amount of energy remains the same during any changes in form.	$Energy_{\text{before}} = Energy_{\text{after}}$

Physics
Chapter Challenge

You will now be completing a second cycle of the *Engineering Design Cycle* as you prepare for the *Chapter Challenge*. The goals and criteria remain unchanged. However, your list of *Inputs* has grown.

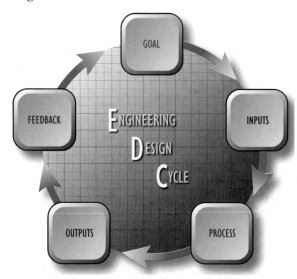

Goal

Your challenge for this chapter is to create a voice-over for an exciting sports event that will educate an audience on the physics behind the action. Review the *Goal* as a class to make sure you are familiar with all the criteria and constraints.

Inputs

You now have additional physics information to help you identify and analyze the various physics concepts that apply to sports activities. You have completed all the sections of this chapter and learned the physics content you will need to complete your challenge. This is part of the *Input* phase of the *Engineering Design Cycle*. Your group needs to apply these physics concepts to put together your presentation.

You also have the additional *Input* of your own personal experience with sports as well as the feedback you received following your *Mini-Challenge* presentation.

Section 1 You investigated Galileo's law of inertia and learned how it relates to the mass of an object. You read about Newton's first law and learned about reference frames for measuring the speed of an object.

Section 2 You measured speed by making speed vs. time graphs using a ticker timer for objects with constant speeds and changing speeds. You also explored the concept of acceleration, or the rate at which speed increases or decreases.

Section 3 You investigated the relationship between forces on an object and the acceleration and change in velocity that they produce. You also read about Newton's second law, which helps to calculate the unbalanced force, mass, or acceleration of an object.

Section 4 You used models to learn about the horizontal and vertical motion of a projectile. You also explored how the horizontal speed and total height of a projectile affects the horizontal distance that it travels.

Section 5 You measured constant acceleration due to gravity and discovered how it causes all objects to speed up as they fall toward Earth. You also used calculations and models to describe the trajectory, or path, of a projectile.

Section 6 You studied examples of force pairs and considered Newton's third law as an explanation for the forces caused by inanimate objects. You also learned to use force diagrams to clearly represent forces on objects.

Section 7 You measured the force of sliding friction between a sports shoe and various surfaces and calculated the coefficient of sliding friction for the different combinations. You also studied the impact of friction on the movement of objects.

Section 8 You explored the idea of conservation of energy and tracked energy through a system as it changed from potential to kinetic, back to potential, and so on. You also learned that energy could be stored by stretching or bending objects and that restorative forces could transform that stored energy back into motion.

Section 9 You calculated work and gravitational potential energy changes for objects that are lifted and learned that gravity applies a constant force on objects moving near the surface of Earth.

Process

In the *Process* phase, you must decide what information you have that you will use to meet the *Goal*. Deciding what physics topics to include is the first step. Select sports footage that is exciting in terms of game play or competition between rivals. Three minutes of exciting sports action from almost any sport will have examples of most of the physics topics you have studied in this chapter. You may want to watch your film several times and simply list the examples that you see. Once you have a list, try to pick about five that are equally spaced throughout the clip. If you use a computer-based video, you may be able to use slow motion and replay certain features to highlight them.

Gather data that will allow you to calculate the magnitude, or size, of forces, masses, and accelerations that you plan to focus on in your sports action. Make sure you know the SI units for each quantity and include a sample calculation for any estimates you make. For example, if you can find the mass of a baseball and time how long it takes to travel a distance on the field, you can estimate its speed and the size of the force required for the pitcher or the batter to accelerate it to get it to that speed in a limited amount of time.

Once you have selected the five examples, have a person in your group write a short script for each one. Then arrange the scripts into one narrative and see what it sounds like. Refine the script each time you practice. You may consider inserting some humor or dramatic narration for emphasis and entertainment. After all, people are not usually watching sports for its educational content. You will not get the job if you cannot keep the viewers in their seats. Manage your time to make sure your group has an opportunity to rehearse before you present. If you are going to record the narration, you may need extra time to edit the final product. Even the experts make mistakes during live narrations!

Outputs

Presenting your information to the class is your design-cycle *Output*. You will provide an auditory sample for the class either through a live reading of the script or a replay of your recorded narration. Some ad-libbing will be fine for entertainment value, but a purely unscripted narration will score very poorly for this challenge.

Feedback

Your classmates will give you *Feedback* on the overall appeal and the accuracy of your presentation, based on the criteria of the design challenge. This feedback will likely become part of your grade but could also be useful for additional design iterations. Remember that you will be viewing other design solutions for the same challenge. The different design solutions may represent feedback in the form of alternative ways you might have solved the problem. No design is perfect; there is always room for optimization or improvement. From your experience with the *Mini-Challenge*, you can see how the design cycle is structured to continuously refine almost any idea.

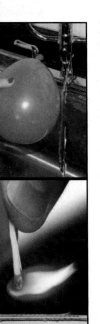

Here are some examples of how the concepts you studied in this chapter relate to other sciences.

Newton's First Law – Inertia

Biology Animals with large body mass are generally unable to change direction quickly when in motion. Smaller animals can often elude their larger predators by making sharp turns while moving quickly.

Chemistry Massive molecules diffuse more slowly than less massive ones, allowing chemists to separate molecules and atoms by mass.

Earth Science When tectonic plates collide, the inertia of their combined mass can cause mountain ranges to rise at the point of intersection.

Newton's Second Law

Biology A flea is able to exert tremendous force for its size, allowing it to accelerate its body into huge jumps, up to 13 in. (33 cm), or 200 times the length of their bodies.

Chemistry The electric force of attraction between water molecules causes them to accelerate and join, forming water droplets.

Earth Science The force of gravity causes water to accelerate as it passes over a waterfall, increasing the erosive power of the water at the bottom of the fall.

Newton's Third Law

Biology An octopus propels itself through water by shooting out a forceful stream of water similar to jet exhaust. The reaction force of the ejected water on the octopus may cause an acceleration of up to 30 m/s^2.

Chemistry When an atom of gas in a balloon strikes the inner surface of the balloon, the force the balloon wall exerts on the atom to change its direction is equal to the force the atom exerts on the balloon. It is this combined force of countless atoms that keeps the balloon inflated.

Earth Science When a hurricane strikes land, the wind exerts tremendous force on topographical features and objects on the land. The reaction force of these objects on the moving air causes it to slow down, which is why hurricanes eventually dissipate as they move over land.

Projectile Motion

Biology Seagulls will often drop clamshells onto rocks to break them open, demonstrating a natural understanding of projectiles.

Chemistry The force of gravity causes settling of insoluble particles in a mixture with water. This is enhanced by spinning of a centrifuge.

Earth Science Volcanic eruptions often blast large rocks into the air. These rocks behave as projectiles, and their landing place may be accurately predicted.

Friction

Biology Air friction limits the speed at which a bird can fly. Friction, exerted as drag, pushes against the outstretched skin of a flying squirrel, allowing it to land safely after jumping from a high tree.

Chemistry Frictional forces provide the activation energy required to begin many chemical processes, such as the lighting of a match.

Earth Science The force of friction between tectonic plates holds them in place as they attempt to slide past each other. When this friction is eventually overcome, earthquakes often result from the sudden, rapid movement of the plates.

Conservation of Energy

Biology The chemical energy in the food a frog eats is converted into potential energy in its leg muscles. When the frog jumps, this energy is transformed into kinetic energy.

Chemistry When two atoms bond together, their electric potential energy decreases and their kinetic energy increases by the same amount.

Earth Science Earth continually receives energy from the Sun and radiates energy back out to the universe at the same rate. But the usefulness, or quality, of energy received from the Sun and that radiated by Earth; is greater. This is important for the continuance of events on Earth, which are characterized by energy conversions to forms that are less useful, or of lower quality. The higher quality energy received from the Sun compensates for the loss of energy quality in energy conversions on Earth.

A. Dean Bell

Writer/Director; New York, NY

A. Dean Bell is an award-winning filmmaker, television writer, director, and producer. He wrote and directed the highly acclaimed show *SportsFigures* that aired on ESPN for 12 years.

SportsFigures is an educational television series designed to teach the principles of physics and mathematics through sports. Bell, having never even taken physics in high school while growing up in Rochester, New York, said he was not worried that he lacked a physics background when it came to writing and directing the show. "I was learning physics from the show's advisors and I felt that my discovery process could be translated into the show," he said.

SportsFigures won four Clarion Awards for best children's television program, and a number of Parents' Choice Awards. Bell knew that when *SportsFigures* was awarded these crowning achievements, his aim to combine education and entertainment had been achieved.

SportsFigures may have taped its last season, but it is still shown in reruns on *Cable In The Classroom*. "It is also used and available in school libraries across the country," said Bell.

Bell is also an assistant professor at SUNY Purchase, New York, his alma mater, where he has been teaching directing and screenwriting since 1995. "I tell my college students that as writers, don't hesitate to take that science course. You just might need to do something like write and direct a television series that teaches physics someday."

Rick Angelo

Producer, ESPN; Fairfield, CT

Rick Angelo began his career in sports television in 1995. Today, Angelo produces games for all college sports for ESPN.

Angelo believes physics plays a phenomenal role in his job. "Everything with sports has something to do with physics," he said. Producers use graphics and animation of the players to show a viewer the athleticism of the athlete. "We will use graphics to show the speed of a ball and what makes it the perfect pitch, to show the viewer what phenomenal athletes they are watching," said Angelo. "Physics enhances our stories about the athletes."

Sandra Giddins

Community Center Director and former Professional Athlete & Coach; Queens, NY

Sandra Giddins grew up in Yonkers, New York and started playing basketball at the age of nine. She played Division I basketball at Cheney University in Pennsylvania on a four-year scholarship. Her athletic career lasted less than two years after suffering a knee injury while playing in Brazil. "I went up for a rebound and came down and my whole knee just twisted," recalled Giddins. Giddins stated that physics and athletics go hand-in-hand. For example, many female basketball players often injure their knees while jumping, due to their low center of gravity. To avert injury, female athletes need to pay attention to their body's center of mass.

Physics

Practice Test

Before you try the Physics Practice Test, *you may want to review sections 1-7, where you will find* **29 Checking Up** *questions,* **7 What Do You Think Now?** *questions,* **28 Physics Essential Questions,** **77 Physics to Go** *questions, and* **11 Inquiring Further** *questions.*

Content Review

1. A cart is rolling along a frictionless, horizontal surface. Which of the following describes the motion of the cart as it continues to roll along the surface?
   a) The cart will slow down as it runs out of the forward force.
   b) The cart will continue to roll with constant speed.
   c) The cart will continue to roll with constant speed only if it is rolling downhill.
   d) The cart will slow down as it uses up its speed.

2. Which object has the most inertia?
   a) a 0.001-kg bumblebee traveling at 2 m/s
   b) a 0.1-kg baseball traveling at 20 m/s
   c) a 5-kg bowling ball traveling at 3 m/s
   d) a 10-kg tricycle at rest

3. An athlete walks with a piece of ticker tape attached to herself with the tape timer running, and produces the tape shown below.

   beginning

   According to the tape, she was traveling with
   a) constant velocity.
   b) positive acceleration.
   c) negative acceleration.
   d) constant velocity, then negative acceleration.

4. A track coach with a meter stick and a stopwatch is trying to determine if a student is walking with constant speed. He should
   a) measure the walker's speed at regular intervals to see if it is always the same.
   b) measure the total distance the student travels and the total time to get the average speed.
   c) measure the beginning and ending speeds only to see if they are the same.
   d) use the meter stick to measure the student's stride length and time how long it takes to take one step.

5. If a cart is traveling with uniform negative acceleration, what conclusions can be drawn about the forces acting on the cart?
   a) The cart must be frictionless.
   b) The cart must be rolling downhill.
   c) The cart must have a net unbalanced force acting on it.
   d) No force is needed; the cart will naturally slow down.

6. A student wants to set up an experiment to determine the effect of a net force on an object's acceleration. To do this, she should
   a) vary the force acting on the object and the mass of the object at the same time.
   b) vary the mass of the object, but not the force acting on the object.
   c) vary the force acting on the object, but not the object's mass.
   d) keep both the force acting on the mass and the mass of the object constant as it rolls along a horizontal surface.

7. A 2-kg block is dropped from the roof of a tall building at the same time a 6-kg ball is thrown horizontally from the same height. Which statement best describes the motion of the block and the motion of the ball? (Disregard air resistance.)
   a) The 2-kg block hits the ground first because it has no horizontal velocity.
   b) The 6-kg ball hits the ground first because it has more mass.
   c) The 6-kg ball hits the ground first because it is round.
   d) The block and the ball hit the ground at the same time because they have the same vertical acceleration.

Active Physics

8. A pitching machine launches a baseball horizontally with no spin. Which of the following statements correctly describes the ball's motion in the air as the launch speed is increased?
    a) The ball's acceleration increases, and the distance it falls in one second decreases.
    b) The ball's acceleration remains the same, and the distance the ball falls in one second decreases.
    c) The ball's acceleration remains the same, and the distance the ball falls in one second increases.
    d) The ball's acceleration remains the same, and the distance the ball falls in one second remains the same.

9. A punter on a football team can kick the ball at an angle of either 30° or 80°. If he wants to maximize both the amount of time the ball spends in the air and the distance the ball travels, at which angle should he kick the ball?
    a) the 30° angle because the ball goes further
    b) the 80° angle because the ball goes further
    c) the 30° angle because the ball spends more time in the air
    d) the 80° angle because the ball spends more time in the air

10. A student is holding a book that has a weight of 20 N in his hand while sitting in a chair. The man claims that the book must be attracting Earth with a force of 20 N. His claim must be
    a) false because books do not attract objects.
    b) false because Earth is much larger than the book.
    c) true because the book has more inertia than Earth.
    d) true due to Newton's third law of action-reaction.

11. Which diagram of a 5-kg mass resting on a table correctly represents the force of the table on the mass?

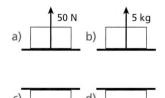

12. Two students have a "tug-of-war" on a smooth gym floor. One student has a mass of 70 kg and is wearing socks, but no athletic shoes. The other student has a mass of 60 kg and is wearing athletic shoes. The student most likely to win will be
    a) the 60-kg student because he can pull harder on the 70-kg student.
    b) the 70-kg student because he can pull harder on the 60-kg student.
    c) the 60-kg student because he experiences a greater frictional force with the floor.
    d) the 70-kg student because he experiences a greater frictional force with the floor.

13. Automobiles with front-wheel drive that have the engine located over the drive wheels have better traction in snow than automobiles with rear-wheel drive. This is most likely because
    a) the tires on front-wheel drive automobiles have a higher coefficient of friction than rear-wheel drive automobiles.
    b) the front tires encounter the snow first.
    c) the front tires have a higher normal force than the rear-wheel tires because the engine is heavier than the rear of the automobile.
    d) the front wheels are used for steering.

14. A student whose mass is 60 kg and a bicycle with a mass of 20 kg are at rest on a horizontal road. The student exerts a force of 120 N to accelerate the bike over a distance of 48 meters. What is the velocity of the bicycle and rider at the end of the 48 meters?
    a) 3 m/s
    b) 6 m/s
    c) 8 m/s
    d) 12 m/s

15. A basketball player is able to jump to a vertical height of 1.25 m. A student calculates that the player must have left the floor with a velocity of 5 m/s. The student can prove this claim by using
    a) conservation of energy.
    b) the principle of friction.
    c) Newton's third law of motion.
    d) the principle of inertia.

Practice Test *(continued)*

Critical Thinking

16. Design an experiment to measure the coefficient of friction between a steel block and the surface of your classroom lab table.
    a) What measuring tools will you need?
    b) What measurements will you take to determine the coefficient of friction?
    c) Show how you will use this data to calculate the coefficient of friction.

17. When you sit on a park bench, the bench exerts an upward force on you.
    a) Compare the force exerted by the park bench on you to your weight.
    b) Explain how the bench is able to provide the force required.

18. During an activity to measure how high a student can jump, the following measurements were made by the student's lab partners:
    • Mass = 65 kg
    • Increase in height of the student's center of mass during jump from the crouched down (ready) position = 0.60 m
    • Change in height from the ready position to the exact point where the student's feet leave the ground = 0.35 m
    a) How much gravitational potential energy did the student have at the peak of the jump?
    b) How much spring potential energy did the student's legs have as he was crouched in the ready position?
    c) Explain why the kinetic energy the student had as he left the ground was less than the spring potential energy when in the crouched down, ready position.

19. A ball is kicked horizontally off a tall building as shown.
    a) Draw a sketch of the ball's positions at 0.1 s intervals for the first 0.4 s as the ball falls to the ground.
    b) Draw arrows to represent the ball's horizontal velocity at positions described in *a)*.
    c) Draw arrows to represent the ball's acceleration for the positions described in *a)*.
    d) Draw arrows to represent the ball's vertical velocity in the positions described in *a)*.

20. Before leaving Earth, the mass of an astronaut is measured to be 60 kg. The astronaut lands on the Moon and measures the acceleration of gravity to be 1.6 m/s^2.
    a) What would the astronaut's weight be on Earth?
    b) What would the astronaut's weight be on the Moon?
    c) What would the astronaut's mass be on the Moon?
    d) Explain your answers to *a)* and *b)* using Newton's second law.

21. Four forces act on a 10-kg mass as shown in the diagram. What would the acceleration of the mass be?

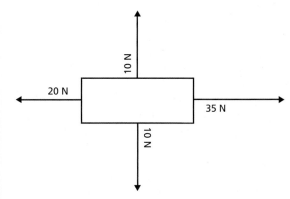

22. A soccer ball is kicked so that at the peak of its trajectory it has a horizontal speed of 15 m/s, and is 5 m above the ground. How far away from the kicker does the soccer ball land?

23. A motorcycle rider starts out on top of a ramp 10 m high, and then rides down and jumps the motorcycle as shown. The rider is at the peak of his jump at 5 m. How fast is the motorcycle going horizontally at this point?

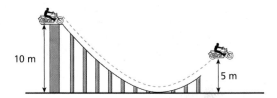

SAFETY

Chapter 3

Safety

Scenario

Traveling can be dangerous. The need to get to a destination quickly and the large number of people and vehicles on the move have made traveling hazardous. There is a greater chance of being killed or injured while traveling than during any other common activity. Realizing this risk, manufacturers of vehicles and governments have begun to take action to alter the statistics. New safety systems have been designed and put into use in automobiles, trains, and airplanes. New laws and an awareness of safety are working together with these systems to reduce the danger in traveling.

What are these new safety systems? You are probably familiar with many of them. In this chapter, you will become even more familiar with some of these systems. Could you design or even build a better safety device for an automobile or a plane? Many students around the country have been doing just that and with great success!

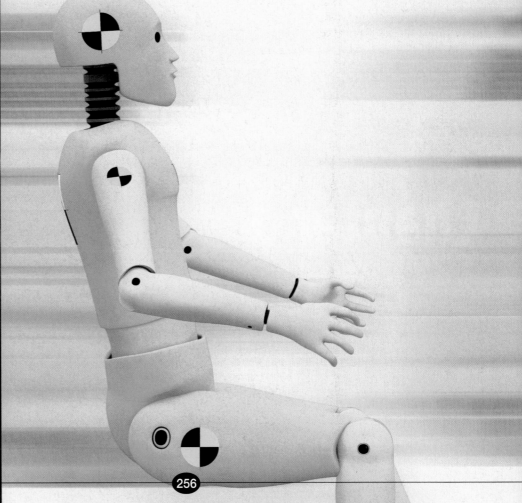

Your Challenge

Your design team will develop a safety system for protecting automobile, airplane, bicycle, motorcycle, or train passengers during a collision. To illustrate this safety system, you will design and build a prototype safety system to protect an egg in a moving cart that undergoes a collision.

When the design teams bring their final products to class, all teams will display their safety systems around the room. Each design team will give a five-minute oral report. Each design team will also be asked to submit a written and/or multimedia report.

Each safety system will also be tested in a collision. Your class as a whole will determine what kind of collision the egg-carrying cart will undergo. It could be a collision with another cart, or it could be a collision with a stationary object. Your class will also decide how fast the carts will be moving prior to the collision. As in real life, you will not be certain about the details of the collision that you are going to have to protect against when you design your system.

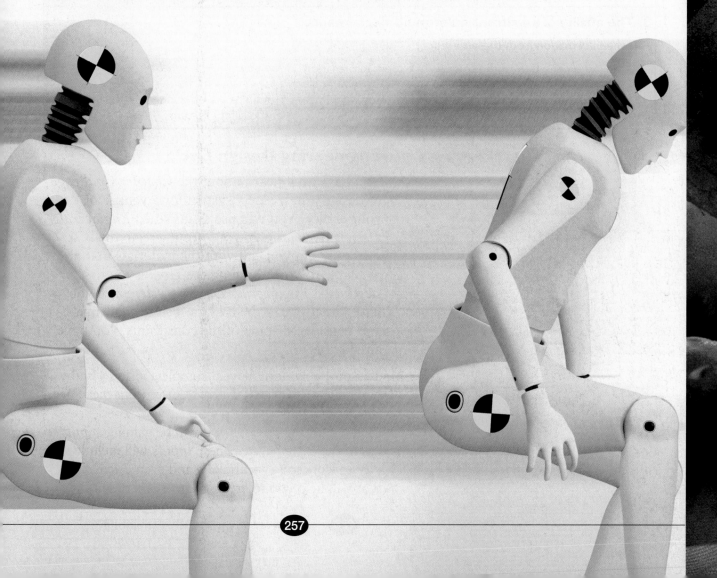

Criteria for Success

You and your classmates will work with your teacher to define the criteria for evaluating your safety system, your presentation, and your written report. After discussion about what features should be included in the grading of each part of the project, you should then read some of the suggestions below. Then you will determine the relative importance of the assessment criteria. Next, assign point values to each. The following are suggestions of point values for each part.

Standard for Excellence	
1. **The quality of your safety-system model or prototype, and the ability of the prototype to protect the egg during the collision**	**40 points**
2. **The quality of a five-minute oral report** • the need for the system • the method used to develop the working model • the demonstration of the working model • the discussion of the physics concepts involved • the description of the next-generation version of the system • the answers to questions posed by the class	**30 points**
3. **The quality of a written and/or multimedia report** • the information from the oral report • the documentation of the sources of expert information • the discussion of consumer acceptance and market potential • the discussion of the physics concepts applied in the design of the safety system	**30 points**

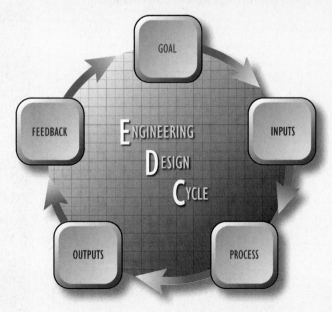

Engineering Design Cycle

You have now heard about the *Chapter Challenge* to design a new safety system for a vehicle of your choice. You will use a simplified *Engineering Design Cycle* to help your group create the best safety system you can with the materials that are available to you. Defining the *Goal* is the first step in the *Engineering Design Cycle*. Since you have already read the criteria for the challenge and considered some of the constraints, you have already begun.

You probably don't have a complete vision of how you will create your safety system yet, but the chapter sections will help you. As you experience each one of the sections you will be gaining *Inputs* to use in the design cycle. These *Inputs* will include new physics concepts, vocabulary, and even calculations that will help you to create a successful design.

During the *Process* step you will combine *Inputs* with your ideas, consider design criteria, compare and contrast potential solutions, and most importantly, make safety-system design decisions.

The first of your *Outputs* in your design cycle will be the safety-system concepts that your group presents to the class as part of the *Mini-Challenge*, including any models, diagrams, and charts you may use to clarify the information you present.

Finally, you will receive *Feedback* from your classmates and your teacher about what parts of your presentation are accurate and which parts need to be refined. You will repeat the design cycle during the second half of the chapter when you gain more *Inputs*, refine your safety system, and make your final safety system presentation.

Physics Corner

Physics in *Safety*

- Acceleration
- Change in momentum
- Collisions
- Effect of forces on motion
- Energy and work
- Force, pressure, and area
- Inertia
- Impulse
- Kinetic energy = $\frac{1}{2}mv^2$

- Law of conservation of momentum
- Mass
- Momentum = $m \times v$
- Newton as a unit of force
- Newton's laws of motion
- Physical properties of matter
- Velocity
- Work = $F \cdot d$

Section 1

Accidents

What Do You See?

Learning Outcomes

In this section, you will

- **Evaluate** your understanding of safety.
- **Identify** and evaluate safety features in selected automobiles.
- **Compare** and contrast the safety features in selected automobiles.
- **Identify** safety features required for other modes of transportation (in-line skates, skateboards, bicycles).

What Do You Think?

Chances are that you will be in an accident one day involving some means of transportation, such as an automobile, in-line skates, or bicycle.

- **How can you protect yourself from serious injury should an accident occur?**

Record your ideas about this question in your *Active Physics* log. Be prepared to discuss your response with your small group and the class.

Investigate

In this section, you will test your knowledge of the risks involved in vehicle collisions. You will also investigate some of the safety features available in vehicles built after 1960.

1. Many people think that they know the risks involved with day-to-day transportation. The "test" on the next page will check your knowledge of these risks.

   The statements are organized in a true and false format. Record a T in your log for each statement you believe is true and an F if you believe the statement is false. Your teacher will supply the correct answers, based on statistics, at the end of the section.

a) More people die of cancer than in automobile accidents.

b) Your chances of surviving a collision improve if you are thrown from the automobile.

c) The fatality rate in motorcycle accidents is less than in automobiles.

d) A large number of people who wear seat belts are killed in a burning or submerged automobile.

e) If you do not have a child restraint seat, you should place the child in your seat belt with you.

f) You can react fast enough during an accident to brace yourself against the impact of the collision.

g) Most people die in traffic accidents during long trips.

h) A person not wearing a seat belt in your vehicle poses a hazard to you.

i) Traffic accidents occur most often on Monday mornings.

j) Male drivers between the ages of 16 and 19 are most likely to be involved in traffic accidents.

k) Automobile accidents resulting in casualties are most frequent during the winter months due to snow and ice.

l) More pedestrians than drivers are killed by automobiles.

m) The greatest number of roadway fatalities can be attributed to poor driving conditions.

n) The greatest number of females involved in traffic accidents are between the ages of 16 and 20.

o) Unrestrained occupant casualties are more likely to be young adults between the ages of 16 and 19.

2. Calculate your score. Give yourself one point for a correct answer. You might want to match your score against the descriptors given below.

14-15 points: Expert Analyst

11-13 points: Assistant Analyst

8-10 points: Novice Analyst

7 points and below: Myth Believer

a) Record your score in your log. Were you surprised about the extent of your knowledge? Some of the reasons behind these facts will be better understood as you continue through this chapter.

3. Look at the photographs of two automobiles. One was built prior to 1960 and the other was built after 2000.

Safety features you may find in an automobile are listed in the first column of the following table. Explain why each safety feature may protect the driver, a passenger, or a pedestrian during an accident. You will record this in the second column in a table in your log. In the third column, state whether you think that the safety feature was present in most pre-1960 automobiles (yes/no). In the fourth column, state whether the safety features are in all new automobiles (1), in some new automobiles (2), or in very few new automobiles, (3).

a) Copy and complete the table in your log.

Safety features	Means of protection	Pre-1960 automobiles (y/n)	New automobiles (1,2,3)
seat belts			
head restraints			
front airbags			
back-up sensing system			
front crumple zones			
rear crumple zones			
side-impact beams in doors			
shoulder belts for all seats			
anti-lock braking systems (ABS)			
tempered shatterproof glass			
side airbags			
turn signals			
electronic stability control			
energy-absorbing collapsible steering column			

Physics Talk

VEHICLE SAFETY

Nobody expects to be in an automobile accident. But accidents do occur. You may have already studied ways to avoid being involved in automobile accidents. In this chapter, you will investigate the systems in vehicles that are designed to keep you safe in case of a collision.

Governments and manufacturers of automobiles can work together to make vehicles safer. If you are in an accident in a safer vehicle, the chances of injury will be limited. People in vehicles are not the only ones in danger. A pedestrian can get hit by an automobile. Engineers can try to build the automobile so that pedestrians may be safer if they are hit by an automobile.

Safety was not always a major consideration in automotive manufacturing. A turning point in the history of automobile safety occurred when Ralph Nader, an American attorney and political activist, wrote the book *Unsafe at Any Speed* in 1965. This book highlighted the problems of not having seat belts in vehicles, having hard chrome dashboards, and solid steering columns. Since then, all automobile manufacturers have improved the safety of their vehicles.

An interesting Australian study of four-wheel drive (4WD) vehicles found that the incidence of fatal 4WD crashes increased by 85 percent between 1990 and 1998 (up 28 percent between 1994 and 1998). By comparison, the incidence of all fatal crashes decreased by 25 percent between 1990 and 1998 (down 10 percent between 1994 and 1998). There are two competing explanations for this. This increase in fatal 4WD crashes could be due to the growing number of kilometers traveled by 4WDs. It could also be due to the tendency of some drivers to increase speed under the impression that the safety features will protect them. Automobiles with anti-lock brakes and four-wheel drive should be safer than automobiles without these features. Some drivers may overcompensate for these added features and end up in accidents that could have been avoided if they had just slowed down.

Checking Up

1. List three ways that manufacturers have made vehicles safer since the 1960s.

2. What are two explanations for the increase in fatal 4WD crashes?

What Do You Think Now?

At the beginning of this section, you were asked

• **How can you protect yourself from serious injury should an accident occur?**

In light of all the safety features you have investigated so far, how would you protect yourself in the event of an accident? What safety device do you think is most effective and why? What actions will not protect you in an accident?

Physics
Essential Questions

What does it mean?

Automobiles today have improved safety devices over older models. Describe three safety features of an automobile and explain how each feature provides passenger safety.

How do you know?

How do you know that safety has become a concern for automobile manufacturers?

Why do you believe?

Connects with Other Physics Content	Fits with Big Ideas in Science	Meets Physics Requirements
Forces and motion	Conservation laws	✱ Good clear explanation, no more complicated than necessary

✱ The laws of physics do not change from day to day. Auto manufacturers add safety devices to automobiles in anticipation of accidents occurring. Compare bicycle helmet laws with laws of physics.

Why should you care?

Safer automobiles can reduce injuries to drivers, passengers, and pedestrians in the event of an accident. How is minimizing injuries in transportation accidents beneficial to society?

Reflecting on the Section and the Challenge

Automobiles accidents can cause serious injuries in a number of different ways. If there are no restraints or safety devices in a vehicle, or if the vehicle is not constructed to absorb any of the energy of the collision, even a minor collision can cause serious injury. Until the early 1960s, automobile design and construction did not even consider passenger safety.

The general belief was that a heavy automobile was a safe automobile. While there is some truth to that statement, today's lighter automobiles may be safer than some of the large, heavy automobiles of the past.

In completing the *Chapter Challenge*, you will want to discuss which safety concerns you are addressing in your improved safety device, and the physics behind each improvement.

Physics to Go

1. Review and list 10 safety features found in today's new automobiles. As you compile your list, write next to each safety feature one or more of the following designations:

   F–effective in a front-end collision.

   R–effective in a rear-end collision.

   S–effective in a collision where the automobile is struck on the side.

   T–effective when the automobile rolls over or turns over onto its roof.

2. Make a list of safety features that could be used for bicycling.

3. Make a list of safety features that could be used for in-line skating.

4. Make a list of safety features that could be used for skateboarding.

5. What safety features do you think should be in every automobile used today?

6. Ask family members or friends if you may evaluate the safety of their automobile. Discuss and explain your evaluation to the automobile owners. Record your evaluation and their response in your log.

7. *Preparing for the Chapter Challenge*

   The safety survey may have provided you ideas for constructing a prototype of a safety system used for transportation. In your log, record ideas that have been generated from this section.

Inquiring Further

1. **Safety and sales**

   Interview a salesperson of automobiles or bicycles, or collect brochures from various automobile and bicycle manufacturers. What new safety features are presented by the salesperson or in the brochures? How much of the advertising is devoted to safety?

2. **Vehicle safety ratings**

   Do an Internet search for automobile safety features and ratings. You may wish to visit the National Highway Traffic Safety Administration Web Site. Compare vehicles from different categories, such as vans, sports cars, or pickup trucks.

Section 2

Newton's First Law of Motion: Life and Death before and after Seat Belts

What Do You See?

Learning Outcomes

In this section, you will

- **Explain** Newton's first law of motion.

- **Describe** the role of seat belts.

- **Identify** the three collisions in every accident.

- **Compare** the effectiveness of various wide and narrow seat belts.

- **Express** the relationship between pressure, force, and area.

What Do You Think?

In a collision, you cannot brace yourself and prevent injuries. Instead of thinking about bracing yourself against a collision when an automobile is going 50 km/h (about 30 mph), think about 10 bowling balls, a mass of 45 kg (a weight of about 100 lb), all hurtling toward you at 50 km/h. You could not use your arms and legs to stop these fast-moving bowling balls. The two situations are equivalent.

- **Suppose you had to design a seat belt for a race car that can go 300 km/h (about 200 mph). How would it be different from one available on a passenger automobile?**

Record your ideas about this question in your *Active Physics* log. Be prepared to discuss your responses with your small group and the class.

Investigate

In this section, you will be investigating what happens to a passenger involved in an automobile accident without and with a seat belt.

Part A: Accidents Without Seat Belts

⚠ Perform the activity outside of busy areas. Do not obstruct paths to exits. Do not leave carts lying on the floor.

1. In this section, you will investigate automobile crashes where the driver or passenger does not wear seat belts. Your model automobile is a laboratory cart. Your model passenger is molded from a lump of soft clay.

   Obtain a lump of soft clay. Mold the clay to represent a human figure.

2. With the "passenger" in place, send the "automobile" at a low speed into a wall.

   ✎ a) Describe, in your log, what happens to the "passenger."

3. Repeat the collision at a higher speed.

   ✎ a) Compare and contrast this collision with the previous one. "Compare and contrast" requires you to find and record at least one similarity and one difference. A better response includes more similarities and differences.

Part B: Accidents With Seat Belts

1. You will test the suitability of different materials for use as seat belts. Your model automobile is, once again, a laboratory cart. Your model passenger is molded from a lump of soft clay.

Give your passenger a seat belt by stretching a thin piece of wire across the front of the passenger. Attach the wire to the cart.

2. Make a collision by sending the cart down a ramp. Start with small angles of incline. Increase the height of the ramp until you see significant injury to the clay passenger.

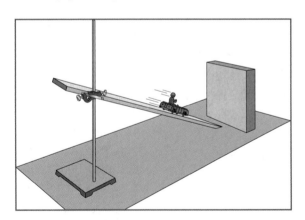

   ✎ a) In your log, note the height of the ramp at which significant injury occurs.

3. Use at least two other kinds of seat belts (ribbons, cloth, and so on). Use the same angle of ramp and release height as in *Step 2*.

   ✎ a) In your log, compare the injury that occurs to the "passenger" using the other kinds of seat-belt material.

Active Physics

b) What accounts for the difference in injury?

4. Crash dummies cost thousands of dollars! Watch the video presentation of a vehicle in a collision, with a crash dummy in the driver's seat. You may have to observe the video more than once to answer the following questions.

a) In the collision, the automobile stops abruptly. What happens to the crash-dummy driver?

b) What parts of the crash-dummy's body are in the greatest danger? Explain what you saw.

Physics Talk

SEAT BELTS AND NEWTON'S FIRST LAW OF MOTION

The Three Parts of Newton's First Law

Physics Words

Newton's first law of motion: an object at rest stays at rest, and an object in motion stays in motion in a straight line with constant speed unless acted upon by a net, external force.

inertia: the natural tendency of an object to remain at rest or to remain moving with constant speed in a straight line.

Newton's first law of motion (also called the law of **inertia**) is one of the foundations of physics. You probably have already encountered Newton's first law. It states:

> An object at rest stays at rest, and an object in motion stays in motion in a straight line with constant speed unless acted upon by a net, external force.

There are three distinct parts to Newton's first law.

Part 1 says that objects at rest stay at rest. This hardly seems surprising.

Part 2 says that objects in motion stay in motion in a straight line with constant speed. This may seem strange indeed. After looking at the collisions in this section, this should seem clearer. The automobile and the clay passenger were moving at constant speed. Even though the automobile stopped, the clay passenger continued moving at the same constant speed until it hit the barrier.

Part 3 says that Parts 1 and 2 are only true when the net force, or total of all forces, on the object is zero. An object may have forces acting on it and still have no change in its motion.

For example, a book at rest on an outstretched arm has two forces acting on it: gravity pulling the book down and the force of the arm on the book, pushing it up. Because these two forces on the book are equal and opposite in direction, the forces are balanced. They cancel each other out. The net force is zero, and the book remains at rest.

In your simulated automobile accident, the cart stopped and the clay figure kept moving until it hit the wall. This action can be explained using Newton's first law. An object at rest stays at rest. An object in motion stays in motion unless acted upon by an unbalanced force. The cart and the clay figure were moving at a constant speed. The wall stopped the cart, but the clay figure continued moving at constant speed until the wall stopped the clay figure.

Human beings have much more complicated anatomies than clay figures. This leads to more complicated actions during a collision.

Three Collisions in One Accident!

Arthur C. Damask analyzes automobile accidents for insurance companies and police reports. This is how Professor Damask describes an accident:

"Consider the occupants of a conveyance moving at some speed. If the conveyance strikes an object, it will rapidly decelerate to some lower speed or stop entirely; this is called the first collision. But the occupants have been moving at the same speed, and will continue to do so until they are stopped by striking the interior parts of the automobile (if not ejected); this is the second collision. The brain and body organs have also been moving at the same speed and will continue to do so until they are stopped by colliding with the shell of the body, for example, the interior of the skull, the thoracic cavity, and the abdominal wall. This is called the third collision."

→

Newton's first law of motion can explain these three collisions when an automobile strikes a pole:

- First collision—The automobile strikes the pole. The pole exerts the force that brings the automobile to rest.

- Second collision—When the automobile stops, the body keeps moving. The structure of the automobile exerts the force that brings the body to rest.

- Third collision—The body stops, but the heart, the brain, and other organs keep moving. The body wall exerts the force that brings the organs to rest.

Even with all the safety features in automobiles, some deaths due to accidents cannot be prevented. In one recorded accident, only a single automobile was involved, with only the driver inside. The automobile failed to follow the road around a turn, and it struck a telephone pole. The seat belt and the air bag prevented any serious injuries apart from a few bruises, but the driver died. An autopsy showed that the driver's aorta (a large blood vessel) had burst, at the point where it leaves the heart. The man's organs were damaged during the "third" collision, when the heart collided with the skeleton.

Force per Unit Area: Designing a Safer Seat Belt

In *Part B* of the *Investigate*, you used a seat belt to stop the clay passenger. Newton's first law states that an object at rest will remain at rest and an object in motion will remain in motion unless acted upon by an unbalanced **force**. The cart stopped, but the passenger continued to move forward until a force acted upon it. In this part, the force stopping the passenger was the force exerted by the seat belt.

Some of the seat belts you used did not work as well as others. Each time you repeated the investigation, the stopping force that the belt exerted on the clay was the same. The force was the same because you released the cart from the same height each time. Yet different materials had different effects on the clay passenger. For example, the wire cut far more deeply into the clay than a broader material did.

The stopping force that each of the seat belts exerted on the clay was approximately the same. When a thin wire was used, all the force was concentrated onto a small area. By replacing the wire with a broader strip of material, you spread the force out over a much larger area of contact.

Force that is spread out over a given area is called **pressure**.

Physics Words

force: an interaction between two objects that can result in an acceleration of either or both objects.

pressure: force per area where the force is normal (perpendicular) to the surface; measured in N/m² (newtons per meter squared) or Pa (pascals).

Pressure is defined as force per unit area. The pressure is much smaller with a ribbon, for example, than with a wire. It is the pressure, not the force, that determines how much damage the seat belt does to the body. A force applied to a single rib might be enough to break a rib. If the same force is spread out across many ribs, the force on each rib can become too small to do any damage. While the total force does not change, the pressure on each rib becomes much smaller.

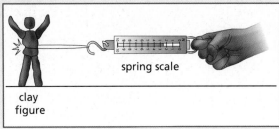

Force can be measured using a spring scale.

Checking Up

1. Explain Newton's first law of motion.

2. Why does the driver in an automobile collision remain in a state of motion when the automobile suddenly stops moving?

3. Use Newton's first law of motion to describe the three collisions.

4. Describe inertia.

5. Why did a broad band of material work better as a seat belt than a narrow wire?

Active Physics Plus

+Math	+Depth	+Concepts	+Exploration
◆	◆		

Calculating Pressure

Physicists are rarely satisfied just to know that the pressure decreases as the width of the seat belt increases. In physics, once a relation between two things is known, everyone wants to know, "Is there an equation?" or "Can you describe this mathematically?"

Pressure is the force per unit area:

$$P = \frac{F}{A}$$

where F is force in newtons (N)
 A is area in meters squared (m²)
 and
 P is pressure in newtons per meter squared (N/m²) which is also called a pascal.

Sample Problem

Two students have the same mass and apply a constant force on the ground of 450 N while standing in the snow.

Student X is wearing snowshoes that have a base area of 2.0 m². Student Y, without snowshoes, has a base area of 0.1 m².

Why does the student without snowshoes sink into the snow?

Strategy: This problem involves the pressure that is exerted on the snow surface by each student. You can use the equation that relates force and area to compare the pressure exerted by each student.

Given:

$$F = 450 \text{ N}$$

$$A_x = 2.0 \text{ m}^2$$

$$A_y = 0.1 \text{ m}^2$$

Solution:

Student Y

$$P = \frac{F}{A}$$

$$= \frac{450 \text{ N}}{0.1 \text{ m}^2}$$

$$= 4500 \text{ N/m}^2$$

Student X

$$P = \frac{F}{A}$$

$$= \frac{450 \text{ N}}{2.0 \text{ m}^2}$$

$$= 225 \text{ N/m}^2$$

Student Y sinks into the snow because the pressure that Student Y exerts on the snow is much greater than the pressure exerted by Student X.

1. What is the pressure exerted when a force of 10 N is applied to an object with each of the following areas?

   a) 1.0 m²

   b) 0.2 m²

   c) 15 m²

   d) 400 cm²

2. A person who weighs 155 lb exerts approximately 700 N of force on the ground while standing. If the person's shoes cover a total area of 400 cm² (0.04 m²), calculate the following:

   a) the average pressure the person's shoes exert on the ground

   b) the pressure the person would exert by standing on one foot

What Do You Think Now?

At the beginning of this section, you were asked the following:

• **Suppose you had to design a seat belt for a race car that can go 300 km/h (about 200 mph). How would it be different from one available on a passenger automobile?**

Using Newton's first law of motion, explain why a seat belt is an important safety feature in a vehicle. Now that you have also investigated the relationship between force and area, what would you need to consider when designing a seat belt for a race car? How do your ideas now compare to the ideas you previously recorded in your log?

Essential Questions

What does it mean?

Newton's first law is a very important part of physics because it describes how objects move in the absence of forces. Use Newton's first law of motion to explain why a passenger keeps moving when a vehicle suddenly stops.

How do you know?

What evidence do you have from your experiment that collisions at higher speeds will have a greater effect on the passenger?

Why do you believe?

Connects with Other Physics Content	Fits with Big Ideas in Science	Meets Physics Requirements
Forces and motion	Systems	∗ Good clear explanation, no more complicated than necessary

∗ Laws in physics can be applied in a wide range of situations. Describe what happens to the passengers when a bus stops quickly. How is this an example of Newton's first law?

Why should you care?

How does what you learned about Newton's first law of motion in this section help you design a safety device for a collision even though you do not know the exact circumstances of the collision?

Reflecting on the Section and the Challenge

In this section, you discovered that an object in motion continues in motion until an unbalanced force stops it. An automobile will stop when it hits a pole. However, the passenger will keep moving until something else stops the passenger, such as the interior of the automobile. The greater the speed of the automobile and passenger prior to the collision, the more damage the passenger will suffer.

Have you ever heard someone say that they can prevent an injury by bracing themselves against a collision in an automobile? This is not true. Even if your muscles were strong enough (which they are not), your bones would break in a serious accident. Restraining devices help to stop the movement of the body. With a restraining system, the force of impact is absorbed by the interior surfaces of the automobile.

In this section, you also gathered data to provide evidence on the effectiveness of seat belts as restraint systems. The seat belt was effective in applying a force to stop the clay passenger. The material used for the seat belt and the width of the restraint affected the distortion of the clay passenger. By applying the force over a greater area, the pressure exerted by the seat belt during the collision can be reduced.

It is important to note that not every safety restraint system will be a seat belt or harness, but that all restraints attempt to reduce the pressure exerted on an object by increasing the area over which a force is applied.

Physics to Go

1. Describe how Newton's first law applies to the following situations:

   a) You step on the brakes to bring your vehicle to a safe stop.

      (Sample answer: You and the vehicle are moving forward. The brakes apply a force and the vehicle stops. Newton's first law states that an object in motion will remain in motion unless an unbalanced force acts upon it. In this case, the force stops the vehicle from moving forward. You stop moving because the interior of the automobile–seat, seat belts, dashboard, floor—apply a force to stop you.)

   b) You step on the accelerator to get going.

   c) You step on the brakes, and an object in the back of the automobile comes flying forward.

   d) A vehicle is involved in a collision and a passenger is wearing a seat belt.

2. Give two more examples of how Newton's first law applies to vehicles or people in motion.

3. The skateboard, shown in the diagram at the right, strikes the curb. Draw a diagram indicating the direction in which the person on the skateboard moves after the impact. Use Newton's first law to explain the direction of movement.

4. Explain, in your own words, the three collisions during a single automobile accident as described by Professor Damask in the *Physics Talk*.

5. Describe why a wire seat belt would not be effective even though the force exerted on you by the wire seat belt is identical to that of a cloth seat belt.

6. Do you think laws making seat belts mandatory are fair? In answering this question, consider how using seat belts affect the society as a whole.

7. Suppose one of your friends wanted a ride in your automobile, but refused to wear a seat belt.

   a) Give two arguments that he or she might make against wearing a seat belt.

   b) How can you challenge these arguments using what you have learned about Newton's first law of motion?

8. Use the diagrams below to compare the second and third collisions described by Professor Damask with the impact of a punch during a boxing match.

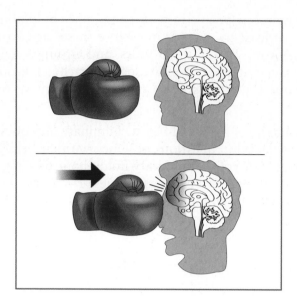

9. **Active Physics Plus**   A famous demonstration around the world has a person lying on a bed of nails. This looks both painful and frightening for those who do not understand physics. Your skin is able to tolerate a certain amount of pressure without tearing. You can hold heavy barbells in your hands, but the pressure is very low because the area of contact is considerably large. In contrast, you can puncture your skin with a single nail because the total area of one nail is very small.

Assume that you can push on the tip of a large, dull nail with a force of 1 N without experiencing pain or puncturing the skin. If you weigh 500 N and you had 1000 nails, then the force would only be 0.5 N per nail. How far apart should the nails be for a person who is 1.6 m tall and 0.5 m wide?

10. *Preparing for the Chapter Challenge*

Describe modifications to a seat belt that you would make if the seat belt were to be used in the following situations:

a) in a plane when it experiences an air pocket and suddenly drops down

b) in a train

c) in a bus

Active Physics

Inquiring Further

1. Opinions about wearing seat belts

Determine what opinions people in your community hold about wearing seat belts. Survey at least five people in each of theses age groups: Group A = 15 to 24 years, Group B = 25 to 59 years, and Group C = 60 years and older. Survey the same number of individuals in each age group. Ask each individual to fill out a questionnaire. Compare the opinions of the different groups.

A sample questionnaire is provided below. Eliminate any question that you feel is not relevant. Develop questions of your own that help you understand what attitudes people in your community hold about wearing seat belts. The answers have been divided into three categories: 1 = agree; 2 = will accept, but do not hold a strong opinion; and 3 = disagree. Try to keep your survey to between five and ten questions.

Age group:		Date of Survey:	
Statement	Agree	No strong opinion	Disagree
1. I believe people should be fined for not wearing seat belts.	1	2	3
2. I wouldn't wear a seat belt if I didn't have to.	1	2	3
3. People who don't wear seat belts pose a threat to me when they ride in my car.	1	2	3
4. I believe that seat belts save lives.	1	2	3
5. Seat belts wrinkle my clothes and fit poorly so I don't wear them.	1	2	3

2. Brakes in an automobile

How is your foot able to stop an automobile? How can the small force of your foot on the brake create a large enough force on the brakes of the automobile to stop the automobile? Investigate how the hydraulic systems in automobile brakes work and relate this to your study of pressure in this section.

Section 3

Energy and Work: Why Air Bags?

What Do You See?

Learning Outcomes

In this section, you will

- **Model** an automobile air bag.
- **Relate** the energy of a moving object to the work required to stop the object.
- **Demonstrate** an understanding about the relationship between the force of an impact and the stopping distance.

What Do You Think?

Automotive engineers often think in terms of energy management when they design safety systems. A good example of energy management is the use of an air bag to protect passengers during an accident.

- **How does an air bag protect you during an accident?**

Record your ideas about this question in your *Active Physics* log. Be prepared to discuss your responses with your small group and the class.

Investigate

In this section, you will use an egg to simulate the head of a passenger traveling in an automobile. An egg is a fairly good model of a human head. It has a fairly thin outer shell with a fragile interior.

1. Wrap an egg in plastic wrap or bag to minimize cleanup, as shown in the diagram on the next page.

2. Drop egg # 1 onto a hard surface (such as a counter) from a very low height. Start with a drop of 2 cm. Check the egg for any cracks. Try to drop the egg so that it always lands the same way, for example, on its side.

For best results, hold the egg with your thumb and index finger as shown in the diagram below.

3. Gradually increase the height of the drop in increments of 2 cm until you get a crack in the shell.

✎ a) Record this as crack height in your log.

4. Continue dropping from greater heights until you get a full break in the shell and the yolk spills out.

✎ a) Record this as smash height # 1.

5. Now create a softer surface for a second egg to fall on. Try a bed of flour, sand, or rice about 2 cm thick. Drop egg # 2 from smash height # 1. Try to drop the egg so that it lands in the same way as your first egg.

✎ a) Record your observations.

6. Measure the depth of the indentation left in the landing material for the drop at smash height # 1. This can be challenging. Try measuring how much of the egg is still sticking out above the original level of the landing material. Then take the difference between the amount above the surface and the total height of the egg. This should be what remains below the surface, or the indentation depth.

✎ a) Record your measurement.

7. Compare the damage of egg # 1 and egg # 2 when dropped from the smash height # 1. When dropped from the same height, egg # 1 and egg # 2 have the same speed just before hitting the landing material. The material must supply a force over a distance (that is, the indentation of the material) for the energy to be dissipated.

✎ a) Compare the force (damage) and distance (indentation) of egg # 1 and egg # 2 when dropped from smash height # 1.

8. The next part of the *Investigate* is best done as a class demonstration. Take a large bed sheet to an area with a clear throwing area. Choose a volunteer that has a good throwing arm, such as a pitcher from the softball or baseball team. Have two other students be the "catchers." They should design a target for the egg-thrower by stretching the sheet out, holding the top two corners of the bed sheet over their heads and the lower two corners a little lower than their waists. The goal for the catchers is to catch the egg in the sheet by creating a cup or scoop at the bottom, which will prevent the egg from rolling off the sheet. Have the pitcher throw the egg as hard as she or he can at the center of the sheet. The pitcher should try to break the egg when it hits the sheet. Everyone else should observe the motion of the sheet when the egg hits it. Have the egg in a plastic bag. It will be a bit harder to throw, but much easier to clean up.

✎ a) Explain why the sheet cannot exert a force large enough to break the egg.

Physics Talk

ENERGY AND WORK

In this section, you observed the damage to an egg from collisions. This is similar to the damage to a person's skull during collisions.

When egg # 1 was dropped from smash height # 1, the shell broke. In contrast, egg # 2 dropped from the same height probably did not experience the same damage because the new surface was softer. How can you describe "softer" in terms of physics concepts?

Kinetic Energy

An automobile traveling down a highway at 100 km/h (about 60 mph) represents a considerable amount of energy. This kind of energy is called **kinetic energy**. Kinetic energy is the energy an object has because of its motion. The adjective "kinetic" comes from the Greek word for motion, "*kinesis*."

Physics Words

kinetic energy: the energy possessed by a moving body is called kinetic energy. $KE = \frac{1}{2}mv^2$

Kinetic energy depends on the mass and the velocity of the object. The following equation shows this relationship.

$$KE = \frac{1}{2}mv^2$$

where *KE* stands for kinetic energy,
        m represents the mass of the vehicle and its occupants, and
        v represent the velocity of the vehicle.

In your investigation, the falling eggs had kinetic energy and approximately the same mass. Both eggs also had the same velocity at the moment before hitting the surface because they were both dropped from the same height (smash height # 1). Both eggs, therefore, had the same kinetic energy (*KE*).

Active Physics

To stop the egg, a surface had to apply a force over some distance. This distance can be seen as the indentation of the surface. For a hard surface, you cannot see the indentation. For the soft surface, you were able to measure the indentation.

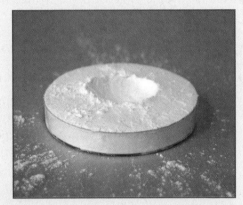

Work and Change in Kinetic Energy

In order to stop an automobile safely, the braking system must decrease the speed of the vehicle and effectively eliminate the kinetic energy by applying a great deal of force over a large distance. When force is applied over a distance, *work* is being done. **Work** is calculated using the following equation:

$$\text{Work} = \text{force} \times \text{distance}$$
$$W = F \cdot d$$

Work is equal to the change in kinetic energy. Work can either increase the kinetic energy or decrease the kinetic energy depending on the direction of the applied force and the distance (displacement) that the object moves.

You can write this as a new equation using the symbol Δ to represent "change in."

$$W = \Delta KE$$

Getting rid of the kinetic energy that an automobile and its occupants have before a collision can be done in different ways. It can be done either safely, or dangerously (causing injury to the passengers). This is what automotive safety engineers call energy management. They need to create a system that transfers the energy of the automobile safely. The work that is needed to stop the automobile traveling at a given speed is a fixed quantity, so it could be done with a small force and a large distance, or a large force and a small distance.

Physics Words

work: the amount of force applied on an object over a certain distance; $W = F \cdot d$

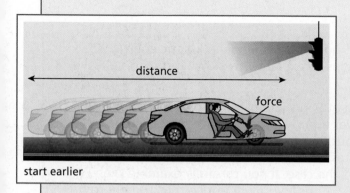

start earlier

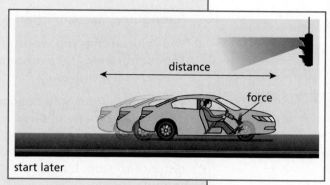

start later

Work = force · **distance** (safely)   Work = **force** · distance (dangerously)

If the change in kinetic energy (*KE*) equals 5000 J (joules), different forces and distances can all provide this change.

Kinetic energy	Force	Distance	Work = F • d
5000 J	50,000 N	0.10 m	5000 J
5000 J	10,000 N	0.50 m	5000 J
5000 J	5000 N	1.00 m	5000 J

You should see that the smaller the stopping distance, the larger the force. You noticed this in the *Investigate* in which egg # 1 hitting the hard surface had more damage than egg # 2 hitting the soft surface which has a larger indentation or distance. This is what happens in a collision, where the automobile and its passengers come to a stop in a very small distance. If a passenger strikes the interior of the automobile, such as an unpadded steering wheel or windshield, the stopping distance will be very small. That would require an extremely large force. Such a force would certainly cause serious injury. That is why air bags are used. An air bag increases the distance over which the stopping force is applied. The force is reduced considerably.

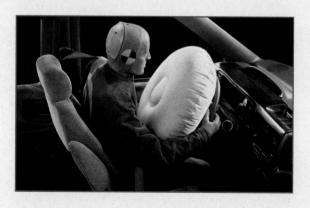

Active Physics

Speed and Kinetic Energy

You noticed that the work, *W*, equals the change in kinetic energy, *KE*. The fact that $W = \Delta KE$, also helps to explain why slowing down is always a good safety move.

To stop an automobile moving at 9 m/s (20 mi/h) requires the force of the brakes to be applied over a fairly large distance. An automobile traveling at 9 m/s requires about 6 m to stop safely. Imagine that an automobile going three times as fast would require three times the distance to stop, but this is not the case. If you carefully examine the formula for kinetic energy ($KE = \frac{1}{2}mv^2$), you will notice that the energy is proportional to the square of the velocity. That is, if you triple the speed, the *KE* is not three times greater, but it is nine times greater (3^2 or 3×3). It would take an automobile traveling at 27 m/s nine times the distance to stop than at 9 m/s, assuming that the brakes apply the same force. That means that it would require 54 m (9×6 m) to stop safely. The fact that kinetic energy is proportional to the square of the velocity also explains why high speed greatly increases the damage done during a collision. The automobile at three times the speed has nine times as much kinetic energy requiring nine times the distance to stop safely.

If you assume that the mass of a car is 1000 kg, you can see the effect of speed on kinetic energy and stopping distance for a given braking force. In the table below, you should notice the following:

• The speed has tripled from 9 m/s in the first row to 27 m/s in the second row.

• The kinetic energy has increased nine times as the speed tripled.

• The work required to stop the car is equal to the kinetic energy at all speeds.

• The braking force of the car is constant irrespective of the speed.

• The stopping distance increased by a factor of nine when the speed tripled.

Speed (meters per second)	$KE = \frac{1}{2} mv^2$ (joules)	Work to stop car $W = \Delta KE$ (joules)	Braking force (newtons)	Stopping distance (meters)
9	40,500	40,500	6740	6
27	364,500	364,500	6740	54

On dry roads, you can safely stop a car traveling at 9 m/s in 6 m. Drivers are used to this speed-to-distance relationship after many years of driving. When the road is wet or icy, there is less force between the tires and the road. With less force you need a larger distance to stop, since the work is still the same for a given amount of kinetic energy. Alternatively, you can decrease the speed of your car so that the kinetic energy decreases and the required work and stopping distance will be smaller. The key to safety when road conditions change is to slow down. Slowing down will permit a safer stop and will also significantly decrease the kinetic energy (and damage) if there is an accident.

For example, imagine a 70.0-kg passenger traveling at a speed of 13 m/s. That person's kinetic energy is

$$KE = \frac{1}{2}mv^2$$
$$= \frac{(70.0 \text{ kg}) \times (13 \text{ m/s})^2}{2}$$
$$= 5915 \text{ J or } 5900 \text{ J (rounded off to two significant figures)}$$

Dimensional Analysis

Notice how the numbers and units were handled in the solution. The numbers were multiplied together to get the numerical answer:

$$\frac{1}{2} \times 70 \times 13^2 = \frac{70 \times 13 \times 13}{2}$$
$$= 5915$$

Active Physics

The units were also multiplied together in the same way:

$$kg \times \left(\frac{m}{s}\right)^2 = kg \times \left(\frac{m}{s}\right) \times \left(\frac{m}{s}\right)$$

$$= kg \cdot \frac{m^2}{s^2}$$

This derived SI unit is given a special name. The unit for energy is called a joule (J).

$$1\ J = kg \cdot \frac{m^2}{s^2} \text{ or } kg \cdot m^2/s^2$$

Paying attention to units is an important problem-solving skill and tool. It is called dimensional analysis.

To stop the person, something has to do the 5900 J of work to get rid of that energy. In an accident, it could be the windshield. What would happen if the person strikes the windshield? Since the windshield is fairly rigid, it might only give 3.0 cm (0.030 m) in stopping the person. So the work done by the windshield is

$$\text{Work} = \text{force} \times \text{distance}$$
$$5900\ J = \text{force} \times 0.3\ m$$
$$\text{Force} = \frac{5900\ J}{0.030\ m}$$
$$= 196,667\ N \text{ or } 197,000\ N \text{ when rounded off}$$

That is a lot of force exerted on the skull. What happens if the passenger strikes a fully inflated air bag instead of the windshield? Suppose that the air bag creates a stopping distance of 30.0 cm (10x greater stopping distance). The amount of work to be done is still the same, 5900 J. But this time, it is applied over a greater distance than the 3 cm of the windshield.

$$\text{Work} = \text{force} \times \text{distance}$$
$$5900\ J = \text{force} \times 0.3\ m$$
$$\text{Force} = \frac{5900\ J}{0.3\ m}$$
$$= 19,667\ N \text{ or } 19,700\ N$$

This is still a lot of force, but it is much less than before (10x smaller force). Air bags are not the only system in the automobile that is designed to absorb energy. Seat belts and crumple zones in the frame of the automobile also help a lot. You will learn more about crumple zones in a later section.

The work done by the air bag decreases the kinetic energy of the person. However, energy in the entire system must remain the same. In this case, the kinetic energy of the person decreases while the energy of the air bag increases. An air bag with increased energy may become a bit hotter as all the molecules in the air bag gain some kinetic energy. Some of the energy during the collision may have produced some sound energy as well.

SI Units of Force, Work, and Energy

Notice that dimensional analysis was used, once again, in calculating the force and the work.

Newton's second law states that force is equal to mass multiplied by acceleration.

$$F = ma$$

The units of mass (kg) multiplied by the units of acceleration (m/s^2) provide the units for force ($\frac{kg \cdot m}{s^2}$ or $kg \cdot m/s^2$).

Since force is such an important concept in physics, this unit is given a special name, the newton (N).

$$1\,N = 1\frac{kg \cdot m}{s^2} \text{ or } 1\,kg \cdot m/s^2$$

Work is equal to force multiplied by distance. $W = F \cdot d$

Referring only to the units

$$
\begin{aligned}
W &= N \cdot m \\
&= \frac{kg \cdot m}{s^2} \cdot m \\
&= \frac{kg \cdot m^2}{s^2} \text{ or } kg \cdot m^2 \cdot s^{-2} \\
&= J
\end{aligned}
$$

Active Physics

Work and kinetic energy are equivalent, and therefore both are expressed in joules.

Also, notice the unit in the following calculation:

$$F = \frac{W}{d}$$

$$= \frac{J}{m}$$

$$= \frac{kg \cdot m^2 \cdot s^{-2}}{m}$$

$$= \frac{kg \cdot m}{s^2} \text{ or } kg \cdot m/s^2$$

$$= N$$

Sample Problem

A total of 12,000 J of work is required to stop a 45-kg cart.

a) What speed would the cart be traveling before it was brought to a stop?

Strategy: This problem involves work required to stop a moving object. Work and kinetic energy are equivalent. That is, 12,000 J of work are necessary to change 12,000 J of *KE* of the cart to 0 J. You are given the mass of the cart. You can use the equation that relates kinetic energy and mass to calculate the speed of the cart.

Given:

$KE = 12,000$ J

$m = 45$ kg

Solution:

$$KE = \frac{1}{2}mv^2$$

$$v^2 = \frac{2KE}{m}$$

$$v^2 = \frac{2(12,000)\,J}{45 \text{ kg}}$$

$$v^2 = 533.3 \frac{J}{kg}$$

$$v = \sqrt{533.3 \frac{\cancel{kg} \cdot m^2 \cdot s^{-2}}{\cancel{kg}}}$$

$$= 23 \text{ m/s}$$

The speed of the cart was 23 m/s.

b) If the cart stopped in a distance of 3 m, what force was needed to stop the cart?

Active Physics

Strategy: This problem involves the kinetic energy and distance it takes to stop. You can use the equation that relates work and distance to calculate the force.

Given:

$W = 12{,}000$ J

$d = 3$ m

Solution:

$W = F \cdot d$

$F = \dfrac{W}{d}$

$F = \dfrac{12{,}000 \text{ J}}{3 \text{ m}}$

$F = 4000$ J/m

$\quad = 4000$ N

Checking Up

1. What factors determine a body's kinetic energy?

2. When work is done on an object, what is the effect on its kinetic energy?

3. How does the force needed to stop a moving object depend upon the distance the force acts?

4. What is the unit of kinetic energy? What is the unit for work?

Active Physics
Plus

+Math	+Depth	+Concepts	+Exploration
◆◆			

Deriving the Equation for the Relationship between Work and Change in Kinetic Energy

In the *Physics Talk*, the equation for work and the relationship that work equals the change in kinetic energy were stated. By using algebra, this relationship can be derived from the definitions of work, Newton's second law and a motion equation that emerges from the definition of velocity and acceleration. (The derivation of the motion equation also uses algebra that is not shown here.)

Derive the equation for

$W = $ change in KE

$W = Fd$

Since $F = ma$

$W = mad$

Using the definitions of $a = \Delta v / \Delta t$ and average $v = \Delta d / \Delta t$, you can derive one of the motion equations:

$v_f^2 = 2ad + v_i^2$

$W = \dfrac{m(v_f^2 - v_i^2)}{2}$

$\quad = \dfrac{1}{2}mv_f^2 - \dfrac{1}{2}mv_i^2$

Work is required to change the KE of an automobile so that it stops.

$W = \Delta\left(\frac{1}{2}mv^2\right)$, where Δ is a symbol for "change."

In order to demonstrate your understanding of this equation:

1. Sketch a graph of the work necessary to bring an automobile to a stop as a function of the automobile's kinetic energy.

2. Sketch a graph of the work required to bring an automobile to a stop as a function of the automobile's speed.

3. Sketch a graph of the work required to bring an automobile to a stop as a function of the automobile's mass.

What Do You Think Now?

At the beginning of the section, you were asked

• **How does an air bag protect you during an accident?**

Explain how an air bag can protect you. Be sure to include the ideas of work and change in kinetic energy in your explanation.

Physics
Essential Questions

What does it mean?

During a crash, you will eventually stop. It can occur when you hit the hard dashboard or the softer air bag. Physics can be used to determine how much force will be exerted on you. Explain how two different forces can cause the same change in the kinetic energy of an object. Include the definition of work in your explanation.

How do you know?

How did you test whether a material is good for cushioning an egg during a collision?

Why do you believe?

Connects with Other Physics Content	Fits with Big Ideas in Science	Meets Physics Requirements
Forces and motion	✳ Conservation laws	Experimental evidence is consistent with models and theories

✳ Energy is an organizing principle of all science. It states that the total energy of a system remains the same. It also allows for a force to be applied by an external force to change the energy. Explain how you can change the energy of an egg or an automobile during a collision without violating the conservation of energy.

Why should you care?

How will you use the physics concept of $Work = F \cdot d = \Delta KE$ to help design your safety system?

Active Physics

Reflecting on the Section and Challenge

In this section, you found that softer surfaces were better able to protect an egg during a collision. Similarly, softer surfaces such as air bags are able to protect you by extending the distance it takes to stop you in an automobile accident. Without the air bag, you will hit something else that will stop you in a shorter distance.

Work produces a change in the kinetic energy. A large force over a short distance or a small force over a large distance are two ways in which work can produce the same change in kinetic energy. The large force can injure you. With an air bag, the stopping distance is larger and therefore, the force required to stop you is smaller.

Energy and work must be considered in designing your safety system. Stopping an object over a large distance reduces the damage. The harder a surface is, the shorter the stopping distance, and the greater the damage. In part, this provides you with a clue to the use of padded dashboards and visors in newer vehicles. Understanding energy and work allows designers to reduce damage both to vehicles and passengers.

Physics to Go

1. There are many situations in which the force of an impact is reduced by increasing the stopping distance. Explain how each of the following actions reduces the force by increasing the stopping distance. Use the terms force, energy, and stopping distance in your answers.

   a) Catching a hard ball with a catcher's mitt

   b) Jumping to the ground from a large height and bending your knees

   c) Bungee jumping

   d) A wrestler's mat

2. If you triple the speed from 20 km/h to 60 km/h, by what factor does the kinetic energy increase?

3. Two eggs are thrown at a blanket. One egg is thrown at twice the speed of the other. If you assume that in both cases the force exerted by the blanket on the egg is the same, how far will the faster egg travel once it hits the blanket as compared to how far the slower egg travels when it hits the blanket?

4. If the work to stop an object is 60 J, list in your log three force and distance combinations that can stop the object.

5. Copy and complete the following table. The first row has been completed for you. In all the other rows, one of the values is missing.

Kinetic energy	Mass	Speed
500 J	1000 kg	1 m/s
	1000 kg	20 m/s
100,000 J		20 m/s
50,000 J	500 kg	
	1000 kg	30 m/s

6. A person with a mass of 60.0 kg is traveling at 18 m/s.

   a) How much kinetic energy does this person have?

   b) How much work is required to stop the person?

   c) Calculate the force required to stop the person if the stopping distance is 50.0 m.

For *Questions 7 and 8*, choose the best answer from those provided.

7. An egg dropped on a pillow is less likely to break than an egg dropped on concrete because:

   a) The pillow provides a larger force over a larger stopping distance.

   b) The pillow spreads the force out over a longer stopping distance.

   c) The egg loses less energy when it is stopped by the pillow as compared to when it is stopped by the concrete.

   d) The concrete contains sharp bits of sand and rock that break the shell.

8. A 60.0-kg runner has 1920 J of kinetic energy. At what speed is she running? Show your work.

   a) 5.66 m/s

   b) 32.0 m/s

   c) 8.00 m/s

   d) 64.0 m/s

9. **Active Physics Plus** In *Active Physics Plus*, you used the equation $v_f^2 = 2ad + v_i^2$. Demonstrate your algebra skills, and use the definitions of $a = \Delta v/\Delta t$ and average $v = \Delta d/\Delta t$, to derive the equation.

10. *Preparing for the Chapter Challenge*

    What safety devices do you know that decrease the force experienced by passengers by increasing the distance over which the collision does work on the passenger? What are the characteristics of those devices that allow them to manage energy better? What can you put in your safety design to manage the energy of a collision?

Inquiring Further

1. **Are air bags always safe?**

   Conduct an Internet search on air bag safety. Do air bags sometimes cause injuries? What are the dangers? What is the physics behind those dangers? How can people reduce the chance of injury due to air bags?

2. **Design a landing pad**

   Design your own landing pad with whatever materials your teacher approves. A pillow might be a good landing pad, but it has one drawback that would make it unsuitable for an automobile. It takes up too much space. Automobile engineers are also limited by other constraints in the design of safety devices. For this problem, you are limited to a landing pad height of 5 cm.

   a) What is the maximum height that you can drop your egg onto your landing pad without getting a crack in the shell?

   b) Do a survey of what other students found and check out their landing pads.

   c) What are the characteristics or properties of a good landing pad?

Section 4

Newton's Second Law of Motion: The Rear-End Collision

What Do You See?

Learning Outcomes

In this section, you will

- **Evaluate,** from simulated collisions, the effect of rear-end collisions on the neck muscles.

- **Describe** the causes of whiplash injuries.

- **Provide** examples of Newton's first and second laws of motion in automobile crashes.

- **Analyze** the role of safety devices in preventing whiplash injury.

What Do You Think?

The whiplash effect is a serious injury that is caused by a rear-end collision. It is the focus of many lawsuits, the inability to work, and discomfort.

- **What is whiplash?**

- **Why is it more prominent in rear-end collisions?**

Record your ideas about these questions in your *Active Physics* log. Be prepared to discuss your responses with your small group and the class.

Investigate

Whiplash injury can occur in automobile collisions at surprisingly low speeds—as low as 2.7 m/s (6 mi/h). In this section, you will simulate a rear-end collision between two carts—a "bullet" cart and a "target" cart. The bullet cart will be moving at a speed of approximately 2.7 m/s (6 mi/h) and will strike a stationary target cart.

You will need to create two clay passengers and two different driver's seats—one with a headrest and one without a headrest.

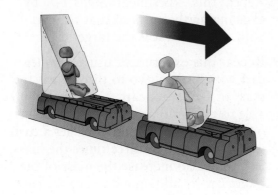

1. Your teacher will provide you with a set of two templates to create driver's seats. Use Template A to create a driver's seat with no headrest. The clay passenger should fit into this seat so that the shoulders of the passenger are level with the top of the seat. (There is no built-in support for the head.)

2. Create the clay passenger in two sections. In the first section, create the torso and legs out of clay.

In the second section, create the head and connect it to the torso with a small piece of clay rolled in the shape of a neck so that the head is not sitting directly on the shoulders. Use a 2.5 cm piece of # 26 wire to fasten the head-neck-torso combination. The wire represents the spinal column in the neck. Do not press the head onto the neck, but rather allow it to rest on it held in place by the wire. The passenger and seat will go in the target cart.

3. Create a similar second clay passenger to go in the bullet cart. Use Template B to create a driver's seat with a headrest.

4. Use masking tape to create seat belts for both dummies.

5. Set up a ramp about 40 cm high, as shown in the diagram on the following page. Use a piece of stiff paper (like card stock) at the bottom of the ramp to smooth out the bump when the cart comes off the ramp.

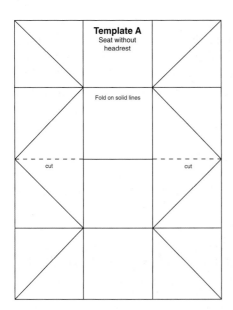

Template A
Seat without headrest

Fold on solid lines

cut   cut

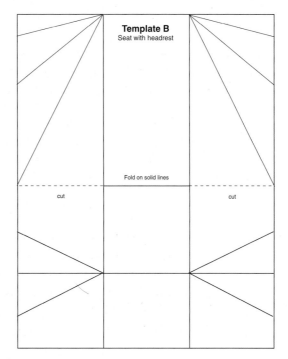

Template B
Seat with headrest

Fold on solid lines

cut   cut

Active Physics

Release the bullet cart from the position on the ramp. This produces an average speed of approximately 2.7 m/s (6 mi/h). This may take several trials.

6. Now place the target cart about 50 cm from the end of the ramp.

7. Release the bullet cart from the same position on the ramp to produce a 2.7 m/s (6 mi/h) collision with the target cart.

   a) What happens to the clay passenger's head in the target cart?

   b) Use Newton's first law of motion to explain your observations.

8. Repeat this experiment (*Steps 1-7*) by exchanging the carts so that the cart with the headrest is the target cart.

9. Repeat this experiment using a bullet cart with a mass two to three times the mass of the target cart. You may be able to tape two or three carts together or one on top of the other to get a cart with about two to three times the mass. You may also increase the mass of the bullet car by adding masses to the cart.

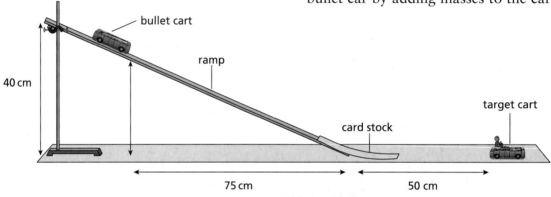

Physics Talk

NEWTON'S SECOND LAW OF MOTION

Newton's first law informs us what happens to objects if no net force acts upon them. Knowing that objects at rest have a tendency to remain at rest and that objects in motion will continue in motion does not provide enough information to analyze collisions. **Newton's second law of motion** allows you to make predictions about what happens when an unbalanced external force is applied to an object. If you were to place a collision cart on a level surface, it would not move. However, if you begin to push the cart, it will begin to move.

Newton's second law of motion states:

> If a body is acted on by an unbalanced force, it will accelerate in the direction of the unbalanced force. The acceleration will be larger for smaller masses. The acceleration can be an increase in speed, a decrease in speed, or a change in direction.

Newton's second law of motion indicates that the change in motion is determined by the net force acting on the object, and the mass of the object itself. Physicists are never satisfied with a verbal explanation and always ask, "Is there an equation that can describe this precisely?"

Physics Words

Newton's second law of motion: if a body is acted on by an unbalanced force, it will accelerate in the direction of the unbalanced force. The acceleration will be larger for smaller masses. The acceleration can be an increase in speed, a decrease in speed, or a change in direction.

Newton's second law does have such an equation that can be written as:

$$F = ma \text{ or } a = \frac{F}{m}$$

From this equation, one can see that "if a body is acted upon by an unbalanced force, it will accelerate in the direction of the unbalanced force." One can also see that the "acceleration will be larger for smaller masses."

What is Whiplash?

In the collision in the investigation you completed, where the target cart did not have a headrest, the clay head swung back during the collision. **Whiplash** is a serious injury that can be caused by a rear-end collision. The back of the automobile seat pushes forward on the torso of the driver and the passengers and their bodies lunge forward. The head remains still for a very short time. The body moving forward and the head remaining still causes the head to snap backward. The neck muscles and bones of the vertebral column (spine) become damaged. The same muscles must then snap the head back to its place atop the shoulders.

Physics Words

whiplash: the common name for a type of neck injury to muscles of the neck.

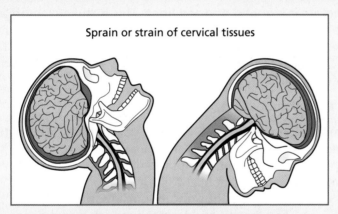

Sprain or strain of cervical tissues

A headrest can prevent whiplash injury. The headrest must be adjusted for the height of the passenger.

Newton's First and Second Laws of Motion and Whiplash

The activity in this section demonstrated the effects of a rear-end collision. Newton's first law and Newton's second law can help explain the "whiplash" injury that passengers suffer during this kind of collision.

Imagine looking at the rear-end collision in slow motion. Think about all that happens.

- An automobile is stopped at a red light. This is the automobile in which the driver is going to receive a whiplash injury. It was the target cart in your investigation. The driver is at rest within the automobile.

- The stopped automobile gets hit from the rear.

- The automobile begins to move. The back of the seat pushes the driver forward and the driver's torso moves with the automobile. The driver's head is not supported and tends to stay back where it is.

- The neck muscles hold the head to the torso as the body moves forward. The muscles then "whip" the head forward. The head keeps moving until it gets ahead of the torso. The neck muscles stop the head, and pull it back to its usual position. Ouch!

Let's repeat the description of the collision and insert all of the places where Newton's first law and Newton's second law apply (in color).

- An automobile is stopped at a red light. This is the automobile in which the driver is going to receive a whiplash injury. The driver is at rest within the automobile. Newton's first law: An object at rest stays at rest, and an object in motion stays in motion unless acted upon by an unbalanced, outside force.

- The stopped automobile gets hit from the rear.

- The automobile begins to move. Newton's second law: The automobile accelerates because of the unbalanced, outside force from the rear: $F = ma$. The back of the seat pushes the driver forward and the driver's torso moves with the automobile. Newton's second law: The torso accelerates because of the unbalanced, outside force from the back of the seat: $F = ma$. The driver's head is not supported and stays back where it is. Newton's first law: an object (the driver's head) at rest stays at rest.

- The neck muscles hold the head to the body as the body moves forward. The muscles then "whip" the head forward. Newton's second law: The head accelerates because of the unbalanced force of the muscles: $F = ma$. The head keeps moving until it gets ahead of the torso. Newton's first law: An object (the head) in motion stays in motion. The head is stopped by the neck muscles. The muscles pull the head back to its usual position. Newton's second law: The head accelerates (slows down) because of the unbalanced force from the neck muscles: $F = ma$. Ouch!

Newton's second law informs you that all accelerations are caused by *unbalanced, outside* forces. It does not say that all forces cause accelerations, only those that are unbalanced.

An object at rest may have many forces acting upon it. When you hold a book in your hand, the book is at rest. There is a force of gravity pulling the book down. There is a force of your hand pushing the book up. These forces are equal and opposite. The "net" force on the book is zero because the two forces balance each other. There is no acceleration because there is no "net" force.

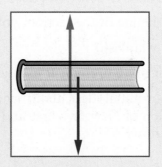

As an automobile moves down the highway at a constant speed, there are forces acting on the automobile but there is no acceleration. No acceleration indicates that the net force must be zero. The force of the engine on the tires and road moving the automobile forward must be equal in magnitude and opposite in direction to the force of the air pushing backward on the automobile. These forces balance each other in this case, where the speed is not changing. There is no net force and there is no acceleration. The automobile stays in motion at a constant speed.

A similar situation occurs when you push a book across a table at constant speed. The push is to the right and the friction is to the left, causing opposing motion. If the forces are equal in size, there is no net force on the book. The book does not accelerate—it moves with a constant speed.

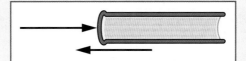

Checking Up

1. What type of safety devices can prevent a whiplash injury?

2. Describe how a whiplash injury occurs in a vehicle collision.

3. Use Newton's first and second laws of motion to analyze how a whiplash injury occurs during a rear-end collision.

+Math	+Depth	+Concepts	+Exploration
◆			

Active Physics

Plus

Using Equations to Analyze a Whiplash Injury

1. Using the model of whiplash and assuming that the driver's head has a mass of 5 kg, calculate the force on the driver's neck muscles during the collision when the target vehicle gets hit and moves at 3 m/s, 5 m/s, 10 m/s, and 15 m/s.

(To give a better sense of these speeds, 27 m/s = 60 mi/h.) Assume this change in motion occurs in 0.2 s (seconds).

2. Draw a graph showing the relationship between force on the neck muscles versus speed of the automobile coming from behind.

3. Repeat the analysis assuming that the time is only 0.1 s (seconds).

What Do You Think Now?

At the beginning of the section, you were asked

• **What is whiplash?**

• **Why is it more prominent in rear-end collisions?**

Revisit your initial ideas about whiplash and rear-end collisions. Based on your investigation of Newton's first and second laws, how would you answer these questions now?

Physics
Essential Questions

What does it mean?

Use Newton's second law of motion to explain what happens to a passenger in a rear-end collision.

How do you know?

How do you know that headrests can improve passenger safety during a rear-end collision?

Why do you believe?

Connects with Other Physics Content	Fits with Big Ideas in Science	Meets Physics Requirements
Forces and motion	Systems	✳ Optimal prediction and explanation

✳ In physics, there is often more than one correct way to describe an event. Describe a rear-end collision using Newton's first law and compare it with your explanation using Newton's second law.

Why should you care?

How can the possibility of a rear-end collision be factored into the design of your safety system?

Reflecting on the Section and the Challenge

Whiplash is a serious injury that can occur during rear-end collisions. The bones that attach the spinal column to the skull are called attachment bones. They are supported by the least amount of muscle. Unfortunately, these smaller bones, with less muscle support, make this area particularly susceptible to injury. The brainstem is very susceptible to damage following whiplash. The brainstem is vital because it regulates blood pressure and breathing movements. By restraining the movement of the head and neck muscles, you can protect against the most severe aspects of whiplash.

Physics to Go

1. Why are neck injuries common during rear-end collisions?

2. Explain why packages in the back of a truck move forward if it comes to a quick stop.

3. As a bus accelerates, the passengers on the bus are jolted toward the back of the bus. Explain what causes the passengers to be apparently pushed backward.

4. Why would the rear-end collision demonstrated in the *Investigate* be more dangerous for someone driving a motorcycle than driving an automobile?

5. Explain in which type of collision headrests serve the greater benefit: during a head-on collision or a rear-end collision?

6. What additional devices have been placed in automobiles to help reduce the impact of rear-end collisions?

7. Consider how your safety device will help prevent whiplash injuries following a collision. What part of the restraining device prevents the movement of the head?

8. As a way to help you learn more about whiplash, rate your whiplash knowledge by taking this whiplash quiz and then check your knowledge against the answers given at the end.

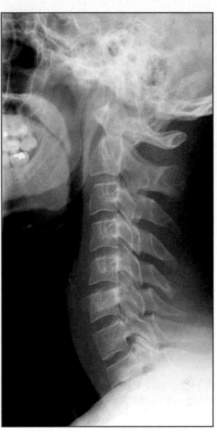

Whiplash Quiz

1. The range of collision speed in which most (nearly 80 percent) rear-impact whiplash injuries occur is:

   a) 10-25 mi/h (4.5 – 11 m/s or about 16-40 km/h)

   b) 15-30 mi/h (7 – 13 m/s or about 25-47 km/h)

   c) 1-5 mi/h   (0.5 – 2.3 m/s or about 2-8 km/h)

   d) 6-12 mi/h (2.7 – 5.4 m/s or about 10-19 km/h)

2. Human-volunteer crash testing, which simulated rear-impact collisions, was conducted at University of California, Los Angeles, and demonstrated the following relationships:

   a) The volunteer's head was subjected to 2 ½ times the acceleration as the vehicle itself.

   b) The volunteer's head was subjected to about ½ the acceleration as the vehicle itself.

   c) The volunteer's acceleration was roughly equivalent to stepping off a curb.

   d) In low-speed collisions, under 8 mi/h (about 12 km/h), no acceleration of the human head can be measured.

3. Regarding the outcome of whiplash injuries, which of the following statements is most accurate?

   a) The vast majority of whiplash injuries resolve in about 6 weeks.

   b) The vast majority of whiplash injuries resolve in 6-12 weeks.

   c) About 25-50 percent of whiplash injuries fail to resolve completely.

   d) Whiplash injuries rarely resolve completely.

4. Although a fairly large percentage of persons will have symptoms on a permanent basis following whiplash injury, what proportion of whiplash patients will have disability?

   a) 2%

   b) 5%

   c) 10%

   d) 18%

   e) 59%

5. The majority of modern automobiles behave relatively stiffly in low-speed, rear-impact collisions. Permanent damage to bumper systems begins to occur at which range of collision speeds?

   a) 20-25 mi/h   (9-11 m/s or about 32-40 km/h)

   b) 2-7 mi/h   (1-3 m/s or about 4-11 km/h)

   c) 8-12 mi/h   (3.6-5.4 m/s or about 13-19 km/h)

   d) 25-30 mi/h   (11-14 m/s or about 40-50 km/h)

6. According to the authors of one series of full-scale, rear-impact crash tests using human volunteers, the threshold for cervical spine soft tissue injury (whiplash injury) occurs at speeds of:

a) 12 mi/h   (5.4 m/s or about 19 km/h)

b) 5 mi/h   (2.3 m/s or about 8 km/h)

c) 2 mi/h   (0.9 m/s or about 3 km/h)

d) 15 mi/h   (7 m/s or about 25 km/h)

(Source: *Dynamic Chiropractic*, August 11, 1997, volume 15, issue 17)

Answers:

1. (d)

2. (a)

3. (c)

4. (e)

5. (c)

6. (b)

Inquiring Further

Crash-test dummies

Investigate crash-test dummies on the Internet. Prepare a 5-minute presentation for the class or a paper including information about how much they cost, their functions, and the variety that exist.

Chapter Mini-Challenge

GOAL Your challenge for this chapter is to create a safety system for a vehicle of your choice. To complete the challenge you will eventually need three products: a 5-minute oral presentation, a written report or multimedia presentation, and a safety system model to protect an egg during a collision in the classroom.

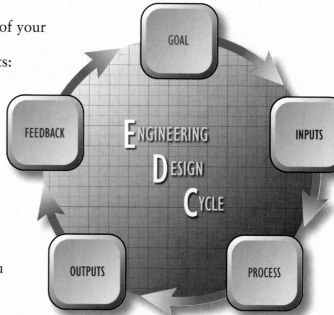

For the *Mini-Challenge* you will create drafts of the first two products; an oral presentation and a written or multimedia report. These drafts could be called prototypes or early versions of the final product in your *Engineering Design Cycle*.

Your group now has some decisions to make. You need to choose a vehicle to design a safety system for. You also have to decide how you can use the physics you have learned to create that system. Then you need to communicate your design ideas to your class. These are very typical problems that engineers need to solve. You can use the simplified *Engineering Design Cycle* to help you meet your *Goal*.

Go back and quickly review your *Goal* that you defined at the start of the chapter. At this point your group will design a safety system that incorporates the physics information you have learned so far in the first four sections.

INPUTS In the *Engineering Design Cycle*, you are adding critical *Inputs* by defining the vehicle that your safety device will be employed in. The type of vehicle will determine some key constraints, like the typical speed of the vehicle, and the mass and velocity of typical obstructions your vehicle may collide with. The physics you have learned so far are the other key *Inputs*. At this point your team should review the physics content from the first four sections to help you design your vehicle safety system.

Section 1: In this section you considered the topic of passenger safety in automobile collisions and explored some of the safety features that are available in modern automobiles. You read that analyzing safety has lead to many safety improvements for automobiles.

Section 2: You investigated Newton's first law of motion and the role it plays in collisions. You also evaluated different seat belt materials and considered the relationship of force, surface area, and pressure.

Section 3: You created a model of a vehicle air bag. You used the ideas of energy and work to help explain why an air bag is helpful to the passengers in an automobile accident.

Section 4: You learned about Newton's second law that explains how objects respond when forces are applied to them by exploring rear-end collisions. Newton's second law describes the relationship between the force applied to a mass and the acceleration it will experience.

Time will be a key constraint for the work you present for the *Mini-Challenge*. You will want to organize your group members so that everyone knows what to do. Assigning roles and responsibilities may be the fastest way to get started. You may want to have a "scriptwriter" to record group thoughts, an "artist" to quickly sketch ideas, a "researcher" who checks chapter sections and returns facts, definitions, and formulas, a "math wizard" who performs calculations and checks the units for all numbers, and maybe even a "multimedia designer" who creates digital files, finds images, or creates a slide presentation of your ideas. The specific roles are not as important as making sure that everyone has a job and knows how to contribute to the group's success.

Once you are organized, you may want to use a short brainstorm to come up with different safety-system ideas. You can use physics principles to help focus your ideas. For instance, ask the group "How can we use a change in force to make a passenger safer?" As soon as you have a list of potential ideas, examine them to see if you want to combine any ideas. For instance, a seat belt and an air bag are both useful, but they work even better together. Finally, vote on an idea that your group will work on.

The time restraints you have to work may prevent you from creating a complete design, so you should focus on describing ideas that you will use based on the physics principles you have learned. You may have an idea for a new seat belt, but instead of detailing what color it will be, focus on explaining why you think a seat belt is necessary and how its specific features will keep the passenger safe. If you have extra time, you can always go back and add more detailed and stylish design elements.

Presenting your information to the class are your design cycle *Outputs*. You will not have to build an egg safety system model yet, but you will want to present some information about how you expect it to work. Even if you change your design before the *Chapter Challenge*, the more ideas you explore now, the more prepared you will be for the *Chapter Challenge*.

Your classmates will give you *Feedback* on the accuracy and the overall appeal of your presentation based on the criteria of the design challenge. This feedback will become an *Input* for your final design in the *Chapter Challenge*.

Remember to correct any parts of your design that were not complete or accurate. Finally, store all of your information in a safe place so that it will be ready to use in the *Chapter Challenge*.

As you complete the remaining sections, look for additional information that will help you improve your safety system. You may learn information that will help you explain why your system is effective by adding details, or even numerical calculations.

Section 5

Momentum: Concentrating on Collisions

What Do You See?

Learning Outcomes

In this section, you will

- **Apply** the definition of momentum.
- **Conduct** analyses of the momentum of pairs of objects involved in one-dimensional collisions.

What Do You Think?

Automobile collisions are a leading cause of injury and death among teenagers.

- **A small sports automobile hits a heavy truck in a collision. What factors determine the outcome for the passengers of the two vehicles?**

- **Which driver will sustain worse injuries? Why?**

Record your ideas about these questions in your *Active Physics* log. Be prepared to discuss your responses with your small group and the class.

Investigate

1. You will stage a head-on collision between two collision carts of equal mass. One of the carts will have a spring or loop of thin metal attached to it so that the carts will collide with a "bounce" rather than with a "thud." A collision of this sort is called an elastic collision. This will serve as a model for the collision of vehicles. Find a level area clear of obstructions, such as the classroom floor, where the one cart can slide into a second cart at rest.

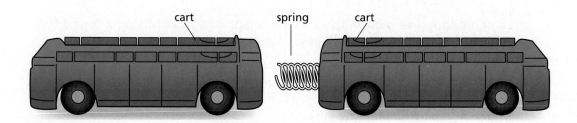

2. Give one cart a small push so that it collides with the second cart. Observe the collision of the moving cart and the target cart.

　a) Record the results in your log. Use a diagram and words to describe what happened to each cart.

3. Repeat the type of collision you just conducted, but this time give the moving cart a larger push so that it hits the target cart with a greater speed.

　a) Describe the results in your log.

　b) How did the results of the collision change from the first time?

　c) Identify a real-life situation that this collision could represent.

4. Double the mass of each cart. Repeat this set of experiments with the two large-mass carts. Compare and contrast the large-mass cart collisions with the small-mass cart collisions.

5. Stage another collision between a stationary small-mass cart and a moving large-mass cart.

　a) Record your observations.

　b) Identify a similar situation in real life, in your log.

　c) Are there any changes in your observations if you increase the speed of the small-mass cart?

6. Stage another collision between a stationary large-mass cart and a moving small-mass cart.

　a) Record your observations.

　b) Identify a similar situation in real life, in your log.

　c) Are there any changes in your observations if you increase the speed of the large-mass cart?

7. You have made observations of what happens when a massive cart hits a less-massive cart. You have also made observations of what happens when the less-massive cart hits the massive cart. Using your observations, conduct an experiment to determine the relative mass of a "mystery" cart of unknown mass compared to a massive cart by staging collisions between them.

　a) Which cart has the greater mass? Describe what you did to decide upon your answer.

　b) Use a scale or balance to check your result. Comment on how well observing collisions between the carts worked as a method of comparing their masses.

Active Physics

Physics Talk

MOMENTUM

Collisions, like a bat hitting a baseball or a racquet hitting a tennis ball, can be fun in sports. Collisions of automobiles are dangerous and cause injuries and deaths.

Physics Words

momentum: the product of the mass and the velocity of an object; momentum is a vector quantity.

What occurs during a collision depends on both the masses of the objects and the velocities of the objects. You observed this with the collisions between carts. **Momentum** is defined as the mass multiplied by velocity and is given the symbol p.

$$p = mv$$

The collision between a small-mass cart with another small-mass cart was very similar to the collision between a large-mass cart and another large-mass cart. In contrast, the large-mass cart hitting the small-mass cart was quite different as was the small-mass cart hitting the large-mass cart. This provides the insight that it is the relative masses (not the absolute masses) of the colliding objects that are important to observe in deciding what will happen in a collision. All vehicles on the road do not have the same mass. Trucks and large SUVs have greater mass than compact vehicles. All vehicles have much greater mass than people walking or people on bicycles. This makes cars and trucks extremely dangerous to pedestrians.

When the large-mass cart hit the small-mass cart, the small-mass cart moved away from the site of the collision with a higher speed than the large-mass cart had before the collision. In a real accident, if a vehicle were to hit a pedestrian, the pedestrian would move a lot faster than the vehicle was moving. The collision would certainly result in injury to, and possibly death of, the pedestrian.

The damage an automobile can produce is related directly to its momentum. All moving automobiles have a very large momentum because of their large mass. A high-speed automobile can have the same momentum as a slow-moving massive truck. For example:

Vehicle	Mass (kg)	Speed (m/s)	Momentum (kg•m/s) $p = mv$
car	1000	20	20,000
truck	10,000	2	20,000

A tennis ball moving very fast can affect a stationary cart more than a tennis ball moving very slowly. This is similar to the damage small pieces of sand moving at very high speeds can cause (such as when a sand blaster is used to clean various surfaces).

In the same way, vehicles have different momenta depending on their mass and velocity. An 18-wheel tractor trailer has a large momentum even if it is moving only a few meters per second, since it has such a large mass. On the other hand, a small automobile (small mass) traveling at very high speeds also has a high momentum due to its speed. The damage done during a collision between objects of such different masses will produce drastically different levels of injury to the passengers in the different vehicles.

Collisions between two objects often involve changes in momentum for each object. When a moving automobile strikes a stationary automobile, the first automobile slows down and the second automobile moves away at some speed. That is, the first automobile loses some of its momentum, and the second automobile picks up some momentum. You will study this relationship in the next section.

Checking Up

1. Which object has greater momentum, a butterfly traveling at 16 km/h (10 mi/h) or an eagle traveling at 16 km/h (10 mi/h)?

2. Describe how the transfer of momentum works.

3. Using what you know of momentum, describe what would happen if a car hit a skateboarder.

Active Physics
Plus

+Math	+Depth	+Concepts	+Exploration
◆			

Calculating Momentum

An automobile with a mass of 1000 kg is moving at 20 m/s (approximately 40 mph). Its momentum is

$p = mv$

$p = (1000 \text{ kg})(20 \text{ m/s})$

$p = 20{,}000 \text{ kg} \cdot \text{m/s}$

Approximate the masses of the following objects and calculate how fast each would have to be traveling to have the same momentum as the automobile.

a) truck

b) SUV

c) bicycle

d) baseball

e) bowling ball

What Do You Think Now?

At the beginning of this activity you were asked:

• A small sports automobile hits a heavy truck in a collision.
What factors determine the outcome for the passengers of the two vehicles?

• Which driver will sustain worse injuries? Why?

Based on the relative amounts of momentum, what is the outcome of a head-on collision between a heavy truck and a small sports automobile if both have the same speed? How do your ideas now compare to your initial ideas?

Physics
Essential Questions

What does it mean?

Define momentum and explain under what circumstances a compact automobile could have the same momentum as a more massive sport utility vehicle.

How do you know?

Explain, using two sets of observations, how you can determine the relative masses of two carts by observing collisions.

Why do you believe?

Connects with Other Physics Content	Fits with Big Ideas in Science	Meets Physics Requirements
Forces and motion	* Conservation laws	Good clear explanation, no more complicated than necessary

* Physicists define new quantities because they are useful in describing real events. Mass and velocity are two easily observable quantities. Why did physicists introduce the term momentum?

Why should you care?

How will the design of your safety system for the *Chapter Challenge* take into account the speed, thus momentum, of the cart carrying the egg?

Reflecting on the Section and the Challenge

In collisions between objects of equal mass, the resulting effect on each object is pretty much the same. But when one vehicle is much more massive than the second one, as in the case of the cart and a tennis ball or a heavy truck colliding head-on with a sports automobile, the results for the smaller vehicle is often disastrous. The object with the low mass suffers the most drastic damage.

The key to understanding collisions is to calculate the momentum of each colliding object. Momentum is mass multiplied by velocity. This is also written as $p = mv$. Objects with a small mass and high speed can have the same momentum as massive objects moving at slow speeds. An automobile with a mass of 1000 kg moving at 5 m/s (10 mph) has an enormous momentum and would severely injure any pedestrian upon contact.

Active Physics

Physics to Go

1. Suppose an automobile collides with another automobile that is stopped. If both automobiles have the same mass, what do you expect to happen in the resulting collision?

2. Describe the collision between two vehicles of equal mass moving toward each other at equal speeds.

3. Describe the collision between two vehicles of very different masses moving toward each other at equal speeds.

4. Why do football teams prefer offensive and defensive linemen who weigh about 140 kg (about 300 lb)?

5. What determines who will get knocked backward when a big vehicle collides with a smaller vehicle in a head-on collision?

6. A 1000-kg automobile is moving at 10.0 m/s. At what speed would a 10,000-kg truck need to travel in the same direction so that the momentum of the two would be equal?

7. *Preparing for the Chapter Challenge*

   Use the words mass, velocity, and momentum to write a paragraph that gives a detailed "before and after" description of what happens when a moving vehicle hits a stationary vehicle of equal mass in a direct collision.

Section 6

Conservation of Momentum

What Do You See?

What Do You Think?

Traffic-accident investigators can determine what happened during an automobile accident by analyzing tire marks and the damage to the automobiles.

- **What physics principles do the traffic-accident investigators use to "reconstruct" the accident?**

Record your ideas about this question in your *Active Physics* log. Be prepared to discuss your responses with your small group and the class.

Investigate

In this *Investigate*, you will use two collision carts of equal masses that will stick together after a collision. Before the collision, one cart will be moving and the other cart will be at rest. After the collision, the two carts should stick together and move as a single object. You may use clay, magnets, or fabric hook-and-loop fasteners to stick the carts together, depending on what is available.

1. Stage a "sticky" collision between the two carts with equal masses. Measure the velocity, in meters per second, of the moving mass before the collision and the velocity of the combined masses after the collision.

Learning Outcomes

In this section, you will

- **Understand** and apply the law of conservation of momentum to collisions.

- **Measure** the momentum before and after a moving mass strikes a stationary mass in a head-on collision.

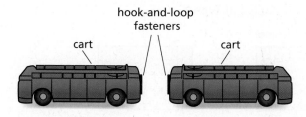

hook-and-loop
fasteners

cart   cart

You can measure the velocities with a ruler and stopwatch, with a ticker-tape timer, with a velocimeter or a computer and motion detector.

✎ a) Prepare a data table in your log similar to the one shown below. Provide enough horizontal rows in the table to enter data for at least four collisions.

Sticky Head-on Collisions:
One Object Moving before Collision

Mass of Object 1 (kg)	Mass of Object 2 (kg)	Velocity of Object 1 before Collision (m/s)	Velocity of Object 2 before Collision (m/s)	Mass of Combined Objects after Collision (kg)	Velocity of Combined Objects after Collision (m/s)
1.0	1.0			0.0	2.0
2.0	1.0			0.0	3.0
1.0	2.0			0.0	3.0
				0.0	

✎ b) Record the measured values of the velocities in the first row of the data table.

2. Stage other sticky collisions using the masses listed in the second and third rows of the data table. Then stage one or more additional collisions using other masses. Measure the velocities before and after each collision.

✎ a) Enter the measured values in the data table.

3. Organize a table for recording the momentum of each object before and after each of the above collisions.

✎ a) Prepare a table similar to the following example in your log.

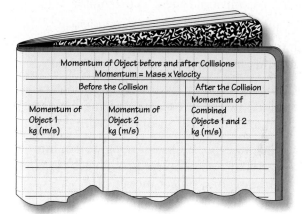

Momentum of Object before and after Collisions
Momentum = Mass × Velocity

Before the Collision		After the Collision
Momentum of Object 1 kg (m/s)	Momentum of Object 2 kg (m/s)	Momentum of Combined Objects 1 and 2 kg (m/s)

✎ b) Calculate the momentum of each object before and after each of the above collisions and enter each momentum value in the table.

✎ c) Calculate and compare the total momentum before each collision to the total momentum after each collision.

✎ d) Allowing for minor variations due to uncertainties of measurement, write in your log a general conclusion about how the momentum before a collision compares to the momentum after a collision.

4. There are a variety of collisions involving two objects. In each collision, momentum is conserved and the same equation is used. The equation gets simpler when one of the objects is at rest and has zero momentum.

Active Physics

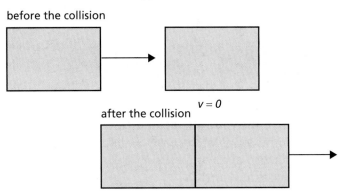

Collision Type 1

before the collision

v = 0

after the collision

a) Draw two sketches for each collision type described at the right—one showing each object before the collision and one showing each object after the collision. By writing the momenta you know directly on the sketch, the calculations become easier. The sketch for Collision Type 1 is provided.

Collision Type 1: One moving object hits a stationary object and both stick together and move off at the same speed.

Collision Type 2: Two stationary objects explode by the release of a spring between them and move off in opposite directions.

Collision Type 3: One moving object hits a stationary object. The first object stops, and the second object moves off.

Collision Type 4: One moving object hits a stationary object, and both move off at different speeds.

Collision Type 5: Two moving objects collide, and both objects move at different speeds after the collision.

Collision Type 6: Two moving objects collide, and both objects stick together and move off at the same speed.

Physics Talk

THE LAW OF CONSERVATION OF MOMENTUM

In this section, you investigated a conservation principle that is a hallmark of physics—the conservation of momentum. You found evidence of the conservation of momentum when a moving cart hit a stationary cart and they stuck together. Momentum is also conserved in all the collisions you illustrated at the end of the investigation. One of these collisions (Type 2) is sometimes called an "explosion." If you add up all of the momenta *before* a collision (or explosion), you know that the sum of all the momenta after the collision will be the same. That is what physicists mean by the word "conserve." The total momentum is conserved because its value remains the same.

In the first collision of the section, a moving cart hit a stationary cart and they stuck together. The same thing happens in a traffic accident. If the momentum before a collision is 5000 kg•m/s, then the momentum after the collision must be 5000 kg•m/s. Imagine a vehicle stops at a red light. The vehicle is not moving and therefore, has a momentum equal to zero. If a second vehicle that has a momentum of 5000 kg•m/s then hits the stopped vehicle, both vehicles move off with (a combined) 5000 kg•m/s of momentum.

Total momentum stays the same or, in other words, total momentum is conserved.

You can write this as an equation and substitute values for the masses and velocities of the vehicles.

Momentum BEFORE collision = Momentum AFTER collision

$$m_1v_1 + m_2v_2 = (m_1 + m_2)v_f$$
$$(1000 \text{ kg})(5 \text{ m/s}) + (1000 \text{ kg})(0 \text{ m/s}) = (1000 \text{ kg} + 1000 \text{ kg})(2.5 \text{ m/s})$$
$$5000 \text{ kg} \cdot \text{m/s} = 5000 \text{ kg} \cdot \text{m/s}$$

You add the masses "after the collision" because they stuck together and travel with the same speed. Conservation of momentum is an experimental fact. Physicists have compared momentum before and after collisions between pairs of objects ranging from railroad cars slamming together to subatomic particles impacting one another at near the speed of light. Never have any exceptions been found to the statement, "The total momentum before a collision is equal to the total momentum after the collision if no external forces act on the system." This statement is known as the **law of conservation of momentum**. In all collisions between vehicles and trucks, between protons and protons, between planets and meteors, the momentum before the collision equals the momentum after the collision.

A single cue ball hits a rack of 15 billiard balls and they all scatter. It would seem as if everything has changed. Physicists have discovered that in this collision, as in all collisions and explosions, nature does keep at least one thing from changing—the total momentum. The sum of the momentum of all of the billiard balls immediately after the collision is equal to the momentum of the original cue ball. Nature conserves momentum. Irrespective of the changes you can see, the total momentum undergoes no change whatsoever. The objects may move in new directions and with new speeds, but the momentum stays the same.

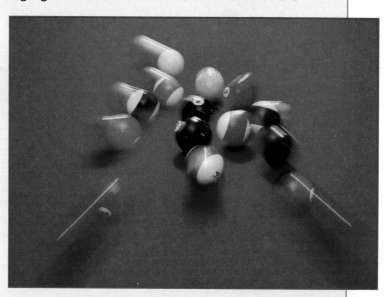

Physics Words

law of conservation of momentum: the total momentum before a collision is equal to the total momentum after the collision if no external forces act on the system.

Active Physics

Conservation of momentum is crucial physics for analyzing any collision between objects. Traffic-accident investigators use tread marks, the positions of the automobiles, and the damage to the automobiles to understand what happened at the time of the accident. They also use the physics principle of momentum conservation to help them in their analysis.

If you know the masses and velocities of two objects before a collision, you can accurately predict the velocities after the collision. Physics allows you to predict the future!

Solving conservation of momentum problems is easy. Using the definition of momentum, $p = mv$, calculate each object's momentum before the collision. Calculate each object's momentum after the collision. The total after the collision must equal the total before the collision.

Sample Problem I

A boy and a girl are riding in bumper cars at an amusement park. A 75-kg boy and car are moving to the east at 3.00 m/s toward a 50-kg girl and car who are moving toward him (west) at 1.80 m/s. If they catch up, stick together, and then move away together, what is their final velocity?

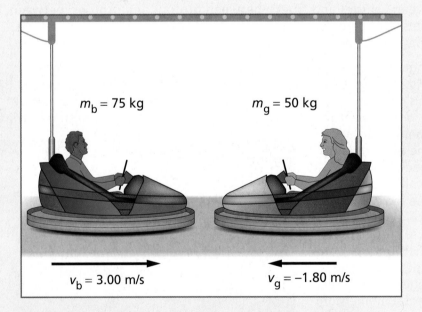

$m_b = 75$ kg $m_g = 50$ kg

$v_b = 3.00$ m/s $v_g = -1.80$ m/s

Strategy: This is a problem involving the law of conservation of momentum. The momentum of an isolated system before an interaction is equal to the momentum of the system after the interaction. As you are working through this problem, remember that the v in this expression is velocity and that it has direction as well as magnitude. Make east the positive direction, and then west will be negative.

Given:

$m_b = 75$ kg

$m_g = 50$ kg

$v_b = 3.00$ m/s

$v_g = -1.80$ m/s

Solution:

$$\left(m_b v_b\right)_{before} + \left(m_g v_g\right)_{before} = \left[\left(m_b + m_g\right)v_{bg}\right]_{after}$$

$$\left(75 \text{ kg}\right)\left(3.00 \text{ m/s}\right)+\left(50 \text{ kg}\right)\left(-1.80 \text{ kg}\right)=\left(75 \text{ kg}+50 \text{ kg}\right)v_{bg}$$

$$v_{bg} = \frac{225 \text{ kg} \cdot \text{m/s} - 90 \text{ kg} \cdot \text{m/s}}{125 \text{ kg}}$$

$$v_{bg} = 1.1 \text{ m/s east (in the direction that the 75-kg boy was going originally)}$$

Sample Problem 2

A steel ball with a mass of 2 kg is traveling at 3 m/s west. It collides with a stationary ball that has a mass of 1 kg. Upon collision, the smaller ball moves to the west at 4 m/s. What is the velocity of the larger ball?

Strategy: Again, you will use the law of conservation of momentum. Before the collision, only the larger ball has momentum. After the collision, the two balls move away at different velocities.

Given:

Before collision

$m_1 = 2$ kg

$v_{1b} = 3$ m/s

$m_2 = 1$ kg

$v_{2b} = 0$ m/s

After collision

$v_{2a} = 4$ m/s

$v_{1a} = ?$ m/s

Solution:

Momentum before = Momentum after

$$\left(m_1 v_{1b}\right)+\left(m_2 v_{2b}\right)=\left(m_1 v_{1a}\right)+\left(m_2 v_{2a}\right)$$

$$\left(2 \text{ kg}\right)\left(3 \text{ m/s}\right)+\left(1 \text{ kg}\right)\left(0 \text{ m/s}\right)=\left(2 \text{ kg}\right)v_{1a}+\left(1 \text{ kg}\right)\left(4 \text{ m/s}\right)$$

$$6 \text{ kg} \cdot \text{m/s} = \left(2v_{1a}\right) \text{ kg} + 4 \text{ kg} \cdot \text{m/s}$$

$$v_{1a} = 1 \text{ m/s}$$

Checking Up

1. Explain the law of conservation of momentum.

2. Compare momentum changes in a collision and an explosion.

3. A vehicle with a momentum of 6000 kg·m/s strikes a stationary vehicle. What is the momentum of the two vehicles as they move off together after the collision?

+Math	+Depth	+Concepts	+Exploration
◆◆	◆◆		

Conservation of Momentum and Newton's Laws

Conservation of momentum can be shown to emerge from Newton's laws. Newton's third law states that if object A and object B collide, the force of object A on B must be equal and opposite to the force of object B on A.

$$F_{A\,on\,B} = -F_{B\,on\,A}$$

The negative sign shows mathematically that the equally sized forces are in opposite directions. Since $F = ma$ by Newton's second law:

$$m_B a_B = -m_A a_A$$

$$\frac{m_B \Delta v_B}{\Delta t} = \frac{-m_A \Delta v_A}{\Delta t}$$

$$m_B \left(\frac{v_f - v_i}{\Delta t} \right)_B = -m_A \left(\frac{v_f - v_i}{\Delta t} \right)_A$$

Since the change in time must be the same for both objects (A acts on B for as long as B acts on A), then Δt can be eliminated from both sides of the equation.

Combining the initial velocities (v_i) on one side of the equation and the final velocities (v_f) on the other side of the equation:

$$m_A v_{iA} + m_B v_{iB} = m_A v_{fA} + m_B v_{fB}$$

Newton's laws have yielded the conservation of momentum. The momentum of object A before the collision plus the momentum of object B before the collision equals the momentum of object A after the collision plus the momentum of object B after the collision.

This equation works in one-dimensional collisions, and also in the extraordinarily complex two-dimensional collisions of multi-vehicle collisions. Momentum is a vector. When analyzing a two-dimensional collision, you must add the momenta using vector diagrams or vector mathematics.

Consider a game of billiards where a cue ball (the white ball) hits a stationary object ball (the red ball). The two balls have the same mass. If the cue ball moves up and to the right (as shown), then the object ball must move down and to the right so that the total momentum is conserved.

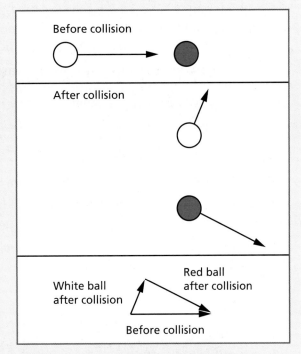

You can see in the vector diagram above that the momentum vector before the collision (the horizontal vector) is identical to the sum of the two other momenta vectors after the collision.

A collision where objects bounce off of each other is an elastic collision. In a perfectly elastic collision, kinetic energy is conserved: the total kinetic energy before the collision is equal to the total kinetic energy after the collision.

When the colliding objects are equal in mass, you can use the conservation of momentum and the conservation of kinetic energy to prove that the angle between the objects after the collision is 90°. In the vector diagram for momentum conservation, you can see that the three vectors create a triangle. Look at the following equation for the conservation of kinetic energy.

$$KE_{Before} = KE_{After}$$

$$\tfrac{1}{2}mv_{iA}^2 = \tfrac{1}{2}mv_{fA}^2 + \tfrac{1}{2}mv_{fB}^2$$

Since all the masses are equal:

$$v_i^2 = v_{fA}^2 + v_{fB}^2$$

You may recognize this as a form of the Pythagorean theorem for a right triangle $a^2 + b^2 = c^2$. The vector triangle for momentum must therefore be a right triangle. The cue ball and the object ball must depart at right angles. You can now use your physics knowledge when you play billiards!

1. The mathematics of collisions becomes a bit difficult since the kinetic energy depends on the square of the velocity. Try to solve for the speed of a pedestrian when hit by an automobile. Assume that momentum is conserved. Also assume that 50 percent of the kinetic energy is conserved. Assume a 1000-kg automobile moving at 10 m/s (only 20 mph) collides with a 70-kg pedestrian at rest. The calculation will give you a sense of how dangerous an automobile is because it has such tremendous momentum.

What Do You Think Now?

At the beginning of the activity you were asked:

- **What physics principles do the traffic-accident investigators use to "reconstruct" the accident?**

Revisit your initial responses. Now that you investigated how the law of conservation of momentum works, how would you answer this question?

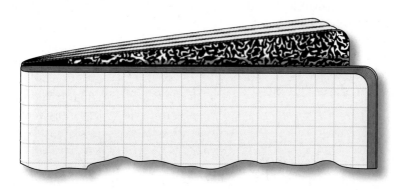

Physics
Essential Questions

What does it mean?

What does it mean to "conserve" momentum in a collision?

How do you know?

All experiments have measurement uncertainties. How accurately were you able to measure the conservation of momentum in your activity? How could the measurements be improved?

Why do you believe?

Connects with Other Physics Content	Fits with Big Ideas in Science	Meets Physics Requirements
Forces and motion	✳ Conservation laws	Good clear explanation, no more complicated than necessary

✳ In physics, concepts are introduced to help make complex situations appear simpler to understand. Describe in words all that happens when a cue ball hits the 15 balls at the beginning of a billiards match. Describe the same event using the concepts of conservation of momentum and conservation of energy.

Why do you care?

How would the principle of conservation of momentum influence the design of a safety system that must protect against collisions with a much more massive object?

Reflecting on the Section and the Challenge

The law of conservation of momentum is a very powerful tool for explaining collisions in traffic accidents. The law works even when one of the objects involved in a collision "bounces back," reversing the direction of its velocity and therefore, its momentum. Whether describing a collision between two people, or between a moving automobile and a tree, you can describe how the total momentum is conserved.

Physics to Go

For the following problems, show your work, as always, and also show a diagram of the momentum "before" and "after."

1. One cart hits and sticks to a second cart. Make a diagram showing the carts before and after the collision. How does the speed of the carts after the collision compare with the initial speed of the moving cart?

2. Two 1-kg carts are each moving toward each other at 2 m/s. They collide and each reverses directions, moving in the opposite directions at 2 m/s. Draw a diagram showing the carts before and after the collision.

   a) Calculate the momentum of each cart before the collision. (Hint: Since they are moving in opposite directions, one momentum will be positive and one will be negative.)

   b) Calculate the total momentum before the collision.

   c) Calculate the total momentum after the collision.

3. In an automobile crash, a vehicle that was stopped at a red light is rear-ended by another vehicle. The vehicles have the same mass. If the tire marks show that the two vehicles moved after the collision at 4 m/s, what was the speed of the vehicle before the collision?

4. Given that the total momentum before a collision must equal the total momentum after the collision, how can one of the cars gain momentum?

5. Vehicle A and vehicle B collide and vehicle A loses 4000 kg•m/s of momentum. What is the change in momentum of vehicle B? What is the total change in momentum due to the collision?

6. A railroad car with a mass of 2000 kg coasting at 3.0 m/s overtakes and locks together with an identical car coasting on the same track in the same direction at 2.0 m/s. What is the speed of the cars after they lock together?

7. In a hockey game, an 80.0-kg player skating at 10.0 m/s overtakes and bumps from behind a 100.0-kg player who is moving in the same direction at 8.00 m/s. As a result of being bumped from behind, the 100.0-kg player's speed increases to 9.78 m/s. What is the 80.0-kg player's velocity (speed and direction) after the bump?

8. A 3-kg hard steel ball collides head-on with a 1-kg hard steel ball. The balls are moving at 2 m/s in opposite directions before they collide. Upon colliding, the 3-kg ball stops. What is the velocity of the 1-kg object after the collision? (Hint: Assign velocities in one direction as positive; then any velocities in the opposite direction are negative.)

9. A 45-kg female figure skater and her 75-kg male skating partner begin their ice-dancing performance standing at rest in face-to-face position with the palms of their hands touching. When their dance-music starts, both skaters "push off" with their hands to move backward. If the female skater moves at 2.0 m/s relative to the ice, what is the velocity of the male skater? (Hint: The momentum before the skaters push off is zero.)

10. A 0.35-kg tennis racquet moving to the right at 20.0 m/s hits a 0.060-kg tennis ball that is moving to the left at 30.0 m/s. The racquet continues moving to the right after the collision, but at a reduced speed of 10.0 m/s. What is the velocity of the tennis ball after it is hit by the racquet?

11. A stationary 3-kg hard steel ball is hit head-on by a 1-kg hard steel ball moving to the right at 4 m/s. After the collision, the 3-kg ball moves to the right at 2 m/s. What is the velocity (speed and direction) of the 1-kg ball after the collision? (Hint: Direction is important.)

12. A 90.00-kg hockey goalie, at rest in front of the goal, stops a puck ($m = 0.16$ kg) that is traveling at 30.00 m/s. At what speed do the goalie and puck travel after the save?

13. A 45.00-kg girl jumps from the side of a pool into a raft ($m = 0.08$ kg) floating on the surface of the water. She leaves the side at a speed of 1.10 m/s and lands on the raft. At what speed will the girl and the raft begin to travel across the pool?

14. Two cars collide head on. Initially, automobile A ($m = 1700.0$ kg) is traveling at 10.00 m/s north and automobile B is traveling at 25.00 m/s south. After the collision, automobile A reverses its direction and travels at 5.00 m/s while automobile B continues in its initial direction at a speed of 3.75 m/s. What is the mass of automobile B?

15. A proton ($m = 1.67 \times 10^{-27}$ kg) traveling at 2.50×10^5 m/s collides with an unknown particle initially at rest. After the collision, the proton reverses direction and travels at 1.10×10^5 m/s. Determine the change in momentum of the unknown particle.

16. A 0.04-kg bullet moving at 200.0 m/s is shot into a 20.00-kg block initially at rest on an icy pond. What is the velocity of the bullet-block combination? The coefficient of friction between the block and the ice is 0.15. How far would the block slide before coming to rest?

17. *Preparing for the Chapter Challenge*

In your description of your design for a safety device, you will need to include an explanation of how it works to reduce injuries. In the past, you have used the ideas "energy management" and pressure to describe what happens in a crash. You can also think of a collision as a transfer of momentum. How does momentum explain what happens when a truck with great mass and an automobile with small mass collide?

Section 7

Impulse and Changes in Momentum: Crumple Zone

What Do You See?

Learning Outcomes

In this section, you will

- **Design** a device that is able to absorb the energy of a collision and reduce the net force on an object in an automobile.

- **Describe** collisions and crumple zones in terms of momentum, impulse, and force.

- **Apply** the concept of impulse in the analysis of collisions.

- **Use** a computer's motion probe (sonic ranger) to determine the velocity of moving vehicles.

- **Use** a computer's force probe to determine the force exerted during a collision.

- **Compare** the change of momentum of a model vehicle before a collision with the impulse applied during a collision.

- **Explore** ways of using cushions to increase the time that a force acts during a primary collision.

What Do You Think?

When an automobile collides with a wall and is brought to a stop, all of the energy of motion that the automobile had has to go somewhere. Also, a force must act to stop the automobile, and any passengers inside. Automotive engineers design something called a crumple zone to absorb the energy of the collision and to lessen the force on the passengers. (*A crumple zone is part of the body of an automobile that compresses during an impact.*)

- **What are some of the factors that automobile designers and engineers must consider when designing a crumple zone as a safety feature?**

Record your ideas about this question in your *Active Physics* log. Be prepared to discuss your responses with your small group and the class.

Active Physics

Investigate

Part A: Designing a Crumple Zone

1. Form teams of three to five students. Each team will design a crumple zone that will attach to the front of a cart. You may use one sheet of paper, 30 cm of tape, 2 rubber bands, and 30 cm of string.

2. The task is as follows:

   • Your cart (automobile) will roll down the ramp from a height of 10 cm, cross 20 cm of level ground, then hit a wall of books and come to a complete halt.

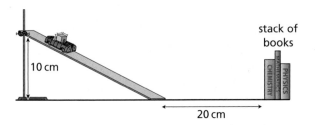

   • A 4 cm by 4 cm by 3 cm block (passenger) will be attached to the cart. The wooden block will be held in the automobile by a single 2-cm length piece of tape attached to the front of the block.

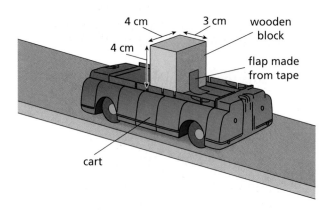

   • The crumple zone which you will design must allow the cart to stop without the block falling over.

If the challenge appears too difficult at first, try heights below 10 cm. You can then demonstrate the height below 10 cm that allows the automobile with the crumple zone to stop without disturbing the wooden block. If the challenge appears too easy, you can try heights above 10 cm.

3. Follow your teacher's guidelines for considering the use of time, space, and materials as you design your crumple zone.

4. Begin by discussing why the tape on the front of the block will not help hold the block in place when the automobile hits the books. (Hint: Use Newton's first law.)

5. Demonstrate your design team's crumple zone for the class. Keep a careful record of your *Engineering Design Cycle.* When you make changes, record the changes and the reason for these changes.

Part B: Cushioning Collisions (Computer Analysis)

1. In this part of the investigation, you will be using a force probe that is attached to a computer to determine the effectiveness of different types of cushions for a cart. A force probe is a device that measures the force of an impact. Before beginning the experiments, investigate how the force probe works. Open the computer files that will display a graph of force versus time. Your teacher will help you locate the program. As the computer is recording data, use your finger to move the lever of the force probe. Investigate how the force of your finger on the lever affects the graph that appears on the computer screen.

   a) Draw the graph that you have generated with the detector.

   b) Beneath the graph, describe what you were doing to create that graph.

2. Release a cart at the top of a ramp and measure the force of impact as the cart strikes a barrier at the bottom. A sonic ranger can be mounted at the top of the ramp to measure the speed of the cart prior to the collision. Open the appropriate computer files to prepare the sonic ranger to graph velocity vs. time and the force probe to graph force vs. time.

3. Mount the sonic ranger at the top of a ramp and place the force probe against a barrier at the bottom of the ramp, as shown in the diagram. Attach an index card to the cart to obtain better reflection of the sound waves and improve the readings of the sonic ranger.

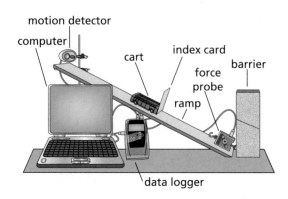

4. To ensure that the data collection equipment is working properly, conduct a few runs of releasing the cart down the ramp so that it collides with the force probe.

a) Make copies of the velocity vs. time and force vs. time graphs that are displayed on the computer.

b) Some computer probe programs calculate the area between the curve and the x-axis. Record this calculated value. Alternatively, you can use a transparency of graph paper to place

over the curve and count the number of boxes that are between the curve and the x-axis.

5. Attach your cushioning material to the front of the cart. Conduct a number of runs with the same type of cushioning. Make sure that the cart is coasting down the same slope from the same position each time.

a) Make copies of the velocity vs. time and force vs. time graphs that are displayed on the computer.

b) Record the area between the curve and x-axis.

6. Repeat *Step 5* using other types of cushioning materials.

a) Record your observations in your log.

7. Using the information from the graphs you obtained in this investigation, answer the following:

a) Compare the force vs. time graphs for the cushioned carts with those for the carts without cushioning.

b) Compare the areas under the force vs. time graphs for all of the experimental trials.

c) Compute the *momentum* of the cart (the product of the mass and the velocity) prior to the collision and compare it with the area under the force vs. time graphs.

d) Summarize your comparisons in a chart.

e) The area under the force vs. time graph is called the *impulse*. How can impulse be used to explain the effectiveness of cushioning systems?

f) Describe the relationship between impulse ($F\Delta t$) and the change in momentum = $\Delta(mv)$.

323

Physics Talk

FORCES AFFECTING COLLISIONS

By examining the different crumple zones designed by other teams in your class, you can get an insight into the physics of collisions. Probably no team just used the flat sheet of paper. Most teams tried to fold the paper in specific ways. It seemed the goal was to have a "softer" collision rather than have the cart hit the wall without any crumple zone.

By trying to make a "softer" collision, you may have used the physics of work and change in kinetic energy.

$$W = F \cdot d = \Delta KE$$

In this case, as in the air bag, you wanted to decrease the force by increasing the distance to stop the automobile. The work done on the cart then reduced the kinetic energy of the cart.

Impulse and Changes in Momentum

There is an equivalent way of describing the physics of a collision. Rather than focusing on the distance that the force acts, you can look at the amount of time that the force acts. By maximizing the time, you can minimize the force. When creating the crumple zone, you increased the time and thereby minimized the force.

It takes an unbalanced, opposing force to stop a moving automobile. Newton's second law of motion, $F = ma$, lets you find out how much force is required to stop any automobile of any mass with a corresponding *acceleration* (or change in speed with respect to time). For example, if a 1000-kg automobile accelerates at –2 m/s², then the force required is

$$F = ma = \left(1000 \text{ kg}\right)\left(-2 \text{ m/s}^2\right) = -2000 \text{ N}$$

Physics Words

velocity: speed in a given direction; displacement divided by the time interval; velocity is a vector quantity; it has magnitude and direction.

Notice that the acceleration is negative because the automobile's **velocity** decreased. Also, notice that the force is negative to indicate that it produces a negative acceleration as it slows the automobile down to a stop.

The overall idea can be shown using a concept map seen at the top of the next page.

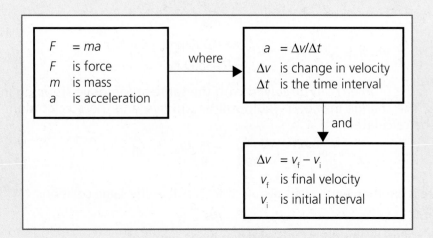

If you know the mass and can determine the acceleration, you can calculate the force using Newtons second law

$$F = ma$$

Suppose a moving automobile has a forward velocity of 15 m/s. Stopping the automobile in 3 s gives it a final velocity of 0 m/s.
The change in velocity

$$= v_{final} - v_{initial}$$
$$= 0 - 15 \text{ m/s}$$
$$= -15 \text{ m/s}$$

(This calculation corresponds to the bottom box in the concept map. Any change in velocity is defined as acceleration. In this case, the change in velocity is −15 m/s .

If the change in velocity occurs in 3 s, the **acceleration** is −15 m/s in 3 s, or −5 m/s every second, or -5 m/s². You can look at this as an equation:

$$a = \frac{\Delta v}{\Delta t} = \frac{(v_f - v_i)}{\Delta t} = \frac{-15 \text{ m/s}}{3 \text{ s}} = -5 \text{ m/s}^2$$

(This calculation corresponds to the upper right box in the concept map.)

Newton's second law informs you that unbalanced outside forces cause all accelerations. The force stopping the automobile may have been the frictional force of the brakes and tires on the road, or the force of a tree, or the force of another automobile. Once you know the acceleration, you can calculate the force using Newton's second law. If the automobile has a mass of 1000 kg, the unbalanced force for the acceleration of −5 m/s every second would be −5000 N. The negative sign tells you that the unbalanced force was opposite in direction to the velocity.

If the automobile has a mass of 1000 kg, the unbalanced force for the acceleration of −5 m/s every second would be −5000 N.

Physics Words

acceleration: the change in velocity per unit time; acceleration is a vector quantity.

Newton's second law of motion: if a body is acted upon by a net external force, it will accelerate in the direction of the net force with an acceleration proportional to the force and inversely proportional to the mass.

$$F = ma$$
$$= (1000 \text{ kg})(-5 \text{ m/s}^2)$$
$$= -5000 \text{ N}$$

The same problem can be solved with the same automobile stopping in 0.5 s. The change in speed would still be –15 m/s, and the acceleration can be calculated.

$$a = \frac{\Delta v}{\Delta t} = \frac{v_i - v_o}{\Delta t} = \frac{-15 \text{ m/s}^2}{0.5 \text{ s}} = -30 \text{ m/s}^2$$

There is another, equivalent picture that describes the same collision:

$$F = ma$$

Multiplying both sides of the equation by Δt, you get

$$F\Delta t = m\Delta v$$

then you can rewrite Newton's second law as

$$F = \frac{m\Delta v}{\Delta t}$$

Physics Words

momentum: the product of the mass and the velocity of an object; momentum is a vector quantity.

impulse: a change in momentum of an object.

The term on the right-hand side of the equation is change in **momentum**. The term on the left side of the equation is impulse.

Any moving automobile has momentum. Momentum is represented with a small p. Momentum is defined as the mass of the automobile multiplied by its velocity $p = mv$.

A change in momentum is called **impulse**. The impulse-momentum equation tells you that the momentum of the automobile can be changed by applying a force for a given amount of time. The impulse is the force multiplied by the time. So a small force exerted over a long time produces the same impulse (change in momentum) as a large force exerted over a short time. "The small force exerted over a long time" is what you found in the effective crumple zones.

Impulse-momentum is an effective way in which to describe all collisions.

Consider this question: "Why do you prefer to land on soft grass rather than on hard concrete?" Soft grass is preferred because the force on your body is less when you land on soft grass. This can be explained by using the impulse-momentum relation.

Whether you land on concrete or soft grass, your change in velocity will be identical. Your velocity may decrease from 3 m/s to 0 m/s.

On concrete, this change occurs very fast, while on soft grass this change occurs in a longer period of time. Your acceleration on soft grass is smaller because the change in velocity occurred in a longer period of time.

$$a = \frac{\Delta v}{\Delta t}$$

When the change in the period of time gets larger, the denominator of the fraction gets larger and the value of the acceleration gets smaller.

When landing on grass, Newton's second law then tells you that the force must be smaller because the acceleration is smaller for an identical mass, $F = ma$. Smaller acceleration on grass requires a smaller force. Smaller forces are easier on your body and that is why you prefer to land on soft grass.

Change in value of momentum $\Delta p = \Delta mv$	Force F	Change in time Δt	Impulse $F\Delta t$
150 kg · m/s	50 N	3 s	150 N/s (150 kg · m/s)
150 kg · m/s	150 N	1 s	150 N/s (150 kg · m/s)
150 kg · m/s	15,000 N	0.01 s	150 N/s (150 kg · m/s)

You can get this change in momentum with a large force over a short time or a small force over a longer time.

If your mass is 50 kg, the amount of your change in momentum will be 150 kg • m/s when you decrease your velocity from 3 m/s to 0 m/s. There are many forces and associated times that can give this change in the value of the momentum.

If you could land on a surface that requires 3 s to stop, it will only require 50 N. A more realistic time of 1 s to stop will require a larger force of 150 N. A hard surface that brings you to a stop in 0.01 s requires a much larger force of 15,000 N.

On concrete, this change in the value of the momentum occurs very fast (a short time) and requires a large force. It hurts. On soft grass this change in the value of the momentum occurs in a longer time and requires a small force that is less painful and is preferred.

Notice that in the chart above, the change in momentum is always equal to the impulse.

"Work and Energy" or "Impulse and Momentum"

The effective crumple zone decreases the force on the passenger. Using the work-energy theorem the force can be minimized by increasing the distance required to stop. Using the impulse-momentum theorem, the force can be minimized by increasing the time required.

As a physics student, it is your job to decide which of these two approaches is best for explaining a particular collision.

$$W = Fd = \Delta KE$$

or

$$F\Delta t = \Delta p$$

Both show that the force can be minimized. In work-energy, force is minimized by an increase in impact distance. In impulse-momentum, force is minimized by an increase in impact time.

Conserving Momentum

In *Part B* of the *Investigate*, a moving cart was brought to rest. The moving cart had momentum. The force probe was able to record the force that was applied to the cart over time to stop the cart. This force over time changed the momentum of the cart.

The force vs. time graphs for two carts with the same initial momentum are sketched below.

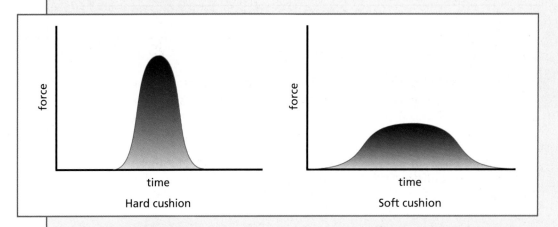

As you can see, the cart with the hard cushion had a larger force acting over a shorter time than the cart with the soft cushion. For the safety of passengers, a small force over a long time is what is needed.

Designing a safety device for an automobile is often determined by finding ways to decrease the force and increase the time during an impact. The change in momentum of a cart or an automobile can be identical, but a smaller force over a larger time will be safer.

You know that during a collision, momentum is always conserved. However, confusion may arise because now you find that a force can change the momentum of a cart by bringing it to rest. How can momentum be conserved in collisions but momentum can be changed by a cushion? It may help to view the collision from two different perspectives. It is true that the total momentum before the collision is equal to the total momentum after the collision. However, during the collision the first cart may lose momentum while the second cart may gain momentum. Each cart changed momentum but the total momentum remained the same. A similar thing happens when the force probe stops the automobile. The automobile loses momentum. The probe gains that same amount of momentum. Since its mass is large (it is connected to the lab table), then this large gain in momentum corresponds to a very small gain in velocity.

You may recall that another way in which to describe the same cushion is to say that the larger force acted over a shorter distance. The work done by the force over the distance was the same for both bumpers, and both bumpers decreased the kinetic energy of the automobile.

Change in Momentum and Impulse

Momentum is the product of the mass and the velocity of an object,

$$p = mv$$

where p is the momentum,
m is the mass, and
v is the velocity.

Change in momentum is the change in the product of mass and velocity. If the mass remains the same, the change in the momentum is the product of the mass and the change in velocity.

$$p = \Delta mv$$

Impulse is the change in momentum.

$$F\Delta t = \Delta mv$$

Change in Kinetic Energy and Work

Kinetic energy is the product of ½ the mass and the square of the velocity.

$$KE = \frac{1}{2}mv^2$$

Work is the product of the force and the distance over which the force acts.

$$W = F \cdot d$$

Work is equal to the change in kinetic energy.

$$W = \Delta KE$$

Checking Up

1. What is a crumple zone?

2. Why is it safer to collide with a soft cushion than a hard surface?

3. What is momentum?

4. What is the relationship between impulse and momentum?

Active Physics

+Math	+Depth	+Concepts	+Exploration
◆◆			

Graphing Momentum Change

An automobile undergoing a collision has a momentum change of 12,000 kg•m/s during a collision. This could occur with a constant force of 4000 N (newtons) over 3 s (seconds).

The graph of the force vs. time for this collision would look like this:

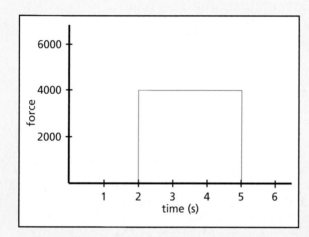

Notice that the area under the graph is the area of the rectangle:

$$A = bh$$
$$A = (3 \text{ s})(4000 \text{ N})$$
$$A = 12,000 \text{ N} \cdot \text{s}$$

You can find the units of 1 N by reminding yourself that the newton is defined in Newton's second law:

$$F = ma$$
$$1 \text{ N} = (1 \text{ kg})(1 \text{ m/s}^2)$$
$$1 \text{ N} = 1 \text{ kg} \cdot \text{m/s}^2$$

The area under the graph has the units of N s. Since 1 N is 1 kg•m/s², the area of the graph has the identical units of kg•m/s.

1. Create a graph that shows the same momentum change of 12,000 kg•m/s where the force is a constant 8000 N. You will have to calculate the corresponding time for the collision.

2. Create a graph that shows the same momentum change where the force is a constant 4000 N for 1 s and then 8000 N for the remainder of the required time to bring the automobile to rest.

3. Create a graph that shows the same momentum change where the force is a constant 4000 N for 1 s, then 8000 N for 0.5 s, and then 4000 N for the remainder of the required time to bring the automobile to a rest.

4. Create a graph that shows the same momentum change where the force gradually increases from 0 N to 4000 N, remains at 4000 N for 1 s and then gradually decreases to 0 N when the automobile comes to rest.

What Do You Think Now?

• **What are some of the factors that automobile designers and engineers must consider when designing a crumple zone as a safety feature?**

Now that you have completed this section on crumple zones, what do you think are some of the important considerations in designing a crumple zone? Compare and contrast crumple zones and air bags.

Physics
Essential Questions

What does it mean?

What is the difference between impulse and momentum?

How do you know?

What were the key design features of your crumple zone and why were they important? What were the physics principles that you used?

Why do you believe?

Connects with Other Physics Content	Fits with Big Ideas in Science	Meets Physics Requirements
Forces and motion	Systems	$*$ Good clear explanation, no more complicated than necessary

$*$ The same physics principles can be applied to many situations. Newton's second law $\left(F = ma\right)$ can describe the effectiveness of air bags or crumple zones. Another form of Newton's second law $\left(F\Delta t = \Delta mv\right)$ provides other insights into the design of air bags or crumple zones. Show how the second equation can be derived from the first equation.

Why should you care?

How could the crumple zone concept be used in your safety system for the *Chapter Challenge?*

Reflecting on the Section and the Challenge

In this section, you found that a crumple zone, as you would find in bumpers or an air bag, is able to protect you by extending the time it takes to stop you. Without the air bags, you will hit something and stop in a brief time. This will require a large force, large enough to injure you. With the air bag (or other crumple device), the time to stop is longer and the force required is therefore smaller.

Force and impulse must be considered in designing your safety system. Stopping an object gradually reduces damage. The harder a surface, the shorter the stopping time, and greater the damage. In part, this provides a clue to the use of padded dashboards and sun visors in newer automobiles. Understanding impulse allows designers to reduce damages both to automobiles and passengers.

You can describe the decrease in force by using work (small force and large distance) or impulse (small force and large time). Which explanation to use depends on whether the stopping distance or stopping time is more easily measured. Work relates to changes in kinetic energy ($KE = \frac{1}{2}mv^2$). Impulse relates to changes in momentum ($p = mv$).

An automobile can be stopped in a very short time or over a longer time. In both cases, there is an identical change in momentum of the automobile. The impulse on the automobile is also identical in both cases since impulse is equal to the change in momentum. However, the potential damage to the automobiles and the passengers is not identical. A large force over a short time can produce severe damage to the automobile and injury to the driver and passengers. Therefore, you will want to consider how you can increase the time (and decrease the force) for your automobile to minimize dangers.

Similarly, an automobile can be stopped in a very short distance or over a longer distance. Although an automobile crashing into a snow bank or a highway barrier can lead to damage and injuries, they are not nearly as severe as what is experienced if the same automobile hits a concrete wall. In this case, you describe the work (force•distance) required to change the kinetic energy of the automobile.

When demonstrating your automobile's safety devices, you may use "momentum and impulse" or "work and kinetic energy" to provide a rationale for your design.

Physics to Go

1. How do impulse and Newton's first law (the law of inertia) play a role in your crumple-zone design?

2. Automobiles today have crumple zones designed into the body of the automobile, and they also have air bags inside the automobile. How do these systems work together to protect the passengers?

3. In automobiles built before 1970, the dashboard was made of hard metal. After 1970, the automobiles were installed with padded dashboards like you find in automobiles today. In designing a safe automobile, why is it better to have a passenger hit a cushioned dashboard than a hard metal dashboard?

    a) Using Newton's second law, explain why the padded dashboard is better.

    b) Using impulse and momentum, explain why a padded dashboard is better.

4. Explain why you bend your knees when you jump to the ground.

5. Helmets are designed to protect cyclists. How would the designers of helmets make use of the concept of impulse to improve their effectiveness?

6. An automobile has a mass of 1200 kg and an initial velocity of 10 m/s (about 20 mi/h). Calculate the change in momentum required to do the following:

   a) Bring it to rest

   b) Slow it to 5 m/s (approximately 10 mi/h)

7. If the braking force for an automobile is 10,000 N, calculate the impulse if the brake is applied for 1.2 s (seconds). If the automobile has a mass of 1200 kg, what is the change in velocity of the automobile over this 1.2 s time interval?

8. A 1500-kg automobile, traveling at 5.0 m/s after braking, strikes a power pole and comes to a full stop in 0.1 s. Calculate the force exerted by the power pole and brakes required to stop the automobile.

9. For the automobile described in *Question 8*, explain why a breakaway pole that brings the automobile to rest after 2.8 s is safer than the conventional power pole.

10. Compare and contrast the two force vs. time graphs shown below.

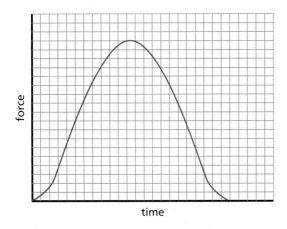

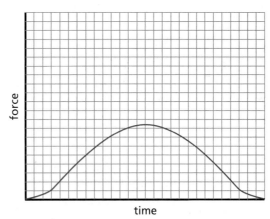

11. *Preparing for the Chapter Challenge*

   How can your safety device reduce the force experienced during an impulse? What features of your device increase the stopping time for the passenger? Record a description of how these features work in terms of impulse and momentum.

Physics
You Learned

Physics Concepts	Is There an Equation?
When an object is moving, it will continue to move at constant speed in a straight line unless there is an unbalanced force to change its motion. If the object is at rest, it stays at rest unless there is an unbalanced force. This is known as **Newton's first law**.	
Active Physics *Plus* Pressure (P) is equal to the force applied (F) divided by the area to which it is applied (A). A large force over a small area will exert a very large amount of pressure.	$P = \dfrac{F}{A}$
Kinetic energy (KE) is the energy of motion. An object's kinetic energy is proportional to the object's mass multiplied by its velocity squared.	$KE = \frac{1}{2}mv^2$
Work (W) done is the product of the force exerted by an object (F) and the displacement in the direction of the force (d). Work may change an object's kinetic energy.	$W = Fd$ $W = \Delta KE$
A small force acting over a large distance can produce the same change in kinetic energy as a large force acting over a small distance.	
An air bag increases the stopping distance available for passengers in the event of a collision, thus decreasing the required stopping force.	
Active Physics *Plus* Work (W) on an object can increase its kinetic energy (ΔKE).	$W = \Delta KE$ $= \left(\frac{1}{2}mv_f^2 - \frac{1}{2}mv_i^2 \right)$
The **acceleration** of an object (a) is directly proportional to the net force applied (F_{net}), and inversely proportional to the object's mass (m). This is known as **Newton's second law**.	$a = \dfrac{F_{net}}{m}$
The net force on an object is the sum of all the forces acting on it at the same time.	
Whiplash is a neck injury often sustained in rear-end collisions, due to the **inertia** of the human head when the torso is accelerated forward.	
Momentum (p) is the product of an object's mass (m) multiplied by its **velocity** (v). Momentum has direction as well as size (a vector quantity), and may be transferred between objects during a collision.	$p = mv$
The **law of conservation of momentum** states that if there are no external forces acting on the system, the total momentum of a system before a collision (mv_b) is equal to the total momentum after the collision (mv_a). During a collision, the objects may gain or lose speed, but the total momentum remains the same.	$m_1v_{1b} + m_2v_{2b} =$ $m_1v_{1a} + m_2v_{2a}$

In an elastic collision, both momentum and kinetic energy are conserved. The sum of the kinetic energies after the collision must equal the sum of the kinetic energies before the collision. When two particles of equal mass collide and one is initially at rest, they must travel off at right angles after the collision for this condition to be met.	$p_{\text{before}} = p_{\text{after}}$ $KE_{\text{before}} = KE_{\text{after}}$
Impulse equals the product of a force acting on an object, and the time period during which the force acts.	$\text{Impulse} = F\Delta t$
When an impulse acts on an object, the momentum of the object changes by an amount equal to the applied impulse.	$F\Delta t = m\Delta v$
The area under a force vs. time graph is the impulse and therefore, equal to the change in momentum of the object.	
Crumple zones are built into automobiles as cushioning devices. A crumple zone increases the time a force may act to bring an automobile to rest, which allows a smaller force to be exerted during the stopping process. The net impulse required to stop an automobile does not change if the automobile has a crumple zone, but the net force applied is decreased as the time it acts is increased.	

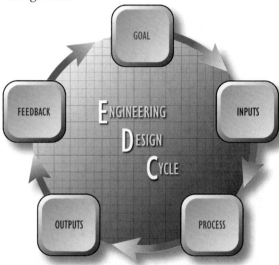

Physics
Chapter Challenge

You will now be completing a second cycle of the *Engineering Design Cycle* as you prepare for the *Chapter Challenge*. The goals and criteria remain unchanged. However, your list of *Inputs* has grown.

Goal

Your challenge for this chapter is to create a safety system to protect passengers in a vehicle of your choice. As part of your design, you will build a model to protect an egg in a collision that you will enact in the classroom during your oral presentation. You will also submit a written or multimedia report of your research and investigation results.

Inputs

You have completed all the sections of this chapter and learned the physics content you need to complete this challenge. You now have additional physics information to help you optimize the design of your safety system. Remember, you will also be protecting an egg using your new physics knowledge. This is part of the *Inputs* phase of the *Engineering Design Cycle*.

Your group must define the vehicle that your safety device will be used in and apply the appropriate physics concepts to build your presentation. The type of vehicle will determine some key constraints, like the typical speed of the vehicle, the mass and velocity of typical obstructions your vehicle may collide with. The other key *Inputs* for this challenge will be the physics principles you have learned from each section of the chapter.

Section 1 You considered the topic of passenger safety in automobile collisions and explored some of the safety features that are available in modern automobiles. You learned that analyzing safety has led to many safety improvements in vehicle design.

Section 2 You learned about Newton's first law of motion and the role it plays in collisions. You also evaluated different seat belt materials and considered the relationships of force, surface area, and pressure.

Section 3 You built a model of a vehicle air bag. You used the ideas of energy and work to help explain why an air bag can be helpful to passengers in the event of an collision.

Section 4 You explored what happens in rear-end collisions and learned about Newton's second law, which describes the relationship between the force applied to a mass and the acceleration it will experience. You recognized how this law explains the way objects respond when forces are applied to them.

Section 5 You learned about momentum through investigating staged collisions. The momentum of an object depends on both its mass and its velocity, which is why speed and size are both factors in the outcome of an automobile accident.

Section 6 You learned about the conservation of momentum, which establishes that the total amount of momentum in a system remains the same. This concept can be used to determine the momentum vehicles have after a collision when no external forces are applied.

Section 7 You compared changes in momentum to the forces applied to objects during a collision. Impulse, or change in momentum, can determine the amount of force applied if you know how much time the change took. You can make the force smaller if you make the time of collision longer!

Process

In the *Process* phase, your group must decide what information you will use to meet the *Goal*. Choose the vehicle that will be the model for your safety system. Your group may brainstorm ideas for many different vehicles. Once you have lots of ideas to choose from, select one that your group agrees is workable and that will also allow you to protect an egg in the classroom collision.

Organization and good communication among your group members will be very important for this challenge. One way to stay organized is to assign roles for each person and make a list of the responsibilities. For instance, one person might have the role of "fact checker" and be responsible for making sure the oral report and written report contain accurate information about the physics principles your safety system applies. Other roles might include model builder, scriptwriter, report writer, and so on. Time constraints are also going to make this challenge difficult, so make sure each person knows when his or her portion of the project must be completed.

When you build your model system to protect an egg, be sure to create a safety system that uses the principles you have chosen to protect human passengers. You may have some constraints, such as time, available materials, or even the shape of the cart your egg will ride on. Engineers are constantly working to meet design goals within constraints.

Make sure that your report or presentation explains why your safety system works and contains the information you want your audience to know. You should include all of the key features of your design along with example calculations and results for all of your safety system. You may also describe differences between your human safety system and your egg safety system. If your class prepares a rubric for this challenge, make sure you refer to it often to ensure that you address each category and include all important information.

Outputs

Presenting your information to the class are your design-cycle *Outputs*. It is very important that your egg safety system be effective since it is the model for your design, so make sure your demonstration is well rehearsed. Each piece of the presentation will have similar information, but it is important to make sure each one is complete.

Feedback

Your classmates will give you *Feedback* on the accuracy and the overall appeal of your presentation based on the criteria of the challenge. This feedback will likely become part of your grade but could also be useful for additional design iterations. Remember that there is always room for some improvement and no design is perfect. From your experience with the *Mini-Challenge*, you should recognize how it is possible to continuously refine any idea by constantly rotating through the design cycle.

Physics
Connections to Other Sciences

Here are some examples of how the concepts you studied in this chapter relate to other sciences.

Newton's First Law – Inertia

Biology Just as an object's motion does not change until a force comes along to change it, a biological species does not change until something changes its genetic makeup. This is the basis of natural selection which leads to the biological evolution of species.

Chemistry The electric polarity of a molecule in a liquid can be demonstrated by the ability of an electrically charged rod to deflect the path of a falling stream of the liquid.

Earth Science If gravity were turned off, all the planets presently orbiting the Sun would continue moving with the same speed, along a line in the direction of their present motion.

Energy and Work

Biology The work done by the tail of a fish as it pushes against the water is responsible for the kinetic energy of a fish as it swims.

Chemistry When heat energy is added to a gas, such as the steam in a steam engine, the gas expands and does work moving a piston. The movement of the piston can then be converted into the kinetic energy of a moving train.

Earth Science Stray particles in the Solar System are constantly bombarding Earth. Smaller particles are stopped over long distances by their frictional contact with gases in the atmosphere. Larger objects that eventually collide with Earth must be stopped in much shorter distances by the ground. This requires huge forces that cause terrible damage if the object is sufficiently large, as was the case with the meteor colliding with the Earth 65 million years ago, believed to have been responsible for making dinosaurs extinct.

Newton's Second Law

Biology The ability of all animals to accelerate and change their velocity depends upon their mass and the net force they can exert.

Chemistry The mass of an ionized atom can be determined by the acceleration that it undergoes when it is placed in an electric field.

Earth Science How quickly rock particles that are picked up by a swiftly flowing stream settle out of the water is determined by the net force on each particle, and the particle's mass. This leads to a sorting of rock particles as the stream runs into a lake or ocean.

Momentum

Biology When an eagle grabs a fish swimming near the top of a lake, the eagle will slow down after the catch, due to conservation of momentum. If the eagle slows too much or if the fish is too large, it may not be able to regain momentum, and may land in the water.

Chemistry The momentum of an atom when it collides with another atom is one factor that determines whether the atoms combine to form a molecule, or simply bounce off each other.

Earth Science The tremendous momentum of a large mass of snow in an avalanche allows it to knock down anything that stands in its path.

Impulse

Biology When animals jump from a height down to the ground, they bend their legs. This results in the exertion of a smaller force over a larger time and prevents injury when they land.

Chemistry The impulse delivered to a wall when gas molecules strike is responsible for the pressure the gas exerts upon the wall.

Earth Science The power of erosion of a waterfall is much greater than the power of a stream flowing down a gently sloping hill from the same height. Stream water stops over a much longer time, requiring less force. Water at the bottom of a waterfall stops quickly, requiring a large force with a greater effect.

338

Joe Nolan

Senior Vice President, Vehicle Research Center; Ruckersville, VA

Joe Nolan realizes his career, much like automobile accidents, was not planned. While earning his graduate degree in engineering, he realized he needed a research position to graduate. "The only research position available was at the Automobile Safety Lab at the University of Virginia's School of Engineering," said Nolan. Today, he is the senior vice president at the Vehicle Research Center for the Insurance Institute for Highway Safety, located in Ruckersville, Virginia.

The Insurance Institute for Highway Safety is a nonprofit, nongovernmental research organization. It is funded by insurance companies and performs over 100 full-scale crash tests per year. The Vehicle Research Center currently reproduces three different real-world crashes to test a vehicle's safety: frontal offset collisions, side impacts, and rear-end whiplash tests. "In the front and side tests, we observe the way the dummies move in the car, the way the restraint system works, and how the car's structure holds up," he said.

While automobile manufacturers continue to upgrade their safety features, Nolan believes that new drivers still need to be more responsible behind the wheel. "Car crashes are the number one cause of death for people under the age of 18, even though vehicles are getting better and belt use is going up," argues Nolan.

Marjorie Cooke

Marine Safety Expert, Robson Forensic; Fairfax County, VA

Dave Cooke

Professional Engineer, Robson Forensic; Fairfax County, VA

Dave and Marjorie Cooke met at the State University of New York Maritime College, and have been working together for over 30 years. According to the couple, their job is never routine. "We may be inspecting a ship or boat to determine its condition, or we may be interviewing someone to determine what happened during the incident."

The couple's understanding of physics is vital during an investigation. "You have to be able to determine what direction and the amount of force applied to various components. In boating accidents, there are no skid marks to help you out."

Michael Jackson

Emergency Medical Technician (EMT); North Apollo, PA

Michael Jackson is an Emergency Medical Technician (EMT) at Allegheny Valley Hospital, located in Natrona Heights, PA. A typical day involves responding to a variety of emergencies, from shortness of breath and chest pains, to automobile accidents. The most severe automobile accident Jackson responded to in his seven-year career was a vehicle that had gone over a hillside. "The passengers were young adults, and luckily, both survived," said Jackson.

Jackson believes that most car accidents are caused by speeding, especially when road conditions are poor. "So many accidents could be prevented if people would drive at safe and appropriate speeds for the current road conditions."

Physics

Practice Test

Before you try the Physics Practice Test, *you may want to review Sections 1–7, where you will find* **24 Checking Up** *questions,* **9 What Do You Think Now?** *questions,* **28 Physics Essential Questions,** **70 Physics to Go** *questions, and* **7 Inquiring Further** *questions.*

Content Review

1. When an elevator going down comes to a stop, blood tends to rush from the occupants' heads. This phenomenon is best explained by
   a) conservation of energy.
   b) Newton's first law of motion.
   c) action-reaction.
   d) the law of universal gravitation.

2. A dull knife does not cut as well as a sharp knife when pushed equally hard. A sharp knife cuts better because it
   a) requires more energy.
   b) continues in motion with constant speed.
   c) has a longer edge.
   d) exerts greater pressure.

3. Two eggs are dropped from equal heights. Egg A lands on a hard floor, while egg B lands on a soft foam pad. Both eggs stop without bouncing, and egg A breaks while egg B does not. Compared to egg A, egg B has
   a) less work done on it, and requires less force to stop.
   b) more work done on it and requires less force to stop.
   c) the same amount of work done on it and requires less force to stop.
   d) less work done on it and requires more force to stop.

4. An egg thrown at a sheet at high speed is stopped and does not break. The best explanation is that
   a) the sheet is made of a soft material and cannot break the egg.
   b) the sheet exerts a small force over a large distance to stop the egg.
   c) the sheet is not held tightly.
   d) the kinetic energy of the thrown egg is not enough to cause the egg to break.

5. An automobile traveling at a speed of 5 m/s brakes to a stop at a distance of 2 m. What distance would be required by the same braking force to stop the automobile at a speed of 20 m/s?
   a) 8 m   b) 16 m
   c) 24 m   d) 32 m

6. As the distance an automobile has available to stop increases, the force required to bring it to a stop decreases. Which physics principle best explains this?
   a) work and energy
   b) conservation of momentum
   c) Newton's first law
   d) pressure depends upon the area over which a force is exerted

7. In the design of some modern automobiles, each headrest automatically snaps forward against the back of a passenger's head if the vehicle is struck from behind, pushing forward with the same acceleration as the rest of the vehicle. This safety device protects a passenger's head by overcoming its
   a) inertia.   b) kinetic energy.
   c) momentum.   d) impulse.

8. Which best describes the forces acting on an automobile moving at constant speed?
   a) There is a constant unbalanced force on the automobile, pushing it forward.
   b) There are no forces acting on the automobile.
   c) All the forces acting on the automobile add up to zero.
   d) There is a small net force on the automobile to keep it moving.

9. Which object would have the greatest momentum?
   a) a 5-kg bowling ball moving at 7 m/s
   b) a 0.4-kg bird flying at 30 m/s
   c) a 20-kg wheelbarrow moving at 2 m/s
   d) a 0.3-kg baseball batted at 60 m/s

340

10. *Diagram 1* below shows two carts of equal mass involved in an elastic collision. Before the collision, cart A is moving to the right at a velocity of 3 m/s and cart B is at rest. After the collision,
    a) both carts will be moving at 1.5 m/s to the right.
    b) both carts will be moving at 3 m/s to the right.
    c) cart A will travel to the left at 3 m/s and cart B will travel to the right at 3 m/s.
    d) cart B will travel to the right at 3 m/s and cart A will be stopped.

Diagram 1: Carts of Equal Mass

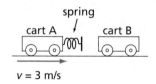

11. In *Diagram 1*, the spring is now removed from cart A, and the two carts collide and become entangled together. After the collision,
    a) both carts will be moving at 1.5 m/s to the right.
    b) both carts will be moving at 3 m/s to the right.
    c) both carts will be stopped.
    d) both carts will be moving to the left at 3 m/s.

12. Two carts of unequal masses are at rest on a level surface with a compressed spring between them. When the spring releases, the carts move apart, with cart A moving as shown below in *Diagram 2*. A student claims that the moment this happens, cart B will move to the right at a velocity of 1 m/s. Her claim is likely based on the principle of
    a) conservation of energy.
    b) conservation of momentum.
    c) Newton's first law.
    d) Newton's second law.

Diagram 2: Carts with Unequal Mass

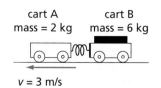

13. In the previous question, what is the combined momentum of the two carts after the spring is released?
    a) 12 kg·m/s
    b) 6 kg·m/s
    c) 3 kg·m/s
    d) 0 kg·m/s

14. The graph shows the force needed to bring a 2-kg mass to rest. What must have been the initial speed of the mass when the force first started to act?
    a) 8 m/s
    b) 20 m/s
    c) 32 m/s
    d) 40 m/s

Force vs. Time Graph

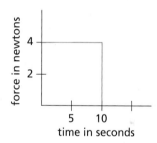

15. A cushioning device such as a crumple zone has no effect on the total impulse required to stop an automobile, but in the event of a collision, such a device will
    a) reduce the automobile's momentum.
    b) reduce the work required to bring the automobile to rest.
    c) reduce the force required to stop the automobile.
    d) reduce the time required to stop the automobile.

Practice Test *(continued)*

Critical Thinking

16. In an "elastic collision," the total kinetic energy as well as the total momentum of colliding objects before and after a collision is the same. Design an experiment to determine if momentum is conserved in an elastic collision between two carts of unequal mass that have springs between them. You should include a description of the equipment setup, the procedure to follow, and the equipment needed to complete the investigation.
    a) What measurements should you take to determine if momentum has been conserved during the collision?
    b) How would you analyze the data to confirm that momentum was conserved?
    c) Would you need to take any additional measurements to determine if the kinetic energy before the collision was equal to the kinetic energy after the collision? If so, what would those measurements be?

17. Imagine you are riding in an automobile and the following events occur. Describe which of Newton's laws applies to each event.
    a) A large box in the trunk slides forward each time the brakes are applied.
    b) You feel you are "pushed back" into the seat when the automobile accelerates.
    c) When you come to a quick stop, your seat belt stops you from moving forward.

18. Automobiles have crumple zones and air bags to protect passengers. Using the concept of impulse equals the change in momentum, explain how these two systems work together to decrease the forces exerted on a passenger in the event of a collision.

19. Two identical cars are equipped with seat and shoulder belts. The first car has narrow belts, and the second car has wider belts.
    a) Which set of belts would be safer for passengers and why?
    b) The seat belts are designed to stretch slightly when a sudden, severe collision occurs and the belts are needed to hold passengers in place. Why would a seat belt that stretches be better than one that does not stretch?

20. The following data was taken when two different amounts of mass were dropped into separate containers of sand and kitty litter. In both cases, the mass did not reach the bottom of the container.

	Trial 1 (sand)	Trial 2 (kitty litter)
Mass	2.0 kg	1.0 kg
Drop height	0.30 m	0.50 m
Leaves an indentation	Yes	Yes
Depth	0.04 m	0.03 m

   a) Calculate the *GPE* of the two masses above the container before they are dropped.
   b) What is the kinetic energy of each mass as it strikes the surface of the sand or kitty litter?
   c) How much work was done on each mass to bring it to rest?
   d) Show your calculations to determine which mass required the greater force to stop once it struck the surface.

Active Physics
Plus

21. An automobile with a mass of 1500 kg is traveling at a speed of 20 m/s when the brakes are applied for a distance of 100 m. If the average braking force during this time is 2500 N, what is the automobile's final speed after braking?

22. In a football game on a muddy field, a 120-kg linebacker running north at 5 m/s tackles an 80-kg running back running west at 10 m/s. If the two players slide off together, what is the speed of the combination?

23. A baseball with a mass of 0.160 kg is thrown at a speed of 40 m/s toward a batter. The batter hits the ball back at 60 m/s. What impulse was provided on the ball by the bat?

Chapter 4

4

Thrills and Chills

Scenario

You are excited and scared as you sit back in the seat. You pull the safety restraints into place. The next thing you know, you are beginning a slow but steady ascent into the sky. Then, with a sudden jolt, you reach the top. This is where the thrill or nightmare begins. You hurtle down the track at ever-increasing speeds. You are flung against one side of your seat as you scream around a curve. You shriek as you hang upside down, fortunately, firmly secured to your seat. All the time, your stomach has no idea where it is or where you are. Finally, you come to rest where you began. What a ride! Want to go again?

Roller coasters have been enjoyed for many years. However, the roller coaster that may appeal to you, may not appeal to your parents or other friends and relatives.

Your Challenge

A roller coaster, called the Terminator Express (see the first section), has been designed for an amusement park. Your challenge is to take the roller-coaster design and modify it for a select group of riders. For instance, you may decide that you will modify the roller coaster so that young children can experience the thrill of a roller coaster in a safe and non-threatening way.

You may prefer to design the roller coaster for adults that are a bit squeamish about the big hills and sharp turns. They want to experience the thrill of a roller-coaster ride, but are ready to pass on the death-defying action. On the other hand, you may choose to design a roller coaster for daredevils that are ready to handle any thrill you can provide. You may also wish to design a roller coaster for people who are physically challenged or visually impaired.

You will present your design as both a model and a written report or poster. The roller coaster you design must be safe and nobody riding it will be in danger. You will also be required to calculate the energy required to get the roller coaster started.

Criteria for Success

You and your classmates will work with your teacher to define the criteria for evaluating your roller coaster and your written report. After discussing features that should be included in the grading of each part of the project, determine the relative importance of the assessment criteria. Then assign point values to each.

Record any notes you have about the *Chapter Challenge* in your *Active Physics* log. You will also need to list the criteria and their point value that your class decided on for assessing the challenge. After class discussions and decisions, turn to the suggested "Standards for Excellence" on the following page for comparison. You may then decide to reconsider your criteria.

Chapter Challenge

Standard for Excellence	
1. The quality of your roller-coaster model and the appeal of the roller coaster to the group of riders that you choose • at least two hills, one vertical loop, and one horizontal loop are included in the design of the roller coaster • the design of the roller coaster clearly takes into account the selected group of riders • the design shows original and creative thinking	**30 points**
2. The safety of the roller coaster • safety data include the height, speed, and acceleration of the roller coaster at five designated locations – bottom of first hill, top of loop, back curve, top of second hill, and horizontal loop • correct equations and correct quantity symbols are used • numerical calculations are accurate • correct units are used in determining safety data • safety data indicate that the roller coaster is safe	**20 points**
3. Calculation of (1) the energy and power required to get the roller coaster rolling, (2) the energy dissipated at the end of the ride to bring the roller coaster to a halt, and (3) a spring system to stop the roller-coaster cars in case the brakes fail • correct equations and correct quantity symbols are used • numerical calculations of work required are accurate • correct units are used	**20 points**
4. The quality of a written report or poster • the length of written report is correct (your class will need to decide this) • the select group for your roller coaster is clearly identified and described • documentation of the sources of expert information is provided • correct science vocabulary is used • diagrams, charts, or graphs are used where appropriate and are accurately labeled • correct spelling and punctuation	**25 points**
5. *Chapter Challenge* completed on time	**5 points**

Engineering Design Cycle

You have now heard about the *Chapter Challenge* to redesign a roller coaster for a group of your choice. You will use a simplified *Engineering Design Cycle* to help your group create the most exciting roller coaster you can with the materials that are available to you. Defining your *Goal* is the first step in the *Engineering Design Cycle*, so you have already begun.

As you experience each one of the chapter sections, you will be gaining *Inputs* to use in the design cycle. These *Inputs* will include new physics concepts, vocabulary, and even equations that will help you to create your design. When your group prepares the *Mini-Challenge* presentation and the *Chapter Challenge* you will be completing the *Process* step of the *Engineering Design Cycle*. During the *Process* step you will evaluate ideas, consider criteria, compare and contrast potential solutions, and most importantly make design decisions.

The *Output* of your design cycle will be the model of the roller coaster that your group presents, including any diagrams, charts, and graphs in your written presentation that you may use. Finally, you will receive *Feedback* from your classmates and your instructor about which parts of your presentation are good and which parts need to be refined. You will repeat the *Engineering Design Cycle* during the second half of the chapter when you gain more inputs, refine your roller coaster, and make your calculations.

Physics Corner

Physics in *Thrills and Chills*

- Acceleration
- Centripetal acceleration
- Circular motion
- Conservation of energy
- Displacement
- Gravitational potential energy
- Hooke's law
- Kinetic energy
- Mass and weight
- Newton's first law of motion
- Newton's second law of motion
- Normal force
- Power
- Scalars
- Spring potential energy
- Vector addition
- Vectors
- Velocity
- Work

Section 1

Velocity and Acceleration: The Big Thrill

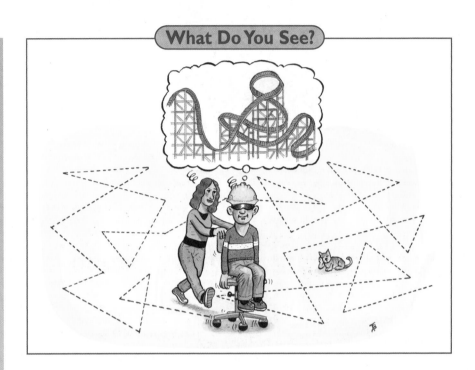

What Do You See?

Learning Outcomes

In this section, you will

• **Sketch** and interpret a top view and a side view of a roller-coaster ride.

• **Identify** whether thrills in roller-coaster rides come from speeds, accelerations, or changes in each.

• **Define** acceleration as a change in velocity with respect to time and recognize the units of acceleration.

• **Calculate** and measure velocity and acceleration.

What Do You Think?

The tallest wooden roller coaster has a height of about 66 m (218 ft). The tallest steel roller coaster is 128 m (420 ft) high. This is as tall as a 40-story high-rise building.

• **Which part of the roller-coaster ride produces the loudest screams? Why?**

Record your ideas about these questions in your *Active Physics* log. Be prepared to discuss your responses with your small group and the class.

Investigate
Part A: Sketch of the Roller Coaster

1. Sketch a roller coaster with a first hill of 15 m that quickly descends to 6 m and then turns to the right in a big circle (radius of 10 m) and then descends back to the ground.

   ✍ a) Include a copy of the sketch in your *Active Physics* log.

2. Compare the sketch of your roller-coaster design with those of others on your design team.

   ✍ a) Which sketch do you like the best? Provide three reasons why you prefer that sketch.

3. Create two sketches with different views for the same roller coaster. The first sketch should be a side view. The second sketch should be a view from the sky.

✎ a) What are the advantages of having two sketches?

4. Below is the roller coaster that has been designed by the professional team that is asking for your help. It is called The Terminator Express. There are two views of the roller coaster. The first view is a side view. The second view is a view from the sky (a top view).

The Terminator Express

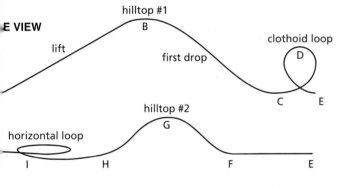

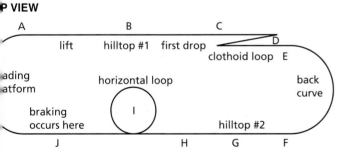

✎ a) Sketch the side and top view in your *Active Physics* log.

5. The Terminator Express roller-coaster car begins from the loading platform at A and then rises along the lift. It reaches the top of hilltop # 1 at B and then makes its first drop. It then goes into a vertical loop at C. This clothoid loop (it has a big radius at the bottom and a small radius at the top)

allows the riders to be safely upside down. The coaster car then goes along the track starting at E, moves through the back curve to F, rises over hilltop # 2 at G and then swings into a horizontal loop at I. The brakes are applied after the loop and the roller coaster comes to a stop at J.

Have one team member read this description as you move your finger along the roller-coaster track and then have a different team member read the description so that the first reader can follow the coaster car along the track.

Repeat the procedure with the top view.

Part B: Roller-Coaster Fun

1. In the next part of the *Investigate*, you will blindfold someone in your group in order to observe the thrilling parts of a roller-coaster ride. The blindfolded person will sit in a chair with wheels. This part of the *Investigate* may be done with the whole class viewing one student.

✎ a) Before you blindfold anyone, write down the safety concerns when one of your team members is blindfolded and you will be pushing him or her. What could go wrong? How can you prevent this? Be sure to check your safety rules with your teacher before proceeding.

2. For each group, choose one person as the rider, one as the recorder, and one as the "driver." The rider should rate each type of move on a 1-to-5 scale (5 being the highest) in terms of its "thrill." The recorder should write a brief description of the move (for example, "sharp left turn") and then record the rider's thrill rating for each move.

3. Have a member of your group sit on the chair with wheels. Blindfold that person. Push on the chair of the blindfolded team member, the rider. While the rider is moving, give the chair another push. Continue pushing the chair but vary the directions of your pushes, for example to the left, to the right, or straight ahead.

a) The recorder should note when the blindfolded team member smiles or laughs or exhibits some emotion as well as the rider's rating of the thrill level.

4. A rider's *velocity* is a measure of the rider's speed and includes information about the direction in which the rider is traveling. The rider's velocity may have been 1.2 m/s north or 1.5 m/s toward the door or 1.0 m/s toward the window. In each case, there is a magnitude or size (1.0 m/s, 1.2 m/s, 1.5 m/s) and a direction (north, toward the door, toward the window).

a) Was the velocity responsible for the "rider's" reactions? Did the blindfolded rider react more when the chair was moving with a fixed velocity (one with the same speed and the same direction) or when the velocity changed, when there was a change in speed or a change in direction of the chair or when there was a change in both the speed and in the direction of the chair?

5. The change in a rider's velocity over time is referred to as *acceleration*. Suppose a rider was moving at 1.1 m/s north and changed velocity to 1.5 m/s north. There is an acceleration because there was a change in speed.

a) In your *Active Physics* log, calculate and record the change in velocity.

6. There would also be acceleration if the rider changed velocity from 1.3 m/s east to 1.3 m/s south. Here the acceleration is due to a change in the direction, with no change in speed.

a) Draw vectors for these two velocities and describe the change in velocity in your log.

7. Suppose a rider was moving at 1.5 m/s toward the door and someone pushed him or her and made the rider move at 1.3 m/s toward the window. There is

acceleration because there was a change in speed and a change in direction.

a) Draw a vector to represent the two velocities for the rider in the above example. Make the direction toward the window to be at right angles to the original direction toward the door. Record the change in speed and the change in direction in your *Active Physics* log for the rider in the example above.

b) Was acceleration responsible for the reactions of the blindfolded rider? Did he or she react more when accelerated?

8. Acceleration is a change in velocity in a specific time. For example, the change from 1.1 m/s north to 1.5 m/s north may have taken 1 s.

The change in velocity is 0.4 m/s in one second. There are a number of ways in which this can be stated: The change in velocity is

- 0.4 m/s in one second
- 0.4 m/s every second
- 0.4 m/s per second
- 0.4 (m/s)/s
- 0.4 m/s^2

Part C: Measuring Velocities and Calculating Accelerations

1. The value 1.5 m/s north is a velocity. The velocity 1.5 m/s tells you that the object can travel 1.5 m in 1 s. The direction of motion is north.

a) If an object were moving across the table, what instruments would you need for measurements to determine if the object were traveling at 1.5 m/s? Describe how you would go about measuring velocity in your classroom.

2. Place a track flat on the top of your table. Place a steel ball in the track and give it a small push to get it moving along the track.

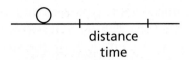

distance
time

a) Measure the distance the steel ball rolls and the time it takes to reach the end of the track using a ruler and a stopwatch. Record this data in your log and calculate the velocity of the steel ball. The equation for calculating average velocity is

$$\text{velocity} = \frac{\text{displacement}}{\text{time elapsed}}$$

$$v = \frac{\Delta d}{\Delta t},$$

where v is the velocity,

Δd is the displacement (change in position), and

Δt is the time elapsed.

The symbol Δ (delta) signifies "change in." Δ always means "final value" – "initial value." So $\Delta t = t_{final} - t_{initial}$.

Remember: a velocity must have a direction. The average velocity will be in the direction of the displacement.

Displacement is itself a vector quantity. For example, you might say that you moved 1.5 m north; so your displacement was 1.5 m north. The change in your position, which is the displacement, is represented as Δd.

3. Do another run with the steel ball but change the speed of the steel ball this time.

a) Record the data and calculate the velocity of the steel ball again.

4. Your teacher will demonstrate the use of a velocimeter that you will use in *Step 6*. A velocimeter (photogate) has two sensors inside and computes the speed of the ball for you. Each sensor can either start or stop the timer when the rolling ball intercepts the beam.

a) How do you think the velocimeter is able to compute the speed?

b) A velocimeter with only a single beam starts when an object breaks a light beam across the opening of the gate. The timer stops when the beam is no longer broken. The time interval can be measured very accurately. The computer measures the opening and closing of the gate as an elapsed time. To determine the velocity of the steel ball, what additional information would you (or the computer) need to know?

5. A large steel ball travels 6 cm. The elapsed time recorded on the velocimeter timer is 2 s.

a) Calculate the speed of the ball. (Since the speed is requested, you do not have to worry about the direction of motion. Speed is a *scalar* — it has no direction. Velocity is a vector — it has direction).

6. Roll a steel ball along a horizontal track. Use the velocimeter to help you find the speed of the steel ball traveling along the track. Place the velocimeter in a position where the ball must intercept the timer's beam. If you don't have a velocimeter available, you may find the speed by using a stopwatch to determine how long it takes the ball to travel a specified distance, say 0.3 m.

7. Raise the track to create a slope for the steel ball to travel down. Allow the steel ball to roll down this ramp. Make certain to start the ball from the same position during your trials when the ramp was horizontal.

a) Measure the speed of the steel ball at two different points. It is easiest to start the ball at rest (speed equals zero) and then use the velocimeter to measure the speed near the bottom of the track. You will also need to measure the time it takes the ball to go from where it starts to when you measure the "final" speed.

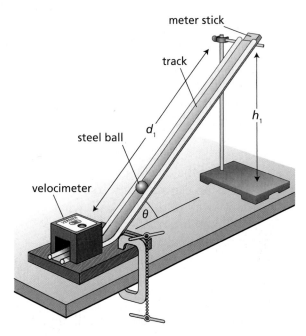

meter stick

track

steel ball

velocimeter

d_1

h_1

θ

Since the direction of the steel ball down the track can be considered to be along a straight path, your measurement is also a velocity. The direction does not change. In your log, record the speeds and the time it took for the ball to go from the starting point to the velocimeter.

b) Calculate the acceleration of the ball from the two speed (velocity) measurements. Acceleration is the change in velocity with respect to time. The equation to calculate acceleration is

$$\text{acceleration} = \frac{\text{change in velocity}}{\text{time elapsed}}$$

$$a = \frac{\Delta v}{\Delta t},$$

where a is the acceleration,
v is the velocity,
t is time,
$\Delta v = v_{final} - v_{initial}$, change in velocity,
$\Delta t = t_{final} - t_{initial}$, time elapsed.

The initial velocity is zero and you recorded the final velocity. You need to know the time it took the steel ball to travel from the start position to the final position. This will provide the change in time necessary for the acceleration calculation. You may have to repeat *Step 7.a)* again in order to measure this time. It may be good to do this several times so that you can compare your measurements and evaluate them.

Part D: Acceleration on the Roller Coaster—Pulling g's

1. On a roller coaster, you often feel heavier or lighter as you whip around curves or go up or down hills. You can feel the accelerations with your body. This is often called "pulling g's." Recall that *g* stands for acceleration due to gravity. The Terminator Express has a number of places where a rider would be pulling *g*'s. Try to imagine a ride on the roller coaster shown in the diagram below.

Top View of the Terminator Express

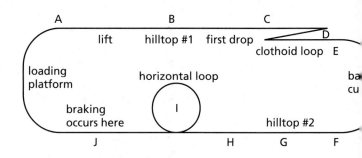

a) Make a new copy of the drawing of The Terminator Express. Indicate where the riders might feel light, and where they might feel heavy. Also indicate on the diagram where you think the coaster is speeding up and where it is slowing down.

Physics Talk

MEASURING VELOCITY AND ACCELERATION

In this section, you were introduced to some terms that you will need to understand in order to redesign The Terminator Express.

Distance, a **scalar** quantity, can be measured with a flexible piece of string or a metric tape measure placed along a path. The unit of measurement used is usually a meter. For example, an object travels 3 m.

Displacement is a measured distance with a direction included. Displacement depends only on the endpoints, not on the detailed path. If an object travels 3.5 m in an eastern direction, the displacement is recorded as 3.5 m, east. Displacement, a **vector**, has magnitude (size or length—3.5 m and direction—east. In the diagram shown, the curve represents the actual path of an object. The straight line represents the displacement.

If you were to walk from your home to school and back again, the distance traveled may be 5 km. The total displacement would be zero because your final position and your initial position are identical.

Speed is the distance traveled divided by the time elapsed. An object's speed may be 4 m/s. This means that the object moves 4 m every second if it continues to move with this speed. Speed is a scalar. It has no direction.

Velocity is the displacement divided by the time elapsed. The object's velocity may be 4 m/s south. Velocity is a vector. It has magnitude (4 m/s) and direction (south).

The equation to calculate average velocity is

$$\text{average velocity} = \frac{\text{displacement}}{\text{time elapsed}}$$

$$v = \frac{\Delta d}{\Delta t},$$

where v is the average velocity,

Δd is the displacement, and

Δt is the time elapsed.

The symbol Δ (delta) signifies "change in."
The symbol Δ always means final value – initial value.

So, $\Delta d = d_{\text{final}} - d_{\text{initial}}$, or change in position,

and $\Delta t = t_{\text{final}} - t_{\text{initial}}$, or time elapsed.

This is the method you used to measure the speed of the ball in the *Investigate*. If you also recorded the direction in which the ball was moving, then you have the information needed to describe the ball's velocity.

For a person walking one lap around a city block, the distance is equal to the perimeter of the city block. The speed is equal to this distance divided by the time to complete the walk. The displacement for the entire trip equals zero (since the person ended up where she started) and the velocity equals zero as a result.

You will find that in some cases it is distance that is important and in other cases displacement is important. It will be important to keep the difference between the two ideas in mind. It may seem that defining both distance and displacement as well as speed and velocity complicates things. However, scientists occasionally introduce terms and distinctions that seem to make simple things more complicated because they are then able to make very difficult things much easier to explain and understand.

Acceleration is the change in velocity divided by the time elapsed. An object's acceleration may be 5 m/s per second. If the direction stays the same, this means that the object changes its speed by 5 m/s every second if it continues with the same acceleration. The speed will increase from 0 m/s to 5 m/s to 10 m/s to 15 m/s with each change requiring one second. The acceleration of 5 m/s every second is also written as 5 m/s^2 (five meters per second squared).

The equation to calculate acceleration is

$$\text{acceleration} = \frac{\text{change in velocity}}{\text{time elapsed}}$$

$$a = \frac{\Delta v}{\Delta t},$$

where a is the acceleration,

Δv is the change in velocity, and

Δt is the time elapsed.

Note that the acceleration (a vector quantity) will be in the direction of the change in velocity.

When you measured the acceleration of the ball rolling down the incline in the *Investigate*, you measured the velocity of the ball at two different times. The acceleration is then given by the change in velocity divided by the time interval between the two velocity measurements. In *Active Physics Plus*, you will explore acceleration when the direction of the velocity changes.

Physics Words

acceleration: the change in velocity divided by the time elapsed; acceleration is a vector quantity, it has magnitude (size) and direction.

Checking Up

1. Explain the difference between distance and displacement.

2. You went to school and back home, a total distance of 2 km. What is your displacement?

3. What is the difference between speed and velocity?

4. How can you find the acceleration of an object?

+Math	+Depth	+Concepts	+Exploration
◆◆	◆◆		

Active Physics

Plus

Subtracting Vectors

In *Part C* of the *Investigate*, you found the acceleration when a steel ball speeds up or slows down while traveling in a straight line. In *Part B*, you probably found that riders get a "thrill" when their velocity changes direction even if they do not speed up or slow down. Whenever velocity changes direction, acceleration occurs. How do you find acceleration when only the direction of the velocity changes and the speed remains the same?

Assume that you are traveling east at 1 m/s and that 1 s later you are traveling north at 1 m/s. Your speed (1 m/s) has not changed but your velocity changed because its direction changed.

$$\text{Acceleration} = \frac{\text{change in velocity}}{\text{time elapsed}}$$

$$a = \frac{\Delta v}{\Delta t}$$

Δv is the change in velocity

$\Delta v = \text{final velocity} - \text{initial velocity}$

You can represent the velocities by arrows (vectors). Here are the vectors for the situation described: The length of the arrow represents the speed. The arrow is drawn to scale, in this case 1 m/s = 2 cm.

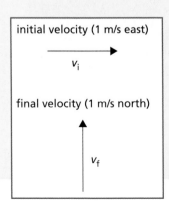

initial velocity (1 m/s east)

v_i

final velocity (1 m/s north)

v_f

To find the change in velocity you need to subtract vectors, but you have only learned how to add vectors. You can turn your subtraction problem into an addition problem. Recall from algebra that subtracting a number is equivalent to adding the negative of the number. For vectors, the negative is represented by an arrow pointed in the the direction opposite to that of the original vector.

$$\Delta v = \text{final velocity} - \text{initial velocity}$$

$$\Delta v = \text{final velocity} + (-\text{initial velocity})$$

You can add the final velocity and the negative of the initial velocity. The negative of the initial velocity has the same magnitude but the opposite direction.

v_i

$-v_i$

The change in velocity is represented by the red vector in the diagram to the right.

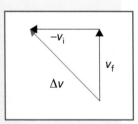

$-v_i$

v_f

Δv

The acceleration (strictly speaking, the average acceleration) will point in the direction of the red arrow Δv and its magnitude will be given by the magnitude (length) of Δv divided by the time elapsed (in this case 1 s).

a) Use the Pythagorean theorem to find the length of Δv.

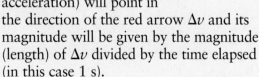

Active Physics

b) Compute the value of the (average) acceleration.

c) The direction of the acceleration will be in the direction of Δv. What is the angle between Δv and the eastward direction?

d) Suppose the initial velocity is 4 m/s north and the final velocity 2 s later is 3 m/s west. Draw a diagram showing the change in velocity. Use the Pythagorean theorem to find the magnitude of Δv and then find the magnitude of the acceleration. Use a protractor to measure the angle of Δv with respect to the westward direction. That will specify the direction of the acceleration.

What Do You Think Now?

At the beginning of this section, you were asked the following:

• **Which part of the roller-coaster ride produces the loudest screams? Why?**

Given what you have learned about velocity and acceleration and what you observed with the student riding in the moving chair, where will the riders in your roller-coaster ride experience acceleration? Which parts will produce the greatest "thrills"?

Physics
Essential Questions

What does it mean?

Scientists need to develop a precise vocabulary to talk about motion. You used the terms speed, velocity, and acceleration to describe the motion of a ball rolling down a ramp. Explain what each of these terms means.

How do you know?

Physicists often find that one concept is particularly important in understanding a given situation. You probably found that the blindfolded rider rated the "thrills" highest while being accelerated. What was the evidence for that? How do you know when the rider is being accelerated?

Why do you believe?

Connects with Other Physics Content	Fits with Big Ideas in Science	Meets Physics Requirements
Forces and motion	✱ Change and constancy	Makes mathematical sense

✱ It is important to distinguish between scientific concepts that are often used interchangeably in everyday language. Speed and velocity are two such concepts. The speedometer in your car indicates the car's speed (usually in miles per hour or kilometers per hour or both). What instrument could cars have that allows you to observe the car's velocity?

Why should you care?

Velocity and acceleration are the two most important concepts in describing motion of all kinds. Give some examples in everyday life where the distinction between velocity and acceleration is important. Why are velocity and acceleration important in a roller-coaster ride? How will understanding the difference between velocity and acceleration help you in your *Chapter Challenge*?

Reflecting on the Section and the Challenge

A big part of roller-coaster fun comes from the physics of velocity and acceleration. Traveling at a high speed is not enough to give a big thrill. The thrills come from accelerating around the curves and along the straight segments. Acceleration may change your speed or your direction (or both) as you ride along the path of the coaster. More rapid changes require greater accelerations. Additional thrills come from changes in acceleration. In designing your variation of The Terminator Express, you will want to ensure that the speeds and accelerations are right for your riders. You are required to have hills and turns, but the loop may be too much for your riders. There are more safety concerns for younger riders.

You are now able to draw top and side views for your variation of The Terminator Express and to note where the accelerations (and fun) may occur. If you were to build a prototype of part of the roller coaster, you could also make measurements of velocity and calculate accelerations.

Physics to Go

1. Draw a top view and a side view of a new version of The Terminator Express with the following characteristics: The roller coaster car begins from the loading platform and then rises along the lift. It arrives at the top of hilltop #1 and makes its first drop. It then climbs hill # 2 that is half the height of hill # 1. The car then goes along the back curve, rises over hilltop # 3, and swings into a horizontal circle. The coaster then comes out of the circle onto a level plane. The brakes are applied and the roller coaster comes to a stop.

2. Identify where the biggest thrill will be in The Terminator Express roller coaster. Explain why this will be the big thrill.

3. Speed by itself does not produce thrills. Living on Earth, you already have a big speed, since Earth is constantly turning.

   a) Earth makes a complete revolution once every 24 h. La Paz, Bolivia is close to the Equator and travels a large circumference in 24 h. Oslo, Norway is close to the Arctic Circle and travels a smaller circumference in 24 h. Which city has the greater speed?

   b) The circumference of Earth's Equator is about 40,000 km. It requires one day or 24 h to complete one revolution. Calculate the speed you are traveling on Earth if you are at the Equator.

   c) Why do you not get a big thrill going at such a high speed?

4. A roller-coaster rider traveling in a straight line changes from a speed of 4 m/s to 16 m/s in 3 s. Calculate the acceleration of the ride.

5. Identify the following situations as an example of either distance, displacement, speed, velocity, or acceleration.

   a) a car traveling at 50 km/h

   b) a student riding a bike at 4 m/s toward home

   c) a roller-coaster ride whips around a left turn at 5 m/s

   d) a roller-coaster car is dragged up a hill 12 m tall traveling at 3 m/s.

   e) a train ride takes you 150 km northwest

6. A lab cart is 10-cm long. It travels through a velocimeter in 2 s. Calculate the cart's speed.

7. A second lab cart is 5-cm long. If it were traveling at the same speed as the cart in *Question 6*, what would the velocimeter record as the elapsed time?

8. Your vehicle accelerates from 0 to 25 m/s (about 55 mi/h) in 10 s while traveling down a straight street. What is the acceleration of your vehicle?

9. As noted in the *Physics Talk*, physicists often introduce terms and distinctions that seem to make simple things more complicated. As you were told, these distinctions can make very difficult things much easier to explain and understand. Give an example outside of physics where you make a distinction for simple things so that complicated things will be easier to understand?

10. *Preparing for the Chapter Challenge*

    Suppose you were designing a roller coaster for young preschool children.

    a) Describe two changes you would make to The Terminator Express roller coaster. Explain why you would make these changes.

    b) Draw the top and side view of the roller coaster with these additional changes.

Inquiring Further

Research roller coasters

Research roller coasters on the Internet. Which are the most modern? What are some innovations in newer roller coasters? What features from historic coasters have been retained? Compare wooden and steel roller coasters.

Section 2

Gravitational Potential Energy and Kinetic Energy: What Goes Up and What Comes Down

Learning Outcomes

In this section, you will

- **Detect** the speed of an object at the bottom of a ramp.

- **Identify** the relationship between the speed at the bottom of a ramp and both the height and the angle of the ramp.

- **Complete** a graph of speed versus height of the ramp.

- **Define** and calculate gravitational potential energy and kinetic energy.

- **State** the conservation of energy.

- **Relate** the conservation of energy to a roller-coaster ride.

What Do You See?

What Do You Think?

The steepest angle of descent on a wooden roller coaster is 70°. The steepest angle of descent on a steel roller coaster is 90°.

Two roller-coaster tracks are shown in the illustration below.

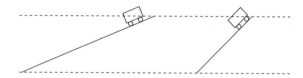

- **Which roller coaster will give the bigger thrill? Why?**

Record your ideas about these questions in your *Active Physics* log. Be prepared to discuss your responses with your small group and the class.

Investigate

Part A: What Affects the Speed of a Ball at the Bottom of a Ramp?

You will use a steel ball and a track to determine if a pattern exists between the placement of the ball and its speed at the bottom of the track. A pattern for speed will allow you to predict the speed for a new roller coaster.

- The basic setup for this experiment is a track and a steel ball (or cart).

- You can measure distances to the nearest tenth of a centimeter with a ruler and speeds with a velocimeter to its precision.

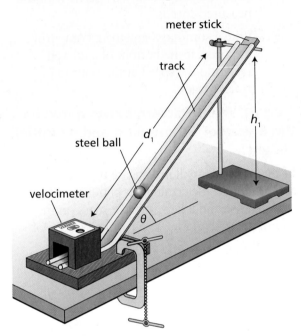

meter stick

track

h_1

d_1

steel ball

velocimeter

θ

1. Your first step is to determine the speed of the steel ball at the bottom of the incline when the ball is placed at different points along the track. Do not vary the angle of the track. For each starting point, record the speed at the bottom of the track, the distance (d) that the ball travels down the ramp, and the height of the ramp (h). Do at least two trials for each height of the steel ball so that you obtain two speed measurements at the bottom of the track. By comparing the results from the two different trials, you will get an idea of the accuracy of your results. If these values are close to each other, record the average speed for the steel ball at the bottom of the track. If the values are very different, make several more trials until you get consistent results.

⚠ Be prepared to stop the ball at the end of the track so it does not roll onto the floor. If the ball rolls onto the floor pick it up right away. If you cannot find the ball, tell your teacher immediately. This is a good safety practice to protect class members from slipping and falling.

a) Complete a data table in your *Active Physics* log for at least four different initial heights and their corresponding distances.

2. You have discovered that the speed of the ball increases if the height and/or distance increase. You will now investigate whether knowledge of one of the variables makes it easier to determine the ball's speed. To do this you will need to change the angle of the track. You will need two data charts to record your measurements. One chart will be for height and speed, and the other for distance and speed.

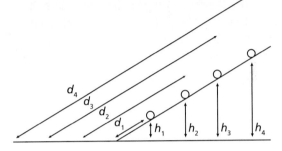

d_4
d_3
d_2
d_1
h_1 h_2 h_3 h_4

a) Use one of the heights you used in *Step 1*. For example, you may choose a height of 30 cm. This height will remain constant as you vary the distance the ball travels. For a height of 30 cm, record the speed of the ball at the bottom of the track and the starting distance. Change the angle of the track. Find a new place along the track where the height is, once again, 30 cm. Record the speed of the ball at the bottom of the track and the starting distance. Change the angle of the track two more times. Record your data.

b) Begin again. Now, use one of the distances up the track you used in *Step 1* (for example, you may choose 40 cm). This distance will remain constant as you vary the height from which the ball travels. With a distance along the track of 40 cm, record the speed of the ball at the bottom of the track and the starting height. Change the angle of the track.

Active Physics

Measure the distance of 40 cm along the track. Record the speed of the ball at the bottom of the track and the starting height. Change the angle of the track two more times. Record your data.

3. Review the data in *Steps 2.a-b)*.

a) Is there a pattern between the starting heights and the speed or between the starting distances and the speed, or both? Describe the pattern(s).

4. Change the angle of the track again to an angle you have not used previously.

a) Predict the speed at the bottom of this track either from the distance the ball travels or from the height that the ball travels using your data from *Step 2* and your conclusion from *Step 3*.

b) Once again, change the angle of the track and make a new prediction for the speed at the bottom of the track.

c) How accurate were your predictions?

5. Conduct the same investigation using a curved track. Measuring the distance along a curved track will require some ingenuity. (Hint: A piece of string may be a useful tool.) Measuring the height is similar to measuring the height for the straight track.

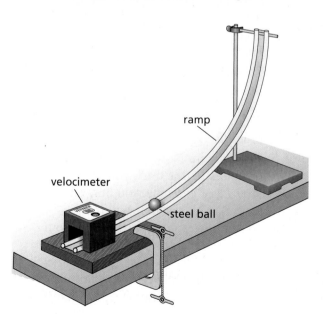

a) Include a column for predicted speeds and measured speeds for each of the heights in your data table. Record your data.

b) Compare your predicted speeds with the measured speeds.

c) Write a summary statement comparing the speed at the bottom of a curved track and the speed at the bottom of a straight track.

Part B: What Pattern Exists between the Speed of a Pendulum and its Initial Height?

In this part, you will investigate the speed of a pendulum to determine if a pattern exists between the initial height of the mass on the end of a string and its speed at the bottom of its swing.

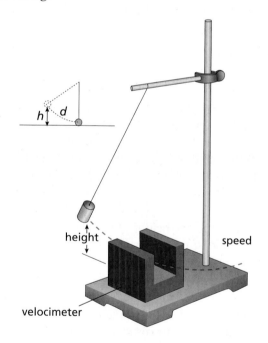

1. Pull the pendulum bob to the side and measure its height (*h*) above its lowest point. You will use a velocimeter to measure the speed of the bob at the bottom of the swing. Make sure that the bob swings cleanly through the velocimeter and does not crash into the side.

a) Construct a data table that includes both the initial height (*h*) and the speed measured at the bottom of the swing.

b) Measure and record the speed at the bottom of the swing for four or five different initial heights.

c) Write a summary statement comparing the initial height to the speed at the bottom of the swing.

2. A valuable way in which to analyze data is with a graph.

a) Take your data set of initial height and speed at the bottom of the swing and construct a graph with height on the *x*-axis and speed at the bottom of the swing on the *y*-axis.

3. You probably found that your graph is a curve. Graphs with curves are difficult to interpret. It is hard to tell if the curve is part of a circle, ellipse, hyperbola, parabola, or none of these. Graphs with straight lines are much easier. Follow these steps to see if your data can be graphed as a straight line by changing the y-axis.

a) Make a second graph now with height on the *x*-axis and the speed squared on the *y*-axis. This will require you to calculate v^2 for each speed.

   Make a third column in your data chart from *Step 1* for the speed squared (v^2).

b) Plot your data for height vs. speed squared.

c) If you find that the new graph is close to a straight line, draw on the graph a straight line that best fits your data points. You could use that straight line to predict the speed at the bottom for other initial heights.

Physics Talk

GRAVITATIONAL POTENTIAL ENERGY AND KINETIC ENERGY

Energy Transformations in the Roller Coaster

By varying the slope of the incline and measuring speeds, you were able to find that the speed of the ball at the bottom of a track is determined not by the length of the incline, but by the initial height of the ball. Similarly, two identical roller-coaster cars traveling down different inclines will have the same final speed if they both start from the same height.

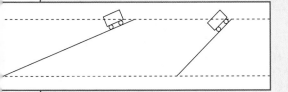

The cars shown in the diagram will have identical speeds at the bottom of the inclines. The second one will get there sooner, but will arrive with the same speed as the first one. This will be true as long as friction is not important.

You saw that this connection between the height and the speed was valid for different inclines, for curved tracks, and for a pendulum.

The concept of energy can be used to describe this relationship. In your *Investigate*, the steel ball or cart at the top of the incline is said to have **gravitational potential energy** (*GPE*). Gravitational potential energy is the energy an object has as a result of its position in a gravitational field. A moving ball has **kinetic energy** (*KE*). Kinetic energy is the energy an object

Physics Words

gravitational potential energy: the energy a body possesses as a result of its position in a gravitational field.

kinetic energy: the energy an object possesses because of its speed.

possesses because of its motion, in particular, due to its speed. *GPE* is dependent on the height of the ball above the ground. The *KE* is dependent on the speed of the ball. In addition, both the *KE* and the *GPE* also depend on the mass of the ball.

When the ball comes down the incline, the *GPE* decreases because the height above the ground level is decreasing. As you saw, when the ball comes down the incline, its speed increases and its *KE* increases. If the starting point on the incline is higher, then the ball experiences a larger change in *GPE* (a larger decrease) and at the bottom of the incline its *KE* is larger. The same will be true for a roller-coaster car.

$$GPE = \text{mass of object} \times \text{strength of gravitational field} \times \text{height}$$

In symbols, the equation for gravitational potential energy is

$$GPE = mgh,$$

where *m* is the mass of the object,

  g is the strength of the gravitational field (*g* is sometimes called the acceleration due to gravity),

  h is the height above the ground or the bottom of the ride.

Near the surface of Earth, $g = 9.8$ N/kg or 9.8 m/s^2. Note that the units for *g* are the same units as acceleration.

You could just as easily have defined *h* as the height above the lab table. You will only concern yourself with the change in height. You will usually set *GPE* = 0 at the lowest point of the object's motion.

The kinetic energy of an object is given by

$$KE = \frac{1}{2} \times \text{mass of object} \times \text{speed} \times \text{speed} = \frac{1}{2} \times \text{mass of object} \times (\text{speed})^2$$

In symbols, the equation for kinetic energy is

$$KE = \frac{1}{2}mv^2$$

where *m* is the mass of the object, and

  v is the speed of the object.

(Velocity is usually represented by *v*, but *KE* is a scalar and the direction is not taken into account.)

Physics Words

joule: the SI unit for all forms of energy; equivalent units for the joule are $\frac{kg \cdot m^2}{s^2}$ or N•m.

The unit for energy is a **joule** (symbol, J), pronounced "jewel." Both *GPE* and *KE* are measured in joules. The table on the next page shows some calculations for a roller-coaster car of mass 200 kg and an initial height of 20 m. Notice that at the top of the roller coaster there are lots of joules of *GPE* and zero joules of *KE* because the roller-coaster car is starting from rest at the top of the incline. At the bottom of the incline, there are zero joules of *GPE* (the car is at it lowest point) and lots of joules of *KE*. At the two other positions listed, there are some joules of *GPE* and some joules of *KE*.

Without knowing the velocity, it would seem that you could not calculate the *KE*. However, in this roller coaster, the sum of the *GPE* and *KE* must always be

Physics Words

mechanical energy: the sum of kinetic energy and potential energy.

40,000 J. This is because that was the total **mechanical energy** at the beginning. Mechanical energy in this case is the sum of GPE and KE. When the roller coaster was at a height of 20 m, there was no movement and 0 J of KE. All of the energy at this point was the 40,000 J of GPE.

This 40,000 J becomes very important for this roller coaster. The sum of GPE and KE must always be 40,000 J at any point on the roller coaster. (There is, of course, in real life, some loss of energy to the environment due to friction that must be taken into consideration. However, you may neglect that for now.)

At the bottom of the roller coaster (see row 2 on the table), there are 0 J of GPE. To total 40,000 J, there must be 40,000 J of KE at the bottom.

Halfway down (see row 3 on the table), the KE must equal 20,000 J, so that the sum of the GPE (20,000 J) and the KE (20,000 J) once again equals 40,000 J.

Mass of car = 200 kg and g = 10 N/kg or 10 m/s² (approximate value)			
Position of car (height) (m)	**GPE (J) = mgh**	**KE (J) = $\frac{1}{2}mv^2$**	**GPE + KE (J)**
top (20 m)	40,000	0	40,000
bottom (0 m)	0	40,000	40,000
halfway down (10 m)	20,000	20,000	40,000
three-quarters way down (5 m)	10,000	30,000	40,000

Three-quarters of the way down (see row 4 on the table), the KE must equal 30,000 J. The sum of the GPE (10,000 J) and the KE (30,000 J) once again equals 40,000 J.

Given any height, you can determine the GPE and then determine the KE. In this roller coaster, the GPE plus the KE must equal 40,000 J.

In a higher roller coaster, the GPE plus KE might equal 60,000 J. You can still calculate the GPE at any height and then find the corresponding KE.

To the right is an energy bar chart that shows GPE and KE at different parts of the car's trip. Notice that when GPE decreases, KE increases and vice versa. The second energy stacked bar chart below shows that the sum of the heights of the two types of energy bars remains the same. That indicates that the sum of KE and GPE remains the same.

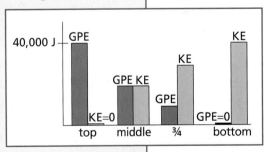

When discussing the conservation of energy, you must recognize that the sum of the GPE and KE only remains the same if there are no losses of energy due to friction, sound, or other outside sources and no additions of energy from motors. At the end of the roller-coaster ride, brakes are applied to bring the roller-coaster cars to a stop. In that process, the KE of the roller-coaster cars is converted into thermal energy, sound, and some light. The brakes certainly get hot! If the track is level at the end of the ride, there is no change in GPE during stopping.

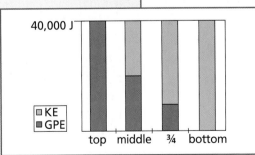

Active Physics

Calculating Kinetic Energy from Gravitational Potential Energy

In a system like your roller coaster, the sum of the *GPE* and *KE* is constant (as long as friction is not important). *GPE* + *KE* = constant.

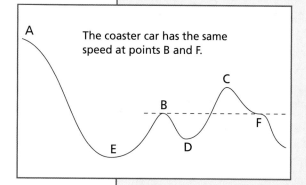

The coaster car has the same speed at points B and F.

In the roller coaster to the left, suppose the *GPE* at point A is 30,000 J and the *KE* at point A is 0 J. Then the total energy at point A and each and every other point on the roller coaster is 30,000 J. The total energy is 30,000 J at points B, C, D, E, and F and every point in between. Since points B and F have the same height, the roller-coaster cart must also have the same *GPE*. That implies that the roller-coaster car also has the same *KE* and is therefore going at the same speed at points B and F.

The height determines the *GPE*. The total energy at every point is the same. If you know the *GPE*, you can easily find the *KE*. The *KE* informs you about the speed.

Calculating Speed from Kinetic and Gravitational Potential Energy

The conservation of energy provides a way to find the kinetic energy if you know the change in height of the roller coaster. From the *KE*, you can find the speed of the roller coaster. Using algebra, you can calculate the speed.

First, you recognize that the total energy, the mechanical energy, of the roller coaster stays the same.

$$\text{Mechanical energy (bottom)} = \text{Mechanical energy (top)}$$

Since you consider only *KE* and *GPE*, the sum of those two must be the same at the top as it is at the bottom.

$$KE \text{ (bottom)} + GPE \text{ (bottom)} = KE \text{ (top)} + GPE \text{ (top)}$$

Since *GPE* = 0 at the bottom and *KE* = 0 at the top, you have

$$KE \text{ (bottom)} + 0 = 0 + GPE \text{ (top)}$$
$$KE \text{ (bottom)} = GPE \text{ (top)}$$

You now use $KE = \frac{1}{2}mv^2$ and $GPE = mgh$

$$\frac{1}{2}mv^2 \text{ (bottom)} = mgh \text{ (top)}$$

Solving for v^2 gives

$$v^2 \text{ (bottom)} = 2gh \text{ (top)}$$

In the preceding equation, the mass (*m*) cancelled out. This means that the speed is independent of the mass of the car. (It doesn't matter whether the roller-coaster car has two or four passengers.)

Sample Problem

The starting height for a roller coaster is 25 m. Its mass with 2 passengers is 300 kg.

a) Calculate the maximum *GPE*.

b) Calculate the maximum *KE*.

c) Calculate the velocity at this maximum *KE*.

d) How would the velocity change if the coaster had 4 passengers and a total mass of 400 kg?

Strategy: Use the equation for *GPE* to calculate the *GPE* at the maximum height. Then use the conservation of energy to find the *KE*. From the value of the maximum *KE*, you can use the equation for *KE* to find the maximum velocity.

Solution:

a) The maximum *GPE* is at the maximum height of the roller coaster, which is equal to the starting height.

$$GPE = mgh$$
$$GPE = (300 \text{ kg})(10 \text{ m/s}^2)(25 \text{ m})$$
$$GPE = 75{,}000 \text{ J}$$

b) Total energy is conserved. The total energy is equal to the maximum *GPE*, which is also equal to the maximum *KE*. The maximum *KE* is therefore equal to 75,000 J.

c) Since the *KE* is equal to $\frac{1}{2}mv^2$ and the mass and *KE* are known, the velocity can be calculated by plugging in the numerical values. It is usually preferable to solve for the missing variable in terms of the other variables before plugging in the numerical values.

$$KE = \frac{1}{2}mv^2$$

$$\text{But } KE_{max} = GPE_{max}$$

$$\frac{1}{2}mv^2 = mgh$$

The mass cancels. Therefore, the velocity does not depend on the mass.

$$\frac{1}{2}v^2 = gh$$

$$v = \sqrt{2gh}$$

$$= \sqrt{2(10 \text{ m/s}^2)(25 \text{ m})}$$

$$= 22 \text{ m/s}$$

d) Note that the speed does not depend on the mass of the coaster as shown in *c*). If the mass changes, both the *GPE* and the *KE* change, but not the speed.

Checking Up

1. What effect does changing the length of the incline have on the speed of a ball when it rolls to the bottom?

2. How does the gravitational potential energy of an object change with its height? With its mass?

3. How does the kinetic energy of an object change with its speed? With its mass?

4. As a roller-coaster car rolls down a hill, what happens to the gravitational potential energy it loses?

5. If a roller-coaster car has 40,000 J of gravitational potential energy when at rest on the top of a hill, how much kinetic energy does it have when it is ¾ of the way down the hill?

+Math	+Depth	+Concepts	+Exploration
◆◆	◆		

Active Physics

Plus

Finding an Equation for the Height vs. Speed Squared Graph

In the *Investigate*, you plotted a graph with height on the *x*-axis and speed squared on the *y*-axis for your pendulum. You can find an equation that describes the straight line you drew. Recall that the equation for any straight line on an *x*-*y* graph is

$$y = (\text{slope} \times x) + b$$

where *b* is the *y*-intercept.

Note that in most math books the equation is written as $y = mx + b$ where *m* is the slope. To avoid confusing *m* for mass with *m* for slope, the word slope was used in the equation.

In your straight-line graph, (speed)^2 is the *y*-variable and starting height is the *x*-variable.

If the car starts out at $h = 0$, (the bottom of the incline), its final speed will be zero.

The graph intersects the origin, and the value of the *y*-intercept, *b*, is 0.

The equation for the graph becomes

$$y = (\text{slope} \times x) + 0 \text{ or}$$

$$y = (\text{slope} \times x)$$

Substituting for the variables in your graph:

$$(\text{speed})^2 = \text{slope} \times \text{height}$$

$$v^2 = \text{slope} \times h$$

1. Calculate the slope (slope = "rise" over "run") of your graph from the pendulum data, and record its value.

2. Compare the value of your slope with those of other groups in the class.

3. Create a similar v^2 versus *h* graph with the data from the ball rolling down the incline from different heights (*Investigate Part A, 2.b*). Calculate the slope of the graph. If your data plotted as v^2 as a function of *h* fall along a straight line (at least fairly close to a straight line), then you can conclude that there is a direct relationship between the square of the speed at the bottom of the ramp and the height at which the ball starts its trip.

In the *Physics Talk*, you saw that $v^2 = 2gh$. Now, you can see why your graph of v^2 versus *h* was a straight line.

If the car were sliding (no rotation of the wheels), the slope of the line representing the car's speed squared versus *h* should also be (approximately): 2×9.8 N/kg $= 2 \times 9.8$ m/s^2 = 19.6 m/s^2. The slope of your graph is equal to 2 *g*. Measurement of the slope is a measurement of "*g*" — the strength of the gravitational field and the acceleration due to gravity. If your slope is 19.6 m/s^2, then $g = 9.8$ m/s^2. When the wheels are rotating or when your steel ball was rolling down the incline, there is some *KE* energy of rotation as well as the *KE* energy of the linear motion of the car or ball. For most roller-coaster cars, the rotational energy is rather small and you can use the equations above to determine the speed of the car.

What Do You Think Now?

At the beginning of this section, you were asked the following:

• **Which roller-coaster will give the biggest thrill? Why?**

Use what you have learned about acceleration and the conservation of energy on the roller-coaster ride to revise your answer. Will the final speed be different at the bottom of the two tracks? Discuss your new answer with other students in your group.

Physics
Essential Questions

What does it mean?

Kinetic energy and gravitational potential energy are two essential concepts in understanding objects moving under the influence of gravity. Explain the meaning of kinetic energy and gravitational potential energy.

How do you know?

Physicists prefer to express relationships among physical concepts using mathematics whenever possible, so that they can make quantitative predictions about what will happen. Use the data you obtained in this *Investigate* to explain the mathematical relationship between initial height and speed at the low point of the motion.

Why do you believe?

Connects with Other Physics Content	Fits with Big Ideas in Science	Meets Physics Requirements
Forces and motion	✳ Conservation laws	Good, clear, explanation, no more complex than necessary

✳ Conservation laws are one of the most important organizing principles of physics. Show how the sum of kinetic energy and gravitational potential energy was used to explain roller coasters and the pendulum. (Note: For the rolling ball, some of the kinetic energy is associated with the rolling of the ball, so the speed of the ball does not directly give you all of the ball's kinetic energy.)

Why should you care?

The interchange between kinetic energy and gravitational potential energy is a way to calculate and compare the kinetic energy and therefore the speed at every point on the roller coaster. How will understanding gravitational potential energy and kinetic energy help you in your roller-coaster design challenge? Relate your answer to your *Engineering Design Cycle*.

Reflecting on the Section and the Challenge

In designing a roller coaster, it is necessary to know how the speed of the roller coaster will vary. Knowing that the sum of the *GPE* and *KE* is constant is crucial in finding the speed at each point on the ride. How to calculate the *GPE* and *KE* will also be important when you want to ensure safety. You cannot let the roller coaster fall off the tracks, nor can you build a roller coaster that injures people. If your roller coaster begins on top of a tall hill, the height of that hill will determine the speed for each and every point along the roller-coaster ride. As you design your roller coaster, you should think about where the *GPE* will be largest and where it will be smallest. You should also think about how the *KE* changes in different parts of the ride.

Physics to Go

1. For which track is the speed of the car the greatest at the bottom? (Assume no friction.)

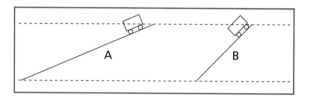

2. State the conservation of energy as it applies to roller coasters. Include in your statement *GPE*, *KE*, *mgh*, and $\frac{1}{2}mv^2$.

3. Complete the table below for a roller coaster starting from rest at the top.

Mass of car = 200 kg and *g* = 10 N/kg or 10 m/s² (approximate value)			
Position of car → height (m)	GPE (J) = mgh	KE (J) = $\frac{1}{2}$ mv²	GPE + KE (J)
top (30 m)	60,000		
bottom (0 m)			
halfway down (15 m)			
three-quarters way down (7.5 m)			

4. Draw a *GPE* and *KE* energy bar chart for the situation given in *Question 3*.

5. Complete the table below for a roller coaster starting from rest at the top.

Mass of car = 300 kg and *g* = 10 N/kg or 10 m/s² (approximate value)			
Position of car → height (m)	GPE (J) = mgh	KE (J) = $\frac{1}{2}$ mv²	GPE + KE (J)
top (25 m)			
bottom (0 m)			
halfway down (12.5 m)			
further down (5 m)			

6. Draw a *GPE* and *KE* energy bar chart for the situation given in *Question 5*.

7. A pendulum is lifted to a height of 0.75 m. The mass of the bob is 0.2 kg.

   a) Calculate the *GPE* at the top.

   b) Find the *KE* of the bob at the bottom.

   c) At what position of the bob will the *GPE* and the *KE* be equal?

8. In the early morning, a roller-coaster train (set of cars hooked together) only has 6 passengers. In the afternoon it has 26 passengers. Will the speed of the roller coaster change with more passengers aboard? Explain your answer.

9. To the right is a side view of a roller coaster that starts from rest at position A.

   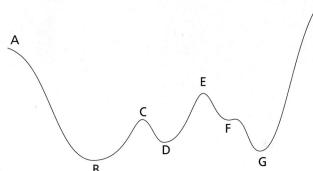

   a) At which point is the roller-coaster car traveling the fastest? Explain.

   b) At which two points is the roller-coaster car traveling at the same speed? Explain.

   c) Is the roller coaster car traveling faster at E or D? Explain.

10. Above and to the right is a side view of a roller coaster that starts from rest at position A.

    a) Determine reasonable values for the *GPE* and *KE* at points B, C, D, E, and F.

    b) Why can't the roller coaster reach point H?

11. ***Preparing For Chapter Challenge***

    Complete this chart for a modified Terminator Express roller coaster. You may wish to try this on a spreadsheet. *h* = 25 m at the top.

Mass of car = 200 kg and *g* = 10 N/kg or 10 m/s² (approximate value)				
Position of car	Height (m)	GPE (J) = *mgh*	KE (J) = $\frac{1}{2}$ *mv²*	GPE + KE (J)
bottom of hill				
top of hill				
top of loop				
horizontal loop				

Inquiring Further

Conservation of energy in skateboarding

As a skateboarder practices on the vert (vertical surface), there are constant changes in the gravitational potential energy *GPE* and the kinetic energy *KE*. Research the size of the vert and report back on how the conservation of energy plays an integral part in this sport. You may also wish to make measurements of skateboarders in the vert from a video on the internet.

Section 3

Spring Potential Energy: More Energy

Learning Outcomes

In this section, you will

- **Calculate** the kinetic energy of a pop-up toy.

- **Calculate** the spring potential energy from the conservation of energy.

- **Calculate** the spring potential energy by using an equation.

- **Relate** spring potential energy with conservation of mechanical energy using an equation.

- **Recognize** the general nature of the conservation of energy as it involves heat, sound, chemical, and other forms of energy.

What Do You Think?

The concept of a "lift hill" for a roller coaster was developed in 1885. This was the initial hill that began a roller coaster ride. A chain or a cable often pulled the train up to the top of this hill.

- **How does the roller coaster today get up to its highest point?**

- **Does it cost more to lift the roller coaster if it is full of people?**

Record your ideas about these questions in your *Active Physics* log. Be prepared to discuss your responses with your small group and the class.

Investigate

Little pop-up toys are fun for all ages. You press the plunger, place it on a table, and "pop!" it flies into the air. In this inquiry investigation, you will determine the kinetic energy, *KE*, of the pop-up toy when it leaves the ground.

 Be sure to use the toy safely, always placing it firmly on the table before releasing it and keeping your face and the faces of your classmates away from where the toy may jump or pop. Eye protection must be worn by everyone during this experiment.

1. Play with the toy to get a sense of how high it jumps.

✍ a) What is the approximate height of a jump?

✍ b) How consistent is the pop-up toy from one jump to the next?

2. Discuss ideas with your group to identify two distinct methods you can use to determine the *KE* when the pop-up toy leaves the table. One method will use the velocimeter. The second method will use a meter stick to measure the height of the jump.

✍ a) Record your two methods in your *Active Physics* log. Since another team may want to understand what you have done, be quite careful to list all the steps. Indicate how all measurements are completed, and what is recorded or calculated.

3. Conduct the investigation into *KE* using both of your methods.

✍ a) Record your results. If you changed your procedure during the experiment, you should also record any changes here. These modifications are similar to the *Process* step of your *Engineering Design Cycle*.

✍ b) Compare the *KE* determinations from the two methods.

4. Measure the mass of the pop-up toy using a balance. Tape some coins to the

top of the pop-up toy in order to approximately double its mass. The mass of a nickel is approximately 5 g. You can probably come close to doubling the mass of the pop-up toy by adding nickels.

5. Repeat the investigation and find the *KE* of the pop-up toy as it leaves the ground. Be sure the coins are taped securely on the toy. Retape after every two or three trials.

✍ a) Why do you think that the heavier pop-up toy behaved differently? Use the terms *GPE* and *KE* in your explanation.

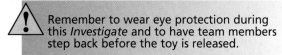
Remember to wear eye protection during this *Investigate* and to have team members step back before the toy is released.

6. Answer the following questions in your *Active Physics* log:

✍ a) What is the *KE* and *GPE* of the toy when it sits on the table?

✍ b) What happens to the *GPE* and *KE* of the toy as it rises from the table?

✍ c) If the total energy of the toy is conserved, where does the *KE* and *GPE* come from as it rises?

✍ d) Where is the toy when its *KE* is greatest and where is it when its *GPE* is greatest?

7. The pop-up toy had both *KE* and *GPE* as it rose above the table. While the toy was sitting on the table, it also had *spring potential energy*, *SPE*. This *SPE* was converted to *KE* when the toy leaped off the table. The *KE* then became increasing *GPE* and decreasing *KE* as the pop-up toy ascended and slowed down. Using the concept of conservation of energy from the last section, you notice that before popping up, the energy of the toy was all *SPE*. Just after popping up, it was all *KE*. When reaching the highest point, the energy was all *GPE*.

The total energy at all other points was the same as the total *SPE* before popping. The total *KE* just after popping or the total *GPE* at its peak also equals the spring potential energy before the toy pops. You can show this in a table. Total energy is conserved, but you now have spring potential energy, *SPE*, as another form of energy in addition to *GPE* and *KE*.

a) Complete the table in your log with other reasonable values for *SPE*, *KE*, *GPE* and the sum in the respective columns.

b) Draw an energy bar chart like the one in the *Physics Talk* in the previous section, but now including *SPE* as well as *KE* and *GPE*.

Position above table (m)	SPE (J)	KE (J)	GPE (J)	SPE + KE + GPE (J)
At rest on table: height = 0 m	20	0	0	20
Just after popping: height = 0 m	0	20	0	20
At peak: height = 0.30 m	0	0	20	20
1/2 way up: height - 0.15 m			10	
With the spring only partially open: height = 0 m				
Some other position: height = ? m				

Physics Talk

CONSERVATION OF ENERGY

Kaitlyn, Hannah, and Nicole share an apartment. Hannah keeps a bowl by the door filled with quarters that she can use for the washer and dryer at the laundromat. On Tuesday, Hannah counts her money and finds that she has 24 quarters, or $6.00 in quarters. This is just the right amount for her laundry on Saturday. On Wednesday morning, Nicole comes rushing up to the apartment because she needs some quarters for the parking meter. She takes three quarters from the bowl and replaces them with six dimes and three nickels. The total money in the bowl is still $6.00. On Wednesday afternoon, Kaitlyn needs to buy a fifty-cent newspaper from the machine that takes all coins but pennies. Kaitlyn takes two quarters from Hannah's bowl and replaces these coins with fifty pennies. The total in the bowl is still $6.00.

Wednesday night, Hannah comes home and notices that her bowl is filled with quarters, pennies, nickels, and dimes. She knows that it still adds up to the $6.00 that was there in the morning, but also knows that she cannot do her laundry unless all the money is in quarters. Her roommates agree to exchange all the coins with quarters the next day.

The money in the bowl could represent the energy in a system. The total amount of energy may have been 600 J. As the coins in the bowl change from quarters to dimes and nickels to pennies and back to quarters, the energy in the system can vary from kinetic energy to gravitational potential energy to **spring potential energy** in any combination. *(Note: In Chapter 2, the term EPE (elastic potential energy) was used. Bungee cords, trampolines, and bent poles in pole vaulting all have elastic potential energy (EPE). The best approximation for EPE is that these behave like springs. In this chapter, we refer to SPE, or spring potential energy.)*

If Kaitlyn had taken the two quarters and not replaced them with pennies, then the total money would be less. The loss in money due to Kaitlyn would have resulted in that money being somewhere else. In some systems, energy is also lost. A bouncing ball does not get to the same height in each successive bounce. Some of the energy of the ball becomes sound energy and heat energy. These can be measured and will indicate that some energy left the system but did not disappear. In the pop-up toy and the roller coaster, the total energy can be *GPE*, *KE*, or *SPE*, but the sum of the energies must always be the same.

As you followed the changes in Hannah's bowl of money, you knew that there were ways to measure the total amount of money. Fifty pennies is identical in value to two quarters. Scientists look for all the energies in a system. There is electrical energy, light energy, nuclear energy, sound energy, heat (thermal) energy, chemical energy, and others. Each one is able to be calculated using measurements. All the energies are measured in joules. If you take into account all forms of energy, the total number of joules must always remain the same. The total energy is conserved.

In this section, you were able to observe how the spring potential energy of the pop-up toy became the kinetic energy of the pop-up toy, which then became the gravitational potential energy of the pop-up toy. A graph of the three types of energy at different locations in the top diagram to the right shows that each type of energy changes in value, but that the total energy remains the same. The total energy can best be shown in a stacked bar chart of the same data in the bottom diagram to the right.

In this *Investigate*, you were also able to observe how the pop-up toy's behavior changed when you doubled its mass.

Physics Words

spring potential energy: the energy stored in a spring due to its compression or stretch.

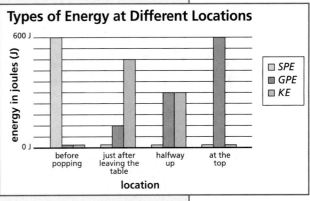

Types of Energy at Different Locations

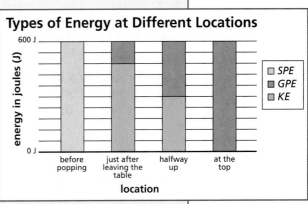

Types of Energy at Different Locations

The larger mass pop-up toy did not go as high as the original, lower-mass pop-up toy. Both pop-up toys had identical spring potential energies. Since "before popping" the *SPE* represents the total energy, both pop-up toys had identical total energies as well. The graphs shown on the previous page could describe the heavier pop-up toy as well. The less massive and more massive pop-up toys can have the same *GPE* if and only if the more massive pop-up toys do not go as high. Since *GPE = mgh*, the larger mass has a smaller height and the smaller mass has a larger height.

In a real roller coaster, the roller coaster has all its energy as *GPE* (gravitational potential energy) as it sits on the highest hill. Most of this energy becomes *KE* (kinetic energy) as the roller coaster is released. Some small amount of the energy is converted to thermal energy and a smaller part to sound energy.

Where does the roller coaster get all of that *GPE* that drives the rest of the ride? Something has to pull the roller coaster up to the top of the hill. The energy to pull the roller coaster is usually electric. The electrical energy comes from a power plant (that burns oil, gas, coal, or uses nuclear energy or water's potential energy) or from a local generator that may use gasoline.

After the cars are pulled to the top of the hill, the total *GPE* and *KE* of the roller coaster remains the same except for losses due to thermal and sound energy. At the end of the ride, the *KE* is converted to thermal energy as the brakes bring the cars to a halt. If the brakes fail, there may be a large spring that will stop the car as the car compresses it.

Calculating Spring Potential Energy

In this section, you extended the conservation of energy principle to include the spring potential energy. It is possible to calculate the spring potential energy.

The equation for spring potential energy is

$$SPE = \frac{1}{2}kx^2,$$

where k is the spring constant and

x is the amount of stretch or compression of the spring.

A spring that is difficult to compress or stretch will have a large spring constant (k). That spring will "pack" more *SPE* for an identical compression than a spring that is easy to compress.

The total energy of a spring toy that can jump into the air is the sum of the *SPE*, the *GPE*, and the *KE*. Once the spring is compressed, the sum of these three energies, *GPE*, *KE*, and *SPE* must remain constant.

$$GPE + KE + SPE = \text{constant}$$
$$mgh + \frac{1}{2}mv^2 + \frac{1}{2}kx^2 = \text{constant}$$

Sample Problem

A spring pop-up toy with a mass of 0.02 kg reaches a maximum height of 0.50 m. The compression length of the spring is 0.03 m. Find the following:

a) *GPE* at the top,

b) *SPE* before the "pop,"

c) the spring constant, k, and

d) *KE* at the moment the spring toy leaves the ground.

Strategy:

You can use the equation for *GPE* to calculate the *GPE* at the top because you are given the mass of the toy and the maximum height. Using the law of conservation of energy, you know that the *GPE* at the top must equal the *SPE* before the pop and the *KE* at the moment the spring toy leaves the ground.

Given:

mass (m) = 0.02 kg
height (h) = 0.50 m
compression length (x) = 0.03 m
Use g = 9.8 m/s^2.

Solution:

a) $GPE = mgh$

$$= (0.02 \text{ kg})\left(9.8 \ \frac{\text{m}}{\text{s}^2}\right)(0.50 \text{ m})$$

$$= 0.098 \text{ J}$$

b) $SPE = GPE$

$$SPE = 0.098 \text{ J}$$

c) $SPE = \frac{1}{2}kx^2$

$$k = \frac{2(SPE)}{x^2}$$

$$= \frac{2(0.098 \text{ J})}{(0.03 \text{ m})^2} \left(\text{Since J} = \text{N} \bullet \text{m, note that the units are } \frac{\text{N} \bullet \text{m}}{\text{m}^2}. \right)$$

$$= 217.78 \ \frac{\text{N}}{\text{m}}$$

$$= 218 \ \frac{\text{N}}{\text{m}}$$

d) $KE = SPE$

$$KE = 0.098 \text{ J}$$

(The *KE* is actually a bit less than this because the toy is 0.03 m above the table when it pops. You can calculate the *GPE* at this height to find the exact *KE*.)

Checking Up

1. What happens to the spring potential energy of a "pop-up" toy after it leaps off the table?

2. A "pop-up" toy has 2 J of spring potential energy before popping. How much kinetic energy will the toy have just after leaving the table?

3. A "pop-up" toy has 2 J of spring potential energy before popping. How much gravitational potential energy will it have at the top?

4. What two factors determine the amount of spring potential energy that is stored in a spring?

+Math	+Depth	+Concepts	+Exploration
♦♦	♦		

Active Physics

Plus

Using Algebra to Derive an Equation for Height

You can use algebra to find out how high the pop-up toy should go.

1. When the spring is completely compressed, but before the toy has popped, what is the *KE* of the toy? What is the equation for the toy's *SPE*?

2. As usual, choose *GPE* to be 0 when the spring is completely compressed. Write an algebraic expression for the total energy = *KE* + *GPE* + *SPE* when the spring is totally compressed but before the toy pops.

3. After the toy pops, it will shoot upward. When it gets to its highest point, what is its *KE*? What is its *SPE* at that point? Explain how you arrived at your answers.

4. If you denote the height of the high point above the starting point as *h*, write an algebraic expression for the *GPE* at the high point.

5. Write an algebraic expression for the total energy = *KE* + *GPE* + *SPE* at the high point.

6. If you assume that the total energy stays the same from before popping to the high point, you may equate the expression from *Question 2.* with the expression from *Question 5.* Solve the resulting expression for *h* and show that

$$h = \frac{\frac{1}{2}kx^2}{mg}$$ where *x* is the original

amount of spring compression.

What Do You Think Now?

At the beginning of this section, you were asked the following:

• **How does the roller coaster today get up to its highest point?**

• **Does it cost more to lift the roller coaster if it is full of people?**

How would your answers to these questions vary, based on what you learned from your investigation? A roller coaster is not lifted up by a spring but by cables and electricity. Will more electrical energy be required to lift a heavier roller coaster? The experiment that you conducted with the pop-up toy when its mass was increased can provide insight into this question. How did the height of the pop-up toy change when the mass changed?

Physics
Essential Questions

What does it mean?

The principle of conservation of energy states that energy may change its form, but the total energy for a system stays the same. Write a short description of a situation in which the energy changes form, but where the total amount of energy stays the same.

How do you know?

All principles of science can be checked with quantitative measurements. Write a short explanation of how your investigation with the pop-up toy with different masses attached illustrates the conservation of energy.

Why do you believe?

Connects with Other Physics Content	Fits with Big Ideas in Science	Meets Physics Requirements
Forces and motion	* Conservation laws	Experimental evidence is consistent with models and theories

* Conservation laws are a major organizing principle of physics. Energy can appear in many forms, but the total energy is always conserved. To understand the behavior of the pop-up toy, you had to include the potential energy of the compressed spring, SPE, and the kinetic energy, KE, and the gravitational potential energy, GPE. Compare the pop-up toy with a child on a trampoline and with a roller coaster in order to demonstrate how the conservation of energy can be used to describe each situation.

Why should you care?

The conservation of energy helps you understand many phenomena in the world around you. How will what you learned about the conservation of energy in this section help you with your roller-coaster design challenge?

Reflecting on the Section and the Challenge

There are other energies — heat, sound, chemical, and so on. In your analysis of the roller coaster, you may decide to ignore heat and sound, but you had better mention this in your report. In the actual construction, it will be important to take into account that a small amount of mechanical energy (KE plus GPE) is being dissipated (lost to other forms of energy).

The roller coaster uses electrical energy to get the cars to the top of the hill. This is similar to using the chemical energy of your body to compress the pop-up toy so that you can watch it jump.

Once the energy is in the spring of the pop-up toy, the SPE can become KE, which becomes GPE. In the same way, once the cars are on top of the hill, the GPE can become KE.

Active Physics

Describing the energy transformations will be a good way to describe the physics of your design of the roller coaster.

You may want to add a spring at the end of the ride to stop a "run-away" roller coaster.

Physics to Go

1. Complete the table with other reasonable values for *SPE*, *KE*, *GPE* for the pop-up toy. In the last column, fill in the sum in the respective columns.

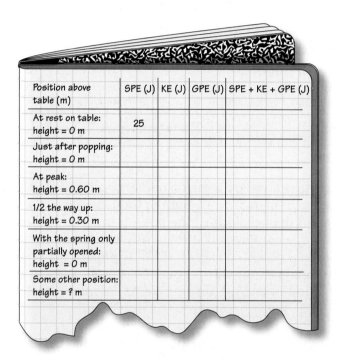

Position above table (m)	SPE (J)	KE (J)	GPE (J)	SPE + KE + GPE (J)
At rest on table: height = 0 m	25			
Just after popping: height = 0 m				
At peak: height = 0.60 m				
1/2 the way up: height = 0.30 m				
With the spring only partially opened: height = 0 m				
Some other position: height = ? m				

2. Draw an energy bar chart for the situation described in *Question 1*. Include bars for *SPE*, *KE*, and *GPE*. Write a brief description of how the energy changes from one form to another during different parts of the pop-up toy's motion.

3. How would the table values in *Question 1* change if some extra mass were attached to the pop-up toy?

4. You throw a ball into the air and catch it on the way down. Beginning with the chemical energy in your muscles, describe the energy transformations of the ball.

5. Why can the second hill of the roller coaster not be higher than the first hill?

6. Why does the roller coaster not continue forever and go back and forth and up and down the hills over and over again?

7. A roller coaster of mass 300 kg ascends to a height of 15 m. How much electrical energy was required to raise the cars to this height?

8. A roller-coaster car has a mass of 400 kg and a speed of 15 m/s.

   a) What is the *KE* of the roller-coaster car?

   b) What will be the *GPE* of this roller-coaster car at its highest point, where *KE* = 0 at that point?

   c) How high can the roller-coaster car go with this much energy?

9. A ball is thrown upward from Earth's surface. While the ball is rising, is its gravitational potential energy increasing, decreasing, or remaining the same?

10. Three people of equal mass climb a mountain using paths A, B, and C shown in the diagram. Along which path(s) does a person gain the greatest amount of gravitational potential energy from start to finish: A only, B only, C only, or is the gain the same along all paths?

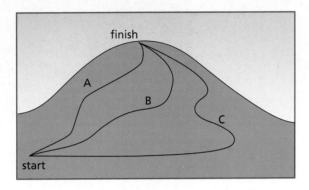

11. In an experiment similar to your toy, the mass of the spring toy was 0.020 kg. The height that the toy rose to was 0.40 m. The initial speed of the spring toy as measured by the velocimeter was 2.7 m/s.

   a) Do the *GPE* and the *KE* both give approximately the same values?

   b) What is the *SPE* before the toy pops?

   c) What height would you expect the pop-up toy to reach if its mass were tripled?

12. A roller coaster begins at a height of 18 m. The mass of the roller coaster and passengers is 300 kg. When the roller coaster reaches the bottom, its brakes fail. An emergency spring must bring the coaster to rest.

   a) What must be the spring constant of this spring if it will be compressed by 4 m?

   b) How much will the spring compress if an additional 100 kg of people are aboard?

13. An umbrella has an automatic opening mechanism. When the umbrella is closed, a spring is compressed. The spring constant is 40 N/m and the spring is compressed 0.3 m. What is the *KE* of the umbrella when it begins to open?

Section 4

Newton's Law of Universal Gravitation: The Ups and Downs of a Roller Coaster

What Do You See?

What Do You Think?

The astronauts "float" around the space station as it orbits Earth. Fish aboard a shuttle orbiting Earth swim in circles. Roller coasters would not work aboard the space shuttle. You are held onto the surface of Earth by its gravity.

- **Does gravity have a direction?**
- **How can people in Australia be held on Earth when they are "upside down"?**

Record your ideas about these questions in your *Active Physics* log. Be prepared to discuss your responses with your small group and the class.

Investigate

Roller coasters require gravity. Once the roller coaster gets to the top of the first hill, gravity allows the gravitational potential energy to become kinetic energy as the coaster and passengers ride the track. Understanding gravity does not require nearly as much courage as riding a roller coaster.

1. Take a small object such as a penny. Hold it up in front you. Let it go. Observe it fall. Consider the horizon line, the "horizontal."

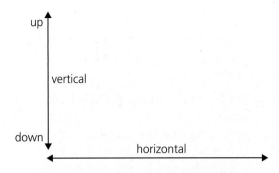

The "vertical" direction is perpendicular to the horizontal and signifies what is usually called "up" and "down."

a) Which direction (horizontal or vertical) does the penny fall?

b) Carefully observe the details of the penny as it falls. Can you agree with members of your group that the penny falls faster and faster as it falls? How could you design an experiment to measure its change in speed (its acceleration)? When experiments are performed, it is found that the acceleration of the penny is almost identical from any location on Earth. The penny always accelerates down with a change in speed of 9.8 m/s every second.

c) Make a map to represent some vertical lines in the room between the floor and ceiling. At five points along this line, draw a little arrow that shows the direction the penny falls. Let the length of the arrow represent the acceleration of the penny (9.8 m/s every second) when released there. This map represents Earth's gravitational influence in the space about Earth in this room. This influence is Earth's gravitational field. The acceleration of the falling body is one way to measure the *gravitational field* of, in this case, Earth.

d) If you have visited another part of the country, did things also fall vertically there? Imagine your little maps all over the country, one for each room where an experimenter drops pennies.

What would their "falling maps" look like at their location?

e) Australia is in the Southern Hemisphere. If someone in Australia drops his or her penny, what direction does it fall there, relative to the Australian's horizontal and vertical? What would his or her "falling map" look like if he or she performed the falling penny experiment in a classroom there?

f) Earth is a sphere. Crumple a piece of paper so that if forms a sphere. Mark your location on the crumpled paper globe. Mark Australia's location.

g) Imagine little copies of your room map, and the Australian's map, placed on the globe. Do you see a trend in the direction that the arrows point? How would you describe it relative to the center of Earth? Sketch the gravitational field around Earth, approximating Earth as a sphere.

h) Earth's gravitational field exerts a force (the force of gravity) on you just as it did on the penny. If you walk up a flight of stairs, the entire Earth pulls on you with its gravity. Yet, you are able to climb the stairs. Would you say that the force of gravity is a strong force, or a weak one?

2. Sea level is 6400 km from the center of Earth. The data table on the next page contains the acceleration of an object like a penny at different distances from Earth's center.

a) Plot these acceleration vs. distance points in a graph. Draw the best possible curve through the points on the graph.

b) How can you use this graph to describe how the acceleration due to gravity is dependent on the distance from Earth?

Active Physics

Distance from the center of Earth (km)	Acceleration due to gravity (m/s²)
6400	9.81 (Earth's surface)
6403	9.80
6411	9.77 (Mount Everest - highest point on Earth)
6560	9.33
6800	8.68 (shuttle orbit)
8000	6.27
14,400	1.93
22,400	0.80
42,000	0.22 (geosynchronous orbit for communications satellite)
391,000	0.003 (orbit of the Moon)

c) From this graph, determine the value of the acceleration due to gravity at the following distances from the center of Earth:

   i) 10,000 km   ii) 20,000 km

   iii) 30,000 km   iv) 40,000 km

d) Recall that the acceleration due to gravity represents the change in velocity with respect to time for a falling object at that location. For example, 9.8 m/s² represents a change in velocity of 9.8 m/s every second. Find the ratios of the acceleration at the following distances:

   i) 20,000 km:10,000 km

   ii) 30,000 km:10,000 km

   iii) 40,000 km:10,000 km

e) The change in acceleration is an *inverse-square rule*. Notice that the acceleration at 20,000 km is ¼ (0.25) the acceleration of the acceleration at 10,000 km. When the distance doubled, the acceleration became ¼ of the original value. When you tripled the distance (30,000 km from 10,000 km), the force became ⅑ (0.11) of the original value.

When you increased the distance by a factor of 4, the force became $\frac{1}{16}$ (0.06) of the original value.

Predict the value of the acceleration when the distance is 50,000 km by assuming that the acceleration should be $\frac{1}{25}$ of the value at 10,000 km. Check this prediction against the graph.

3. Imagine a sphere with a radius of 10 cm. This will represent Earth. Inserted into this sphere are toothpicks at equal distances around the sphere so that it looks something like a blowfish shown in the photograph. These toothpicks represent the gravitational field lines of Earth as you move out from the center. Back on Earth's surface, the influence of the gravitational field had a certain magnitude (such as 9.81 m/s² on Earth's surface). At a distance above the surface, this gravitational field and lines now have to be "spread out" over a larger area. The source of the field is Earth's mass, *m*. Since the surface area of a sphere is proportional to r^2, the gravitational field is getting weaker by the square of the distance from Earth.

a) Describe how the mathematical model (values of the acceleration due to gravity), the graphical model, and the toothpick model are all similar and how they are different.

Physics Talk

NEWTON'S LAW OF UNIVERSAL GRAVITATION

Earth's Gravitational Field

You have made a map of Earth's **gravitational field** that exists in your room, and about the entire Earth. A "field" is an influence that one object (in this case, Earth) sets up in the space around it. The first object is called the source of the field. Earth is the source of its gravitational field.

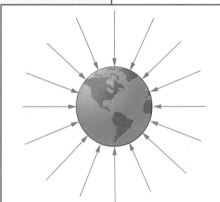

A second object (your penny, your body, or the Moon) interacts with this field. The second object is called the response object or the test object. It responds to the field, and you can use it to test for the existence of the field and map it.

The lines of the gravitational field in the model you imagined were created using toothpicks.

These gravitational field lines show you

- The direction of the gravitational field is the direction of the force on a mass. (All objects will accelerate along these field lines toward the center of Earth.)

- The gravitational field is stronger where the lines are close together and weaker where the lines are further apart. (The acceleration due to gravity is largest near Earth and gets weaker as you move further from Earth.)

- The gravitational field is present everywhere. The lines just show the field at some points.

- The gravitational field extends out to infinity.

The gravitational field lines from a large mass such as Earth resemble the points on a blowfish like the one shown on the previous page.

In the case of gravitational fields, the field is mapped with objects that have mass; in the case of magnetic fields, you have to use magnets; in the case of the electric field, you have to use electric charges. In mapping the gravitational field about Earth, your map gives information about the direction and size of the force that Earth's gravity would exert on an object with mass that is placed there.

The Inverse-Square Relationship

You saw a pattern in the *Investigate*. You were told that acceleration due to gravity becomes less as an object moves further from the surface of Earth. In simple terms for gravity, the **inverse-square relationship** says that the force of gravity between two objects decreases by the square of the distance between them.

Physics Words

gravitational field: the gravitational influence in the space around a massive object.

inverse-square relationship: the relationship between the magnitude of a gravitational force and the distance from the mass. This also describes how electrostatic forces depend on the distance from an electrical charge.

Active Physics

If you triple (3×) the distance, the force is $\frac{1}{3^2}$ or $\frac{1}{9}$ the original force. If you quadruple (4×) the distance, the force is $\frac{1}{4^2}$ or $\frac{1}{16}$ the original force. If you increase the distance by 10 times (10×), the force is $\frac{1}{10^2}$ or $\frac{1}{100}$ the original force.

Newton's law of universal gravitation describes the gravitational attraction of objects for one another. Isaac Newton first recognized that all objects with mass attract all other objects with mass. The strength of gravity is quite small. (Recall how you can climb stairs despite the entire Earth pulling down on you.) It takes a very large concentration of mass, such as a planet, to exert large gravitational forces.

All objects have mass and Earth attracts all objects. Newton reasoned that the Moon must have mass, and that Earth must also attract the Moon. This he called universal gravitation. The same field of **gravity** that pulls an apple to the ground goes on reaching out across space, all the way to the Moon. Before Newton, people thought there was "terrestrial gravity" that described the falling of apples and projectiles near Earth's surface, but some other kind of "celestial force" held the Moon in its orbit. Newton unified these "terrestrial" and "celestial" conceptions into one principle: universal gravitation. He calculated the acceleration of the Moon in its orbit and measured the acceleration of an apple falling in Earth's gravity and saw that both were related by the inverse-square relationship. It is a tribute to Newton's genius that he then guessed that not only Earth, but all bodies with mass attract each other. Yes, you and the table attract each other with a gravitational force.

Newton initially had astronomical quantitative evidence for his inverse-square force concept. Almost 100 years passed before Newton's idea that all bodies with mass attract all other bodies with mass was supported by table-top laboratory experiments. To do so, the very small gravitational force that small bodies exert on one another had to be measured. Because this force is very small compared to the force of the massive Earth, the experiments were very difficult. But in 1798, Henry Cavendish, a British physicist, finally measured the gravitational force between two masses (lead spheres) of a few kilograms each. He used the tiny twist of a quartz fiber caused by the force between two suspended lead spheres to detect and measure the force between them. Gravitation was, indeed, universal.

Physics Words

Newton's law of universal gravitation: all bodies with mass attract all other bodies with mass; the force is proportional to the product of the two masses and gets stronger as either mass gets larger; the force decreases as the square of the distances between the two bodies increases.

gravity: the force of attraction between two bodies due to their masses.

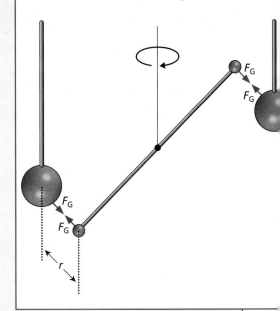

The Cavendish Experiment

Active Physics

Newton's law of universal gravitation states

• All bodies with mass attract all other bodies with mass.

• The force is proportional to the product of the two masses and gets stronger as either mass gets larger.

• The force decreases as the square of the distance between the two bodies increases.

Is There an Equation?

Complex laws often look easier in mathematical form. You can express Newton's law of universal gravitation mathematically as

$$F_G = \frac{Gm_1m_2}{r^2}$$

where F_G is the force between the bodies,
   r is the distance between their centers,
   m_1 and m_2 are the masses of the bodies, and
   G is a universal constant equal to $6.67 \times 10^{-11} \text{N} \bullet \text{m}^2/\text{kg}^2$.

You can see that the equation says exactly the same thing as the words in a much smaller package.

With Newton's law of gravitation, you now have a concept in terms of which you can reason about how things behave in a gravitational field. When this force law is put into Newton's laws of motion, you can show, by calculation, that according to this inverse-square relationship, the Moon would orbit Earth and the planets would orbit the Sun in elliptical paths. This calculation, based on the concept of universal gravitation with its inverse-square dependence, can be checked against the real orbits of the planets. The planets do move in ellipses (to the first approximation), hence to that degree of precision, these "laws" are confirmed.

The planets do not move exactly in ellipses because the planets also tug on one another besides each being "tethered" by or "tied" to the Sun. But these small changes from the ellipse can also be calculated and checked against data, and that program has shown Newton's laws of motion, with universal gravitation as a force, to be very reliable. This back-and-forth of guessing a principle within the pattern of facts, then working out the consequences of that principle, testing it against reality, and using the results of those tests to refine the principles, is how you do science.

Newton's law of gravitation can describe and predict accurately the forces. It does not describe a mechanism for the force. For example, it does not explain how Earth "communicates" to the falling penny which way is "down." What is the mechanism for this "force at a distance?" Newton was puzzled by this and chose not to answer it. Scientists today are still exploring how this force at a distance is transmitted.

Checking Up

1. What is the direction of the gravitational field in your classroom?

2. Using the idea of field lines, where is the gravitational field the strongest?

3. If you triple the distance between two masses, what happens to the force of gravity between the two masses?

4. What is the force that holds the Moon in its orbit around Earth?

5. Approximately what is the shape of the orbit of the planets around the Sun?

Active Physics

+Math	+Depth	+Concepts	+Exploration
♦♦	♦	♦♦	

Active Physics

Plus

Acceleration of the Moon

The Moon is 60 times further away from the center of Earth than objects on the surface of Earth, and moves about Earth in an approximately circular path.

1. If the acceleration due to gravity on the surface of Earth is 9.8 m/s^2, use the inverse square relationship and your calculator to determine the acceleration due to gravity at the Moon's distance.

   Since the Moon orbits Earth, you can calculate its acceleration. The equation for acceleration of any object moving in a circle at constant speed is

   $$a = \frac{v^2}{r}$$

   where v is the speed
      r is the distance (radius)
         of the object from the center

The Moon's distance is 60 times the radius of Earth ($60 \times 6.4 \times 10^6$ m = 3.84×10^8 m). The Moon travels once about Earth in 28.25 days.

2. Find the speed of the Moon using the equation $v = d/t$ where d is the circumference of the Moon's orbit ($2\pi r$).

3. Calculate the acceleration of the Moon.

4. Compare the acceleration of the Moon using these two different approaches. (When Newton made this comparison, he was confident that his inverse square law of gravity was correct.)

Kepler's Laws

Newton once stated, "If I have seen further than others, it is because I have stood on the shoulders of giants." Tycho Brahe and Johannes Kepler were two of those giants. Tycho Brahe observed and recorded the positions of the planets every night over many years. Kepler viewed the data and tried for years to form mathematical relationships that could explain all of Brahe's data. At first, it appeared that the planet's data could be adequately described by stating that the planets moved in circles about the Sun. This description was only approximately true. Kepler had to decide if Brahe's data was a bit imprecise or whether the circular path was incorrect. Kepler's confidence in Brahe's observations forced him to keep trying other descriptions of the paths. Kepler eventually did find three mathematical relationships that fit the data very well. These are now known as Kepler's laws.

Kepler's first law: The planets travel in ellipses about the Sun. An ellipse is a mathematical shape that is defined by two foci. The Sun is at one focus. There is nothing at the other focus.

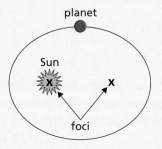

Kepler's second law: The planets sweep out equal areas in equal times. Imagine a pizza in the shape of an ellipse. Slices of pizza are cut from one of the foci. Each slice of pizza has the same area. The planets would travel along the edge of the ellipse. The time needed to travel along the edge of each slice of pizza would be identical. Since the edge of the pizza represents the path of the planet around the Sun, this means that the planet travels faster when it is near the Sun and slower when it is further from the Sun.

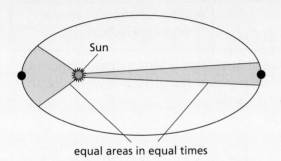

equal areas in equal times

Kepler's third law: There is a mathematical relationship that defines the time it takes for a planet to complete an orbit about the Sun and the average distance of the planet from the Sun.

$$\frac{T^2}{R^3} = \text{a constant}$$

where T is the time to complete one orbit and R is the average distance from the Sun.

The quantity $\frac{T^2}{R^3}$ is identical for all planets orbiting the Sun.

Kepler found this equation from the experimental data of Brahe. Newton derived the same equation from his assertion that the Sun and each planet have an attractive gravitational force.

$$F_G = \frac{Gm_1 m_2}{r^2}$$

1. Earth travels about the Sun in 1 year. The average distance of Earth from the Sun is 1.50×10^{11} m. Convert the 1 year to seconds and find the value of $\frac{T^2}{R^3}$ for Earth.

Defining Earth's average distance from the Sun as 1 AU (astronomical unit), all other planets' average distance and period can be defined in terms of Earth.

2. Show that Kepler's value $\frac{T^2}{R^3}$ is identical for all planets, using the table below. A spreadsheet program will allow you to make these calculations in very little time.

	Mercury	Venus	Earth	Mars	Jupiter	Saturn	Uranus	Neptune
Mean distance from the Sun (AU)	0.3871	0.7233	1	1.524	5.203	9.539	19.19	30.06
Sidereal period of orbit (years)	0.24	0.62	1	1.88	11.86	29.46	84.01	164.79

What Do You Think Now?

At the beginning of this section, you were asked

• **Does gravity have a direction?**

• **How can people in Australia be held on Earth when they are "upside down"?**

Now that you have completed this section, how would you revise your answers to these questions?

Physics
Essential Questions

What does it mean?

Newton's law of gravitation says that all massive objects attract each other with a force that decreases with the square of the distance between them. How does the equation $F_G = \dfrac{Gm_1 m_2}{r^2}$ also communicate this relationship?

How do you know?

You observe the force of gravity when a penny is dropped. Earth attracts the penny. How did Cavendish demonstrate that two objects attract each other?

Why do you believe?

Connects with Other Physics Content	Fits with Big Ideas in Science	Meets Physics Requirements
Forces and motion	Models	* Good, clear explanation, no more complex than necessary

* Newton's law of gravitation states that Earth attracts the Moon in the same way that Earth attracts an apple. Why do you believe that the physics laws on Earth work equally well for the objects outside of Earth?

Why should you care?

As you design your roller coaster on Earth, you may also wonder – would the roller coaster behave identically on the Moon? What changes would you expect if your roller coaster was on the Moon where the acceleration due to gravity is only ⅙ that on Earth?

Reflecting on the Section and the Challenge

In this section, you mapped the gravitational field by using data of the acceleration of objects falling at specific locations. Patterns help you understand the world around you, such as Newton's law of universal gravitation, with its inverse square relationship. With this concept, you have a reason for the flights of projectiles and the elliptical orbits of satellites. You have both a field model and a mathematical model, $F_G = \dfrac{Gm_1 m_2}{r^2}$.

Both can be and have been tested experimentally, and they both are successful.

Gravity is required for any roller-coaster ride. The acceleration due to gravity at Earth's surface is 9.8 m/s every second or 9.8 m/s^2. This will not only determine the speed at different parts of the coaster ride, but will also have an impact on your apparent weight during the roller-coaster ride.

Physics to Go

1. The gravitational force between two asteroids is 500 N. What would the force be if the distance between them doubled?

2. A satellite sitting on the launch pad is one Earth radius away from the center of Earth (6.4×10^6 m).

   a) How would the gravitational force between them be changed after launch when the satellite was two Earth radii (1.28×10^7 m) from the center of Earth?

   b) What would the gravitational force be if the satellite was three Earth radii (1.92×10^7 m) from the center of Earth?

   c) What would the gravitational force be if the satellite was four Earth radii (2.56×10^7 m) from the center of Earth?

3. Why does everyone trust in gravity?

4. Compare the acceleration due to gravity at the top and bottom of a roller-coaster ride.

5. a) Which is closer to the Moon—the middle of Earth or the water on the side of Earth facing the Moon?

   b) Suggest an explanation for high tides on the side of Earth facing the Moon. *Please note these diagrams are not to scale.*

   c) Use your answer to *a)* to propose an explanation for the uneven distribution of water on Earth's surface, as shown in the diagram.

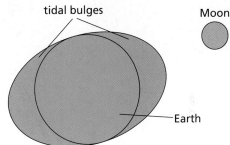

6. Astronauts on many Shuttle flights study the effects of "free fall." Fish taken aboard the Shuttle react to "free fall" by swimming in circles. "Free fall" mimics what you feel if gravity were not present.

   a) How would a fish's life be different without gravity?

   b) Does gravity hold a fish "down" on Earth?

7. Two objects have a tiny, but measurable gravitational force of attraction between them. How will that force change if the distance between the objects is
   a) doubled   b) tripled   c) quadrupled   d) halved

8. Two objects have a tiny, but measurable gravitational force of attraction between them. How will that force change if the mass of one of the objects is
   a) doubled   b) tripled   c) quadrupled   d) halved

9. Two objects have a tiny, but measurable gravitational force of attraction between them. How will that force change if the mass of both of the objects is
   a) doubled   b) tripled   c) quadrupled   d) halved

10. Two objects have a tiny, but measurable gravitational force of attraction between them. How will that force change if the following changes in mass occur?

Mass 1	Mass 2
same	doubles
triples	triples
doubles	triples

Active Physics

Section 5

Hooke's Law: Finding Your "At Rest" Weight

What Do You See?

Learning Outcomes

In this section, you will

- **Distinguish** between mass and weight.

- **Calculate** weight in newtons for a given mass.

- **Measure** the effect of weight on the vertical stretch of a spring.

- **Illustrate** the relationship between weight and stretch of a spring in a graph.

- **Use** a spring to create a scale and explain how Newton's second law is used in the creation of the scale.

- **Calculate** spring forces using Hooke's law.

What Do You Think?

A canary and an elephant have enormous differences in weight. The elephant may weigh more than 100,000 times as much as the canary weighs.

- **Can you use the same scale to weigh a canary and an elephant?**

- **How does a bathroom scale work?**

Record your ideas about these questions in your *Active Physics* log. Be prepared to discuss your responses with your small group and with the class.

Investigate

Part A: Mass and Weight

1. Fruits and vegetables at a supermarket are often priced by weight. Apples may cost 79 cents per pound and watermelon may cost 22 cents per pound.

a) What is a pound?

b) Is the unit, pound, related to mass? Explain your answer.

c) How would you define weight?

2. In physics, weight is defined as the force of gravity on an object. The weight (force) is the mass of an object multiplied by the strength of the gravitational field at the location of the object. Large masses are heavy (have large weights) and small masses are light. In the metric system, the mass of an object is measured in kilograms. The strength of the gravitational field near the surface of Earth is 9.8 N/kg (newtons per kilogram). The unit newton per kilogram is equivalent to meters per second every second. Using this information, you can calculate a student's weight (force). The student has a mass of 50 kg.

weight (force) = mass × strength of gravitational field

$$F_w = mg$$
$$= (50 \text{ kg})(9.8 \text{ N/kg})$$
$$= 490 \text{ N (newtons)}$$

The unit for weight is the newton (N). *Weight* is a force and has the same units as any other force.

a) Calculate and compare the weights of a gymnast with a mass of 40 kg and a football player with a mass of 110 kg.

3. On the surface of the Moon, the strength of the gravitational field is only about 1.6 N/kg.

a) What would be the weights of the gymnast and the football player in *Step 2.a)* if they were on the Moon?

4. The newton is the metric unit for weight. However, you may wish to compare this to a pound, with which you are more familiar. Each kilogram (mass) has a weight of 2.2 lb on Earth. A 220-lb football player has a mass of 100 kg. The weight (force) exerted on 100 kg, according to the equation $F_w = mg$, is 980 N.

a) Find the weight in newtons of a bowling ball that weighs 11 lb.

b) Find the weight in newtons of a ¼-lb burger (a patty that has a weight of ¼-lb).

5. The weight of a ¼-lb burger is close to 1 N. In a country that uses metric measurements, a restaurant could call their ¼-lb burger a "Newton Burger." You can use this as an approximate way to determine how much something weighs in newtons if you know the weight in pounds. A 50-lb person has the equivalent weight of 200 quarter-pound burgers (200 × ¼-lb). Therefore, the 50-lb person has an approximate weight of 200 N.

a) Using this technique, find the approximate weight in newtons of a roller-coaster car that weighs 1500 lb.

Part B: The Properties of Springs

1. Make a spring from a piece of paper. Take a piece of 8½ × 11 paper. Fold it like an accordion.

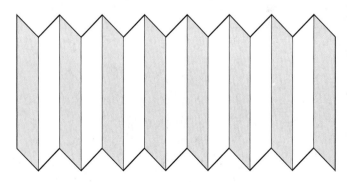

2. With a small force, stretch the paper spring slightly.

a) Record what happens when you release the paper.

3. With a small force, compress the paper spring slightly.

a) Record what happens when you release the paper.

4. Does the paper spring return to its original size and shape as the force of the stretch increases? Try it.

✎ a) Record your observations.

5. A metal spring has properties like those of the paper spring. The metal spring is usually better able to restore itself to its original shape than the paper spring. However, the metal spring can also be stretched past its load limit so you should be careful not to do this.

6. The stretch of a metal spring can be measured precisely. You can use a set of masses to determine the properties of springs. Secure the spring vertically as indicated in the diagram. Attach a metric ruler to the ring stand or support holding the spring. Use a file card to note the bottom-most position of the spring. Set this measurement as the zero measurement for the stretch of the spring. You are now ready to measure the stretch of the spring with a given set of masses.

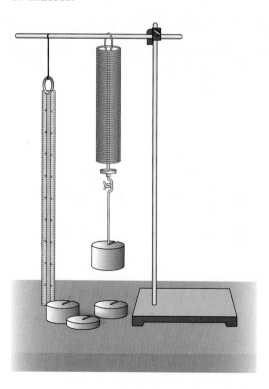

You may have to convert from grams to kilograms to newtons. If a 100-g mass is used, this is equivalent to 0.1 kg. The mass of 0.1 kg has a weight of 0.98 N. This can be written as a single equation:

$$F_w = mg$$

$$= (100 \text{ g}) \left(\frac{1 \text{ kg}}{1000 \text{ g}} \right) \left(9.8 \frac{\text{N}}{\text{kg}} \right)$$

$$= 0.98 \text{ N}$$

Notice that you converted grams to kilograms by multiplying by 1 kg/1000 g. In math class, you learned that you could always multiply a number by 1 and not change its value. For instance, $27 \times 1 = 27$. Since 1 kg is equal to 1000 g, the fraction 1 kg/1000 g has an equivalent numerator and denominator and the fraction equals 1. When you use this fraction in the equation, the 100 g-mass gets converted to 0.1 kg. The gram units "cancel" and you are left with kilogram units. This unit conversion was done because you want the mass in kilograms.

✎ a) In your *Active Physics* log, create a data table with four columns. Label the first three columns mass, weight (of the mass hung on the spring), and stretch of spring. The fourth column will be left blank for the time being.

7. Measure the stretch of the spring (from its "relaxed" or zero position length to its stretched length) for different masses.

⚠ Be careful when placing and removing masses so that the spring does not snap and hurt anyone. Have one person hold the bottom and top of the spring as another person adds or removes each mass.

✎ a) Record your measurements in the data table.

✎ b) Plot a graph with the stretch of the spring on the *x*-axis and the weight on the *y*-axis. (Keep in mind that this is a bit unconventional since the independent variable is usually placed on the *x*-axis.)

c) From your graph, predict what the stretch would be for a weight that you have not tried, but between the weights that you have measured. This type of prediction from a graph is called *interpolation*.

8. Test your prediction by measuring the stretch of the spring for that weight.

a) How accurate was your prediction?

9. Repeat the investigation for a second spring that looks different from the first. The spring may have larger or smaller coils, or the coils may be closer together or further apart. You should have a new data table, a new graph, and a new interpolation.

a) Describe how the springs differ in physical appearance.

b) Describe how the springs differ in terms of the data tables and corresponding graphs.

c) Draw the best-fit line for your two graphs. How is the slope of the line related to the force necessary to stretch the spring?

10. Suppose you have another spring whose spring constant is different from the two springs you investigated.

a) Draw a graph for this "invented" third spring. Plot spring force versus amount of stretch on your graph.

b) Write a description of a spring that would have such data. The description should include the ease or difficulty of stretching the spring.

11. Return to the first data table you made in *Step 6.a*). Divide the weight of the mass hung on the spring by the stretched distance for each measurement.

a) Record the values in the fourth column.

b) What do you notice about these calculated values?

c) Repeat the calculations for the second data table.

d) What value might your invented spring have for this column?

e) How do the values in the fourth column relate to the slope of the graph?

f) The slopes of these graphs are the spring constant (*k*) for each spring. Explain why it is called a spring constant.

Part C: The Spring as a Weighing Machine

1. The spring stretches a different amount for each hanging mass or weight. Create a scale for weighing objects using one of the two springs that you have previously used. A scale has a spring and an arrow (a pointer) that points to the number representing the weight of the hanging object.

2. Choose three known masses.

a) Measure their weight on your scale. Record your values.

3. Choose two objects of unknown weight.

a) Measure their weight on your scale. Describe each object and record its weight.

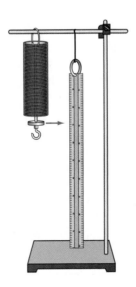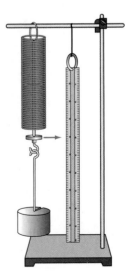

Active Physics

Physics Talk

HOOKE'S LAW

Hooke's Law Describes the Restoring Force a Spring Exerts

Stretching a rubber band or a spring requires a force. If you want to stretch a spring more, a larger force is required. There are many different relationships that could be imagined between the applied force and the stretch of the spring. The graph could have looked like any of the ones shown to the right.

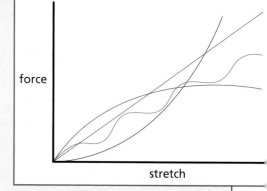

In this section, you measured the amount of force required for each stretch of the spring. You found that there was a linear relationship. The graph was a very precise straight line. To get a sense for how wonderful this is, you can try to imagine other straight lines you have experienced in nature. Other than the Sun's rays as you sometimes see them coming through the clouds and the line of a quarter moon (sometimes called a half-moon), there are very, very few straight lines in nature. By graphing the force and stretch, you have discovered a straight line of nature.

When Robert Hooke (1635-1703) discovered this property of springs, he knew it was a big discovery and kept it to himself to see if it could lead to other discoveries.

Many springs have the property that the stretch of the spring is directly proportional to the force applied to it. This means that if you double the force, the stretch of the spring doubles. If you triple the force, the stretch of the spring triples. And if you make the force 2.7 times larger, the stretch of the spring is 2.7 times as large. If the spring is not moving, the spring exerts a restoring force equal in magnitude to the force that stretched the spring.

Hooke's law describes springs that behave in this way. The law explains very simply what restoring force a spring exerts if it is stretched. The more you stretch a spring, the larger the restoring force of the spring. You can describe this relationship in words or with a graph or with a mathematical equation. The equation for Hooke's law is

force exerted by the spring $=$ $-$spring constant $\times$ spring stretch

(or compression)

$$F_s = -kx$$

Physics Words

Hooke's law: the restoring force exerted by a spring is directly proportional to the distance of stretch or compression of the spring.

where F_s is the force exerted by the spring,
x is the stretch (or compression) of the spring, and
k is the spring constant.

The negative sign in the equation indicates that the pull by the spring is opposite to the direction it is stretched or compressed. Stretch a spring down and it pulls up. Stretch a spring to the right and it pulls to the left. Compress a spring to the left and it pushes to the right.

The spring constant (k) is an indication of how easy or difficult it is to stretch or compress a spring. You can determine the value of the spring constant (k) by measuring the force exerted by the spring and the stretch of the spring. This is what you did in the *Investigate*. You varied the force by using different weights and measured the stretch. The measure of the stiffness of the spring is represented by k. A stiff spring will have a large value for k; a "soft" spring will have a small value for k. The spring constant, k, depends on the material from which the spring is made and the shape and size of the coils.

Sample Problem I

A 3.0-N weight is suspended from a spring. The spring stretches 2.0 cm (0.020 m). Calculate the spring constant.

Strategy: If a 3.0-N weight is suspended at rest from the spring, the spring must be applying a force of 3.0 N. If the spring were applying a force of less than 3.0 N, the weight would accelerate down. If the spring were applying a force of more than 3.0 N, the weight would accelerate up. When the force of gravity on the mass is 3.0 N down and the spring exerts a force of 3.0 N up, then the mass has no net force on it and it remains at rest once the friction brings it to rest. In the *Investigate*, you always took your measurements when the mass had stopped moving.

Given:

$F = 3.0$ N

$x = 0.020$ m

Solution:

The magnitude of the force is

$$F_s = kx$$

Solving for k $\quad k = \dfrac{F_s}{x}$

$$= \frac{3.0 \text{ N}}{0.02 \text{ m}}$$

$$= 150 \text{ N/m}$$

Note that the stretch of the spring, x, was converted from centimeters to meters. The result tells you that it would take a force of 150 N to stretch the spring 1 m. You also ignored the negative sign in calculating the magnitude (size) of the force. From here on, the negative sign in the equation will be omitted. In mathematics, you would say that you are calculating the absolute value of F using the absolute value of the stretch, x. You must always keep in mind that the direction of the force is opposite to the direction of the stretch.

With a set of data points for the weight and the stretch, you would find that all values of k are the same or constant (at least approximately) for a given spring. The spring constant is k. As you determined in the *Investigate*, you can also record the data on a graph. The graph can also be used to determine the spring constant (k).

$$F_s = kx$$
$$y = \text{slope} \times x$$

If the data are graphed so that the force is on the y-axis and the stretch is on the x-axis, then the spring constant will be the slope of the graph. You can see this if you compare the equations for Hooke's law and the equation for a straight line (when the y-intercept is zero).

Sample Problem 2

Weights are hung from a spring and the stretch is measured. The data collected is shown in the graph to the right. Calculate the spring constant from the graph.

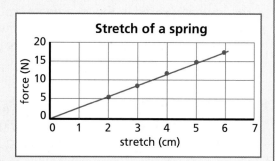

Strategy: Since the force is on the y-axis and the stretch is on the x-axis, you can compare the equations for a straight line and Hooke's law.

Hooke's law: $F_s = kx$ Straight line: $y = \text{slope} \times x$

The slope of the graph will be equal to the spring constant, k.

Given:

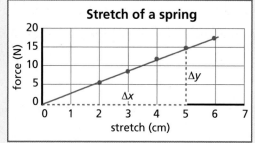

Solution:

$$\text{slope} = \frac{\text{rise}}{\text{run}} = \frac{\Delta y}{\Delta x}$$
$$= \frac{15 \text{ N}}{5.0 \text{ cm}}$$
$$= 3 \text{ N/cm}$$

Mass and Weight

In this section, you used specific masses as weights. A 1-kg mass on Earth has a weight of 9.8 N.

$$\text{weight} = mg$$

where m is mass in kilograms and
g is the gravitational field strength of the Earth (9.8 N/kg = 9.8 m/s^2).
$$\text{weight} = (1 \text{ kg})(9.8 \text{ N/kg})$$
$$= 9.8 \text{ N}$$

A 1-kg mass has a specific amount of matter and a specific volume. Of these three properties, only the mass is related to the weight. When the 1-kg mass is on Earth, there is a force attracting the 1-kg mass to Earth. This force is also referred to as the weight of the 1-kg mass. If this 1-kg mass were taken to the Moon, the "Moon weight" of the 1-kg mass would be less than the "Earth weight" of the same mass. There will be other opportunities in *Active Physics* to study the differences between mass and weight. In this *Investigate*, you hung the mass from a spring and used its weight as the force on a spring.

The equation for the relationship between mass and weight on Earth is weight = *mg*. This equation is similar to Newton's second law (*F* = *ma*). In that case, *a* is equal to 9.8 m/s².

$$\text{weight} = mg$$

$$\text{Force} = ma$$

Weight is a force. When an object is moved from Earth to the Moon, its mass stays the same, but its weight changes due to the change in the gravitational field strengths of Earth (*g* = 9.8 N/kg) and the Moon (*g* = 1.6 N/kg).

Stretch and Compress

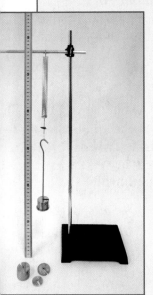

You began the *Investigate* by both compressing and stretching a paper spring. You then made measurements on a stretched spring. Conducting an investigation with a compressed spring would produce similar results.

Many bathroom scales work by compressing a spring. Inside the bathroom scale is a spring. When you step on the scale, the spring compresses just enough to provide an upward force equal to your weight. The more weight, the more compression of the spring is required. The spring is connected to a scale that has been calibrated to give your weight (usually in pounds). As the spring gets compressed, the arrow points to a different number corresponding to the compression and force of the spring.

The scale does not read the weight of the object directly. The scale reads the compression of the spring. Of course, under normal circumstances the compression of the spring provides a force equal to your weight. You can then say that the scale reads your weight.

You can express this mathematically. A person steps on a scale. The scale moves a bit and then comes to rest. There are two forces acting on the person. There is the force of gravity pulling down on the person. There is also the force of the spring pushing up on the person. These two forces are equal but in opposite directions. The net force on the person is zero and the person remains at rest.

$$\text{Net force} = ma \text{ (Newton's second law)}$$

$$\text{Net force (sum of the forces)} = 0 \text{ (zero acceleration)}$$

$$\text{Force due to gravity} + \text{force due to the spring} = 0$$

$$mg + (-kx) = 0$$

$$mg = kx$$

Physics Words

weight: the force exerted on a mass as a result of gravity; the weight force on an object due to Earth is downward, in the vertical direction.

Checking Up

1. A spring obeys Hooke's law. If the force on the spring is increased five times, how much does the stretch of the spring increase?

2. What is meant by the "spring constant" of a spring?

3. How does the weight of an object in newtons compare to its mass in kilograms?

4. When you stand on a bathroom scale, how does the force of compression of the spring compare to your weight?

+Math	+Depth	+Concepts	+Exploration
◆◆	◆	◆	◆◆

Graphing Force on the *X*-axis

If a graph for a stretched spring is constructed so that the force is on the *x*-axis and the stretch is on the *y*-axis, then the slope will be the reciprocal of the spring constant or $1/k$. You can see this by comparing the equations for Hooke's law and for a straight line.

In the following equation, capital X and Y are used to label the axes to avoid confusion with x, for stretch. The equation for a straight line passing through the origin is

$$Y = \text{slope} \times X$$

Hooke's law for the magnitude of the force (omit the minus sign) is

$$F_s = kx$$

$$x = \left(\frac{1}{k}\right)F_s$$

Since the force is on the X-axis and the stretch x is on the Y-axis, the slope of the straight-line graph is $1/k$.

$$x = \boxed{\frac{1}{k}}F_s$$
$$Y = \boxed{\text{slope}} \times X$$

Graph the data in *Physics to Go*, *Question 7* by putting the amount of stretch (x) on the y-axis and the force on the x-axis. From the slope of the graph, find the spring constant, k.

Hooke's Law and the Stretch of a Rubber Band

Design an experiment to see if the amount of stretch of a rubber band is described by Hooke's law. With your teacher's permission, carry out the experiment.

What Do You Think Now?

At the beginning of this section, you were asked the following:

• **Can you use the same scale to weigh a canary and an elephant?**

• **How does a bathroom scale work?**

Now that you have completed this section, how would you answer these questions? Include the concepts of weight and Hooke's law and springs in your answer.

Physics
Essential Questions

What does it mean?

A stretched or compressed spring can exert a force. Explain what is meant by spring force, spring stretch, and spring constant.

How do you know?

Physicists like to find mathematical relationships among concepts whenever possible. Explain how what you learned in this section shows that Hooke's law describes real springs.

Why do you believe?

Connects with Other Physics Content	Fits with Big Ideas in Science	Meets Physics Requirements
Forces and motion	* Models	Good, clear, explanation, no more complex than necessary

* Many principles of science have a broad, but limited range of application. Hooke's law describes the relationship between the stretching force and the amount of stretch for some springs under some conditions. Hooke's law may not accurately describe a rubber band with a really heavy mass hung from it. But any time you observe a force due to a stretch or a compression, Hooke's law is a good place to start. How would you determine if stretching an old rubber band is described by Hooke's law?

Why should you care?

While riding on roller coasters, your stomach may get queasy and you may feel as if your weight changed. How can you use a spring to determine if there are weight changes?

Reflecting on the Section and the Challenge

Part of the fun of a roller coaster is the sensation you get as your weight appears to change at the peaks and valleys of the ride. In the next section, you will use your understanding of how spring scales work to understand these apparent weight changes. All spring scales are based on Hooke's law. The stretch (or compression of a spring) is directly proportional to the force pulling or pushing on the spring. When everything is at rest, the spring exerts a restoring force equal in magnitude to the force stretching or compressing the spring. Mathematically, you can write Hooke's law as $F_s = -kx$, where F_s is force exerted by the spring and x is the stretch. The spring constant, k, is constant for a specific spring. A bathroom spring scale measures the compression of the spring. The force exerted by the compressed spring, when everything is at rest, is equal to your weight. Imagine bringing a spring scale with you on the roller coaster. When the roller coaster is moving, the scale will read many different values. You may want to include the apparent weight changes in your design for your roller coaster.

Physics to Go

1. Calculate the weight of the following objects:

   a) a football player with a mass of 100 kg

   b) a toddler with a mass of 10 kg

   c) an adult with a mass of 60 kg

2. Use the approximation that the weight of a ¼-lb burger is one newton. (Likewise, one stick of butter = ¼-lb butter has a weight of one newton.) Write down the approximate weights (in newtons) of the following objects:

   a) a 130-lb student   b) a 1000-lb roller-coaster car   c) a 50-lb child

3. Weights were hung from a spring and the stretch of the spring was measured. The data is given in the table below.

Weight (N)	Stretch (cm)
0.0	0.0
0.3	2.0
0.7	4.6
1.2	8.0
2.0	13.0
2.4	16.2
3.1	21.0

   a) Graph the data with the stretch of the spring on the x-axis and the weight on the y-axis.

   b) If the data points do not fall exactly on a straight line, draw the best-fit line through the data points.

   c) Find the slope of the graph.

   d) What is the meaning of the slope?

   e) Devise a graph for a second spring. Sketch the devised spring's graph. Write a description of a spring that would have such data. The description should include the ease or difficulty of stretching the spring.

4. A weight of 12 N causes a spring to stretch 3.0 cm. What is the spring constant (k) of the spring?

5. When Robert Hooke first described the relationship that has come to be known as Hooke's law, he wrote "as the force, so the stretch." Explain in a full sentence or two what Hooke meant by this. (Hooke wrote this as a footnote in Latin with the letters all mixed up. This allowed him to keep his discovery a secret for a while.)

6. Two springs have spring constants of 10.0 N/cm and 15.0 N/cm. Which spring is more difficult to stretch?

7. Calculate the spring constant (k) from the graph of a stretched spring below.

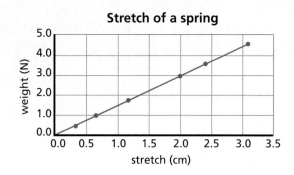

Stretch of a spring

8. *Preparing for the Chapter Challenge*
To include the apparent weight changes in your design for your roller coaster, you will need to describe how a spring scale works. Write a brief description of how a spring scale works.

Inquiring Further

Investigating the parts of a bathroom scale

Get permission to take apart a bathroom scale. Investigate the parts. Create sketches to explain how the scale works and the function of all of the parts. When your explanation is complete, put the scale back together. Present your information to the class.

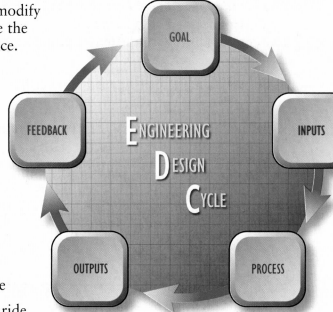

Your challenge for this chapter is to modify the design of a roller coaster to create the optimum thrill for your target audience. You will have to give some careful consideration to each feature of the ride and decide how your audience would most likely enjoy it. Then, you will use the physics you've just learned to make it happen.

For your initial design you will need the following:

- A target audience — a particular group of riders with similar thrill tolerances

- A model of the design containing two hills, a vertical curve, and a horizontal curve

- Safety calculations at five points during the ride

- A calculation of the work required to start the ride

- A written poster or report

You still have more to learn before you can complete the challenge, but now is a good time to give the *Chapter Challenge* a first try. Your *Mini-Challenge* is to produce a thorough description of your target audience, a list of good ideas about which features of a ride will appeal to them, and to practice some calculations based on your ideas. You can describe what your target audience would like to experience in a roller-coaster ride, even if you are unsure of exactly how your coaster will deliver that type of movement. If your group is planning to make a poster, you might consider sketching the sections of the poster on print paper and taping them together to give the class an idea of how you will organize the information from your final design.

The physics you have learned so far will enable you to complete some of your safety calculations. If you assign a mass to each car on your coaster, you can begin to quantify how much potential energy there will be at the top of a hill and how much kinetic energy there should be at the bottom, too. You also know how to find the speed at the bottom of the hill using that same information.

Go back and quickly read the *Goal* at the start of the chapter. You will find all of the details for completing the entire challenge. At this point, you will focus on the portions you can complete with the physics you have learned so far. You can now complete a thorough description of your target audience, since you don't need any additional physics knowledge to describe their thrill-tolerance level.

In the *Engineering Design Cycle*, you are adding a critical *Input* by defining the target audience for your roller-coaster design. Additionally, you have your personal experience with roller coasters and the information you have learned in *Sections 1 to 5* to use as *Inputs*.

Your team should review the physics content from the first five sections to help you compose your roller-coaster design.

Section 1: You devised a method for drawing your roller-coaster model, a method for calculating velocities, and calculating accelerations. You also discovered that accelerations are more thrilling than high speeds.

Section 2: You investigated gravitational potential energy and its impact on velocity for objects going down a ramp. This should help you with your safety calculations of speed.

Section 3: You analyzed kinetic energy and the conservation of energy. Use this information to help decide how tall your hills can be and how fast you will be going.

Section 4: You investigated the force of gravity. You may wish to explain how your roller-coaster design would work on the Moon!

Section 5: You explored the weight of objects and how a spring scale works. What if you had a spring for a seat?

 Brainstorm with your group to come up with potential target audiences. After you have a good list, pick two or three groups and make a list of ride characteristics that would be most appealing to each one: fast, lots of loops, big accelerations, gentle turns, and so on.

Next, have each member of your group rank each of the groups in the order they would most like to work on them—1, 2, 3, and so on (with 1 being the best). Add up the ranks for each group. The target audience with the lowest number should be the most popular one in your group.

At this point, you can do some very powerful analysis by calculating the potential and kinetic energy associated with each hill in your coaster design. Even if you change the height of the hill later, the calculation will be similar and simple to change to optimize your design. You will also be able to calculate the speed at any point for which you calculate the kinetic energy.

 Presenting your information to the class is the *Output* for your design cycle. You should have a description of your target audience and a list of the features you will provide for them. You should present your *PE*, *KE*, and velocity calculations. Finally, you should present or describe the written portion of your final design presentation. This can be a sketched poster, brochure, or written paper.

 Your classmates will give you *Feedback* on the accuracy and the overall appeal of your presentation based on the criteria of the design challenge. This feedback will become an *Input* for your final design in the *Chapter Challenge*.

Remember to correct any parts of your design that did not meet design constraints for speed for your target group. It will be harder to remember if you wait until the chapter is complete to go back and correct your mistakes. Then, store all of your information in a safe place so that it will be ready to use in the *Chapter Challenge*.

Section 6

Forces Acting During Acceleration: Apparent Weight on a Roller Coaster

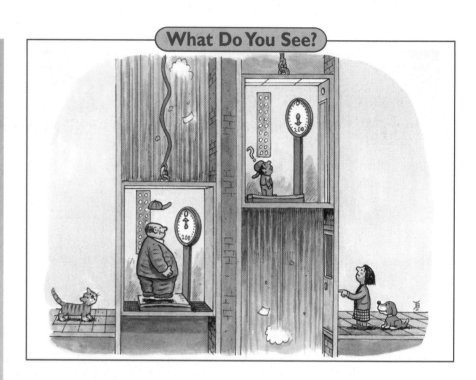

What Do You See?

Learning Outcomes

In this section, you will

- **Explore** the change in apparent weight as an object moves up or down with constant speed.

- **Explore** the change in apparent weight as an object accelerates up or down.

- **Analyze** the forces on a mass at rest, moving with constant velocity, or accelerating by drawing the appropriate force-vector diagrams.

- **Predict** mathematically the change in apparent weight as a mass accelerates up or down.

What Do You Think?

As the roller coaster moves down that first hill, up the second hill, and then over the top, you feel as if your weight is changing. As you go over the top of the hill, you have the feeling of floating when your body rises up out of the seat. In roller coaster terms, this is called airtime.

- **Does your weight change when you are riding on a roller coaster?**

- **If you were sitting on a bathroom scale, would the scale give different readings at different places on the roller coaster?**

Record your ideas about these questions in your *Active Physics* log. Be prepared to discuss your responses with your small group and the class.

Investigate

In this experiment, you will investigate the apparent weight changes you feel when you are on a roller coaster. You will use the spring scale for your observations. However, you will explain what you observe with both the spring scale and the bathroom scale.

Part A: Moving the Mass at a Constant Speed

1. Hang a mass from the spring scale and note the force indicated by the spring scale. When the mass is not moving and the acceleration equals 0, the force of gravity pulling the mass down and the force exerted by the spring pulling the mass up must be equal. The force of the spring has the same magnitude as the force of gravity. You could also just say, "The spring is measuring the weight."

 Be careful when lifting and lowering the weight, as it could cause injury if it were to fall. Make smooth, unhurried movements.

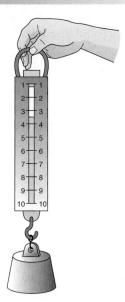

▲ a) Record the weight of the mass in your log.

2. With your arm extended down, move the mass up until your arm is as high as you can reach. Once you start the mass moving, you want to keep lifting it at a constant speed.

Your group members will try their best to read the spring scale during the time that the mass is moving at constant speed. Ignore the readings when you first start moving the mass and when you stop it. You will return to those observations later. It may help if the mass is behind a barrier

and not visible when you begin or stop the motion. Setting this up will require some ingenuity.

You may have to repeat this step a few times so that you can lift the mass at a constant speed so that your group members can observe it.

▲ a) In your log, make a table similar to the one below.

	Acceleration (up, down, zero)	Scale reading (larger, smaller, equal to weight)
Mass at rest	zero	equal
Mass up at constant speed	zero	
Mass accelerating upward	up	larger
Mass at rest at top	zero	
Mass moving down at constant speed	zero	
Mass accelerating downward	down	

▲ b) In the table in your log, record your finding for mass moving up at a constant speed.

3. The observations in *Step 2* may have been difficult for you to make accurately. The spring scale should have displayed the same reading when the scale moved at constant speed as it did when it was suspended at rest. The same result will occur in an elevator. If you are on a bathroom scale, the scale will compress and display your weight when the elevator is at rest. It will display the same weight when the elevator is moving at a constant speed between floors. Repeat the observation with the spring scale moving down at a constant speed.

Is the weight once again the same? Note that you are only interested in the weight reading as the mass descends at a constant speed, not when you first get it to move or when you stop it.

✍ a) In the table in your log, record your finding for mass moving down at a constant speed.

4. Newton's first law states that an object at rest remains at rest and an object in motion continues to move with constant velocity, unless acted upon by an unbalanced force. Newton's second law states that an accelerating object must have a net force acting upon it; $F_{net} = ma$. When the mass is being lifted at constant speed in a straight line, there is no acceleration since acceleration is defined as a change in velocity with respect to time. If there is no acceleration, then the net force is zero.

✍ a) Draw a box (representing the mass) in your log. Draw arrows to show the forces on the box hanging on the spring when the box is not accelerating.

5. Recall that in physics and mathematics, the arrows you drew to represent the forces are called vectors. Check your drawing to see if the arrows (vectors) have the following features:

✍ a) Was the vector representing the weight force drawn pointing down? Why did you draw it this way?

✍ b) Was the vector representing the force of the spring drawn pointing up? Why did you draw it this way?

✍ c) Were there any other force vectors? What do they represent?

✍ d) Were the weight vector and the spring force vector equal in length? The length of the vector is proportional to the magnitude of the force. If the forces are equal in magnitude, then the lengths of the vectors should be the same. If needed, change your force diagram so that the length of

the vectors correctly represents the magnitude of the forces.

✍ e) You may have drawn a vector indicating the force applied by the hand. The hand holds the spring scale, and not the mass, so this would not be a force on the mass. If needed, modify your force diagram.

6. Now consider the box when it was moving down with constant speed.

✍ a) Draw a second box with the force vectors when the box is moving down at a constant speed. Provide an explanation using Newton's first law and Newton's second law (similar to *Step 4*) as a rationale for your diagram.

Part B: Accelerating the Mass

1. It is now time to return to the scale readings when you first started moving the mass. With your arm extended down, accelerate the mass up until your arm is as high as you can reach. Your group members will try their best to read the spring scale during the time that the mass is accelerating. Once again, you may have to repeat this a few times so that others can lift as you observe.

✍ a) Record your observation in your *Active Physics* log.

✍ b) Use Newton's second law ($F_{net} = ma$) to make sense of the observation in your log.

✍ c) Draw a box representing the mass and draw the force vectors acting on the box as it first begins to move and is accelerating upward.

2. Check your drawing to see if the force vectors have the following features:

✍ a) Was the weight vector drawn pointing down?

✍ b) Was the force of the spring vector drawn pointing up?

✍ c) Were there any other force vectors? What do they represent?

▲ d) How do the weight vector and the spring-force vector compare in length? The length of the vectors is proportional to the magnitude of the force.

3. Since the box is accelerating up, the force of the spring must have been larger than the force of gravity. Newton's second law indicates that acceleration up requires a net force up. In your force-vector diagram, the vector representing the spring scale should be longer than the vector representing the force of gravity.

▲ a) If necessary, modify your diagram to show the spring-scale vector as longer than the force-of-gravity vector.

4. From your observations, you can see that when the mass is accelerating upward, the spring scale displays a value larger than the mass's weight. Suppose you were standing on a bathroom scale in an elevator. The elevator begins to move up. How would the reading on the bathroom scale compare to your weight at rest?

▲ a) Record your answer in your log.

5. Returning to the mass hanging on the spring scales, predict what would happen to the scale reading when the mass stops moving upward.

▲ a) Record your prediction in your log.

▲ b) Repeat the observations for the moments when the mass stops its upward motion. Describe your observation in your log.

6. Suspend a mass from a spring scale. Raise the spring scale and mass slightly above eye level.

▲ a) Slowly lower the spring scale and mass. Observe what happens to the value on the scale and write a description in your log.

▲ b) Draw a force-vector diagram that has a net force in the direction of the acceleration.

▲ c) Predict whether you think the scale will read a higher or lower value when it is accelerating downward as opposed to when the mass is at rest? Record your prediction.

▲ d) Now try lowering the spring scale and mass quickly. Observe the scale and see if the value changes. Was your initial prediction correct? Explain.

7. As a summary of what changes occur to the spring-scale reading, complete the chart under *Part A, Step 2* in your log. Some responses are provided to help you get started.

▲ a) Create a similar chart showing what would happen if you rode in an elevator while standing on a bathroom scale.

8. Riding in an elevator is similar to riding in a roller coaster. Although the physics is the same, the elevator ride does not have the excitement of a roller coaster.

▲ a) Compare elevator rides and roller coasters by providing three similarities and three differences.

9. There is a ride at the amusement park today in which all you do is drop straight down. If you were to record your motion, you would find that your speed increases by 9.8 m/s every second. This value of 9.8 m/s^2 is the acceleration due to gravity near the surface of Earth. All objects near the surface of Earth fall at this same rate of change of velocity with respect to time if gravity is the only significant force acting on them.

You have Galileo (1564-1642) to thank for this insight. As the story goes, he dropped two objects from the Leaning Tower of Pisa in Italy and observed them hitting the ground at the same time. The story may not be true, but Galileo did perform many experiments with balls rolling down inclined planes. The "dropping experiment" has been repeated many times with very precise equipment and with the effects of air resistance minimized or eliminated.

a) If you were at the Leaning Tower of Pisa and dropped a baseball and a bowling ball at the same time, which would hit the ground first? Explain your answer.

b) If you dropped a baseball and a piece of paper, which would hit the ground first? Explain your answer. Does the shape of the paper influence the way it

drops? Do you think you could modify a sheet of paper to drop at the same time you drop a baseball? Try this and record your observations in your log.

c) How would you modify the statement, "All objects fall at the same acceleration" to account for your observation of a baseball and a sheet of paper?

The numerical value of the acceleration of falling objects, if gravity is the only significant force, is equal to the strength of the gravitational field (9.8 N/kg = 9.8 m/s^2 near the surface of Earth). That is why g is sometimes called "the acceleration due to gravity." But you should remember that in many cases, the object may experience other forces in addition to its weight. In these cases, the acceleration will not be equal to g. If you are falling under the influence of gravity alone, you are in "free fall."

Physics Talk

FORCES ACTING DURING ACCELERATION

Using Newton's First and Second Law to Explain Forces Acting During Constant Speed and Acceleration

As the roller coaster moves you about, you feel funny things happening in your stomach. These, however, are more than just feelings. These changes can be measured. You can use physics to explain these feelings.

When an object is at rest, the sum of the forces on that object equal zero. Both Newton's first law and Newton's second law can be used to explain this. Using Newton's first law (an object at rest stays at rest and an object in motion stays in motion unless acted upon by a force), the object is at rest and no net force acts on it. Using Newton's second law ($a = F/m$), you realize that the object is at rest and, therefore, has zero acceleration and, therefore, no net force acting on it.

When the object moves up at constant speed, many people are too quick to jump to the wrong conclusion that there must

be a larger force up than down to keep the object moving up at constant speed. Both Newton's first and second laws can once again be used to explain correctly that the sum of the forces on that object equals zero. Using Newton's first law (an object at rest stays at rest and an object in motion stays in motion unless acted upon by a force) the object is in motion at constant speed and no net force acts on it. Using Newton's second law ($a = F/m$), you realize that the object is moving at constant speed and, therefore, has zero acceleration and, therefore, no net force acting on it.

The object moving down at constant speed is identical (in terms of forces and accelerations) to the object moving up at constant speed.

Your evidence for this is the observation in the *Investigate* that the spring scale exhibited the same weight whether the object was at rest or moving at a constant speed. You also observed that if the object accelerated up, there was an increase in the spring scale reading.

If you were sitting on a scale in a level roller-coaster cart, at rest or moving with a constant velocity, the scale reading would be equal to your weight. The force of Earth pulling on you (your weight), which is shown as a blue vector in the force diagram on the right, would be equal in magnitude to the force of the compressed spring within the bathroom scale, which is shown as a red vector.

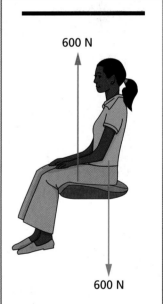

600 N

600 N

Suppose you weigh 600 N. Then, the bathroom scale would have to provide a force of 600 N to make the net force on you zero. If the force were any smaller, you would accelerate down. Any larger, and you would accelerate up. When you first stand on the scale, the compression is too little and you do move down. The spring compresses and provides a larger force but you continue to move down. You go past the compression you need, and the spring then pushes up. You go back up and down and up and down and continue this movement until the spring's force is exactly equal to your weight.

As the roller coaster starts moving up, there is acceleration up. (Remember that acceleration is a change in velocity with respect to time.) For you to accelerate up, there must be a net force pushing you up. Since you are in contact with the bathroom scale, it must be the bathroom scale that is pushing you up. Yes, the roller coaster is pushing on the scale, but you only have to worry about the forces on you. Newton's second law states that it is the net force acting on you that is responsible for your acceleration.

The scale reading will be greater in magnitude than your weight (the force on you due to Earth's gravity). The magnitude of the force of the Earth pulling on you (your weight) would be less than the magnitude of the force of the compressed spring within the bathroom scale.

411

If your weight is 600 N (blue vector), then the bathroom scale would have to be providing a force of greater than 600 N (red vector).

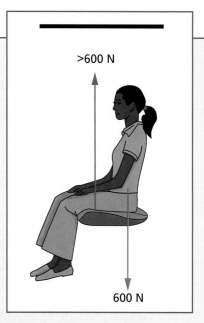

>600 N

600 N

Another way of looking at the situation is to look first at the forces. According to the vector diagram, the force of the scale is larger than the force of gravity. The net force is, therefore, up and according to Newton's second law, the object will accelerate up, $F_{net} = ma$. You observed this in the *Investigate* when you accelerated the mass up and observed the increased scale reading.

Calculating Acceleration

Suppose you are standing on a bathroom scale in an elevator. You can calculate the acceleration of the elevator if you know your weight and measure the force as read on the spring scale during the acceleration. Assume you weigh 600.0 N and the force of the scale on you is 700.0 N up.

$$F_{net} = 700.0 \text{ N} - 600.0 \text{ N}$$
$$= 100.0 \text{ N (upward)}$$

To find the acceleration, you need to know your mass. If your weight is 600.0 N ($F_w = 600.0$ N), you can calculate your mass.

$$F_w = mg, \text{ where } g = 9.8 \text{ N/kg}$$

$$m = \frac{F_w}{g}$$

$$= \frac{600.0 \text{ N}}{9.8 \text{ N/kg}} \text{ (units: } \cancel{N} \times \frac{kg}{\cancel{N}})$$

$$= 61 \text{ kg}$$

Knowing the mass and the net force, you can calculate the acceleration using Newton's second law.

$$F_{net} = ma$$

$$a = \frac{F}{m}$$

$$= \frac{100.0 \text{ N}}{61 \text{ kg}} \text{ (units: } \frac{\cancel{kg} \times m/s^2}{\cancel{kg}})$$

$$= 1.6 \text{ m/s}^2$$

Similarly, you can calculate the reading of the spring scale if you know the acceleration of the elevator.

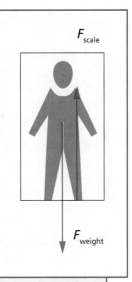

Sample Problem

An elevator at the top floor begins to descend with an acceleration of 2.0 m/s² downward. What will a bathroom scale read if a 50.0-kg person is standing on the scale while the elevator is accelerating?

Strategy: Since the elevator and the person are accelerating down, the net force on the person must be down. The force vectors are shown in the diagram on the right.

Newton's second law states that
$$F_{net} = ma$$

where F_{net} is the net force.

Since the weight is greater than the force of the spring and in the opposite direction, you can write this as

Weight – force due to bathroom scale = *ma* (downward)

Given:

$m = 50.0$ kg

$a = 2.0$ m/s²

Solution:

First find the person's weight: Weight = *mg*

$$= (50.0 \text{ kg})(9.8 \text{ N/kg})$$
$$= 490 \text{ N}$$

Using Newton's second law,

Weight – force due to scale = *ma*

$$490 \text{ N} - F_{scale} = (50.0 \text{ kg})(2.0 \text{ m/s}^2)$$

Solve for the force due to the scale.

$$F_{scale} = 490 \text{ N} - (50.0 \text{ kg})(2.0 \text{ m/s}^2)$$
$$= 390 \text{ N}$$

The scale would read 390 N instead of the person's weight, which is 490 N.

If the elevator accelerates up, the scale reads a value higher than the person's weight of 490 N. There is really no limit to the upward acceleration although the person would become unconscious if the acceleration were greater than about nine times the acceleration due to gravity. This has been experimentally determined by test pilots.

If the elevator accelerates down, the scale reads a value lower than the weight of 490 N. There is a lower limit on the scale reading. If the elevator accelerates down at 9.8 m/s² (For example, the cable broke and the elevator is in free fall.), the scale would not push up at all and its reading would be 0 N.

Active Physics

Using Newton's second law,

$$F_{scale} = ma$$

$$\text{Weight} - \text{Force by spring} = ma$$

Substitute the numerical values.

$$(50.0 \text{ kg})(9.8 \text{ N/kg}) - F_{scale} = (50.0 \text{ kg})(9.8 \text{ N/kg})$$

$$490 \text{ N} - F_{scale} = 490 \text{ N}$$

Solve for the force due to the scale.

$$F_{scale} = 0 \text{ N}$$

This is what you experience when you jump off a diving board. It is also felt for a few moments in the amusement park ride where you are in free fall.

Apparent Weight

When the elevator is at rest or moving up or down at constant velocity, your weight readings are identical. That's because at rest or moving at a constant velocity requires no net force. The force of the scale up on you is equal to the weight force down. The bathroom scale denotes the value of the force up on you.

When an object accelerates (changes its velocity), you know there must be a net force acting on the object. When the elevator accelerates up, you also accelerate up. This is because Earth pulls down on you with a force that is smaller than the force that the scale exerts on you upward. The scale reads a larger force than before.

You also feel as if you weigh more. Why is that? You feel your weight because of the contact forces between your body and other objects. When you stand on the floor, you feel the floor pushing up on you. Also, some parts of your body are only loosely connected to other parts. For example, when you are standing straight up, your stomach moves down a bit until the connective tissues in your body (acting like springs) exert a large enough force upward to hold your stomach in place against the force due to gravity. Nerve endings in those tissues allow you to feel that stretching. When the elevator accelerates upward, you feel the larger contact force between you and the bathroom scale. Also, the connective tissues have to stretch more to get your stomach to accelerate. All of this leads to a feeling of larger apparent weight.

When the elevator accelerates down, you also accelerate down. This is because the force of the scale up on you is less than the force of your weight down. The scale reads a smaller force than before. You also feel as if you weigh less because the contact force with the bathroom scale is smaller and because the connective tissues stretch a bit less. If the elevator cable were to break, you would have only the force of your weight pulling you down. The scale would not push up and you and the force reading on the scale would be zero. You feel "weightless" because the contact force between you and the bathroom scale is zero and because the connective tissues within your body relax. (People often describe the feeling as "stomach floating.") Roller coasters, like elevators, have parts of their motion where the acceleration is up or down. At these locations, people feel as if they weigh more or less.

Air Resistance

A roller coaster in free fall will accelerate at 9.8 m/s every second. Every second, the speed will increase by 9.8 m/s. This acceleration due to gravity is identical for all objects falling on Earth, if there are no other forces acting on the object. You know that raindrops, snowflakes, and leaves falling to the ground do not accelerate at this rate. The air must be applying a force to these materials that opposes the force of gravity. This force is often referred to as air resistance. Often, in introductory physics courses, you are told to ignore air resistance. Ignoring this force makes the analysis of moving objects simpler, but incorrect. When analyzing a roller coaster, ignoring air resistance also means pretending that there is no wind on your face or clothing as you descend a big hill. When analyzing falling rain, ignoring air resistance means pretending that the rain can be going so fast that it could seriously harm you. Whenever you consider the forces on an object and decide to "ignore air resistance" you have to be aware of how much this analysis differs from the real world you live in.

Checking Up

1. What is the sum of all the forces acting on an object when it is moving up a constant speed?

2. A person sitting on a bathroom scale on a roller coaster is accelerating upward. How does the reading on the bathroom scale compare to the person's weight?

3. When you accelerate upward, why do you feel as if you weigh more?

4. Suppose you are standing on a bathroom scale in an elevator when the cable breaks. What does the bathroom scale read when you are falling with the elevator?

5. What is the force that slows a falling raindrop?

Active Physics

Plus

+Math	+Depth	+Concepts	+Exploration
	◆◆	◆◆	◆

Einstein's Theory of Gravity

When an object is falling under the influence of gravity alone, the object is in "free fall." You learned that in free fall, all objects fall with the same acceleration. Let's look at that issue more closely.

When a ball, for example, is in free fall, it is accelerating (downward) because there is a net force (gravity) acting on the ball. That force is the ball's weight, $F_{net} = F_w = mg$. Note that weight (force) is determined by the ball's mass and the strength of the gravitational field at the location of the ball.

The mass m tells you how strong the gravitational force will be. Newton's second law tells you how the net force and the ball's acceleration are related ($F_{net} = ma$). Here the mass, m, plays the role of inertia. It tells you how much the ball "resists" being accelerated.

If you combine the two equations, $mg = ma$, the mass terms cancel out and you find that in free fall, the acceleration of the ball is equal to g ($a = g$). This tells you that all objects, no matter what their mass, should have the same acceleration under free-fall conditions.

Active Physics

If you stop and think for a moment, it may be surprising to recognize that mass plays two different roles here. On one hand, it determines the strength of the gravitational force acting on the ball. On the other hand, it determines the inertia of the ball (its resistance to being accelerated). Why should those two effects be the same? Most scientists took this relationship for granted until Albert Einstein, in about 1915, recognized the deep significance of having the same "mass" for both the gravitational force and for inertia. From this insight, he developed an entirely new theory of gravity based on ideas such as curved space-time.

The following exercise will provide some insights into Einstein's theory of gravity (the General Theory of Relativity).

1. Rewrite the equations on the previous page using subscripts to distinguish between $m_{inertial}$ and $m_{gravitational}$.

2. Below is a diagram of two balls of different mass being dropped. The student is at rest on Earth and drops the massive red ball and the less-massive blue ball at the same time from the same height.

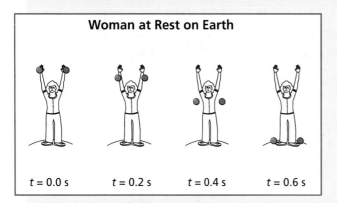

Woman at Rest on Earth

$t = 0.0$ s $t = 0.2$ s $t = 0.4$ s $t = 0.6$ s

a) How does the student describe the motion of the ball?

b) What value will the student get for her measurement of the acceleration of the ball?

3. In the diagram below, the procedure is repeated, only this time in a rocket ship accelerating up at 9.8 m/s every second. The rocket ship is in deep space and there is no net gravitational force acting on it.

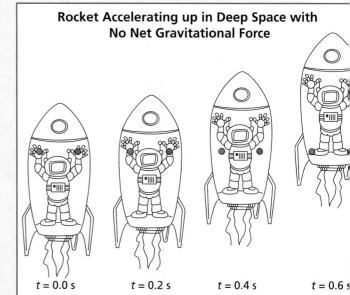

Rocket Accelerating up in Deep Space with No Net Gravitational Force

$t = 0.0$ s $t = 0.2$ s $t = 0.4$ s $t = 0.6$ s

a) What does the astronaut in the rocket ship see?

b) How does the astronaut explain this?

c) What would the astronaut measure for the acceleration of the massive red ball and the less massive blue ball?

4. You have the ability to see that the rocket is accelerating up.

a) How do you explain the ball's positions after each 0.2 s?

b) How do you explain the rocket's position after each 0.2 s?

5. Can you think of an experiment that the student in the room or the astronaut in the rocket could perform to determine if gravity is pulling the ball down or if the rocket is accelerating up?

What Do You Think Now?

At the beginning of this section, you were asked the following:

- **Does your weight change when you are riding on a roller coaster?**

- **If you were sitting on a bathroom scale, would the scale give different readings at different places on the roller coaster?**

Revise your answers to these questions using what you have learned about apparent weight and acceleration. Discuss your revisions with other students in your group.

Physics
Essential Questions

What does it mean?

Force, mass, and acceleration are key concepts in the study of motion. Explain what F_{net} means, what m means, and what a means.

How do you know?

In physics, you use reliable instruments to verify your sense perceptions. In your investigation, how did you use a spring scale to explore the way you feel on a roller coaster as it goes up and down?

Why do you believe?

Connects with Other Physics Content	Fits with Big Ideas in Science	Meets Physics Requirements
Forces and motion	✳ Change and constancy	Experimental evidence is consistent with models and theories

✳ General principles of science allow you to learn new things about a situation. Newton's second law, $F_{net} = ma$, says that if an object is not accelerating, then the net force on the object must be 0. How was Newton's second law able to help explain weight changes as you accelerate up and down?

Why should you care?

Force, mass, and acceleration are important in all kinds of motion. How will what you learned about force and acceleration in this section help you with your challenge?

Reflecting on the Section and the Challenge

A ride in an elevator is a lot like a ride in a roller coaster. Roller coasters, like elevators, accelerate up or down. However, the elevator moves at too slow a pace and with too little acceleration to provide a great deal of excitement. In a roller coaster, these accelerations are much greater and they are what make a roller-coaster ride thrilling. At the locations where these accelerations occur, people feel as if they weigh more or less. When you design your roller coaster, you may want to take into consideration how large an acceleration your sample population would enjoy.

Physics to Go

1. Objects near the surface of Earth accelerate at a rate of 9.8 m/s every second if gravity is the only significant force acting on them. Based on this information, how fast will an object be going after it has fallen from rest after each of the following lengths of time?

   a) 2 s   b) 5 s   c) 10 s

2. Objects near the surface of the Moon accelerate at a rate of 1.6 m/s every second. Based on this information, how fast will an object be going after it has fallen from rest after each of the following lengths of time?

   a) 2 s   b) 5 s   c) 10 s

3. The vector diagram on the right shows a block of wood that can move up and down. The red vector represents the force pushing up on the block. The blue vector represents the weight of the block.

   a) Could the block be at rest?

   b) Could the block be moving up at a constant speed?

   c) Could the block be accelerating down?

   d) If you wrote "no" for any of the above questions, sketch a force diagram for that description.

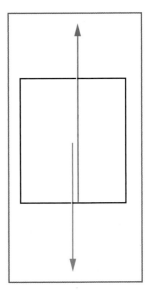

4. Complete the table on the right in your log. Some responses are provided in the table.

5. A student weighs 140 lbs. On an elevator, the person is surprised to find that the scale only reads 137 lbs for a few moments. Describe the motion of the elevator.

6. A person in an elevator at rest weighs 600 N. The elevator is about to move from the second floor to the fifth floor. When it first starts to move, what will the passenger observe about the weight indicated by a bathroom scale on which the passenger is standing?

7. An elevator at the top floor begins to descend with an acceleration of 1.5 m/s². A person is standing on a bathroom scale in the elevator.

   a) Will the bathroom scale's reading increase or decrease once the elevator starts?

   b) What will a bathroom scale read if a 50-kg person is standing on the scale during the acceleration?

	Acceleration (up, down, zero)	Scale reading (larger, smaller, equal to weight)
A. Elevator at rest on top floor	zero	equal
B. Elevator starts moving down		
C. Elevator moves down at constant speed		
D. Elevator comes to rest on bottom floor		
E. Elevator is at rest at bottom floor		
F. Elevator begins to move up	up	larger
G. Elevator moves up at constant speed		
H. Elevator comes to rest on top floor		
I. Elevator at rest on top floor	zero	equal

Active Physics

8. A 50-kg student is on a scale in the elevator.

   a) What will be the scale reading when the elevator is at rest?

   b) What will be the scale reading when the elevator accelerates up at a rate of 2 m/s²?

   c) What will be the scale reading as the elevator travels up at a constant speed?

9. Explain the meanings of the three sketches below. Specifically, why is there a different scale reading for the same student in each elevator?

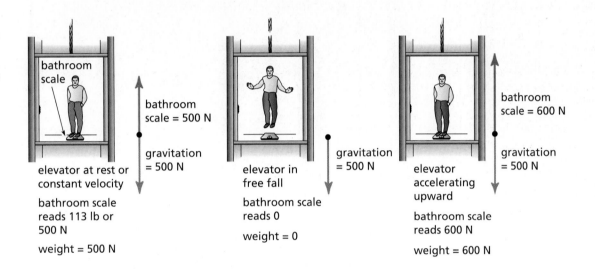

10. *Preparing for the Chapter Challenge*
    Think about the group of people for whom you are designing your roller coaster. What amount of acceleration would they find exciting? How much acceleration would be safe for them? In your log, record which parts of the Terminator Express you would modify and why.

Inquiring Further

Apparent weight on elevators

Use a digital camera or video camera and record some bathroom scale readings while riding in an elevator. Go with an adult to a place where there is an elevator that moves up and down several floors. Take photographs of the readings of the bathroom scale on which you are standing while the elevator starts, moves steadily and then stops. Illustrate as many of the results described in this section as possible.

Visit interactive Web sites on apparent weight changes in elevators and explore what happens to your weight as you ride an elevator in a tall building. Write notes about your findings and draw vector diagrams to represent the interaction of the forces of gravity pulling you down and the scale pushing you up as you accelerate or ride at a steady speed in the elevator.

Active Physics

Section 7

Circular Motion: Riding on the Curves

What Do You See?

Learning Outcomes

In this section, you will

- **Recall** the idea that an object in motion remains in motion with a constant velocity unless acted upon by a force - Newton's first law.

- **Explain** how a force directed toward a center (a centripetal force) will allow a roller-coaster cart to travel in circular motion.

- **Describe** how the centripetal force is dependent on the speed and the radius of the curve and the mass of the cart.

- **Solve** problems using the equation for centripetal force.

- **Recognize** that safety considerations limit the acceleration of a roller coaster to below 4 *g*.

What Do You Think?

The first looping coaster was built in Paris, France. It had about a 4-m (13 ft) diameter loop. One of the largest loops today is about 35 m (120 ft) wide.

- **Why don't you fall out of the roller-coaster cart when it goes upside down during a loop?**

Record your ideas about this question in your *Active Physics* log. Be prepared to discuss your response with your small group and the class.

Investigate

In this *Investigate*, you will explore the behavior of the roller coaster on horizontal curves where you feel pushed to the side and on vertical curves where you find yourself upside down. The more you understand about the requirements of curves on roller coasters, the better your roller-coaster design will be.

Part A: Moving on Curves

1. A battery-operated car can move when you turn on the switch. Investigate the toy car's motion under different circumstances.

a) Turn on the car and let the car run on the floor. Describe its motion in your *Active Physics* log.

b) Attach one end of a string to the side of the car. Loosely tie the other end of the string around a pencil, and hold the eraser end of the pencil firmly on the floor. Turn on the car, and describe the car's motion.

c) Predict what will happen to the motion of the car when you let go of the pencil end of the string. Provide a reason for your prediction.

d) Test your prediction and record your observations in your log.

⚠ Be sure to pick up the car from the floor when it is not in use so it does not present a hazard for people walking in the room.

2. Your investigation with the toy car demonstrates that a force is needed for circular motion. This is a big idea that takes some getting used to. Whenever you see anything moving in a circle or on any curve, you should remind yourself of the movement of the toy car and the string. Without the force of the string, the car moves in a straight line.

If something moves in a circle, there must be a force that constantly veers it away from the straight line to keep it moving in a circle.

a) What force kept the toy car moving in a circle?

b) In which direction must this force point?

3. There is no string that keeps a real automobile moving around a curve. However, if the automobile is to move around the curve, there must be a force pointing toward the center of the curve. Imagine a curved road surface covered with slick ice. The automobile would not "make the curve" but would keep moving in a straight line and go off the road. It wouldn't matter which way you pointed the wheels — no turning would occur. What is the force that keeps a real automobile moving around a curve in normal traffic conditions?

4. In a roller coaster, there are horizontal curves similar to those on the road.

a) Sketch the coaster moving around a horizontal curve.

b) Draw an arrow coming from the coaster car that shows the direction of the velocity of the coaster when the car is part way around the curve. (Remember, the toy car went straight when you released the string.)

c) Now, add another arrow to the coaster car showing the direction of the force that keeps the coaster moving in a circle. Note that the arrow in *b*) represents the velocity vector. In this case, the arrow represents a force vector.

5. There are two orientations of the roller-coaster car you will investigate as it travels in a horizontal circle. The passengers can be sitting up as they would in an automobile with the wheels of the roller coaster down. They could also be on their sides with the wheels of the roller coaster facing away from the center of the circle. In each of these orientations, the force moving the cart in a circle will be toward the center of the circle.

a) Look at the diagrams on the next page. Is this the way that you drew the force arrow in *Step 4.c*)?

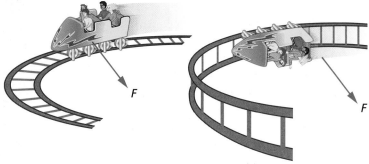

Make any changes necessary to your diagram and talk your ideas over with your team if you have questions.

b) Identify the force that causes the roller coaster to move in the circle in each of the following cases: with passengers sitting in the usual sitting position, and with passengers and the coaster cart turned sideways.

c) The coaster car, whether stationary or moving also has forces in the vertical direction – its weight and the force of the ground pushing up. Draw a small box to represent the coaster car and the passengers. Attach arrows to this box that represent all of the forces acting on the coaster and passengers as it goes in a circle.

Part B: How Much Force is Required?

1. Your teacher will supply you with three rubber stoppers and a string. Put on your safety goggles. Twirl the stopper at a slow speed in a horizontal circle like helicopter blades. Gradually increase the speed.

⚠️ Wear safety glasses to protect your eyes in case the string should break or your partner accidentally loses grip of the string. Everyone must be wearing safety glasses. Stand clear of anything that is breakable, such as glass.

a) Observe and record the force that your fingers are applying to the string at a slow speed and as you increase the speed of the stopper.

b) Write down a description of what you observed about the relationship between the speed of the stopper and the force of your fingers.

2. Now twirl a string with two or three rubber stoppers attached. Hold the string so that the length of the string for the multiple stopper is the same as the length of the string for one stopper.

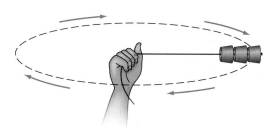

a) Compare the force that your fingers applied to a string with one rubber stopper and a string with more than one stopper.

b) In comparing one stopper with three, why did you keep the speeds and radii (length of string) of the circular twirls identical?

c) Write down your observations about the force of your fingers and the mass of the stoppers.

3. Twirl one stopper, but this time, change the length of the string.

a) Write down a description of what you observed concerning the length of the string and the force on your fingers.

b) What properties of the twirling stopper must you keep constant if you wish to compare only how changes in length affect the required force?

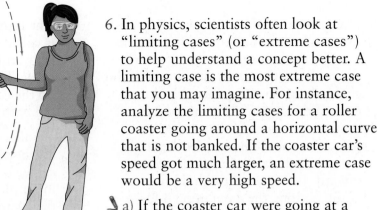

4. Now twirl the stopper in a vertical circle.

a) Observe how the force your fingers exert on the string is different when the stopper is near the top of the circle and when it is at the bottom of the circle.

b) Write down a description of how this force changes. Is it larger when the stopper is at the top of the loop or when it is at the bottom?

c) Twirl the stopper in a vertical circle and gradually reduce the speed of the stopper. At some point, the speed will be so low that the string goes slack and the stopper no longer moves in a circular path. When the string goes slack, it is no longer exerting a force on the stopper. Record your observation of where the string goes slack.

5. To keep a roller coaster moving in a circle, a force is required toward the center of the circle. The track pushing on the edges of the wheels, the surface of the track pushing on the rims of the wheels, the force of gravity on the coaster car, or some combination of these forces can supply this force.

a) How does the required force change when the speed of the roller coaster changes?

b) How does the required force change when the mass of the roller coaster changes?

c) How does the required force change when the radius of the curve changes?

d) If the speed of a roller coaster were increased, how might you strengthen the track to provide the additional force required?

6. In physics, scientists often look at "limiting cases" (or "extreme cases") to help understand a concept better. A limiting case is the most extreme case that you may imagine. For instance, analyze the limiting cases for a roller coaster going around a horizontal curve that is not banked. If the coaster car's speed got much larger, an extreme case would be a very high speed.

a) If the coaster car were going at a very high speed, would the force required from the track to keep the car moving in the curve be very large or very small? Write your response down in your *Active Physics* log.

b) The other extreme case is a coaster car with zero speed. Would the force that the track would have to provide if the car were moving very slowly around a curve be very large or very small? Write your response down in your *Active Physics* log.

7. The roller coaster may also do a loop as it travels in a vertical circle. If the loop were a perfect circle, as illustrated to the right, there would always have to be a force toward the center of circle.

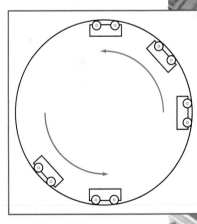

a) Make a sketch of the loop in your *Active Physics* log.

b) Draw the velocity vector for the coaster at each of the positions shown in the diagram.

c) Draw the centripetal force vectors at each position. This is the force toward the center of the circle that keeps the roller-coaster car moving in a circle at each position in a circle.

8. The gravitational force F_w is acting on the coaster car at all times. To move in a circle, there must be a force toward the center of the circle. At the top of the circle, the gravitational force is down toward the center of Earth and acts toward the center of the circle. For a coaster car at the bottom of the circle, the gravitational force remains down toward the center of Earth. However, at the bottom, the gravitational force is in the opposite direction to the force required for circular motion. The only other force at the bottom of the loop is the force due to the track pushing up on the car. This upward force must be responsible for the car moving in a circle.

a) Draw the gravitational force and the force of the track on the coaster car when the car is at the bottom of the loop and moving in a circle.

9. Check your force diagram for the coaster car at the bottom by answering the following questions.

a) Is the gravitational force (weight force) vector pointing down?

b) Is the force of the track pointing up?

c) Is the force of the track pointing up larger than the weight force pointing down? (Hint: at the bottom of the circular loop, the coaster car's net force is up toward the center of the circle.)

10. The force of the track on the coaster car is called the *normal force*, F_N, because it is "normal" or "perpendicular" to the track. This normal force must be present on the car when it rounds the loop at the bottom.

11. A roller-coaster car in a vertical loop always requires a net force toward the center of the loop. At the top of the loop, the car requires a force toward the center of the loop, which is straight down. This net force can be supplied by a combination of the downward force of gravity, and by the downward normal force of the track.

a) In the extreme case, where the coaster car is traveling at very high speed, would the force required to keep it moving in the circle be very large or very small? Since the force of gravity is *mg* and doesn't change its value, what produces most of the very large force?

b) Describe how the construction of a roller-coaster track in a vertical loop is impacted by the speed of the roller coaster. Enter comments and ideas into your engineering design process, too.

Physics Talk

CENTRIPETAL FORCE AND ACCELERATION

A battery-operated car can move in a straight line at constant speed. As you saw in the *Investigate*, this same car can move in a circle if a string is attached to the car and the end of the string is held fixed at a point on the floor. The string supplied a force toward the center of the circle that kept the car moving in a circle. All objects moving in circles or curves must have a force toward the center of the circle.

Much of the fun of riding a roller coaster comes from whipping around the turns and flipping upside down. All objects moving in circles are accelerating and require a force toward the center of the circle. In a roller coaster moving around a horizontal curve, there is no string toward the center, but there is a force due to the track pushing on the wheels of the roller-coaster car.

In a roller-coaster curve where the car tilts vertically and the wheels face the outside of the circle, the force toward the center is the **normal force** of the track on the wheels. Of course, there must be some support that holds the track in place, but it is the track that acts directly on the wheels of the car. It is called a normal force, F_N, because it is normal (perpendicular) to the track.

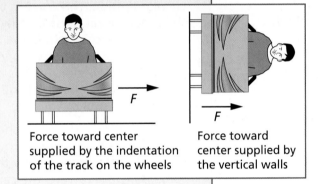

Force toward center supplied by the indentation of the track on the wheels

Force toward center supplied by the vertical walls

In any circular motion when the object is moving at constant speed, the force that keeps the object moving in a circle is called the **centripetal force**. The centripetal force is always directed toward the center. Centripetal means "center seeking." The toy car moving in a circle had a centripetal force that was the force of tension in the attached string acting on the toy car. An automobile moving around a curve has the force of friction between the tires and road as the centripetal force. Earth moving around the Sun has a force of gravity toward the Sun. The clothes in a dryer have the walls of the dryer keeping the clothes moving in a circle (the water flies out in straight lines through the holes). The roller-coaster car rounding a turn on its side may have the force of the track as the centripetal force. *The centripetal force is not an additional force.* It is the name given to a force like friction, tension, gravity, or the normal force when that force causes an object to move in a circle. The centripetal force could be a combination of these forces.

In your experiments with the rubber stoppers on the string, you experienced producing the centripetal force (acting via the string) required to keep the stopper moving in a circle. You observed that the centripetal force is larger if the speed of the stopper increases. Also, you observed that the centripetal force is larger if the mass of the stoppers is larger. Finally, you observed that the centripetal force is larger if the radius of the circle is smaller (with the mass and speed remaining the same).

Physics Words

normal force: the force acting perpendicular to the surface.

centripetal force: any force directed toward the center that causes an object to follow a circular path at constant speed.

Active Physics

All of these observations are summarized in the equation for centripetal force.

$$F_c = \frac{mv^2}{r}$$

where F_c is the centripetal force,

   m is the mass of the object,

   v is the speed, and

   r is the radius of the circle.

When you are riding in the roller-coaster car and the car goes around a curve, you are also accelerating. You know from Newton's second law that if there is a net force, an object must be accelerating. In the case of circular motion, this force is toward the center of the circle. Therefore, the acceleration must be toward the center of the circle. This is called **centripetal acceleration**. You can feel the contact forces between you and your seat and between you and the side of the coaster car that cause you to accelerate. It is the acceleration and the related contact forces that give you the thrill of riding on the roller coaster.

When the roller coaster is in a vertical loop, the direction of the centripetal force is always changing to ensure that the centripetal force vector always points toward the center of the circular track. Pay particular attention to how this is phrased. Although the centripetal force is always toward the center, the direction is always changing since in the circle, the centripetal force may be toward the left or the right or up, but still point toward the center.

Physics Words

centripetal acceleration: the acceleration directed toward the center of a circle experienced by an object traveling in a circular path at constant speed.

In the vertical loop, this centripetal force can be either the gravitational force, the normal force of the track on the coaster car or a combination of the two. When it is a combination of the two, you must add the forces as vectors. At the bottom of the circle, the normal force (red vector) points toward the center of the circle (upward) while the gravitational force (blue vector) points downward. The vector sum of these two forces must be toward the center of the circle. You can therefore conclude that the normal force is larger than the gravitational force. The normal force corresponds to your apparent weight, as it did in the investigation in the previous section. This is why you feel as if you weigh more at the bottom of the loop of the roller coaster.

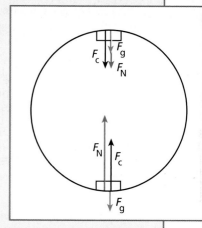

At the top of the loop-the-loop, the gravitational force (blue vector) and the normal force (red vector) both act downward, toward the center of the loop. The sum of these two vectors provides the required centripetal force.

How much of the normal force required to keep the car moving in a circle will depend on the mass and speed of the car.

The black force vectors show the net centripetal force required to keep the car moving in a circular path at the top and bottom of the loop. Notice that the length of the black vectors is different since the coaster car has a larger speed at the bottom of the loop. The directions are different because the centripetal force must always point toward the center of the circle.

The blue force vector represents the force of gravity or weight of the coaster cars. Both weight vectors are identical because the weights of the roller-coaster car are identical at the top and bottom.

The red vector represents the normal force of the track on the car. The sum of the normal force plus the weight must be equal to the required net (centripetal) force. At the top, the normal force is smaller since the weight contributes to the centripetal force. If the speed decreases, the required net centripetal force would be less and less. There comes a point where the gravitational force (weight) would be all that is required to keep the coaster car moving in a circle. In that case, the normal force is zero. In this special situation, where no normal force is required, you could actually have a small gap at the top between the track and the car. The car would continue to move in a circle. If the car were to slow down more, the car would leave the track completely and no longer travel in a circle. That is something you don't want to have happen with your roller coaster!

At the bottom of the roller-coaster loop, the car would need a normal force of the track on the car greater than the weight since the weight is downward and the car needs a net upward force (toward the center of the circle).

This is summarized in the following tables.

Fast-moving Roller Coaster

	Required centripetal force	Force of gravity (weight)	Normal force (the force of the track on the car)
at the top of the loop	5000 N	1000 N	4000 N
at the bottom of the loop	9000 N	1000 N	10,000 N

Slow-moving Roller Coaster

	Required centripetal force	Force of gravity (weight)	Normal force (the force of the track on the car)
at the top of the loop	2100 N	1000 N	1100 N
at the bottom of the loop	6100 N	1000 N	7100 N

Apparent Weight and the Roller-Coaster Ride

You discovered earlier that an elevator ride could give you a sense of weight changes during accelerations. In the roller coaster loop-the-loop, the passenger will also experience changes in apparent weight. The normal force on the passenger due to the seat is an indication of the apparent weight, as it was in the elevator. A passenger on the roller coaster feels lighter at the top of the loop because the contact force between the passenger and the seat is smaller. This is similar to the elevator because in both cases you feel lighter because acceleration is directed downward. A passenger on the roller coaster feels heavier at the bottom of the loop. Once again, this is similar to the elevator because in both cases you feel heavier because acceleration is upward.

In the slow-moving roller coaster in the chart, the apparent weight (normal force) at the top of the loop may only be 1100 N, while the apparent weight (normal force) at the bottom of the loop may be 7100 N.

Three locations can be used to summarize the discussion on forces and weight. On a level track with the coaster car moving at constant speed, the sum of the forces must be zero.

At the bottom of the loop, there must be a net force up toward the center of the circle to keep you moving in a circular path.

At the top of the loop, there must be a net force down toward the center of the circle to keep you moving in a circular path.

Roller coasters do not use loops that are circular. They use a clothoid loop (it has a big radius at the bottom and a small radius at the top). In this way, at the top of the loop the roller coaster is moving in a small circle (smaller radius), while at the bottom it is moving in a larger circle (larger radius). This kind of loop is used to ensure that the roller-coaster car can make the turn at the top but not have an acceleration at the bottom of the loop that exceeds about 4 *g's*. The speed at the bottom is determined by the height of the loop as you saw in *Section 2*. If *r* is larger at the bottom of the loop, then the acceleration experienced by the riders at the bottom of the loop will be smaller, keeping it within a thrilling but safe range.

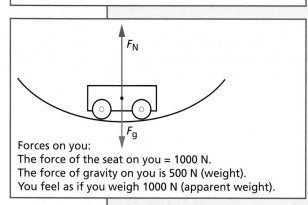

Forces on you:
The force of the seat on you = 500 N (apparent weight).
The force of gravity on you is 500 N (weight).

Forces on you:
The force of the seat on you = 1000 N.
The force of gravity on you is 500 N (weight).
You feel as if you weigh 1000 N (apparent weight).

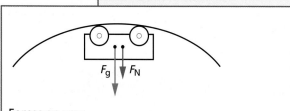

Forces on you:
The force of the seat on you = 100 N.
The force of gravity on you is 500 N (weight).
You feel as if you weigh 100 N (apparent weight).

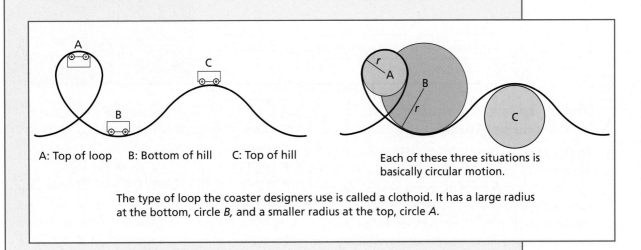

A: Top of loop   B: Bottom of hill   C: Top of hill

Each of these three situations is basically circular motion.

The type of loop the coaster designers use is called a clothoid. It has a large radius at the bottom, circle *B*, and a smaller radius at the top, circle *A*.

Safety on the Roller Coaster

Test pilots and astronauts experience lots of accelerations during their job performance. To prepare for this, they all go through physical training to see how much acceleration they can endure without getting sick or becoming unconscious. Experiencing an acceleration of more than nine times gravity for a sustained period will cause unconsciousness in most people. Since the acceleration due to gravity is 9.8 m/s^2 or approximately 10 m/s^2, you can refer to other accelerations in terms of 1 *g*. An acceleration of 2 *g*'s is approximately 20 m/s^2 while an acceleration of 8 *g*'s is approximately 80 m/s^2. Astronauts sometimes experience as much as 6 *g*'s during liftoff.

Safety on a roller coaster requires that you stay below 4 *g*'s for the entire ride. You must never go beyond 4 *g*'s for even a short time. Changes in small accelerations may make a better ride than one big thrill from a single large acceleration.

Checking Up

1. What is required to make an object travel in a circle?

2. If you are traveling in a circle at constant speed, are you accelerating?

3. At the top of a roller-coaster loop, what two forces provide the centripetal force?

4. What force is responsible for your apparent weight on a roller coaster?

5. How does the centripetal force acting on an object depend upon the object's mass? On the radius of the curve? On the object's speed?

Active Physics

+Math	+Depth	+Concepts	+Exploration
◆◆	◆◆		

Understanding the Equation for Centripetal Force

The success of physics in describing the world is due to the discovery that mathematics can describe events precisely, accurately, and concisely. You can bring together all of your observations about circular motion into one equation relating the force required to keep an object in circular motion, the object's mass, its speed, and the radius of the circle. First, you note that if there is a net force toward the center of the circle, the object must be accelerating toward the center of the circle. That acceleration is centripetal acceleration. The centripetal acceleration is given by

$$\text{centripetal acceleration} = \frac{\text{speed}^2}{\text{radius of the circle}}$$

$$a_c = \frac{v^2}{r}$$

where a is the object's acceleration,

v is the object's speed, and

r is the radius of the circle.

By Newton's second law there must be a net force in the direction of the acceleration.

$$F_{net} = ma_c$$

$$F_{net} = \frac{mv^2}{r}$$

Recall that the net force F_{net} might be composed of several different forces.

This equation concisely describes your observations. Let's see how this works. If the speed of the object moving around the circle increases, the force required to keep it moving in a circle increases (as the square of the speed). If the radius of the circle is made larger while the speed stays the same, the net force required to keep it moving in a circle gets smaller (r is in the denominator). If the mass of the object increases, the net force required to keep it moving in a circle increases.

The net force, F_{net}, on the left side of the equation is the force required to move something in a circle. It is always directed toward the center of the circle. Such a force is called the centripetal force. When something moves in a circle a force is required. Remember the toy car with the string attached? The string always supplied a force toward the center of the circle and the car moved in a circle. For the toy car, the string force acting on the car was the centripetal force.

$$F_{net} = ma_c$$

$$F_{string} = \frac{mv^2}{r}$$

On the right side of the equation are variables that can change when objects move in circles. They were tested in your investigation as you twirled the cork on a string. The finger force F was equal to mv^2/r.

1. a) As the mass increases on the right side of the equation, then the right side of the equation gets larger. What happens to the F_{net}? Describe in your log how this agrees with your observations.

   b) If the velocity increases on the right side of the equation, what happens to the F_{net}? Describe in your log how this agrees with your observations.

The equation tells you more about how the change in velocity affects the force than you could determine from your qualitative

430

exercise. The equation says that the force increases as the square of the velocity, v^2. If the velocity triples, then v^2 is nine times as large. Tripling the velocity requires nine times the force. If the velocity quadruples (four times as large), then v^2 is sixteen (4×4) times as large. And, if the velocity increases by a factor of 10, then v^2 is 100 times as large.

2. A rollercoaster car going with twice the speed around a banked curve needs a stronger track. Write down in your log how much stronger the track must be for a doubling of the speed.

3. If the radius of the curve increases on the right side of the equation, then the right side of the equation gets smaller since the r is in the denominator of the fraction. What happens to the F_{net}?

4. Complete the following sentence in your log: The larger the radius for the curve, the _____ the force required to keep the car moving along the curve. If the curve is tight (r is very small) then a _____ force is required.

5. The limiting case of the large curve is where the curve's radius is so very large that the curve and a straight line are hardly distinguishable. On a straight path, no force is required. Describe in your log how this agrees with your observations of the stopper on a string.

Sample Problem

A roller-coaster cart moving at 12.0 m/s

enters a horizontal turn with a radius of curvature equal to 20.0 m.

a) What is the centripetal acceleration of the roller coaster?

b) If the mass of the passengers and car is 300 kg, what is the net centripetal force required to keep the car on its tracks?

Strategy: Since you know the speed of the car and the radius of the circle, you can directly calculate the centripetal acceleration. You can then use Newton's second law to calculate the magnitude of the centripetal force. You know that its direction will be in toward the center of the circle.

Given:

$v = 12.0$ m/s

$r = 20.0$ m

$m = 300.0$ kg

Solution:

$$a_c = \frac{v^2}{r}$$

$$= \frac{(12.0 \text{ m/s})^2}{20.0 \text{ m}}$$

$$= 7.2 \text{ m/s}^2$$

Next, find the net centripetal force

$$F_{net} = ma$$

$$= (300.0 \text{ kg})(7.2 \text{ m/s}^2)$$

$$= 2200 \text{ N}$$

The force will be in the direction of acceleration, toward the center of the circle. Since the track is the only object in contact with the car, this force will have to be supplied by the track to the wheels of the coaster.

What Do You Think Now?

At the beginning of this section, you were asked the following:

• **Why don't you fall out of the roller coaster car when it goes upside down during a loop?**

Review, and if necessary, revise your answer to the question. Use the concepts of circular motion, centripetal force, and force diagrams in your response. Discuss your revisions with other students in your group. How would you explain the answer to a friend who has not done this investigation?

Physics
Essential Questions

What does it mean?
General concepts such as acceleration and force are often given special names
for particular circumstances. The crucial concept in this section is centripetal
acceleration and centripetal force. Explain the meanings of centripetal
acceleration and centripetal force and give some examples of when each applies.

How do you know?
What evidence do you have that a force is required to move a toy car in a circle?
Describe the observations you made in this *Investigate* that give evidence that
the centripetal acceleration increases if v increases while r stays the same?

Why do you believe?

Connects with Other Physics Content	Fits with Big Ideas in Science	Meets Physics Requirements
✳ Forces and motion	Models	Good, clear explanation, no more complex than necessary

✳ The toy car had a string to move it in a circle. Tires on the car provide frictional
force on the road that allows your car to make a turn and move in a circular
path. When you are moving upside down in the loop of a roller coaster, why do
you believe that there must be a force pulling you in a circle? What is that force?

Why should you care?
Traveling along curves occurs in many situations. Give some examples of
centripetal acceleration in everyday life. How will what you learned in this
section about centripetal acceleration help you with your challenge?

Reflecting on the Section and the Challenge

All objects moving in circles require a centripetal force toward the center. With
a toy car attached to a string, the tension in the string is the centripetal force. A
roller-coaster car rounding a horizontal turn has the track pushing on the wheels
providing the centripetal force. A roller coaster making a turn on its side has the
track's normal force as the centripetal force. The upside-down roller coaster has
gravity and the normal force from the track combining to produce the centripetal
force. At the bottom of the loop, the normal force is larger than the weight force
to provide a net centripetal force upward. Since the normal force must be larger
than the gravitational force, the passengers feel much heavier at the bottom of
the loop. In designing your roller coaster, you will have to ensure that the roller
coaster has enough speed to make the full circle. You will also have to ensure
that it doesn't have so much speed at the bottom that the apparent weight is too
great. You don't want the passengers to be injured!

432

The loop is one of the big thrills of riding a roller coaster. People are always worried that they will fall out of the roller coaster when it is upside down. This does not happen because they arrive at the top of the loop with a large speed. The gravitational force (weight) at the top of the roller coaster combines with the normal force from the track to serve as the centripetal force that moves the roller coaster in a circular path.

Physics to Go

1. A battery-operated toy car is attached to a string.

   a) If the loose end of the string is held to the ground, draw the path of the car while the battery is running.

   b) If the string were to break while the car was moving in a circle, draw the path that the car would follow.

2. Consider a real car on a road making a turn.

   a) What force has replaced the string of the toy car in *Question 1.a*)?

   b) If the car were to hit a section of ice, draw the path that the car probably would follow.

3. A girl twirls a key chain in a circle. If she twirls it faster, she finds that she holds the chain tighter. Explain why this is necessary.

4. It is a cold night and the roads are icy. If your car is filled with friends, will it be easier or more difficult to make a turn? Explain why.

5. The force equation for circular motion at constant speed is $F_{net} = mv^2/r$. Explain what each of the terms represents.

6. A roller-coaster car is traveling east at 20 m/s. After 2 s, it is traveling north at 20 m/s.

   a) Did the speed of the roller-coaster car change?

   b) Did the velocity of the roller-coaster car change?

   c) What was the change in velocity of the roller-coaster car? Give both magnitude and direction for the change in velocity.

7. **Active Physics** **Plus** A roller-coaster car is traveling east at 20 m/s in a circular path. After 16 s, it is traveling north at 20 m/s. The circular curve had a radius of 200 m. Calculate the acceleration of the car and give its direction.

8. A roller-coaster car is traveling in a circular loop. Identify the six force vectors in the diagram to the right.

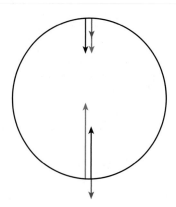

9. In explaining circular motion, someone correctly states that the centripetal force is a name for a combination of forces, but it is not an additional force. Explain what this means.

10. Fill in the missing values in the tables that you created in your *Active Physics* log:

Fast-moving roller coaster			
	Required centripetal force	Force of gravity (weight)	Normal force (the force of the track on the car)
At the top of the loop	4000 N	500 N	
At the bottom of the loop	6000 N		
Slow-moving roller coaster			
	Required centripetal force	Force of gravity (weight)	Normal force (the force of the track on the car)
At the top of the loop	800 N		
At the bottom of the loop	2800 N		

11. At which section of a vertical loop would the roller-coaster passengers feel the heaviest? Why?

12. Safety requires the roller coaster to be able to make the complete vertical loop and to keep the acceleration under 4 *g*. How can both of these safety features be accomplished at the same time?

13. Use the diagram of the Terminator Express roller coaster. Indicate at which of the following points the passengers will feel heavy, where they will feel light, and where it is uncertain.

The Terminator Express

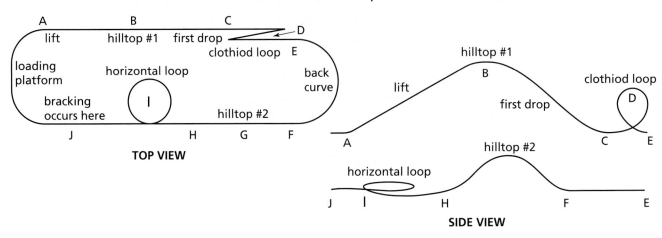

a) C (bottom of hill #1)

b) D (top of the vertical loop)

c) E (bottom of the vertical loop)

d) F (bottom of hill #2)

e) lift hill (going up at constant speed)

14. Using the diagram of the Terminator Express, indicate at which of the following points the centripetal force is up, when it is down, when it is zero, and when it is sideways.

a) C (bottom of hill #1)

b) D (top of the vertical loop)

c) E (bottom of the vertical loop)

d) F (bottom of hill #2)

e) lift hill (going up at constant speed)

f) horizontal loop

g) back curve

15. *Preparing for the Chapter Challenge*

The *Chapter Challenge* requires you to calculate the accelerations and forces on the roller coaster at different positions. In discussions with your teacher, determine whether the "calculations" should be comparisons of the forces at different positions or involve solving the equations for centripetal acceleration and force.

Inquiring Further

Circular motion on a swing

Imagine that you are swinging back and forth on a playground swing. Use the ideas developed in this section (centripetal acceleration and centripetal force) to explain how the contact force between you and the swing seat changes as you swing back and forth. If you have the opportunity, ride on a swing and pay close attention to how the force that the seat exerts on you changes as you swing back and forth and how that force changes if you get the swing to higher heights.

Section 8 Work and Power: Getting to the Top

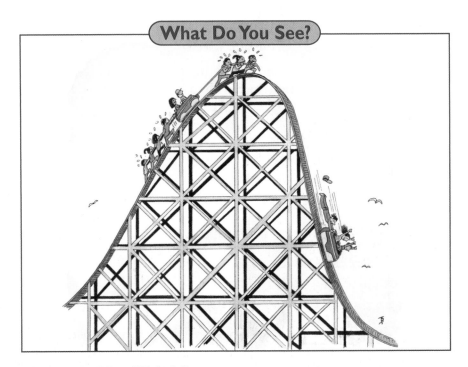

What Do You See?

Learning Outcomes

In this section, you will

- **Calculate** and compare the product of force and distance for lifting an object up a ramp to the same height for different angles of the ramp.

- **Define** work in terms of force *F* and displacement, *d*, in the direction of the force.

- **Explain** the relationship between work and gravitational potential energy and spring potential energy.

- **Define** power as the rate of doing work and the units of power as watts.

What do You Think?

The greatest drop for a roller coaster is 125 m (400 ft). The roller coaster must be pulled up to that height to get the ride started.

- **Does it take more energy to pull the roller coaster up a steep incline than a gentle incline?**

- **Why is it more difficult to walk up a steep incline than a gentle incline?**

Record your ideas about these questions in your *Active Physics* log. Be prepared to discuss your response with your small group and the class.

Investigate

1. The roller coaster at the top of the hill is ready to go. It goes up and down the hills and around the curves without any energy input. An idealized roller coaster would keep going forever. The car on the track pictured will go from point A to B to C to D to E to F to G. It will then reverse and go from G to F to E to D to C to B to A. It will then begin the trip again. Of course, in a real system some of the kinetic energy and gravitational potential energy will be converted to other forms of energy. Friction turns the mechanical energy into thermal energy, sound energy, and so on, and the roller coaster carts will eventually stop.

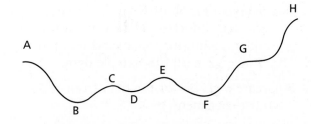

 a) Why do you think that the roller coaster cannot scale a higher hill than the one from which it began?

2. You will now investigate the force required to lift a roller-coaster cart to a certain height. You will use a cart and a ramp in your classroom. You can pull the cart to the top of the ramp with the use of a spring scale. The spring scale will indicate the force required to pull the cart.

A meter stick can be used to record the distance that the cart moved along the ramp. You can then vary the distance along the ramp by varying the ramp angle *while keeping the height to which you raise the cart the same.*

The ramp should be measured from the bottom of the ramp to the height of the support for the ramp.

> ⚠️ Be careful when lifting and lowering the weight, as it could cause injury if it were to fall. Make smooth, unhurried movements.

Height remains constant as you change the angle.

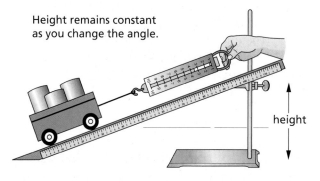

height

 a) Create a data table in which you can record the force required to pull the cart up the ramp the four different distances at the four different angles.

 b) Measure the force required to pull the cart up the ramp to a specified height at constant speed. Reminder: You must always pull the cart to the same height and parallel to the ramp. How will you determine if the speed is constant?

 c) Measure the distance that the cart travels along the ramp from the bottom to the specified height.

3. Complete your investigation.

 a) Record your information in your data table.

 b) What conclusion can you reach about the force required to move the cart and the distance the cart moves along the ramp to attain a specific height?

4. Any time you take measurements, there is some uncertainty in the measurement. When you weigh yourself on a scale, the weight reading may be off by a little bit. If the scale reads 143 lb, you may actually weigh 143 lb and a few ounces. The scale does not give you an exact measurement. No measurement is ever exact.

 a) What are the uncertainties in your measurements of distance? Could your measurement of distance be off by as much as 3 cm? Could your measurement of distance be off by as much as 1 cm? What is the largest amount that your distance measurement may be off? Write down this value with the notation ± to signify that you may have been under or over by that amount. For instance, if you think that your distance measurement could have been off by 2 cm, you would write this as ±2 cm.

Active Physics

b) Record the uncertainties in your measurements of force by noting the accuracy of your spring-scale reading. If the uncertainty is 0.1 N, record this as ±0.1 N. These uncertainties will be important when you analyze your data in the *Investigate*.

5. Another way that you can get the cart to the top of the incline is to lift it vertically. Use the spring scale to lift the cart vertically.

a) Record the force required to lift the cart vertically and the height that you lifted it.

6. There are other ways that the cart could be lifted to the top of the incline. For example, you could have an electric motor pull the cart to the top. Brainstorm and generate a list of at least three ways in which the cart could be brought to the top of the incline. (Brainstorming allows for all ideas to be included, even those that appear silly or impractical.)

a) Record your ideas in your *Active Physics* log.

7. Did you find that when the distance the cart travels to reach height *h* increases, the required force decreases? When one quantity increases and a second quantity decreases, this is referred to as an "inverse relation." If *F* is one quantity and *d* is the other quantity, one inverse relation can be described mathematically by the equation $F \cdot d = c$ where *c* is a constant. In the following table are some *F* and *d* values forming an inverse relation where $F \cdot d = 12$.

F	d	F•d=c
1	12	12
2	6	12
3	4	12
4	3	12
6	2	12
12	1	12

a) Make a graph of *F* (vertical axis) versus *d* (horizontal axis) to show the relationship for the inverse relation $F \cdot d = 12$ with this sample data.

8. Create a graph for the data from your experiment.

a) In the equation $F \cdot d = 12$, the product of the *F* and *d* values always equals 12. Does the product of the force and distance in your experiment always equal a certain value? Make the calculations and record the results on the side of your chart.

b) Why would the values in your experiment not be expected to be exactly the same?

c) For one pair of force and distance, repeat the calculation force × distance with the force value raised by the force uncertainty and the distance value increased by the distance uncertainty.

d) Now calculate the difference between the original product and the new product in *c*). That difference is a good estimate of the uncertainty to be associated with the results of your calculations in *Step 6*.

e) Do your results agree if you take this uncertainty into account? For example, one product might be 6.1 N•m , while another product is 6.3 N•m . If the uncertainty estimated for the product is 0.3 N•m , you see that the difference between the two products is less than the uncertainty, and you can say that "the results agree within the experimental uncertainty."

Physics Talk

WORK

The roller coaster must get to the top of the first hill to begin the ride. In the *Investigate*, you moved a cart to the top of an inclined ramp by applying a force with the spring scale over a certain distance and you find that the product of the force you applied and the distance through which it acted is the same, regardless of the slope of the ramp. In physics, the product of force multiplied by distance is called **work**. The work done by a force F on an object as the object undergoes a displacement parallel to the force is defined through the following equation:

Work = force (parallel to the displacement) × displacement

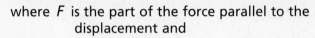
$$W = F \bullet d$$

where F is the part of the force parallel to the displacement and

d is the displacement.

Note that the definition of work involves only that part of the force that is in the same direction or opposite direction to the displacement.

In this *Investigate*, the spring scale pulled the lab cart up the incline and the force was in the same direction as the displacement. You found that the product of force times displacement (work) was the same regardless of the angle of the incline. The force was larger for a steeper incline, but the distance along the incline was smaller. The product of the force and distance moved along the ramp was always the same. That quantity was the work that was done by the spring scale on the cart. The work done by a force on an object is a measure of the energy transferred to the object. In the case of the cart, the gravitational potential energy (*GPE*) of the cart increased as a result of the work done by the spring scale. Recall that gravitational potential energy is energy of position relative to the surface of Earth or of an identified surface such as a table or a floor. Pulling the cart up the ramp changed the elevation of the cart and increased its gravitational potential energy.

To bring the roller coaster to the top of its first hill, work must be applied to the roller-coaster system. The work will increase the energy of the roller-coaster system. The work to lift the roller coaster up the ramp to a certain height is identical to the work to lift it vertically to that height. When you lift it vertically, the force required is about equal in magnitude to the weight of the cart. The vertical displacement is the height that it must be lifted.

$$W = F \bullet d$$
$$= \text{weight} \times \text{height}$$
$$= mgh$$

Physics Words

work: the product of displacement and the force in the direction of the displacement; the energy transferred to an object.

Active Physics

The work done on the roller coaster is *mgh*. This is equal to the change in gravitational potential energy, *GPE*, of the roller coaster.

Sample Problem I

A lab cart that weighs 300 N is lifted to the top of an incline 2 m above the ground.

a) What is the work done on the cart by the force that lifted the cart?

b) How much force would be required to lift the same cart to the same height using a 10-m long inclined ramp?

a) *Strategy:* The force required to lift the cart at constant velocity is equal in magnitude to its weight. The displacement is the height that the cart was lifted. The force and the displacement are both in the vertical direction.

> **Given:**   **Solution:**
>
> $F = 300$ N $W = F \bullet d$
>
> $d = 2$ m $W = (300 \text{ N})(2 \text{ m})$
>
> $= 600$ N$\bullet$m
>
> $= 600$ J

b) *Strategy:* The work required to lift the cart would be identical since the cart began at the same height and ended at the same height. Since you know the new displacement, you can find the new force.

> **Given:**   **Solution:**
>
> $W = 600$ J $W = F \bullet d$
>
> $d = 10$ m $F = \dfrac{W}{d}$
>
> $= \dfrac{600 \text{ N} \bullet \text{m}}{10 \text{ m}}$
>
> $= 60$ N

By using the ramp, you need a force of only 60 N to slide the cart up the ramp, instead of the 300 N to lift it. That is why truckers use a ramp when loading a truck. The ramp is considered to be a simple machine. The same work is done, but with much less force. Of course, the force must be applied over a longer distance because the energy transfer is the same.

More Roller-Coaster Energy

The roller-coaster car is usually raised with electrical energy supplied by a motor. Electrical energy can be calculated by measuring the voltage, current, and time. Creating steam to push it up the incline could also have raised the roller-coaster cart. In this method, the heat energy can also be calculated. In all of these methods, work is done by the spring, by the electricity, or by the heat. The roller-coaster system gains that amount of energy. The roller coaster has increased its *GPE* by that amount.

In any system, the total energy remains the same. This is an organizing principle of physics and is referred to as the conservation of energy.

Although you treat the roller-coaster's energy as primarily *KE* and *GPE*, real roller coasters have some energy transferred to other forms such as heat energy and sound energy. There is work done by friction and work done by air resistance. This work removes *KE* and *GPE* from the roller coaster. The work done by friction, for instance, becomes heat energy that is dissipated into the air surrounding the roller coaster.

Braking the Roller Coaster

Your roller coaster must have a means of stopping the cars at the end of the ride. Normally, brakes stop the coaster cars. The brakes use friction to convert the *KE* of the car's motion into thermal energy. The brakes might fail; so you need to have a back-up mechanism to stop the coaster cars. One way to do this is to have a large spring that the car can compress. As the spring is compressed, the *KE* of the cars is stored as spring potential energy. The expression for spring potential energy is $\frac{1}{2}kx^2$, where x is the distance that the springs are stretched or compressed.

Power

Sometimes it is important to know how fast work is done. In this *Investigate*, you pulled the lab cart up the incline. You could have pulled it up with a variety of speeds. To take the time into account, you divide the work done by the time elapsed. The result is called **power**. The definition of power is

$$\text{power} = \frac{\text{work done}}{\text{time elapsed}}$$

$$P = \frac{W}{\Delta t}$$

Note that the scientific definition of power is different from the ordinary usage of the word in sentences like, "I have power over you," or "She has lots of political power."

Physics Words

power: the work done divided by the time elapsed; the speed at which work is done and energy is transferred.

Active Physics

Sample Problem 2

Tomas runs up the stairs in 24 s. His weight is 700 N and the height of the stairs is 10 m.

a) What is the work done by Tomas to get to the top of the stairs?

b) How much power must Tomas supply?

Given: $F = 700$ N

$d = 10$ m

Strategy: You can use the definition for work and power to solve this problem. Since it is assumed that Tomas goes up the stairs at a constant speed, the force acting upward on Tomas must equal his weight.

Solution:

a) $W = F \bullet d$

$= (700 \text{ N})(10 \text{ m})$

$= 7000$ J

b) $P = \dfrac{W}{\Delta t}$

$= \dfrac{7000 \text{ J}}{24 \text{ s}}$

$= 290$ J/s or 300 J/s

Physics Words

watt: the SI unit for power; 1 W = 1 J/s.

Checking Up

1. When a spring scale is used to do work pulling a cart to the top of an incline, where has the energy gone when the cart is at rest at the top?

2. Where does the roller coaster get its gravitational potential energy when it is at the top of the first hill?

3. Why do truckers use a ramp when loading a truck if the work required is the same with or without a ramp?

4. When the brakes stop a roller coaster, what happens to the coaster's kinetic energy?

5. What is the unit for power?

Notice that the unit for power is joules per second, which is given the name **watts**. You are familiar with the power ratings of light bulbs in watts. You may have heard of horsepower as another unit for power. One horsepower is the energy output of a horse over a specific time. One horsepower is approximately 750 W (watts). A "one horsepower electric motor" uses electrical energy at a rate of about 750 W.

Sometimes the letter W is used for watts. Be sure not to confuse this W with the *W* used for work.

Active Physics
Plus

+Math	+Depth	+Concepts	+Exploration
♦	♦	♦	

Direction of Force in Work Done

It may seem that the force would always be in the same direction as the displacement. This is not always the case. Consider a push lawn mower. The push lawn mower has no motor. It moves because someone pushes it.

The force is applied along the handle of the lawn mower. The displacement of the lawn mower is the distance along the ground. The force and the displacement are not in the same direction, but there is some work done. That is, there is some energy transfer to the mower.

Although the entire force is not in the same direction as the displacement, some of the force is in the same direction as the displacement.

That part of the force is called $F_{\parallel}$. The symbol $\parallel$ stands for parallel. This force is parallel to the displacement

The force along the handle can be broken into its two vector components by finding the horizontal and vertical forces that, when added together, would be identical

to the original vector. In the diagram on the left, the horizontal and vertical component forces are approximately equal in size. The symbol $\perp$ stands for perpendicular. This force is perpendicular to the displacement.

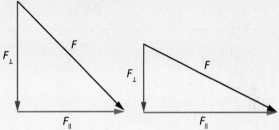

In the diagram on the right, the horizontal vector is much larger than the vertical component. Most of the force applied to the handle is now in the same direction as the displacement. Even though the total force is identical (note that the length of the force vector is the same in each diagram), the horizontal component is larger as the angle between the handle and the ground gets smaller. The same total force and the same displacement, but more work is done when the horizontal component is greater.

Why then don't you push the lawn mower with a small angle? Although more work would be done, it would hurt your back. Therefore, you sacrifice some work in order to make using the lawnmower more comfortable.

1. A student is asked to use a window pole to slide a window up. If the window moves the same distance up, is the work applied equal in the two cases shown on the next page? Is the force applied equal in the two cases?

443

Active Physics

2. A child is seated in a cart. Explain why it is easier to pull the child with a longer rope? (Hint: Draw two diagrams — one for a short rope and one for a long rope.)

Spring Energy

Recall the pop-up toy investigation. In that *Investigate*, the potential energy stored in the spring was converted into the kinetic energy of the toy. How much energy was stored when the toy spring was compressed? The force of a spring that obeys Hooke's law is $F = kx$. The force is not constant but changes as the

stretch or compression of the spring changes. The spring force is zero when the spring is not compressed at all and a maximum value of kx when the spring is compressed the maximum distance x. If you compress the spring a distance x, then the average force that you exert on the spring will be $\frac{1}{2}kx$.

For an ideal spring, the force that compresses the spring must be equal to the force that the spring pushes back with. The work done on the spring is

$$W = F_{\parallel}d$$

$$= \left(\frac{1}{2}kx\right)x$$

$$= \frac{1}{2}kx^2$$

The same expression applies if the spring is stretched by the distance x.

The work done on the spring is equal to the potential energy stored in the spring (*SPE*).

1. Could you get your roller coaster to the top of its first hill using the energy stored in a (very large) spring? What would be the advantages and disadvantages of starting the roller coaster that way?

What Do You Think Now?

At the beginning of this section, you were asked the following:

- **Does it take more energy to pull the roller coaster up a steep incline than a gentle incline?**

- **Why is it more difficult to walk up a steep incline than a gentle incline?**

Revise your answers to these questions using the concepts of work and energy. Relate your answers to the *Investigate* activities. Discuss your revisions with other students in your group.

444

Essential Questions

What does it mean?

Lifting the roller coaster to the top of the first hill requires work. Work is the crucial concept in this section. Explain what work means as a scientific concept.

How do you know?

Physicists prefer to express concepts in mathematical form. The concept of work involves the product of force and displacement as long as the two are parallel to each other. Describe the evidence from this section that shows that it is the product of force and displacement in the direction parallel to the force that is important for work.

Why do you believe?

Connects with Other Physics Content	Fits with Big Ideas in Science	Meets Physics Requirements
Force and motion	Conservation laws	✻ Optimal prediction and explanation

✻ Conservation of energy is an organizing principle of physics. In a roller coaster, losses in gravitational potential energy (*GPE*) produce gains in kinetic energy (*KE*). Work by an external force can add to or remove from energy to the roller coaster. Give an example of a force doing work on the coaster to either increase or decrease the total energy of the coaster.

Why should you care?

Scientists often use everyday words in ways that don't agree with everyday usage. This precision in language is crucial to the communication of scientific ideas. Compare some examples of the scientific meaning of work with the common use of the work that shows up in everyday life. How will what you learned about work in this section help you with your challenge?

Reflecting on the Section and the Challenge

A roller-coaster ride always begins with a slow, suspenseful ride to the top of the first hill. On the way up, the roller coaster is designed to shake a bit and to make a few extra noises in order to add to the drama. The roller coaster is gaining gravitational potential energy (*GPE)* on the way up. The motor is performing work on the roller coaster cart. Work is a precisely defined term in physics: $W = F \cdot d$. The work supplied by the motor increases the energy of the roller coaster. At the top of the incline, the motor is disengaged and the roller coaster is on its own. There is some work by friction with the air and track that removes energy from the roller coaster. At the end of the ride, the brakes are applied and negative work is done because force and distance are in opposite directions. The kinetic energy of the roller coaster cars is converted to thermal (heat) energy by the brakes.

In designing your roller coaster, you will have to include a motor to lift the roller coaster. You will have to decide on the slope of the track going up and the time you want the ride to take to get to the top of the first hill. Work and energy will be useful ways of describing what is needed in your design. You will also want to know how fast this work is done. For that you will use the concept of power where power = (work done) ÷ (time elapsed).

Physics to Go

1. A lab cart starts at the top of the incline. It slides down the incline a distance *l* and comes to rest after compressing a spring a distance *x*.

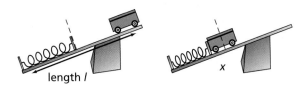

length *l*

x

a) Compare the *GPE* of the cart at the top of the incline and at the bottom.

b) How much work was done on the cart by the force of gravity (the cart's weight) as the cart went from the top to the bottom?

c) How much work was done on the cart by the spring as the spring was compressed?

d) What is the spring's *SPE* when it is compressed by the distance *x*?

e) Describe the total energy of the cart just before it hits the spring.

f) At which point does the cart begin to slow down?

2. Calculate the work done in the following situations:

a) A waiter applies a force of 150 N to hold a tray filled with plates on his shoulder. He then moves 7 m toward the kitchen door. What is the work done on the tray by the waiter?

b) A bowler lifts a 60-N bowling ball from the rack to his chest, a vertical distance of 0.5 m. What is the work done on the bowling ball by the bowler?

c) A girl pulls her sled up a hill. The length of the hill is 40 m and the pulling force required was 75 N. What is the work done by the girl on the sled if she pulls the rope on the sled while the string is parallel to the hill?

d) The weight of a dumbbell is 500 N. It is lifted over a body-builder's head, a distance of 0.7 m. What is the work done by the body-builder on the dumbbell?

3. Why are you told to conserve energy if the conservation of energy tells you that energy is always conserved? Create a better way of saying "conserve energy."

4. If you were to fill the lab cart you used in the *Investigate* with clay to represent the people in the roller coaster, what would have changed in the experiment?

5. An electric motor lifts a roller-coaster car that weighs 10,000 N to the top of the first hill that is 20 m above the ground. To add suspense, the ride up takes 150 s.

    a) Calculate the work done by the motor.

    b) Calculate the power of the motor.

6. ***Preparing for the Chapter Challenge***
   In the Terminator Express roller coaster, describe one trip of the coaster car around the ramp in terms of work and energy.

Inquiring Further

Power from an electric motor

Have the lab cart pulled up to the top of the incline with a motor. Measure the energy of the motor using voltage, current, and time. Compare the energy from the motor with the increase in *GPE* of the cart.

Active Physics

Section 9 Force and Energy: Different Insights

What Do You Think?

"The Snake" roller coaster stays at ground level throughout the ride. The passengers move left, then right, then left again.

- **Which parts of The Snake will be the most thrilling?**

- **If the speed of The Snake always remains the same, why will it still be fun?**

Record your ideas about these questions in your *Active Physics* log. Be prepared to discuss your response with your small group and the class.

Investigate

Part A: Energy and Forces in a Roller Coaster

1. Your study of roller coasters has actually taken two turns. You have investigated energy changes in roller coasters. You have also investigated forces and accelerations in roller coasters.

 a) Copy this beginning of a concept map into your log.

Learning Outcomes

In this section, you will

- **Describe** instances in which two cars will attain the same speed but require different times to reach those speeds.

- **Recognize** that force is described by vectors and energy is described by scalars.

- **Explain** how force and energy considerations provide different insights into roller-coaster rides.

- **Discover** whether energy or force considerations are more appropriate for analyzing aspects of roller-coaster rides.

```
         Roller coaster
        /              \
   Energy          Forces and
                   accelerations
```

A concept map is a way to organize your thoughts. It serves as a good review of what you have learned. Creating a concept map often helps you increase your understanding. On a set of note-sized pieces of paper (or sticky-note paper), write down at least four things you know about energy and how it relates to roller coasters. Each note should have one concept only. (Review *Sections 2 and 3* for assistance.)

2. Sort the concepts into a map that connects the concepts in a logical fashion. Add these concepts to your log.

3. On a new set of note-sized pieces of paper (or sticky-note paper), write down at least four things you know about forces and accelerations and how they relate to roller coasters. Each note should have one concept only. (Review *Sections 1, 4, 5 and 6* for assistance.)

4. Sort the concepts into a map. Add these concepts to your log.

5. The left half of your map reminds you of the relationships between energy concepts. The right half of your map reminds you of the relationships among force and acceleration concepts.

   a) Is there a bridge between these two sides of the map? Describe how energy is related to forces and accelerations. (Review *Section 7* for assistance.)

You use both energy and force approaches to understand roller coasters because they both provide you with valuable information. Sometimes it is easier to look at a roller coaster as an energy ride, while other times it is best to look at a roller coaster as a force ride. As you become more comfortable with physics, you will become better at matching what you want to know with the energy or the force approach. Sometimes you need both and sometimes they are redundant.

6. In the roller coaster below, the initial height of the roller coaster is given.

   a) At which two points does the roller coaster have the same speed if friction is negligible?

   b) How did you determine your answer? Write down your approach in your log.

   c) At which point would the roller-coaster car experience the largest contact (normal) force from the track? Write down in your log how you arrived at an answer.

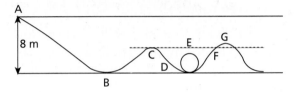

7. Describe how the new roller coaster shown below is different from the roller coaster in Step 6.

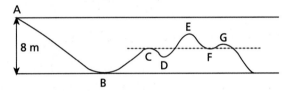

   a) In this roller coaster, at which two points does the roller coaster have the same speed if friction is insignificant?

   b) How did you determine your answer? Write down your approach in your log.

8. In either roller coaster, part of the track could have been replaced with horizontal track indicated by the dotted line.

   a) Why would the flat track be less fun than the roller-coaster track?

9. Look at the following diagram.

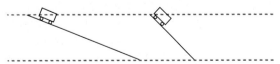

   a) Using energy principles, predict which cart would have the greater speed when it reaches the bottom.

Active Physics

b) Predict which car will get to the bottom in the least time. On what did you base your response? Record your explanation in your log.

Part B: Using Vectors to Describe a Path

1. Your teacher will give you a penny or a piece of wrapped candy.

a) Record the date stamped on the penny or write your initials on the candy wrapper. Hide the penny or piece of candy somewhere in the room.

b) Provide a set of detailed instructions to allow another student to find your penny or piece of candy if they start at your desk.

2. Exchange directions and try to find your partner's penny or piece of candy.

a) Did their instructions include how far you have to walk?

b) Did their instructions include any changes in direction (left turns or right turns)?

c) Did their instructions include reaching up or down?

d) Rewrite the instructions so that each instruction describes how far the person should move in meters and in which direction.

e) Compare this new set of directions with your first set. What advantages and disadvantages does each set have?

Physics Talk

ADDING SCALARS AND ADDING VECTORS

You can walk 30 m east. You can ride at 60 mph toward Mexico. Both descriptions include a number and a direction. Both are vectors. There are some descriptions that include a number, but no direction. There are 26 students in the classroom. The temperature is 18°C. Physicists have found that whether a number has a direction or not is an extremely important distinction. You can understand the world better if you recognize which quantities can have directions and deal with them accordingly.

It is fairly obvious that some quantities, like force, always have directions. Some quantities, like your age, never have direction. There are some quantities, like how fast you are traveling, that can include direction. Your car can be traveling at 30 mph or you can describe the car traveling at 30 mph north.

Recall that a quantity with both a number (often referred to as magnitude) and a direction is called a vector. A quantity with a number and no direction is a scalar.

Scalars are easy to add, subtract, multiply, and divide. If you walk 15 km and then walk another 20 km, the total distance traveled is 35 km. After walking 35 km, you know how tired you will be and how worn your shoes will be. This scalar quantity is called distance. Traveling from New York to Florida, your average speed might be 50 mph. This takes into account the total distance traveled and the total time, but does not take into account any turns you made. Speed is also a scalar.

Displacement is described by a vector. You may walk 15 km north and then walk another 20 km east; both displacements have a magnitude (the distance traveled) and a direction. Your total displacement is only 25 km. To add vectors, you must draw them and use vector addition. In this case, when the two vectors are perpendicular to each other, vector addition is an application of the Pythagorean theorem. You can also draw the diagram to scale and measure the distance and the angle. The distance can be measured using a ruler and the scale of the diagram. Using a protractor, you find the angle is close to 53° east of north (east of the north direction).

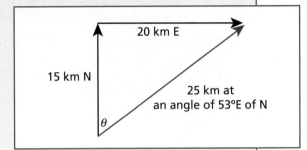

20 km E

15 km N

25 km at
an angle of 53°E of N

θ

Energy – A Scalar Quantity

Energy is a scalar and addition of scalars is simple. As you explored in earlier activities, the roller-coaster ride may have *GPE* (gravitational potential energy) and *KE* (kinetic energy). It may have used electrical energy to lift the roller coaster to the top of the first hill. All energies can be calculated, and they are all measured in the same units, joules. To find the total energy at any place or at any time, you just add up all the energies. This is what makes the roller-coaster analysis using energies so powerful. After the roller coaster begins moving downhill, the sum of *GPE* and *KE* remains the same. The roller coaster begins with *GPE* and as the coaster car moves, the *GPE* converts to *KE* as the roller coaster picks up speed and then converts the energy back to *GPE* as the cart goes higher and loses speed. Whatever the energy of the roller coaster is at the beginning of the ride, that is the energy at all times as long as friction is not significant. If two points on the roller-coaster ride have the same height, then they must have the same *GPE*. If they have the same *GPE*, then they also have identical *KE*. It doesn't matter what the cart did between the two points. It may have gone up, down, or in a loop-the-loop, but the *KE* will be the same at all points a specified distance above the ground.

In this *Investigate*, you looked at a roller coaster in *Step 6*. The speeds of the coaster carts are the same at points C and F. Both points C and F have the same height and therefore have the same *GPE*. Since all points on the roller coaster have the same total mechanical energy (*GPE* + *KE*) then both points must have the same *KE*. The same *KE* implies the same speed ($KE = \frac{1}{2}mv^2$).

In the roller coaster in *Step 7* of this section, the speeds of the coaster cars were still the same at points C and F even though the track changed between C and F.

In roller-coaster physics, energy considerations tell you three things:

Active Physics

- The total mechanical energy (*GPE* + *KE*) is the same at every point (as long as friction is not significant or motors do not add energy).

- The *GPE* depends only on the height from a reference position (*GPE* = *mgh*) since the mass and the gravitational force remain the same.

- If two points on a roller coaster have the same height, the roller coaster is moving at the same speed at those two points.

Energy considerations are path independent. You can look at the energy at one point and compare it to the energy at a later point. The energy will remain the same. It does not matter what happens between the places that are of interest.

In the four roller-coaster sections shown in the diagram, the coaster cars begin at the top with zero *KE* and 20,000 J of *GPE*. When they reach the bottom, all will have the same *KE* (kinetic energy). This means that they will all have the same speed. To find this *KE* or speed, you only have to look at the beginning point and the final point. The path does not affect the final speed since you are not considering friction as a factor.

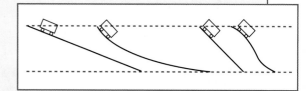

Force – A Vector Quantity

Although the roller-coaster cars all get to the bottom with the same speed, they do not get there in the same time. To find the time, you would have to look at the forces and this becomes a vector problem. In all tracks, the force of gravity is always down. The normal contact force between the track and the carts is always perpendicular to the track.

The straight tracks are the easiest to analyze. The force of gravity and the normal force remain in fixed directions. You move down the incline and go faster and faster. The steeper the slope, the larger the gravitational force down the incline and the quicker you get to the bottom. It is a big acceleration for a short time and you reach the maximum speed. On a small incline, there is a small resultant force down the incline. It is a small acceleration for a long time, but you reach the same maximum speed.

The inclines with shifting directions add to the thrill. Your speed changes as you move to different heights. As you move closer to the ground, your speed increases. The normal force (the force of the track on the carts) and the contact force of the cart on you are always changing direction. This causes you to accelerate in lots of different directions. The changes in the acceleration (both in size and in direction) give you that bouncy feeling and the thrill of the roller coaster. The diagram on the next page shows the gravitational force and normal forces at different points on a roller coaster.

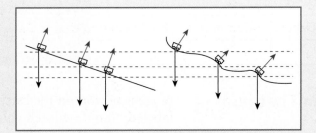

- On the straight incline, the gravitational force and the normal force remain in fixed directions. The car has an acceleration that is constant in magnitude and direction.

- On the curved incline, the normal force changes direction (it must be perpendicular to the incline) and changes in magnitude. The cart has an acceleration that changes both in magnitude and in direction. This provides big thrills.

- The speeds of the carts are identical on the two inclines at the points shown. When the heights above the ground are the same, the *GPE* is the same. If the *GPE* is the same and the total energy is the same, the *KE* is the same. If the *KE* is the same, then the speed is the same.

When to Consider Force and When to Consider Energy

The mathematics of energy conservation requires simple addition. The mathematics of forces and accelerations requires vector addition. When the roller coaster looks complex, with lots of curves, physicists think of energy first because of the ease of using simple addition rather than vector addition.

When asked about how much time something will take, physicists think about forces and accelerations because acceleration is the change in velocity with respect to time.

Force and energy are related. The force of gravity does work on the roller coaster and increases its *KE*. Changes in energy always require work by a force. Work is a force applied over a distance $(W = F \bullet d)$.
The only external force doing work on the roller coaster once it is moving downward is gravity. There is positive work on the roller coaster since work increases the *KE* of the coaster carts. The normal force never does any work since it is always perpendicular to the displacement. No part of the normal force is ever in the direction the roller-coaster cart is moving.

Checking Up

1. What process is needed to add vector quantities?

2. Is energy a vector or a scalar? Is force a vector or a scalar?

3. For roller coasters, what three things do energy considerations tell you about the coaster at different points?

4. Does the energy of the roller coaster depend upon the path the roller coaster takes?

5. What is required to provide a change in the energy of a roller coaster?

+Math	+Depth	+Concepts	+Exploration	Active Physics
◆◆				*Plus*

Using the Pythagorean Theorem

1. A roller coaster at a 25° incline makes a sharp right turn as it descends the hill. The velocity of the roller-coaster cart is 5.0 m/s south before the turn. After the turn, the velocity of the roller-coaster cart is 12.0 m/s west but it is also pointing downward at an angle of 25°. Ignore the downward angle.

   a) Determine the change in velocity of the roller coaster using a vector diagram. Recall that $v_f - v_i$ is identical to $v_f + (-v_i)$.

   b) Determine the magnitude of the change in velocity of the roller coaster using the Pythagorean theorem. (Hint: Use your vector diagram of the two velocity vectors and the change in velocity vector.)

   c) Use a protractor to determine the direction of the change in velocity vector. Express your answer as an angle relative to the direction south.

2. How would your answer to *Question 1* change if you took into account the downward angle of the incline?

3. Just as you can find the length (magnitude) of the change in velocity vector mathematically using the Pythagorean theorem, you can also find the angle. You may have learned in mathematics that the tangent function of an angle in a right triangle is the ratio of the length of the side opposite the angle to the length of the side adjacent to the angle. The inverse tangent button on the calculator, often labeled "tan⁻¹" will tell you the angle if you know the lengths of the sides. For the velocities given in *Question 1*, you can find the angle for the change in velocity vector. First, divide the side opposite the angle (= 5) by the side adjacent to the angle (= 12). By pushing the "inverse tan" button, the calculator will provide the angle of 23°.

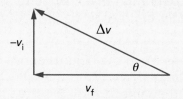

4. Displacement is described by a vector. Suppose that you walk 15 km north and then walk another 20 km east; both displacements have a magnitude (the distance traveled) and a direction. In this case, your net displacement from your starting point is only 25 km.

   a) Draw a vector diagram for this situation. Draw the displacement vectors carefully to scale and determine the magnitude (length) and direction (angle) of the net displacement vector from the diagram.

   b) Use the Pythagorean theorem to find the length of the net-displacement vector.

   c) Use the tangent function to find the angle for the net-displacement vector.

   d) Compare the results of *b*) and *c*) with the results found from your vector diagram.

What Do You Think Now?

At the beginning of this section, you were asked the following:

• **Which parts of The Snake will be the most thrilling?**

• **If the speed of The Snake always remains the same, why will it still be fun?**

Review and, if necessary, revise the answers to these questions in terms of forces acting on the riders at various parts of the ride. The Snake roller coaster stays at ground level throughout the ride. The passengers move left, then right, then left again. Discuss your revisions with other students in your group.

Physics
Essential Questions

What does it mean?

Scientists introduce concepts like force and energy that help you understand many different phenomena. The crucial concepts in this section are force and energy. Explain what force means and what energy means and how they are different.

How do you know?

Science often provides several ways of understanding a given situation. Describe an example of some aspect of a roller-coaster ride in this section where force is a useful concept. Describe an example of some aspect of a roller-coaster ride in this section where energy is a useful concept.

Why do you believe?

Connects with Other Physics Content	Fits with Big Ideas in Science	Meets Physics Requirements
Forces and motion	Conservation laws	✳ Good, clear explanation, no more complex than necessary

✳ For concepts to be useful in science they should apply to many different situations. Force and energy are important concepts in all areas of science. Describe some examples from other *Active Physics* units where force and energy play a role. Explain how force or energy, or both, help you understand what is going on in those examples.

Why should you care?

Both force and energy help you understand many different situations. Give some examples of where energy shows up in everyday life. (Hint: A calorie is a unit of energy; a kilowatt-hour is a unit of energy.)

Give some examples of where force shows up in everyday life. (Hint: A pound is a unit of force; a ton is a unit of force.)

How will what you learned in this section about force and energy help you with your challenge?

Reflecting on the Section and the Challenge

The thrill of the roller coaster comes from the changing velocities. You can analyze the changes in speed using energy considerations. Energy is a scalar. *GPE* can be easily calculated at every point on the roller coaster. Once you know the *GPE*, you can find the *KE* and then determine how fast the roller coaster moves. Understanding the mathematics of energy is as simple as 3 + 4 = 7. Energies add with simple arithmetic just like all scalars.

You can also analyze the thrills of changing velocities by noting the forces acting on the roller coaster. Forces are described by vectors. Vectors have both magnitude and direction. When more than one force acts on a roller coaster (e.g., the gravitational force and the normal force), you have to add forces using vector arithmetic. You can always do this with a vector diagram. When the forces are perpendicular, you can readily use mathematics and the Pythagorean theorem to find magnitude, and a protractor or more mathematics to determine the angle and direction.

Designing a roller coaster requires you to know how fast it will be going at each point along the path. You can use energy considerations to determine this.

You will also have to know how large the forces are because you will need to figure out the strength of the materials needed to provide the forces by the track. If too large a force is applied, the track may break. Adding the forces can provide you with this information.

You will also have to know the accelerations of the passengers. Too large of an acceleration or a change in acceleration and the riders may get sick or become unconscious. Newton's second law relating forces and accelerations ($F_{net} = ma$) can help you with this.

Making an exciting roller coaster requires changes in forces. The whips and turns and the ups and downs will change the speeds, the accelerations, and the forces on the passengers.

Physics to Go

1. A roller coaster makes a sharp right turn. The velocity of the roller coaster car is 5.0 m/s south before the turn and 5.0 m/s west after the turn.

   a) Determine the change in velocity of the roller coaster cart using a vector diagram.

   b) Determine the change in velocity of the roller coaster cart using the Pythagorean theorem. You can figure out the angle in this case from the vector diagram.

2. All roller coasters that begin at the same height have the same speeds at the bottom. Explain why these two roller-coaster tracks provide the same change in speed when a cart goes from the top to the bottom.

3. Identify the following as vectors or scalars:

   a) distance

   b) displacement

   c) speed

   d) velocity

   e) acceleration

   f) force

   g) kinetic energy

   h) potential energy

   i) work

4. Which of the following statements are about vectors and which are about scalars?

   a) Mark traveled 30 km.

   b) Maia's weight (the force of gravity on her) is 600 N.

   c) The roller-coaster car had a kinetic energy of 1200 J.

   d) The cart was traveling at 30 m/s toward the center of town.

5. Sometimes it is easier to look at a roller coaster as an energy ride, while other times it is best to look at a roller coaster as a force ride. Give an example of each approach.

6. a) Draw the forces acting on roller coaster 1 at points A, B, C, and D

   b) Draw the forces acting on roller coaster 2 at points A, B, C, and D.

   c) Why is it easier to use forces to analyze roller coaster 2?

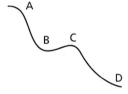

roller coaster 1

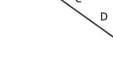

roller coaster 2

7. a) Label three points on roller coaster 3 that have the same *GPE*.

   b) Compare the total energies of the roller coaster at these points.

   c) Compare the *KE* of the roller coaster at these points.

   d) Why are you able to ignore the other points of the roller coaster when comparing the *GPE* and *KE* and total energy?

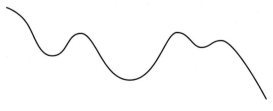

roller coaster 3

Active Physics

Section 10

Safety Is Required but Thrills Are Desired

What Do You See?

Learning Outcomes

In this section, you will

- **Calculate** the speed of the roller coaster at different positions using conservation of energy.

- **Calculate** the acceleration of the roller coaster at turns.

- **Determine** if the acceleration is below 4 *g* for safety.

- **Determine** if the speed at the top of a loop is sufficient for safety concerns.

- **Construct** sounds and scenery to enhance the thrills of a roller-coaster ride.

What Do You Think?

Occasionally, people are severely injured or killed on a roller coaster. However, these type of accidents are rare.

- **Does the knowledge that people can get hurt or die on a roller coaster change the thrill of the ride?**

- **Would your answer change if you found out that one-half of all roller-coaster rides ended in the death of its passengers?**

Record your ideas about these questions in your *Active Physics* log. Be prepared to discuss your responses with your small group and the class.

Investigate

1. Safety is one of the criteria that you must meet in designing your roller coaster.

   a) List three reasons why safety is a major concern for roller-coaster designers.

   b) How safe is safe? Your answer may depend on what injuries you describe for the roller coaster. Nausea and vomiting are one type of injury, broken bones are a second type of injury, becoming unconscious is a third type of injury, and death is the greatest injury. For the four types of injuries listed, make an estimate of how many people could get injured on a roller coaster ride before it would be closed to the public. Be sure to include whether these are injuries in a day, a month, or a year.

2. Astronauts going into space have to withstand very large accelerations during rocket launch. After many tests of test pilots and race-car drivers, it was determined that people will become unconscious if the acceleration is greater than about 9 g (or 9 times the acceleration due to gravity, that is, 9×9.8 m/s^2). Some people black out at 5 g or 6 g. This unconsciousness results from the blood leaving the brain during the high acceleration.

The roller-coaster manufacturer has indicated that the maximum acceleration at any place on the roller coaster should not exceed 4 g (or 4 times the acceleration due to gravity, that is, 4×9.8 m/s^2).

a) At what locations on the roller coaster are there accelerations?

b) If the roller coaster were to fall straight down, what would be the acceleration?

c) Is this a safe acceleration?

d) If you find that your roller coaster accelerations are greater than 4 g at the position shown, what changes in speed or shape of the curve can be made to decrease the acceleration?

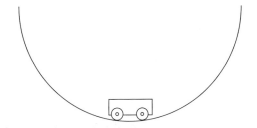

3. The roller-coaster designer can play all sorts of tricks to produce extra thrills on the same roller coaster.

a) Describe how you can add suspense to the trip up to the top of the first hill.

b) Describe how you can use sounds during the roller-coaster ride to add to the thrills.

4. The choice of scenery surrounding the roller coaster can also add to the thrill. The roller coaster can look like it will dive into water when it is descending. The roller coaster can look like it will hit a building when it rounds a curve.

a) Describe three visual effects through the use of scenery that will add to the thrill of your roller coaster.

5. Thrills can come from high speeds. Thrills more often come from acceleration (changing velocity with respect to time). Change in velocity can be a change in speed or direction.

a) Describe three ways in which you can add thrills to a roller-coaster design by having changes in velocity.

b) Describe three ways in which you can add thrills to a roller-coaster design by having changes in acceleration.

6. The photo shows a roller coaster at an amusement park.

a) Using what you have learned in this chapter, describe the different parts of the roller-coaster ride shown in the picture. Where are you likely to experience the most thrills? Why?

Active Physics

b) In the vertical loops you will notice that the track is more sharply curved at the top than in the curved sections between the loops? Why is the track designed that way? (Hint: Think about speed and the *g*'s you would pull on various parts of the loop.)

Physics Talk

ROLLER-COASTER SAFETY

The roller coaster has to be safe in order to be fun. Analysis of the safety requirements of the roller coaster is a valuable way of reviewing some of the physics in earlier sections. Your class and teacher can decide the level of mathematics that will be required for your challenge. In each of the examples below, there is both a qualitative and quantitative discussion.

You know from research with test pilots that people will not be safe if their acceleration is greater than 4 *g*. A free fall provides an acceleration of 1 *g*. Roller coasters may have steep inclines but they are generally not in free fall and therefore have an acceleration less than 1 *g* on straight inclines.

When the roller coaster rips around a corner or moves through the bottom of a vertical loop, the acceleration can be much more than 1 *g*. Analyze the acceleration at the bottom of a loop. The acceleration can be computed by recognizing that the roller coaster at this location is moving in an arc of a circle. The centripetal acceleration must be toward the center of the circle and can be calculated by using the equation

$$a = \frac{v^2}{r}$$

By varying the speed or the radius of the circle in the roller-coaster design, you can limit the acceleration to less than 4 *g*.

Qualitative (no numbers): Decreasing the speed at that point will lower the acceleration. This can be accomplished by changing the height from which the coaster descends. Less gravitational potential energy, *GPE*, will result in less kinetic energy, *KE*, and therefore a lower speed. Alternatively, you can make the curve gentler. This increases the radius of the curve and decreases the acceleration as well.

Sample Problem 1 (Quantitative – with numbers)

A roller-coaster car with a mass of 800 kg is traveling at 15.0 m/s at the bottom of a loop. The loop has a radius of 5.0 m.

a) What is the centripetal acceleration required to keep the car moving in a circle?

Strategy: Use the equation for centripetal acceleration.

Given: $v = 15.0$ m/s

$r = 5.0$ m

Solution: $a = \dfrac{v^2}{r}$

$= \dfrac{(15.0 \text{ m/s})^2}{5.0 \text{ m}}$

$= 45 \text{ m/s}^2$

This acceleration is greater than 4 g (4×9.8 m/s^2 = 39.2 m/s^2) and is therefore unsafe.

b) One way to lower this acceleration would be to lower the speed. Assume that the new design gives the coaster car a speed of 12.0 m/s. Calculate the centripetal acceleration if the car is moving in a circle.

Strategy: Use the equation for centripetal acceleration, again.

Given: $v = 12.0$ m/s

$r = 5.0$ m

Solution: $a = \dfrac{v^2}{r}$

$= \dfrac{(12.0 \text{ m/s})^2}{5.0 \text{ m}}$

$= 29 \text{ m/s}^2$

This acceleration is now less than 4 g (4×9.8 m/s^2 = 39.2 m/s^2) and is therefore safe.

c) Another way to lower the acceleration is to make the loop larger. Using the original speed of 15.0 m/s, calculate the centripetal acceleration if the radius of the loop were 7.0 m.

Strategy: Use the equation for centripetal acceleration, again.

Given: $v = 15.0$ m/s

$r = 7.0$ m

Solution: $a = \dfrac{v^2}{r}$

$= \dfrac{(15.0 \text{ m/s})^2}{7.0 \text{ m}}$

$= 32 \text{ m/s}^2$

This acceleration is now less than 4 g (4×9.8 m/s^2 = 39.2 m/s^2) and is therefore safe.

The largest centripetal acceleration (at the bottom of the loop) also requires the largest centripetal force. This maximum force will inform you as roller-coaster designer of the strength of materials required to build this part of the roller coaster. The force acting on the coaster car is a combination of its weight and the normal force from the track. The normal force required when the coaster car is moving in a circle at the bottom of the loop is much greater than the normal force that would support the car at rest at the bottom of the incline. The at-rest cart requires no net force. The normal force up (provided by the track) must equal the gravitational force (weight) down. This is shown with the first vector diagram to the right.

When the car is moving in a vertical circle, a centripetal force is required. The sum of the normal force from the track and the gravitational force must equal the centripetal force required. Since the gravitational force is down, the normal force, must be greater at the bottom of the loop to provide the additional upward force needed. This is shown in the second vector diagram to the right.

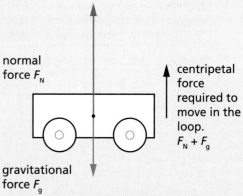

The centripetal force required can be calculated using Newton's second law:

$$F_{net} = ma.$$

In this case $F_{net} = \dfrac{mv^2}{r}$.

In this section, you equated an acceleration with the concept of pulling "g's." Pulling 4 g's is actually different that experiencing an acceleration of 4 x 9.8 m/s². For example, when you stand still on Earth your acceleration is 0 g's, but you are experiencing 1 g. Here, 1 g means you feel normal. The support force under your feet is equal to your weight. Experiencing 2 g's means that you feel twice as heavy as normal, because the support force (often normal force) is twice your weight. The heaviness that you experience is strictly based on the support force. When you are in free fall, your acceleration is 1 g, but you feel weightless because there is no support force.

In the chapter, it indicates that an acceleration of greater than 4 g's (as produced by $a = v^2/r$) is the maximum acceptable. Actually, if you are at the bottom of the loop, an acceleration of 4 g's will require a support of 5 g's (five times the rider's weight) and you will feel five times as heavy as normal. At the top of the loop, an acceleration of 4 g's only requires 3 g's of support force, because gravity is providing a force toward the center as well.

Sample Problem 2

A roller-coaster car with a mass of 800.0 kg is traveling at 15.0 m/s at the bottom of a loop. The loop has a radius of 5.0 m.

a) What is the centripetal force required to keep the car moving in the circle?

Strategy: Use Newton's second law to relate net force and acceleration.

Given:
$$v = 15.0 \text{ m/s}$$
$$r = 5.0 \text{ m}$$
$$m = 800.0 \text{ kg}$$

Solution:
$$F_{net} = ma = \frac{mv^2}{r}$$
$$= \frac{(800.0 \text{ kg})(15.0 \text{m/s})^2}{5.0 \text{ m}}$$
$$= 36,000 \text{ N}$$

This net force of 36,000 N up will allow the car to move in the vertical circle.

b) What is the normal force that the track exerts on the car?

Strategy: The normal force must be 36,000 N greater than the gravitational force to provide a net force of 36,000 N as required.

Solution: The gravitational force (weight) is:
$$F_w = mg = (800.0 \text{ kg})(9.8 \text{ m/s}^2)$$
$$= 7840 \text{ N}$$

Therefore, the normal force must equal 36,000 N + 7840 N = 43,840 N or about 44,000 N.

This indicates that the track and support structure of the roller coaster must be able to exert a force of at least 44,000 N or the track will break.

Similar calculations can be completed with the force required to make a turn on a horizontal part of the roller coaster and a turn where the roller coaster banks on its side as it whips around a turn.

Active Physics

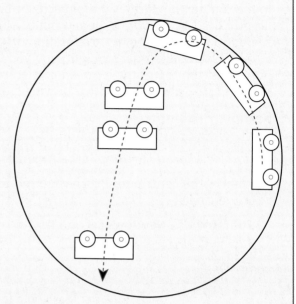

Another safety feature requires that the speed at the top of the loop is great enough to complete the loop. A cart that has too little speed will not make it to the top of the roller coaster and will not be able to move in the circle. It will fall to the ground, as shown in the diagram at the right.

If gravity were the only force acting at the top of the roller coaster, then the car must require a centripetal acceleration equal to that of free fall.

Sample Problem 3

What is the minimum speed required at the top of the loop to ensure that the coaster car does not leave the track? The car has a mass of 800.0 kg. The loop has a radius of 5.0 m.

Strategy: The minimum speed pertains to the centripetal acceleration of 9.8 m/s². Using the equation for centripetal acceleration, you can find the required speed.

Given: $a = 9.8$ m/s²
$r = 5.0$ m

Solution: $a = \dfrac{v^2}{r}$

$$v = \sqrt{ar}$$

$$= \sqrt{(9.8 \text{ m/s}^2)(5.0 \text{ m})}$$

$$= 7.0 \text{ m/s}$$

A coaster car traveling with a speed of 7.0 m/s will be able to complete the upper part of the loop. A speed greater than 7.0 m/s will also be able to make the loop. The greater speed will require a larger centripetal force. The additional force will be provided by the track pushing down on the car. In real roller coasters, the cars have special attachments under the wheels to keep the cars on the track if, for some reason, the speed gets too low near the top of the loop.

Checking Up

1. What is the maximum safe acceleration for a roller coaster?

2. List two ways to keep the acceleration of coaster cart low enough to be safe.

3. At what part of the loop is the acceleration the greatest on a roller-coaster cart?

4. At what part of the loop is the normal force the greatest?

+Math	+Depth	+Concepts	+Exploration
◆◆			

More Quantitative (with numbers) Analysis

1. A roller-coaster car is traveling at 30.0 m/s at the bottom of a circular loop. The radius of the loop is 9.0 m.

   a) Using the conservation of mechanical energy,
   $$KE + GPE = constant$$
   $$mgh + \frac{1}{2}mv^2 = constant$$
   calculate the initial height of a roller-coaster car to give it a speed of 30.0 m/s at the bottom of a loop. At the highest point of the roller-coaster ride, the velocity is 0 m/s. At the bottom of the loop of the roller-coaster ride, the height h equals 0 m.

   b) Using the equation $a = \dfrac{v^2}{r}$, calculate the acceleration at the bottom of the loop.

   c) Is this a safe acceleration?

   d) At what speed would this loop with a radius of 9.0 m begin to be a safety concern?

   e) At what speed would a loop with a smaller radius of 7.0 m begin to be a safety concern?

   f) How fast would the roller-coaster car be traveling at the top of the loop? (Because the loop's radius is 9.0 m and the top of the loop is 18.0 m above the ground, the diameter is 18.0 m.) You must use the initial height of the roller coaster that you calculated above to solve this problem.

   g) Using the equation $a = \dfrac{v^2}{r}$, calculate the acceleration at the top of the loop.

   h) Is this a safe acceleration?

   i) There are two safety concerns regarding accelerations in a loop. The acceleration cannot exceed 4 g. This excessive acceleration would occur at the bottom of the loop, if at all. The acceleration at the top must be greater than 1 g (9.8 m/s²). If the acceleration required for circular motion at the top of the loop is less than 1 g, the roller-coaster car will leave the track and plummet to the ground. The speed at the top of the roller coaster must be large enough to require acceleration at least as great at 9.8 m/s².

   j) Describe if the results you found in b) – g) fit these safety limits.

2. The track must be strong enough to hold the roller-coaster car without breaking. You can calculate the minimum strength of a track by assuming that the roller-coaster car is filled with big football players or Sumo wrestlers.

   What force would a roller-coaster track on a horizontal section of track have to supply to hold up a car filled with passengers if the total mass were 1000.0 kg? (Remember the equation for weight is $F_w = mg$ where $g = 9.8$ N/kg.)

3. When the roller-coaster car makes turns, there must be a centripetal force pushing the roller-coaster car toward the center of the circle.

The following are three types of turns that will be analyzed:

- a sharp left turn on a flat track,

- a sharp left turn where the car is turned on its side and the track is vertical, and

- a loop where the car is moving in a vertical circle.

a) For each of the three turns, identify the direction of the force keeping the car moving in a circle.

b) For each of the three turns, identify the source of this force. (The force could be the force of friction, the gravitational force, the normal force, the force of tension on a rope, the force of the wheels in the track or any combination of these forces.)

4. A roller-coaster car has a mass of 1000.0 kg and takes a sharp left turn where the car is turned on its side and the track is vertical with a radius of 12.0 m and the car is moving at 15.0 m/s. Calculate the centripetal force required to keep the car moving in the curve.

5. A roller-coaster car has a mass of 1000.0 kg and takes a sharp left turn on a flat track with a radius of 12.0 m and the car is moving at 15.0 m/s. Calculate the centripetal force required to keep the car moving in the curve.

6. A roller-coaster car has a mass of 1000.0 kg and is about to enter a vertical loop that has a radius of 12.0 m. The car is moving at 15.0 m/s.

a) Calculate the centripetal force required to keep the car moving in the curve.

b) This centripetal force that you calculated is the sum of the normal force of the track up toward the center of the roller-coaster car and the force of gravity down to the ground. Copy the following diagram into your log:

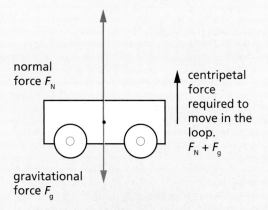

normal force F_N

centripetal force required to move in the loop.
$F_N + F_g$

gravitational force F_g

c) Calculate the force of gravity on the car.

d) Calculate the normal force on the car. This is the magnitude of the force that the tracks and frame of the roller-coaster structure must be able to exert on the car to keep it moving in a circle.

What Do You Think Now?

At the beginning of this section, you were asked the following:

- **Does the knowledge that people can get hurt or die on a roller coaster change the thrill of the ride?**

- **Would your answer change if you found out that one-half of all roller-coaster rides ended in the death of its passengers?**

Record you ideas about these questions now. What aspects of the roller-coaster ride are most likely to be dangerous if the ride is not properly designed? Describe how you would use what you have learned about the physics of roller coasters to make sure your roller-coaster ride is safe.

Physics
Essential Questions

What does it mean?

Scientific concepts are often useful in helping you understand safety issues. Explain why 4 g is the maximum acceleration that should be designed into the roller coaster. If a given design exceeded this acceleration, how could you alter the design?

How do you know?

Cars, trains, and planes can all go much faster than a roller-coaster ride, but don't produce the thrills of the roller-coaster ride. How do roller coasters produce the thrills?

Why do you believe?

Connects with Other Physics Content	Fits with Big Ideas in Science	Meets Physics Requirements
Forces and motion	✳ Models	Experimental evidence is consistent with models and theories

✳ Different scientific principles can explain the same phenomenon. Compare and contrast the use of forces and energy as ways to describe roller-coaster rides.

Why should you care?

Safety is a primary concern of any roller-coaster ride. How can you increase safety and increase thrills through the use of scenery surrounding your ride?

Reflecting on the Section and the Challenge

There is lots of creativity in designing a roller coaster. There is lots of creativity in designing a bridge, a building, and a table. All designs are constrained by the physics of the world.

A beautiful bridge must also be a bridge that does not collapse. In this section, you learned about the safety features that you must take into account in your design for the roller coaster. You have to ensure that the accelerations are never above 4 g. This will require you to design the curves and loops with radii that limit the accelerations. You must also make sure that if your roller coaster does have a loop, the cart will be able to complete the loop. You can vary the radius of any part of the track in the design. You can vary the velocity of the car by changing the launch height for the roller coaster. The higher the first hill, the more speed the coaster will have at the bottom. Safety is required, but thrills are desired. The section also discussed ways in which you can use sound and scenery to improve the thrills of your design.

Physics to Go

1. An engineering company submits a plan for a roller coaster. What factors will you check to ensure that the roller coaster is safe?

2. **Active Physics** **Plus** A roller-coaster car is traveling at 20.0 m/s at the bottom of a loop. The radius of the loop is 12.0 m.

   a) Using the conservation of mechanical energy ($KE + GPE$ = constant) $\left(mgh + \dfrac{1}{2}mv^2 = \text{constant}\right)$, calculate the initial height of a roller-coaster car when it starts from rest to give it a speed of 20.0 m/s at the bottom of a loop.

   b) Using the equation $a = \dfrac{v^2}{r}$, calculate the acceleration at the bottom of the loop.

   c) Is this a safe acceleration?

   d) At what speed would this loop with radius of 12.0 m begin to be a safety concern?

   e) At what speed would the acceleration in a loop with a smaller radius of 7.0 m begin to be a safety concern?

3. A roller-coaster car is traveling at 25.0 m/s at the bottom of a loop. The radius of the loop is 10.0 m.

   a) Calculate the acceleration of the car at the bottom of the loop.

   b) Is this a safe acceleration?

4. **Active Physics** **Plus** A roller coaster has an initial height of 50.0 m above the bottom of an incline.

   a) What will be the speed of the roller-coaster car at the bottom of the incline?

   b) The roller-coaster car goes into a loop with a radius of 10.0 m. What is the acceleration required to keep the cart moving in the circular loop?

   c) What will be the speed of the roller-coaster car at the top of the loop?

   d) What will be the acceleration of the car at the top of the loop if the car is moving in a circle?

   e) Explain whether this roller coaster is safe at the bottom and the top of the loop.

5. **Active Physics** **Plus** A roller coaster has a loop with a radius of 8.0 m (diameter = 16.0 m).

   a) What speed must the roller-coaster car have at the top of the loop if the only force acting on the car at the top is the force of gravity and the acceleration is therefore 9.8 m/s²?

   b) How high must the first hill be to provide this speed at the top of the loop?

6. A roller-coaster car, when filled with people, has a mass of 900.0 kg. The roller-coaster car rounds a curve on the ground with a radius of 18.0 m at a speed of 12.0 m/s.

a) What is the centripetal acceleration of the car?

b) What is the centripetal force on the car?

c) What will provide this centripetal force?

7. A roller-coaster car, when filled with people, has a mass of 900.0 kg. The roller-coaster cart rounds a curve on the ground with a radius of 15.0 m at a speed of 20.0 m/s.

a) What is the centripetal acceleration of the car?

b) What is the centripetal force on the car?

c) The wheels in the tracks can provide a force of 25,000 N. Is the roller coaster safe?

8. A roller coaster is able to complete a loop when the car has two passengers. The car is loaded with six people.

a) Will the centripetal acceleration change as a result of the change in mass?

b) Will the roller coaster be going faster, slower, or the same speed at the bottom of the loop with the extra passengers?

c) Will the roller-coaster track require a stronger material because of the increased number of riders?

Inquiring Further

Amusement-park physics

Visit an amusement-park physics site as directed by your teacher and explore some of the safety factors in designing roller coasters. Report your findings back to your team.

Active Physics

Physics You Learned

Physics Concepts	Is There an Equation?
A **scalar** is a quantity that is completely described with a number and units. Scalars add, subtract, multiply, and divide like normal numbers.	
A **vector** is a quantity that needs direction as well as a number with the correct units to completely describe it. There are special rules for vector addition and vector multiplication.	
Displacement is a distance in a certain direction from a specified reference point. Displacement is a vector quantity.	
Velocity (v) is the change in displacement (Δd) of an object divided by the time interval (Δt) for that displacement to occur. Velocity is a vector quantity having both a speed and a direction.	$v = \dfrac{\Delta d}{\Delta t}$
Acceleration (a) is the change in velocity (Δv) of an object divided by the time interval (Δt) for that change to occur. Acceleration is a vector quantity.	$a = \dfrac{\Delta v}{\Delta t}$
Active Physics Plus To find the magnitude of the change in velocity (Δv) of an object changing direction by 90 degrees, the **Pythagorean theorem** is used to find the square root of the sum of the squares of the velocities. The acceleration is this change in velocity divided by the time interval and is in the direction of the difference between the vectors.	$\Delta v = \sqrt{\left(v_1^2 + v_2^2\right)}$ $v_1 = $ velocity before $v_2 = $ velocity after
Earth's gravitational field is the region of space where Earth's gravitational force is acting. A gravitational field is a vector quantity that points toward the center of the mass.	
The force of gravity (F_{G}) between any two masses $(m_1$ and $m_2)$ depends upon the product of the masses divided by the distance between their centers, squared (r^2). For a planet, the gravitational field falls off with the inverse square of the distance.	$F_{\mathrm{G}} = \dfrac{Gm_1m_2}{r^2}$
Because the gravitational force exerted by the Sun on each planet varies inversely as the square of the distance between the Sun and the planet, the planet's orbits are elliptical.	
Kinetic energy (KE) is proportional to an object's mass (m) multiplied by the mass's velocity squared (v^2). Kinetic energy is the energy of motion.	$KE = \dfrac{1}{2}mv^2$
Gravitational potential energy (GPE) equals an object's mass (m) multiplied by the acceleration of gravity (g) and its vertical height above Earth (Δh). GPE is energy as a result of an object's vertical position above Earth's surface.	$GPE = mg\Delta h$
When an object is falling or freely descending, the object's gravitational potential energy (GPE) is being converted into kinetic energy (KE) as it descends, and the sum of the GPE and KE is a constant.	$GPE + KE = $ constant
Active Physics Plus The square of the velocity (v^2) of a falling object equals twice the acceleration of gravity (g) multiplied by the height of fall (Δh). For a mass falling or freely descending in a gravitational field, the fall speed is independent of the mass.	$v^2 = 2g\Delta h$
Spring potential energy (SPE) is proportional to the strength of the spring, indicated by the spring constant (k) multiplied by the change in length of the spring squared $(\Delta x)^2$. SPE is the energy stored in a spring when it is stretched or compressed.	$SPE = \dfrac{1}{2}k\left(\Delta x\right)^2$

For a system that uses spring potential energy (like a pop-up toy), the sum of the *SPE, KE,* and *GPE* is a constant. The law of conservation of energy states that for a closed system where no outside energy is added or subtracted, the total energy of the system remains the same, although it may switch forms.	$GPE + KE + SPE$ $= \text{constant}$
The weight of an object (F_w) equals the object's mass (m) multiplied by the strength of the gravitational field at that point (g). Different planets will have different values for g.	$F_w = mg$
The spring force (F_s) equals the spring constant (k) multiplied by the change in length of the spring (Δx), and is in the direction opposite the change in length.	$F_s = -k\Delta x$
The net force on an object is found by adding the vectors of all the forces acting on the object.	
Newton's first law states an object traveling with constant speed without direction change has no net force acting upon it.	$F_{net} = 0$
The acceleration of an object (a) equals the net force acting on the object (F_{net}) divided by the object's mass.	$a = \dfrac{F_{net}}{m}$
Active Physics **Plus** Inertial mass and gravitational mass are equal quantities.	
Active Physics **Plus** The centripetal acceleration (a_c) equals the square of the velocity (v^2) divided by the radius of the circle (r) and points toward the center of the circle.	$a_c = \dfrac{v^2}{r}$
For an object to travel in a circle, a net force toward the center of the circle, called the centripetal force, is required.	
Active Physics **Plus** The centripetal force (F_c) acting on an object equals the object's mass multiplied by its centripetal acceleration. The centripetal force on a roller-coaster car may come from a perpendicular force provided by the track (the normal), the car's weight, or a combination of the two forces.	$F_c = \dfrac{mv^2}{r}$
The apparent weight of a rider on a roller coaster is the normal force provided by the seat.	
Work (W) equals the force (F) acting in the direction of motion multiplied by displacement of the object (d).	$W = F \cdot d$
The work done on an object increases the object's energy. This increase can be in any form: *KE, GPE,* or *SPE.*	$W = \Delta KE + \Delta GPE + \Delta SPE$
Power (P) equals the work done (W) divided by the time required to do the work (Δt). Power is measured in watts (J/s).	$P = \dfrac{W}{\Delta t}$

Physics
Chapter Challenge

You will be completing a second process of the *Engineering Design Cycle* as you prepare for the *Chapter Challenge*. The goals and criteria remain unchanged, however, your list of *Inputs* has grown.

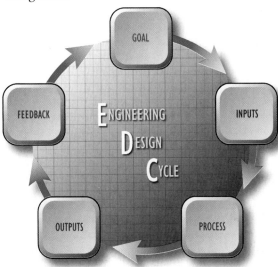

Goal

Your challenge for this chapter is to modify the design of a roller coaster to create the optimum thrills and chills for your target audience. Review the *Goal* as a class to make sure you are familiar with all the criteria and constraints.

Inputs

You now have additional physics information to help you identify and address the different physics concepts that apply to the design of a roller coaster. You have completed all the sections of this chapter and learned the content you will need to complete your challenge. This is part of the *Input* phase of the *Engineering Design Cycle*. Your group needs to apply these physics concepts to build your presentation. You also have the additional *Input* of your own personal experience with roller coasters as well as the feedback you received following your *Mini-Challenge* presentation.

Section 1 You determined the best method for drawing a model of a roller coaster. You also calculated velocities and accelerations. You discovered that acceleration can be more thrilling than high speed.

Section 2 You investigated gravitational potential energy and its impact on velocity for objects going down a ramp. This is important information for calculating the safety limitations of speed.

Section 3 You explored kinetic energy and the conservation of energy. These concepts are critical for determining the height of the "hills" in your roller-coaster design and how fast the roller coaster can go.

Section 4 You investigated the force of gravity. You may wish to explain how your roller-coaster design would work on the Moon!

Section 5 You explored the weight of objects and how a spring scale works. What if you had a spring for a seat?

Section 6 You investigated apparent weight, or the force acting to hold you up. You will use this to construct hidden thrills in your ride and to calculate how much "up" force a passenger will need to stay safely in the seat at all times.

Section 7 You calculated centripetal force and learned an important safety factor in roller-coaster design. You discovered that a roller coaster must never exceed forces of 4 *g*'s in its turns, which may be too high for some passengers.

Section 8 You calculated work and compared that value to potential energy. This is significant in determining how much work is needed to start your roller coaster.

Section 9 You used scalar and vector quantities to analyze speeds and energies in your roller-coaster ride. You also learned a way to compare and explain different slope designs for your model.

Section 10 You completed the safety calculations for the height, speed, and acceleration of your roller coaster. You learned to pay special attention to the design criteria that are specific to your target audience.

Active Physics

Process

In the *Process* phase, you need to decide what information you will use to meet the *Goal*. Defining your target audience is a good way to start. Your target audience is a specific group of potential riders with similar thrill tolerances. Also, it is important to clearly identify what types of "thrills and chills" you intend your ride to deliver, which will help your audience assess how successful you were.

You can either construct a physical model or create a design poster to explain the twisting path of your roller coaster. This model is part of the criteria and is a powerful tool for explaining design concepts clearly to an audience. Make sure your design contains all of the required features as defined in the criteria.

To maximize the thrills of your ride, you will need to figure out the optimum size for your roller coaster's hills, loops, and turns. For this, you may need to perform an *Iterative Analysis*, repeating analysis steps. You can start by calculating the potential and kinetic energy associated with each hill in your roller-coaster design. You can also calculate the forces involved with different accelerations. Your results will be important for determining if you are pushing the 4-*g* limit or maintaining a low-*g* experience for riders. Once you complete the calculations, you should be able to deduce what changes will move you closer to the results you want in your design. Alternatively, you could use a programmable calculator or a spreadsheet program to perform repetitive calculations and simply try various different values until you are satisfied with the result. Both are valid approaches and each has its advantages.

You will need safety calculations for at least five points on the ride. You should include them for each major feature in the ride, even if there are more than five. Be sure to add one or two examples of safety calculations to your poster or model so that the class can follow your explanations. In many cases, you will have to repeat calculations as you use the results to optimize the sizes of hills, loops, and turns.

Your poster should include all the required data and highlight the information you want your audience to know. Make sure you identify all of the key features of your design along with example calculations and results for all of your safety analyses. You should also clarify how your design addresses the particular needs of your target audience.

Outputs

Presenting your information to the class is your design cycle *Output*. You should offer a clear description of your target audience and explain how the features of your roller coaster are designed for that audience. You will need to present your *PE*, *KE*, and velocity calculations and explain the factors that determine how much work must be done on the system to get it started. This will effectively be the energy bill for your design. While this is not one of the design criteria, minimizing energy consumption is an added bonus to almost any situation.

Feedback

Your classmates will give you *Feedback* on the accuracy and the overall appeal of your presentation based on the criteria of the design challenge. This feedback will likely become part of your grade, but could also be useful for additional design iterations. No design is perfect; there is always room for optimization or improvement no matter how slight. From your experience with the *Mini-Challenge,* you should see how you could continuously rotate through the design cycle to refine almost any idea.

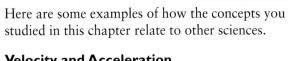

Physics
Connections to Other Sciences

Here are some examples of how the concepts you studied in this chapter relate to other sciences.

Velocity and Acceleration

Biology An animal's ability to accelerate, and the velocity it is able to achieve, determine its means of survival. Slower-moving animals such as turtles must rely upon defensive mechanisms to survive, while faster-moving animals such as cheetahs or rabbits either become predators or use their speed and ability to evade predators.

Chemistry Atoms and molecules are in constant motion, and gas molecules are constantly accelerating by changing speed and direction as a result of collisions.

Earth Science Changes in Earth systems are due to movement. Earthquakes, weather patterns, and landform erosion require movement with some velocity. When land rapidly accelerates during an earthquake, tremendous damage may occur.

Kinetic Energy

Biology The energy of food atoms that have been consumed are used up by exercise, which is kinetic energy.

Chemistry The temperature of a gas is determined by the average kinetic energy of its molecules.

Earth Science The kinetic energy of wind and water is responsible for the erosive power of these elements.

Potential Energy

Biology Plants store the energy of sunlight in the form of compounds like *ATP*, which participate in chemical reactions that release energy.

Chemistry GPE which is stored by an elevated object becomes *KE* as the object falls and becomes more tightly bound to the Earth. Molecules interacting in a chemical reaction can rearrange their atoms into new product molecules in which their atoms are more tightly bound. When this happens, the atoms that become more tightly bound experience a decrease in their electric potential energy, and there is an increase in the *KE* of the product molecules.

Earth Science The potential energy stored within high-temperature compressed gases in lava is the source of violent volcanic explosions.

The Force of Gravity and Weight

Biology The force of gravity acts on all elements of the biosphere and determines phenomena such as the height of a tree, or the maximum size and mass an animal may attain.

Chemistry Gravitational forces on the gases in our atmosphere determine its composition, and explain why light atoms such as hydrogen and helium are not normally found in air.

Earth Science The tremendous force of gravity acting on layers deep within Earth transforms sedimentary rock into metamorphic rock.

Springs

Biology The spring-like action of muscles and tendons allows animals to move and jump.

Chemistry Chemical bonds are often modeled in terms of springs, as atoms vibrate back and forth within these bonds.

Earth Science When large glaciers cover a landmass, they often compress the ground. When the glaciers retreat, the ground may "rebound" like a spring, causing small earthquakes to occur.

Work and Conservation of Energy

Biology The work done by a bird to fly to a greater height is converted into kinetic energy as the bird swoops down, gaining speed.

Chemistry Work done compressing a gas is converted into heat which may be sufficient to provide the "activation energy" required to ignite a fuel-air mix in a diesel engine.

Earth Science A boulder launched by an explosive volcano starts with a fixed amount of kinetic energy, which is converted into gravitational potential energy as it rises and then back to kinetic energy as it falls to Earth.

474

Sushma Sharma

High School Physics Teacher Chicago, IL

Sushma Sharma's love for physics and teaching began at an early age. Growing up in New Delhi, India, she attended public schools and entered many science fairs. Her high school physics teacher first sparked her interest in physics, and her first teaching experience was as a tutor to her fellow students and neighbors. She earned her undergraduate and master's degrees in physics at Delhi University, and upon moving to the United States, she earned a degree in education. "Teaching and learning are my lifelong passions," said Sushma.

After 26 years in the field, she is still learning new things every day. "The most exciting parts of the job for me are the 'eureka' moments when students realize that the concepts they are learning work in their everyday experiences," she said. Currently, Sushma is an instructional science coach with Northwestern University and provides support and training in the *Active Physics* curriculum to Chicago Public School teachers. The feedback so far has been very encouraging.

Sushma likes teaching *Thrills and Chills*, because her students love roller coasters. Her students especially enjoyed seeing the physics principles at work during their trip to a local amusement park. "They loved the *Chapter Challenge*, which has them design a roller coaster," said Sushma.

Sushma thinks that *Active Physics* is one of the best ways to teach physics to students. "They have an opportunity to really understand how physics principles work in day-to-day life and not just as abstract concepts. This curriculum allows students from all backgrounds and all levels of ability to learn and enjoy physics," she said.

Dr. David Wright

Physics Professor and Educational Consultant to Busch Gardens Amusement Park; Virginia Beach, VA

Dr. David Wright teaches introductory physics and astronomy at Tidewater Community College, and he does a lot to try to engage his students. "The most fun thing is playing with my physics toys and seeing my students get excited about how things work," he said.

When he is not teaching, Dr. Wright is at Busch Gardens Amusement Park performing for students at his theme park laboratory. "My objective is to help them see how physics relates to thrill rides." In one of his demonstrations, he rides a skateboard, powered by a fire extinguisher, to help illustrate Newton's laws.

Stacey Smilek

Pharmacy Manager and American Coaster Enthusiasts member; Pocono's, PA

Stacey Smilek grew up in New Jersey, only 20 minutes away from Six Flag Great Adventure. A pharmacist by day, she gets her kicks as a member of the American Coaster Enthusiasts (ACE) club, along with over 8,000 devoted roller-coaster fans, who travel throughout the United States and other countries to experience the thrills of riding roller coasters.

"What I love about roller coasters is the airtime, or negative g's that you experience. If I could build a roller coaster, I would want as much airtime as possible," said Smilek.

Physics

Practice Test

Before you try the Physics Practice Test, *you may want to review Sections 1-10, where you will find* **46 Checking Up** *questions,* **17 What Do You Think Now?** *questions,* **40 Physics Essential Questions,** **99 Physics to Go** *questions, and* **7 Inquiring Further** *questions.*

Content Review

1. A roller coaster undergoes different changes in velocity during the ride, with each change taking one second. Which change in velocity would cause a passenger to experience the greatest magnitude of acceleration?
   a) 20 m/s to 24 m/s
   b) 16 m/s to 22 m/s
   c) 4 m/s to 8 m/s
   d) 2 m/s to 6 m/s

2. A ride on a roller coaster with a 900-m track lasts two minutes. What are a passenger's average speed and average velocity for the ride?
   a) Both the average speed and the average velocity are 7.5 m/s.
   b) The average speed is 7.5 m/s and the average velocity is zero.
   c) The average speed is zero, and the average velocity is 7.5 m/s.
   d) Both the average speed and the average velocity are zero.

3. A ball starts from rest and rolls down a track toward a velocimeter, as shown below. If the mass is already known, the data from the velocimeter makes it possible to calculate the
   a) kinetic energy and starting gravitational potential energy.
   b) potential energy and the ball's acceleration.
   c) kinetic energy and the ball's acceleration.
   d) ball's acceleration and starting gravitational potential energy.

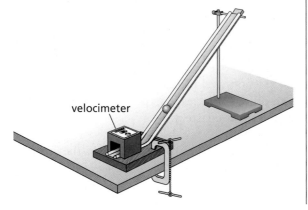

velocimeter

4. A ball swinging on a string has a total energy of 4 J. Which statement below correctly describes the kinetic and gravitational potential energies of the pendulum system as the ball swings back and forth?
   a) The kinetic energy at the bottom is 4 J and the potential energy at the top is zero.
   b) The kinetic energy at the bottom is zero and the potential energy at the top is 4 J.
   c) The kinetic energy at the bottom is 2 J and the potential energy at the top is 2 J.
   d) The kinetic energy at the bottom is 4 J and the potential energy at the top is 4 J.

5. A pop-up toy with a spring constant of 100 N/m and a mass of 0.005 kg is compressed 0.02 m. What is the toy's spring potential energy?
   a) 1 J   b) 0.02 J
   c) 5 J   d) 0.0005 J

6. A 0.20-kg mass hangs on the end of a spring as shown. The spring stretches 0.30 m. What is the weight of the mass on the spring?
   a) 1.5 N   b) 2.0 N
   c) 3.0 N   d) 6.0 N

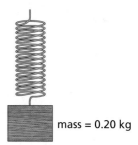

mass = 0.20 kg

7. A different mass now hangs on the above spring and the spring stretches to a length of 0.75 m. According to Hooke's law, what is the value of this new mass?
   a) 0.75 kg   b) 0.60 kg
   c) 0.5 kg   d) 0.4 kg

8. As a mass suspended from a spring scale accelerates uniformly downward, the reading on the spring scale would be
   a) lower than the weight of the mass.
   b) higher than the weight of the mass.
   c) equal to the weight of the mass.
   d) first lower, then equal to the weight of the mass.

9. A person with a mass of 60 kg stands on a bathroom scale in an elevator that is accelerating. If the scale reads 720 N, what is the magnitude and direction of the acceleration?
   a) 7.2 m/s^2 upward
   b) 2 m/s^2 upward
   c) 12 m/s^2 downward
   d) 9.8 m/s^2 downward

10. A toy plane attached to a wire is flying in a horizontal circle. What point will the plane move toward if the wire breaks when the plane is in the position shown below?
   a) 1   b) 2
   c) 3   d) 4

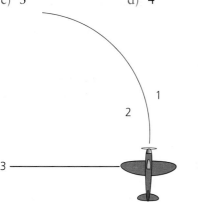

11. The centripetal force acting on the plane in the position in *Question 10* is directed toward point
   a) 1   b) 2
   c) 3   d) 4

12. A diver with a mass of 50 kg runs off the end of a diving board with a kinetic energy of 200 J. If the board is 3 m above the surface of a pool, what is the diver's kinetic energy when she hits the water?
   a) 350 J
   b) 650 J
   c) 1700 J
   d) 6050 J

13. A lab cart is being pulled up a ramp to the top of a ledge as shown below. As the angle between the ramp and the horizontal is increased, what happens to the force required and the work done?
   a) The force increases and the work decreases.
   b) The work increases and the force increases.
   c) The force remains the same and the work increases.
   d) The force increases and the work remains the same.

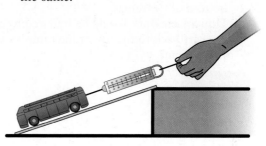

14. If the cart in the diagram above is always pulled to the top of the ramp in the same amount of time once the ramp angle is changed, what happens to the power needed to pull the cart up the ramp?
   a) The power increases as the angle increases.
   b) The power decreases as the angle decreases.
   c) The power remains the same regardless of the angle.
   d) The power decreases as the angle increases.

15. An automobile goes over a hill that has a radius of 50 meters and collides with another vehicle. The driver claims the automobile was not airborne when it passed over the top of the hill. Knowing that the centripetal force on the automobile is provided only by the force of gravity, what else would an accident investigator need to know to determine if the driver is telling the truth?
   a) the automobile's speed only
   b) the automobile's speed and mass
   c) the automobile's mass only
   d) the automobile's speed and the height of the hill

Practice Test *(continued)*

Critical Thinking

16. A cart with a mass of 0.5 kg is at the top of a ramp as shown in the diagram below.
    a) What is the cart's gravitational potential energy at the top of the ramp?
    b) If the cart is allowed to roll down the ramp freely, what would be its kinetic energy at the bottom of the ramp?
    c) What would be the cart's velocity at the bottom of the ramp?
    d) How much work would be required to pull the cart back to the top of the ramp from the bottom?

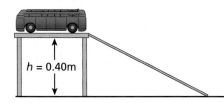

$h = 0.40m$

17. Design an experiment to show that the amount of work required to pull a cart to the top of a table from the floor is independent of the angle of the ramp used to pull the cart.
    a) What measuring instruments will you need?
    b) What measurements will you take?
    c) How will you use this data to prove that the angle has no effect on the work done?

18. The data below pertains to the stretch of a spring given the amount of mass hanging from it.

Mass	Stretch
0.200 kg	0.15 m
0.400 kg	0.28 m
0.600 kg	0.44 m
0.800 kg	0.59 m
1.000 kg	0.75 m
1.200 kg	0.89 m

    a) Graph the data above.
    b) Using the data, calculate the spring constant of the spring.
    c) Calculate the spring potential energy of the spring when it is stretched a distance of 0.80 m.
    d) If a 0.500-kg mass were suspended from the spring, how far would the spring stretch?

19. A 60-kg person is standing on a spring scale in an elevator. Provide answers to the following in newtons:
    a) What will the scale read when the elevator is at rest?
    b) If the elevator accelerates upward for a short period of time at 1 m/s², what will the scale read during the acceleration?
    c) What will the scale read if the elevator continues at constant speed upward?
    d) When coming to rest, the elevator has a negative acceleration of 1.5 m/s². What does the scale read now?

20. An 800-kg roller-coaster cart traveling at a constant speed of 20 m/s goes around a vertical loop with a radius of 25 meters.
    a) What is the weight of the coaster cart?
    b) What is the roller-coaster cart's centripetal acceleration?
    c) The cart now goes around the vertical loop at a different constant speed requiring a centripetal force of 10,000 newtons to travel in a circle with a radius of 25 meters. What is the magnitude and direction of the net force that the track must supply on the cart at the bottom of the loop?
    d) What is the magnitude and direction of the net force the track must supply on the cart at the top of the loop?

Active Physics
Plus

21. A pop-up toy with a spring constant of 50 newtons/meter and a mass of 0.005 kg is compressed 0.04 meter, and then released. If all the spring potential energy is converted to gravitational potential energy, how high will the toy pop up?

22. A roller-coaster cart with a mass of 300 kg goes around a vertical loop that has a 10-meter radius. The maximum normal force exerted by the rail during the loop is 9700 newtons. What is the cart's speed at this point?

Chapter 5

LET US ENTERTAIN YOU

5

Let Us Entertain You

Scenario

Most entertainment today, such as movies, television and video games, all involve the communication of sound and light signals. The sound signals that entertain you usually come from voices or musical instruments. Light signals make the images you see on TV or in the movies, and specially designed light patterns add to the effect of an event.

Your Challenge

You have been made part of a committee to design a two- to four-minute sound and light show to entertain other students your age. Unlike music stars or TV producers, you have neither the funds nor the technology they use available to you. All the sounds you use must come from musical instruments that you build yourself, or from human voices. Some of these sounds may be prerecorded and then played back during your show. If your teacher has a laser and is willing to allow you to use it, you may do so. All other light must come from conventional household lamps. You will then have to follow up the show with an explanation of the physics principles that allowed you to be so creative.

Criteria for Success

What criteria should be used to evaluate your sound and light show? Since the intention is to entertain students your age, your show will need to be interesting and enjoyable. You are restricted in the funds and technology you can use, so you will need to be innovative in your presentation to capture the attention of other students.

You will have to follow up the show with an explanation of the physics principles you used, so you will need to understand the physics concepts behind your show. However, remember that physics principles are not enough. Your sound and light show will also need to be entertaining. Your class will decide on a way to assign points for creativity. Note that an entertaining and interesting show need not be loud or bright.

Work with your classmates to brainstorm what features are important for your sound and light show and your explanation of the physics principles. As a class, you will decide if your explanation will be given in an oral report or presented as a written report. Next, with your class, determine the relative importance of the assessment criteria. Assign point values to each.

After you and your classmates make a list of features and point values, you may wish to compare it to the list on the next page. Each item in the list has been given a point value, but the values are only suggestions. Your class must decide what kind of grading system you will use.

Standard for Excellence	
1. The variety and number of physics principles used to produce the sound and light show	30 points
2. The quality of the oral or written explanation	40 points
• name of the physics principles that you used	10 points
• explanation of each principle	10 points
• example of something that each principle explains or an example of how each principle is used	10 points
• explanation of why each concept is important	10 points
3. Entertainment value	25 points
4. Meet the time limitations	5 points

You will have a chance later in the chapter to discuss these criteria again. At that time, you may have more information on the concepts and how you might produce your show. You may then want to propose changes in the criteria and the point values.

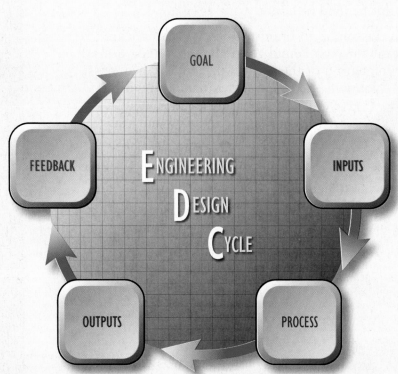

ENGINEERING DESIGN CYCLE

GOAL

INPUTS

PROCESS

OUTPUTS

FEEDBACK

Engineering Design Cycle

Your *Chapter Challenge* is to create and present an entertaining sound and light show. You will use a simplified *Engineering Design Cycle* to help your group create your production. Establishing a clear *Goal* is the first step in this cycle. You have defined the problem you need to solve, identified the *Criteria for Success*, and thought about some of the constraints that you will need to face. You may also already be thinking of some possible ways to entertain an audience. You are on your way to establishing your *Goal*.

As you experience each one of the chapter sections, you will be gaining *Inputs* to use in the design cycle. These *Inputs* will include new physics concepts, vocabulary, and some unique techniques to help you create and explain your show.

When your group prepares the *Mini-Challenge* and the *Chapter Challenge*, you will be completing the *Process* step of the *Engineering Design Cycle*. During the *Process* step you will evaluate ideas, consider criteria, compare and contrast potential solutions, and make design decisions.

The first *Outputs* of your design cycle will be an entertaining sound show accompanied by a short explanation of the physics principles involved. After completing several sections, you will work on part of your presentation. Finally, you will receive *Feedback* from your classmates and your instructor about which parts of your presentation are solid and which parts are shaky and need to be refined. You will then repeat the *Engineering Design Cycle* during the second half of the chapter when you gain more *Inputs* about light and refine your production into a complete sound and light show.

Physics Corner

Physics in *Let Us Entertain You*

- Color addition, color shadows
- Frequency and pitch
- Law of reflection
- Law of Refraction (Snell's law)
- Lens equation
- Lenses: focal point, focal length
- Longitudinal (compressional) and transverse waves
- Periodic waves
- Real images formed by curved mirrors
- Reflection of light
- Refraction of light
- Shadows
- Sound and vibration
- Sound waves in air-filled tubes
- Standing waves
- Tension, string length, and pitch
- Virtual images
- Wave motion
- Wave pulses
- Wavelength, frequency, speed

Section 1 — Sounds in Vibrating Strings

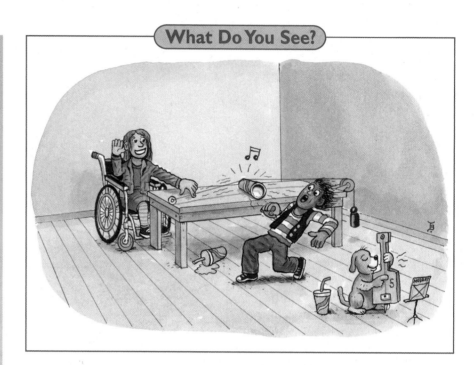

What Do You See?

Learning Outcomes

In this section, you will

- **Observe** the effect of string length on the pitch of the sound produced.

- **Observe** the effect of tension on the pitch of the sound produced.

- **Control** the variables of tension and length.

- **Summarize** experimental results.

What Do You Think?

When the ancient Greeks made string musical instruments, they discovered that cutting the length of the string by half or two-thirds produced other pleasing sounds.

- **How do guitarists or violinists today make different sounds?**

- **If someone were pretending to play a guitar (for example, the air guitar), how would the player position his or her fingers to make the highest pitch notes?**

Record your ideas about these questions in your *Active Physics* log. Be prepared to discuss your responses with your small group and with your class.

Investigate

In this section, you will make sounds by plucking a string. You will first investigate how the length of the string affects the *pitch* (how high or low the note is) of the sound produced, and then how the tension in the string affects the pitch. The following steps will guide you in setting up the equipment and changing the length and tension of the string.

1. Carefully mount a pulley over one end of a table. On the opposite side of the pulley, securely tie one end of the string to the clamp.

2. Tie the other end of the string around a 500-g mass. Extend the string over the pulley. Place a plastic or styrene-foam cup under the string near the clamp. The string should be able to vibrate (move back and forth) without hitting the table, as shown in the diagram below. You can adjust the length of the vibrating string by sliding the cup back and forth.

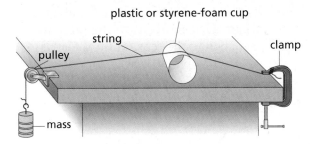

Put on your impact goggles. Be sure to have your impact goggles on anytime you put your eyes or ears close to the vibrating string.

Make sure the area under the hanging mass is clear (no feet, no legs). Check to make sure that the string is not fraying. Replace the string if it is showing signs of wear.

3. Hang one 500-g mass on the string. Pluck at the string and listen to the sound. The sound will be easier to hear if you place your ear near the opening of the plastic or styrene-foam cup. Pay attention to the pitch you hear. A high pitch is like the squeal of a vehicle's brakes as the vehicle comes to a screeching halt. A low pitch is like the rumble of thunder or the boom of bass notes from a loud radio. Observe the string vibrate. Use a finger to feel the vibrations in the string. Measure the length of the vibrating string (the distance between the cup and the pulley).

a) Record your observations in your log in a table similar to the following.

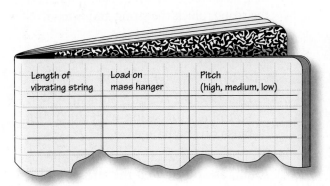

Length of vibrating string	Load on mass hanger	Pitch (high, medium, low)

4. Now change the length of the section of the string that is vibrating by sliding the cup. Measure the length of this section. Pluck this section of the string and observe changes in the pitch. Repeat this several times as you vary the length of the string between the cup and the pulley to observe changes in the pitch.

a) Record the different lengths of the vibrating string and the relative pitches of the sound in the table in your log.

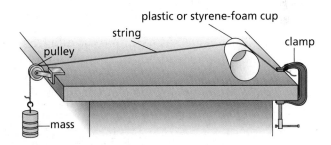

b) Make a general statement about what happens to the pitch you hear as you change the length of the vibrating string.

You will now investigate how the size of the mass affects the pitch of the sound. In this part of the investigation, you should keep the length of the string constant. The next step will guide you in changing the mass on the mass hanger.

5. Set the cup at the length of string that you will be using for this part of the *Investigate*. Make the length of the vibrating string as long as possible. With the 500-g mass on the string, pluck the string and listen to the pitch of the sound.

✎ a) Make up a new table to record your data in your log.

✎ b) Describe the sound you hear when you pluck the string with the 500-g mass on the hanger.

6. To investigate what happens to the sound as you tighten the string, add a second 500-g mass to the first 500-g mass, making the total mass 1000 g.

Pluck the string again. Observe the vibration, and listen to the pitch of the sound.

✎ a) Continue adding mass and describing the sound made by the string when you pluck. Do this until the total mass is 2000 g.

 Make sure the string is capable of holding 2000 g.

✎ b) Look over your data. Increasing the mass tightens the string and increases its tension. Make a general statement about what happens to the pitch as you change the tension on the string.

Physics Talk

CHANGING THE PITCH

Investigating Variables

To produce sound, something must **vibrate**. You observed the vibration of the string as it produced sound. You investigated two of the **variables**, length and tension, that affect the **pitch** of the sound of a vibrating string.

As you moved the cup, you changed the length of the vibrating string. You observed that shortening the string increased the pitch. The shorter string resulted in a higher pitch. Musicians who play string instruments, such as a guitar or violin, change the length of the string on the instrument to change the pitch of the sound produced. They do this by pressing their fingers down on the strings at different places along the neck of the instrument.

Physics Words

vibrate: move back and forth rapidly.

variable: something that can change or vary during an investigation.

pitch: (in music) how high or low a note is.

When you added mass to the mass hanger on the end of the string, you also changed the pitch. Increasing the hanging mass tightened the string by creating more tension in it. As the string tension increased, the pitch of the sound also increased. In tuning a string instrument, the performer changes the string tension by turning a peg attached to one end of a string. As the peg pulls the string tighter, the pitch rises.

Combining these two results into one expression, you can say that increasing the tension or decreasing the length of the string will increase the pitch. To write a mathematical equation to describe these relationships, you would have to accurately measure the pitch of each sound in a further investigation.

In percussion instruments (instruments such as a xylophone or drum that are struck to produce a sound), the object that is struck vibrates. In a xylophone, pieces of wood and metal vibrate. In drums, the head of the drum vibrates. In all of these instruments, you can expect that the length or area of the vibrating surface will behave in much the same way as the length of the string.

Checking Up

1. What happens to the pitch of the sound produced by a string when its tension is increased?

2. When you decrease the length of a string in an instrument, how does the pitch of the sound you hear change?

3. What effect did adding mass to the mass hanger have on the string in the *Investigate*?

4. How is sound produced in a percussion instrument?

Active Physics

+Math	+Depth	+Concepts	+Exploration
◆◆	◆		

Active Physics

Plus

Is There an Equation?

After repeating investigations similar to yours but with meters to measure the frequencies of the sounds, student scientists, as well as professional scientists, have found that there is an equation that can accurately predict the frequency of vibrating strings.

The equation that relates frequency of sound produced to the tension, length, and mass of the string is

$$f = \sqrt{\frac{T}{4\,mL}}$$

where f is the frequency or pitch of the sound,
T is the tension in the string,
L is the length of the string, and
m is the mass of the string.

A thick string will have a larger m than a thin string of the same material. Frequency is measured in cycles per second ($\frac{1}{s}$). If tension is measured in newtons, length is measured in meters, and mass is measured in kilograms, the units make sense:

$$f = \sqrt{\frac{T}{4\,mL}} \rightarrow \sqrt{\frac{N}{(kg)(m)}} = \sqrt{\frac{kg\,\frac{m}{s^2}}{kg \cdot m}} = \frac{1}{s}$$

1. Make a graph that shows how the frequency varies with the length of the string when the tension of the string is held constant. As the length of the string changes, so does its mass. For example, one half the length has only one half the mass.

From the graph, determine by what factor you would have to shorten the string to get a pitch that is double the frequency of the original pitch. (Musicians would say that the new pitch is one octave higher.)

2. Make a graph that shows how the frequency varies with the tension of the string when the length and mass of the string are held constant.

From the graph, determine by what factor you would have to tighten the string to get a pitch that is double the frequency of the original pitch.

3. From the equation, predict what would happen to the frequency as the mass of the vibrating string increases.

4. In a piano, short, thin, light metal wires are used for the high-pitch notes (those activated at the right end of the keyboard). Long, thick, heavy metal wires are used for the low-pitch notes (those activated at the left end of the keyboard). Explain why different thicknesses of wires are used in a piano. Explain how the sounds made with piano strings are related to what you learned in this section about making sounds with vibrating strings.

What Do You Think Now?

At the beginning of this section, you were asked the following:

• **How do guitarists or violinists today make different sounds?**

• **If someone were pretending to play a guitar (for example, the air guitar), how would the player position his or her fingers to make the highest pitch notes?**

You investigated the effects that changing the length of the string and the tension of the string have on the pitch of the sound produced. How do you now think that these musicians make sounds with different pitches? Use evidence from your investigation to support your answer.

Physics

Essential Questions

What does it mean?

A violin is less than 0.5 m long. A bass fiddle is more than 1.5 m long. Which instrument do you expect to be able to play notes with a lower pitch and why?

How do you know?

What experiment can be conducted to demonstrate that higher-pitched sounds can be produced by either shortening the length of a vibrating string or by increasing the tension of a vibrating string?

Why do you believe?

Connects with Other Physics Content	Fits with Big Ideas in Science	Meets Physics Requirements
Waves and interactions	Models	✳ Experimental evidence is consistent with models and theories

✳ A goal of physics would be to identify principles that can accurately predict all sounds from all instruments. Although you worked with strings in this investigation, as student scientists you can probably predict correctly how different pieces of wood or metal could be used to make a xylophone or a marimba (often played in Zimbabwe, Zambia, and other African nations). How might the length of the string and the tension of the string relate to properties of the wooden bars in these instruments?

Why should you care?

Vibrations occur in many situations. In this section, you investigated vibrations that give rise to sound. List some examples where vibrating strings show up in musical instruments. Describe how a drum produces a sound. How will what you learned in this section help you with your challenge of creating sound?

489

Reflecting on the Section and the Challenge

Part of the *Chapter Challenge* is to produce a sound show. In this section, you investigated the relationship of the pitch to the length of the string and to the tension in the string. The shorter the string, the higher the pitch. The greater the tension in the string, the higher the pitch. That is the physics of string instruments!

If you wanted to design a string or multi-string instrument for your show, you would now know how to adjust the length and tension to produce the notes you want. If you were to make such a string instrument, you could explain how you change the pitch by referring to the results of this section.

Physics to Go

1. a) Explain how you can change the tension in a vibrating string.

   b) Describe how changing the tension changes the pitch of the sound produced by the string.

2. a) Explain how you can change the length of a vibrating string on a guitar or violin with your finger during a performance.

   b) How does changing the length change the pitch of the sound produced by the string?

3. a) How could you change the tension in a string and keep the pitch the same?

   b) How could you change the length of a string and keep the pitch the same?

4. Suppose you changed both the length and the tension of the string at the same time. What do you think would happen to the sound?

5. a) Tell how a performer plays different notes on a guitar and on a violin that has been tuned.

   b) Tell how a performer or an instrument tuner changes the pitch of the strings to tune a guitar and to tune a piano.

6. a) Look at a guitar. Find the tuners (knobs at the end of the neck). What is the purpose of these knobs on a guitar?

   b) Why do you think a guitar needs tuners?

   c) What do you think happens to the pitch as strings stretch due to increases in temperature?

7. a) What is the purpose of the frets on a guitar?

   b) Does a violin or a cello have frets? If you don't have access to a violin or cello, find some pictures of those instruments.

   c) Why do violinists and cellists require more finger-placement accuracy in playing their instruments than a guitarist?

tuners

fret

8. *Preparing for the Chapter Challenge*

Design a string instrument that you could use in your sound and light show. Provide the explanation that will meet the requirements of the challenge. Use the rubric to grade yourself on this piece of the challenge.

Inquiring Further

1. **Pitch and the diameter of the string**

   Design an investigation to find how the diameter (thickness) of the string affects the pitch you hear. Submit your design to your teacher for approval before carrying out your investigation.

2. **Pitch and the material of the string**

   Design an investigation to find how the material the string is made of affects the pitch you hear. Submit your design to your teacher for approval before carrying out your investigation.

3. **Dame Evelyn Glennie**

   Dame Evelyn Glennie is a celebrated and accomplished percussionist. (A percussionist is a person who plays a musical instrument, such as the drum, cymbal, triangle, or xylophone that is struck to produce a sound.) She is also deaf. She explains that being deaf does not mean that she cannot hear, it means that her ears do not work. She says that she can "hear" the vibrations of sounds on her body. Go to the Internet, locate her Web site, and read her essay on "hearing." Be prepared to give a report to your class.

Active Physics

Section 2

Making Waves

What Do You See?

Learning Outcomes

In this section, you will

- **Observe** the motion of a wave pulse.

- **Calculate** the speed of a wave pulse.

- **Observe** standing waves.

- **Investigate** the relationship among wave speed, wavelength, and frequency.

- **Make** a model of wave motion.

- **Distinguish** between transverse and longitudinal waves.

What Do You Think?

On December 26, 2004 a giant tsunami (tidal wave) spread across the Indian Ocean with a wave height of about 0.8 m to 1.0 m in the open ocean. When it reached the shore, the wave grew to heights of tens of meters, causing widespread destruction, death, and many injuries.

- **How does water move to make a wave?**

Record your ideas about this question in your *Active Physics* log. Be prepared to discuss your responses with your small group and with your class.

Investigate

In the previous section, you learned that vibrating strings produce sounds. In this section, you will look at another vibrating system, a coiled spring. Using a coiled spring, you will be able to observe and control the vibrations more readily than in a string. The strings in your musical instruments behave similarly to the vibrations in the coiled spring.

Part A: Producing a Class "Stadium Wave"

1. Before you begin investigating *waves* on a spring, your teacher will have the class produce a "stadium wave" in the class.

One row of students will stand with their hands up and then sit, lowering their hands, as the next row of students stand up and then sit. This continues across the classroom. After a few attempts, answer the following questions:

a) Which way did the wave move?

b) Which way did you move?

c) How did the wave move without you moving in that direction?

d) What variables can you change in your "class wave"? (For example, you can change the speed of the wave. Can you change anything else?)

As you learn more about waves in the upcoming section, remind yourself of your experience with the "class stadium wave."

Part B: Producing Transverse Waves on a Spring

1. Obtain a coiled spring from your teacher. One member of your group should hold one end of the coiled spring firmly on the floor in an area free of obstacles. Stretch out the coiled spring

until the coils are about 4 cm apart. Mark the positions of the ends of the coiled spring by sticking pieces of tape on the floor. Measure the distance between the pieces of tape.

 A coiled spring can easily get tangled and ruined. Your group is responsible for making sure that the coiled spring does not get tangled. One way to do this is to not let it "snap back."

Make sure that the area in which you are working with the spring is free of obstacles.

a) In your log, record the distance between the pieces of tape.

2. Hold the ends of the stretched-out coiled spring at the tape marks. One group member will hold one end of the coiled spring fixed to the floor. Another student will whip back and forth the other end of the coiled spring sideways 20 cm to generate a *transverse wave* pulse. The quicker you whip the end back, the more distinct the pulse wave will be. Observe what happens. (The student holding the fixed end of the coiled spring must keep it fixed and should not let go. This is a safety issue. It also helps to keep the coiled spring from getting tangled.)

a) In what direction do the coils of the spring move as the pulse goes by? In your log, draw an arrow representing the direction in which the wave moved (from one person to the other person). Draw another arrow representing the direction in which a part of the spring moved away from its original position. What is the angle between your two arrows?

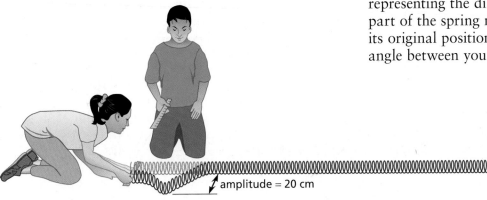
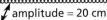
amplitude = 20 cm

b) Place a small piece of tape or colored yarn on a segment of the coiled spring roughly in the middle of the spring. Describe the movement of the piece of tape or yarn as a wave pulse travels along the coiled spring from the generating end to the fixed end. Draw two arrows—one showing the motion of the wave, the other showing the motion of the tape or yarn. What is the angle between these two arrows? How does this answer relate to your answer in *Step 2.a)*?

c) A dictionary definition of transverse is "situated or lying across." Another definition is "in a crosswise direction" and a third is "at right angles to the long axis." Why is transverse a good name for the pulse you observed?

d) The distance you disturb the coiled spring from its original position is called the *amplitude*. The amplitude tells you how much the spring is displaced. What was the original amplitude of your wave?

e) Notice that the wave pulse reflects (turns back) from the fixed end and returns. Draw a sketch in your log showing the shape of the wave pulse on the way to the fixed end and on the way back from the fixed end.

3. Send one wave pulse, with an amplitude of 20 cm, along the coiled spring. Have your partner simultaneously (at the same time) send a second pulse of the same size toward you. Do this by having both you and your partner whip the coiled spring on the same side of the spring. This will generate two pulses on the same side of the coiled spring. Another way to say this is that you generated two displacements on the same side of the coiled spring.

a) Describe what happens as the two pulses move along the coiled spring. Carefully describe what happens as the two pulses meet each other.

4. Even in the slow-moving wave of a coiled spring, it may be difficult to see what happens when two waves meet going in opposite directions. To show more clearly what is occurring, do the following: Place four styrene-foam cups or paper triangles parallel to the coiled spring on each side near the center of the stretched spring, but 30 cm away from the spring. Send a pulse with an amplitude of 20 cm down the coiled spring.

Notice that the cups are not disturbed when the wave travels down the coiled spring. This is because the amplitude of the wave is smaller than the distance to the cups.

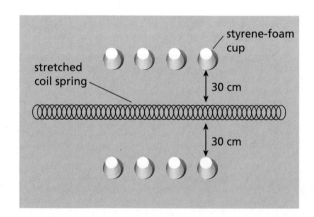

5. Now repeat *Step 3* and notice what happens when both waves meet in the area of the cups.

a) How was the amplitude of the combined wave different from the amplitude of the original waves? How does this show what happens when two waves meet? Record your observations.

6. Next, you will calculate the speed of the wave pulse. The speed of the wave pulse is equal to the distance traveled by the pulse divided by the elapsed time.

$$\text{Speed} = \frac{\text{distance traveled}}{\text{time elapsed}} \quad \text{or} \quad v = \frac{\Delta d}{\Delta t}$$

494

You have measured the length between the pieces of tape in *Step 1*. Now, you can measure the elapsed time.

Start a pulse on the spring and measure the time it takes the pulse to travel the length of the spring. Take three measurements and then calculate the average. Keep your amplitude the same for each trial and record its value.

a) Record your data in a table like the one shown.

b) Calculate the average speed of the wave pulse. Record the speed in your data table in your log.

Amplitude	Time for pulse to travel from one end to the other	Average time	$\text{Speed} = \dfrac{\text{length of spring}}{\text{average time}}$

7. Measure the time it takes for wave pulses with two other amplitudes to travel the length of the spring. Make one pulse with an amplitude larger and one smaller than the value used in *Step 6*.

a) Take three measurements in each case and calculate their average.

b) Record the results in the table in your log.

c) Calculate the average pulse speeds and record them in your data table.

d) Does the speed of the pulse depend on the amplitude? You may find that there is some difference when you compare pulse speed with amplitude.

You must decide if the difference is large or small. Compare your results with those found by other groups of students.

8. Carefully bring the ends of your coiled spring back together so that the spring does not get tangled, and return it to your teacher.

9. Obtain another, more tightly coiled spring from your teacher. Stretch the coiled spring on the floor so that the coils are about 1 cm apart. Be careful to hold the end of this spring very tightly on the floor so that it does not slip from your grip. This is a safety issue. Send a pulse down the spring, as before, by using a quick back and forth "whip" motion.

a) Does this pulse seem to go faster or slower than the one on the less tightly coiled spring? Record your observations in your log.

b) Calculate the average speed of the wave pulse in the spring. Show your calculations in your log.

c) Record any difference you noticed in the wave speed of the tightly coiled spring compared to the coiled spring you used in the previous steps of the *Investigate*.

10. Now use this tightly coiled spring to make periodic (repetitive) waves. Make certain that the person on the other end of the spring is still holding that end tightly on the floor. Keeping the ends of the spring the same distance apart as before, whip one end of the coiled spring back and forth three times along the floor. The result you observe is called a *periodic wave*.

a) Describe the appearance of the periodic wave you created. Notice that the wave reflects off the fixed end and returns.

b) You can make parts of the coiled spring remain still by sending periodic waves continuously down the coil and having them "overlap" with the reflected waves. Change how rapidly you whip one end until you see points where the spring does not appear to move at all. You will see other parts of the coiled spring move back and forth rapidly. These wave patterns are called *standing waves*. To get these waves, the person holding the other end of the spring must keep it fixed.

11. If you were to take two photos and overlap them it may look like this:

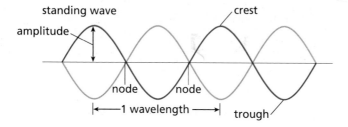

The distance from one *crest* (peak) of a wave to the next is called the *wavelength*. Notice that the overlapping waves have crests and troughs that switch places. Some parts of the coiled spring do not move (*nodes*). At a single instant, the distance between adjacent nodes is 1/2 the wavelength. The wavelength is the distance from crest-to-crest or trough-to-trough (the *trough* is the large displacement on the opposite side of the peak).

a) Keeping the rate at which you move the spring back and forth constant, measure the wavelength of your standing wave several times. Find the average wavelength.

b) Record the average wavelength of your standing wave in your log.

12. You can also measure the wave frequency. The *frequency* is the number of times the wave moves up and down each second. Measure the frequency of your standing wave. You can do this by watching the hand of the person shaking the coiled spring. Count the number of back-and-forth motions in 10 s. Divide this number by 10. The frequency is the number of back-and-forth motions of the hand in one second.

a) Record the wave frequency in your log. The unit of frequency is the *hertz* (Hz). One hertz (1 Hz) means one full oscillation (back-and-forth motion) per second. Two hertz (2 Hz) means two full oscillations per second.

13. Make several different standing waves by changing the wave frequency. Try to make each standing wave shown in the diagrams. Measure the wavelength. Measure the frequency.

wavelength = twice coiled spring length

wavelength = coiled spring length

wavelength = 2/3 coiled spring length

a) Record the frequency and wavelength in a table like the one shown on the next page.

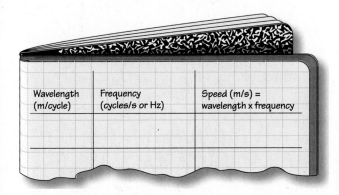

Wavelength (m/cycle)	Frequency (cycles/s or Hz)	Speed (m/s) = wavelength x frequency

b) For each wave, calculate the product of the wavelength and the frequency. Compare these values with the average speed of the pulse that you found in *Step 9*.

14. Fold a small rectangle about 1.5 cm by 5 cm (about ½" by 2") of paper in half and place it over one of the coils of the coiled spring near the far end. Send a transverse wave pulse down the coiled spring. Notice that the paper "jumps" as the wave pulse goes by. This observation shows that you have sent energy down the coiled spring in the form of the wave pulse. The paper is first at rest and has no (kinetic) energy. When it starts moving, it gains kinetic energy. The energy was carried from your hand to the paper via the wave on the coiled spring.

15. Summarize the results of *Part B* by completing the following statements.

a) A transverse pulse is one in which the motion of the wave is perpendicular to…

b) As the amplitude of a transverse pulse on a spring increases, its speed…

c) As the frequency of a standing wave increases, the wave length…

Part C: Producing Longitudinal (Compressional) Waves on a Spring

1. You have only created transverse waves so far. A different kind of wave is the *compressional* (or *longitudinal*) wave. Have the members of your group stretch out the tightly coiled spring between the pieces of tape that marked the ends of the spring in *Part A* and hold the ends firmly. To make a compressional wave, squeeze part of the spring by bringing a handful of edges toward you and let them go. Observe the compressed part of the coiled spring move along the length of the coiled spring. Listen to the sound it makes. Ask the person at the far end of the coiled spring what he/she feels. Calculate the speed of the compressional wave from the distance traveled and the time elapsed using the equation $v = d/t$. Compare it with the speed of the transverse wave.

a) Record your results in a table like the one in *Part B, Step 6*.

b) With the spring still stretched, have a member of your group place a small piece of tape or yarn on the coils of the spring roughly in the middle. In what direction does the piece of tape move as the compressional wave moves along the coiled spring?

c) A dictionary definition of compressional is "a) The act or process of compressing; b) The state of being compressed." A dictionary definition of longitudinal is "Placed or running lengthwise." Explain why compressional or longitudinal wave is a suitable name for this type of wave.

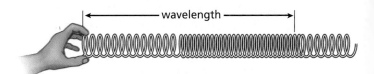

wavelength

d) If multiple compressions are sent along the spring, the wavelength can be measured. Instead of crests and troughs, the compressional wave has compressions and rarefactions. Compare the distances between the two compressions with the distance between two rarefactions.

Part D: Using a Wave Viewer

1. To help you understand waves better, construct a wave viewer by cutting a slit in a file card and labeling it as shown.

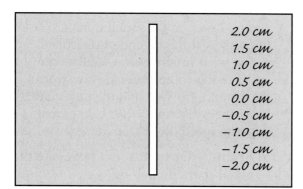

2.0 cm
1.5 cm
1.0 cm
0.5 cm
0.0 cm
−0.5 cm
−1.0 cm
−1.5 cm
−2.0 cm

2. Make a drawing of a periodic transverse wave on a strip of adding-machine tape.

Place this strip under the wave viewer so you can see one part of the wave through the slit.

3. With the slit over the tape, pull the tape so that the wave moves. You will see a part of the wave (through the slit) going up and down.

4. Draw periodic transverse waves with different wavelengths on other pieces of adding-machine tape. Put these under the slit and pull the adding-machine tape at the same speed.

✎a) Describe what you see.

Physics Talk

UNDERSTANDING WAVES
Waves Transfer Energy

Physics Words

wave: a transfer of energy with no net transfer of mass.

medium: (in physics) the material through which a wave can travel.

In this section, you were able to send energy from one end of the coiled spring to the other. The coiled spring "transferred" the energy from one end to the other but the spring remained in essentially the same place before and after the pulse moved. A **wave** is a transfer of energy with no net transfer of mass. When a baseball is thrown down a hallway, the kinetic energy of the ball also moves from one place to another. However, in contrast to the wave in the spring, the ball "transfers" the energy with a transfer of its mass.

To transfer energy along the coiled spring in the *Investigate*, you used chemical energy stored in the muscles of your arm. This energy was transferred to your arm as mechanical energy. You passed that on to the coiled spring at one end by whipping it over a certain distance. The coiled spring then had energy. A piece of paper at the other end of the coiled spring moved when the wave arrived there. The ability to move the piece of paper indicates that energy is present. If you whip the coiled spring with a greater amplitude, you have to provide more energy, and the piece of paper will have more energy when the wave goes by. The energy was transferred from one form to another, but the total energy remained the same. Energy is always conserved. The coiled spring is the **medium** through which the wave travels and through which the energy is transferred. You will learn later in the course that light is a transverse wave that requires no medium!

Physics Words

periodic wave: a repetitive series of pulses; a wave sequence in which the particles of the medium undergo periodic motion: that is, after a fixed amount of time, the medium returns to its starting point and then repeats its oscillation.

crest: the highest point of displacement of a wave.

trough: the lowest point of displacement of a wave.

amplitude: the maximum displacement of a particle as a wave passes; the height of a wave crest; it is related to the wave's energy.

For water waves, the medium is the surface of the water. Leonardo da Vinci stated, "The wave flees the place of creation, while the water does not." Imagine dropping a ball into a pool of water. Waves come from the center of the ball's position in the water. As the water moves up and down, the wave moves out from the center of its source, often in concentric circles.

A unique feature of a wave is that as waves pass each other, they "add" as they pass. Then they continue to travel as if the other wave had never been present. You noticed this when you sent pulses in different directions along the coiled spring. Below are computer simulations of pulses passing each other.

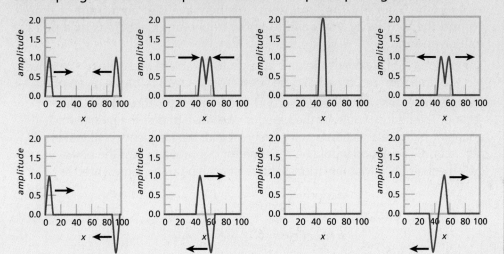

Wave Vocabulary

In discussing waves, a common vocabulary helps to communicate effectively. In this section, you observed waves in a coiled spring. Here is a summary of some of the observations. As you read, try to become more familiar with the terminology.

A **periodic wave** is a repetitive series of pulses. The diagram shown can be thought of as a photograph of a periodic wave. The highest point on the periodic wave is called the **crest.** The lowest point is called the **trough.** The maximum disturbance, the **amplitude** of this wave, is 5.00 cm. By the standard definition used in science, this is the height of the crest or the depth of the trough. It is not the distance from the crest to the trough.

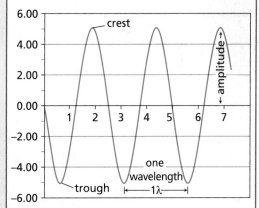

When there is a large amplitude in a vibrating string, the sound is loud. A soft sound has a small amplitude. A large amplitude corresponds to a large amount of energy. In the coiled-spring activity you completed, a large amplitude would give the paper attached to the coiled spring more kinetic energy.

In the case of light, a large amplitude corresponds to a bright light. In coiled springs, the large amplitude is a large disturbance of the medium away from the original position of the coiled spring.

Physics Words

wavelength:
the distance between two identical points in consecutive cycles of a wave.

frequency:
the number of waves produced per unit time; the frequency is the reciprocal of the amount of time it takes for a single wavelength to pass a point.

period: the time required to complete one cycle of a wave.

transverse wave: a wave in which the motion of the medium is perpendicular to the motion of the wave.

longitudinal (compressional) wave: a wave in which the motion of the medium is parallel to the direction of the motion of the wave.

standing wave: a wave pattern that remains in a constant position (also called a stationary wave pattern).

The **wavelength** (λ) of a periodic wave is the distance between two consecutive crests or between two consecutive troughs. (The Greek letter λ, *lambda*, is the symbol for wavelength.) In the diagram, the wavelength (λ) is 2.5 cm.

The **frequency** (*f*) of a periodic wave is the number of vibrations occurring per unit of time. A frequency of 10 waves per second may also be referred to as 10 vibrations per second, 10 cycles per second, 10 s^{-1}, or 10 Hz (hertz). Generally, humans can hear frequencies ranging from very low (20 Hz) to very high (20,000 Hz). You cannot tell the frequency by examining the wave in the diagram. The "snapshot" of the wave is at an instant of time. To find the frequency, you have to know how many crests pass by a point in a given time.

The **period** (*T*) of a wave is the time it takes to complete one cycle of the wave. It is the time required for a full cycle (crest-trough-crest) to pass a given point.

If three waves pass a point every second, the frequency is three waves per second. The period would be the time for one wave to pass the point, which equals $\frac{1}{3}$ s. If 10 waves pass a point every second, the frequency is 10 waves per second. The period would be the time for one wave to pass the point, which equals $\frac{1}{10}$ s. Mathematically, this relationship can be represented as

$$\text{period} = \frac{1}{\text{frequency}} \quad \text{or} \quad T = \frac{1}{f}$$

$$\text{frequency} = \frac{1}{\text{period}} \quad \text{or} \quad f = \frac{1}{T}$$

The period and the frequency are inversely related to one another.

Different points in a periodic wave are said to be "in phase" if they have the same displacement and are moving in the same direction. All crests of the wave shown below are "in phase."

In the wave shown, the following pairs of points are in phase:

- A and B
- C and D
- E and F

A **transverse wave** is a wave in which the direction the medium moves is perpendicular to the direction of the wave. A **compressional (longitudinal)** wave is a wave in which the direction the medium moves is parallel to the direction the wave moves.

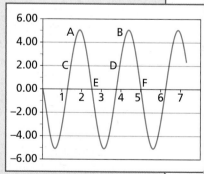

In the *Investigate*, you first sent a pulse down the coiled spring. You noticed that the pulse reflected off the end and returned back to the beginning. When you sent a periodic wave down the coiled spring, those waves also reflected off the end and returned back along the coiled spring. It is the combination of the wave moving up the coiled spring and the reflected wave moving back down the coiled spring that produces the **standing waves** you observed.

Active Physics

A **node** is a spot on a standing wave where the medium is motionless. At a node, the medium does not move while other places of the standing wave move up and down. The locations of these nodes do not change as the wave medium vibrates in a standing wave pattern. An **antinode** is a spot on a standing wave where the displacement is the largest. The locations of these antinodes do not change as the wave medium vibrates in a standing-wave pattern.

Sound Is a Compressional Wave

Compressional waves on a coiled spring are similar to sound waves in air. Just as you compressed a part of the coiled spring, when someone speaks, some of the air molecules get compressed. Just as the tightly coiled wave moved along the spring, these compressions move through the air. Just as the spring returned to its original uncompressed state after the wave passed, the air molecules move back and forth, (returning to their original location) after the sound wave has passed. Just as the part of the spring closest to you did not move along the spring, the air molecules do not move across the room. The sound waves move across the room. These sound waves eventually impact the air next to your ear and cause your eardrum to vibrate. These vibrations are then electrically coded and sent to your brain where you recognize the voice and can make sense of the language.

Calculating the Speed of Waves Using Distance and Time

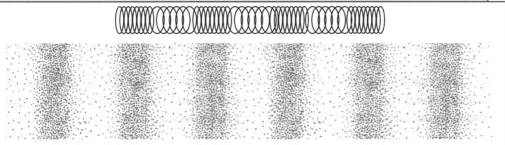

The molecules in the air bunch up in a similar fashion as coils of the spring bunch up in a compressional wave on a coiled spring.

You can find the speed of a wave by measuring the distance the crest moves during a certain time interval.

$$\text{Speed} = \frac{\text{distance traveled}}{\text{time elapsed}}$$

In mathematical language

$$v = \frac{\Delta d}{\Delta t}$$

where v = speed,

Δd = distance traveled, and

Δt = time elapsed.

Physics Words

node: a point on a standing wave where the medium is motionless.

antinode: a point on a standing wave where the displacement is the largest.

Sample Problem 1

The distance the crest of a wave moves is 2 m in 0.2 s. Calculate the speed of the wave.

Strategy: You can divide the distance traveled by time lapsed to calculate the speed of the wave.

$$v = \frac{\Delta d}{\Delta t}$$

Given: $\Delta d = 2$ m

$\Delta t = 0.2$ s

Solution: $v = \dfrac{\Delta d}{\Delta t}$

$$= \frac{2 \text{ m}}{0.2 \text{ s}}$$

$$= 10 \text{ m/s}$$

Calculating the Speed of Waves Using Frequency and Wavelength

The distance from one crest of a periodic wave to the next is the wavelength. The number of crests that go by in one second is the frequency. Imagine you saw 5 crests go by in 1 s. You measure the distance between crests (the wavelength) to be 2 m. The speed is $\left(5 \dfrac{\text{crests}}{\text{s}}\right) \times \left(2 \dfrac{\text{m}}{\text{crest}}\right) = 10$ m/s .

Thus, the speed can also be found by multiplying the wavelength and the frequency.   Wave speed = wave frequency × wavelength

In mathematical language

$$v = f\lambda$$

where v = speed,

f = frequency, and

λ = wavelength.

Sample Problem 2

Determine the speed of a transverse wave with a frequency of 4 Hz, a wavelength of 0.75 m, and an amplitude of 1.5 m.

Strategy: You can multiply the frequency by the wavelength to calculate the speed of the wave.

Given:

$$v = f\lambda$$

$$f = 4 \text{ Hz or } \left(4 \frac{\text{cycles}}{\text{s}}\right)$$

$$\lambda = 0.75 \text{ m}$$

Solution:

$$v = f\lambda$$

$$= \left(4 \frac{\text{cycles}}{\text{s}}\right)(0.75 \text{ m})$$

$$= 3 \text{ m/s}$$

Notice that cycles is used so that there is a unit in the numerator $\left(4 \dfrac{\text{cycles}}{\text{s}}\right)$ but it is not used when there is a measurable unit in the numerator $\left(3 \dfrac{\text{m}}{\text{s}}\right)$.

Checking Up

1. What is a wave?

2. What is the difference between a transverse and a longitudinal wave?

3. What is the difference between a node and an antinode?

Active Physics

+Math	+Depth	+Concepts	+Exploration
◆		◆	

Active Physics
Plus

Representing Waves Graphically

What happens when waves meet? They pass through each other and continue unaffected. At the instant the waves are in the same place at the same time, something interesting occurs. The waves add their amplitudes to momentarily form a new wave that is made up of the two waves together. This is called the principle of superposition. The waves are superimposed or added on top of one another. If one wave that is pulling up the spring meets an equal wave pulling the spring down, the two waves cancel, leaving a spring that is momentarily at rest.

The diagram below shows what happens when two square pulses meet. Each pulse has a height of 2 cm and a width of 1 cm. When they reach the same point, the resultant pulse is the sum of the two pulses: 4 cm high and 1 cm wide. After passing through each other, the waves will again resume their original shape.

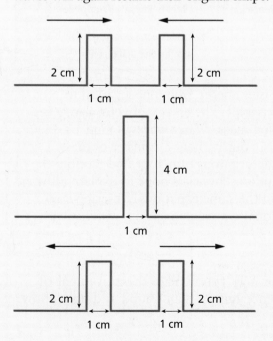

1. Use graph paper to show the resultant pulses when the pair of pulses shown below reach the same point.

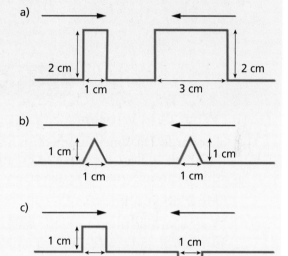

a)

b)

c)

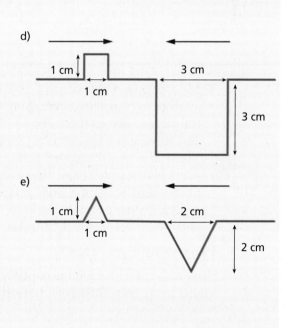

d)

e)

Active Physics

What Do You Think Now?

At the beginning of this section, you were asked the following:

• **How does water move to make a wave?**

Although you did not investigate water waves, you could design an experiment to see how water waves behave. They are very similar to transverse waves on a coiled spring. You can use the same physics words used in this section to explain how a water wave moves. The concepts of amplitude, transverse, wavelength, frequency, period, and speed are all applicable.

Physics
Essential Questions

What does it mean?

Leonardo Da Vinci summed up his understanding of waves by stating that "The wave flees the place of creation, while the water does not." What does this mean in terms of transverse waves on a spring?

How do you know?

You were able to measure the speed of a wave by using two different equations: $v = \Delta d/\Delta t$ and $v = f\lambda$. Both equations should have produced the same value for the speed. Show how both equations yield the units of speed, meters per second (m/s).

Why do you believe?

Connects with Other Physics Content	Fits with Big Ideas in Science	Meets Physics Requirements
Waves and interactions	Models	✳ Experimental evidence is consistent with models and theories

✳ Most people recognize that you can transfer energy from one location to another by throwing something like a baseball. The energy of your arm gets transferred across the room by the moving mass. Water waves, sound waves, and waves on a spring also transfer energy but without a transfer of mass. These are considered two fundamental descriptions of matter and motion: the particle description and the wave description. Physicists hope to explain all wave phenomena using the same language and the same equations. Describe how transverse waves on a spring, compressional waves on a spring, water waves, and sound waves are all similar.

Why should you care?

How can your knowledge of wave motion help you explain the movement of sound from your instruments to the audience during your sound and light show?

Reflecting on the Section and the Challenge

Coiled-spring waves are easy to observe. You have produced transverse and compressional coiled-spring waves and have measured their speed, wavelength, and frequency. For the *Chapter Challenge*, you may want to build musical instruments. Your instruments probably will not be made of coiled springs. You may, however, use strings that behave just like coiled springs. When you have to explain how your instrument works, you can relate its production of sound in terms of the coiled-spring waves that you observed in this section.

Physics to Go

1. Four characteristics of waves are amplitude, wavelength, frequency, and speed.

   a) Tell how you measured each characteristic when you worked with the coiled spring.

   b) Give the units you used for each characteristic in your measurement.

   c) Which wave characteristics are related to each other? Tell how they are related.

2. Suppose you shake a long, coiled spring slowly back and forth. Then you shake it rapidly.

   a) Describe how the waves change as you shake the coiled spring more rapidly.

   b) What wave characteristics change?

   c) What wave characteristics do not change?

3. Suppose you took a photograph of a periodic wave on a coiled spring. How can you measure wavelength by looking at the photograph?

4. Suppose you mount a video camera on a tripod and aim the camera at one point on a coiled spring. You also place a clock next to the coiled spring, so the video camera records the time. When you look at the video of a periodic wave going by on the coiled spring, how could you measure the frequency?

5. a) **What are the units of wavelength?**

   b) What are the units of frequency?

   c) What are the units of speed?

   d) Tell how you find the wave speed from the frequency and the wavelength.

   e) Use your answer to show how the units of speed are related to the units of wavelength and frequency.

6. a) What is a standing wave?

   b) Draw a standing wave on a coiled spring. Add labels to your drawing to show how the coiled spring moves.

   c) Tell how to find the wavelength by observing a standing wave.

7. a) Explain the difference between transverse waves and compressional (longitudinal) waves.

   b) Coiled-spring waves can be either transverse or compressional. Describe how the coiled spring moves in each case.

   c) Standing waves require two periodic waves traveling in opposite directions. In the *Investigate*, one student was sending waves down the coiled spring. How was the other wave generated?

8. a) When you made standing waves, how did you shake the coiled spring (change the frequency) to make the wavelength shorter?

   b) When you made standing waves, how did you shake the coiled spring (change the frequency) to make the wavelength longer?

9. A coiled spring is stretched out to 5.0 m in length between you and your partner. By shaking the coiled spring at different frequencies, you are able to produce standing waves with one antinode, two antinodes, three antinodes, four antinodes, and even five antinodes.

   a) What are the wavelengths of each of the wave patterns you have produced?

   b) How are the frequencies of the wave patterns related to each other?

10. A tightrope walker stands in the middle of a high wire that is stretched 10 m between the two platforms at the ends of the wire. The tightrope walker bounces up and down, creating a standing wave with a single antinode and a period of 2.0 s.

   a) What is the wavelength of the wire wave being produced?

   b) What is the frequency of this wave?

   c) What is the speed of the wave?

11. A transverse pulse with an amplitude of 3 cm is sent to the right along a coiled spring. A second transverse pulse with an amplitude of 2 cm is sent to the left along the same coiled spring and on the same side as the first pulse.

   a) What will be the amplitude of the pulse at the moment the centers of each pulse meet?

   b) How would your answer change if the pulses were on opposite sides of the coiled spring?

12. During the coiled-spring investigation, your partner generates a wave pulse that takes 2.64 s to go to the far end of the coiled spring and back to your partner. The coiled spring stretches 4.5 m along the floor. What is the speed of the wave pulse on the coiled spring?

13. A clothesline is stretched 9 m between two trees. Clothes hang on the line as shown in the diagram below. When a particular standing wave is produced in the line by shaking the line, the clothes remain stationary.

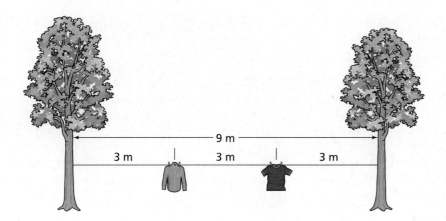

a) What is the term for the positions occupied by the clothes?

b) What is the wavelength of this standing wave?

c) What additional wavelengths could exist in the line that the clothes remain stationary?

14. *Preparing for the Chapter Challenge*

Explain how the sound from a vibrating-string instrument travels from the instrument to the ears of the audience.

Inquiring Further

1. **Using the wave viewer to investigate the speed of a wave**

   Use the wave viewer and adding-machine tape to investigate what happens if the speed of the wave increases. Pull the tape at different speeds and report your results.

2. **Adding waves using a calculator**

   You can add waves on your calculator in incremental steps. If you have a graphing calculator, simulate the addition of waves and show their sum.

Section 3   Sounds in Strings Revisited

What Do You See?

Learning Outcomes

In this section, you will

- **Calculate** the wavelength of a standing wave on a string.

- **Organize** data in a table.

- **Describe** how the pitch of the sound produced by a vibrating string depends on the wave speed, wavelength, and frequency of the waves on the string.

What Do You Think?

You investigated how the pitch of a vibrating string depends on the length of the string and the tightness (tension) of the string. How is the length of the vibrating string related to the wavelength of the standing wave set up on the string?

- **Why does the pitch change when you change the tension in the string?**

Record your ideas about this question in your *Active Physics* log. Be prepared to discuss your responses with your small group and with your class.

Investigate

1. Carefully mount a pulley over one end of a table, as you did in the *Investigate* in the first section. Securely tie one end of a string to the clamp on the other end of the table.

 Be sure to wear impact goggles while doing the experiment.

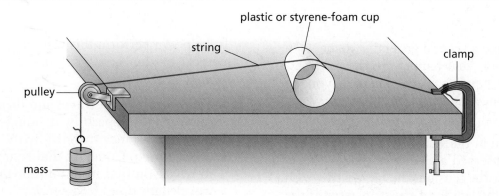

plastic or styrene-foam cup

string

clamp

pulley

mass

2. Tie the other end of the string around a 500-g mass. Extend the string over the pulley. Place a plastic or styrene-foam cup under the string near the clamp, so the string can vibrate without hitting the table, as shown in the diagram above. You can adjust the length of the vibrating string by sliding the cup back and forth.

3. Hang one 500-g mass on the string. Pluck the string, listen to the sound, and observe the string vibrate.

The vibrating string is producing a standing wave. When you pluck the string, it does not move at the ends. Just as you could transmit a standing wave on the coiled spring, you can produce a standing-wave pattern on the string with the two fixed ends being nodes and the center being an antinode. It is more difficult to see the vibration of the antinode on the string because the string vibrates so quickly.

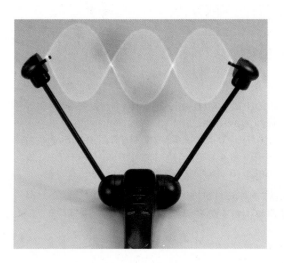

4. Measure the length of your vibrating section of string, and calculate the wavelength of the vibration. The length of the string equals ½ of the total wavelength (½ λ).

🖊 a) Record the length of the vibrating string and the wavelength in a table in your log.

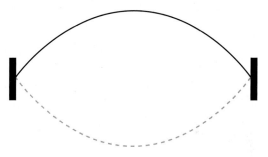

wavelength = twice string length

5. Shorten the vibrating part of the string.

🖊 a) Record how the pitch (frequency) of the sound changed.

🖊 b) Record the new length of the vibrating string and the new wavelength of the standing wave for this shortened string.

6. Repeat *Step 5* for two new lengths.

7. Look at the data in your table.

🖊 a) In your log, make a general statement about what happens to the wavelength as you change the length of the string.

✎ b) Make a second general statement about what happens to the pitch or frequency of the sound as you change the length of the string.

8. In the first section, you changed the tension in the string by adding weights and observed a change in pitch—the greater the tension, the higher the pitch. Since the length of the string stayed the same, the wavelength must have also stayed the same.

✎ a) What wave property changed to make the frequency higher? (Hint: Recall the wave equation, $v = f\lambda$. If the wavelength remains the same and the frequency changes, what else needs to change?)

9. You can explore the relationship among wave speed, wavelength, and wave frequency with the following investigation. You may have to do this investigation in the hall or outside on the sidewalk or athletic field.

Place small pieces of masking tape about 30 cm apart on the floor. Cover a distance of about 10 m in a straight line. Now walk, stepping on each piece of tape by taking one step each second. Your "frequency" is one step per second and your "wavelength" is 30 cm (the distance between pieces of tape).

To help you perform this task, have a member of your group call out the time using a stopwatch.

✎ a) Time your overall travel and then calculate your speed by dividing the total distance traveled by the time elapsed. Compare that result to what you find from multiplying wavelength times frequency.

10. Now change your "wavelength" by stepping on every other piece of tape. Keep the same frequency (one step per second).

✎ a) Again, compare your speed for the trip with the result obtained by multiplying wavelength by frequency.

11. Now change your frequency by taking one step every two seconds. Make your wavelength 30 cm.

✎ a) Again, compare your speed for the trip with the result of multiplying wavelength by frequency.

12. Make up your own combination of frequency and wavelength and see how they affect your speed.

✎ a) Record your findings in your *Active Physics* log.

Physics Talk

WAVELENGTH, WAVE SPEED, AND FREQUENCY

Frequency and Wavelength

The vibrating string producing the sound is actually setting up a standing wave between its endpoints. The length of the string determines the wavelength of this standing wave. If the string is 40 cm, then the wavelength of the lowest-frequency standing wave is 80 cm. The length of the string is always ½ the wavelength of the lowest-frequency standing wave.

The pitch that you hear is related to the frequency of the wave. The higher the pitch, the higher the frequency. You expressed this with a mathematical equation.

To get a higher frequency, you have to shorten the string or generate a smaller wavelength. Recall the wave equation:

Wave speed = wave frequency × wavelength

In symbolic form,

$$v = f\lambda$$

where v = speed,

f = frequency, and

λ = wavelength.

You can rewrite this equation to solve for frequency. Divide both sides of the equation by the wavelength:

$$f = \frac{v}{\lambda}$$

Now analyze the equation and ensure that it is consistent with your experimental findings in the *Investigate*. When you shortened the length of the string, you also shortened the wavelength of the standing wave. You found that this shorter wavelength increased the pitch. An increase in pitch corresponds to an increase in frequency. When you shortened the wavelength of the string's standing wave, you increased the frequency.

The equation above shows this as well. When the wavelength gets shorter, the denominator on the right side of the equation gets smaller. When the denominator gets smaller, the value of the fraction gets larger (as long as the numerator stays the same). For example, $\frac{1}{100}$ is much smaller than ½. If the fraction on the right side of the equation gets larger, then the left side of the equation also gets larger. In the equation, $f = \frac{v}{\lambda}$, the frequency gets larger.

This is what your experiment demonstrated. The shorter the wavelength is, the higher the frequency. This is called an **inverse relationship**. In an inverse relationship, decreasing one variable increases the other variable or vice versa. In this instance, decreasing the wavelength increases the frequency and pitch.

decreasing the wavelength increases the frequency and pitch

Tension and Thickness of a String and Frequency

How are tension and pitch related? In the first section of this chapter, you also found that changing the tension in the string by adding masses would change the frequency or pitch of the sound. When you increased the tension, you did not change the wavelength of the standing wave.

You can use the equation $f = \frac{v}{\lambda}$ to help you understand what happened.

Since the wavelength did not change, and the frequency increased, you must conclude that the speed of the wave increased.

Physics Words

inverse relationship: a relationship in which decreasing one variable increases the other variable or vice versa.

Active Physics

The increased tension in the string means that a portion of the string that is displaced to the side will feel a larger force pulling it back toward its rest position. An increase in tension produces a larger force. A larger force will produce a greater acceleration on that portion of the string that is displaced and make it vibrate faster. This vibration makes the disturbance travel more quickly down the string.

In the equation, $f = \frac{v}{\lambda}$, increasing the wave speed increases the value of the right side of the equation. This corresponds to an increase of the left side of the equation or an increase in frequency. This a **direct relationship.** Increasing one variable also increases the other variable. In this case, the wave speed increases and therefore the frequency or pitch must increase.

Physics Words

direct relationship: a relationship in which increasing one variable increases the other variable or decreasing one variable also decreases the other variable.

increasing the wave speed increases the frequency and pitch

How does increasing the thickness of the string lead to a different wave speed in the string? You know from looking at guitars or violins or the inside of pianos that the thick strings produce the lower frequency sounds. The increased mass in the string means that a portion of the string that is displaced to the side will require an increased force to pull it back toward its rest position. This force is the tension produced in the string. For a given amount of tension force, a heavier mass will have a smaller acceleration on the displaced portion of the string and hence, it will move more slowly back and forth. The decrease in acceleration will make the disturbance travel more slowly down the string.

Because the tension changes the wave speed, a weaker tension would mean a wave travels more slowly on the spring.

In the equation, $f = \frac{v}{\lambda}$, decreasing the wave speed decreases the value of the right side of the equation. This corresponds to a decrease of the left side of the equation or a decrease in frequency.

Is There an Equation?

Standing waves occur when the length of the coiled spring or string and the wavelength have a particular relationship. The length of the coiled spring must equal ½ wavelength, 1 wavelength, ³/₂ wavelengths, 2 wavelengths, and so on. Mathematically, this can be stated as

$$L = \frac{n\lambda}{2}$$

where *L* is the length of the coiled spring,

      λ is the wavelength, and

      n is a number (1, 2, 3...).

The number *n* is the number of antinodes in the standing wave pattern.

Sample Problem I

You and your partner sit on the floor and stretch out a coiled spring to a length of 3.5 m. You shake the coiled spring so that the pattern has one antinode between the two of you. Your partner measures the time for 10 vibrations and finds that it takes 24.0 s for the coiled spring to make 10 vibrations.

    a) What is the wavelength of this wave?

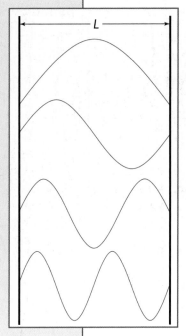

Strategy: Draw a sketch of the wave you made. It should look like the first wave pattern in the diagram. It is one-half of a full cycle of the wave. This is the maximum wavelength for a standing wave on this length of coiled spring. You can use the equation that shows the relationship between the length of the coiled spring and the wavelength.

Given:

$L = 3.5$ m

$n = 1$

Solution:

$$L = \frac{n\lambda}{2}$$

Rearrange the equation to solve for λ.

$$\lambda = \frac{2L}{n}$$
$$= \frac{2(3.5 \text{ m})}{1}$$
$$= 7.0 \text{ m}$$

Notice that the wavelength is twice the length of the coiled spring.

    b) What is the period of vibration of the wave?

Strategy: The period is the amount of time for one vibration. You have the amount of time for 10 vibrations.

Solution:

$$T = \frac{\text{time for 10 vibrations}}{\text{10 vibrations}} = \frac{24.0 \text{ s}}{10} = 2.4 \text{ s}$$

Active Physics

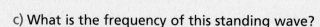

c) What is the frequency of this standing wave?

Strategy: The frequency represents the number of vibrations per second. It is the reciprocal of the period.

Given:

$T = 2.4$ s

Solution:

$$f = \frac{\text{number of vibrations}}{\text{time}} \text{ or } f = \frac{1}{T}$$

$$= \frac{1}{2.4 \text{ s}}$$

$$= 0.42 \text{ vibrations per second}$$

$$= 0.42 \text{ Hz}$$

d) Determine the speed of the wave you have generated on the coiled spring.

Strategy: The speed of the wave may be found by multiplying the frequency times the wavelength.

Given:

$f = 0.42$ Hz or $0.42 \text{ s}^{-1}\left(\dfrac{1}{\text{s}}\right)$

$\lambda = 7.0$ m

Solution:

$$v = f\lambda$$

$$= 0.42\left(\frac{1}{\text{s}}\right) \times 7.0 \text{ m}$$

$$= 2.94 \text{ m/s or } 2.9 \text{ m/s}$$

Checking Up

1. How does decreasing the wavelength increase the frequency of a wave? Explain, using an equation that relates the two variables of frequency and wavelength to wave speed.

2. How is the tension of a string related to its pitch?

3. Explain how tension relates to wave speed.

4. What is the equation that relates the length of a coiled spring and the wavelengths of the standing waves that can be produced on the spring?

Sample Problem 2

You stretch out a coiled spring to a length of 4.0 m, and your partner generates a pulse that takes 1.2 s to go from one end of the coiled spring to the other. What is the speed of the wave on the coiled spring?

Strategy: Use the equation for speed.

Given:

$\Delta d = 4.0$ m

$\Delta t = 1.2$ s

Solution:

$$v = \frac{\Delta d}{\Delta t} = \frac{4.0 \text{ m}}{1.2 \text{ s}}$$

$$= 3.3 \text{ m/s}$$

Active Physics

Plus

+Math	+Depth	+Concepts	+Exploration
◆◆			

Is There an Equation?

A vibrating string sets up a standing wave. The frequency of the sound can be increased by shortening the string length, by increasing the tension, or by using a thinner string (thereby decreasing the mass). You can derive an equation that combines all of these relationships.

$$f = \frac{v}{\lambda}$$

Since the wavelength is ½ the length of the string: $\lambda = 2L$

$$f = \frac{v}{2L}$$

From other studies, physicists have found

$$v = \sqrt{\frac{T}{m/L}}$$

where m = mass of one string,
   L = length of the string, and
   T = tension of the string.

By combining these equations:

$$f = \frac{\sqrt{\dfrac{T}{m/L}}}{2L} = \sqrt{\frac{T}{4mL}}$$

1. A standard acoustic guitar has six strings. For the highest pitch notes, a thin string is used. For the lowest notes, a thick string is used. For the intermediate pitch notes, a medium thickness string is used. The string tension is controlled by the tuning pegs at the end of the guitar. To keep the neck of the guitar from bending to one side or the other, you want to have the tension in all of the strings about the same. Using what you learned in this section, explain why the guitar designer decided to use thick strings for the low notes and thin strings for the high notes.

What Do You Think Now?

At the beginning of this section you were asked the following:

• **Why does the pitch change when you change the tension in the string?**

Use what you learned in this section to explain how the length of a vibrating string is related to the wavelength of a standing wave on the string, how the pitch of a vibrating string changes when you change the tension of the string, and how the thickness of the string affects the velocity and the frequency of a standing wave on a string.

Active Physics

Essential Questions

What does it mean?

When you plucked a string instrument, you set up a standing wave on the string. What is a standing wave?

How do you know?

Physicists want to know how the quantities like wave speed depend on the properties of the medium in which the wave is traveling. How does the speed of a wave on a string depend on the string's length and its tension? How does the wave speed depend on the thickness of the string? Describe the evidence you have for this from your experiments.

Why do you believe?

Connects with Other Physics Content	Fits with Big Ideas in Science	Meets Physics Requirements
Waves and interactions	Models	* Experimental evidence is consistent with models and theories

* Physicists develop models and mathematical relationships that apply to many different situations. Waves and their interactions are big ideas in physics and the same models of waves can explain sound, water, light, and waves on a string. Explain how what you learned in this section about string vibrations illustrates the general relationships that link wavelength, wave frequency, and wave speed.

Why should you care?

Physicists are always looking for general principles that apply to many different situations. You care about relationships connecting wavelength, wave speed, and wave frequency because you are interested in music and how you can generate sounds on string instruments for the *Chapter Challenge*. You may also care because you or your friends play string instruments in a band or an orchestra. Give some examples of where different kinds (different materials) of vibrating strings or cords show up in everyday life. How will what you learned in this section help you create musical instruments for your challenge?

Reflecting on the Section and the Challenge

In this section, you related your observations of the pitch of vibrating strings in *Section 1* to the wave vocabulary developed in the previous section. You learned that the length of the vibrating string determines the wavelength of the standing wave. The tension in the string determines the wave speed. Together, these effects determine the wave frequency, which is what determines the pitch of the sound that you hear. That's the physics of string instruments!

If you wanted to create a string or multi-string instrument for your show, you would now know how to adjust the length and tension and mass of the string to produce the notes you want. If you were to make such a string instrument, you could explain how you change the pitch by referring to the results of this section.

Physics to Go

1. Tell how changing the tension of a vibrating string changes the frequency of the wave produced.

2. Tell how changing the length of a vibrating string changes the wavelength of the standing wave in the string.

3. How would you change both the tension and the length of a vibrating string and keep the frequency the same?

4. Suppose you changed both the length and the tension of a vibrating string at the same time. What would happen to the sound in terms of wavelength and frequency?

5. For the guitar, tell how a performer changes the frequency of vibration of the strings to tune the instrument.

6. A guitar has six strings of the same length. The thickness or mass of the strings is different and each string has a different pitch and frequency. Explain why the mass of the string affects the frequency of the wave. (Hint: Think about how force, mass, and acceleration are related.)

7. *Preparing for the Chapter Challenge*

   Design a string instrument that you may consider using in your sound and light show. Provide the explanation that will meet the requirements of the challenge. You will want to describe how the string forms a standing wave, the wavelength of that standing wave, and how wavelength relates to the frequency and pitch you hear. Use the rubric to grade yourself on this part of the challenge.

Inquiring Further

Investigate frequency using a frequency meter

1. Set up the vibrating string as you did in the *Investigate*. This time, you will measure the frequency of the sound. Set up a frequency meter on your computer. (A free frequency-counter program for your computer can be found on the Internet.) Pick up the sound with a microphone. Investigate how changing the length of the string changes the frequency of the sound. Sketch a graph to describe the relationship.

2. Set up the vibrating string, computer, and microphone as you did in *Step 1*. This time, investigate how changing the string tension changes the frequency of the sound. Sketch a graph to describe the relationship.

3. Set up vibrating strings of differing thicknesses and investigate how the mass of the string changes the frequency of the sound. Does the wave speed remain the same in all of the strings? Use the frequency obtained from your frequency meter and the wavelength that you measured in this section to calculate the wave speed. Is the wave speed slower in thick, heavy strings, than in thin, lighter strings under the same tension?

Section 4

Sounds from Vibrating Air

What Do You See?

Learning Outcomes

In this section, you will

- **Identify** standing waves in different kinds of air-filled tubes.

- **Observe** how pitch changes with the length of the tube.

- **Observe** the effect of closing one end of the tube on the pitch of the sound.

- **Observe** sound bending around corners and spreading.

- **Relate** observations of pitch to drawings of standing waves.

- **Summarize** experimental results.

- **Organize** observations to find a pattern.

What Do You Think?

The longest organ pipes are about 11.0 m long and flutes are about 0.5 m long.

- **How do flutes and organ pipes produce sound?**

Record your ideas about this question in your *Active Physics* log. Be prepared to discuss your responses with your small group and with your class.

Investigate

In this *Investigate*, you will blow air across different-length straws and test tubes filled with different amounts of water to observe the differences in the sounds produced. You will investigate how sound can travel around a corner. You will also explore how to make your own reed instrument.

Part A: Vibrations in Tube-Shaped Instruments

1. Carefully cut a drinking straw in half. Cut one of the halves into two quarters. Cut one of the quarters into two eighths. Give a cut-up piece of the straw to each member of your group.

   (Your teacher may decide to distribute lengths of PVC tube as a substitute for the straws.)

2. Gently blow into the top of the piece of straw (or tap the PVC tube on the palm of your hand).

   a) Describe what you hear.

   b) Listen as the members of your group blow into their straw pieces one at a time. Describe what you hear.

   c) Write a general statement about how changing the length of the straw changes the pitch you hear.

3. Now cover the bottom of your straw piece with your finger and blow into it again. Uncover the bottom and blow again.

   a) Compare the sound the straw makes when the bottom is covered to when it is uncovered.

   b) Listen as the members of your group blow into their straw pieces, with the bottom covered and then uncovered. Write a general statement about how covering the end of the straw changes the pitch.

   c) Write a general statement about how changing the length of the straw changes the pitch you hear when one end is covered and then uncovered.

 Make sure the outsides of the test tubes are dry.

4. Obtain a set of four test tubes. Leave the first one empty. Add water to the second until it is about 1/5 full. Fill the third to 1/3 full and the fourth to 1/2 full. Give a test tube to each member of your group. Blow across your test tube.

   a) Describe what you hear.

   b) Listen as the members of your group blow, one at a time, across their test tubes. Record what you hear.

   c) Describe the pattern you find in the observations you recorded.

   d) Compare the results of blowing into the straws with blowing across the test tubes. How are the results consistent?

5. Review your observations and then answer the following questions.

   a) What is vibrating in the straw and in the test tube to make the sound that you hear?

   b) Is the test tube similar to the straw with the bottom covered or uncovered? Why?

Part B: The Spreading and Bending of Sound Waves

1. Have one lab partner stand around the corner of the door and out of sight. Have your partner make a sound.

   ✎a) Make a drawing that shows how the sound waves travel from beyond the corner of the doorway to your ear.

2. Roll a sheet of paper into the shape of a megaphone.

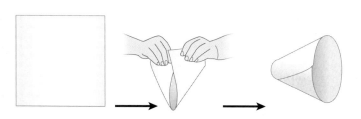

Emit a sound without the use of the megaphone and then emit the same sound with the megaphone in front of your mouth. Have your lab partners report on the difference between the two sounds.

✎a) Record this observation in your log.

Part C: Making a Reed Instrument

1. To make a musical instrument, obtain a straw and cut the ends to form a V-shape as shown in the diagram above.

2. Flatten the V-shaped end of the straw by gently biting on it with your teeth. Blow into the straw.

3. Make a sound by blowing into the straw, and as you emit the sound, use scissors to cut off the end of the straw. Cut the straw into shorter pieces in quick succession to enable you to continue making the sound with the straw without running out of breath.

> ⚠ Be careful that the scissors do not get too close to your eyes or face.

✎a) Listen to the different frequencies of the sound as you shorten the straw. Record your findings.

4. Begin with a new straw. Add a horn to one end of the straw to construct a trombone. Make the horn out of a sheet of paper, as shown below.

✎a) Record the effect that the horn has on the sound that your lab partners hear.

5. Try to make a trombone by inserting a second straw with a smaller diameter inside the first straw.

✎a) Record any engineering design strategies you used to make the trombone.

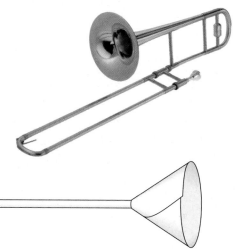

Physics Talk

SOME PROPERTIES OF SOUND WAVES

Compressing Air to Make Sound

Sound is a compressional (longitudinal) wave. The molecules of air squeeze together or spread out as the sound wave travels through the air, just like the coils of the spring that you observed in a previous section.

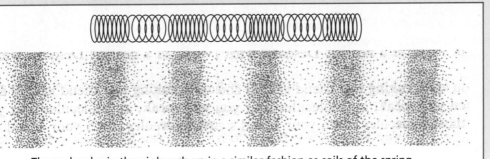

The molecules in the air bunch up in a similar fashion as coils of the spring bunch up in a compressional wave on a coiled spring.

In the *Investigate*, the air in the straw or the test tube was the medium through which the sound waves traveled. Standing waves were set up in the air. These waves traveled to your ears where you heard the sounds. These waves are similar to the standing waves made by the playing of the string instruments. At the bottom of the test tube, the air molecules cannot vibrate, because their motion is stopped by the glass at the end of the test tube. The wave's amplitude is zero at the bottom of the test tube. This point is a node of the standing wave. At the open end of the test tube, the amplitude of the wave is as large as it can possibly be. This vibration of air at the open end makes a sound wave that moves from the test tube to your ear. This point is an antinode of the standing wave.

Imagine 10 or 20 students lined up in a straight line, about one arm's length apart. The last person in the line moves closer to the person in the front. That person then moves closer to the next person in the line and this movement continues through the line. The closer spacing eventually forms a compressional wave that travels along the line of people.

If the person farthest in the line is standing against a wall, that person will not be able to move. That situation is similar to the closed end of a tube where the air molecules cannot move, and hence, have no displacement.

Active Physics

Wave Diffraction

Sound waves travel by spreading out or bending around barriers. When you speak to a friend, the sound waves leave your mouth and spread out in front of you and off to the sides. In *Part B* of the *Investigate,* you observed the spreading out and bending of the sound waves when your lab partner made a sound from around the corner of the door.

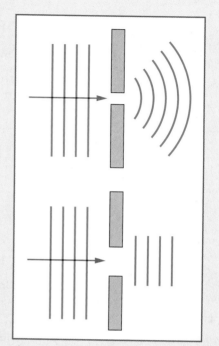

Physics Words

diffraction: the ability of sound waves to spread out or change direction as they emerge from an opening.

This ability of sound waves to spread out or change direction as they emerge from an opening is called **diffraction.** The smaller the opening, the more the sound waves diffract. The diffraction of the sound waves as they emerge from two openings can be shown with a diagram.

The wave in the top diagram goes through a small opening (in comparison to its wavelength) and diffracts a great deal. The wave on the bottom goes through a large opening (in comparison to its wavelength) and shows little diffraction.

In the *Investigate,* you noticed how much louder a sound you made was when you used a megaphone. You have probably seen cheerleaders use megaphones at sports events to change the amount of the diffraction. Therefore, cheerleaders are able to project a louder sound in front of the cheering crowds.

A smaller opening produces more diffraction that a large opening. How do you determine the size of an opening? The size of the opening may be determined by the wavelength of the sound wave. Whether an opening is large or small depends on the size of the opening compared to the wavelength of the wave.

Vibrating Columns of Air

The sound you heard when you blew into the straw and across the test tube was produced by a standing wave in air. If both ends of the straw are open, the air molecules at both ends move back and forth forming a vibrating column of air. The drawing below shows the movement of the air as a standing wave. Where the blue lines are far from the axis of the straw, the displacement of the air molecules is large. Where the blue lines cross the axis, the displacement of the air molecules is zero.

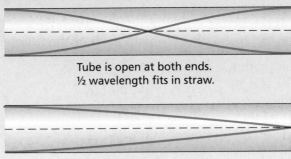

Tube is open at both ends.
½ wavelength fits in straw.

Tube is closed at one end.
¼ wavelength fits in straw.

When you covered the bottom end of the straw, you prevented the air molecules from moving at the covered end and the pitch and frequency of the sound decreased. This drawing shows the pattern of displacement of the air molecules as a standing wave. Notice that the blue lines hit the axis at the closed end of the straw indicating that the displacement of the air molecules there is zero.

Recall that the speed of a wave is equal to the frequency multiplied by the wavelength. This formula can be expressed mathematically as $v = \lambda f$. Using your previous knowledge of an inverse relationship, you can infer the following from $v = \lambda f$: If the wave speed stays the same, the frequency decreases as the wavelength increases.

In the straw open at both ends, $\frac{1}{2} \lambda$ (one-half wavelength) fits in the length of the straw L. Therefore, the wavelength of the sound is $2L$.

In the straw closed at one end, $\frac{1}{4} \lambda$ fits in the length of the straw L. Therefore, the wavelength of this sound is $4L$. The wavelength in the open straw is half the wavelength in the straw closed at one end. This equation predicts that the frequency of the standing wave in the open straw is twice the frequency of the standing wave in the straw closed at one end.

Checking Up

1. How does sound travel through air?

2. How do sound waves diffract?

3. How do you express the speed of a wave in terms of its wavelength and its frequency? What is the relationship between wave frequency and wavelength if wave speed remains constant?

+Math	+Depth	+Concepts	+Exploration	Active Physics
◆	◆			*Plus*

Wave Diffraction

Wave diffraction (bending of waves through an opening, for example) becomes important when the size of the opening is about the same size as or smaller than the wavelength of the waves

1. a) Using the equation $v = f\lambda$, calculate the wavelength associated with a pitch of "middle A" (440 Hz) for sound waves traveling through air. Use the value of 340 m/s as the average wave speed in air.

b) Would you expect to have significant diffraction of sound waves when they go through an open door? An open window? A garage door opening?

2. Calculate the wavelength of the note with each of the following frequencies.

a) 22 Hz

b) 220 Hz

c) 880 Hz

d) 8800 Hz

What Do You Think Now?

At the beginning of the section, you were asked the following:

• **How do flutes and organ pipes produce sound?**

Use what you learned in this section to explain how flute and organ pipes produce sound. How does the wave speed affect the frequency and wavelength of sound?

clarinet   oboe   bassoon   trumpet

Physics
Essential Questions

What does it mean?

When a vibrating string produces sound, a standing wave is set up along the string. Air in a tube can also set up a standing wave to produce a sound. Describe the standing wave in the air in the tube and compare it to the standing wave on a string.

How do you know?

Physicists want to know how wave characteristics like wavelength and wave frequency depend on the properties of the medium in which a wave is traveling. How does the pitch of the sound produced in a tube depend on the tube's length? Does it matter if one end of the tube is open or closed? What evidence do you have for this from your experiments?

Why do you believe?

Connects with Other Physics Content	Fits with Big Ideas in Science	Meets Physics Requirements
Waves and interactions	Models	* Experimental evidence is consistent with models and theories

* Physicists like to develop general principles and models that apply to many different situations. By listing two similarities and two differences, compare and contrast the sound produced by vibrating strings and the sound produced by air in tubes.

Why should you care?

Scientists always like to find new situations that can be explained in terms of what they have learned in other situations. Give some examples of where sounds are produced by vibrating air in tubes. Include examples outside of the classroom where air or wind causes strings or pipes to vibrate to produce sounds.

Reflecting on the Section and the Challenge

In this section, you observed the sounds produced by different kinds of tubes and pipes. If the pipe is cut to a shorter length, the pitch of the sound increases. Also, when the pipe is open at both ends, the pitch is much higher than if the pipe were open at only one end. You have seen how simple drawings of standing waves in these tubes help you find the wavelength of the sound. If the tube is closed at one end, the air has zero displacement at that end. If the tube is open at one end, the air has maximum displacement there.

For your sound show, you may decide to construct some "wind" instruments using test tubes or straws, or other materials approved by your teacher. When it comes time to explain how these work, you can refer to this section to explain the physics.

Physics to Go

1. You can produce a sound by plucking a string or by blowing into a pipe.

   a) How are these two ways of producing similar sound?

   b) How are these two ways different?

2. a) For each piece of straw your group used, make a full-sized drawing to show the standing wave inside. Show both the straw closed at one end and open at both ends.

   b) Next to each drawing of the standing waves, make a drawing, at the same scale, of one full wavelength. For the long pieces of straw, you may need to tape together several pieces of paper for this drawing.

   c) For a periodic wave, wave frequency times the wavelength is the wave speed. The speed in air is the same for all frequencies. Based on your drawing in *Part 2.b*), what can you predict about the frequencies of the standing waves in the straw pieces?

   d) How well do your predictions from *Part 2.c*) agree with your observations in this experiment?

3. Find some information on the length of organ pipes.

   a) What is the length, in meters, of the longest organ pipe?

   b) Assume this pipe is closed at one end. Draw the standing wave pattern.

   c) For this pipe, what is the wavelength of this standing wave?

   d) Why does a large wavelength indicate that the frequency will be low? Give a reason for your answer.

4. Suppose you are listening to the sound of an organ pipe that is closed at one end. The pipe is 3 m long.

   a) What is the wavelength of the sound in the pipe?

   b) The speed of sound in air is about 340 m/s. What is the frequency of the sound wave?

   c) Now suppose you are listening to the sound of an organ pipe that is open at both ends. As before, the pipe is 3 m long. What is the wavelength of the sound in the pipe?

   d) What is the frequency of the sound wave?

5. Suppose you listen to the sound of an organ pipe that is closed at one end. This pipe is 1 m long. How does its frequency compare with the frequency you found in *Question 4.b*)?

6. Waves can spread into a region behind an obstruction.

   a) What is this wave phenomenon called?

   b) Draw a diagram to illustrate this phenomenon.

7. A drum corps can be heard practicing at a distance of 1.6 km (about 1 mile) from the field. What is the time delay between the drumstick hitting the drum and the sound heard by an individual 1.6 km away? (Assume the speed of sound in air to be 340 m/s.)

8. *Preparing for the Chapter Challenge*

   List some ideas for producing sounds from air in tubes that can be used in a sound and light show. Describe how the instrument produces sounds with different frequencies.

Inquiring Further

1. **Musical test tubes**

   If you have a good musical ear, add water to eight test tubes, adjusting the amount of water to the pitch that you desire. Your goal is to create a musical scale when you successively blow over the top of each of the test tubes. Play a simple piece for the class.

2. **Measuring the frequency of vibrating columns of air**

   Carefully cut new straw pieces, as you did in *Investigate, Step 1*. This time, you will measure the frequency of the sound. Set up a frequency meter on your computer. Place the microphone near an open end of the straw. (A free frequency-counter program for your computer can be found on the Internet.)

   As before, each person blows into only one piece of straw. Make the sound and record the frequency. Now cover the end of the straw and predict what frequency you will measure. Make the measurement and compare it with your prediction. Repeat the measurements for all of the lengths of straw. Record your results, and describe what patterns you find.

3. **Investigating the effect of the diameter of a vibrating column of air on frequency**

   In this section, you found the relationship between the length of a tube and the pitch the sound produced. You also considered the differences between sounds made by air vibrating in open tubes and closed tubes.

   Design an experiment that will test to see if the pitch of a sound from a tube changes due to a change in the diameter of the tube. Use the frequency meter to measure the frequency of the sound made by your tubes. You could extend this investigation by measuring frequencies of sounds made in tubes of the same diameter but of different materials.

4. **History of wind instruments**

   Research for information about the Aeolian harp, an ancient musical instrument played by the wind. Present your findings to the class.

Your challenge for this chapter is to create a sound and light show to entertain students your age. The show should be between two and four minutes long, and must contain sound and light effects that you create using classroom materials. While you might be able to imagine an awesome display of blinding lights and deafening sound effects, you will have to work to incorporate those ideas in a show that works within the constraints of the challenge. The success of this challenge will likely rely more on your group's creativity than your access to technical equipment. For your initial design you will need the following:

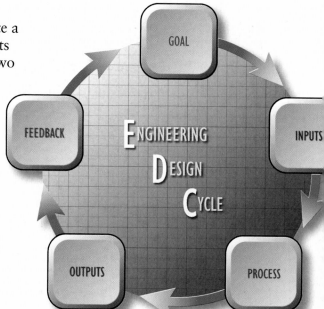

- Sound-producing devices based on classroom activities

- Light effects based on classroom activities

- Entertaining ideas and additional props

- A script for your show

- A written explanation of the physics concepts behind your effects

Your *Mini-Challenge* for this chapter is to entertain your classmates for one or two minutes using sounds that your group creates and to explain the physics concepts that make your show possible.

At this point, you can only address one half of the *Chapter Challenge*. Since you have only studied sounds and waves so far in this chapter, you will be making an entertaining sound show to present to your class. It may be argued that a sound show will not be very interesting without lights, but think of your radio. Not too far back in time, radio was the only entertainment media available and entire families would gather around their radio to be entertained by radio programs. Competing with today's image-rich media options will be difficult, so that is why your group's creativity will be very important.

Go back and quickly revisit the *Goal* you established at the start of the chapter. Review your *Goal* as a class. To prepare for and get the most out of the *Mini-Challenge*, you will need to make sure you have all the criteria and necessary constraints.

The *Inputs* phase of the *Engineering Design Cycle* are also constraints. Your group is limited to using sounds that you can create using techniques similar to the ones used in *Sections 1* to *4* of this chapter. Remember, you are also required to explain the physics involved, so using different types of sound makers will complicate that part of your presentation.

Your team should review the physics content from the first four sections to help you compose your sound and light show.

Section 1: You created sounds of different pitch by independently changing the length and tension of a vibrating string.

Section 2: You produced both transverse and longitudinal (compressional) waves in a spring. You also characterized many wave properties including amplitude, wavelength, wave speed, and frequency.

Section 3: You characterized the relationship between wave speed, wavelength, and the frequency of vibration for a vibrating string. You also considered a human model for that relationship. Remember, the relationship could be expressed in the equation $v = f\lambda$.

Section 4: You explored the sounds produced by vibrating air in a tube. You learned that you could change the pitch by changing the length of the straw or by covering one end of the straw. Both methods resulted in a change in the wavelength of the sound you produced. You also learned about the bending of sound waves, called diffraction.

 The *Process* phase is when you decide what information you have to help you meet the criteria of the *Goal*. This *Mini-Challenge* will rely heavily on your group's ability to come up with an entertaining idea. One way you can generate a lot of ideas is to research existing ideas and then brainstorm using those ideas as starting points. One of the most important rules of brainstorming is to ignore constraints and avoid criticisms until you have a long list of ideas. You can shorten the list later.

Make a short list of different sorts of sound presentations that people in your group enjoy. Have each student research one or two ideas to see what types of equipment are used to produce the sounds involved in those shows. Finally, make a list of adjectives that describe any of the types of shows on your list. These adjectives will give you an idea of what your show might include.

Now, assign a recorder for your group and start brainstorming. For each adjective on your list, ask your group to come up with ten ideas that would match it. For example, if funny is on your list, you might write a silly song about your teacher, play a popular children's tune, or play the melody of a current pop song. Repeat this step for each adjective you started with. You should end up with a long list of ideas that can be refined to fit the constraints of the challenge.

 Your group's *Outputs* of your *Engineering Design Cycle* will be to perform your sound show for the class and explain the physics concepts you used to make it happen. You should make sure you take notes on the instruments you used and your explanation should be written out to hand in. Remember, anything you create for your *Mini-Challenge* can be used to complete your final *Chapter Challenge*.

 Your classmates will give you *Feedback* on the entertainment value and the overall appeal of your presentation based on the criteria of the design *Mini-Challenge*. This *Feedback* will become an important *Input* for your final design in the *Chapter Challenge*. You will have enough time to make corrections and improvements, so pay attention to the valuable information provided by your classmates' feedback.

At this point, remember to correct any parts of your explanation that were not complete or correct. It will be harder to remember the changes you need to make if you wait until the chapter is complete to go back and correct your mistakes. Then, store all of your information in a safe place so that it will be ready to use in the *Chapter Challenge*.

If you were satisfied with your sound show, you will want to keep your idea in mind as you complete the remaining sections on light so you can add appropriate lighting effects to improve your show. If you liked other groups' ideas you may want to change your presentation to include those new ideas. In either case, keep your final design *Goal* in mind as you complete the remaining sections of the chapter.

Section 5

Shadows

What Do You See?

Learning Outcomes

In this section, you will

- **Observe** that light rays travel in straight lines.

- **Analyze** shadow patterns.

- **Explain** the size of shadows.

What Do You Think?

When the Sun is high in the sky, around noon, your shadow is very short. But early in the morning, when the Sun has just come up, or in the evening, just before the Sun sets, your shadow is long.

- **Explain why the length of your shadow in sunlight changes during the day.**

- **Sometimes your shadow looks fuzzy, sometimes it is very crisp. What causes a crisp shadow and a fuzzy shadow?**

Record your ideas about these questions in your *Active Physics* log. Be prepared to discuss your responses with your small group and with your class.

Investigate

In this *Investigate*, you will explore the formation of shadows using a white light bulb as a source of light and a cardboard puppet to cast the shadow.

 Lamps get very hot. Be careful not to touch the bulb or housing surrounding the bulb.

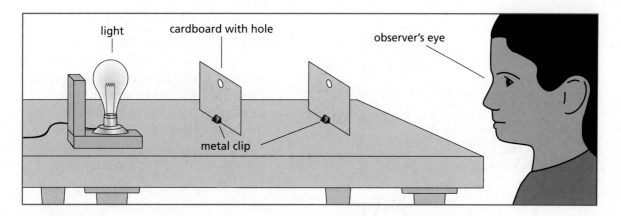

1. Set up a white light bulb in a light-bulb holder at one end of your lab table.

2. Make a hole about 1 cm in diameter in a piece of cardboard. Place the hole about 20 cm above the bottom of the piece of cardboard. (The hole should be about the same height as the light bulb above the tabletop.) Then do the same for a second piece of cardboard. Use flexible metal clips or clay to stand the cardboard pieces on a table.

3. Turn on the light bulb. Place the two pieces of cardboard between you and the light bulb. (Don't forget to turn off the light bulb when not in use.)

a) How do you have to position the holes so that you can see the light bulb?

b) Draw a sketch of the light bulb and the cardboard pieces and holes as seen in the diagram above.

You should notice that the light bulb and two holes must fall along a straight line with your eye in order for you to see the light bulb through the holes. One model of light says that the light bulb emits light rays, and these rays travel in straight lines. In order to see the light, the light ray must enter your eye.

4. Carefully cut out a cardboard puppet that you will use to make shadows.

5. Turn on the white light bulb again. Use a white piece of cardboard as a screen.

Move the puppet around between the light and the screen. Observe the shadow on the screen.

a) Describe the shadow you see.

b) What happens to the shadow if you move the puppet sideways or up and down?

c) What happens to the shadow if you move the puppet close to the screen?

d) What happens to the shadow if you move the puppet close to the bulb?

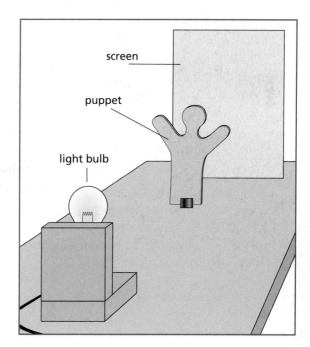

6. Look at the top-view diagram of the light, the puppet, and the screen on the next page. It shows the puppet halfway between a source of light and the screen.

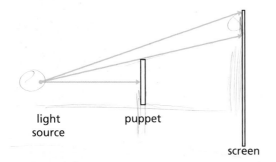

light source   puppet

screen

🖊 a) Make a copy of this drawing in your log. Draw several light rays coming from the light source and extend these light rays in straight lines to the point at which they get stopped (on the puppet or on the screen). A few lines are shown in the diagram.

🖊 b) Use the top-view drawing you made to answer these questions:

  i) Which part of the screen receives light from the light bulb?

  ii) Which part receives no light?

🖊 c) Label the part of the screen that does not receive any light as the shadow. How does the size of the shadow compare to the size of the puppet?

7. Repeat the drawing with the puppet closer to the screen, and then further from the screen.

🖊 a) Explain whether your diagrams properly model what you observed when you moved the puppet earlier in *Step 5*.

8. The light source that you used in your experiment was not a point source. Light emerges from the entire width of the bulb. Replace the point of light with a small vertical line of light.

light ray

penumbra

light

shadow (umbra)

puppet   penumbra

screen

🖊 a) Draw rays of lights from points on both sides of the light (top and bottom in the drawing) to the screen. Light rays will go in straight lines in all directions from all parts of the light. (Hint: You may want to draw the light rays from the top and bottom with different colors.)

🖊 b) Use the top-view drawing you drew to answer these questions:

  i) Which part of the screen receives light from both the top and bottom of the light bulb?

  ii) Which part receives no light?

  iii) Which part receives some light producing a gray part of the shadow?

🖊 c) Note on your drawing which part of the screen is in shadow. Are there parts of the screen that are in the shadows formed by all points of the light bulb? If so, identify and label them on your diagram as full shadow, and in parentheses write *umbra*.

🖊 d) If there are parts of the screen that receive light from one point of the light but do not receive light from the other part, identify these positions on your diagram and label them as partial shadow and in parentheses write *penumbra*.

9. Explore the phenomenon of shadows further. Turn on the white light bulb. Move the puppet around in order to explore and observe the shadow on the screen.

a) Describe the shadow you see. Identify the *umbra* (full shadow) and *penumbra* (fuzzy shadow).

b) What happens to the shadow (the umbra and penumbra) if you move the puppet sideways or up and down?

c) What happens to the shadow (the umbra and penumbra) if you move the puppet close to the screen?

d) What happens to the shadow (the umbra and penumbra) if you move the puppet close to the light bulb?

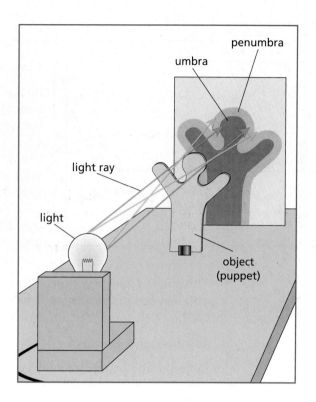

Physics Talk

SHADOWS

Light Travels in a Straight Line

In the *Investigate*, you noticed that the light bulb and the two holes in the cardboard must be in a straight line with your eye in order for you to see the light bulb. One model of light explains this by saying that the light bulb emits light rays. In order to see the light, the light ray must enter your eye. Since you can only see the light when the bulb, the two holes, and your eye are in a straight line, it appears that light must travel in a straight line. You may have seen a light from a laser or the Sun traveling in straight lines.

You also saw evidence that light travels in a straight line when you put a puppet in the path of the light rays from the light and the screen. A dark area appeared on the screen due to the absence of light. This dark area is the shadow of the puppet.

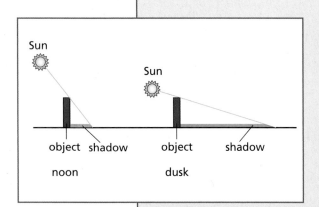

noon

dusk

How Can a Shadow Change Length?

In the *Investigate*, you observed that the size of a shadow depends on the distances between the light source, the object, and the screen. You may have noticed that during the day, your shadow changes size. At noon, your shadow is small, while at dusk your shadow may be many, many times larger than you. This change in size occurs, not because the distances between the Sun, you and the ground change, but because the angle of the Sun changes.

This angle change is similar to changing the orientation of the screen. As you can see in the contrasting diagrams, the size of the shadow changes as the position of the Sun in the sky changes.

Umbra and Penumbra

When shadows are formed by objects that obstruct light from light bulbs or from the Sun, the shadow has several parts. One part of the shadow gets no light at all from the light source. That area is called the **umbra** or full shadow. The outer part of the shadow gets some light from the light source but is not fully illuminated. That area, which makes the edge of the shadow look fuzzy, is called the **penumbra**, or partial shadow.

You can model the light and shadows using ray diagrams. Each ray signifies a bit of the light. When a point source of light emits light in all directions, the puppet will block some of the light, creating a dark shadow on the screen.

Physics Words

umbra: the part of the shadow that gets no light.

penumbra: the part of the shadow that gets partial light.

Since light bulbs are extended sources, not point sources, a set of rays emerges from all parts of the bulb. This produces a dark shadow (the umbra) and a gray shadow (penumbra). The penumbra gets light from some parts of the light but not from other parts.

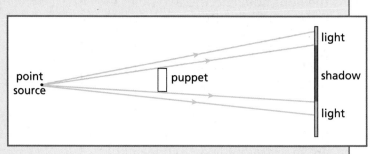

Checking Up

1. How does light travel?

2. Explain how a dark shadow is formed.

3. What causes a shadow to be fuzzy?

+Math	+Depth	+Concepts	+Exploration
◆	◆		

Active Physics

Plus

Predicting the Size of a Shadow

The ray model that you used to determine the size of the shadow can provide accurate predictions if the diagram is drawn to scale. You can also note that similar triangles are formed by the ray diagram and a ratio can be set up to provide accurate predictions.

Sample Problem

One side of a 10 cm puppet is 20 cm from the light source as shown in the diagram. The screen is 50 cm from the light source as shown in the diagram. Find the length of the shadow.

Given:

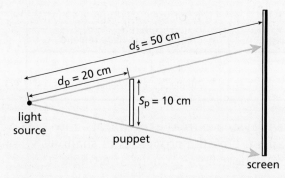

Solution:

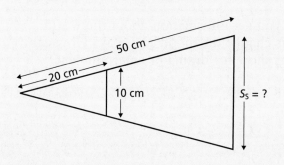

Setting up similar triangles, the following ratio is formed:

$$\frac{S_p}{d_p} = \frac{S_s}{d_s}$$

$S_p =$ the size of the puppet
$S_s =$ the size of the shadow

$$\frac{10 \text{ cm}}{20 \text{ cm}} = \frac{S_s}{50 \text{ cm}}$$

$$S_s = 25 \text{ cm}$$

Solve the following problems using a scale diagram or ratios.

1. A small light bulb is shining light on a basketball (diameter is 23 cm or 9 inches), which is 3 m from the light bulb. Behind the basketball, on the side away from the light bulb, is a wall 4 m from the basketball. Calculate the size (diameter) of the basketball's shadow on the wall.

2. The basketball is replaced with a 23 cm long rod. Calculate the size of the rod's shadow on the wall if the angle of the rod varies from 0° to 30° to 45° to 60°.

3. The basketball is placed back in position. The wall (screen) is now rotated. Calculate the size of the ball's shadow on the screen if the angle of the screen varies from 0° to 30° to 45° to 60°.

Active Physics

What Do You Think Now?

At the beginning of this section, you were asked the following:

• **Explain why the length of your shadow in sunlight changes during the day.**

• **Sometimes your shadow looks fuzzy, sometimes it is very crisp. What causes a crisp shadow and a fuzzy shadow?**

Use your observations from the *Investigate* to explain why the length of your shadow changes during the course of a day. Now that you know how shadows are formed, describe the different parts of a shadow. Which part is the "crisp" shadow and which part is the "fuzzy" shadow?

Physics
Essential Questions

What does it mean?

What is a shadow and how is it formed?

How do you know?

How does the size of the shadow depend on the size of the puppet and the distance of the screen and light source from the puppet?

Why do you believe?

Connects with Other Physics Content	Fits with Big Ideas in Science	Meets Physics Requirements
Waves and interactions	Models	✳ Experimental evidence is consistent with models and theories

✳ Physicists will accept ideas only if there is evidence from experiments and observations to support those ideas. Explain how the properties of shadows you learned about in this section illustrate the general principle that light travels in straight lines.

Why should you care?

Light is one of the most important ways you get information about the world around you. How can the use of shadows change the mood of a play? How can you add shadows to your sound and light show for drama or entertainment?

Reflecting on the Section and the Challenge

When an object blocks all light from a light source, it creates a shadow. Since some light comes from all parts of the light source, there are places where the shadow is black, (no light) and places where the shadow is gray (some light reaches this area). In your sound and light show production, you may choose to use shadows.

By moving the object or the lights during the show, you may be able to produce some interesting shadow effects. By having three-dimensional puppets, you can produce some interesting optical effects for your show. Lighting design is used in all theater productions. It requires a knowledge and understanding of how lights work and how shadows are formed, as well as an aesthetic sense of what creates an enjoyable display.

Physics to Go

1. Draw a diagram to show how a shadow is formed.

2. How can moving the light, the object, and the screen all lead to changes in the size of the shadow?

3. Explain why a gray halo surrounds a dark shadow made by a light bulb and an object.

4. a) Why is your shadow in sunlight different at different times of the day?

   b) What is the position of the Sun when your shadow is the longest? The shortest?

5. Why is the gray halo (the penumbra) about your shadow so thin when you are illuminated by the Sun?

6. *Preparing for the Chapter Challenge*

   Design puppets that you may want to use as part of your light show. How will you explain the physics of shadows in order to meet the criteria of the challenge?

Inquiring Further

Using two light bulbs as sources of light

Suppose your puppet is illuminated by two light bulbs that are placed about 20 cm apart. What kind of shadow will be formed? Make a sketch of what you see. Then draw ray diagrams that explain why some areas are dark, some are somewhat brighter, some are gray, and some are fully lit.

Active Physics

Section 6   Reflected Light

Learning Outcomes

In this section, you will

- **Observe** the reflection of light by a mirror.
- **Identify** the normal of a plane mirror.
- **Measure** angles of incidence and reflection for a plane mirror.
- **Collect** evidence for the relationship between the angle of incidence and the angle of reflection for a plane mirror.
- **Observe** changes in the reflections of letters.
- **Identify** patterns in multiple reflections.

What Do You Think?

Astronauts placed a mirror on the Moon in 1969 so that a light beam sent from Earth could be reflected back to Earth. By timing the return of the beam, scientists found the distance between Earth and the Moon. They measured this distance to within 30 cm.

- **How are you able to see yourself in a mirror?**
- **If you want to see more of yourself in the mirror, what can you do?**

Record your ideas about these questions in your *Active Physics* log. Be prepared to discuss your responses with your small group and with your class.

Investigate

In this section, you will investigate the reflection of light from a plane mirror. You will also make measurements to find the relationship between the angle of incidence and angle of reflection.

1. Look at your face in a small mirror. Keeping the mirror vertical and close to your face, note how much of your face you can see (for example, from your eyebrows to the top of your lips).

   a) Predict what will happen if you move the mirror further from your face.

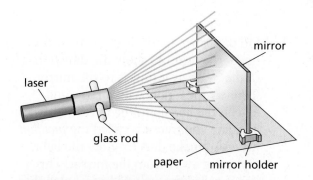

laser

glass rod

paper   mirror holder

mirror

b) Observe how much of your face you can see with your arm extended and record your findings.

2. Arrange a large piece of cardboard between you and a light bulb on a table, as shown in the diagram, so you cannot see the light bulb directly.

3. Carefully stand a plane mirror on the table. Then adjust the mirror so that you can see the light bulb.

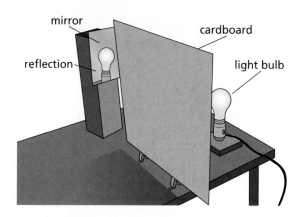

mirror

cardboard

reflection

light bulb

 Never look directly at a laser beam or shine a laser beam into someone's eyes. Always work above the plane of the beam and beware of reflections from shiny surfaces.

5. Carefully stand the plane mirror on your desk in the middle of the piece of paper. It can be held in place with a mirror holder or modeling clay. Draw a line on the paper along the front edge of the mirror. Now remove the mirror and draw a dotted line perpendicular to the first line, as shown, crossing the middle of the first line. In geometry this dotted line is called the *normal*, which means the same as the perpendicular line.

a) Where does the image of the light bulb appear to be located?

b) Place a pencil where the image appears to be. Do all members in your group agree on this location? Record the position of the pencil.

 Do not use mirrors with chipped edges. Make sure the ends of the glass rod are polished.

4. Place a piece of paper on your desk. Carefully aim a laser pointer, or the light from a ray box, so the light beam moves horizontally, as shown in the diagram. If you are using a laser, place a glass rod in the path of the light beam so that the beam spreads up and down. The glass rod can be fixed to the laser temporarily with masking tape or by constructing a cylinder that slides over the end of the laser and has two holes in the side for the glass rod. (A small sleeve with two holes is placed around the tip of the laser. The glass rod is inserted through the two holes.)

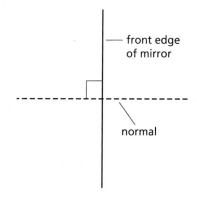

front edge of mirror

normal

6. Aim the light source so the beam approaches the mirror along the normal. Be sure the glass rod is in place to spread out the beam.

a) What happens to the light after it hits the mirror?

7. Keeping the output end of the light source at the same point, tilt the light source so that the light hits the mirror at a different angle.

a) What happens to the light beam?

Active Physics

b) On the paper, mark three or more dots under the beam to show the direction of the beam as it travels to the mirror. Connect these dots with a ruler and extend the line up to the mirror surface. The line you traced is called the *incident ray*. Also make dots to show the light ray going away from the mirror. This line is called the *reflected ray*. Label this pair of lines to show they go together. Draw the *normal* line where these rays touch the mirror.

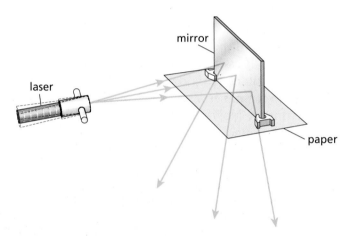

8. Repeat *Step 7* for several different angles.

a) For each angle, mark dots on the paper to show the direction of the incident and reflected rays. Also, label each pair of rays. Describe how the direction of the reflected ray changes when you change the direction of the incident ray.

9. Turn off the light source and remove the paper. Look at one pair of rays. Your mirror may have the reflecting surface on the back of the glass. If so, the light bends as it enters and leaves the glass part of the mirror. In your drawing, the incident and reflected rays may not meet on the line drawn at the mirror surface.

The following diagram shows a top view of the mirror, the normal, and an incident and reflected ray. Notice the *angle of incidence*, the angle formed

between an incident ray and the normal, and the *angle of reflection*, the angle formed between a reflected ray and the normal in the drawing.

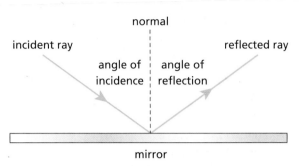

a) Using a protractor, measure the angles of incidence and reflection for all of your pairs of rays. Record your data in your log in a table similar to the following.

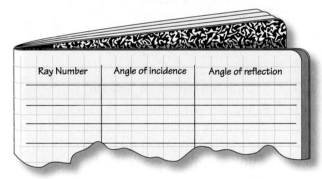

Ray Number	Angle of incidence	Angle of reflection

b) What is the relationship between the angles of incidence and reflection?

c) Look at the reflected rays in your drawing. Extend each reflected ray back behind the mirror. What do you notice when you have extended all the rays? The position where the rays meet (at least approximately) is the location of the image of the light source. All of the light rays leave the light source at one point in front of the mirror. The reflected rays all seem to emerge from one point behind the mirror. If you observed the reflected light, you would see the image of the light source at this point behind the mirror.

d) Tape a copy of your diagram in your log.

10. Hold the light source, or some other object, near the mirror and look at the image of the object reflected in the mirror. Now hold the object far away and again look at the reflection.

   a) How is the size of the image related to the size of the object?

   b) Since things far away appear smaller to your eyes, how does the position of the image appear to change as the object is moved away from the mirror?

11. Set up a mirror on another piece of paper, and draw the normal to the mirror on the paper. Print your name in block capital letters along the normal (the line perpendicular to the mirror). Observe the reflection of your name in the mirror.

   a) How can you explain the reflection you see?

b) Which letters in the image are closest to the mirror? Which are farthest away?

c) In your log, make a sketch of your name and its reflected image.

12. Carefully stand up two flat mirrors so they meet at a right angle. Be sure they touch each other, as shown.

13. Place an object in front of the mirrors.

   a) How many images do you see?

   b) Slowly change the angle between the mirrors. Make a general statement about how the number of images you see changes as the angle between the mirrors changes.

Physics Talk

REFLECTION OF IMAGES IN A PLANE MIRROR

Locating an Image in a Plane Mirror

People look in a mirror every day, yet few people know how a mirror works. Most people think that if they step away from a mirror that they will see more of themselves. Your investigation disproved this. As the mirror was moved farther from your face, you could not see any more of your face (unless you tilted the mirror).

Mirrors are important for many reasons. They are used in personal grooming and are also used in automobile safety, telescopes, cameras, CD players, and many more technologies.

Understanding mirrors begins with an understanding that when a light ray hits a mirror, the **angle of incidence** is equal to the **angle of reflection**. You observed this in the investigation. The ray of light that strikes a surface is called the **incident ray**, while the ray of light that reflects off a surface is called the **reflected ray**.

The angle of incidence and angle of reflection are shown in the diagram at the top of the next page.

Physics Words

angle of incidence: the angle formed between an incident ray and the normal.

angle of reflection: the angle formed between a reflected ray and the normal.

incident ray: the ray of light that strikes a surface.

reflected ray: the ray of light that reflects off a surface.

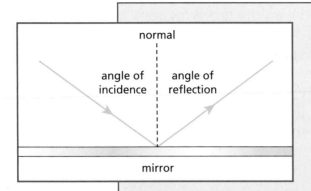

The angle of incidence is the angle between the incident ray and the **normal** (line drawn perpendicular to the mirror — as shown as a dotted line). The angle of reflection is the angle between the reflected ray and the normal.

Most objects do not reflect light like a mirror. An object like the tip of a nose reflects the light of the incident ray in all directions. That is why everybody in a room can see the tip of the nose.

You can look at the light leaving the tip of a nose and hitting a mirror to see how an image is produced and where it is located. Each ray of light leaves the nose at a different angle. Many of these rays of light then hit the mirror. The **law of reflection** for mirrors states that the angle of incidence for a ray equals the angle of reflection for that ray. There are now a set of rays diverging from the mirror. If you assume that the light always travels in straight lines, you can extend these rays behind the mirror and find from where they seem to emerge. That is the location of the image. The mirror does such a good job of reflecting that it looks as if there is a tip of a nose (and all other parts of the face) behind the mirror. That is how a mirror works.

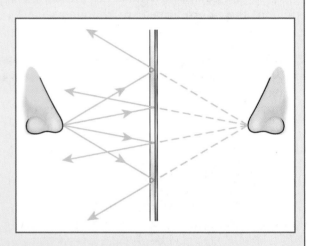

Physics Words

normal: a line that is perpendicular.

law of reflection: a law for mirrors that states that the angle of incidence is equal to the angle of reflection.

If you measure the distance of the image behind the mirror, you will find that it is equal to the distance of the nose (object) in front of the mirror. This can also be proved using geometry.

Sample Problem 1

Light is incident upon the surface of a mirror at an angle of 40°. Sketch the reflected ray. What is the angle between the incident ray and the reflected ray?

Strategy: The angles of incidence and reflection are always measured from the normal. The law of reflection states that the angle of incidence is equal to the angle of reflection. Since the angle of incidence is equal to 40°, the angle of reflection is also 40°.

Given:

$\angle_i = 40°$

Solution:

The angle of incidence and the angle of reflection are measured from the normal. As the two angles are equal, the angle between the incident ray and the reflected ray is twice the angle of incidence. In this case the angle between the incident ray and the reflected ray is 40°+ 40°, or 80°.

Sample Problem 2

Suppose that the mirror is turned clockwise (as viewed from above) 10° so the angle of incidence is now 50°. How much has the angle between the incident ray and the reflected ray changed?

Strategy: Since the angle of incidence is now 50°, the angle of reflection is also 50° according to the law of reflection.

Given:

$\angle_i = 50°$

Solution:

The angle of incidence and the angle of reflection are measured from the normal, the line perpendicular to a surface. So, the angle between the incident ray and reflected ray is now 100°. It has increased by 20°, or twice the angle through which the mirror was rotated.

Light Waves

As you begin to study the reflection of light rays, it is worthwhile to recognize that light is a wave and has properties similar to sound waves.

In studying sound waves, you learned that sound waves are compressional or longitudinal. The disturbance is parallel to the direction of motion of the wave. In sound waves, the compression of the air is left and right as the wave travels to the right. You saw a similar compressional wave using the compressed coiled spring.

Light waves are transverse waves. They are similar to the transverse waves of the coiled spring. In a transverse wave, the disturbance is perpendicular to the direction of the wave. In the coiled spring, the disturbance was up and down as the wave traveled to the right. In light, the fields that make up light (the disturbance) are perpendicular to the direction of motion of the waves. Unlike the transverse waves of a coiled spring, the transverse light waves do not need a medium to travel. Light waves can travel in a vacuum.

Light waves also carry energy. You know that when you are in full sunlight, you feel warmed by the light. Light waves are transferring energy from the Sun to you.

→

Checking Up

1. Explain the law of reflection.

2. Define the angle of incidence.

3. Describe the behavior of light waves hitting a mirror.

Active Physics

+Math	+Depth	+Concepts	+Exploration
◆		◆	◆

Active Physics

Plus

Reflection of a Reflection

Have you ever found yourself between two mirrors? If the mirrors are not quite parallel to one another, you can see hundreds of images of yourself. The first mirror creates an image. The second mirror creates an image of the image. The first mirror then creates an image of the image of the image.

Carefully tape together one edge of two mirrors so they can move like a hinge, with the mirrored surfaces facing each other.

1. Place a small object between the mirrors. When the angle between the mirrors is 90°, you should see three images.

a) Draw a ray diagram that shows how the first image is created by a reflected light from the object to the first mirror and into your eye.

b) Draw a ray diagram that shows how the second image is created by a reflected light from the object to the second mirror and into your eye.

c) Draw a ray diagram that shows how the third image is created by a reflected light from the first image to the second mirror and into your eye.

d) Draw a ray diagram that shows how the third image is also created by a light reflected from the second mirror to the first mirror and into your eye.

2. Investigate how the number of images you see depends on the angle between the mirrors. You will need a protractor to measure this angle. (If you have polar coordinate paper available, you will not need a protractor.)

a) Plot a graph of the number of images versus the angle between the two mirrors.

b) What mathematical relationship can you find between the angle and the number of images?

What Do You Think Now?

At the beginning of this section, you were asked the following:

• **How are you able to see yourself in a mirror?**

• **If you want to see more of yourself in the mirror, what can you do?**

Now that you have completed this section, how would you answer these questions? Compare your answers now to those you wrote in your log at the beginning of the section. If they are different, what evidence did you see in the *Investigate* that made you change your answers?

Physics
Essential Questions

What does it mean?

In this section, you learned that light travels in straight lines until it interacts with materials such as mirrors where light can be reflected. Then light travels in straight reflected lines until it interacts with another material or object. In order to talk about the reflection of light, scientists use angles of incidence and angles of reflection. How are these angles defined?

How do you know?

Physicists prefer to find quantitative relationships among properties. These relationships should be based on observations and experiments. How are the angle of incidence and the angle of reflection related? What evidence do you have for this from your investigations?

Why do you believe?

Connects with Other Physics Content	Fits with Big Ideas in Science	Meets Physics Requirements
Waves and interactions	✻ Interactions of matter, energy, and fields	Experimental evidence is consistent with models and theories

✻ When scientists observe new phenomena, they often have to modify previously stated general principles. Does light always travel in straight lines? How does what you learned about reflection in this section modify how you would express the general principle about light traveling in straight lines?

Why should you care?

You use mirrors every day. Make a list of some of the ways that mirrors are used in your everyday life. Compare your list with those of your classmates. Suggest two ways that mirrors can be used in creative ways in your sound and light show.

Reflecting on the Section and the Challenge

In this section, you aimed light rays at mirrors and observed the reflections. From your investigation, you discovered that the angle of incidence is equal to the angle of reflection. Therefore, you can now predict the path of a reflected light beam. You also experimented with reflections from two mirrors. When you observed the reflection in two mirrors, you found many images of one object that made interesting patterns.

This section has given you experience with many interesting effects that you can use in your sound and light show. For instance, you may want to show the audience a reflection in one mirror or two mirrors placed at angles. You can probably build a kaleidoscope using the directions supplied in *Inquiring Further*. You will also be able to explain the physics concepts you use in terms of reflected light.

Physics to Go

1. How is light reflecting from a mirror similar to a tennis ball bouncing off a wall?

2. a) What is the normal to a plane mirror?

   b) When a light beam reflects from a plane mirror, how do you measure the angle of incidence?

   c) How do you measure the angle of reflection from a plane mirror?

   d) What is the relationship between the angle of incidence and the angle of reflection?

3. Make a top-view drawing to show the relationships among the normal, the angle of incidence, and the angle of reflection.

4. Suppose you are experimenting with a mirror mounted vertically on a table, like the one you used in this section. Make a top-view drawing. Use a heavy line to represent the mirror and a dotted line to represent the normal.

   a) Show light beams that make angles of incidence of 0°, 30°, 45°, and 60° to the normal.

   b) For each of the above beams, draw the reflected ray. Add a label if necessary to identify each of the rays or use colored pencils for individual sets of incident and reflected rays.

5. Stand in front of a mirror.

   a) Move your hand toward the mirror. Which way does the reflection move?

   b) Move your hand away from the mirror. Which way does the reflection move?

   c) Use what you learned about the position of the mirror image to explain your answers.

6. Suppose you printed the whole alphabet in block (upper case) letters along the normal to a mirror in the way you printed your name in *Step 11* of the *Investigate*.

   a) Which letters would look just like their reflections?

   b) Write three words that would look just like their reflections.

   c) Write three words that would look different from their reflections.

   d) Draw the reflection of each letter you gave in *6.c*).

7. Why is the word *ambulance* written in an unusual way on the front of the ambulance pictured at the right?

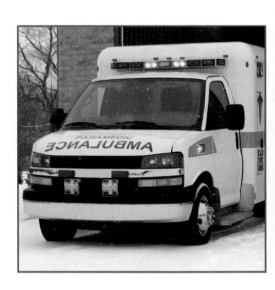

8. Use a ruler and protractor and a ray diagram to locate the image of a small, glowing light bulb placed in front of a plane mirror. Be careful! You must measure as carefully as you can to obtain the most accurate answer.

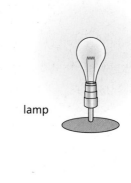

9. Locate the image of the lamp shown in the diagram at right.

10. After reflecting off the mirrors A, B, and C, which target will the ray of light hit?

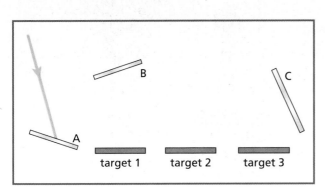

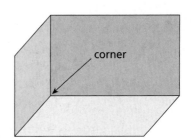

Inquiring Further

1. Reflection from three mirrors

Carefully tape together three small, flat mirrors to make a corner reflector. Shine a laser down into the corner. Where does the reflected beam go? Move the laser beam around so that it always strikes all three mirrors. Does the reflected beam change direction?

2. Building a kaleidoscope

Build a kaleidoscope by carefully inserting two mirrors inside a paper-towel holder. You can also use three identical mirrors. Do not force the mirrors into the tube. Tape the edges of the mirrors together, with the mirrored surfaces inside. Describe what you see through your kaleidoscope.

To make this more interesting, get a small piece of clear plastic tubing and put small pieces of glitter of different colors and baby oil in the tubing. Seal off the ends with sealing wax used when making jellies. This is a safe wax and available in grocery stores. The tubing might be from a spray bottle of window cleaner. Put this filled tube in the center of the paper kaleidoscope tube. Try both the vertical and the horizontal direction and see what the falling pieces of glitter do to make the images produced.

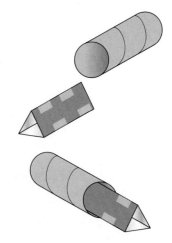

547

Section 7

Curved Mirrors

What Do You See?

Learning Outcomes

In this section, you will

- **Identify** the focal point and focal length of a curved mirror.

- **Observe** virtual images in a convex mirror.

- **Observe** real and virtual images in a concave mirror.

- **Measure** and graph image distance vs. object distance for a concave mirror.

What Do You Think?

The curved mirror of the Palomar telescope is 5 m across. The Hubble Space Telescope has a curved mirror about 2.4 m across. Mirrors with varying curvatures are used in amusement parks as fun-house mirrors. Store mirrors, external mirrors on school buses, and car side-view (passenger-side) mirrors are also curved.

- **How is what you see in curved mirrors different from what you see in ordinary flat mirrors?**

Record your ideas about this question in your *Active Physics* log. Be prepared to discuss your responses with your small group and with your class.

Investigate

In this *Investigate*, you will observe the images formed by a concave and a convex mirror.

1. Look into a *concave mirror*. In a concave mirror, the reflecting surface "caves in."

   a) Record your observations as you change the distance from your face to the mirror.

2. Look into a *convex mirror*. In a convex mirror, the reflecting surface bulges out.

✎ a) Record your observations as you change the distance from your face to the mirror.

3. Carefully set up a laser pointer or the light from a ray box, so the light beam moves horizontally. If you are using a laser, place a glass rod in the light beam so that the beam spreads up and down. Be sure that the laser light is directed safely so that no one's eyes are exposed to the direct beam or to the reflected beam.

4. Place a convex cylindrical mirror in the light beam, as shown in the diagram. Use a pencil to draw a line that follows the outside curved base of the mirror.

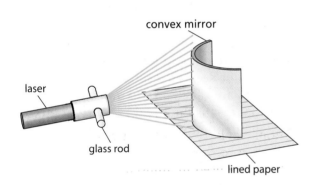

5. Shine a beam directly at the center of the mirror. If you use lined paper, you will find this easy to do. This is the incident beam. Show its path by placing three or more dots on the paper, as you did when tracing rays to and from plane mirrors. Connect the dots to make a straight line. Find the reflected ray and mark its path like you did with the plane mirror. Label the two rays so you will know that one is a reflection of the other.

6. Move the light source sideways to make a series of parallel beams (that is, each new beam is parallel to the original beam). To make sure the incident beams are parallel, use the lines on the paper as a guide. Mark the path of each incoming ray with three dots.

 Never look directly at a laser beam or shine a laser beam into someone's eyes. Always work above the plane of the beam and beware of the reflections from shiny surfaces.

7. Mark the reflected beam that corresponds with each parallel incident beam. Draw the path of each of these reflected rays. Label each incident and reflected ray so you will know that they go together.

8. Examine your incident and reflected rays.

✎ a) Write a sentence to tell what happens to the incident beams after they are reflected.

✎ b) Make a drawing in your *Active Physics* log to record the paths of the light rays.

9. Remove the mirror. With a ruler, extend each reflected ray backward to the part of the paper that was behind the mirror. All the lines converge in a single point (at least approximately). The place where the extended reflected rays meet is called the *focal point of the mirror*. The distance from this point to the mirror is called the *focal length*.

✎ a) Measure and record this focal length.

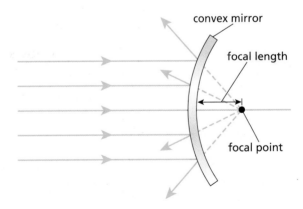

10. Now place the concave side of the cylindrical mirror in the light beam. To help you remember the name concave, think of the concave mirror as "caving in." Repeat *Steps 4* through *6* for this mirror.

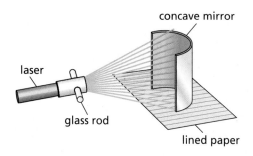

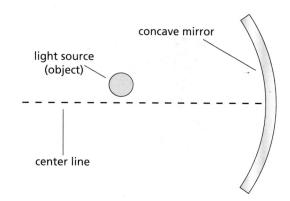

a) Is it true that all the reflected light beams from the concave mirror converge in a single point (at least approximately)?

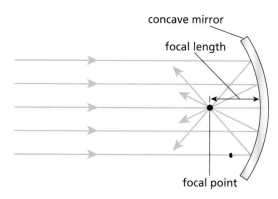

b) Make a drawing in your *Active Physics* log to record the path of the light.

c) Measure and record the focal length.

11. Now that you have located the focal point, move the laser back along the parallel lines as before. As you move the laser, you will notice that the reflected beam always moves through the focal point.

12. How do concave and convex mirrors reflect light differently?

a) Record your answer in your log.

13. Now set up the concave spherical mirror as shown in the diagram. Use a 40-W light bulb as a light source. The light bulb will be called the "object." Carefully mount your mirror so its center is at the same height as the light source. Place the light source about a meter away from the mirror. Put the source slightly off the centerline, as shown.

14. Try to find the image of the light source on an index card. (You may need to move the light source a bit more to the side of the centerline so the index card does not block the light from hitting the mirror.) Move the card back and forth until the image is sharp. The image you found is called a *real image* because you are able to project it on a card or a screen. The images you saw in a flat mirror are not real images because they cannot be seen on a screen or card. Such images are called *virtual images*. Here, virtual means "not real." A virtual image is an apparent source of light rays. The light rays do not actually converge at a virtual image location.

a) Record the distance of the bulb from the reflecting surface of the concave mirror and of the focused image on the index card from the mirror. Put your results in the first line of a table like the one below.

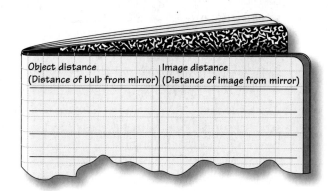

Object distance (Distance of bulb from mirror)	Image distance (Distance of image from mirror)

Active Physics

15. Carefully move the mirror closer to the object. Find the sharp image, as before, by moving the index card back and forth.

 a) Record the image and object distances in your table.

 b) Repeat and record the measurement for at least six object locations.

 c) Draw a graph of the image distance (*y*-axis) versus the object distance (*x*-axis).

 d) Write a sentence that describes the relationship between the image distance and the object distance.

16. The focal length of this concave mirror can be found by finding the location of an object that is very far away from the mirror. Try to locate the image from something visible from the window of your classroom. It is best to stand away

from the window in a slightly darkened room. Alternatively, you can find the image of the bulb when it is placed many meters from the mirror.

 a) Record the focal length.

 b) Investigate what happens if the object distance is less than the focal length. Place an object close to your concave mirror (between the focal point and the mirror) and describe what you see.

17. A convex mirror cannot form a real image that can be projected onto a screen. It can form a virtual image behind the mirror, like a plane mirror.

 a) Record descriptions in your log of the image in a convex mirror when the mirror is held close and when the mirror is held far from the object.

Physics Talk

MAKING REAL IMAGES

You were able to tell the difference between real and virtual images by observing real images produced by a **concave mirror** and virtual images produced by a **convex mirror**.

A **real image** is an image that will project on a screen or on the film of a camera; the rays of light are actually brought together at the image location. A virtual image is an apparent image. A **virtual image** cannot be projected on a screen or on the film of a camera. Light rays after reflection from the mirror diverge and appear to come from a point beyond the mirror.

To find how a concave mirror makes a real image, you can choose three rays of light. Each ray of light obeys the relation you found for plane mirrors (angle of incidence = angle of reflection).

Physics Words

concave mirror: a curved mirror in which the reflecting surface caves in.

convex mirror: a curved mirror in which the reflecting surface bulges out.

real image: an image that can be projected on a screen or on the film of a camera. The rays of light actually pass through the image location.

virtual image: an apparent image from which light rays appear to diverge; it cannot be projected on a screen or on the film of a camera. Light rays do not actually converge at the virtual image location.

Active Physics

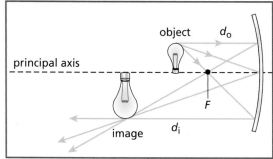

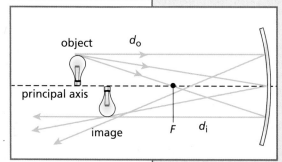

Look at the first diagram. It shows rays coming toward a concave mirror from a point on a light bulb. One ray approaches the mirror parallel to the dotted line, which is the principal axis of the mirror. As you found in the *Investigate*, this ray reflects through the **focal point**. Another ray approaches the center of the mirror. This ray reflects and makes the same angle with the mirror axis going away from the mirror as it did when approaching it. A third ray of light emerges from the bulb and goes through the focal point labeled F in the diagram. This ray hits the mirror and reflects parallel to the principal axis. The image of the top of the light bulb forms where these three reflected rays meet. All other rays leaving the bulb and hitting the mirror also meet at this point. Actually, you can find the location with only two of the three rays shown. The two rays going through the focal point do not require the use of a protractor.

The next drawing shows the same mirror, but with the object much further from the mirror. The image in the second diagram is much smaller and much closer to the focal point. These ray diagrams can account for the real images that you observed with the concave mirror as you moved the light bulb to different distances and observed the images.

The virtual images from the concave mirror can be explained by a similar ray diagram. If the object is closer to the mirror than the **focal length**, the ray of light emerging from the object and parallel to the principal axis will reflect off the mirror and go through the focal point. A second ray of light, which goes from the object as if it came from the focal point, will reflect off the mirror parallel to the principal axis. A third ray of light will leave the object and reflect off the mirror at the point where the principal axis and the mirror meet. This ray reflects and makes the same angle with the mirror axis going away from the mirror as it did when approaching it. These three reflected rays are all diverging. They will never meet on the side of the concave mirror and will therefore, not be able to be projected on a screen. If these three reflected rays enter your eye or a camera, it appears as if they all come from a point beyond the mirror. (The extended rays beyond the mirror are shown as dotted lines in the ray diagram.) This is the location of the virtual image. It is very similar to the virtual image that you investigated from a plane mirror. In the plane mirror, the image was identical in size to the object. In the concave mirror, the image can be larger than the object.

The virtual image from a convex mirror can be explained with the ray diagram shown at right.

Physics Words

focal point (of a mirror): the point where the extended reflected rays that originate from incident rays parallel to the principal axis meet.

focal length (of a mirror): the distance from the focal point to the mirror.

Checking Up

1. Explain how a real image is different from a virtual image.

2. How does a concave mirror produce a real image?

3. How does the object distance relative to the focal length affect the size of the image formed by a curved mirror?

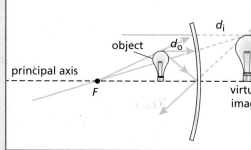

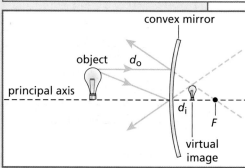

Active Physics

+Math	+Depth	+Concepts	+Exploration
◆			

Active Physics

Plus

Is there an Equation to Relate Focal Length with Object and Image Distances?

A mathematical relation that describes focal length, object distance, and image distance for concave mirrors is

$$\frac{1}{\text{focal length}} = \frac{1}{\text{object distance}} + \frac{1}{\text{image distance}}$$

In mathematical symbols, the relationship is

$$\frac{1}{f} = \frac{1}{d_o} + \frac{1}{d_i}$$

where
f is the focal length of the mirror,
d_o is the object distance, and
d_i is the image distance.

You have measured d_o and d_i in the *Investigate*. Use the values from the log table in *Step 14* to calculate the sum of $\frac{1}{d_o}$ and $\frac{1}{d_i}$ for each pair of data.

1. Record your calculations in your log using a table like the following:

d_o	d_i	$\frac{1}{d_o}$	$\frac{1}{d_i}$	$\frac{1}{d_o} + \frac{1}{d_i}$	f

a) Are your sums approximately equal? If so, you have mathematically found the value of $\frac{1}{f}$ for the mirror you used. From that result, find the focal length.

As you have seen, the distances of the object and image and the focal length are related by the equation below.

$$\frac{1}{f} = \frac{1}{d_o} + \frac{1}{d_i}$$

Look at the graph of the equation that relates focal length, object distance, and image distance. Notice that as the object distance decreases, the image distance becomes very large. As the object distance increases, the image distance approaches the focal length (f).

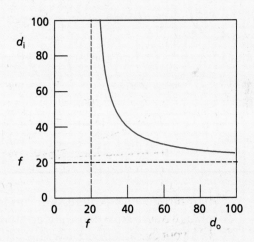

The equation $\frac{1}{f} = \frac{1}{d_o} + \frac{1}{d_i}$ can also be derived from this graph. You can attempt this derivation by recognizing that the graph is a hyperbola that has been shifted by a distance equal to the focal length in both the x- and y-axes.

Active Physics

What Do You Think Now?

At the beginning of this section, you were asked the following:

- **How is what you see in curved mirrors different from what you see in ordinary flat mirrors?**

Use your observations from the *Investigate* to compare the images. Be sure to include the difference between real and virtual image and the size of the images with the two mirrors.

Physics
Essential Questions

What does it mean?

A general simple principle such as the law of reflection can help explain curved mirrors as well as plane mirrors. Where is the angle of incidence and angle of reflection when light travels from the object to a concave mirror and then reflects off the concave mirror and moves through the focal point?

How do you know?

What evidence do you have that the image produced by a concave mirror can be a different size than the object? How could you demonstrate this to someone?

Why do you believe?

Connects with Other Physics Content	Fits with Big Ideas in Science	Meets Physics Requirements
Waves and interactions	Models	✳ Good, clear explanation, no more complex than necessary.

✳ When physicists "explain" or "understand" some effect, such as the formation of images with mirrors, they apply fundamental principles or laws to show how the effect occurs. How does the law of reflection help you understand the relationship among object distance, image distance, and focal length for a curved mirror?

Why should you care?
Technology allows you to take ideas in science and design and build useful objects. Give some examples of the use of curved mirrors in everyday life. How can curved mirrors be used in your challenge?

Reflecting on the Section and the Challenge

You have observed how rays of light are reflected by a curved mirror. You have seen that a concave mirror can make a real image (an image on a screen). In addition, you have seen that there is no real image formed by a convex mirror, and the image is always smaller than the object.

You may want to use a curved mirror in your sound and light show. You may want to project an image on a screen or produce a reflection that the audience can see in the mirror. What you have learned will help you explain how these images are made.

Since the image changes with distance, you may try to find a way to have a moving object so that the image will automatically move and change size. A small ball suspended by a string in front of a mirror may produce an interesting effect. You may also wish to combine convex and concave mirrors so that some parts of the object are larger and others are smaller. Convex and concave mirrors could be shaped from pliable materials covered with aluminum foil or coated with reflective materials to make a kind of fun-house mirror.

Remember that your sound and light show will be judged partly on creativity and partly on the application of physics principles. This section has provided you with some useful principles that can help with both criteria.

Physics to Go

1. Make a drawing of parallel laser rays aimed at a convex mirror. Draw lines to show how the beams reflect from the mirror.

2. Make a drawing of parallel laser rays aimed at a concave mirror. Draw lines to show how the beams reflect from the mirror.

3. a) Look at the back of a shiny spoon. What do you see?

   b) Look at the inside of a spoon. What do you see?

4. a) If you were designing a shaving or makeup mirror, would you make it concave or convex? Explain your answer.

   a) Why do some makeup mirrors have two sides? What do the different sides do? How does each side produce its own special view?

   b) How does a curved passenger-side mirror on a car produce a useful view? What kind of curved mirror is used?

   c) Why does a dentist use a curved mirror?

5. A ball is hung on a string in front of a flat mirror. The ball swings toward the mirror and back. How would the image of the ball in the mirror change as the ball swings back and forth?

6. A ball is hung on a string in front of a concave mirror. The ball swings toward the mirror and back. How would the image of the ball in the mirror change as the ball swings back and forth?

7. A student found the real image of a light bulb in a concave mirror. The student moved the light bulb to different positions. At each position, the student measured the distance of the image and the light bulb from the mirror. The results are shown in the table.

d_o (cm)	d_i (cm)
15	100
25	35
50	20.8
90	17.5

a) Draw a graph of this data.

b) Make a general statement to summarize how the image distance changes as the object distance changes.

c) Estimate where the image would be if the light bulb were twice as far away as the greatest object distance in the data.

d) Estimate what would happen to the image location if the object were only half as far from the mirror as the smallest object distance in the data.

8. Outdoors at night, you use a large concave mirror to make an image on a card of distant automobile headlights. What happens to the image as the car gradually comes closer?

9. The diagram shows a light ray R parallel to the principal axis of a concave (converging) mirror. Point F is the focal point and C is the center of curvature. If you would extend the mirror surface to form a complete circle, C would be at the center of the circle.

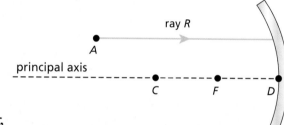

a) The light ray R is parallel to the principal axis, reflects from the mirror, and travels through the focal point F. Draw this ray in your diagram.

b) A line drawn from C to the mirror is perpendicular to the mirror surface. That line can serve as the normal when measuring the angle of incidence and the angle of reflection. Draw the ray R and its reflected ray by measuring the angle of incidence relative to the normal and drawing the reflected ray at the appropriate angle of reflection relative to the normal.

c) The new ray should go through the focal point. If your mirror is too curved, this does not happen. That is why in some ray diagrams the mirror is depicted as a straight line. Repeat *Steps a) and b)* with a curved mirror depicted as a straight line.

10. The diagram to the right shows a curved mirror surface, a light bulb, and its image. In relation to the focal point of the mirror, where is the light bulb (object) most likely located?

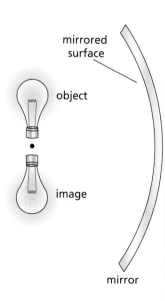

Active Physics

11. A candle is located beyond the center of curvature, C, of a concave mirror having a focal point, F, as shown in the diagram. Sketch the image of the candle.

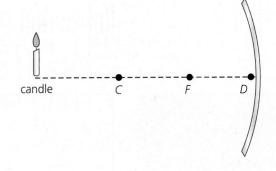

12. The diagram below shows four rays of light from object *AB* incident on a concave mirror with a focal length of 0.04 m. Point *F* is the principal focus of the mirror, point *C* is the center of curvature, and point *O* is located on the principal axis.

   a) Which ray of light will pass through *F* after it is reflected from the mirror?

   b) As object *AB* is moved from its position toward the left (away from the mirror), what will happen to the size of the image produced?

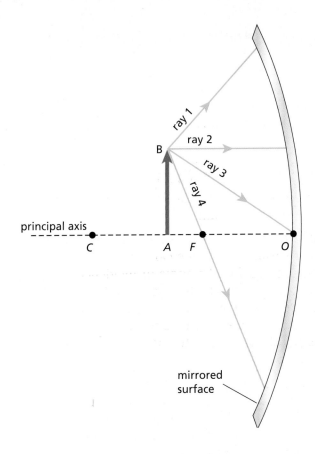

13. *Preparing for the Chapter Challenge*

   Write down a few ideas that can show how a concave or convex mirror could be used in your sound and light show.

Section 8

Refraction of Light

What Do You See?

Learning Outcomes

In this section, you will

- **Observe** refraction.

- **Measure** angles of incidence and refraction.

- **Measure** the critical angle.

- **Observe** total internal reflection.

What Do You Think?

The Hope Diamond is valued at about 100 million dollars. A piece of cut glass of about the same size is worth only a few dollars.

- **How can a jeweler tell the difference between a diamond and cut glass?**

Record your ideas about this question in your *Active Physics* log. Be prepared to discuss your responses with your small group and with your class.

Investigate

In this section, you will use an acrylic block and the light from a laser beam to observe the refraction of light.

1. Place an acrylic block on a piece of white paper on your desk. Have one member of your group hold a pencil or some other thin, tall object behind the acrylic block while you look at the object through the block.

   a) Describe what you see as you move your head back and forth sideways. Record your observations in your *Active Physics* log.

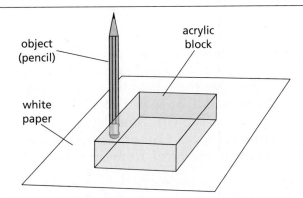

2. Trace the outside of the acrylic block on the paper. Carefully aim a laser pointer, or the light from a ray box, so the light beam moves horizontally, as you did in previous sections. Remember to follow the safety rules when using lasers and never allow any of the transmitted or reflected light to fall on a student's eye.

Place a glass rod in the light beam so that the beam spreads up and down.

3. Shine the laser pointer or light from the ray box through the acrylic block. Be sure the beam leaves the acrylic block on the side opposite the side the beam enters.

a) Mark the path of each beam. You may wish to use a series of dots as you did before.

b) Label each path on both sides of the acrylic block so you will know that they go together.

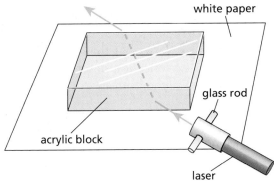

You may notice that some of the incident light is reflected off the acrylic block. Use a series of dots to mark the reflected ray.

4. Remove the acrylic block.

a) Connect the paths you traced to show the light beam hitting the front surface of the acrylic block, traveling through

the acrylic block, and emerging from the acrylic block. You cannot see the laser beam traveling through the acrylic block, but you can tell where the beam entered and left. To get the path of the laser beam through the block, just connect these points with a straight line. Note that the direction of the beam is not the same as that in air. The light has been *refracted* by the block.

b) Draw perpendicular lines (the normals) at the point where rays enter and leave the acrylic block. Label these lines as normal.

c) Measure the angles of incidence (the angle between the incident ray and the normal in the air), reflection (the angle between the reflected ray and the normal in the air), and refraction (the angle between the refracted ray and the normal in the acrylic block).

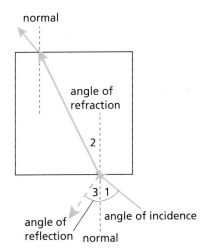

d) Record your measurements in a table like the one shown.

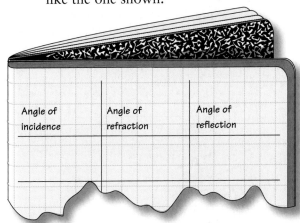

Angle of incidence	Angle of refraction	Angle of reflection

5. Repeat *Steps 2, 3,* and *4* for two more (different) angles of incidence. Use a separate sheet of paper for each trial.

  a) Draw a graph of angle of refraction (*y*-axis) versus the angle of incidence (*x*-axis).

  b) Use your graph to predict the angle of refraction if the angle of incidence is 45°.

  c) Set up the acrylic block and light source so the angle of incidence is 45°. Find the angle of refraction. Compare the angle of refraction to your prediction.

6. Some of the incident light reflected off the acrylic block. Does the law of reflection hold true for the light reflected from the surface of the acrylic block?

7. Replace the acrylic block with the 45°-90°-45° glass prism, lying flat on a piece of paper. Aim the laser beam as shown in the diagram so that the beam enters a short side of the triangle and leaves on the long side.

  a) Trace the outline of the prism and make some dots to mark the incident ray and refracted ray.

  b) Draw the normals where the incident ray enters the prism and where the refracted ray leaves the prism.

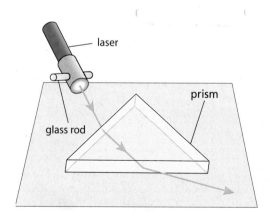

8. Put the prism on a new sheet of paper. Now direct the laser beam so that it approaches the side of the prism along the normal (that is, perpendicular to the side as shown). Note that the laser beam no longer exits at the bottom but now exits the prism from the other side.

  a) Trace the outline of the prism and make some dots to mark the incident ray and refracted ray.

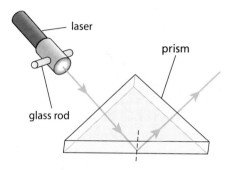

Note that the long side of the prism is acting as a mirror. This situation is called *total internal reflection* because the inside of the prism acts like a perfect mirror (total reflection) and the reflected light stays inside the prism (until it gets to the other side).

  b) Extend the lines indicating the incident rays and refracted rays to see where they hit the bottom of the prism. Draw the normal at that point. Does the law of reflection describe what happens at the bottom of the prism?

9. Swivel the incident beam at various angles and determine when the beam refracted at the bottom just disappears. (This may be difficult to find precisely because the refracted beam gets weak just before it disappears.) The angle of incidence at the bottom of the prism when the refracted beam at the bottom just disappears—skimming the bottom— is called the *critical angle* of refraction.

10. It is possible to bend a long, thin acrylic rod so the light enters the narrow end of the acrylic rod, reflects off one side of the acrylic rod, then reflects off the other and back again, emerging from the other narrow end. Try to bend a long acrylic rod so that the light is reflected as described. A flexible glass or plastic rod used in this manner is called an optical fiber. You may have seen such fibers on lamps in novelty stores.

Physics Talk

SNELL'S LAW (THE LAW OF REFRACTION)

A light ray refracts (bends) when it goes from one material to another. You have explored light going from air to acrylic and from acrylic back into air. This bending occurs whether the substances are acrylic, glass, water, or diamond. The amount of bending depends on the properties of the two materials. Each transparent material has a specific property called the **index of refraction**.

A diamond with a high index of refraction (lots of bending when light comes in from the air) can be distinguished from glass with lower index of refraction (less bending when light comes in from the air). If neighboring materials have nearly the same index of refraction, the bending is small as light travels from one material to the other. For example, if you submerge your acrylic block in a container of water (use a container with flat sides), you will find that the amount of bending of light when it goes from water to acrylic or from acrylic back into water is relatively small. The index of refraction for water is close to that for acrylic. The index of refraction for air is 1.0003. For water, the index of refraction is 1.33; for acrylic it is about 1.5, and for diamond about 2.5.

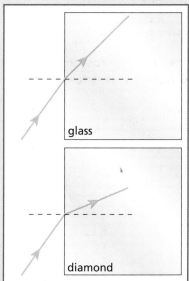

Light entering glass and diamond at the same angle bends much more when it enters the diamond.

The relationship between the index of refraction and the ratio of the sine of angle of incidence to the sine of angle of refraction for each of the two materials is called the **law of refraction** or **Snell's law**.

Physics Words

index of refraction: a property of the materials at an interface that determine the relationship between the angle of incidence and the angle of refraction.

Snell's law: the relationship between the index of refraction and the ratio of the sine of angle of incidence to the sine of angle of refraction at the boundary of the two media where refraction takes place.

Snell's law states that as light enters a substance such as acrylic (high index of refraction) from air (low index of refraction), the light bends toward the normal. When light leaves a substance such as acrylic (high index of refraction) and enters the air (low index of refraction), it bends away from the normal. The larger the difference in the index of refraction for the two materials, the larger the difference between the angle of incidence and the angle of refraction.

If the light is entering material such as air (with a low index of refraction) from a substance with a higher index of refraction, the angle in that substance may be such that the angle of refraction is 90°. In this special case, the angle in the substance is called the **critical angle**. If the angle in the substance is greater than this critical angle, then the light does not enter the air but reflects back into the substance as if the surface were a perfect mirror. This is the basis for optical fibers in which laser light reflects off the inner walls of glass or plastic and travels down the fiber, regardless of the bend in the fiber.

You noticed in the investigation at every air-glass interface, some of the light was reflected and some of the light was refracted. The exception to this was the light's angle of incidence was greater than the critical angle. In this case, all of the light was reflected back into the glass. The result is **total internal reflection**.

Physics Words

critical angle:
the angle of incidence, for a light ray passing from one medium to another, that has an angle of refraction of 90°.

total internal reflection:
a phenomenon in which the refracting medium acts like a perfect mirror and the reflected light stays inside the medium.

In the diagram, rays 1-3 leave the glass and bend away from the normal as they enter the air. Ray 4 leaves the glass and bends away from the normal such that its angle of refraction is 90°. The angle of incidence is defined as the critical angle. Ray 5 has an angle of incidence greater than the critical angle. It reflects back into the glass. The angle of incidence is equal to the angle of reflection.

It turns out that the index of refraction is also related to the speed with which light travels in vacuum and also to the average speed with which light travels through the material. The relationship is expressed as

$$\text{index of refraction} = \frac{\text{speed of light in vacuum}}{\text{speed of light in the material}}$$

The speed of light in a vacuum is 2.99×10^8 m/s, a very high speed! In fact, it is the fastest speed that anything can attain.

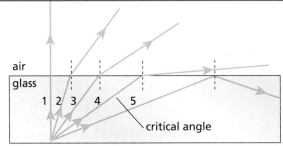

Checking Up

1. Why do light rays bend when they travel from one substance to another?

2. Explain how you can measure a diamond's index of refraction.

3. Explain Snell's law.

Active Physics Plus

+Math	+Depth	+Concepts	+Exploration
◆			

Using Snell's Law to Analyze Your *Investigate* Data

The law of refraction (Snell's law) can be expressed in mathematical terms. The expression involves the trigonometric sine of the angle of incidence (θ_i), the sine of the angle of refraction (θ_r), and the index of refraction of each of the two materials. This relationship can be mathematically expressed as

$$n_i \sin \theta_i = n_r \sin \theta_r$$

$$\text{or} \quad \frac{\sin \theta_i}{\sin \theta_r} = \frac{n_r}{n_i}$$

1. Using your data from this section, find the sine of the angles using a calculator. (Use the SIN button and be sure the calculator is set for angles in degrees.)

2. For each angle of incidence and angle of refraction pair, calculate the ratio

$$\frac{\sin \theta_i}{\sin \theta_r}$$

3. According to the law of refraction, this ratio should be the same for all pairs of angles. The ratio should equal the ratio of the two indexes of refraction $\frac{n_r}{n_i}$.

   Does this relationship work for your combination of air and acrylic?

What Do You See Now?

The cartoon at the beginning of *Section 8* shows how a person can see a fish behind a rock due to the bending of light. In the cartoon, the arrow shows the direction the person is looking. The light actually travels from the fish to the person's eye. Should the cartoonist reverse the arrow?

What Do You Think Now?

At the beginning of the section, you were asked the following:

• **How can a jeweler tell the difference between a diamond and cut glass?**

Now that you know how refraction occurs, what would be different between diamond and cut glass to allow a jeweler to recognize a diamond? How does your answer relate to Snell's law and critical angles?

Physics
Essential Questions

What does it mean?

In this section, you learned that light travels in straight lines until it interacts with materials. When light travels from one medium to another, its direction can be changed by the process of refraction. Explain what you mean by the term "refraction of light."

How do you know?

Physicists prefer to find quantitative relationships among basic properties based on observations and experiments. How are the angle of incidence and the angle of refraction related? Tell how you know this from your experiments in the *Investigate*.

Why do you believe?

Connects with Other Physics Content	Fits with Big Ideas in Science	Meets Physics Requirements
Waves and interactions	✳ Interactions of matter, energy and fields	Experimental evidence is consistent with models and theories

✳ When scientists observe new phenomena, they often have to modify previously stated general principles. Does light always travel in straight lines? How do your observations of refraction modify your statement about the general principle that light travels in straight lines?

Why should you care?

The aspect of light behavior such as refraction is very general and occurs in many different situations. Give some examples of the use of refraction in everyday life. How can the refraction of light be used as part of the entertainment in your sound and light show?

Reflecting on the Section and the Challenge

The bending of light as it goes from one material into another material is called refraction. It is mathematically expressed by Snell's law, which involves the material property called the index of refraction. The higher the index of refraction, the slower the average speed of the light traveling in that material.

As you design your light show for the *Chapter Challenge*, you may find creative uses of refraction. You may decide to have light bending in such a way that it spells out a letter or word or forms a picture. You may wish to have the light travel from air into glass to change its direction. You may have it bend by different amounts by replacing one material with another. Regardless of how you use refraction effects, you can now explain the physics principles behind them.

Physics to Go

1. A light ray goes from the air into an acrylic block. In general, which is larger, the angle of incidence or the angle of refraction?

2. a) Make a sketch of a ray of light as it enters a piece of acrylic block and is refracted.

   b) Now turn the ray around so it goes backward. What was the angle of refraction is now the angle of incidence. Does the turned-around ray follow the path of the original ray?

3. A light ray enters an acrylic block from the air. Make a diagram to show the angle of incidence, the angle of refraction, and the normal at the edge of the acrylic block.

4. Light rays enter an acrylic block from the air. Make drawings to show rays with angles of incidence of 30° and 60°. Use your data from this section to find the angle of refraction for each of these rays. For each incident ray, sketch the refracted ray that passes through the acrylic block.

5. a) Light is passing from the air into an acrylic block. What is the maximum possible angle of incidence that will permit light to pass into the acrylic block? Refer to your data for refraction of a light ray entering the acrylic block from the air.

   b) Make a sketch to show your answer. Include the refracted ray (inside the acrylic block) in your sketch.

6. a) A ray of light is already inside an acrylic block and is heading out. What is the name of the maximum possible angle of incidence that will permit the light to pass out of the acrylic block?

   b) If you make the angle of incidence greater than this special angle, what happens to the light?

   c) Make a sketch to show your answer. Be sure to show what happened to the light.

7. a) Make a drawing of a light ray that enters the front side of a rectangular piece of acrylic block and leaves through the back side.

   b) What is the relationship between the direction of the ray that enters the acrylic block and the direction of the ray that leaves the acrylic block?

8. You have seen the colored bands that a prism, cut glass, or water produce from sunlight. Light that you see as different colors has different wavelengths. Since refraction makes these bands, what can you say about the way light of different wavelengths refracts?

9. Active Physics Plus Light enters a piece of glass ($n = 1.50$) from air ($n = 1.00$) at an angle of 45°. Calculate the angle of refraction in glass using Snell's law.

10. **Active Physics Plus** To investigate whether a stone in a ring is a real diamond ($n = 2.42$) or a piece of cut glass ($n = 1.50$), a student/physicist observes a laser beam emerging from the stone. The angle of incidence in the stone is 20°. The angle of refraction in air is 56°. What does the physicist conclude from this data? Is the stone in the ring a diamond or glass?

11. **Active Physics Plus** Compare the angle of refraction in water ($n = 1.33$), glass ($n = 1.50$), and diamond ($n = 2.42$) if the angle of incidence is 45° for each.

12. *Preparing for the Chapter Challenge*

Design a light effect that uses refraction of light. You may wish to look at one of the suggestions in *Inquiring Further* for ideas. Explain your light effect using what you have learned about refraction in this section.

Inquiring Further

1. **Setting up a special effect using total internal reflection**

Find some small-diameter, clear, flexible tubing, about 2 m long. Plug one end of the tube. Pour clear gelatin in the other end, through a funnel, before the gelatin has had time to set. Arrange the tubing into an interesting shape and let the gelatin set. You may wish to mount your tube on a support or a sturdy piece of cardboard, which can be covered with interesting reflective material, such as iridescent paper. Fasten one end of the tube so laser light can easily shine straight into it. When the gelatin has set, turn on the laser. What do you see? This light-trapping phenomenon is called total internal reflection.

2. **Using different media to observe refraction**

Place your acrylic block in a clear, rectangular container of water. The water container should be large enough so that the acrylic block can be turned in different directions. Shine a laser beam perpendicular to the side of the water container so the beam hits the acrylic block. Rotate the acrylic block and observe how the angle of incidence and angle of refraction change when the block is immersed in water. Explain what is happening.

3. **The "magic" reappearing penny**

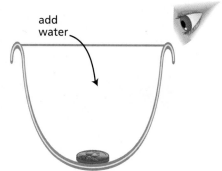

add water

Place a penny in the bottom of an opaque drinking glass. Position your eye so that the penny is just out of view when you look over the rim of the glass. Predict what will happen when you fill the glass with water. Then try it and see what happens. How can you explain the results?

Section 9

Effect of Lenses on Light

What Do You See?

Learning Outcomes

In this section, you will

- **Observe** real images formed by a convex lens.

- **Project** a slide using a lens.

- **Relate** image size and position to object size and position and the properties of your lens.

What Do You Think?

Lenses are used in binoculars, telescopes, microscopes, and cameras.

- **How is a lens able to project movies or take photographs?**

Record your ideas about this question in your *Active Physics* log. Be prepared to discuss your responses with your small group and with your class.

Investigate

1. Look at the lens your teacher gives you.

   a) Make a side-view drawing of this lens in your log. This is a *convex lens*. A convex lens is thicker in the middle and thinner toward the edges.

2. Point the lens at a window or at something distant outside. Use a file card as a screen. Look for an image on the screen as you move it toward and then away from the lens. Keep moving the card until you see a sharp image of a distant object.

   a) Sketch the arrangement of the lens, the screen, and the window that allows you to see the image of the distant object on the card.

Active Physics

b) Describe what you see. Is the image large or small? Is the image right-side up or upside down? Is it reversed left to right? This image is called "real" because you can project it on a screen.

⚠️ Do not use a lens with chipped edges. Mount the lens securely in a holder. Use only light sources with enclosed or covered electrical contacts.

3. If the object is very far away, the position of this image is very near the focal point (focus) of the lens. The distance from the center of the lens to the image is about equal to the focal length of the lens. It is the same location at which parallel rays of light coming through the other side of the lens would converge.

a) Measure or approximate the object distance (the distance between the object and the lens).

b) Measure the image distance (the distance between the image and the lens).

c) Record your object and image distance. Note that in this case, the image distance is also about equal to the focal length of the lens.

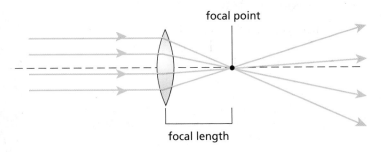

focal point

focal length

4. Set up a clear-filament 40-W light bulb as a light source. Mount the lens at the same height as the light source. Point the light bulb right at the lens, as shown. You can first explore the lens qualitatively by trying to form different images with the same lens.

⚠️ Caution: Lamps get very hot.

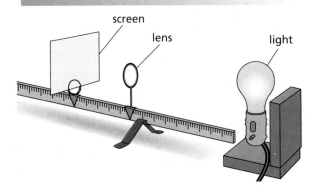

screen

lens

light

a) Adjust the lens, light source, and screen such that a crisp image is formed that is *smaller* than the light source. Record the arrangement in your log.

b) Adjust the lens, light source, and screen such that a crisp image is formed on the screen that is *larger* than the light source. Record the arrangement in your log.

c) Adjust the lens, light source, and screen such that a crisp image is formed that is the *same size* as the light source. Record the arrangement in your log.

5. After exploring the images formed by a lens, you will now investigate the images more quantitatively. By varying the object distance, you will locate the image and record the image distance. By gathering such data, you will learn more about the lens and its properties.

Place the light bulb about a meter away from the lens. Find the image of the light bulb on a screen.

a) Record your results in a table, including the distance of the image from the lens and the appearance of the image. (Is it upside down or upright? Is it bigger or smaller than the object?)

6. Repeat *Step 5* for a variety of smaller object distances.

a) Collect your data in an organized table with columns d_o (distance of the object from the lens) and d_i (distance of the image from the lens).

b) Include in your log a statement about image size relative to object size.

c) Look at your table and see if there are any basic patterns relating d_o, d_i, and image size. What are the patterns and what is the evidence for them?

7. Make an object by carefully cutting a hole in the shape of an arrow in an index card. Position the card close to the light bulb.

a) Observe the image of the object on the screen. Describe what you see in your log.

b) Position the arrow cards at different distances between the light bulb and the convex lens. Record happens to the image.

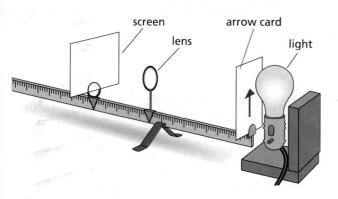

8. Project the image of the arrow onto the wall. Can you make what you project larger or smaller?

a) In your log, indicate what you did to change the size of the image.

9. Make a small slide by drawing an arrow with a marking pen on a clear transparency sheet. Place the slide in different positions between the light bulb and a screen.

a) Describe how you can project a real, enlarged image of your slide onto a screen or wall.

b) How can you use the lens position to change the size of the image?

c) In your log, record how you think this effect might be part of your light and sound show.

10. Your teacher will now give you a new lens. Your group should figure out how to do the following. Record your procedures in your *Active Physics* log.

a) Determine the focal length of the lens.

b) Using a 1-cm long arrow object, find at least three combinations of object distance (d_o) and image distance (d_i) and the appearance/size of the image.

c) Find an object distance that produces an image the same size as the original object.

d) Find an object distance that produces an image twice the size as the original object.

11. With your teacher's approval, carry out your procedure and record the data.

12. The equation $\dfrac{1}{f} = \dfrac{1}{d_o} + \dfrac{1}{d_i}$ that you used for relating d_o, d_i, and focal length f for mirrors also works for lenses. Use this equation with your results from *Steps 3, 5,* and *11* to see if it provides a good description of your results. (Hint: Use your calculator to determine f from d_i and d_o.)

Physics Talk

RAY DIAGRAMS

Images Formed by a Convex Lens

You are probably more familiar with images produced by lenses than you are with images from curved mirrors. The lens is responsible for images formed by projectors, cameras, microscopes, and binoculars.

Physics Words

convex lens: a lens that is thicker in the middle and thinner toward the edge. Rays that enter the lens parallel to the axis of the lens will converge toward the axis and cross the axis on the far side of the lens at the focal point. A convex lens is also called a converging lens.

focal point: for a convex lens, the place where light rays that approach the lens parallel to the principal axis converge on the far side of the lens. For a concave lens, the place from which the rays that originated from rays that approach the lens parallel to the principal axis seem to diverge.

Light refracts (bends) as it enters glass and bends again when it leaves the glass. The **convex lens** is thicker in the middle and thinner toward the edge. Rays that enter the lens parallel to the axis of the lens will converge toward the axis and cross the axis on the far side of the lens at the **focal point** (**F**). The distance between the focal point and the center of the lens is called the focal length of the lens. A convex lens is also called a converging lens. Because light can go either way through a lens, there are two focal points, one on each side of the lens.

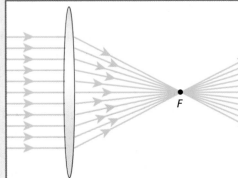

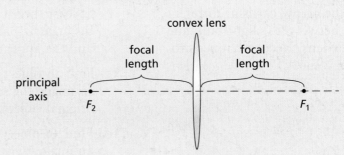

If an object is illuminated, it reflects light in all directions. If these rays of light pass through a lens, an image may be formed. You observed this with the image from outside the window produced by a lens on your index-card screen. You also observed this with the image of the arrow produced by a lens.

Although all of the light rays from the object help to form the image, you can locate an image by choosing two easy rays to draw—the ray that is parallel to the principal axis and travels through the focal point, and the ray that travels through the center of the lens and continues undeflected. (These rays are in red in the diagram.)

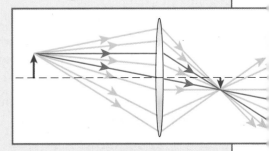

You can use this technique to see how images that are larger (movie projector), smaller (camera), and the same size (copy machine) as the object, can be formed with the same lens. A movie projector puts the film very close to the focal point of the lens and makes a very large image that you observe at the movies. The film is placed upside down so that the image you see is right-side up. A camera lens uses an object (for example, a tree, a person) at a distance much larger than the focal length of the lens. The lens produces a very small image that can either fit onto a small piece of film or can be recorded digitally. A copy machine uses a lens to produce an image that is the same size as the original.

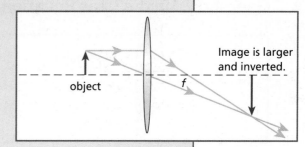

If the object is close to the lens (an object distance smaller than the focal length), then a real image is not formed. However, if you were to view the rays emerging, they would appear to have come from a place on the same side of the lens as the object. To view this virtual image, you put your eye on the side of the lens opposite the object and peer through the lens—it's a magnifying glass!

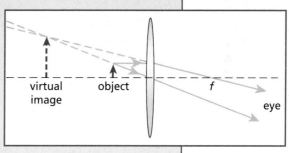

Sample Problem

The diagram shows a lens and an object.

a) Using a ray diagram, locate the image of the object shown.

b) Describe the image completely.

Strategy: Choose a location on the object to be the origin of the rays. A simple choice would be the tip of the arrow. At least two rays must be drawn to locate the image.

Given: See the diagram.

Solution:

a)

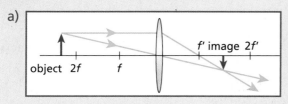

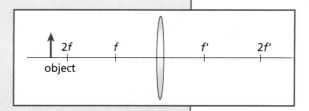

b) The image is real, reduced in size, and inverted (relative to the object).

As the object moves closer to the lens, its image size will increase. At $d_o = f$ there will be no image and at $d_o < f$ the image will be virtual and upright.

Checking Up

1. How would you locate an image formed by a convex lens?

2. Is it possible to change the size of an image using a convex lens? Explain your answer.

3. How does a convex lens form a virtual image?

+Math	+Depth	+Concepts	+Exploration
◆◆			

Plus

Geometry for the Lens Equation

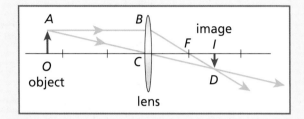

By using some geometry and algebra and the diagram shown here, you can derive the lens equation

$$\frac{1}{d_o} + \frac{1}{d_i} = \frac{1}{f}.$$

Note that the object distance is given by $d_o = \overline{OC}$, the image distance is given by $d_i = \overline{CI}$, and the focal length (the distance from the lens to the focal point) is given by $f = \overline{CF}$. The object height is $h_o = \overline{AO}$ and the image height is $h_i = \overline{ID}$.

The figure above shows two representative light rays leaving the tip A of the object arrow on the left. The ray traveling from A to B is parallel to the principal axis of the lens and hence passes through the focal point F on the far side of the lens.

The second ray passes through the center of the lens C and is not deviated (for a thin lens).

The two rays cross at point D, which is the location of the image of the tip of the arrow. It is a real image because the rays of light actually converge there. Also note that the tip of the arrow is in the reverse position on the opposite side of the lens so that the image will be inverted or upside down.

a) Opposite angles are equal. Hence, $\angle ACO = \angle ICD$.

b) Triangles AOC and CID are right triangles because the original arrow is perpendicular to the optic axis. Use geometry to show that the two triangles, AOC and CID are similar.

c) Since triangles AOC and CID are similar, use geometry to show that $\dfrac{\overline{AO}}{\overline{OC}} = \dfrac{\overline{ID}}{\overline{CI}}$ or in terms of object distance, object height, image distance, and image height $\dfrac{h_o}{d_o} = \dfrac{h_i}{d_i}$.
(Note that this result can be rearranged to give the magnification expression $\dfrac{h_i}{h_o} = \dfrac{d_i}{d_o}$.)

d) Triangles BCF and FID also are similar triangles. Use geometry to show that this is true.

e) Since triangles BCF and FID are similar triangles, you can use geometry to prove that $\dfrac{\overline{BC}}{\overline{CF}} = \dfrac{\overline{ID}}{\overline{FI}}$ or $\dfrac{h_o}{f} = \dfrac{h_i}{(d_i - f)}$.

f) Use the magnification expression from c) with the result from d) to write $\dfrac{h_i}{h_o} = \dfrac{d_i}{d_o} = \dfrac{d_i - f}{f} = \dfrac{d_i}{f} - 1$, where you broke up the last fraction into two parts to get $\dfrac{d_i}{d_o} = \dfrac{d_i}{f} - 1$.

g) Divide both sides of the previous equation by d_i to show that $\dfrac{1}{d_o} = \dfrac{1}{f} - \dfrac{1}{d_o}$ or $\dfrac{1}{d_o} + \dfrac{1}{d_i} = \dfrac{1}{f}$, which is the lens equation.

What Do You Think Now?

At the beginning of the section, you were asked the following:

• **How is a lens able to project movies or take photographs?**

Now that you have investigated how images are formed using a convex lens, explain how the distance between an object and a lens relates to the formation of an image.

Physics

Essential Questions

What does it mean?

Applications of the law of refraction can lead to a wonderful and useful technology like the lens. What is a lens? What is meant by the focal length of a converging lens?

How do you know?

What evidence do you have that the same lens can be used to create large images and small images?

Why do you believe?

onnects with Other Physics Content	Fits with Big Ideas in Science	Meets Physics Requirements
ves and interactions	Models	✳ Experimental evidence is consistent with models and theories

✳ Physicists create models to explain and predict phenomena. The ray diagram is a model that shows how and where the image is formed. Explain how you know that the ray-diagram model does a good job at explaining the size and location of images. Specifically, is your experimental evidence consistent with this model?

Why should you care?

When scientists and engineers invent new devices, they like to apply them to many new situations. Give some examples of the use of lenses in everyday life. How will what you learned in this section help you with your challenge?

Reflecting on the Section and the Challenge

You have explored how convex lenses make real images. You have found these images on a screen by moving a card back and forth until the image was sharp and clear, so you know that the sharp images occur at a particular place. Bringing the object near the lens moves the image away from the lens and enlarges the image, but if the object is too close to the lens, there is no real image. The real images are reversed left to right and are upside down. You may be able to use this kind of image in your sound and light show. You have also projected images of slides on a wall. You may be able to add interest by moving the lens and screen to change the size of these images. You may also be able to project a real image at a spot in space that does not have a screen. The image will not appear until you wave a wand in that location in space or until a student, or something, moves into that space to reflect the image.

Physics to Go

1. If the image of an object is at the focal point of a lens, where is the object located?

    a) What is the focal length of a lens?

    b) How can you measure the focal length of a lens?

2. In the *Investigate*, you set up a lens and screen to make an image of a distant light source.

    a) Is the image right-side up or upside down?

    b) Did the lens bend light to make this image? How can you tell?

    c) A distant light source begins moving toward a fixed (stationary) lens. What must you do to keep the image sharp?

3. You make an image of a light bulb with a convex lens.

    a) What can you do to make the image smaller than the light bulb?

    b) What can you do to make the image larger than the light bulb?

4. You have two lights, a lens, and a screen, as shown in the diagram. One light is a great distance from the lens. The other light is much closer.

light   light   lens   screen

    a) If you see a sharp image of the distant light, describe the image of the closer light.

    b) If you see a sharp image of the closer light, describe the image of the more distant light.

    c) Could you see a sharp image of both lights at the same time? Explain how you found your answer.

5. Using a ray diagram, locate the image formed by the lens at the right.

2f   f   f′   2f′

6. An object is placed 20 cm from a convex lens. A real image of the object is formed 50 cm on the other side of the lens. What is the focal length of the lens?

7. An object 1.5 cm tall is placed 5.0 cm in front of a converging lens of focal length 8.0 cm.

   a) Determine the location of the image.

   b) Is the image a real image or a virtual image? (Hint: Draw a ray diagram for this situation.)

   c) Is the image upright or inverted? Is it larger or smaller than the object?

8. A relative wants to show you slides from her wedding in 1972. She brings out her slide projector and screen.

   a) If she puts the screen 2.8 m from the projector and the lens has a focal length of 10.0 cm, how far from the lens will the slide be so that her pictures are in focus?

   b) Why does she put the slides into the projector upside down?

9. The right diagram shows an object 0.030 m high placed at point X, 0.60 m from the center of the lens. An image is formed at point Y, 0.30 m from the center of the lens. Describe the image completely.

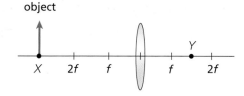

10. The second diagram represents an object placed two focal lengths from a converging lens. At which point will the image be located? Base your prediction on both your data on object and image distances and on a result calculated from the lens equation.

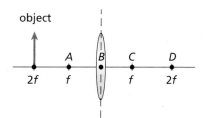

11. The third diagram shows a lens with an object located at position A. Describe what will happen to the image formed as the object is moved from position A to position B.

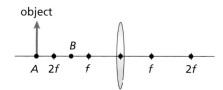

12. a) What kind of lens is used in your classroom overhead (transparency) projector? Does it form a real image or a virtual image?

   b) When you focus the projector to make a clear image of the transparency sheet, are you changing the object distance or the image distance (or perhaps both)?

   c) Why is the image on the screen not inverted in comparison with the object (the transparency sheet)?

13. *Preparing for the Chapter Challenge*

   Describe how you could use a convex lens in your sound and light show. What could you use as an object? Where in relationship to the focal length of the lens will you place the object?

Inquiring Further

1. **Graphing image distance vs. object distance for a convex lens**

   To investigate how the image position depends on the object position, find a convex lens, a white card, and a light source. Find the image of the light source, and measure the image and object distance from the lens. Make these measurements for as wide a range of object distances as you can. In addition, make an image of an object outside, such as a tree. Estimate the distance to the tree.

   The image of a distant object, like the tree, is located very near the focal point of the lens. Draw a graph of the results. Compare the graph with the lens equation

   $$\frac{1}{\text{focal length}} = \frac{1}{\text{object distance}} + \frac{1}{\text{image distance}}$$

   $$\frac{1}{f} = \frac{1}{d_o} + \frac{1}{d_i}$$

2. **Convex lenses and cameras**

   a) Research how a camera works. Find out where the image is located. Also find out how the lens changes so that you can photograph a distant landscape and also photograph people close up.

   b) Find a camera with a zoom lens and a shutter that you can keep open (with a bulb or time-setting). Place a piece of waxed paper or a piece of a plastic bag behind the lens, where the film would be if you took a picture. Find the image and compare it to the images you made in this section. Focus the lens for objects at different distances. Investigate how well the object and image location fit the lens equation,

   $$\frac{1}{f} = \frac{1}{d_o} + \frac{1}{d_i} \ .$$

   Note that the focal length of the lens is typically printed on the lens.

   c) Research how the concept of "depth of field" is important in photography. Report to the class on what you learn.

Section 10

Color

What Do You See?

Learning Outcomes

In this section, you will

- **Observe** combinations of colored lights.
- **Predict** patterns of colored shadows.

What Do You Think?

When a painter mixes red and green paint, the result is a dull brown. But when a lighting designer in a theater shines a red and a green light on an actor, the actor's skin looks bright yellow.

- **How could these two results be so different?**
- **What would you see if light from a red flashlight and light from a green flashlight were aimed at the same spot on a piece of white paper?**

Record your ideas about these questions in your *Active Physics* log. Be prepared to discuss your responses with your small group and with your class.

Investigate

In this *Investigate*, you will explore the mixing of colored lights.

1. Carefully cut out a cardboard puppet that you will use to make shadows. You can use the one you used in a previous section to make shadows.

 Lamps get very hot. Be careful not to touch the bulb or housing surrounding the bulb.

2. Set up three lamp holders and a screen. Place red, green, and blue light bulbs into their holders so they can shine on a white screen 1 m from the bulbs.

3. Turn on red and green bulbs. They should be aimed directly at the center of the screen.

a) What colors do you see on the screen? Record what you see.

b) Predict what color the shadows will be if you bring your puppet between the bulbs and the screen. Record your prediction, and give a reason for it.

c) Put your puppet between the light bulbs and the screen. Record what you see.

d) Predict what you would see if you turn off the red bulb, then try it. Record what you see. Turn on the red bulb and turn off the green bulb. Record what you see.

e) Make a top-view drawing to show the path of the light rays from the red and green bulbs.

f) On your drawing, label the color you will see on each part of the screen.

4. Turn off the green bulb and turn on a blue one. Repeat what you did in *Step 3*, but with the blue and red bulbs lit.

5. Turn off the red bulb and turn on the green one. Repeat what you did in *Step 3*, but with the blue and green bulbs lit.

6. Turn on the red bulb so all three—red, blue, and green—are lit. Repeat what you did in *Step 3*.

7. Obtain some paints (either acrylic or water colors will do, although acrylic works best).

a) Mix the red and green paints. What color do you produce? Is this the same color you got by mixing red and green lights?

b) Mix other combinations of paint colors. For each case, record the colors that you produce.

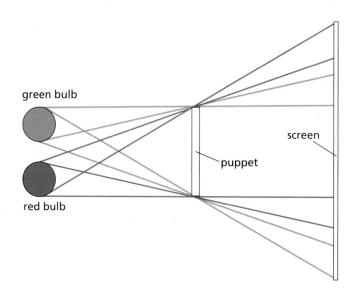

green bulb

puppet

screen

red bulb

Physics Talk

MIXING DIFFERENT COLORED LIGHTS AND PAINTS

When you see a red tomato, red light is reflected from the tomato and enters your eyes. The color of the reflected light is the color you see. The tomato absorbs all colors of light other than red. Similarly, plant leaves look green because they reflect green light and absorb light of all other colors. The chlorophyll in the leaves is what gives the leaves their green color, so you recognize that chlorophyll reflects green light while absorbing the light of other colors. This is an important issue in the ecology of plants, where nearby plants can affect the environment for other plants.

If you illuminate objects with the pure red light, all objects will look red. This is because only red light is present to enter your eye. If you were to illuminate an object with a red and green light, the object would look yellow. When lights of different colors are mixed new colors result. This is called **additive color mixing** because colors are "added" together. If you add the right amounts of red, green, and blue lights you will get white light, a combination of all colors of light. In theaters, different color lights are used to produce all sorts of effects to enhance the performance.

Physics Words

additive color mixing: mixing colored lights on a screen or other object.

In this investigation, you explored how shadows are affected by colored lights. As you observed in an earlier section, an object in white light casts a black shadow called the umbra (where no light reaches the screen) and a gray shadow called the penumbra (where some light reaches the screen.

The shadow produced by an object illuminated by a red light will produce a black shadow as the umbra and a dimmer red shadow as the penumbra. The rest of the wall or screen is red. You observed similar effects with the green and blue light bulbs.

The surprising shadows occur when the object is illuminated by two (or three) different colors. The umbra is easy to understand. No light from either the red bulb or the green bulb reaches the screen and that part of the shadow is black.

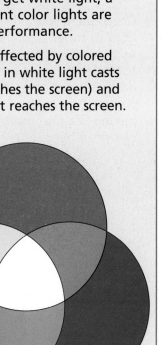

The penumbra has a number of distinct parts. One part of the penumbra is illuminated by the red light but not by the green light. This part of the penumbra looks red. Another part of the penumbra is illuminated by the green light but not by the red light and appears green. Other parts have some illumination from the red light and some illumination from the green light. The screen that is illuminated by both the green and red lights appears yellow.

When the green light was turned off, you observed more complete shadow (umbra) and the yellow sections became red. When the green light was turned back on, some of the umbra became green and the red sections became green.

Green paint looks green because it reflects green light and absorbs light of other colors. Red paint looks red because it reflects red light and absorbs light of other colors. If you mix red paint and green paint together, the mixture will absorb almost all colors and ends up looking dark brown or gray (depending on the exact color of the red and green paints). Getting new colors by mixing paints is called **subtractive color mixing** because each paint "subtracts" (absorbs) colors other than the color it reflects.

Physics Words

subtractive color mixing: mixing pigments or dyes that absorb light of different colors

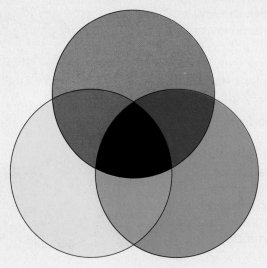

Checking Up

1. Explain the difference between subtractive and additive color mixing.

2. What three color lights can be mixed to produce white light?

Active Physics

+Math	+Depth	+Concepts	+Exploration
	♦♦		

Active Physics

Plus

Predicting Size and Color of Shadows

1. You already know how to predict the size of the shadows (umbra and penumbra) from an extended light source. You can use this approach to predict the positions and color of the shadows when a red light and a green light are used to illuminate an object. Use the diagram below as a starting point to draw the shadows from the two light sources.

You may find it helpful to use a diagram to the right of the screen to help locate all the different umbra and penumbra from the two light sources.

2. Using your model of the shadows from below, describe what you would see in each part of the screen. You can then create a second column to show what would happen to the shadows if your green light were turned off. You can then create another column to show what would happen if the red light were turned off.

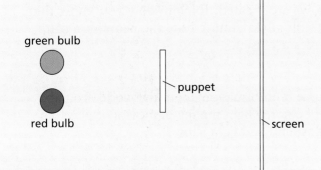

green bulb

red bulb

puppet

screen

What Do You Think Now?

At the beginning of the section, you were asked the following:

- **How could the results of mixing red and green paint and red and green light be so different?**

- **What would you see if light from a red flashlight and light from a green flashlight were aimed at the same spot on a piece of white paper?**

How would you answer these questions now? Using your knowledge of additive and subtractive color mixing, explain the difference in color between mixing paints and mixing colored lights.

Physics
Essential Questions

What does it mean?

Color involves both the physical aspects of light and how your eyes (and brain) respond to the light. What is meant by a color shadow? If "shadow" means "absence of light," how can a shadow have a color?

How do you know?

What you see in terms of color depends on both the object you are looking at and the kind of light that is shining on the object. What evidence do you have from this section that the color of light shining on an object may affect the color you see when you look at the object?

Why do you believe?

Connects with Other Physics Content	Fits with Big Ideas in Science	Meets Physics Requirements
Waves and interactions	Models	✳ Experimental evidence is consistent with models and theories

✳ Physicists create models to explain and predict phenomena. The ray diagram is a model that shows how shadows are created. Explain how you know that the shadow diagram does a good job at explaining how the penumbra can have a color when two light sources are used.

Why should you care?

Color perception is an important source of information about the world around you. Give some examples of the use of colored light mixing in movies or plays. Can you use colored shadows in your sound and light show?

Reflecting on the Section and the Challenge

Different colored lights can combine to make white light. When an object blocks all light from a light bulb, it forms a shadow. Since some light comes from all parts of the bulb, there are places where the shadow is black (no light) and places where the shadow is gray (some light reaches this area). An object illuminated by different colored lights can form shadows that prevent certain colors from reaching the wall and allowing other colors to pass by.

In your sound and light show creation, you may choose to use the ideas of colored shadows to show how lights can be added to produce interesting combinations of colors. By moving the object or the lights during the show, you may be able to produce interesting effects.

Colored lights are often used in theater productions, and even in big sports events. Making a good lighting design requires that you understand how colored lights mix and how colored shadows are formed. You also need to know how color can affect the mood of the audience to enhance what the director of the show wants to accomplish.

Physics to Go

1. Suppose you shine a red light on a screen in a dark room. The result is a disk of red light. Now you turn on a green light and a blue light. The three disks of light overlap as shown.

   a) Copy the diagram into your log. Label the color you will see in each part of the diagram.

   b) Add the labels "bright," "brighter," and "brightest" to describe what you would see in each part of your diagram.

2. An object casts a shadow on a screen when colored lights shine on it.

   a) Make a drawing of an object in blue light. Label the color of the shadow and the rest of the screen.

   b) Repeat *a)* for an object in green light.

   c) Now make a copy of your drawing for *b)*. Add a blue light. Label the color of all the shadows.

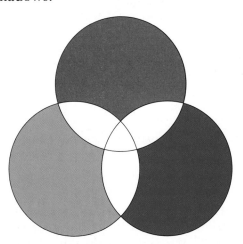

3. *Preparing for the Chapter Challenge*

   List some imaginative ways that you can add colors to your light show.

Inquiring Further

Mixing colors with a computer program

You can explore additive color mixing using a computer. The easiest way is to use a "drawing program" or a "presentation program."

Active Physics

Physics You Learned

Physics Concepts	Is There an Equation?
The length, mass, and tension of a vibrating string determine the vibration rate. As the length of the string increases, the vibration rate decreases. As the mass of the string increases, the vibration rate decreases. As the tension in the string increases, the vibration rate increases.	
Frequency (f) is the number of vibrations that are produced per second. The frequency determines what the ear hears as **pitch**.	$f = \#$ of cycles/second
The **period** of a **wave** (T) is the time it takes for a wave to complete one cycle and is equal to one divided by the wave's frequency (f).	$T = \dfrac{1}{f}$
Active Physics *Plus* — The fundamental frequency of vibration (f) of a stringed instrument is equal to the square root of the string tension (T) divided by four times the mass multiplied by the length of the string.	$f = \sqrt{\dfrac{T}{4mL}}$
Wave motion is the energy of vibration transferred through a material (the **medium**).	
A **transverse wave** occurs when the particles of the medium **vibrate** at right angles to the path in which the wave travels.	
A **longitudinal wave** occurs when the particles of a medium vibrate parallel to the direction of the path in which the wave travels.	
The **amplitude** of a wave is the maximum distance the vibrating particles move from their rest position. The **crest** is the highest point of displacement of the wave, and the **trough** is the lowest point. The speed of a wave in a medium is independent of the wave's amplitude.	
When two waves in a medium meet, their amplitudes add together.	
A **periodic wave** is a wave that repeats at definite intervals.	
Standing waves are produced when two waves of equal amplitudes and frequencies travel in opposite directions. Points on a standing wave that do not move are called nodes.	
The velocity (v) of a periodic wave traveling in a medium is equal to the wave frequency (f) multiplied by the **wavelength** (λ).	$v = f\lambda$
The wavelength (λ) of a periodic wave is equal to twice the distance (L) between successive nodes, or the distance between identical points on successive waves.	$\lambda = 2L$
Vibrating air columns produce standing longitudinal waves in musical instruments. Tubes closed at one end set up standing waves when the tube length is one-fourth the wavelength. Tubes open at both ends set up standing waves when the tube length is one-half the wavelength.	
Diffraction of waves occurs when the waves pass through an opening. The degree of diffraction is determined by the ratio of the wavelength to the size of the opening.	
Because the wavelength of light is very short, light travels in straight lines unless it passes through a very narrow opening.	
When light is blocked from an area because it travels in straight lines, a shadow is formed. If the source of light is larger than a point, the shadow will either be completely dark (the **umbra**), or partially dark, with lighter edges (the **penumbra**).	
Active Physics *Plus* — The shadows formed by light rays obey simple geometric rules that allow the size of shadows from an object's size and distance to be calculated.	

When a beam of light strikes a mirror and reflects, the **angle of incidence** (i) is equal to the **angle of reflection** (r). This is known as the law of reflection.	$\angle i = \angle r$
All angles in optics are measured to a perpendicular (the normal) to the surface.	
Plane mirrors form **virtual images** located behind the mirror. The image has the same size as the object and is the same distance behind the mirror as the object is in front of it.	
Active Physics *Plus* Multiple images are formed by two plane mirrors placed at an angle to each other.	
Concave, circular mirrors focus parallel rays of light to a point called the focus. **Concave mirrors** can form images, called real images, that can be projected onto a screen. The size and location of the image depends upon the distance of the object from the mirror. If the object is closer to the mirror than the **focal length**, the images formed are virtual and enlarged.	
Active Physics *Plus* For a concave mirror, one divided by the focal length $(1/f)$ equals one divided by the image distance $(1/d_i)$ plus one divided by the object distance $(1/d_o)$. This formula can be used to locate the position of the image formed by a concave mirror.	$\dfrac{1}{f} = \dfrac{1}{d_o} + \dfrac{1}{d_i}$
Convex mirrors are able to produce only virtual images that cannot be projected onto a screen.	
Refraction occurs when light passes from one transparent medium to another.	
The **index of refraction** of a medium (n) relative to air equals the sine of the angle of incidence $(\angle i)$ in air divided by the sine of the angle of refraction $(\angle r)$ in the medium.	$n = \dfrac{\sin \angle i}{\sin \angle r}$
Active Physics *Plus* The index of refraction of light in the incident medium (n_i) times the sine of the angle of incidence in that medium equals the index of refraction in the refracted medium (n_r) times the sine of the angle of refraction. This is known as **Snell's law**.	$n_i \sin \theta_i = n_r \sin \theta_r$
The speed of light in a transparent medium (v) equals the speed of light in a vacuum (c) divided by the index of refraction of the medium (n). The speed of light in any medium is always less than the speed of light in a vacuum.	$v = c/n$
If light travels from a medium of higher index of refraction to one of lower index, at an angle greater than the **critical angle**, the light will undergo **total internal reflection**.	
Lenses use the principle of refraction to form images.	
A **convex lens** is thicker in the center than the edges, and focuses parallel rays of light to a point. Convex lenses can form images that can be projected onto a screen. The size and location of the image depends upon the distance of the object from the lens. If the object is closer to the lens than the focal length, the images formed are virtual and enlarged (like those formed by a magnifying glass).	
The formula used to locate the image formed by a convex lens is the same formula used for image location by a concave mirror.	$\dfrac{1}{f} = \dfrac{1}{d_o} + \dfrac{1}{d_i}$
A concave lens can produce only virtual images that are smaller than the object.	
Colors that you see are due to reflected light. When illuminated with white light, some colors are absorbed, and the reflected colors are what you observe.	
When light of different colors are added together, a new color is produced. This is called **additive color mixing**.	

Physics
Chapter Challenge

You will now be completing a second cycle of the *Engineering Design Cycle* as you prepare for the *Chapter Challenge*. The goals and criteria remain unchanged. However, your list of inputs has grown.

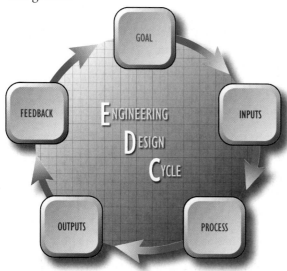

Goal

Your challenge for this chapter is to create an entertaining sound and light show for students your age. The *Mini-Challenge* presentations that were given earlier by your class should give you a good idea of the types of shows your classmates find entertaining. Now you must determine how to incorporate one of those ideas with some of the lighting and sound effects you learned in this chapter, and explain the physics concepts behind them. Review the *Goal* as a class to make sure you are familiar with all the criteria and constraints.

Inputs

You have learned all the physics content you need to complete your challenge. You have completed all the sections of this chapter and now have additional information to help you identify and analyze the various physics concepts that apply to lighting and sound effects. This is part of the *Inputs* phase of the *Engineering Design Cycle*. Your group needs to apply these physics concepts to put together your presentation. You also have the additional *Inputs* of feedback you received following your *Mini-Challenge* presentation.

Section 1 You created sounds of different pitch by independently changing the length and tension of a vibrating string.

Section 2 You produced both transverse and longitudinal (compression) waves in a spring. You also learned to characterize many wave properties including amplitude, wavelength, wave speed, and frequency.

Section 3 You explored the relationship between wave speed, wavelength, and the frequency of vibration for a vibrating string. You also considered a human model for that relationship and learned that the relationship could be expressed in the equation $v = f\lambda$.

Section 4 You examined the sounds produced by vibrating air in a tube. You learned that you could change the pitch by changing the length of the straw or by covering one end of the straw. Both methods resulted in a change in the wavelength of the sound you produced. You also learned about the bending of sound waves, called diffraction.

Section 5 You used ray diagrams to explain the size and shape of shadows and learned that light travels in straight lines to create shadows. You also examined the parts of a shadow— the darker umbra toward the center, and the fuzzy, lighter edges called the penumbra.

Section 6 You studied images reflected in a plane mirror and determined that the angle of incidence for a light ray is equal to the angle of reflection for the reflected ray. You learned that both of those angles are measured relative to the normal line, perpendicular to the mirror's surface.

Section 7 You looked at images created by convex and concave mirrors. You also used ray diagrams to find the focal point and measured the focal length for both types of mirror to help explain how the virtual images were formed.

Section 8 You observed refraction, the bending of light. You also used ray diagrams to trace the path that light traveled and measured the angles of incidence and angles of refraction. You also discovered an interesting phenomenon known as total internal reflection when you shined your light at an angle greater than the critical angle for the block material.

Section 9 You discovered why refraction is a key physics principle as you explored the effect of lenses on light. By observing the relationship between the locations of an object, a lens, and the resulting real image, you realized the basic technology behind many optical devices.

Section 10 You observed shadows generated by multiple bulbs of different colors.

Process

In the *Process* phase, you need to decide what information you have that you will use to meet the *Goal*. Decide on a format for your presentation. Will your group play a song, perform a play or show, or create some other type of presentation? Creativity is encouraged and will make your project memorable. Once you have that focus determined, it will be easier to decide how to proceed. You can organize your creative process in a number of ways, but make sure that every member of your group is included and knows how he or she can contribute to the presentation.

Your experience with the *Mini-Challenge* and with the investigations will provide you with some ideas regarding techniques that were found to be entertaining. Now you can concentrate on optimizing some of those effects. Start with a technique you used in class and see if you can make it more impressive by changing one or more of the features. You can anticipate what feature to change and estimate the amount of change that might produce the result you want. For example, in the case of stringed instruments, you would change lengths and tensions to adjust the sound. For projecting images, you could alter the distances between the light, the object, the lens, and the

screen to change the effect. In all cases, it will be useful to record the trials you conduct and the results you obtain. This information will help you recreate the successful trials and you can share this information as part of your physics explanation.

Remember that the sound-producing devices and the light effects in your presentation must be based on classroom investigations. Be sure to include a script for your show, a written explanation of the physics concepts behind the effects, and any additional props that can enhance your presentation. If your class prepares a rubric to go along with the criteria for this challenge, make sure you refer to it often to ensure that you address each category without leaving out any important information.

Outputs

Your presentation to the class are your design-cycle *Outputs*. Entertain your classmates for two to four minutes with a show using sounds and lights that your group creates, and be sure you accurately convey the physics concepts you exploited to make it all happen. A combination of creativity, good analysis, solid project development and presentation skills are required to create a successful *Chapter Challenge*.

Feedback

Your classmates will give you *Feedback* on the accuracy and overall appeal of your presentation based on the criteria of the design challenge. This feedback will likely become part of your grade but could also be useful for additional design iterations. No design is perfect; there is always room for further improvement in any design. Your experience with the *Mini-Challenge* should demonstrate how you could continuously rotate through the design process to refine almost any idea.

Physics
Connections to Other Sciences

Here are some examples of how the concepts you studied in this chapter relate to other sciences.

Waves

Biology Nerve cells transmit messages from the brain to the muscles through waves of electrical impulses. These electrical waves are associated with the motion of positive and negative ions into and out of the nerve cells.

Chemistry Light waves can transmit energy that is absorbed by molecules. Similarly, molecules can emit energy in the form of light waves.

Earth Science Water waves play an important role in shaping land masses. Like all waves, water waves carry energy. This energy can be used to break up rocks, move sand around, and redefine the contours of beaches and inlets.

Vibrating Strings

Biology Vocal cords are similar to vibrating strings. Since the length remains the same, tightening the vocal cords increases the wave speed in the cords and the frequency of vibration increases.

Chemistry Polymers are long-chain molecules found in rubber and plastics that can vibrate like strings. By studying those vibrations, chemists can determine the composition and structure of the polymers.

Earth Science Standing waves similar to those set up in vibrating strings can occur in the ground when the soil is saturated with water during an earthquake. This phenomenon increases the destructive power of the earthquake.

Refraction

Biology Cells are somewhat transparent to light. By observing light as it refracts through cells, biologists can learn about cell structure.

Chemistry Different combinations of a set of elements, such as FeO, Fe_2O_3, and FeO_2, refract light differently. Chemists can use this refraction pattern to determine the particular elemental combination in a sample.

Earth Science The refraction of light passing through Earth's atmosphere during a lunar eclipse allows some light to pass into the shadow of Earth on the Moon. This light, which is predominantly in the red region, gives rise to the "blood moon" phenomenon.

Lenses

Biology Eyes are equipped with variable focal length lenses that allow us to form clear images of objects by adjusting the focus.

Chemistry Lenses made of material other than glass allow focusing of images from non-visible spectral lines to assist in compound identification.

Earth Science Telescopes have lenses that magnify images of the planets. The gravitational lens effect of distant galaxies helps determine their mass.

Mirrors and Reflection

Biology Tigers and other animals can hunt successfully at night due to a reflective layer of cells inside their eyes. This layer allows light a second chance to interact with the light detecting cells of the eye, improving night vision. Such animals can often be spotted at night due to the reflection of light from their eyes.

Chemistry Chemists analyze the structure of organic compounds using infrared spectrophotometers. These instruments use a light source, a series of mirrors, and a light detector to determine the functional groups in a compound.

Earth Science We see the Moon because sunlight is reflected by the Moon. Similarly, when astronauts are in space, they see Earth only because it is reflecting sunlight.

Color

Biology Color plays an important role in nature. Birds and insects may be attracted to a plant by its color, and thus aid in pollination. The colors of some animals can provide camouflage, making it more difficult for predators or prey to spot them, or color can serve as an attraction to mates.

Chemistry Many substances change color as a reaction to chemical environment. Substances used to measure pH change color as a reaction to the pH content of a given solution. Other substances change color depending on their valence state.

Earth Science The color of the minerals in a rock is an important indicator in rock identification. Rocks are scraped across porcelain plates and the streaks that are left are analyzed for their color.

Dr. Stephon Alexander

Theoretical Physicist; University Park, PA

At a very young age, Stephon Alexander learned to embrace the unknown, and explore his two greatest passions: science and music.

Alexander was born in Trinidad & Tobago and moved with his family to the Bronx, New York at the age of eight. His father, who was a taxi driver by day and a computer technician by night, inspired him to expand his knowledge of computers. "My curiosity took me to the local library when I discovered the words 'quantum mechanics...' this was my first introduction to physics."

He attended De Witt Clinton High School, also in the Bronx, where the dropout rate was 60 percent. Alexander found inspiration from his physics teacher, Mr. Kaplan, who was also his music teacher. "I came to school solely to be in his classroom and get my daily dose of kindness and, his knowledge about the laws of nature."

Alexander earned his B.S. in physics from Haverford College, his Ph.D. in physics from Brown University, and also completed postdoctoral work at Imperial College in London and the Stanford Linear Accelerator Center. Currently, he is an assistant professor in the Penn State University physics department.

When Dr. Alexander's research of quantum mechanics, string theory and relativity becomes too intense, he unwinds by playing and composing music. He believes that physics and music have more similarities than people think: "Exploring a physics problem is like jazz improvisation – understanding the basic rules and themes lets you take off in new directions. Music is a wonderful device to communicate the beauty of physics. I like to demystify the Big Bang Theory by breaking it down in terms of sound."

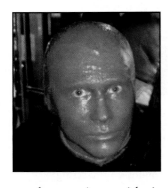

Shaneca Adams

Professional Performer; New York, NY

Shaneca Adams is a professional performer who grew up in Missoula, Montana. When he first moved to New York, he created his own dance-theater pieces with simple light and sound, creating a world where the main theme was free expression and artistic experimentation.

In 2004, he joined the Blue Man Group. Adams believes that the performances are so popular because of their unique mix of science and theater. "The Blue Man is a scientific character that interacts with the audience, using timing and sensitivity. The Blue Man constantly formulates theories about how things work and then tries experiments to see if they are correct."

Jon Varo

Performer, Composer and Music Store Manager; Nashville, TN

Music has always been a part of Jon Varo's life. He received his bachelor's degree in music, with an emphasis on music synthesis and film scoring. He is currently the store manager at World Music Nashville and an aspiring songwriter.

Varo believes that physics and music share many similarities. "The more you understand about the science of acoustics, the more you truly understand music. For performance purposes, physics is needed in order for an audience to hear music being played. The act of tuning a guitar requires the instrument to be adjusted to a specific frequency; a frequency is a part of physics," stated Varo.

Physics
Practice Test

Before you try the Physics Practice Test, *you may want to review Sections 1–10, where you will find* **31 Checking Up** *questions,* **14 What Do You Think Now?** *questions,* **40 Physics Essential Questions,** **94 Physics to Go** *questions, and* **19 Inquiring Further** *questions.*

Content Review

1. If you want to tune a guitar string to a higher frequency, you should
   a) increase the tension in the string.
   b) decrease the tension in the string.
   c) replace the string with a longer one.
   d) replace the string with a more massive one.

2. A student measures the pitch of several strings of different lengths that are all under the same tension and records the data. The student finds she needs to produce a pitch that falls between the values she has measured, and must select a string to produce that pitch. The best choice to make would be to
   a) choose a length she measured that provides a pitch closest to the frequency she needs.
   b) choose a length that has not yet been measured.
   c) graph the data from the measurements she has made, and find a length that matches the frequency she needs.
   d) try different string lengths until she finds one that is close to the pitch she needs.

3. Two waves with different shapes as shown below are moving toward each other on a coiled spring.

   Which diagram below best shows the shape of the spring when the two waves meet?

   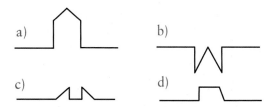

4. A wave is traveling along a spring as shown in the diagram below. If the wave frequency is 8.0 hertz, what is the wave speed?
   a) 0.75 m/s   b) 6.0 m/s
   c) 12 m/s   d) 4.0 m/s

   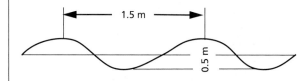

5. Besides a meter stick, what would you need to measure the velocity of a wave on a spring?
   a) the wave frequency
   b) the wavelength of the wave
   c) the wave amplitude
   d) a stopwatch

6. In the diagram below, one end of a string is attached to a side of a table, while a weight hanging on a pulley is attached to the opposite side. Which of the following would have no effect on the pitch of the string when it is plucked?

   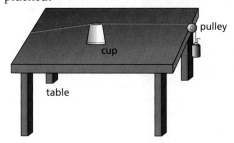

   a) the size of the mass hanging on the string
   b) the length of the string
   c) the thickness of the string
   d) how hard the string is plucked

7. If you slit one end of a straw and blow through it, the reed will vibrate and create a sound. If you want the sound to be louder, you could
   a) use a longer straw.
   b) add a funnel to the end of the straw.
   c) reverse the straw and blow through the opposite end.
   d) not blow as hard through the straw.

Active Physics

8. The diagram shows light from a source being blocked by an object, and then falling on a screen. Area A is part of the penumbra, while area B is the umbra. As the object is moved toward the screen, what happens to the sizes of areas A and B?

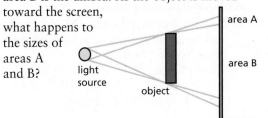

a) Area A gets larger and area B gets smaller.
b) Area A gets smaller and area B gets larger.
c) Areas A and B both get larger.
d) Areas A and B both get smaller.

9. A student stands 2 m from a plane mirror and sees her image. How far from the student is the image?
a) 1 m   b) 2 m
c) 3 m   d) 4 m

10. An object is placed at position X as shown in the diagram, and a person is looking at the image from position Y. At what position will the image of the object appear to be?

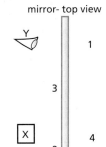

a) 1   b) 2
c) 3   d) 4

11. Wording on the mirror on the passenger side of an automobile reads "Objects in the mirror may be closer than they appear." This is because the image of an object seen in the mirror is smaller than would normally be expected. The image is not inverted, so the mirror must be
a) convex.
b) concave.
c) a plane.
d) any of the above, depending upon the viewing angle.

12. A laser beam is sent into a "black box" and comes out as shown. The object inside the black box is most likely

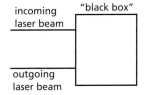

a) a single plane mirror.   b) a concave mirror.
c) a right angle prism.   d) a convex lens.

13. A laser beam enters an acrylic block as shown in the diagram. When the light beam exits the block, it will travel along the path labeled

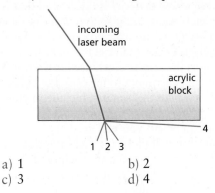

a) 1   b) 2
c) 3   d) 4

14. A man starts from a distance and begins to approach a convex lens that forms a real image of him on a screen. He gets closer and closer to the lens until his image disappears. As he nears the lens, his image
a) gets larger until he reaches the focal point.
b) gets larger until he reaches the lens.
c) is right-side up until he reaches the lens.
d) is right-side up until he reaches the focal point.

15. In order to create the illusion of partial invisibility in stage productions, an actor who is dressed entirely or partly in dark blue is illuminated with a red spotlight. The result is that parts of the performer will seem to "magically" disappear. This special effect works because
a) dark blue reflects red light to the audience.
b) dark blue absorbs red light but does not reflect any red light.
c) red light gives a dark blue shadow behind the performer.
d) dark blue light and red light form yellow light.

Critical Thinking

16. In an investigation, you shake a long, coiled spring back and forth slowly while your partner holds the other end fixed.
a) How do waves in the coil change when you move the spring back and forth more quickly?
b) Which characteristics stay the same?
c) While shaking the spring, you set up a standing wave. If you observe three nodes, and the spring is 6-m long, what is the wavelength of the standing wave?
d) If you shake the spring back and forth 2 times each second, what is the wave speed on the spring?

Practice Test *(continued)*

17. Suppose a new material is discovered that is completely transparent so that you cannot see a beam of light as it passes through the material. If a sample of this material has parallel faces similar to the acrylic block used in *Section 8*, design an experiment to measure the index of refraction of this sample. Include in your description
    a) the equipment you will need.
    b) how you will make the measurements you need (a drawing might be helpful).
    c) how you will use your measurements to calculate the index of refraction.

18. The diagram to the right shows the top view of an object (an arrow) placed in front of a plane mirror.
    a) Copy the drawing onto a separate sheet of paper, then use a ruler and protractor to locate the image of the object in the mirror. Use at least two lines to locate the head and the tail of the arrow to show the image.
    b) If the plane mirror could be bent into an arc to make a convex mirror, what would happen to the size of the image of the arrow?
    c) If the plane mirror is replaced with a concave mirror with focal length *f*, where should the arrow be placed to form a real image of the same size?

19. A student investigating the relationship between the object distance and the real image distance formed by a convex lens took the following data:

position	object distance	image distance
1	100 cm	25 cm
2	80 cm	27 cm
3	60 cm	30 cm
4	40 cm	40 cm
5	30 cm	60 cm
6	25 cm	100 cm

    a) From the data, determine the focal length of the lens.
    b) When the object is 60 cm from the lens, is the image formed larger, smaller, or the same size as the object?
    c) When the object is 30 cm from the lens, is the image right side up or inverted?

20. A guitar has six strings the same length but of different mass and thickness.
    a) If all the strings are under the same tension, explain how the mass of a string affects the frequency of vibration.
    b) When the tension on a guitar string is increased, what characteristic of the sound produced from plucking the string increases?
    c) What characteristic remains the same?
    d) Use an equation to describe what happens to the speed of the wave on the guitar spring when the tension is increased.

21. A beam of light traveling in water strikes the side of an aquarium at an angle of 30°. If the index of refraction of water is 1.33, and the index of refraction of glass is 1.50, what is the angle of refraction of the light beam as it enters the glass?

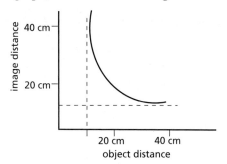

22. The graph shows the object distance vs. the image distance for a convex lens. According to the graph, what is the focal length of the lens?

23. An object is placed 20.0 cm from a concave, circular mirror that has a focal length of 5.0 cm. How far from the mirror is the image of the object formed?

Chapter 6

ELECTRICITY FOR EVERYONE

Electricity for Everyone

Scenario

Imagine you and your team members are part of an international group called Homes For Everyone (HFE). The purpose of your organization is to address housing and electricity needs in areas throughout the world. HFE would like you to develop an appliance package that would help meet the basic needs for healthy, enjoyable living for the families who reside in different parts of the world.

The source of electrical energy chosen for this particular project is a wind generator. The following is a description of the wind-generator system chosen for HFE. Some of the words will be unfamiliar to you. That's all right. Try to get a sense of the meaning of unfamiliar words. When the chapter is completed, you will understand these terms.

The wind-generator system is a highly reliable, mass-produced model that has an output of 2400 W (watts), or 2.4 kW (kilowatts). Experience has shown that in areas having only moderate average wind speed (6 to 8 km/h) the generator system will deliver a monthly energy output of about 90 kWh (kilowatt-hours) to the home, or about 3 kWh per day. Batteries allow storage of electrical energy from the wind-driven generator to keep the home going for four windless days. The batteries deliver direct current (DC) electricity, but most home appliances are designed to use alternating current (AC).

An inverter changes the DC from the batteries into AC before it enters the home. A circuit breaker rated at 2400 W protects the batteries from overheating if too much energy is asked for at any single time. Finally, a kilowatt-hour meter is provided to keep track of the amount of electrical energy that has been used. The result is that the dwelling will have the same kind of electricity delivered to it as do most homes in the United States, but less electrical power and energy will be available than for the average home in the United States.

Your Challenge

You will use your experience with electricity in your home and what you learn in this chapter to decide which electrical appliances, powered by a wind generator, can and should be provided for in the HFE dwellings.

- Your first task is to decide which electrical appliances can and should be used to meet the basic needs of the people living in the home serviced by the wind generator. As part of your decision-making process, you will need to determine if it seems best to provide a basic appliance package that would be the same for all dwellings, or if packages should be adapted with "options" to allow for factors, such as different family sizes, climates, or other local conditions. You will also need to describe how each appliance in your package will contribute to the well-being of the people who live in the dwelling.

- Your second task is educational. The people will need to be instructed how to stay within the power and energy limits of their electrical system as they use their appliances. You must develop an outline for a training manual for volunteers who will be teaching the people about the HFE wind-generator system and the appliances. The volunteers have no special knowledge of electricity. Therefore, the volunteers need a "crash course" that will prepare them to teach the people to use their electrical system with success. Two factors will be especially important to teach: The power demand of the combination of appliances being used at any one time may not exceed 2400 W, and the average daily total consumption of electrical energy should not exceed 3 kWh.

- Your third task is to include a wiring diagram to show how the electricity will be distributed in the home. This will include decisions your team will make about placement of outlets, switches, and fuses.

Criteria for Success

How will each part of the project be graded? The challenge has three major parts. Should each of these parts be worth the same amount? Decide with your class how many points should be allocated for each part of the challenge. Also, discuss and record what you must do to earn all of the points in each part and get an A for the challenge. Once you have discussed and decided on the point allocation, you can compare your criteria with the criteria and points values shown in the rubric on the following page.

Standard for Excellence

1. The HFE appliance package • number of physics principles used • physics concepts from the chapter are integrated in the appropriate places • physics terminology and equations are used where appropriate • correct estimates of the magnitude of physical quantities are used • additional research, beyond the basic concepts presented in the chapter	**40 points**
2. Outline for training manual for HFE volunteers • the content that you will need to teach • how you will teach the content	**35 points**
3. Wiring diagram • the placement of all the outlets, fuses, and switches	**20 points**
4. Challenge completed on time	**5 points**

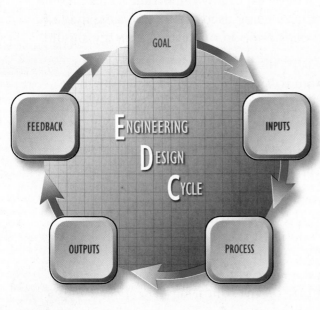

Engineering Design Cycle

You have now heard about the *Chapter Challenge* to design an appliance package and electrical system to be used by HFE to help many deserving families. You will use a simplified *Engineering Design Cycle* to help your group complete this design challenge. Defining the problem is the first step in the design cycle, so you have already begun.

As you experience each one of the chapter sections, you will be gaining *Inputs* to use in the design cycle. These *Inputs* will include new physics concepts, vocabulary, and even equations that will help you to create your electrical system.

When your group prepares the *Mini-Challenge* presentation and the *Chapter Challenge*, you will be completing the *Process* step of the cycle. During the *Process* step you will evaluate ideas, consider criteria, compare and contrast potential solutions, and most importantly, make design decisions.

Physics Corner

Physics in *Electricity for Everyone*

- Conservation of energy
- Electrical efficiency
- Energy $E = Pt$
- Entropy
- Fuses
- Generators
- Heat energy and specific heat
- Heat transfer
- Load limits
- Ohm's law
- Parallel circuits
- Power $P = VI$
- Resistance, voltage, and current
- Series circuits
- Simple circuits
- Switches
- Thermodynamics
- Utility bills

The *Output* of your design cycle will be the electrical system that your group presents to the class, including any charts, diagrams, or calculations you may use to clarify the information you present. Finally, you will receive *Feedback* from your classmates and your instructor about what parts of your presentation are good and which parts need to be refined. You will repeat the *Engineering Design Cycle* during the second half of the chapter when you gain more *Inputs*, refine your electrical system, and make your final appliance package and electrical system presentation.

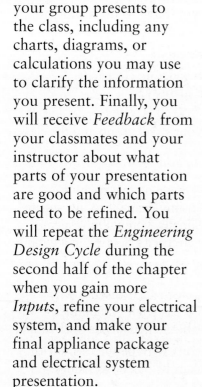

Section 1

Generating Electricity

What Do You See?

Learning Outcomes

In this section, you will

- **Trace** energy transformations.

- **Plan** a model for electricity.

- **Construct** a circuit that lights a bulb.

- **Adjust** the brightness of a light bulb with a hand generator.

What Do You Think?

Usually, when you need electricity, all you have to do is plug an appliance into the wall.

- **How is the electricity that you use generated?**

- **Oil can be used as an energy source to generate electricity. What other sources of energy can you identify?**

Record your ideas about these questions in your *Active Physics* log. Be prepared to discuss your responses with your small group and the class.

Investigate

In this *Investigate*, you will explore how people use electricity to improve their lives. You will then set up a simple circuit to investigate the energy required to light a light bulb. Finally, you will investigate how a light bulb produces light from the electricity flowing in a circuit.

Part A: What Electrical Appliances Do You Really Need?

1. Before embarking on your study of electricity, discuss why some people may not, or cannot, use electricity available through utility power lines. Think about their needs and wants.

   a) In your log, list some of the reasons why people do not or cannot access electrical power from utility power lines.

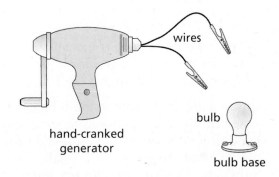

wires

hand-cranked
generator

bulb

bulb base

 b) What sources of electricity would be available to those who do not obtain their electrical power from utility companies?

 c) If you did not have electricity available to you, how could you store and prepare your food?

 d) What forms of entertainment do not require electricity?

2. If you had a limited amount of electricity, which electrical appliances would you choose to use? Which appliances would you eliminate?

 a) In your log, list the five top electrical appliances that you would choose.

3. Compare the lists as a class. You will return to these lists at the end of the chapter as you complete the *Chapter Challenge*. Since the wind generator will probably not be able to supply all the electricity required for these appliances, you will have to learn about electricity to improve your list.

Part B: Investigating a Closed Circuit

1. You will be provided with a bulb, bulb base, connecting wires, and a generator. Assemble the bulb, bulb base, connecting wires, and hand generator. Turn the crank of the generator to make the bulb light.

> ⚠ Never turn the crank too fast.
> You can strip the gears!

 a) Draw a diagram of how you assembled the equipment for the bulb to light. This is called a closed *electric circuit*. Under what conditions will the bulb not light? Use words and a diagram in your answer.

 b) What are the effects of changing the speed or direction of cranking the generator?

 c) What are the effects of reversing the connections of the wires to the bulb or to the generator?

2. Replace the bulb that you have been using with a blinking bulb, the kind used in some toys, flashlights, and holiday decorations. As before, use the generator to make it light. Keep cranking the generator to make the bulb go through several on-and-off cycles.

 a) Describe any difference that you can feel in cranking the generator when the bulb is on compared to when the bulb is off.

 b) How do you think that the blinking bulb works? What makes it go on-and-off?

> The steel wool will get very hot. Do not touch it while conducting the experiment. Allow the steel wool to cool before removing it.

3. Replace the blinking bulb with tiny strands of steel wool within the bulb socket. (Hint: The fewer strands you use, the better this works.) Crank the generator and observe what happens to the steel wool. Be careful not to touch the hot steel wool. You may push the steel wool with the point of a pencil to provide a better contact with the socket. You may also remove the socket and connect the ends of the steel wool to the alligator clips.

 a) Describe the appearance of the steel wool when the generator is being cranked.

 b) What factors affect whether or not the steel wool glows, how much it glows, and for how long?

 c) What were the similarities and differences between the steel wool and the light bulbs that were used?

d) What would happen if too much electrical energy flowed through a wire in the wall of a house?

4. Unscrew the bulb from its bulb base. Assemble the bulb, connecting wire, and hand generator (no bulb base), and turn the crank of the generator to make the bulb light. Experiment with placing the wires on different parts of the bulb to try to make it light. Draw a diagram of how you assembled the equipment for the bulb to light.

5. Was the electrical energy that you used to "light things up" in this investigation "free"? Did you get something for nothing? Using your observations in this *Investigate*, write a short paragraph to answer each of the following questions:

a) What was the energy source for each part of the *Investigate* (bulb, blinking bulb, steel wool)? Was it free energy, at no cost?

b) How did you make the hand generator work? What is it doing? What forms of energy were involved in the investigation, and in what order did the forms appear?

c) How is the energy source used in this investigation different from the source used to light a bulb in a flashlight, or in a house lamp?

Physics Talk

GENERATING ELECTRICITY

Electrical Circuit

Physics Words

electrical circuit: a route along which electricity can flow.

In this section, you created a closed **electrical circuit** that could light a bulb. The electricity appeared to go from the generator to the light bulb and then back to the generator. The circuit resembled a "closed loop," like a circle.

To get the bulb to light, you had to turn the crank of the hand generator. The faster you turned the crank, the more electrical energy was generated and the brighter the bulb became. When you used the blinking bulb, you probably noticed that when the bulb went off, it was very easy to turn the crank. That is because you did not need to generate any energy to light the bulb.

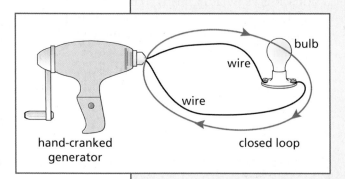

hand-cranked generator

closed loop

Energy Transformations

The energy to turn the crank came from your hand. You got the energy from eating food. The chemical energy from your food became mechanical energy to turn the crank of the generator. The mechanical energy you supplied became electrical

Active Physics

energy. This electrical energy then turned into the light and heat of the bulb. There are lots of energy transformations required to light a bulb.

Electricity for your home is also created by a generator. The details of how a generator produces electricity will be explored in another chapter. The generators needed to produce the amounts of electricity required in a city are much, much larger than your hand generator. People cannot turn these large turbines. Wind or falling water is needed to turn the turbines in similar ways to you turning the crank of the hand generator. Steam can also be used to turn the turbines. To make the steam, heat is produced by burning oil, coal, or gas, or causing uranium to fission.

The production of electricity requires a source of energy. That energy can come from you (as in the *Investigate*), the wind (as in the dwelling in the *Chapter Challenge*), or from large power plants.

How Does a Light Bulb Work?

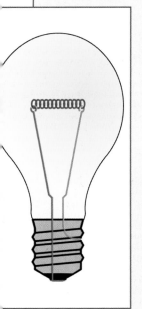

When you used a tiny strand of steel wool, you found that the steel wool would glow when electricity flowed through it. When Thomas Edison invented the light bulb, he tried thousands of different materials until he found one that would not burn out but would continue to glow when electricity ran through it. It was necessary to put that tiny piece of material (the filament) in a glass-enclosed container. To make the connection to the wires, the light bulb you used has two terminals — one for each side of the wire.

One side of the wire is connected to the bottom of the bulb. The other side is connected to the metal on the side of the bulb that also is used to screw the bulb into the socket. That was a clever technology — to use the metal screw threads as one end of the wire.

The glowing and burning steel wool also shows you the danger of too much electricity in a circuit. Without safety measures, wires get overheated and cause fires. Fuses are one such safety measure that you will learn about in a later section.

Light bulbs are just one device that uses electricity to do something useful. Electric motors convert electricity into mechanical work. Ovens and stoves convert electrical energy into heat to cook food. Refrigerators and air conditioners use electrical energy to cool things. Fans convert electrical energy into mechanical energy to move air. Electrical energy is also used to produce light and sound in your televisions and computers. Try living for a weekend without using any electrical device of any kind!

Checking Up

1. Energy is necessary to make a light bulb light. Where did the energy come from to light the bulb during your investigation?

2. Why was it easier to turn the handle of the generator connected to the blinking bulb when the blinking bulb was off?

3. Compare and contrast the glowing steel wool with the filament of a light bulb.

+Math	+Depth	+Concepts	+Exploration
	◆		◆

Closed Electrical Circuit

1. Using only a single wire and a battery, construct a circuit that will make a bulb light. Keep a record of all of your attempts. Identify the diagram for the circuit that lights the bulb, and include in your diagram the picture of the wiring inside the bulb.

2. Identify which of the circuits shown below will or will not light the bulb.

3. The blinking bulb you investigated must have some mechanism to make it turn on and off. Design a blinking bulb.

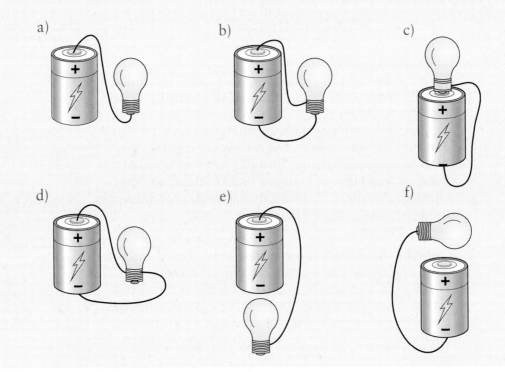

What Do You Think Now?

At the beginning of this section, you were asked the following:

• **How is the electricity that you use generated?**

• **Oil can be used as an energy source to generate electricity. What other sources of energy can you identify?**

How would you answer these questions now? Use what you have learned about electricity using generators to create a circuit to revise your previous answers, if needed.

What does it mean?

A person describes a flashlight that uses a battery and a bulb. It looks like this:

Is this the complete circuit?
Will the bulb light?

How do you know?

Given a generator or a battery, two wires, and a bulb, draw a circuit that will light the bulb and one that will not the light the bulb.

Why do you believe?

Connects with Other Physics Content	Fits with Big Ideas in Science	Meets Physics Requirements
Electricity and magnetism	✳ Conservation laws	Experimental evidence is consistent with models and theories

✳ "You can't get something for nothing." When generating electrical energy, where does the energy come from?

Why should you care?

Physics allows you to describe electricity, but cultural and economic factors determine how much electricity you use and how you use it. Describe why considering culture and economics along with physics would be important in the selection of electrical appliances for a home.

Reflecting on the Section and the Challenge

This section has given you some experience with using a generator to provide energy for electric light bulbs. The generator and the light bulb used in this section are scaled-down versions of the ones in the home for which you are designing an appliance package. The one in that dwelling will have the wind turn the crank to produce the electricity. One additional feature will exist in the electrical system for the dwelling: The electrical energy from the generator will be able to be stored in batteries until it is needed to operate lights and other appliances.

Part of your challenge is to write a training manual to help instructors teach the local people about their wind-generator system. You will want to include something about the necessity for a complete circuit and an illustration of such a circuit in the training manual. You will probably also want to include something about how the energy is generated and transformed. The key point is that you cannot get electrical energy without some input of energy. You can turn the crank of a generator using human energy, the wind, or other sources of energy.

Physics to Go

1. Electrical appliances plug into the wall with a single plug, but a plug has at least two prongs (sometimes there is a third one, but the minimum is two). Why do you think that this is the case? Refer to what you know about closed circuits in your answer.

2. You know that electricity comes "out of the wall." You also know that it "starts" in a power plant. Draw a picture that shows how you think the electricity is "created" and how it gets to your home.

3. Explain what you think electricity is, how it behaves, and how it does what it does.

4. A bulb holder has two terminals. Draw a diagram to show how these terminals connect to the light bulb.

5. There is a flashlight that you squeeze again and again to get the light bulb to light. How is this similar to the hand generator you used in this section?

6. A light bulb has output energy of light and heat. List five other electrical appliances. For each appliance, the input energy is electrical. What is the output energy?

In the following questions, choose the best answer from those provided.

7. Electrical energy can be transformed into

   a) light

   b) heat

   c) sound

   d) all of the above

8. Which of the following is designed to convert energy into mechanical work?

   a) electric fan

   b) kerosene heater

   c) flashlight

   d) baking oven

9. Choose the correct sequence of energy transformations in the *Investigate* with the hand generator:

   a) light to heat to mechanical

   b) mechanical to electrical to light and heat

   c) mechanical to heat to light

   d) electrical and mechanical to light and heat

Active Physics

10. *Preparing for the Chapter Challenge*

Part of your challenge is to write an outline for a training manual. Write down the key point(s) from this section that you will need to include in your manual.

Inquiring Further

1. **Energy-efficient light bulbs**

The kind of light bulb you used in this section is an incandescent bulb. Another kind of light bulb that is sold is labeled "energy efficient." Research these kinds of bulbs by visiting a home supply store. Look at the labels for these bulbs and make note of factors such as the number of lumens (the amount of light) produced and the amount of power (watts) consumed. Compare these with traditional incandescent bulbs.

2. **History of light bulbs**

Research the history of the light bulb. Be prepared to present your research to the class.

Section 2

Modeling Electricity: The Electron Shuffle

What Do You See?

Learning Outcomes

In this section, you will

• **Develop** a physical model for electric current and potential energy.

• **Use** this physical model to trace the flow of electric charges in series and parallel circuits.

What Do You Think?

Electricity is one of the most widely used forms of energy. Every day, you use electricity to perform a multitude of tasks. Yet, like water and air, you probably tend to take electricity for granted.

• **What is electricity and how does it move through a circuit?**

Record your ideas about this question in your *Active Physics* log. Be prepared to discuss your responses with your small group and the class.

Investigate

In this investigation, the class will create a model of an electric circuit by students playing the roles of the battery, the electric charge, and the load (light bulb). The model is not a perfect model — few seldom are. However, it will give you a better idea of what is happening in an electric circuit, as energy is passed from the battery to the electric charges to the light bulb.

Part A: Modeling a Simple Circuit

1. Begin with a simple circuit containing a battery and a light bulb. One member of the class will role-play the part of the battery. This student will supply plenty of energy — a bag of pretzels. Food is the source of energy for your body and gets

used up as you play. A second student will play the part of the light bulb. For example, this person will have to shake, jump, dance, or move in some way. Other students will play the parts of the electric charges in the circuit.

2. Form a large circle of the electric charges as if you were all waiting in line for something. You should be facing the back of the charge in front of you.

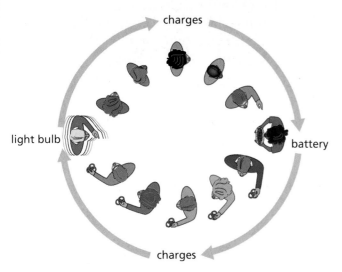

charges

light bulb

battery

charges

3. Have the battery stand at one side of the circle ready to give out the energy, the particles sent out by the batteries to carry energy to the light bulb (a pretzel to each charge). Have the light bulb stand at the opposite side of the circle ready to receive and be energized by the charges as they come past (takes the pretzel). Each unit of charge, called a *coulomb*, will pick up one *joule* of energy (represented by one pretzel).

4. The teacher will act as the switch and tell you when to begin and when to stop. On a signal from the teacher (closing and opening the switch), the charges will begin and stop moving in a clockwise circle.

5. When the energized charge passes by the light bulb, it gives its energy to the light bulb by dropping the energy into the hand of the light bulb. The light bulb needs to show that it has become energized by getting "excited" (a little dance will do). The charge now must continue on its path back to the battery to pick up more energy, and repeat the cycle. Notice that only the energy gets used up, not the charges themselves. The charges continue on their path through the circuit.

You have now completed round 1 of the "Electron Shuffle." In round 1, the battery (source of pretzels) gave each packet of charge (a student) a certain amount of energy (one pretzel). The charge then gave that energy to the light bulb (a student) who converted that electrical energy into light (a dance). The charges continue to the battery to get more energy and repeat the process.

6. In round 2 of the Electron Shuffle, the moves are the same. However, in round 2, there is a vocal part added. The person representing the battery announces once, "the battery voltage is one *volt* which equals one joule of energy for each coulomb of charge." The student receiving the pretzel then responds "one coulomb of charge receiving one joule of energy." The battery then distributes the pretzels to the students as they file through. The battery announces periodically, "Please move along, one coulomb per second is one *ampere* (often shortened to amp) of current." When the light bulb dances, he or she must occasionally say, "I just received one joule of energy from that coulomb of charge."

a) What are the variables that could change in the Electron Shuffle?

In the next two rounds, you will vary the voltage and current.

7. Round 3: The voltage of the battery is three volts. A three-volt battery gives each coulomb of charge three joules of energy. The current is still one amp.

8. Round 4: The voltage of the battery returns to one volt. The current in the circuit is two amps. A current of two amps has two coulombs of charge moving by every second.

9. In your log, record how the Electron Shuffle would change under the following conditions:

a) There is a five-volt battery. (Remember: voltage is the energy for each coulomb of charge.)

b) The current is increased to three amps (Remember: current is the number of coulombs that pass through the battery every second.)

c) There is a two-volt battery.

d) The current is increased to five amps.

e) A two-volt battery is replaced with a four-volt battery.

f) The current increases from two amps to three amps.

Part B: Modeling a Series Circuit

1. You will now investigate what happens when there are two light bulbs in the circuit.

a) Describe how the Electron Shuffle could be performed if the circle included two light bulbs, one after the other, and each light bulb must get some energy.

2. Set up the Electron Shuffle circuit as before with a one-volt battery. This time use two light bulbs, one after another, in a series. When an electric charge reaches the first light bulb it will need to drop some of its energy there, but

hold onto some of its energy for the next light bulb. All electrons go through the first light bulb and then through the second light bulb. The exact amount of energy dropped at each light bulb depends on the light bulbs themselves. This property is called their electrical resistance. For now, assume that the light bulbs are identical. They need to share equally the energy of each charge. Each charge will drop half of its energy with each bulb (break the pretzel in half). Once the charge has dropped its remaining energy at the second light bulb, it will continue on its path back to the battery for more energy.

a) Since the brightness of a bulb depends on how much energy is used up in the bulb during a given time, how would the brightness of each of the two bulbs in series compare with the brightness of a single bulb hooked up to the battery?

3. In your log, record how the Electron Shuffle would change under the following conditions:

a) Four identical light bulbs are placed in series.

b) The series circuit of two light bulbs has the battery replaced with a three-volt battery.

c) The circuit of two light bulbs has a larger current.

d) The light bulbs are not identical. The first light bulb requires more energy than the second light bulb.

4. In the first rounds of the Electron Shuffle, the bulb received one joule of energy every second. This was modeled by a one-volt battery providing a joule of energy for each coulomb of charge. The charges flowed at the rate of one amp or one coulomb per second. The number of joules per second that a bulb receives determines how bright

the bulb is. This is referred to as the power of the bulb. Power is measured in *watts*. One watt is equal to one joule per second. When you use a 100-W (watt) bulb in your home, it is using 100 J (joules) of energy every second. A 40-W bulb is using 40 J of energy every second. If the bulbs are manufactured the same way and have the same efficiency, the 100-W bulb is much brighter than the 40-W bulb.

a) Compare a circuit with one bulb and two identical bulbs in series by completing a table similar to the one on the right in your log. The one bulb is not identical to the pair of identical bulbs.

One bulb		Two bulbs in series		Comparison
Battery voltage (volts)	Current in the circuit (amps)	Battery voltage (volts)	Current in the circuit (amps)	Which circuit has the brighter bulb(s)?
1	1	1	1	
1	1	2	1	
1	1	1	2	
1	1	2	2	
2	2	4	1	
2	2	2	3	
4	1	3	2	

Physics Talk

A MODEL FOR AN ELECTRICAL CIRCUIT

Have you ever felt really exhausted at the end of a very strenuous period of activity such as a long soccer practice? Your muscles are really tired because you have "burned" a lot of energy in them. When you get this tired feeling, you need to "recharge your batteries," so to speak, with the energy you get from eating food. Electric circuits are like that in a way. As electric charge moves around in a circuit, it picks up energy at the battery (like you eating food) and loses or "drops" its energy at devices like light bulbs or appliances (like you using that energy to play hard). Just as your blood carries energy to your muscles, electric charge carries energy in a circuit. Notice that in this process, only the energy gets used up, not you or your blood. In an electric circuit, the electric charge does not get used up either, only its energy.

Sometimes, when you are not ready to use the energy right away, your body stores the energy. This gives you the potential to use the energy later. That is why it is called **potential energy**. An electric charge can do that too. **Electric potential energy**, or simply **electric potential** for short, is the energy of an electric charge waiting to be used by some load.

Electrical circuits have **batteries**, **resistors** (for example, light bulbs), and wires. The battery provides the energy for each **coulomb** of electrical charge that will move in the circuit. The rate of flow of this charge is the **current**. ➡️

Physics Words

potential energy: the energy of a system due to its positions in a force field.

electric potential energy: energy per unit charge.

battery: an electronic device serving as a source of electric power.

resistor: a conductor whose function is to control the current in a circuit.

coulomb (C): the SI unit of charge; one coulomb (1 C) is approximately equal to the charge of a lightning bolt, the charge of 6.25×10^{18} electrons.

current: the rate of flow of electric charge; the number of coulombs passing a point in one second.

Active Physics

Physics Words

voltage: the energy (in joules) for each coulomb of charge.

volt (V): the SI units of electric voltage or potential; one volt is equal to one joule per coulomb (1 V = 1 J/C).

joule (J): the SI unit of energy.

ampere: the SI unit of current; one ampere is the flow of one coulomb/second (1 A = 1 C/s).

series circuit: a circuit in which the current flows in a single line, so that all resistance in the circuit (light bulbs, etc.) has the same current flowing through them.

watt (W): the SI unit of power; one watt is equal to one joule per second (1 W = 1 J/s).

Checking Up

1. How is the unit of current (the ampere) related to the unit of charge (the coulomb)?

2. In an electric circuit, what happens to the energy of each charge?

3. If a circuit has four identical light bulbs, and a battery that provides 24 V, how many volts are lost (dropped) to each light bulb?

4. A light bulb is connected in a circuit. List two things that could be increased to make the bulb glow more brightly.

The Electron Shuffle is a model for electrical circuits that can help you understand what happens in a circuit as the **voltage**, current, or number of resistors is changed.

The Electron Shuffle models the electrical circuit by making the comparisons in the table to the right.

All of the energy of the charges is "dropped" into the resistors of the circuit. Suppose the voltage of the battery

Electron Shuffle	Electrical circuit
bag of pretzels	battery
students delivering pretzels	charges
student receiving pretzels	light bulb
number of pretzels	voltage (1 V = 1 J/C)
number of students passing a point every second	current (1 A =1 C/s)
number of pretzels per second received by the student	power–brightness of bulb (1 W = 1 J/s)

is six **volts** (6 V). That means that the battery provides 6 V, or six **joules** for each coulomb of charge. All 6 V will be provided to the single light bulb in the circuit. This can happen often if there is a large current. The current is measured in **amperes** or **amps** (A). A 2-A current has two coulombs of charge passing a point every second.

A Series Circuit

There is only one way to connect a single light bulb in a circuit. There is more than one way to connect two or more bulbs in a circuit. In this section, you connected the bulbs in a series, to make a **series circuit**. In a series circuit, the electric current has only a single path that it can follow.

If the battery provides 6 V and the circuit contains three identical resistors in series, then each resistor will get 2 V. The total voltage provided to the resistors is equal to the voltage of the battery: 2 V + 2 V + 2 V = 6 V. Since each coulomb of charge goes through the first resistor, then the second resistor, and then the third resistor, the current (flow of charge) is the same throughout the circuit.

People are concerned with the brightness of a light bulb. The brightness of a bulb is dependent on the energy per second that the bulb receives. The energy per second is also referred to as the power delivered to the bulb and is measured in **watts (W)**. One watt is equivalent to a flow of energy of one joule per second (1 W = 1 J/s). You can increase the brightness of a bulb by increasing either the energy/coulomb (voltage) or the rate the coulombs are delivered (current) or both.

Diagram of a Series Circuit

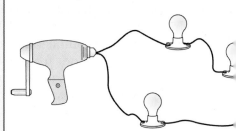

Schematic Diagram of a Series Circuit

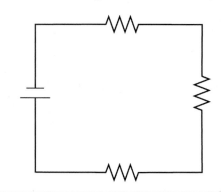

Active Physics

Plus

+Math	+Depth	+Concepts	+Exploration
	◆	◆	

Improving the Electron-Shuffle Model

In describing a series circuit consisting of a battery and three light bulbs, it was assumed that all the energy of the charges was "dropped" into the light bulbs. If a 6-V battery was used, then each coulomb provided has two joules to each of the three light bulbs. In this model, the wires were assumed to have no resistance and none of the energy was required to move the charges through the wires. That is not true. The wires are made of materials that do not use much of the energy, but they do use some of the energy. In your Electron-Shuffle model, it is as if a few crumbs of the pretzel must be provided to each wire in the circuit. A few additional crumbs are required to move the electrons through the battery as well.

1. Write a description of how to perform the Electron Shuffle that includes the voltage drops through each wire and the battery.

2. In a series circuit, all the light bulbs do not have to be identical. Calculate the voltage drops in each of three light bulbs if one of the bulbs requires twice the voltage of the other two. The voltage of the battery is 12 V.

3. How does the solution to *Question 2* change, if each of the wires requires 0.1 V?

What Do You Think Now?

At the beginning of this section, you were asked:

• **What is electricity and how does it move through a circuit?**

Now that you have completed this section, how would you answer the question now? What else do you think you need to know to answer the question more completely?

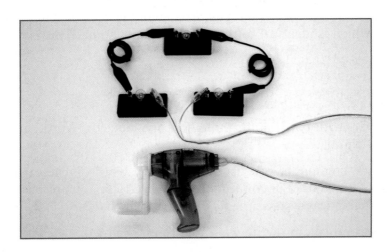

> ## Physics
> ## Essential Questions
>
> **What does it mean?**
>
> How do voltage and current relate to the brightness of a bulb?
>
> **How do you know?**
>
> How would you know if the Electron-Shuffle model is a useful model of current flow in circuits?
>
> **Why do you believe?**
>
> | Connects with Other Physics Content | Fits with Big Ideas in Science | Meets Physics Requirements |
> |---|---|---|
> | Electricity and magnetism | ✳ Models | Experimental evidence is consistent with models and theories |
>
> ✳ Physicists use models to describe and better understand many phenomena. A description of how electricity works is called a "model." The Electron Shuffle is a model that helps support the description of how electricity works. Is a scientific model the same thing as reality, or is it just a convenient (and sometimes limited) description of reality?
>
> **Why should you care?**
>
> Part of your challenge is to create an outline for a training manual that will help people become acquainted with electrical use. Explain voltage and current using the Electron-Shuffle model and without using the Electron-Shuffle model.

Reflecting on the Section and the Challenge

In this section, you developed a concrete model for the flow of current in a series circuit. You modeled how the voltage of the battery provides energy to each light bulb in the circuit. You have also introduced new vocabulary words in this section. You will get an opportunity to practice this vocabulary in this chapter. You may want to use the Electron Shuffle in your training manual to help others learn about electric circuits. Your wind generator will provide 120 V of electricity, which is identical to the 120 V in your home. This allows all home appliances to work properly with your wind generator.

Physics to Go

1. Make a chart with two columns, the first one labeled "Word" and the other labeled "Meaning."

   a) In the first column make a list of "electricity words." These are words that you have heard used in connection with electrical units of measurement, parts of electrical systems, or how electricity behaves.

   b) In the second column write what you think each word means or describes.

Active Physics

2. Suppose you had two one-volt batteries in series.

   a) How many pretzels would a "charge" pick up passing through both batteries in the Electron Shuffle?

   b) Predict what would happen if a light bulb were to be connected with two batteries in series and explain using your physical model of current and voltage.

   c) Would the light bulb be brighter? (Remember: Brightness is dependent on the energy per second delivered to the bulb.)

3. Compare a circuit with one bulb and three identical bulbs in series by completing the table in your log:

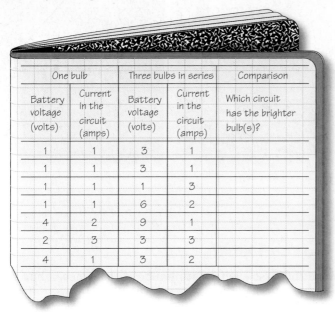

One bulb		Three bulbs in series		Comparison
Battery voltage (volts)	Current in the circuit (amps)	Battery voltage (volts)	Current in the circuit (amps)	Which circuit has the brighter bulb(s)?
1	1	3	1	
1	1	3	1	
1	1	1	3	
1	1	6	2	
4	2	9	1	
2	3	3	3	
4	1	3	2	

4. Compare a circuit with two bulbs and three identical bulbs in series by completing the table in your log:

Two bulbs in series		Three bulbs in series		Comparison
Battery voltage (volts)	Current in the circuit (amps)	Battery voltage (volts)	Current in the circuit (amps)	Which circuit has the brighter bulb(s)?
2	1	3	1	
2	1	3	1	
2	1	3	2	
4	1	6	2	
2	4	6	1	
2	4	6	3	
4	1	6	2	

Section 3

Series and Parallel Circuits: Lighten Up

Learning Outcomes

In this section, you will

- **Compare** series and parallel circuits.

- **Recognize** generator output limit.

- **Modify** the Electron-Shuffle model of electricity.

What Do You Think?

Lights were the first electric appliances for homes. They replaced gas lamps. Hotels that began using Edison Electric Lights had to have warning signs explaining how to turn on the light. "Warning: You should not put a match by the bulb. To turn on the light, move the switch."

- **When one light bulb in your house goes out, can the other light bulbs remain on?**

- **How can a circuit be set up to allow this?**

Record your ideas about these questions in your *Active Physics* log. Be prepared to discuss your responses with your small group and the class.

Investigate

In this *Investigate*, you will simulate the movement of charge in a *parallel circuit* in the same way you did for a series circuit in the previous section. You will then compare series and parallel circuits using a hand generator. Finally, you will investigate what happens in a series circuit when one bulb is removed.

Part A: Modeling a Parallel Circuit

1. A parallel circuit is a bit more complicated than a series circuit. It contains multiple pathways through which the charge can flow. In order to do this, there are forks in the path, called junctions, where some of the charge goes in one direction and some in another. Set up the Electron Shuffle with a one-volt battery and with three lights in parallel, one behind the next.

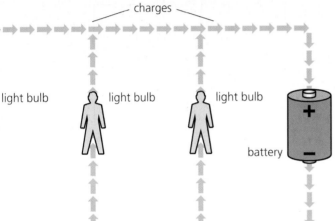

When charge reaches the first junction, some of it must go through the first light bulb, with the remainder continuing to the second and third light bulb. Each electron goes through only one bulb before returning to the battery. Assuming that all the bulbs are identical, ⅓ of the charges will go through the first bulb, ⅓ of the charges will go through the second bulb, and ⅓ of the charges will go through the third bulb.

2. Perform the Electron Shuffle with a one-volt battery. A one-volt battery provides one joule for each coulomb of charge. In the Electron Shuffle, the battery will provide one pretzel to each student. You and your classmates will move through the circuit. Each student will have to make a decision as to which path to travel. If a student's birthday is in January, February, March, or April, that student goes through the first bulb. If a student's birthday is in May, June, July, or August, that student goes through the second bulb. If a student's birthday is in September, October, November, or December, that student goes through the third bulb.

3. During this round of the Electron Shuffle, the person representing the battery announces once, "The battery voltage is one volt, which equals one joule of energy for each coulomb of charge." The student receiving the pretzel then responds, "One coulomb of charge receiving one joule of energy." The battery then distributes the pretzels to the students as they file through. The battery announces periodically, "Please move along, one coulomb per second is one ampere of current." When any light bulb dances, he or she must occasionally say, "I just received one joule of energy from that coulomb of charge."

While performing the Electron Shuffle, pay attention to the voltage "drop" across each light bulb and the current through each light bulb.

4. After completing the Electron Shuffle, parallel style, answer the following questions:

   a) The battery provided each coulomb of charge with one joule of energy. How much energy did each light bulb get from each coulomb of charge?

   b) The charges left the battery at the rate of one coulomb per second. What was the current through each light bulb?

In the next two rounds, you will vary the voltage and current.

5. Round 3: The voltage of the battery is three volts. A three-volt battery gives each coulomb of charge three joules of energy. The current is still one amp.

6. Round 4: The voltage of the battery returns to one volt. The current in the circuit is two amps. A current of two amps has two coulombs of charge moving by every second.

7. In your log, record how the Electron Shuffle, parallel style, would change under the following conditions:

a) Four identical light bulbs were placed in parallel.

b) The circuit of three light bulbs had the battery replaced with a three-volt battery.

c) A circuit of three new light bulbs had a larger current with the original one-volt battery.

d) Four identical light bulbs were placed in parallel with a six-volt battery.

e) Three bulbs that are not identical are placed in parallel.

Part B: Comparing Series and Parallel Circuits

1. Before you begin this investigation, remind yourself about the "feel" of the generator and the brightness of the bulb when the generator was used to energize one bulb in *Section 1*. Connect a single bulb to the generator and crank. Use your observations of a single bulb as a basis for comparison when you use two or more bulbs during this *Investigate*.

2. There are two distinct ways to connect more than one light bulb to the generator. Look at the two pairs of diagrams showing three bulbs connected in series and in parallel. The diagrams show the apparatus you will use. The diagrams also show schematic representations of each circuit.

a) Describe in your log how the two circuits are different.

b) Make predictions about how each circuit operates.

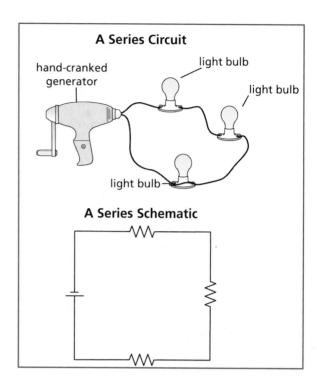

A Series Circuit

A Series Schematic

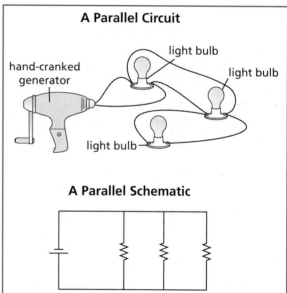

A Parallel Circuit

A Parallel Schematic

3. Connect two bulbs in series with the generator. Use the diagram showing three bulbs connected in series to help you. Crank the generator, and notice the "feel" of the generator and the brightness of the bulbs. Repeat this for three bulbs, and four bulbs in series.

a) Describe what happens and try to explain why it happens.

4. What would happen if, in a series circuit of several bulbs, one bulb were to be disconnected, or burn out? Try it by unscrewing one bulb from its base while the circuit is operating.

 a) Describe what happens, and try to explain why it happens.

5. Connect two bulbs in parallel with the generator and, again, observe the "feel" of the generator and the brightness of the bulbs. Repeat this for three bulbs, and four bulbs.

 a) Describe your observations and compare them to your predictions for a parallel circuit.

6. What would happen if one bulb were to fail in a parallel circuit? Try it by unscrewing one bulb.

 a) Describe what happens, and try to explain why it happens.

Physics Talk

COMPARING SERIES AND PARALLEL CIRCUITS

In series circuits, all the coulombs of charge travel through the first light bulb, then the second light bulb, and then the third light bulb. The electrons require a complete circuit or pathway from the battery to the light bulbs and back to the battery to flow. If one of the light bulbs is broken or removed, then the circuit path is no longer complete and there will be no flow of charge or current. All of the light bulbs will go out.

In **parallel circuits**, some of the coulombs of charge go through the first light bulb, while other coulombs of charge go through the second light bulb, and still other coulombs of charge travel through the third light bulb. Each light bulb has a complete circuit or pathway from the battery to the light bulbs and back to the battery. If one of the light bulbs is broken or removed, then the circuit path to the other light bulbs is not affected. All the other bulbs will continue to light.

If the battery provides six volts and the circuit contains three resistors in parallel, then each resistor will get six volts of energy but only from some of the charge. The total voltage provided to each of the resistors is equal to the voltage of the battery: 6 V. That is because all of the energy of the coulomb of charge is given to only one resistor.

Because each coulomb of charge goes through only one resistor, then the current leaving the battery is split among the three resistors. If the current leaving the battery is split amongst three amps (three coulombs per second), then each resistor gets one amp of current (for identical resistors). This means that the one coulomb that passes the first resistor every second will drop six volts there. The same thing will happen at the other two resistors.

Physics Words

parallel circuit: a circuit that provides separate paths for current to travel through each resistor; the same voltage is provided across each resistor (lamp, etc.).

Active Physics

The Language of Electricity

A formal study of physics requires use of some of the basic language of electricity that was introduced in this and previous sections. (The terms to which you were introduced in the previous sections are shown in *italics*.)

- There are two kinds of **electric charges**, positive and negative. **Protons**, which have a positive charge, and **electrons**, which have a negative charge, are the source of these charges.

- Like charges repel, and opposite charges attract.

- There is a smallest amount of the property called electric charge, the amount possessed by one proton or one electron. While protons and electrons differ in several ways (such as mass), an electron and a proton have an identical amount of charge.

- Electrons move in *electric circuits* of the kind you have been exploring. They carry the *electric current* as they flow through the circuit path, delivering energy that is transformed into light and heat by the light bulb. Protons, although present in the materials from which circuits are made, do not flow because they are locked within atoms.

- Scientists have agreed upon a standard "package" of electric charge, called the *coulomb* (C). The charge of a single proton or electron is 1.6×10^{-19} C. In order to get a single coulomb of charge, it would take 6.25×10^{18} electrons (6.25 billion-billion, an amount equal to one over the charge of the electron). One coulomb is approximately the charge transferred during a lightning bolt.

- Scientists have agreed upon a standard rate of flow of the electric current in circuits. When one coulomb of charge passes through a point in a circuit during each second of time, the current is said to be one *ampere*, often abbreviated to amp and written with the symbol A.

- Different materials offer different electrical resistance, or opposition, to the flow of electric charge through them. That's what the word "resistance" means, opposition to the flow of electric charge. A material in an electric circuit that offers resistance is called a *resistor*. Tungsten, from which light bulb filaments are made, has high electrical resistance. When electricity flows through a light bulb, for instance, the part that glows is a metal called tungsten. It "robs" energy from the moving electrons, gets hot and glows. Copper, by contrast, has low resistance; electrons transfer very little energy when flowing through copper. That is why copper wire is used to conduct electricity in electric circuits. Electrical resistance is measured in **ohms**. The symbol for an ohm is the Greek letter *omega*, or Ω.

- *Batteries* or generators provide energy to the electrons. These electrons are then able to light bulbs, heat wires, or make motors turn. The energy given to each coulomb of charge is measured in *volts* (V).

Physics Words

electric charge: a fundamental property of matter; charge is either positive or negative.

proton: a positively charged particle with a charge of 1.6×10^{-19} C and a mass of 1.7×10^{-27} kg.

electron: a negatively charged particle with a charge of 1.6×10^{-19} C and a mass of 9.1×10^{-31} kg.

ohm: the SI unit of electrical resistance; the symbol for ohm is Ω.

Checking Up

1. One of three light bulbs in a circuit is removed from its socket. Describe what happens to the other light bulbs if it is a series circuit.

2. One of three light bulbs in a circuit is removed from its socket. Describe what happens to the other light bulbs if it is a parallel circuit.

3. Which part of the atom moves around the circuit carrying energy?

4. What happens to the energy that a tungsten filament "robs" from the electrons as they pass through a circuit with a light bulb?

+Math	+Depth	+Concepts	+Exploration
	◆		

Active Physics

Plus

More About Parallel Circuits

1. Three identical light bulbs are connected in series with a 6-V battery. A second circuit has three identical light bulbs connected in parallel with a 6-V battery. The current leaving the battery in the series circuit is 1 A. The current leaving the battery in the parallel circuit is 9 A.

   a) Compare the voltage drops in each light bulb in the two circuits.

   b) Compare the currents in each light bulb in the two circuits.

   c) Compare the brightness of each bulb in the two circuits.

2. A circuit consisting of three light bulbs is shown below. When light bulb B is removed, what happens to the brightness of the remaining two bulbs? (Use your model of the Electron Shuffle to guide you.)

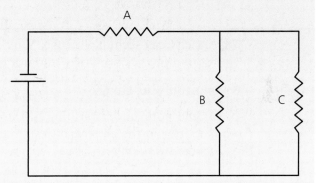

What Do You Think Now?

At the beginning of this section, you were asked the following:

• **When one light bulb in your house goes out, can the other light bulbs remain on?**

• **How can a circuit be set up to allow this?**

How would you answer these questions now? What else do you think you need to know to answer the questions more completely?

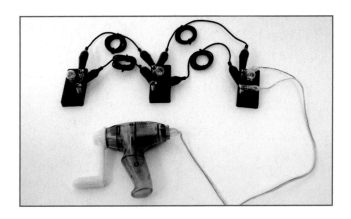

Active Physics

Physics
Essential Questions

What does it mean?

Why is a house wired using parallel circuits rather than series circuits?

How do you know?

What evidence do you have from the activities you performed that series and parallel circuits behave differently?

Why do you believe?

Connects with Other Physics Content	Fits with Big Ideas in Science	Meets Physics Requirements
Electricity and magnetism	Models	✶ Experimental evidence is consistent with models and theories

✶ Electricity can seem like magic. Why do you believe that electricity is based on sound physics principles and not magic?

Why should you care?

Why should your understanding of the differences between series and parallel circuits matter in the electrical design and wiring of your appliance package in the *Chapter Challenge*?

Reflecting on the Section and the Challenge

In this section, you were introduced to parallel and series circuits and to electrical terms that you will need to know and be able to use for planning electric circuits to be used in the wind-powered home.

It is a fact that homes are wired using parallel circuits. Individual houses, apartments, mobile homes, or any other dwellings that receive electricity from a power company, have parallel circuits. Some older homes have as few as four circuits, and newer homes usually have many more. Each circuit in a home may have several light bulbs and other electrical appliances "plugged in," all in parallel. When electrical appliances are hooked up in parallel, if one is off or disconnected, the others can still be on. In a series circuit, if any appliance is disconnected, the other appliances cannot work. In your training manual, you will need to explain why the circuits in the home are wired in parallel.

Physics to Go

1. Did the generator used in this investigation seem to have an "output limit"? In other words, did you arrive at conditions when the generator could not make the bulbs glow brightly even though you tried to crank the generator? Discuss this in a few sentences.

2. There is a great big generator at the power plant that sends electricity to your home. The wind generator chosen for HFE is much smaller than the generators used at power plants, but much larger than the one used for this investigation. What implications might the output limit of the HFE electrical system have for the number of light bulbs and other electrical appliances that can be used in the HFE appliance package that you will recommend? Discuss this in a short paragraph.

3. As you add more and more bulbs in series to a circuit with a constant voltage, what will happen to the brightness of the bulbs? (Remember: Brightness is dependent on the energy every second delivered to the bulbs.)

4. There are two lit light bulbs in a circuit. One bulb burns out but the other stays lit. Which statement is correct?

   a) The two bulbs are wired in series.

   b) The two bulbs are wired in parallel.

   c) This is an impossible circuit — if one bulb goes out, the other bulb must also go out.

5. Draw a series circuit with three identical light bulbs. If the battery in the circuit has 12 V, determine the voltage impressed across the bulbs. Compare the current in each light bulb with the current leaving the battery.

6. Draw a parallel circuit with three identical light bulbs. If the battery in the circuit has 12 V, determine the voltage impressed across the bulbs. Compare the current in each light bulb with the current leaving the battery.

7. Discuss what would happen to the current in a circuit if two batteries were connected in parallel in the circuit. Would a light bulb in that circuit be brighter than the same circuit with only one battery? (Remember: Brightness is dependent on the energy per second delivered to the bulb.)

8. Look at the circuit at the right that has three different light bulbs in parallel — one with a high resistance, one with a medium resistance, and one with a low resistance. Using the Electron-Shuffle model, explain why each light bulb will receive an equal voltage.

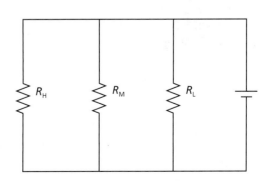

Active Physics

9. Look at the following set of circuit diagrams — one has two equal batteries in series and the other has two equal batteries in parallel. Using the Electron-Shuffle model:

a) Compare the voltage (energy per coulomb) that each bulb receives.

b) Compare the current (charge every second) that each bulb receives.

c) How will the brightness of the bulbs compare in the two cases?

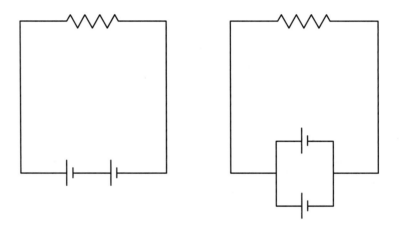

10. *Preparing for the Chapter Challenge*

Part of your challenge is to write what kind of circuit, series or parallel, you would choose for household wiring, and why. Write a short paragraph to explain your choice.

Inquiring Further

Thomas Edison

Thomas Edison is arguably one of the greatest inventors in world history. When you think of Edison, you probably think of the light bulb and the changes that this invention has made on the world. Edison dreamed of a world where you could read at night, where you could walk down a lit street, and where you could enjoy daytime all the time. Electricity and the light bulb have made that dream a reality. You live in Edison's dream! Edison once said that genius is 1% inspiration and 99% perspiration. Explain the meaning of this phrase. Construct a list of Edison's major inventions. (Edison had 1093 patents in his name!)

Section 4

Ohm's Law: Putting up a Resistance

What Do You See?

Learning Outcomes

In this section, you will

• **Calculate** the resistance of an unknown resistor given the voltage drop and current.

• **Construct** a series circuit.

• **Use** a voltmeter and ammeter in a series circuit accurately.

• **Express** the relationship between voltage and current for a resistor that obeys Ohm's law in a graph.

What Do You Think?

Lighting makes some rooms conducive to work and other rooms more relaxing.

• **What determines the brightness of a light bulb?**

• **What determines how much current flows in a circuit?**

Record your ideas about these questions in your *Active Physics* log. Be prepared to discuss your responses with your small group and the class.

Investigate

Imagine a "black box," a box that you cannot see inside. Inside the box is a resistor. In this *Investigate*, you will determine the contents of the black box electrically by measuring the voltage across and the current through the resistor inside.

1. In order to predict what is in the black box, you first will have to complete an investigation of three different resistors, a 5-Ω (ohm), a 10-Ω, and a 15-Ω resistor.

    You will need to set up a simple circuit with a resistor, a voltmeter, and an ammeter, as shown in the diagram on the next page. By varying the voltage of the battery, you can learn how the current of the circuit and the voltage across a resistor changes.

623

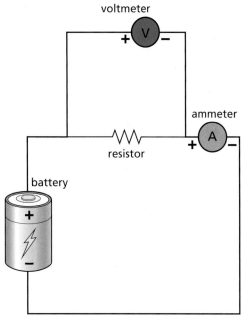

Before beginning your study, please note the following circuit rules:

- The ammeter is always placed in series in the circuit.

- The positive terminal of the ammeter is always closest to the positive terminal of the battery.

- The voltmeter is always placed in parallel in the circuit. The simplest way to measure the voltage drop across the resistor is to take the two leads from the voltmeter and touch the two ends of the resistor simultaneously.

- The positive terminal of the voltmeter is always closest to the positive terminal of the battery.

- Keep the connection in the circuit on for as long as it takes to read the ammeter and voltmeter, and no longer.

- You can vary the voltage with a variable voltage supply or by adding additional batteries into the circuit.

2. Begin with the 5-Ω resistor. Plan your experiment to find out how the voltage and current vary for a 5-Ω resistor.

a) Record your plan.

b) Make a table that will summarize the data you intend to collect.

3. After your teacher has approved your plan, conduct your experiment.

a) Record your data for the voltage and current of the 5-Ω resistor.

4. Repeat your investigation for the 10-Ω and 15-Ω resistors.

a) Record your data for the 10-Ω resistor.

b) Record your data for the 15-Ω resistor.

c) Given a voltage and current, how would you determine if the circuit had a 5-Ω, 10-Ω, or 15-Ω resistor?

5. A black box for a resistor yielded the following data:

Voltage (volts)	Current (amps)
1.00	0.17
1.50	0.25
2.00	0.33
2.50	0.42
3.00	0.50
3.50	0.58
4.00	0.67

a) Did the student's circuit have a 5-Ω, 10-Ω, 15-Ω, or some other resistor?

6. Your teacher will supply you with a resistor inside a black box.

a) Record data to determine which resistor is inside the black box. Explain how you know.

b) How confident are you about the contents of the black box? (1 = I have no idea; 10 = I am completely sure; nothing else is possible.)

Physics Talk

OHM'S LAW RELATES RESISTANCE TO VOLTAGE AND CURRENT

Scientists study "black boxes" all the time. A black box is an object or a phenomenon that you cannot see directly. Scientists will often define something to be a black box and describe it in terms of how it interacts with the world around it. In this section, you investigated a black box electrically to discover the resistor that was inside.

You first measured the voltage and current of three known resistors. The measurements of voltage and current showed that increasing the voltage increased the current in the circuit. This was true for all three resistors.

The ratio of the voltage to current was constant for any single resistor. For example, data of the voltage and current for the 3-Ω may have looked like the first two columns of the chart. The third column is the ratio of voltage to current.

Voltage (V)	Current (A)	$\dfrac{\text{Voltage}}{\text{Current}}$ $\dfrac{V}{I}$
1.00	0.33	3
1.50	0.50	3
2.00	0.67	3
2.50	0.83	3
3.00	1.00	3
3.50	1.17	3
4.00	1.33	3

Georg Simon Ohm, a German physicist.

The ratio of the voltage to current is equal to the **electrical resistance**. This relationship is referred to as **Ohm's law**. Many resistors obey Ohm's law, which states that as the voltage increases at a fixed rate, the current increases at the same rate. This is expressed mathematically:

$$R = \frac{V}{I}$$

where R is the resistance in ohms (Ω),

  V is the voltage in volts (V), and

  I is the current in amperes (A).

Physics Words

electrical resistance: the ratio of the voltage across a conductor divided by the current.

Ohm's law: voltage increases at a fixed rate as the current increases at the same rate.

Active Physics

The unit of resistance is the ohm. A one-ohm resistor connected to a one-volt battery will draw one ampere of current. The symbol for ohm is the Greek letter *omega* (Ω).

This equation can be rearranged to calculate the value of any of the terms.

$$V = RI \qquad I = \frac{V}{R}$$

The helpful algebra circle can be used to solve for any of the three variables, by covering up the variable you are solving for and viewing the equation.

If you want to solve for voltage, cover the *V* and you will see that you must multiply *I* by *R* (since they are side by side).

If you want to solve for current, cover the *I* and you will see that you must divide *V* by *R*.

If you want to solve for resistance, cover the *R* and you will see that you must divide *V* by *I*.

Some resistors obey Ohm's law over a wide range of voltages. For these resistors, the value of *R* always remains the same.

Sample Problem

A 2-Ω resistor is placed in a circuit. Record the currents corresponding to voltage measurements of 10 V and 30 V.

Strategy: You are asked to calculate current for a known resistor. You can use Ohm's law, which shows the relationship among voltage, resistance, and current.

Given: $R = 2\ \Omega$

$V = 10$ V and 30 V

Solution: $I = \dfrac{V}{R}$

$$I = \frac{10\ \text{V}}{2\ \Omega} \qquad\qquad I = \frac{30\ \text{V}}{2\ \Omega}$$
$$= 5\ \text{A} \qquad\qquad\qquad = 15\ \text{A}$$

Dimensional Analysis and Ohm's Law

In the sample problem, you used the equation
$$I = \frac{V}{R}$$

Recall that resistance (*R*), measured in ohms (Ω), is the ratio of the voltage to the current, measured in $\frac{V}{A}$. Also, recall that mathematically

$$\frac{V}{\dfrac{V}{A}} = \cancel{V} \times \frac{A}{\cancel{V}} = A$$

Notice how the units cancel, leaving the unit for current, amperes (A).

Checking Up

1. What is the name for the ratio of the voltage applied to a circuit and the current in a circuit?

2. A single 5-Ω resistor is placed in a circuit that has a battery supplying 10 V. What current will flow in this circuit?

3. When the voltage is increased in a circuit with a single resistor that obeys Ohm's law, what will happen to the current in the circuit?

Active Physics

+Math	+Depth	+Concepts	+Exploration
◆◆	◆◆	◆	

Active Physics

Plus

Graphing Ohm's Law

Ohm's law expresses the relationship between the voltage and current

$$R = \frac{V}{I}$$

For most resistors, the ratio of the voltage and current is a constant.

Recording the varying voltage and the corresponding current would allow you to make a graph. If the resistor obeys Ohm's law, the ratio of the voltage and current remains the same and the graph would be a straight line. If the current is on the *x*-axis and the voltage on the *y*-axis, the slope of the line is equal to *R*.

For the data given in the *Physics Talk* for a 3-Ω resistor, the graph would look like the one shown.

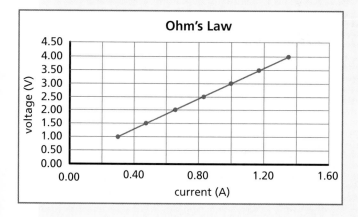

1. Calculate the slope of the line and determine if, in fact, it is equal to 3 Ω.

   It makes sense to calculate the slope. The equation for a straight line is $y = mx + b$, where *m* is the slope of the line, and *b* is the *y*-intercept. The *y*-axis has the value of voltage (*V*) and the *x*-axis has the values of current (*I*). The *y*-intercept is zero. Lining up the equations for a straight line and Ohm's law, you can see that the slope *m* is equal to the resistance (*R*).

   $$\begin{array}{ccc} y & = & m & x & + b \\ V & = & R & I \end{array}$$

   Recognize that this graph is a bit unusual. Usually, the independent variable (the one you vary) goes on the *x*-axis and the dependent variable goes on the *y*-axis. If your data were plotted like that, the slope of the line would be equal to $1/V$ which is equal to $1/R$.

2. Plot the data as current versus voltage. Calculate the slope and determine if, in fact, it is equal to 1/(3-Ω).

3. Using either the *V-I* format or the *I-V* format, graph the data from the three resistors, 3 Ω, 10 Ω, and 15 Ω on a single graph.

What Do You Think Now?

Lighting makes some rooms conducive to work and other rooms more relaxing.

- **What determines the brightness of a light bulb?**

- **What determines how much current flows in a circuit?**

How would you answer these questions now? What else would you think you need to know to answer the questions more completely?

Active Physics

Essential Questions

Physics

What does it mean?

What is Ohm's law?

How do you know?

How do you know that Ohm's law is a valid description of the relationship between voltage, current and resistance?

Why do you believe?

Connects with Other Physics Content	Fits with Big Ideas in Science	Meets Physics Requirements
Electricity and magnetism	Models	✳ Experimental evidence is consistent with models and theories

✳ In physics, mathematical models are created that express relationships between quantities. Explain why you believe that Ohm's law can be applied to a wide variety of objects.

Why should you care?

How will you use Ohm's law to help design the electrical system for the limited power and energy of your wind generator?

Reflecting on the Section and the Challenge

Ohm's law expresses the relationship between voltage and current for many resistors. Your appliances are all electrical resistors. These resistors can get hot (in toasters) or help a motor turn (in fans) or create light (in bulbs). Knowing the resistance allows you to use Ohm's law to compute the voltage and current required in a circuit. As you develop your appliance package, you will need to consider the voltage and currents used in the circuit. You may wish to choose appliances that have different resistances to limit the power required in the circuit.

Active Physics

Physics to Go

1. Copy and fill in the table at right that provides two of the following three quantities: voltage drop across a resistor, the current through the resistor, and the resistance of the resistor. As an example, in the first row the resistance is 2 Ω and the current is 1 A. From $V = IR$, the value of the voltage should be 2 V.

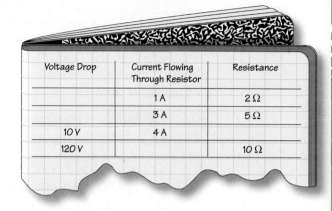

Voltage Drop	Current Flowing Through Resistor	Resistance
	1 A	2 Ω
	3 A	5 Ω
10 V	4 A	
120 V		10 Ω

2. A resistor is placed in a circuit. Calculate the resistance in each of the following cases.

   a) The current in the circuit is 3 A and the voltage drop across the resistor is 12 V.

   b) The current in the circuit is 2 A and the voltage drop across the resistor is 6 V.

3. A resistor of 5 Ω is placed in a circuit. The voltage drop across the resistor is 12 V. What is the current through the resistor?

4. A resistor is placed in a circuit. The current in the circuit is 2 A and the voltage drop across the resistor is 8 V. The voltage is then increased to 12 V. What will be the new current?

5. **Active Physics** **Plus** Using the information in the data table, construct a graph following the directions below.

   • Mark an appropriate scale on the x-axis labeled "Current (A)."

   • Mark an appropriate scale on the y-axis labeled "Voltage (V)."

   • Plot the data points for voltage versus current.

   • Draw the best-fit line.

Current (A)	Voltage (V)
0.010	2.3
0.020	5.2
0.030	7.4
0.040	9.9
0.050	12.7

   a) Using your graph, find the slope of the best-fit line.

   b) What physical quantity does the slope of the graph represent?

6. Your hair dryer has a resistance of 9.6 Ω and you plug it into the bathroom outlet. Assume household voltage to be 120 V and that different parts of your house are connected in parallel.

   a) What current will it draw?

   b) Suppose your brother has an identical hair dryer and plugs it into the same part of the circuit. What current will the two hair dryers draw?

   c) If the maximum current the circuit breaker in the system can handle is 20 A, what do you think will happen?

7. **Active Physics** **Plus** Two wires are tested in a lab setting. Current was measured as the voltage across the wire was varied. The results of the experiment are shown in the graph to the right. Both wire A and B obey Ohm's law. Which wire has the greatest resistance?

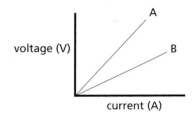

8. A 12-V battery is hooked up to a 3-Ω resistor. The current through the resistor is

   a) 36 A   b) 12 A   c) 4 A   d) ¼ A

9. A 2-Ω resistor has 4 A of current running through it. The voltage drop (or potential drop) across the resistor is

   a) ½ V   b) 2 V   c) 4 V   d) 8 V

Inquiring Further

Write ohm (home) about it

The ohm is a unit of electrical resistance and is given the symbol Ω, the Greek letter *omega*. You can have some fun with the ohm by creating an "ohm-expression." A few examples are given below. Try to develop one of your own "Ω-expressions."

ohm plate
or home plate

ohm on the range,
or home on the range

Sherlock ohms
or Sherlock Holmes

Section 5

Electric Power: Load Limit

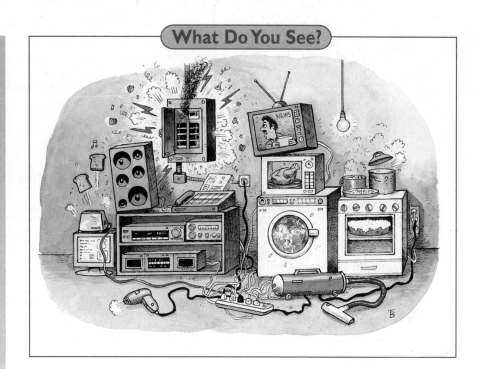

What Do You See?

Learning Outcomes

In this section, you will

- **Define** power, insulator, and conductor.

- **Use** the equation for power, $P = IV$.

- **Calculate** the power limit of a 120-V household circuit.

- **Differentiate** between a fuse and a circuit breaker.

- **Identify** the need for circuit breakers and fuses in a home.

What Do You Think?

Everybody has at one time blown a fuse, or tripped a circuit breaker causing the lights to go off in a circuit in the house.

- **What is the function of a fuse or circuit breaker?**

- **Exactly what conditions do you think make a fuse blow or a circuit breaker trip?**

Record your ideas about these questions in your *Active Physics* log. Be prepared to discuss your responses with your small group and the class.

Investigate

1. Create your own *fuse* by taping a very thin strand of steel wool to an inflated balloon. Connect the hand generator to one end of the steel wool. Connect the other end of the steel wool to a light bulb. Complete the circuit by connecting the other end of the light bulb to the generator. (You can use additional wires.)

   Begin cranking the generator, slowly at first, and observe the steel wool. Gradually increase the speed of the generator and watch what happens to your fuse.

Active Physics

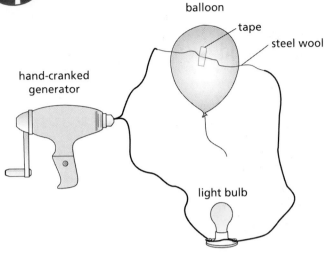

balloon

tape

steel wool

hand-cranked
generator

light bulb

a) What happens to the light when your fuse blows?

2. Your teacher will do the next part of the *Investigate* as a demonstration for the entire class. You will intentionally exceed the load limit of the power strip that is specially fitted with an external fuse. Household circuits operate at dangerous voltage and current levels, so you should never experiment with those kinds of circuits. Your teacher will add light bulbs, heat lamps, hot plates, hair dryers, and other appliances to the circuit until the fuse blows. Observe the number of appliances needed to reach the load limit and the manufacturer's ratings of the appliances.

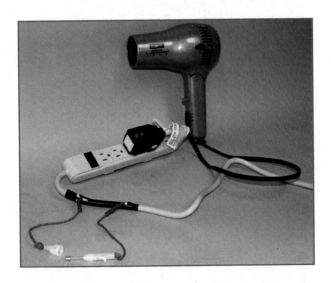

a) Why do you think that the fuse blew?

b) Why did the circuit require multiple appliances to blow the fuse?

c) Can you develop a model that explains why the fuse behaves the way it does?

3. In your log, create a table like the one shown.

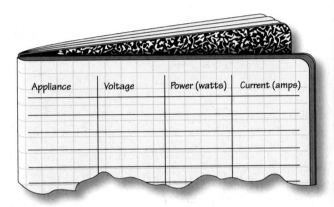

Appliance	Voltage	Power (watts)	Current (amps)

4. Fill in the table in your log.

a) List each of the appliances needed to blow the fuse in the first column of the chart.

b) House circuits in the United States are all 120 V. Complete the second column of your chart by listing 120 V for each appliance.

Appliances have either power ratings or current ratings noted somewhere on the appliance.

- Power is the amount of energy used per unit time and is measured in watts. One watt (1 W) is equal to one joule per second (1 J/s).

- Current is the flow of electric charge and is measured in amperes (amps, for short). One amp (1 A) is equal to one coulomb per second (1 C/s).

c) Record either the current rating or the power rating of each appliance in the chart.

5. The product of voltage and current is power.

$$P = VI$$

You could derive this equation by looking at the definitions of each quantity.

Quantity	Definition	Units
voltage (V)	energy/charge	J/C or V
current (I)	charge/second	C/s or A
power (P)	energy/second	J/s or W

a) Show that the units on both sides of the equation $P = VI$ are identical.

b) Complete the remainder of your appliance chart by calculating the current or power for each appliance using $P = VI$.

6. Based on the table in *Steps 2* and *3*, answer the following questions.

a) Find the total current and total power of the appliances that blew the fuse.

b) If the fuse had a current rating, did the total current of the appliances exceed that rating?

Physics Talk

ELECTRICAL POWER

What Is Power?

The brightness of a bulb is dependent on the **power**, or the rate at which energy is supplied to the bulb. What is power, and how it is different from energy?

Think back to your Electron Shuffle. Each student was a unit of charge and carried a certain amount of energy (a pretzel) through the circuit to the light bulb. Imagine repeating this investigation, only this time keep track of the amount of energy (number of pretzels) left with the light bulb in a certain amount of time, for example 30 s.

First, consider what will happen if the circuit is set up with a 1-V battery (each student carrying one pretzel) and turned on for 30 s. During this time, 30 pretzels leave the battery, and 30 pretzels are left at the light bulb.

Now suppose this is repeated using a 2-V battery, that is, the battery gives out two pretzels to each student unit of charge. Remember, that with twice as much voltage, the current will be twice as much, so students would walk faster with the 2-V battery than with the 1-V battery. In 30 s, 120 pretzels leave the battery, and 120 pretzels are left at the light bulb. If only the voltage had changed, it would have been 60 pretzels. If only the current had changed, it would have been 60 pretzels. With both the current and voltage changing, there are 120 pretzels.

The amount of energy delivered (number of pretzels) for the 2-V battery is four times the energy delivered with the 1-V battery.

Physics Words

power: the rate at which energy is transmitted, or the amount of energy used in a given unit of time.

If more electric charges were delivering their energy (voltage) at a higher rate of flow (current), it makes sense that you get more power as the current and/or the voltage increase. Increasing the voltage increases the current as well as the amount of energy delivered. This, in turn, increases the power to the light bulb. More power is more energy every second and that will make the bulb brighter.

Is There an Equation?

Power equals voltage multiplied by current.

Power (P) is the energy per time. The units are joules per second (J/s), or watts (W).

Voltage (V) is energy per charge. The units are joules per coulomb (J/C) or volts (V).

Current (I) is the flow of charge per unit time. The units are coulombs per second (C/s) or amps (A).

Think of this in terms of dimensional analysis. Voltage is the amount of energy per unit of charge, and current is the amount of charge per unit of time.

$$\text{Power} = \text{voltage} \times \text{current}$$
$$= (\text{energy per charge}) \times (\text{charge per second})$$
$$= \frac{\text{energy}}{\text{charge}} \times \frac{\text{charge}}{\text{second}}$$
$$= \text{energy/second}$$

Using symbols:

$$P = VI$$
$$= \frac{J}{\cancel{C}} \times \frac{\cancel{C}}{s}$$
$$= J/s$$

Physics Words

fuse (electrical): a device placed in an electrical circuit that melts when too much current flows through it, thereby breaking the circuit; it protects the other parts of the circuit from damage due to too much current.

circuit breaker: a device placed in an electrical circuit that operates like an automatic switch to open the circuit when too much current flows through.

Blowing a Fuse or Tripping a Circuit Breaker

A **fuse** and a **circuit breaker** are devices that are placed in an electrical circuit to protect it from damage due to too much current. A fuse is designed to melt when too much current flows through, thereby breaking the circuit. A circuit breaker operates like an automatic switch to open the circuit when there is too much current flowing. Unlike a fuse that must be replaced once it has been blown, a circuit breaker can be reset to close the circuit again and return to normal operation. When the wire in a fuse melts and the circuit is opened, the expression used is "blow a fuse." When a circuit breaker opens a circuit when too much charge is flowing through, the expression used is "trip a circuit breaker."

Physics Words

conductor: a material through which electric current can move easily; metals are good conductors.

insulator: a material through which electric current cannot move easily; air, glass, plastic, rubber, and wood are examples of insulators.

Some materials are considered to be good **conductors** of electricity. In a conductor, electric charge can flow easily. Metals, such as copper, are good conductors of electricity. That is why copper is commonly used for electrical wires. In a conductor, the outer electrons of each atom are loosely bonded and can be easily shared among atoms. Therefore, the electrons can move freely through the material. Conductors have a very low resistance to electric current. (You will learn more about electrons and bonds when you study the atom.)

Insulators do not allow electric charge to flow easily. The outer electrons of the atoms of insulators are tightly bonded. The electrons cannot be easily shared between neighboring atoms. Examples of insulators include air, glass, plastic, rubber, and wood. Insulators are used to provide protection from potentially dangerous amounts of current flowing through a conductor. The rubber coating on electrical wires protects you from the current flowing through the wire. Insulators have a very high resistance to electrical current. You unfortunately do not!

Did you ever wonder why some appliances cause a fuse to blow or a circuit breaker to trip? Why might turning on a hair dryer blow a fuse but turning on a radio would not? Devices that generate lots of heat also use lots of energy. In the appliance package that you will be creating for the wind generator, there is a load limit of 2400 W. In your own home, you are not restricted to a load limit. If you have the money, the electric company will set up more circuits, allowing you to use more electricity. The company can then collect more money from you.

Many people have plugged in a hair dryer and blown a fuse. If you think back, it always seems to be that a blown fuse or a tripped circuit breaker is due to someone plugging in a hair dryer, a toaster oven, or a hot plate (all heat-generating devices). It never seems to happen when someone plugs in a radio or a clock. The table below shows the power ratings of some appliances.

The appliances with high power ratings are responsible for blowing a fuse or tripping the circuit breaker.

In the *Investigate*, you were able to burn a wire and explode a balloon by increasing the current. During

Appliance	Power rating (W)
hair dryer	1200
toaster oven	1500
radio	70
clock	3

the demonstration, something similar happened. As you added appliances, you kept increasing the current until a small wire in the fuse burned (or a circuit breaker tripped) and an open, incomplete circuit resulted. For this reason, a fuse must always be connected in series, so that when it burns out, the circuit will be open and current flow will stop.

Active Physics

Why have a fuse? It seems like a nuisance. If the power company will supply the electricity, why do you need fuses to limit the current and power you use? The fuse is a safety device. The fuse or circuit breaker is there to limit the total current in a typical circuit to 15 A or 20 A, depending upon the wires. All electrical currents generate heat. This is because the movement of electric charge in the resistors of the circuit involves transforming energy into heat. Even wires that typically have very low resistance can get hot. Since the job of the wires is to deliver energy to the circuit loads, you do not want the wires to get too hot, or they might cause a fire. Electrical fires within the walls are exceedingly dangerous because they often go undetected while building up deadly fumes. Limits must be set on how much current a wire may carry safely. That is the job of a fuse or circuit breaker.

If the fuse is rated at 15 A, you can use as many appliances as you like in that circuit as long as the total current is less than 15 A. Once you exceed 15 A, the fuse will blow, opening the circuit and reminding you to unplug some appliances.

Thinking About Your Appliance Package

Home circuits in the United States provide 120 V. Knowing this, you can calculate the current of each appliance.

Appliance	Power rating (W)	Voltage (V)	Current (A)
hair dryer	1200	120	10
toaster oven	1500	120	12.5
radio	70	120	0.6
clock	3	120	0.03

Brightness of a bulb is related to the rate of light energy emitted, which is related to the energy per second or power used. If bulbs are manufactured the same way, a 100-W bulb will be brighter than a 60-W bulb.

However, there are now 20-W compact fluorescent bulbs that can produce the same amount of light as 100-W conventional bulbs. Much of the 100 W of power used in the conventional bulb generates heat and not light. Replacing a conventional bulb with a compact fluorescent bulb saves quite a lot of power. When you are limited to 2400 W of peak power from the wind generator, the compact fluorescent bulbs may be just what you want to recommend.

Since the appliances you will use are all designed to operate at 120 V, the voltage of the circuits in your home needs to be 120 V. If the fuse or circuit breaker can handle a maximum of 15 A, then the power limit is 120 V × 15 A or 1800 W. If a toaster is 1200 W and a hair dryer is 1000 W, they cannot both be operating simultaneously on any one line in your house since they total 2200 W, which is more than the 1800-W limit. If you want to run both appliances at the same time, you must use different circuits, each with its own 1800-W limit.

A second way of viewing the circuit is to look at the current requirements of each appliance. Since the appliances are in parallel, the total current will be the sum of all of the individual currents. In the example above, the current of the 1200-W toaster can be found using the power equation. The current is 1200 W ÷ 120 V or 10 A. Similarly, the hair dryer requires about 8 A. The total current is about 18 A. This is more than the 15-A fuse can tolerate.

Sample Problem 1

A 12-V starter battery in a car supplies 48 A of current to the starter. What is the power output of the battery?

Strategy: You are asked to find the power, so you use the power equation that is specific to electrical circuits.

Given:
$$V = 12 \text{ V}$$
$$I = 48 \text{ A}$$

Solution:
$$P = VI$$
$$= (12 \text{ V})(48 \text{ A})$$
$$= (12\, \frac{\text{J}}{\cancel{\text{C}}})(48\, \frac{\cancel{\text{C}}}{\text{s}})$$
$$= 576 \text{ J/s or about } 580 \text{ W}$$

Sample Problem 2

A 75-W study lamp is plugged into the 120-V household outlet in your room. What current does the outlet supply to the light bulb?

Strategy: Again, use the power equation but rearrange the equation to solve for current.

Given:

$P = 75$ W

$V = 120$ V

Solution:

$$I = \frac{P}{V}$$

$$= \frac{75 \text{ W}}{120 \text{ V}}$$

$$= \frac{75 \text{ (J/s)}}{120 \text{ (J/C)}}$$

$$\frac{75}{120}\left(\frac{\cancel{J}}{s}\right) \times \left(\frac{C}{\cancel{J}}\right)$$

$$= 0.63 \text{ C/s or } 0.63 \text{ A}$$

Light bulbs do not draw a lot of current.

Sample Problem 3

A light bulb operating at 120 V draws 0.50 A. Determine the bulb's

   a) resistance

   b) power

Strategy: Ohm's law can be used to determine the resistance of the light bulb. The power can be determined using $P = VI$.

Given:

$V = 120$ V

$I = 0.50$ A

Solution:

a) $V = IR$

Solving for R,

$$R = \frac{V}{I}$$

$$= \frac{120 \text{ V}}{0.50 \text{ A}}$$

$$= 240 \ \Omega$$

b) $P = VI$

$$= (120 \text{ V})(0.50 \text{ A})$$

$$= 120\frac{J}{\cancel{C}} \times 0.50\frac{\cancel{C}}{s}$$

$$= 60 \text{ J/s or } 60 \text{ W}$$

Checking Up

1. What is the purpose of a fuse in a circuit?

2. How must a fuse be connected in a circuit to prevent current from flowing when the circuit becomes "overloaded"?

3. A household circuit that uses 120 V has a 15-A fuse in the circuit. How many total watts from different appliances can the circuit supply before the fuse is in danger of burning out?

4. A 60-W and a 100-W bulb are each plugged into a 120-V circuit. Which light bulb will have the larger current?

+Math	+Depth	+Concepts	+Exploration
◆◆	◆		

Active Physics

Plus

Combining the Power Equation and Ohm's Law

Algebraically combining the power equation and Ohm's law can provide you with some very helpful equations.

Since $P = VI$ and $V = IR$

Substitute IR for V in the power equation

Then $P = (IR)I$

$$P = I^2R$$

This form of the power equation is helpful when you know the values of current and resistance. You do not need to find the voltage across the resistor.

Since $P = VI$ and $V = IR$

Substitute $\dfrac{V}{R}$ for I in the power equation

Then $P = V\left(\dfrac{V}{R}\right)$

$$P = \dfrac{V^2}{R}$$

This form of the power equation is helpful when you know the values of voltage and resistance. It saves you from the need to find the current through the resistor.

1. In a series circuit, all resistors have identical currents.

    a) What is the relationship between the power and resistance of these resistors?

    b) In a parallel circuit, all resistors have identical voltages. What is the relationship between the power and resistance of these resistors?

2. Two identical resistors ($R = 6\ \Omega$) are connected in series to an 18-V battery.

    a) Calculate the current, voltage, and power of each resistor.

    b) These same identical resistors ($R = 6\ \Omega$) are now connected in parallel to an 18-V battery. Calculate the current, voltage, and power for each resistor.

3. A circuit consisting of three light bulbs is shown below. When light bulb B is removed, what happens to the brightness of the remaining two bulbs? (Use your model of the Electron Shuffle to guide you.)

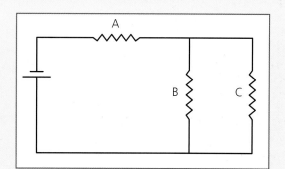

Active Physics

What Do You Think Now?

At the beginning of this section, you were asked:

- **What is the function of a fuse or circuit breaker?**
- **Exactly what conditions do you think make a fuse blow or a circuit breaker trip?**

Now that you have completed this section, how would you now answer these questions? What else would you think you need to know to answer the questions more completely?

Physics
Essential Questions

What does it mean?

What does it mean to blow a fuse or trip a circuit breaker?

How do you know?

In a typical household circuit, what evidence do you have that a 15-A fuse will blow when more than 1800 W are plugged in?

Why do you believe?

Connects with Other Physics Content	Fits with Big Ideas in Science	Meets Physics Requirements
Electricity and magnetism	*Models	Experimental evidence is consistent with models and theories

*Physicists use models to help understand and make sense of a wide variety of phenomena. How does the Electron-Shuffle model help you to understand the relationship among power, voltage, and current?

Why should you care?

The wind generator available for Homes For Everyone is limited to a maximum power of 2400 W at any one time. How will you use this information when you develop your appliance package? How can a fuse help to limit people's power consumption?

Reflecting on the Section and the Challenge

The total power capacity of the wind generator is 2400 W, so the load limit of the electrical system for the HFE dwelling is 2400 W, as outlined in the *Scenario* of the *Chapter Challenge*. Since most electrical appliances are designed around an industry standard of 120 V, the power plant of the wind generator will provide 120 V to circuits within the dwelling. In this *Investigate*, you learned what load limit means, and how to relate it to current and voltage. If the people in the dwelling try to run appliances that require more than 2400 W, the fuse will blow. If this were to happen in your own home, you could always choose a different line to run the extra appliances. With only one generator, this is not an option in the HFE dwelling. This will have direct application soon when you begin selecting appliances to be used in the dwelling.

Physics to Go

1. In your *Active Physics* log, complete the table below. The table provides two of the following four quantities in a circuit: voltage, current, power, and resistance. If you know two of these, you can find the others.

   Example: In the first row the resistance is 2 Ω and the current is 1 A. Using Ohm's law, $V = IR$, you can find the value of the voltage (V). The value of the voltage is 2 V. The power is given by $P = IV$. The power is 2 W.

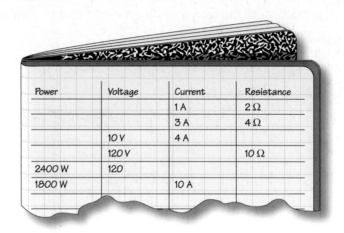

Power	Voltage	Current	Resistance
		1 A	2 Ω
		3 A	4 Ω
	10 V	4 A	
	120 V		10 Ω
2400 W	120		
1800 W		10 A	

2. Explain in detail what load limit means, and include maximum current, in amperes, as part of your explanation.

3. An electric hair dryer has a power rating of 1200 W and is designed to be used on a 120-V household circuit. How much current flows in the hair dryer when it is in use?

4. A 120-V circuit for the kitchen of a home is protected by a 20-A circuit breaker. What combinations of the appliances listed below can be used on the circuit at the same time without the circuit breaker shutting off the circuit?

   - 1000-W toaster
   - 1200-W frying pan
   - 300-W blender
   - 600-W coffee maker

5. How many 60-W incandescent light bulbs can be operated at the same time on a 120-V, 15-A circuit in a home? How many energy-efficient 22-W bulbs can operate on a similar circuit?

6. Some electrical appliances are rated in horsepower (HP). 1 HP = 746 W. What amount of current flows in a 0.8 HP vacuum cleaner operating on a 120-V circuit?

7. Some electrical appliances are rated in amps. What is the power in watts of a 6-A appliance designed to operate on a 120-V circuit?

8. A 1500-W hair dryer is plugged into the outlet in your bathroom. How much current does this hair dryer draw?

9. When you turn on the toaster in the kitchen, it draws 8.0 A of current from the line.

   a) Find the power output of the toaster.

   b) You plug another toaster in the same outlet and the circuit breaker trips. What is the maximum current for the type of breaker you are using?

10. A 3-W clock operates at 120 V.

   a) How much current does the clock draw?

   b) Determine the clock's resistance.

   c) If the maximum current that can be drawn from the outlet is 15 A, how many clocks would it take to blow the fuse? (Assume all clocks could be plugged into the outlet.)

11. An iron has a resistance of 13.1 Ω. Could two identical clothing irons operate on the same fuse? (Assume $V = 120$ V and $I_{max} = 15$ A.)

12. The load limit for a household circuit operating at 120 V is 2400 W. Exceeding that limit will result in a blown fuse. Which combination of the following devices would blow the fuse: mini-refrigerator ($P = 300$ W), microwave oven ($R = 19$ Ω), hair dryer ($I = 12$ A), coffee maker ($R = 9.2$ Ω).

13. How much current, in amps, must exist in the filament of

   a) A 60-W light bulb when it is operating in a 120-V household circuit?

   b) A 100-W light bulb?

   c) Fuses and circuit breakers are rated in amperes, usually 15 or 20 A for most household circuits. Use the equation $P = VI$ to show how you can calculate the load limit, in watts, of a 120-V household circuit protected by a 15-A circuit breaker.

14. *Preparing for the Chapter Challenge*

   a) Find out about the power rating, in watts, of at least six electrical appliances. You can do this at home, at a store that sells appliances, by studying a catalog, or on the Internet. Some appliances have the watt rating stamped somewhere on the device itself, but for others you may have to check the instruction book for the appliance or find the power rating on the original package. Also, your local power company probably will provide a free list of appliances and their power ratings on request. If the appliance lists the current in amperes, you can assume a voltage of 120 V and calculate the power (in watts) by using the equation $P = VI$.

b) List three appliances you would include in the HFE appliance package that will be part of the *Chapter Challenge*. For each appliance, list the power demand. For each appliance, describe how it will contribute to the well-being of the people living in the dwelling.

Inquiring Further

Electrical system of a house

Find out about the electrical system of your home or the home of a friend or acquaintance. With the approval of the owner or manager, and with adult supervision, locate the load center, also called the main distribution panel, for the electrical system. Open the panel door and observe whether the system uses circuit breakers or fuses. How many are there, and what is the ampere rating shown on each fuse or circuit breaker?

You may find some larger fuses or breakers that control large, 240-V appliances such as a kitchen range (electric stove); if so, how many are there and what are their ampere ratings? If you can, determine what they control.

In some load centers there is a list of what rooms or electrical devices are controlled by each fuse or breaker, but often the list is missing or incomplete.

With the approval of the owner or manager, and with adult supervision, you can develop a list that indicates what each fuse or breaker controls. To do so, shut off one circuit and go through the entire house to find the lights and outlets that are "dead" (check outlets with a lamp that you can carry around easily). Those items that are "off" are controlled by that fuse or breaker. List them. Then turn that circuit back on and repeat the same process with another circuit.

Report your findings to your teacher in the form of a list or diagram of the house showing what is controlled by each fuse or circuit breaker.

Section 6

Current, Voltage, and Resistance in Parallel and Series Circuits: Who's in Control?

What Do You See?

Learning Outcomes

In this section, you will

- **Assemble** a switch in a circuit with parallel components to control a particular lamp.

- **Use** the conservation of energy to determine how currents and voltages are distributed in series and parallel circuits.

- **Use** Ohm's law to derive equations for the total resistance of multiple resistors in series and parallel circuits.

What Do You Think?

Many electrical switches are operated manually (by hand), and many others are automatic, turning appliances on and off in response to a variety of conditions.

- **List at least three different kinds of automatic switching devices.**

- **What are the conditions that cause the on/off action of the switch?**

Record your ideas about these questions in your *Active Physics* log. Be prepared to discuss your responses with your small group and the class.

Investigate

1. Assemble the circuit as shown in the diagram at the top of the next page. Each number corresponds to a different wire. You may wish to place masking tape on each wire with the corresponding number on it.

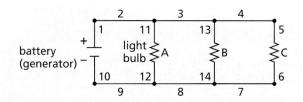

a) Draw a diagram of the circuit. Label the bulbs: A, B, C in your log. Copy the diagram in pencil (you will need to do some erasing later). Notice that the diagram shows 14 different wires. It is sometimes easier to place switches into circuits if you use a few additional wires in the circuit.

2. Compare the circuit you assembled with the one in the following diagram that shows the circuit you used in *Section 3*.

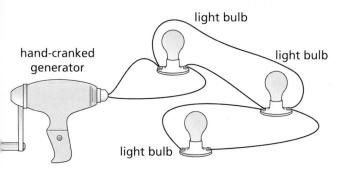

Connect the battery to be sure that all bulbs operate in the circuit you assembled in *Step 1*.

a) Identify the additional new wires on your circuit diagram from *Step 1.a*).

b) What type of circuit (series or parallel) is represented in both diagrams?

3. Predict which wire in the schematic diagram from *Step 1.a)* should be replaced with a switch if you wished to turn all three bulbs on and off. (There will be more than one correct answer.)

Before you proceed with any of the following steps, have your teacher approve the circuit that you have set up.

a) Record your prediction in your log.

b) Replace that wire with a switch. Does it work as predicted?

4. Predict which wire could be replaced with a switch if you wished to turn only bulb A on and off? (There will be more than one correct answer.)

a) Record your prediction in your log.

b) Replace that wire with a switch. Does it work as predicted?

c) Mark the location of the switch on the circuit diagram in your log by writing "switch A" and drawing an arrow from the word "switch A" to the place where the switch should be placed. Erase the wire you took out of the circuit diagram and replace it with the symbol for a switch.

5. Repeat *Step 4* for bulb B and then for bulb C.

a) Remember to record your predictions.

b) Replace the wire you chose with a switch. Are your predictions beginning to improve?

c) Draw two additional diagrams to show the location of switch B and switch C.

6. Placing a voltmeter in the circuit to measure the voltage across any light bulb is relatively simple. Take the two wires from the voltmeter and place them on the two sides of any light bulb. The positive side of the voltmeter should be closer to the positive side of the battery. If you inadvertently reverse the wires, you will note a negative voltage, or see the needle attempt to go below zero. The voltmeter is always placed in parallel with the resistor (light bulb). Place the voltmeter and measure the voltage across the first bulb.

7. Placing an ammeter in the circuit to measure the current through a light bulb is similar to placing a switch next to the bulb to control it.

Active Physics

The ammeter is always placed in series with the resistor (light bulb). Place the ammeter and measure the current through the first bulb.

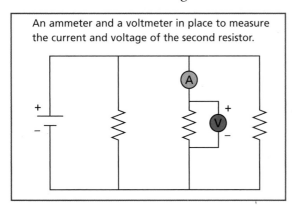

An ammeter and a voltmeter in place to measure the current and voltage of the second resistor.

✎ a) Record your measurements in a table in your *Active Physics* log.

✎ b) Measure and record the voltage and current in the other two bulbs.

8. Measure the total voltage and current in the circuit.

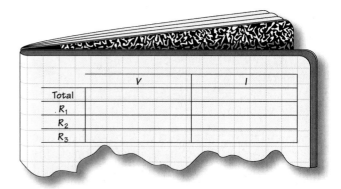

	V	I
Total		
R₁		
R₂		
R₃		

✎ a) Predict where you should place the meters to measure the total voltage and current. Draw a circuit diagram showing where the meters should be placed.

✎ b) After your teacher approves your circuit, measure and record the total voltage and current.

Physics Talk

RELATING CURRENT, VOLTAGE, AND RESISTANCE IN SERIES AND PARALLEL CIRCUITS

Multiple resistors, such as light bulbs, can be set up in series or parallel. The properties of the series and parallel circuits are quite different. Light bulbs in series will all go out when one bulb is removed. Light bulbs in parallel will remain on when one bulb is removed.

In this *Physics Talk*, you will read about the principles of current and voltage in series and parallel circuits. You will also be introduced to the equations for relating total current, total voltage, and total resistance in both series and parallel circuits. It will be helpful to recall the model you created when you did the Electron Shuffle as you read each part.

In the *Active Physics Plus*, you will see how you can combine the equations for total current and total voltage with Ohm's law to derive the equations for total resistance in both series and parallel circuits.

Switches

In the *Investigate*, you learned how switches could control which resistors in a parallel circuit will get current. Regardless of how an electrical switch may be activated, most switches work in the same basic way. Switches are always in series with the device they control. When a switch is "on," a good conductor of electricity, usually copper, is provided as the path for current flow through the switch. Then, the circuit containing the switch is said to be "closed," and the current flows. When a switch is turned "off," the conducting path through the switch is replaced by an air gap. Since air has very high resistance, the current flow through the switch is interrupted, and the circuit is said to be "open."

Current in a Series Circuit

The current, measured in amperes (A), in an electrical circuit, is a measure of the amount of charge that flows past a given point in a given amount of time. One ampere is defined as one coulomb per second. In the Electron-Shuffle model, each person represented one coulomb of charge. The current was defined as the number of students (coulombs) that moved past a point every second. The charge that flows into one end of a wire must flow out the other end of the wire. In a series circuit, the current that goes through the first light bulb

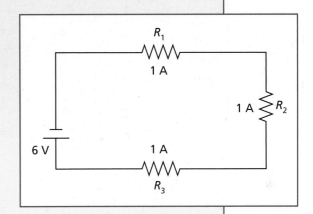

must go through the second light bulb, and then through the third light bulb. Think of how all of the charges went through all of the light bulbs in the Electron Shuffle when the light bulbs were in series. The circuit diagram above shows a circuit with three bulbs in series. The same 1-A current flows through each bulb, even if the bulbs are not identical. The following equation describes this relationship (T stands for total).

$$I_T = I_1 = I_2 = I_3$$

Current in a Parallel Circuit

In a parallel circuit, the current splits at certain junctions and then joins together at other junctions. The current entering any junction must equal the current leaving that junction if charge is to be conserved. Consider a circuit with three identical light bulbs in parallel. Since the bulbs are identical they have equal currents flowing through them. Assume that the total current in the circuit is 9 A, so that 3 A must flow through each light bulb. You can see that 9 A of current enter junction A, and two currents, a 3-A and 6-A (a total of 9 A) leave the junction. The current that goes into a junction is equal to the current that comes out of that junction. This is true everywhere in the circuit. At junction D, 9 (3 + 6) A enter and 9 A exit.

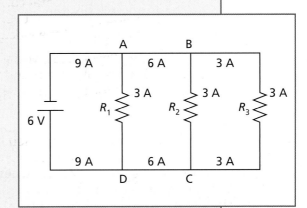

In the next parallel circuit diagram, the 9 A are shown in packets of 3 A, with each packet a different color. You can see how the packets of charge split at the junctions and then join again as they approach the battery.

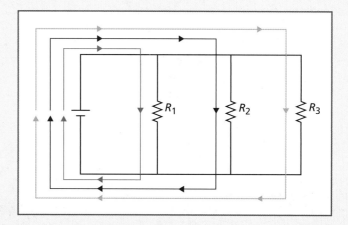

The total current leaving the battery is equal to sum of the currents through the paths in the parallel circuit.

$$I_T = I_1 + I_2 + I_3$$

Your measurements of the current in the investigation provided experimental evidence of this relationship.

Voltage in a Series Circuit

The voltage (also called the potential difference), measured in volts, is a measure of the energy per charge. One volt is defined as one joule per coulomb. The battery provides a certain amount of energy to every coulomb of charge. The energy in the circuit is distributed to the resistors (lamps or appliances) in the circuit.

In a series circuit, all of the charges go through all of the resistors, so the current going through each light bulb in the figure must be the same ($I_1 = I_2 = I_3$). If the three resistors are identical, as in the Electron Shuffle, each resistor will get the same energy. If a battery provides 6 V, then 2 V are transferred to the first resistor, 2 V are transferred to the second resistor, and 2 V are transferred to the third resistor. However, if the resistors are different, each will get a different amount of the energy. For example, if a 6-V battery is used, 2 V may be transferred to the first resistor, 3 V to the second resistor, and 1 V to the third resistor. In either case, the sum of the voltages must total the voltage of the battery. The following equation describes this relationship.

$$V_T = V_1 + V_2 + V_3$$

This is a statement about the conservation of energy. The battery provides a certain amount of energy to each coulomb of charge. This energy is then distributed to the three resistors.

Voltage in a Parallel Circuit

In a parallel circuit, the charges that go through one resistor do not go through any other resistor. All of the energy of that charge must be transferred to that one resistor, as we saw in the Electron Shuffle investigation. If a battery provides 6 V, then 6 V must be transferred to each resistor. For instance, in the circuit with the three light bulbs in parallel, each bulb sees the same voltage, 6 V. The following equation describes this relationship.

$$V_T = V_1 = V_2 = V_3$$

Your measurements of the voltages of each bulb in the investigation provided experimental evidence across this relationship.

Resistance in Series and Parallel Circuits

Combining the equations above and Ohm's law, it is possible to derive equations that relate total resistance in series and parallel circuits. The following equation describes this relationship for a series circuit.

$$R_T = R_1 + R_2 + R_3$$

The following equation describes this relationship for a parallel circuit.

$$\frac{1}{R_T} = \frac{1}{R_1} + \frac{1}{R_2} + \frac{1}{R_3}$$

The *Active Physics Plus* shows you how these equations were derived.

Series Circuit Summary

All components have the same (equal) current.

$$I_T = I_1 = I_2 = I_3$$

Voltage drops add to equal total voltage.

$$\text{Voltage: } V_T = V_1 + V_2 + V_3$$

Resistances add to equal total resistance. The more resistors in the circuit, the larger the total resistance.

$$\text{Resistance: } R_T = R_1 + R_2 + R_3$$

Ohm's law: Ohm's law can be applied to the entire circuit or to any resistor in the circuit.

$$V_T = I_T R_T \qquad V_1 = I_1 R_1 \qquad V_2 = I_2 R_2 \qquad V_3 = I_3 R_3$$

Power: Power can also be calculated for the entire circuit or for any resistor in the circuit.

$$P_T = V_T I_T \qquad P_1 = V_1 I_1 \qquad P_2 = V_2 I_2 \qquad P_3 = V_3 I_3$$

Parallel Circuit Summary

Currents through each component add to equal total current.

$$\text{Current: } I_T = I_1 + I_2 + I_3$$

All components have the same (equal) voltage.

$$\text{Voltage: } V_T = V_1 = V_2 = V_3$$

The more resistors in the circuit, the smaller the total resistance of the circuit.

$$\text{Resistance: } \frac{1}{R_T} = \frac{1}{R_1} + \frac{1}{R_2} + \frac{1}{R_3}$$

Ohm's law: Ohm's law can be applied to the entire circuit or to any resistor in the circuit.

$$V_T = I_T R_T \qquad V_1 = I_1 R_1 \qquad V_2 = I_2 R_2 \qquad V_3 = I_3 R_3$$

Power: Power can also be calculated for the entire circuit or for any resistor in the circuit.

$$P_T = V_T I_T \qquad P_1 = V_1 I_1 \qquad P_2 = V_2 I_2 \qquad P_3 = V_3 I_3$$

Sample Problem I

Given the following series circuit, find:

a) the total resistance

b) the total current

c) the current through each resistor

d) the voltage across each resistor

e) the total power

f) the power dissipated by each resistor

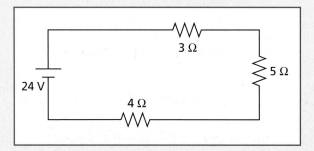

Strategy: This is a series circuit. All the current goes through each of the resistors. First calculate the total resistance. Then, using Ohm's law, calculate the total current. You can also use Ohm's law to calculate the voltage across each resistor. Then, using the equation for power, calculate the total power and the power through each resistor.

Given:

$V = 24$ V
$R_1 = 3\ \Omega$
$R_2 = 5\ \Omega$
$R_3 = 4\ \Omega$

Solution:

a) Total resistance:

$$R_T = R_1 + R_2 + R_3$$
$$= 3\ \Omega + 5\ \Omega + 4\ \Omega$$
$$= 12\ \Omega$$

b) Total current:

$$V_T = I_T R_T$$
$$I_T = \frac{V_T}{R_T}$$
$$= \frac{24\ V}{12\ \Omega}$$
$$= \frac{24\ \cancel{V}}{12\ \dfrac{\cancel{V}}{A}}$$
$$= 2\ A$$

c) You know that the total current is 2 A. In a series circuit, $I_T = I_1 = I_2 = I_3$, so the current through each resistor is 2 A.

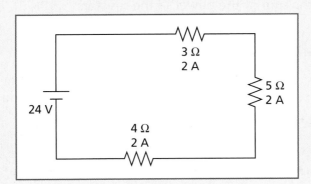

It is helpful to place this information in the diagram.

When you do your dimensional analysis, recall:

• Current (*I*) is measured in amps (A), which are equivalent to coulombs per second (C/s).

• Voltage (*V*) is measured in volts (V), which are equivalent to joules per coulomb (J/C).

• Resistance (*R*) is measured in ohms (Ω), which are equivalent to volts per amp (V/A).

• Power (*P*) is measured in watts (W), which are equivalent to joules per second (J/s).

Active Physics

d) Once you know two of the four variables (V, I, P, R), you can find the other two variables. In this case, you know I and R and can find the voltage using Ohm's law for each resistor.

$$V_1 = I_1 R_1 \qquad\qquad V_2 = I_2 R_2 \qquad\qquad V_3 = I_3 R_3$$
$$V_1 = (2\ \text{A})(3\ \Omega) \quad\ V_2 = (2\ \text{A})(5\ \Omega) \quad\ V_3 = (2\ \text{A})(4\ \Omega)$$
$$V_1 = 6\ \text{V} \qquad\qquad V_2 = 10\ \text{V} \qquad\qquad V_3 = 8\ \text{V}$$

Notice the sum of the voltage drops:

$$6\ \text{V} + 10\ \text{V} + 8\ \text{V} = 24\ \text{V}$$

This is the voltage supplied by the battery.

e) You can now find the total power.

$$P_T = V_T I_T$$
$$= (24\ \text{V})(2\ \text{A})$$
$$= 48\ \text{W}$$

f) $\quad P_1 = V_1 I_1 \qquad\ P_2 = V_2 I_2 \qquad\ P_3 = V_3 I_3$

$\qquad P_1 = (6\ \text{V})(2\ \text{A}) \quad P_2 = (10\ \text{V})(2\ \text{A}) \quad P_3 = (8\ \text{V})(2\ \text{A})$

$\qquad P_1 = 12\ \text{W} \qquad\ P_2 = 20\ \text{W} \qquad\ P_3 = 16\ \text{W}$

Notice the sum of the power in the resistors:

$$12\ \text{W} + 20\ \text{W} + 16\ \text{W} = 48\ \text{W}$$

That is the power supplied by the battery.

It is often useful to draw the circuit diagram and to place the values you calculate directly on the diagram to help keep track of all the variables.

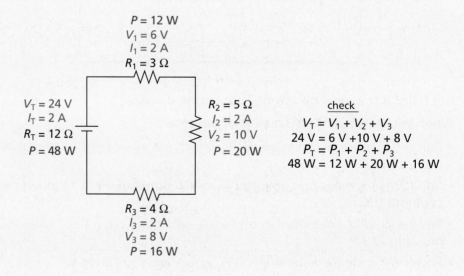

Sample Problem 2

Given the following parallel circuit, find:

a) the current through each resistor

b) the total current

c) the total power

d) the power in each resistor

e) the total resistance

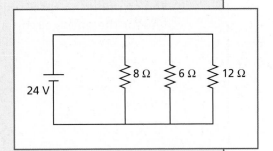

Strategy: This is a parallel circuit. The current follows different paths to each resistor. In a parallel circuit, the voltage drops across each resistor are equal. In this case, the voltage of each resistor equals 24 V.

$$V_T = V_1 = V_2 = V_3 = 24 \text{ V}$$

You can put this information in the diagram immediately.

Once you know two of the four variables (V, I, P, R), you can find the other two variables. In this case, you know V and R. You can find the current using Ohm's law for each resistor.

Solution:

a) $V = IR$

$$I = \frac{V}{R}$$

$$I_1 = \frac{V_1}{R_1} \qquad I_2 = \frac{V_2}{R_2} \qquad I_3 = \frac{V_3}{R_3}$$

$$I_1 = \frac{24 \text{ V}}{8 \ \Omega} \qquad I_2 = \frac{24 \text{ V}}{6 \ \Omega} \qquad I_3 = \frac{24 \text{ V}}{12 \ \Omega}$$

$$I_1 = 3 \text{ A} \qquad I_2 = 4 \text{ A} \qquad I_3 = 2 \text{ A}$$

b) You can find the total current by adding the currents through each resistor. If the resistors have currents of 3 A, 4 A, and 2 A, then the total current must be equal to $3 \text{ A} + 4 \text{ A} + 2 \text{A} = 9 \text{ A}$.

c) Use the power equation to calculate the power once you know the current.

$$P_T = V_T I_T$$
$$= (24 \text{ V})(9 \text{ A})$$
$$= 216 \text{ W}$$

d) $P_1 = V_1 I_1 \qquad P_2 = V_2 I_2 \qquad P_3 = V_3 I_3$

$\quad P_1 = (24 \text{ V})(3 \text{ A}) \quad P_2 = (24 \text{ V})(4 \text{ A}) \quad P_3 = (24 \text{ V})(2 \text{ A})$

$\quad P_1 = 72 \text{ W} \qquad P_2 = 96 \text{ W} \qquad P_3 = 48 \text{ W}$

Notice the sum of the power in the resistors:
$$72 \text{ W} + 96 \text{ W} + 48 \text{ W} = 216 \text{ W}$$
That is the power supplied by the battery.

Active Physics

e) You can find the total resistance of the circuit easily by using Ohm's law for the entire circuit

$$V_T = I_T R_T$$

$$R_T = \frac{V_T}{I_T}$$

$$= \frac{24 \text{ V}}{9 \text{ A}}$$

$$= 2.67 \ \Omega \text{ (or about 3 } \Omega\text{)}$$

You can also find the total resistance by adding the individual resistors in parallel. Notice that in this equation, you are dealing with fractions.

$$\frac{1}{R_T} = \frac{1}{R_1} + \frac{1}{R_2} + \frac{1}{R_3}$$

$$= \frac{1}{8 \ \Omega} + \frac{1}{6 \ \Omega} + \frac{1}{12 \ \Omega}$$

Using the least common denominator of 24:Notice that the total resistance is less than any single resistance in the parallel circuit. This is

$$\frac{1}{R_T} = \frac{3}{24 \ \Omega} + \frac{4}{24 \ \Omega} + \frac{2}{24 \ \Omega}$$

$$= \frac{9}{24 \ \Omega}$$

$$R_T = 2.67 \ \Omega \text{ (or about 3 } \Omega\text{)}$$

always true and agrees with the simpler method above, as it must.

You can keep track of all values you calculate on a circuit diagram.

Checking Up

1. Are switches connected in series or parallel with the devices they control?

2. Would a switch be used in a series or parallel circuit if you wanted to turn off one of several light bulbs?

3. What is the resistance of a switch when it is open? When it is closed?

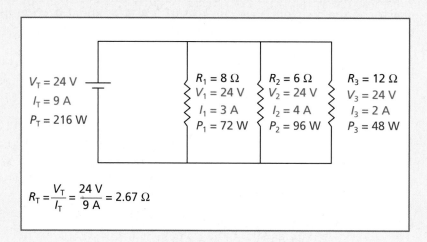

Active Physics

Active Physics

+Math	+Depth	+Concepts	+Exploration
◆◆	◆◆		

Plus

Deriving the Equation to Calculate Total Resistance in Series and Parallel Circuits

Series and parallel circuits distribute the current and voltage differently and require different analysis.

Series Circuits with Three Resistors

In a series circuit

Current $\qquad I_T = I_1 = I_2 = I_3$

Voltage $\qquad V_T = V_1 + V_2 + V_3$

Ohm's law can be applied to the entire circuit or to any resistor in the circuit.

$$V_T = I_T R_T$$
$$V_1 = I_1 R_1$$
$$V_2 = I_2 R_2$$
$$V_3 = I_3 R_3$$

Combining these equations yields an equation that relates the total resistance to the individual resistors in a series circuit.

$$V_T = V_1 + V_2 + V_3$$
$$I_T R_T = I_1 R_1 + I_2 R_2 + I_3 R_3$$

Since $I_T = I_1 = I_2 = I_3$

$$I_T R_T = I_T R_1 + I_T R_2 + I_T R_3$$
$$I_T R_T = I_T \left(R_1 + R_2 + R_3 \right)$$
$$R_T = R_1 + R_2 + R_3$$

Parallel Circuits with Three Resistors

In a parallel circuit

Current $\qquad I_T = I_1 + I_2 + I_3$

Voltage $\qquad V_T = V_1 = V_2 = V_3$

Ohm's law can be applied to the entire circuit or to any resistor in the circuit.

$$V_T = I_T R_T$$
$$V_1 = I_1 R_1$$
$$V_2 = I_2 R_2$$
$$V_3 = I_3 R_3$$

Combining these equations yields an equation that relates the total resistance to the individual resistors in a parallel circuit.

$$I_T = I_1 + I_2 + I_3$$
$$\frac{V_T}{R_T} = \frac{V_1}{R_1} + \frac{V_2}{R_2} + \frac{V_3}{R_3}$$

Since $V_T = V_1 = V_2 = V_3$

$$\frac{V_T}{R_T} = \frac{V_T}{R_1} + \frac{V_T}{R_2} + \frac{V_T}{R_3}$$
$$\frac{1}{R_T} = \frac{1}{R_1} + \frac{1}{R_2} + \frac{1}{R_3}$$

The more resistors you add in parallel the smaller is the total resistance of the circuit. This is because each resistor in parallel provides another pathway for the current to flow, resulting in more total current for the same voltage. That is why circuit breakers and fuses are needed in a household circuit to limit the total current in the circuit.

655

1. As identical resistors are added in a series circuit, the total resistance changes. Graph the total resistance of a series circuit versus the number of 12-Ω resistors in the circuit.

2. As identical resistors are added in a parallel circuit, the total resistance changes. Graph the total resistance of a parallel circuit versus the number of 12-Ω resistors in the circuit.

3. In a parallel circuit, the total resistance is always smaller than any of the individual resistors.

    a) Show that this is true for a circuit with 1-Ω, 10-Ω, and 20-Ω resistors.

    b) Show that this is true for a circuit with two unknown resistors.

4. Shown below is a series/parallel circuit.

    a) Calculate the total resistance of the series/parallel circuit shown below.

    b) Calculate the current through each resistor.

    c) Calculate the voltage across each resistor.

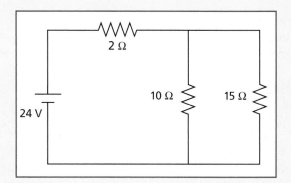

What Do You Think Now?

At the beginning of this section, you were asked:

• **List at least three different kinds of automatic switching devices.**

• **What are the conditions that cause the on/off action of the switch?**

Now that you have completed this section, how would you answer these questions?

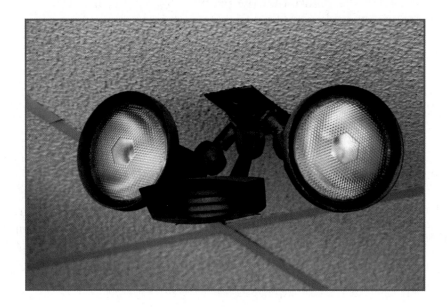

Physics
Essential Questions

What does it mean?

Explain how the voltage of each light bulb in a parallel circuit can be equal to the voltage of the power source.

How do you know?

What experimental evidence do you have that the voltage across each light bulb in a parallel circuit is equal to the voltage of the battery?

Why do you believe?

Connects with Other Physics Content	Fits with Big Ideas in Science	Meets Physics Requirements
Electricity and magnetism	* Conservation laws	Experimental evidence is consistent with models and theories

* Conservation of energy is one of the major organizing principles of physics. How can the voltage relationship of the individual resistors and the voltage of the battery in both series and parallel circuits be explained in terms of energy conservation?

Why should you care?

Circuits in your home make use of both series and parallel circuits. How can your knowledge of circuits be expressed in a meaningful way in your training manual?

Reflecting on the Section and the Challenge

Part of the problem you are facing with the electrical system for the Homes For Everyone (HFE) dwellings is to assure that the people who live in them will not exceed the 2400 W power limit of the system by having too many appliances in use at any one time. Depending on what you choose to include in the HFE appliance package, it may be necessary to use switching devices—automatic, manual, or both—to assure that the people who live in the homes will stay within the power limit as they use their appliances.

Perhaps you could also use automatic switches as "fail safe" devices to prevent accidentally using up too much electrical energy by, for example, forgetting to shut off lights that are not in use.

You may decide that you want a switch to turn off all lights and appliances in a room. Alternatively, you may decide that a certain appliance should never be turned off. You now know how to set up circuits and switches with these properties.

Your calculations of current can help you to prevent a fuse from blowing. You can now explain in your manual how the total current varies as more and more appliances are added in parallel. Your understanding of current, voltage and resistance calculations can guide your explanations in your manual.

Physics to Go

1. In your log, describe several possibilities for using switching devices to address the power limit problem in your universal dwelling. Write your ideas in your log.

2. Electric switches are available which act as timers to turn appliances on and off at chosen times or for chosen intervals. Identify one or more ways a timer switch would be useful in an HFE dwelling.

3. Look at the wiring diagrams shown. Copy each into your log. Position and draw a single switch in each circuit that would allow you to have two lights on all the time, and one light that you could turn on or off.

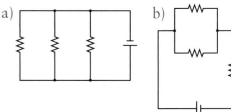

4. A 15-V battery is hooked up to three resistors in series. The voltage drop across the first resistor is 3 V and the voltage drop across the second resistor is 10 V. What is the voltage drop across the last resistor?

5. A 15-V battery is hooked up to three identical resistors in series. What is the voltage across each resistor?

6. A 15-V battery is hooked up to three identical resistors in parallel. What is the voltage across each resistor?

7. In each of the circuits below, all the ammeters (denoted with circles surrounding an A) but one have the current displayed. What is the current in the unknown ammeter?

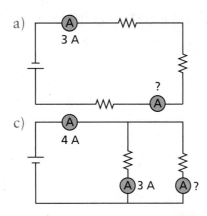

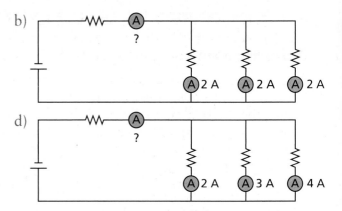

8. Three resistors are hooked up in series. The voltage drops across the resistors are 4 V, 8 V, and 2 V. The current through the first resistor is 2 A.

   a) What is the voltage of the battery?

   b) What is the current through the second resistor?

9. Two identical resistors are hooked up in parallel. The total voltage of the circuit is 6 V. The total current of the circuit is 2 A.

   a) What is the voltage drop across each resistor?

   b) What is the current through each resistor?

Active Physics

10. Three resistors of 12 Ω, 14 Ω, and 4 Ω are connected in series to a 12-V power supply. Find

    a) the total resistance of the circuit

    b) the current flowing through each resistor

    c) the voltage drop across each resistor

11. Three resistors of 8 Ω, 6 Ω, and 4 Ω are connected in series to a battery of six 1.5-V dry cells, which are also connected in series. (Remember when you added batteries in series in the Electron Shuffle?)

    a) Draw a circuit diagram for this situation.

    b) Calculate the total voltage provided by the battery.

    c) Calculate the total resistance.

    d) Find the total current.

    e) What is the voltage drop across each individual resistor?

12. The table to the right represents a set of three resistors arranged in series. Draw a diagram of the circuit. Then use the facts that you know about series circuits to fill in the empty spaces.

	V	I	R
Total	120 V		
R_1			10 Ω
R_2			5 Ω
R_3			25 Ω

13. A 6-Ω, 3-Ω, and 18-Ω resistor are connected in parallel to an 18-V power supply. Draw a diagram of the circuit. Make and complete a chart like the one in the previous problem. Find

    a) the total resistance of the circuit

    b) the total current through the circuit

    c) the current flowing through each resistor

14. **Active Physics** **Plus** You are given three 10-Ω resistors by your teacher. You are told to arrange them in the following ways. Sketch a diagram for each arrangement and make a table with the given values. Complete each chart by finding the unknown values. What values will you have for total resistance in each case?

    a) All three resistors in series.

    b) All three resistors in parallel.

    c) One resistor in series and two in parallel.

    d) Two resistors in series with one in parallel.

    (Hint: In a combination series/parallel circuit, always simplify the parallel resistors first, then the series combinations.)

15. The table to the right represents a set of three resistors arranged in parallel. Draw a diagram of the circuit. Then use the facts that you know about parallel circuits to fill in the empty spaces.

	V	I	R
Total	24 V		
R_1			18 Ω
R_2			12 Ω
R_3			36 Ω

16. Which circuit segment below has the same total resistance as the circuit segment shown in the diagram to the right? (Hint: Whenever two resistors are placed in parallel, the combination has to be smaller than the smallest single resistor. Think about it—each time you add a resistor in parallel, you are making it easier for the charge to flow. So the total resistance always goes down when you add a new resistor.)

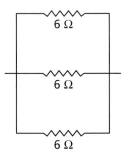

a)

2 Ω   2 Ω   2 Ω

b)

2 Ω

4 Ω

6 Ω

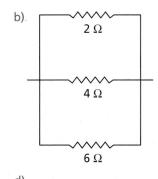

c)

12 Ω

12 Ω

d)

1 Ω   1 Ω

17. The diagram to the right shows the current in three branches of an electric circuit. What is the value and the direction of the current between junction P and point W?

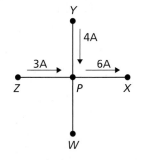

18. What is the current in the circuit represented by the diagram below?

1 Ω   2 Ω   3 Ω

6 V

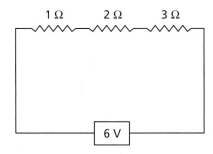

Active Physics

19. What is the current in the ammeter A in the diagram below?

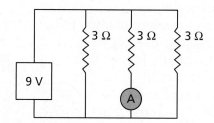

20. A mercury switch is often used as a silent switch for turning lights on and off. The mercury switch is a glass cylinder with a large drop of the liquid metal mercury inside it. When the mercury switch tilts one way, the circuit is completed. When the mercury switch tilts the other way, the circuit is open and the light goes out. Draw a design for how a mercury switch could be manufactured so that when you flip a switch the lights go on and when you lower the switch, the lights go off.

Inquiring Further

1. "Automatic" switching devices

Shop, in a store or catalog, for electrical switching devices controlled by a variety of conditions such as light/dark, high/low temperature, motion, sound, etc. The devices may be either "built-in" to appliances (e.g., the thermostat built into an oven that allows you to set the oven for a specific temperature) or separate (e.g., a clock timer designed to automatically turn lights on and off). Find as many different kinds of switching devices as you can, and note which ones may be useful for the HFE electrical system, and for what purpose. In your log, write a brief report on your findings.

2. Three-way switches

Occasionally, you want to have a light in your house controlled by two switches. For example, you may want to be able to turn a light on from the bottom of the stairs and then turn it off when you get to the top of the stairs. Later, you may want to turn it on from the top of the stairs and then off at the bottom. This is called a three-way switch.

a) Design a circuit diagram for a three-way switch.

b) Design a circuit diagram for a four-way switch (this has three switches that can control the same light.)

Active Physics

Chapter Mini-Challenge

Your challenge for this chapter is to create an appliance package and training manual to be used with the HFE wind generator to supply electricity to a family home. You will have to give some careful consideration to each appliance you select and explain how each one can be used within the system. You will need the physics you have learned so far to help you make your selections and to illustrate how much energy and power each appliance will require. For the *Mini-Challenge* you will complete two very important steps.

1. Develop a preliminary list of appliances that your home might need. You can revise this list later once you have more information about how much power different appliances require. Provide a rationale for the appliances you chose.

2. Create a circuit diagram for your house, including switches, one or more fuses (for safety), and symbols (like the light bulb) to represent the appliances in your list. Assume a single voltage source, which is the windmill generator and batteries. Provide an explanation for how you have designed your circuit based on the electrical requirements of the house.

Go back and quickly read the description of the *Goal* you established at the start of the chapter. Review the *Goal* as a class to make sure you have all of the criteria and necessary restraints. You are now more than halfway through the chapter and you have learned a lot about electricity that will help you design the electrical system for the HFE dwelling.

In addition to the physics you have learned so far, you will be adding most of the *Inputs* for this phase of the *Engineering Design Cycle*. You will be selecting appliances for the appliance list based on your own experience with using electricity. The constraints for this design are the wind generator that will be supplying the electricity and the design goal of creating a universal list of appliances.

Your team should review the physics content from the first six sections to help you compose your appliance package and training manual.

Section 1: You generated electricity and created a circuit that allowed you to light up a light bulb. The transformations of the energy from your body, to the wires, and then to the bulb are very important parts of understanding electricity.

Section 2: You used a physical model for the flow of electricity in a circuit. By acting out the parts of the battery, the electric charge, and the bulb, you now have a very strong understanding of where energy goes when you are working with electricity.

Section 3: In this section, you explored two different types of electrical circuits and compared their similarities and differences. You also learned how to draw a simple circuit diagram for each type of circuit.

Section 4: You explored an electrical "black box" using tools to measure the voltage and current in a circuit. Using this information you learned about resistance in electrical circuits and how it affects the movement of electric charge, or electric current. The relationship among resistance, voltage, and current in an electrical circuit is known as Ohm's law.

Section 5: You learned about load limits and electric power. Part of your challenge requires you to stay within a 2400-W power limit at all times. The physics you learned in this section will help you do that.

Section 6: You explored the role of simple electrical switches. You also considered the wiring diagram that would provide for the best distribution of electricity in your electrical system design.

The *Process* phase is when you decide what information you have to help you meet the criteria of the *Goal*. Brainstorm with your group to come up with a list of potential appliances. After you have a list of ten or more appliances, have each member of your group put them in order from most important to least important by assigning a number to each one. Add the numbers from each group member to get a total rank value for each appliance. This would be an objective way to select the most important appliances using the input of every group member. Remember to include the reasons why each appliance is necessary.

Your first circuit diagram will become a prototype for your final circuit design. Have each student in the group make a sketch of a circuit diagram including switches, fuses, appliances, and the single voltage source. Review each diagram and discuss the advantages and disadvantages of each one. You could make a pros and cons table to help you keep track of your information. Select the circuit diagram that best meets the requirements of the electrical system design. You might find that you want to combine elements from several circuit diagram sketches.

Finally, remember to include an explanation for the design of your circuit diagram. Describe why you placed switches where you did, how your fuses will protect the system, and why you have the wiring layout that you do. You could also discuss how the design of your circuit will affect the electrical current at different points of the circuit using Ohm's law.

Presenting your information to the class is your *Output* for your *Engineering Design Cycle*. You should have a list of appliances, including the reason why each one is important. You should present your circuit diagram. Finally, you should describe the features of your circuit diagram that will enable it to function properly and meet the design goals.

Your classmates will give you *Feedback* on the accuracy and the overall appeal of your presentation based on the criteria of the *Mini-Challenge*. This *Feedback* will become an *Input* for your final design in the *Chapter Challenge*. You will have enough time to make corrections and improvements, so you will want to pay attention to the valuable information your classmates provide.

At this point, remember to correct any parts of your design that did not meet the design goals of the *Mini-Challenge*.

Finally, identify those goals that have not been addressed through research (*Investigates* and reading) and were therefore not addressed in your *Mini-Challenge*. Look for additional information in the remaining sections that will help you calculate power and kilowatt-hours of electricity consumption. Also, find out how to stay within the power and energy limits set in the original design challenge.

Section 7

Laws of Thermodynamics: Too Hot, Too Cold, Just Right

What Do You See?

Learning Outcomes

In this section, you will

- **Assess** experimentally the final temperature when two liquids of different temperatures are mixed.

- **Assess** experimentally the final temperature when a hot metal is added to cold water.

- **Calculate** the heat lost and the heat gained of two objects after they are placed in thermal contact.

- **Discover** if energy is conserved when two objects are placed in thermal contact and reach an equilibrium temperature.

- **Explain** the concept of entropy as it relates to objects placed in thermal contact.

What Do You Think?

As you add cold milk to hot coffee, you expect that the milk will get a bit warmer and the coffee will get a bit colder.

- **What determines the final temperature of the coffee and milk?**

Record your ideas about this question in your *Active Physics* log. Be prepared to discuss your responses with your small group and the class.

Investigate

In this investigation, you will determine the final temperature of a cold water and hot water mixture. Styrene-foam cups work well as containers for this investigation. The insulation "protects" the experiment from the environment by reducing heat transfer with anything outside of the cup.

 Use a heat-proof holder, such as a glove or tongs, while pouring.

1. Pour 100 mL of hot water into a styrene-foam cup and measure the temperature of the water. Pour 100-mL of cold water into a second styrene-foam cup and measure its temperature.

   🖎 a) Record the temperature of the hot water.

   🖎 b) Record the temperature of the cold water.

   🖎 c) Predict the final temperature of the mixture of hot and cold water.

2. Add the cold water to the hot water. Measure the final temperature.

   🖎 a) Record the temperature of the mixture.

   🖎 b) Compare your predicted value with the recorded value.

hot water
cold water
styrene-foam cup

3. Vary the experiment by changing the amount of cold water. Mix 100 mL of hot water with 50 mL of cold water; 75 mL of cold water; 125 mL of cold water; and 150 mL of cold water.

   🖎 a) Make a data table. Record your observations.

   🖎 b) Construct a graph of the results. Plot the final temperature on the *x*-axis and the amount of cold water added on the *y*-axis.

   🖎 c) Use your graph to predict the final temperature when 108 mL of cold water is added to 100 mL of hot water.

4. Cool water can be heated with the addition of hot water. How well would a piece of hot metal heat the cool water? Plan an experiment to compare: (1) the effect of adding 100 g of hot water to a styrene-foam cup with 60 g of cool water, with (2) the effect of adding 100 g of metal heated to the same temperature as the hot water to a separate styrene-foam cup with 60 g of cool water.

 Clean up any spilled water immediately, especially off the floor so that no one slips.

One way to heat the metal is to place it in a bath of hot water for three to five minutes. The length of time you need to keep the metal in the water bath depends upon the size of the metal. You can then use tongs to gently lift the metal from the hot water. As soon as the metal is out of the water, you will need to hold it over several pieces of paper towel folded to make a small mat and shake off drops of the hot water so that none of the hot water enters the beaker with the cold water. You want to try to place only the metal gently into the cold water.

🖎 a) Record your experiment design in your log.

🖎 b) Predict whether the individual cups of cool water will reach the same final temperature.

🖎 c) Do you think it matters what kind of metal you use? For example, will equal masses of copper or aluminum produce the same final temperature? Explain your answer.

Make sure that your design is approved before you continue with the experiment.

5. Conduct the experiment.

✎ a) Record the final temperature of each trial:

  • hot water mixed with cool water

  • hot metal mixed with cool water

✎ b) Did the hot metal warm the cool water as much as an equal mass of hot water?

6. Read the first part of the *Physics Talk*, Specific Heat.

✎ a) Calculate the value of the specific heat, *c*, for the metal that you used to heat the water.

✎ b) Your teacher will tell you the accepted value for the specific heat of the metal you used. How does the specific heat that you calculated compare with the accepted value of specific heat for that metal?

✎ c) Explain any differences between the two values.

Physics Talk

LAW OF CONSERVATION OF ENERGY

Specific Heat

In the first part of the *Investigate*, you saw that adding equal amounts of hot water and cool water produced a final temperature halfway between the initial temperatures of both. When the proportions of the hot and cold water were varied, the temperature changed. The final temperature was somewhere between the two initial temperatures, and nearer to the temperature of the water with the larger mass.

Physics Words

law of conservation of energy: the total amount of energy in a closed system is conserved; energy can neither be created nor destroyed.

The **law of conservation of energy** informs you that if the cold water gained thermal energy through the transfer of heat (as indicated by its rise in temperature), then the hot water must have lost an equal amount of thermal energy. The total energy change must be zero.

An equation to express this might look as follows:

$$\Delta Q_h + \Delta Q_c = 0$$

$$(m_h)(T_f - T_h) + (m_c)(T_f - T_c) = 0$$

where ΔQ is a measure of heat in joules,

  m_h is the mass of the hot water in grams,

  m_c is the mass of the cold water in grams,

  T_f is the final temperature of the water in degrees Celsius,

  T_c is the temperature of the cold water, and

  T_h is the temperature of the hot water.

Notice that the change in temperature $(T_f - T_c)$ for cold water is positive since the final temperature is larger than the initial temperature. The

Active Physics

change in temperature $(T_f - T_h)$ is negative for hot water since the final temperature is smaller than the initial temperature. The cold water gains thermal energy, while the hot water loses thermal energy. In this equation, if the mass of the hot water is less, its change in temperature (ΔT_h) must be larger than the cold water's.

The equation requires you to use the mass of the water. For water, a volume of 1 mL has a mass of 1 g. Converting from volume to mass is easy for water, since the density of water is 1 g/mL. That is, a mass of 1 g occupies a volume of 1 mL.

Energy is conserved whether the cool water is mixed with hot water or hot metal. To understand what happened with the hot metal, look at the factors that determine the amount of heat transferred.

The effect of adding an equal mass of hot metal to the cool water was less than the hot water by a factor called the **specific heat** of the metal (c). Specific heat is defined as the heat energy (in joules) required to raise the temperature of a mass (one gram) of a substance a given temperature interval (one degree Celsius). The unit for specific heat is joules per gram degrees Celcius (J/g°C). Water has a very high specific heat, a value of 4.18 J/g°C.

Physics Words

specific heat: the heat energy required to raise the temperature of a mass of a substance a given temperature interval.

When the material that is being added is taken into account, the equation for the transfer of heat becomes

$$\Delta Q = mc\Delta T$$

where ΔQ is a measure of heat in joules,

   m is the mass of the substance in grams,

   c is the specific heat of the substance
        (the specific heat of water is 4.18 J/g°C), and

   ΔT is the change in temperature in degrees Celsius.

Since the hot metal did not warm the cool water as much as an equal mass of hot water, the specific heat will be smaller for the metal than for water.

Look at this equation again for the trial where the hot metal is added to the cool water:

Heat change of metal + Heat change of water = 0

$$(mc\Delta T)_{metal} + (mc\Delta T)_{water} = 0$$

The value of c for the metal will be different from the value of c for the water. From this equation, you should be able to calculate the value of the specific heat, c, for the metal that you used to heat the water.

Sample Problem

When 100.0 g of hot water at 80.0°C is mixed with 60.0 g of cold water at 20.0°C, the final temperature is 57.5°C. Show that energy was conserved.

Strategy: Heat is a form of energy. The law of conservation of energy tells you that the thermal energy (heat) lost by the hot water is going to equal the thermal energy (heat) gained by the cold water. The sum of these two changes must equal 0.

Given:

$m_h = 100.0$ g $\qquad T_h = 80.0°C$

$m_c = 60.0$ g $\qquad T_c = 20.0°C$

$c = 4.18$ J/g°C $\qquad T_f = 57.5°C$

Solution:

Heat lost by hot water + Heat gained by cold water $= 0$

$$(mc\Delta T)_{hot\ water} + (mc\Delta T)_{cold\ water} = 0$$

$$(100.0\ g)(4.18\ J/g°C)(57.5°C - 80.0°C) + (60.0\ g)(4.18\ J/g°C)(57.5°C - 20.0°C) = 0$$

$$-9405\ J + 9405\ J = 0$$

Conservation of Energy

Energy is conserved. It is not created or destroyed. It only changes from one form to another. If no energy is allowed to enter or leave a system, the total energy of a system remains the same. When an object like a book is dropped to the ground, you can trace the transfer of energy. Initially all the energy is gravitational potential energy. As the book falls, it loses gravitational potential energy and gains kinetic energy as it increases its speed. Eventually the book hits the ground. As the book hits the ground and stops, some of the kinetic energy is converted to sound, as you hear a "thump." The rest of the kinetic energy of the book becomes heat, and the temperatures of the book and of the ground both rise a bit.

You can calculate changes in gravitational potential energy $(\Delta GPE = mg\Delta h)$ and changes in kinetic energy $(\Delta KE = \frac{1}{2}mv_f^2 - \frac{1}{2}mv_i^2)$. You also now know how to calculate changes in thermal energy $\Delta Q = mc\Delta T$. Heat is part of the total energy picture. Conservation of energy means that the total amount of energy in a closed system stays the same, so that the sum of all of the energies remains constant. If a system is not closed, the amount of energy change in the system is equal to the amount of energy that enters or leaves the system. This may seem like simple common sense, but the conservation of energy is one of the most profound principles in physics.

Temperature and Heat

Temperature and heat are not the same, but they are related. **Temperature** is a measure of the average kinetic energy of the molecules of the material due to the random motion of the molecules. You can measure temperature with a thermometer. You can also perceive the temperature through your sense of touch. Since your sense of touch is subjective, the use of an

Physics Words

temperature: a measure of the average kinetic energy of the molecules of a material.

Active Physics

objective tool like a thermometer is required. The temperature and the kinetic energy of the molecules change when the object touches a material of a higher or lower temperature.

At the molecular level, the faster-moving, high kinetic-energy molecules collide with the slow-moving, low kinetic-energy molecules, giving them some of their energy. After many collisions, the average kinetic energy of the two original materials cannot be distinguished. The final temperature is that average kinetic energy.

If object A and object B have the same temperature and object B and object C have the same temperature, then object A and object C must have the same temperature. Even though object A and object C may never interact, you would know that their temperatures are the same because they are both compared to object B. This relation is referred to as the **zeroth law of thermodynamics**. Without this assumption, the study of thermal energy would be exceedingly difficult.

Heat is a common word used in many different contexts. However, in physics, heat has a very specific meaning. Although you may often see the terms heat and **thermal energy** used to mean the same thing, scientists recognize a difference between the two terms.

Thermal energy is the total energy of the particles that make up an object. It is a form of energy that results from the motions of atoms and molecules, and it is associated with the temperature of the object. When the thermal energy of an object increases, there is an increase in temperature. You can think of thermal energy as the energy that an object possesses.

Heat is the thermal energy that is transferred from one object to another. Heat is a transfer of thermal energy from an object at a higher temperature to an object at a lower temperature.

Thermal energy is a form of energy that results from the motions of atoms and molecules. The internal energy of a substance is the amount of energy in the random motions of atoms and molecules. (Random motion means that the atoms and molecules are moving in no specific pattern.) This includes kinetic energy and potential energy of the interacting molecules. The amount of internal energy in an object has to do with the nature of the material, the mass of the material, and the temperature of the material. For example, 100 g of hot water has more energy than 100 g of cold water because of a difference in temperature. A swimming pool of 10,000 kg of cold water will have more energy than 1 kg of hot water, mainly because of a difference in mass. If the 1 kg of hot water is poured into the swimming pool of 10,000 kg of cold water, the temperature of the pool water will rise a tiny amount. The temperature of the hot water will drop considerably. Thermal energy is a measure of both the temperature and the amount of matter.

Physics Words

zeroth law of thermodynamics: if two objects have the same temperature as a third object, then the two objects must also have the same temperature.

heat: energy transferred from one place to another by virtue of a temperature difference.

thermal energy: a form of energy that results from the motions of atoms and molecules; the energy associated with the temperature of a substance.

thermodynamics: the study of the relationships between heat and other forms of energy and the transformation of one form into another.

Active Physics

The First Law of Thermodynamics

Thermodynamics is the study of the relationships between thermal energy and other forms of energy and the transformation of one form into another. In this *Investigate*, you mixed hot and cold water and observed how the final temperature of the mixture was related to the initial temperatures of the hot and cold water. The change in thermal energy of the hot and cold water were equal. The sum of the changes in the thermal energy was equal to zero.

The change in thermal energy of the water was dependent on the mass, the specific heat of water, and the change in temperature.

$$\Delta Q = mc\Delta T$$

When you mix cold milk with hot coffee, you expect the cold milk to warm a bit and the coffee to cool a bit. They will soon arrive at the same temperature. This can be explained using the conservation of energy. The milk gained some energy and the hot coffee lost some energy. It might be clearer if you look at some numbers. If the cold milk is at 5°C and the hot coffee is at 90°C, the final temperature of the milk-coffee mixture could be 80°C. In this case, the temperature of the milk rose 75°C and the temperature of the coffee fell 10°C. Energy was conserved. If you knew the mass of the coffee and the milk, you could compute the gain and loss of the energy by each substance using the relation $Q = mc\Delta T$. The change in energy of both the milk and the coffee would be the same.

This situation is quite common. If you put a cup of hot coffee in a cold metal cup, there would be a similar effect. The coffee could cool from 90°C to 80°C and the metal could warm from 5°C to 80°C. If you knew the masses of the metal and the coffee and the specific heat of the metal, you could again compute the gain and loss of the energy with the relation $Q = mc\Delta T$. Again, the change in energy would be the same for the metal and for the coffee.

The conservation of energy with respect to hot and cold objects is referred to as the **first law of thermodynamics**. In the situations you have studied, the hot and cold materials did not interact with other materials. The hot and cold materials did not get heated from the outside nor did they use any of their thermal energy to do work by moving something. The first law of thermodynamics can also explain what happens if one of these two situations did occur.

Physics Words

first law of thermodynamics: the thermal energy added to a system is equal to the change in internal energy of the system plus the work done by the system on its surroundings.

Imagine a gas that is enclosed in a container with a movable top (a piston). Initially, the gas has a certain amount of thermal energy. The kinetic energy of the molecules that keep colliding with the piston keep it up. If an external flame were to heat the gas, the piston would move up. The gas did work on the piston by lifting it.

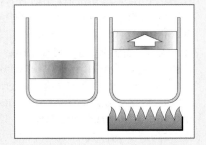

The conservation of energy would state that $\Delta Q = \Delta U + W$

The thermal energy (ΔQ) added is equal to the change in internal energy (ΔU) of the gas plus work (W) done lifting the piston. This is another way of stating the first law of thermodynamics.

The Second Law of Thermodynamics

When hot coffee is poured in a cold metal cup, it never happens that the metal gets even colder and the coffee gets even hotter. It never happens that the coffee heats up from 90°C to 92°C and the metal cools from 5°C to 1°C. In principle, the conservation of energy would be satisfied if the cold metal lost thermal energy and the coffee gained an equal amount of thermal energy so that no energy was created or destroyed. However, this never happens. It also never happens that if you leave a can of warm cola on the kitchen table that the cola gets colder and the room gets warmer.

If something never happens, you must assume that nature has placed a restriction on it. In this case, the restriction is called **entropy**. It informs you that the two materials in contact will reach a common equilibrium temperature. The transfer of heat can only take place in one direction — from hot to cold. Temperature tells you which way the thermal energy is transferred. A cooler metal will heat up (gain heat) when placed in contact with the hot coffee, but the cooler metal will never become cooler (lose heat) when placed in contact with the hot coffee.

Physics Words

entropy: a thermodynamic property of a substance associated with the degree of disorder in the substance; a substance is more ordered as a solid than a liquid, and a liquid is more ordered than a gas.

This irreversibility of heat flow helps to distinguish the past from the future. If you watch a movie of a pendulum moving back and forth, you may not be able to tell whether the film is being played forward or backward. If you watch someone break an egg and fry it, the film would look quite silly when played backward. It doesn't make sense that the egg could get un-fried and then return to its shell. Similarly, water in a glass in a warm room will never suddenly freeze into ice cubes and make the room warmer.

The irreversibility of heat flow is related to the entropy of the substances and is related to the order and disorder of the system. When hot and cold water are mixed, entropy (disorder) increases. When a solid turns to liquid or a liquid turns to gas, entropy (disorder) increases as well. A mathematical understanding of entropy requires a careful look at the possible distributions of energies of the molecules and can be described using statistical physics.

You can get a sense of order and disorder and entropy by considering two gases reaching an equilibrium temperature. On one side of a container, you may have 50 fast-moving molecules. The other side of the container has 10 slow-moving molecules. If the two sides came into contact, you would expect that eventually the fast-moving molecules and the slow-moving molecules would collide often enough that the fast-moving molecules would slow down and the slow-moving molecules would speed up. This is an example of entropy increasing or disorder increasing.

Imagine the opposite occurring. If you had a container with 60 moving molecules, could you imagine all the fast-moving molecules speeding up, the slow-moving molecules slowing down and the fast molecules all going to the left side of the container and the slow molecules all going to the right side of the container? This would be an example of entropy decreasing or disorder decreasing. It is possible, but it is very, very improbable. The only way you would expect to see the entropy decreasing is if someone deliberately did this and expended energy sorting the molecules.

Physics Words

second law of thermodynamics: thermal energy is transferred from hot objects to cold objects and never goes from cold to hot spontaneously.

Checking Up

1. How is temperature defined in terms of molecular action?

2. When cold milk is added to hot coffee, the milk warms up and the coffee cools down. What can be said about the energy of the milk and the energy of the coffee when this happens?

3. The amount of thermal energy that is gained or lost by an object depends upon what three things?

4. In a process that is not reversible in a closed system, what always happens to the entropy of the system?

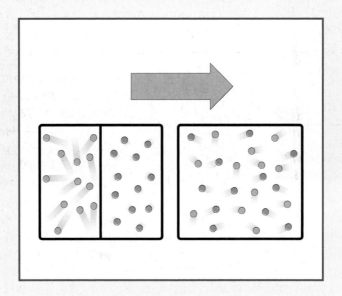

The **second law of thermodynamics** can be stated in a number of different ways:

- In irreversible processes, entropy or disorder always increases.

- Time is irreversible.

- Thermal energy is transferred from hot objects to cold objects and never goes from cold to hot spontaneously.

+Math	+Depth	+Concepts	+Exploration
◆◆◆		◆	

Active Physics

Plus

Entropy

Imagine that there are three spheres in a box that has two sides. Each sphere is a different color—red, blue, purple. The possible configurations of the box are as follows:

Left side of the box	Right side of the box
R, B, P	
R, B	P
R, P	B
B, P	R
R	B, P
B	R, P
P	R, B
	R, B, P

Of the eight possible configurations, only one has all the particles on the left side of the box. That makes this configuration less likely than others where the particles are on both sides of the box. The configuration where all particles are on the left side of the box can be said to have low entropy and low disorder. If all the particles were to start on the left side of the box and were free to move about, you would expect at some later time to observe the particles more evenly distributed. There are six configurations where the particles are on both sides of the box. These represent higher entropy or higher disorder.

1. Repeat this example and find the probability for all the particles in the box to be on one side if there were four, five, or ten particles in the box. For ten particles in the box, you will probably want to find a mathematical pattern rather than writing out all possible configurations.

2. Using your calculations, explain why it appears that entropy or disorder will increase as the number of particles increases. In other words, if you were to start with all the particles in a box on one side, explain why you would expect to never see them on one side again.

In a one-liter bottle, there are over 10^{20} molecules of air. Can you imagine the probability that all the molecules would be in the bottom half of the bottle?

The Heat Engine and the Second Law of Thermodynamics

Once again, imagine a gas that is enclosed in a container with a movable top (a piston). Initially, the gas has a certain amount of thermal energy. The kinetic energy of the molecules keep colliding with the piston and keep it up. If an external flame were to heat the gas, the piston would move up. The gas did work on the piston by lifting it.

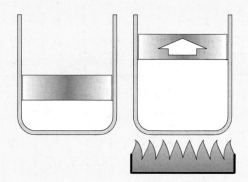

If the gas were then cooled by placing it in touch with a cold object, the gas molecules would lose kinetic energy and the piston would move down.

673

Active Physics

This is the basis of a simple heat engine: Heat the gas and move the piston up; cool the gas and move the piston down. If you keep repeating this, the piston moves up and down over and over and can turn the wheels of a car.

It would be great if this engine could be 100% efficient. That would mean that all the heat would get converted to mechanical energy. The laws of nature do not allow this 100% efficiency. This is another statement of the second law of thermodynamics.

Sample Problem

A heat engine consists of a quantity of gas in an enclosed cylinder with a mass located on top as shown in the diagram below. The mass can move freely up and down as the gas expands.

weight of piston = 500 N

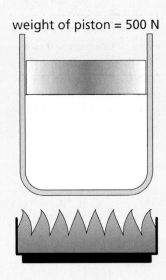

a) If 2000 J of heat are added to the cylinder and the internal energy of the gas increases by 1900 J, causing the gas to expand, how much work is done by the gas as it expands and moves the piston?

b) How high will the piston rise?

a) *Strategy:*

Since the gas and the flame represent a closed system, the energy added by the flame must go to either increasing the internal energy of the gas, or toward work done by the gas.

Given:

$\Delta Q = 2000$ J

$\Delta U = 1900$ J

Solution:

Using the first law of thermodynamics:
$\Delta Q = \Delta U + W$

Solving for W
$W = \Delta Q - \Delta U$

$\quad = 2000$ J $- 1900$ J

$\quad = 100$ J

b) *Strategy:*

Work done equals force × distance, where the force the gas expands against is the weight of the piston that holds it in the cylinder.

Given:

$W = 100$ J

$F = 500$ N

Solution:
Using the equation for work:

$W = F \times d$

Solving for d

$d = \dfrac{W}{F}$

$\quad = \dfrac{100 \text{ J}}{500 \text{ N}} = 0.2$ m

If heat were now extracted from the cylinder, the gas would typically cool and the piston would fall as the gas contracts.

What Do You Think Now?

As you add cold milk to hot coffee, you expect that the milk will get a bit warmer and the coffee will get a bit colder.

• **What determines the final temperature of the coffee and milk?**

Now that you have completed this section, how would you answer this question now?

Physics
Essential Questions

What does it mean?

How does energy conservation help predict the final temperature when hot and cold water are mixed together?

How do you know?

What measurements did you have to record to show that energy was conserved when hot water was placed in cool water?

Why do you believe?

Connects with Other Physics Content	Fits with Big Ideas in Science	Meets Physics Requirements
Thermodynamics	✱ Conservation laws	Experimental evidence is consistent with models and theories

✱ Conservation of energy is a bedrock principle of science. Conservation of energy is considered one of the greatest insights into how nature works. What do people mean when they ask you to conserve energy when you know that energy is always conserved?

Why should you care?

Electricity can be used to heat water. People often heat an entire pot of water to make one cup of tea. This is a very wasteful use of resources. Write a note to people to convince them to only heat the water they need. Emphasize the amount of energy required to heat water.

Active Physics

Reflecting on the Section and the Challenge

Heating water for purification or cooking food is a matter of survival. You may decide to use your limited amount of electrical energy to perform these important tasks. It will be crucial to calculate the energy required to change the temperature of water or foods. You know that a cold drink will warm up if it sits on the table and that a hot drink will cool down if it sits on the same table. All objects in the dwelling will reach the same final temperature—the equilibrium temperature. You can now calculate the energy changes when cold objects and warm objects are put in contact.

Physics to Go

1. A hot cup of coffee at 90°C is mixed with an equal amount of milk at 80°C. What would be the final temperature if you assume that coffee and milk have identical specific heats?

2. Explain why heating up a whole pot of water when you only need enough for one cup of tea is wasteful of time and wasteful of energy consumption.

3. A container of water can be heated with the addition of hot water or the addition of a piece of hot metal. If the mass of the water is equal to the mass of the metal, which material will have the greatest effect on the water temperature? Explain your answer.

4. Suppose 200 g of water at 50°C is mixed with 200 g of water at 30°C.

   a) What will be the final temperature?

   b) Calculate the energy gained by the cold water.

   c) Calculate the energy lost by the hot water.

5. Suppose 200 g of water at 50°C is placed in contact with 200 g of iron at 30°C. The final temperature is 48°C.

   a) Calculate the energy gained by the iron. The specific heat (c) of iron is 0.45 J/g°C.

   b) Calculate the energy lost by the hot water.

   c) If the final temperature could have been measured more accurately, would you expect that it would have been a bit more or less than 48°C? Why?

6. Suppose 100 g of water at 50°C is placed in contact with 200 g of iron at 30°C. The final temperature is 46.5°C.

   a) Calculate the energy gained by the iron. The specific heat of iron is 0.45 J/g°C.

   b) Calculate the energy lost by the hot water.

   c) If the final temperature could have been measured more accurately, would you expect that it would have been a bit more or less than 46.5°C? Why?

7. Suppose 300 g of water at 50°C must be cooled to 40°C by adding cold water. The temperature of the cold water is 10°C. How much of the cold water must be added to the hot water to bring the temperature down to 40°C?

8. 100 g of water at 80°C is placed in contact with 100 g of water at 40°C.

   a) Show that energy is conserved if the final temperature of all the water is 60°C.

   b) Show that energy is conserved if the final temperature of the 100 g of hot water is 100°C and the final temperature of the cool water is 20°C.

   c) Both of these situations are possible according to the conservation of energy. Only one happens. Explain why.

9. Approximate the final temperature if water is mixed in the following proportions:

   a) 100 g of water at 80°C is mixed with 100 g of water at 20°C.

   b) 100 g of water at 80°C is mixed with 1 g of water at 20°C.

   c) 1 g of water at 80°C is mixed with 100 g of water at 20°C.

10. **Active Physics** *Plus* Imagine that 300 J of work is done on a system and 400 J of heat is removed from the system. Using the first law of thermodynamics, what are the values of

    a) W?

    b) ΔQ?

    c) ΔU?

11. **Active Physics** *Plus* Consider a piston that is supported by gas at a certain temperature. The heat added to the gas is 20 J. The work done on the piston is 18 J. What happened to the other 2 J of energy?

12. **Active Physics** *Plus* An ice cube placed in a warm drink melts. Describe any energy and entropy changes.

Active Physics

Section 8

Energy Consumption: Cold Shower

What Do You See?

Learning Outcomes

In this section, you will

- **Calculate** the heat gained by a sample of water.

- **Calculate** the electrical energy converted into heat by a resistor.

- **Calculate** the efficiency of a transformation of electrical energy to heat.

- **Explore** the power ratings and energy consumption levels of a variety of electrical appliances.

What Do You Think?

The entire daily energy output of a Homes For Everyone (HFE) generator would not be enough to heat water for an average American family for a day.

- **If an electrical heating coil (a type of resistor) were submerged in a container of water, and if a current were to flow through the coil to make it hot, what factors would affect the temperature increase of the water?**

Identify as many factors as you can, and predict the effect of each on the water temperature. Record your ideas about this question in your *Active Physics* log. Be prepared to discuss your responses with your small group and the class.

Investigate

1. Assemble and use an electric calorimeter according to the directions given by your teacher.

   Alternatively, your teacher may provide you with a heating coil and two nested styrene-foam cups. If a cover could be created for the styrene-foam cups, it will improve the data you can collect.

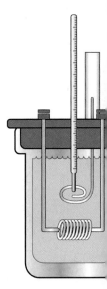

If a heating coil is used, you must be sure to never have the heating coil plugged in if the coil is out of the water. This requires you to place the coil in the water and then plug it in. You can then unplug the coil and remove it from the water. If the coil is plugged in while it is out of the water, it will be permanently broken in a very short time.

Add a measured amount of cold tap water to the calorimeter.

a) Record the mass of the water. (You will need to find the mass of an empty container, as well as the mass of the container plus the measured amount of water.)

b) Measure and record the beginning temperature of the water.

c) Record the watt rating of the resistor that will be used to heat the water. (The watt rating is often written on the appliance.)

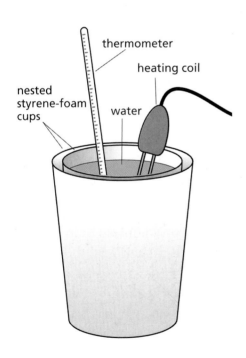

2. Note the time at which you begin sending electric current through the resistor. Keep the electric heater operating for the amount of time recommended by your teacher.

When you stop the current, note the time, stir the water, and measure the final, maximum temperature of the water.

a) In your log, record the final water temperature (°C) and the heating time (seconds).

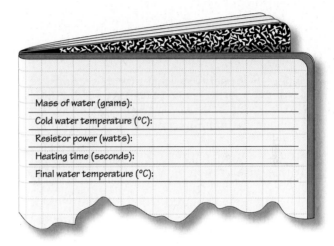

Mass of water (grams):	
Cold water temperature (°C):	
Resistor power (watts):	
Heating time (seconds):	
Final water temperature (°C):	

 Always make sure the coil (or heater) is completely submerged in the water.

 Promptly dry up any spilled water.

 Do not try to stir the water with the thermometer. If the thermometer should break, immediately notify your instructor.

3. Recall that the heat gained by an object can be found using the equation:

$$\Delta Q = mc\Delta T$$

where ΔQ is a measure of heat in joules,

m is the mass of the substance in grams,

c is the specific heat of the substance, and

ΔT is the change in temperature in degrees Celsius.

Active Physics

Use the equation to calculate the heat gained by the water in the calorimeter. The specific heat of water is 4.18 J/g°C.

✎ a) Show your calculation in your log.

4. Recall also that power rating, in watts, is expressed as the amount of energy, in joules, that something consumes per unit of time. Mathematically, power is expressed as

$$P = \frac{E}{t} \text{ so } E = Pt$$

where E is energy in joules (watt-seconds),

    P is power in watts (joules/second),

    t is time in seconds.

Energy can be expressed in watt-seconds (otherwise known as a joule).

The energy calculated from the temperature change of the water should be equal to the energy calculated from the power rating of the appliance and the time.

✎ a) Compare these two values for the heat gained by the water. If the values are not the same, you cannot conclude that the conservation of energy principle is wrong. Rather, you have to assume that the electrical energy was not all used to heat the water.

✎ b) Where could the "lost" energy have gone?

5. If all of the electrical energy used did not go into heat in the water, then you know your system for heating water is less than 100% efficient. Calculate the efficiency of your water-heating device.

If the appliance were 100% efficient, all of the electrical energy would have heated the water; if the appliance were 50% efficient, only half of the electrical energy would have heated the water.

$$\text{Efficiency} = \frac{\text{useful energy output}}{\text{energy input}} \times 100\%$$

✎ a) Record your calculations in your log.

Physics Talk

ENERGY CONSUMPTION

Electric power companies usually charge for the energy used in units of "kilowatt-hours," where a kilowatt, or 1000 W (watts), is the power that would be used, for example, by placing ten 100-W light bulbs in parallel. If you left these ten light bulbs on for one hour, the amount of energy that would be used would be

    1 kilowatt-hour of energy = power × time

                                 = 1000 W × 1 h

                                 = 1000 W × 3600 s

                                 = 3,600,000 J

A joule is a much smaller quantity of energy than a kilowatt-hour and would be the equivalent of having a 1-W bulb on for 1 s. That is, one joule equals one watt-second.

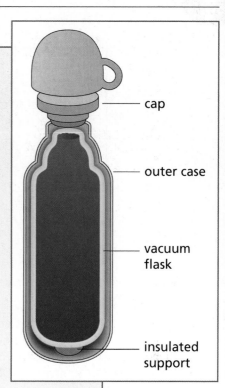

cap

outer case

vacuum flask

insulated support

What is the world's greatest invention? A comedian once replied: "The thermos. When you put a cold drink in it, it stays cold. When you put a hot drink in it, it stays hot. How does the thermos know?"

A cup of hot water left on a table cools down. A cup of cold water left on the same table warms up. How can you change the temperature or keep the temperature constant?

Heat is a transfer of thermal energy. Energy in one form must come from energy in another form. Energy must be conserved. If you wish to heat up water, you must supply it with a source of energy like a flame, an electrical heater, or a hot metal.

If a system is isolated from outside sources of energy, one part of the system may warm up and another part may cool down, but the total energy must remain constant. In this *Investigate*, you calculated the electrical energy that was used to heat the water. Thermal energy, like all forms of energy, is measured in units of joules (J). You used the following equation.

Change in heat
= mass of object × specific heat of material × temperature change
$$\Delta Q = mc\Delta T$$

where ΔQ is a measure of change in heat in joules,

m is the mass of the substance in grams,

c is the specific heat of the substance, and

ΔT is the change in temperature in degrees Celsius.

Energy used to heat the object can also be calculated using the following equation:

Since energy = power × time
and power = voltage × current
then, energy = voltage × current × time

$$E = VIt$$

where E is the energy in joules (J),

V is the voltage in volts (V),

I is the current in amperes (A), and

t is the time in seconds (s).

Active Physics

Sample Problem

A 12-V starter battery in a car supplies 48 A of current to the starter. If the starter draws energy for 15 s, how much energy does the starter use?

Strategy: You can use the equation to calculate energy.

Given:

$$V = 12 \text{ V}$$
$$I = 48 \text{ A}$$
$$t = 15 \text{ s}$$

Solution:

$$E = VIt$$
$$= (12 \text{ V})(48 \text{ A})(15 \text{ s})$$
$$= (12 \tfrac{J}{C})(48 \tfrac{C}{s})(15 \text{ s})$$
$$= 8640 \text{ J (or about 8600 J)}$$

Recall that voltage was energy per unit of charge, and current is unit of charge per second. Multiplying these two will produce energy per second, the unit of power. Multiplying this by seconds gives you units of energy, in this case joules.

Efficiency

In the *Investigate*, you would expect that the heat energy you calculated from the temperature change of the water should be equal to the electrical energy you calculated from the power rating of the heater. The law of conservation of energy states that energy cannot be created or destroyed. However, when you compared the two values, you found that they were not equal. You calculated the efficiency of this transfer of energy using the following equation.

$$\text{Efficiency} = \frac{\text{useful energy output}}{\text{total energy input}} \times 100\%$$

The efficiency you calculated was probably less than 100%. Therefore, you realized that some energy must have been "lost." You should expect this loss because energy is lost from the system and is transferred to the surrounding environment. Thermal energy may have escaped as heat through the insulation of the cup or calorimeter or the top of the water surface of the cup. Some of the energy could have been transferred to the thermometer and the resistor may still have been warm when you removed it from the cup. This is the case any time energy is transferred. Some of the energy is transformed into forms of energy that are not useful at the moment.

Checking Up

1. How is the energy used by a light bulb related to the power of the light bulb? What equation would you use to determine the energy used?

2. What units do physicists use to measure heat energy and electrical energy?

3. What equation could you use to calculate energy used by an appliance if you knew the voltage, current, and time during which the current flows?

4. How is the percentage efficiency of an energy transformation calculated?

Active Physics

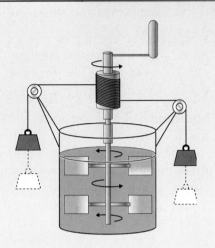

+Math	+Depth	+Concepts	+Exploration
♦♦	♦	♦♦	

Mechanical Equivalent of Heat

In this section, you were able to find the relationship between electrical energy and thermal energy. By stirring water, you can also increase its temperature. By measuring the amount of work that is done by stirring, you can find the mathematical relationship between mechanical work and heat.

The experiment was first performed by Sir James Joule. (Yes, the joule was named after him.) In his experiment, he had two weights fall to the ground. As they fell, they turned paddles that were immersed in water. He then measured the change in the temperature of the water. By calculating the change in energy of the falling weights and the increase in temperature of the water, Joule calculated the mechanical equivalent of heat.

The change in gravitational energy is equal to

$$m_f g \Delta h$$

where m_f is the mass of the falling object,

g is the acceleration of the object due to gravity in meters per second squared, and

Δh is the change in height in meters.

The change in thermal energy is equal to

$$m_w c \Delta T$$

where m_w is the mass of the water in grams,

c is the specific heat of the water,

ΔT is the change in temperature in degrees Celsius.

Joule found that 4.18 J of work were required to raise the temperature of 1 g of water 1°C.

1. In a fitness center, an athlete may be able to lift 20 kg from the floor to her waist (a distance of 1 m) over and over again every second.

   a) Calculate the change in gravitational potential energy ($mg\Delta h$) every time she lifts the 20 kg. (Assume that $g = 10$ m/s^2.)

   b) Someone has a clever idea. Why not have the energy that the athlete is expending be used for heating up water for coffee? How much energy is required to heat 1 cup of water (250 g) from 20°C to 100°C?

   c) How many seconds would the athlete have to lift weights to produce the energy required to heat up the water for a cup of coffee?

2. Chemical energy in your food can be measured in joules. In the United States, people are accustomed to the energy in food being measured in calories. One food calorie is written as 1 C and is equivalent to 4185 J. Since many humans eat 2000 C a day, this is a staggering amount of energy. Where does it all go?

   a) Using the fitness center example, calculate the total energy expended if the athlete were to lift the weights for a one-hour workout without any rest whatsoever.

   b) What percentage of her 2000 C of food was used in lifting the weights.

   c) Where do you think the rest of the consumed energy goes?

3. A cup of hot coffee will eventually cool off until it reaches room temperature. If you wanted to keep the coffee warm, you would have to keep providing some energy transfer to the coffee. This is often done with heat from a hot plate or an electrical heating coil that you used in the investigation. The human body must stay at approximately 98.6°F. A change in body temperature of just 10°F will kill a person. A 110-lb person has a mass of approximately 50 kg.

   a) Devise a way to find out how much energy is required to keep this 50-kg person at 98.6°F (37°C), when they are in a room that is 20°C.

   b) What percentage of that person's 2000 C of food would be used to maintain body temperature?

What Do You Think Now?

At the beginning of this section, you were asked:

• **If an electrical heating coil (a type of resistor) were submerged in a container of water, and if a current were to flow through the coil to make it hot, what factors would affect the temperature increase of the water?**

Having completed this section and the previous section, identify as many factors as you can, and predict the effect of each on the water temperature.

Active Physics

Physics
Essential Questions

What does it mean?

Electrical appliances are rated in watts and energy is measured in joules. Utility companies calculate total energy use in kilowatt-hours. How can a utility company calculate the energy use in joules or kilowatt-hours if they know the power in watts of an appliance and the time that the appliance is used?

How do you know?

Electrical energy can be used to increase the temperature of a clothing iron and a cup of water, or decrease the temperature of items in a refrigerator or a room with an air conditioner. How can you measure the electrical energy used to heat water?

Why do you believe?

Connects with Other Physics Content	Fits with Big Ideas in Science	Meets Physics Requirements
Electricity and magnetism	* Conservation laws	Good, clear, explanation, no more complex than necessary.

* Energy conservation is a guiding organizing principle of all science. Describe and give a specific example of energy transfer that includes electrical energy, thermal energy and mechanical energy.

Why should you care?

Each appliance in your Homes For Everyone (HFE) package is going to require a certain amount of energy. The wind generator has an upper energy limit. How can this limited energy be used to maximum advantage to enhance the well being of the people?

Reflecting on the Section and the Challenge

In this section, your knowledge of how to calculate electric power consumption was extended to include how to calculate electric energy consumption. You also learned that heating water electrically requires a lot of energy and can be quite inefficient. All of this knowledge applies directly to the selections you will make for your HFE appliance package.

Active Physics

Physics to Go

1. The calorimeter did not allow the water to trap 100% of the energy delivered to it by the resistor. Some of the heat probably escaped from the water. Identify and explain ways in which you think heat may have escaped from the water, reducing the efficiency of the calorimeter.

2. The calorimeter used in this investigation can be thought of as a scaled-down, crude version of a household hot-water heater. The efficiencies of hot-water heaters used in homes range from about 80% for older models to as much as 92% for new, energy-efficient models. Identify and explain ways in which you think heat escapes from household hot-water heaters, and how you could improve the efficiency of the heater.

3. From what you have learned so far, discuss the possibilities for providing electrically heated water for Homes For Everyone (HFE). Is a standard water heater of the kind used in American homes desirable, or possible, for HFE? What other electrical options exist for accomplishing part or all of the task of heating water for HFE?

4. For most Americans, the second biggest energy user in the home, next to the heating/air-conditioning system, is the water heater. A family of four that heats water electrically (some use gas or oil to heat water) typically spends about $35 per month using a 4500-W heater to keep a 160-L (40 gallon) tank of water hot at all times. The water is raised from an average inlet temperature of 10°C (50°F) to a temperature of 60°C (140°F), and the average family uses about 250 L (60 gallons) of hot water per day for bathing and washing clothes and dishes.

   In the above description, explain what each of the following numbers represents: 35, 4500, 160, 40, 10, 50, 60, 140, 250, 60.

5. Electrical appliances are designed to convert electrical energy into some other form of energy. Choose five appliances from the list of Home Electrical Appliances beginning on the next page that have a wide range of power. In your log, make a list like the one shown.

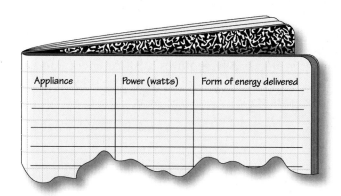

Appliance	Power (watts)	Form of energy delivered

Home Electrical Appliances

Average Power and
Average Monthly Energy Use for a Family of Four

Family Data

	Power (watts)	Energy/mo (kWh/mo)
Big Appliances		
Air Conditioner		
(Room)	1360	
(Central)	3540	
Clothes Washer	512	
Clothes Dryer	5000	
Dehumidifier	645	
Dishwasher	1200	
Freezer	400	
Humidifier	177	
Pool Filter	1000	
Kitchen Range	12,400	
Refrigerator	795	
Space Heater	1500	
Waterbed	350	
Water Heater	4500	
Small Refrigerator	300	
Lights & Minor		
Appliances (combined)		
Kitchen		
Baby Food Warmer	165	
Blender	300	
Broiler (portable)	1200	
Can Opener	100	
Coffee Maker		
Drip	1100	
Percolator	600	
Corn Popper		
Oil-type	575	
Hot Air-type	1400	
Deep Fryer	1500	
Food Processor	370	
Frying Pan	1200	
Garbage Disposal	445	
Sandwich Grill	1200	
Hot Plate	1200	
Microwave Oven	750	
Mixer	150	

Home Electrical Appliances

	Power (watts)	Energy/mo (kWh/mo)
Roaster	1400	
Rotisserie	1400	
Slow Cooker	200	
Toaster	1100	
Toaster Oven	1500	
Trash Compactor	400	
Waffle Iron	1200	
Entertainment		
Computer	60	
Radio	70	
Television	90	
Stereo	125	
VCR	50	
Personal Care		
Air Cleaner	50	
Curling Iron	40	
Hair Dryer	1200	
Hair Rollers	350	
Heat Blanket	170	
Heat Lamp	250	
Heat Pad	60	
Iron	1100	
Lighted Mirror	20	
Shaver	15	
Sun Lamp	300	
Toothbrush	1	
Miscellaneous		
Auto Engine Heater	850	
Clock	3	
Drill (1/4")	250	
Fan (attic)	375	
Fan (window)	200	
Heat Tape	240	
Sewing Machine	75	
Skill Saw	1000	
Vacuum Cleaner	650	
Water Pump (well)	335	

Please note: Average values of power are shown. The power of a particular appliance may vary considerably from the value in the table. Energy use will vary with family size (a four-member family is assumed for the tabled values), personal preferences and habits, climate, and season. Similar information in greater detail is available free upon request from most electric utilities.

Use information from the list of appliances to fill in the first two columns. In the third column, write the form of energy (heat, light, motion, sound, etc.) that you think each appliance is designed to deliver.

What pattern, if any, do you think exists between the power rating of an appliance and the form of energy it is designed to provide? Explain your answer.

6. Make a new list with six columns similar to the one shown. Choose five to ten appliances from the list. Record the name and power rating of that appliance. Record the approximate time that this appliance is used in one day. Calculate the time that this appliance is used in one month (assuming that a month has 30 days). Calculate the electrical energy that the appliance consumes.

The energy used by an appliance in watt-hours (W•h) is found by multiplying the power of the appliance times the time it is used in hours in one month. Calculate the energy in kilowatt-hours (kW•h) by dividing the watt-hours by 1000 since there are 1000 W in 1 kW.

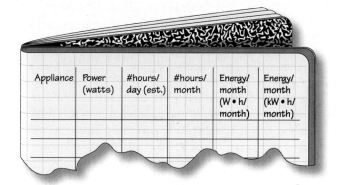

Appliance	Power (watts)	#hours/ day (est.)	#hours/ month	Energy/ month (W•h/ month)	Energy/ month (kW•h/ month)

7. You use a 1500-W hair dryer for 5 min every morning to dry your hair.

a) How much electrical energy are you changing to heat every day?

b) If you could transfer all of that energy to heating up water for a shower, how much water could you heat from 20°C to 45°C?

c) If one kilogram of water is about 0.26 gal (gallons), how many gallons of water does that represent? Is that enough water to take a shower? How much water do you think you use in a typical shower in your own home?

d) Make a statement in your log about which use of this amount of energy would make most sense in your appliance package—using the hairdryer to dry your hair for 5 min, or taking a shower with that amount of energy?

8. Electric companies charge by the kilowatt-hour. Which of the following is the most expensive use of electricity over the course of a week? Show your calculations for each in your log.

a) a 100-W light that is left on for 6 h per day

b) a 1500-W hair dryer for 10 min every morning

c) a 5000-W clothes dryer used for 70 min a week

d) a 1200-W dishwasher that is run for 45 min, four times a week

e) a 900-W water pump that is run for 50 min each day

Inquiring Further

1. EnergyGuide® labels

Find out about EnergyGuide® labels. The United States government established a federal law that requires EnergyGuide labels to be displayed on major appliances such as water heaters, refrigerators, freezers, dishwashers, clothes washers, air conditioners, furnaces, and heat pumps. The bright yellow EnergyGuide label allows consumers to compare the energy costs and efficiencies of appliances. Visit a store where appliances are sold and record the information given on the EnergyGuide labels of competing brands of one kind of appliance, such as water heaters. Prepare a short report on which appliance you would purchase, and why.

2. Reducing electric energy to heat water

Research ways to reduce the amount of electrical energy needed to provide hot water for your own home or an HFE dwelling. Some possibilities may include using solar energy and/or a "tempering tank" to heat the water partially, followed by "finishing off" the heating electrically, and tankless "instant" water heaters which use electricity to heat water, but only when hot water is needed. Prepare a report on your findings.

3. An average shower

Measure the amount of water the average member of your family uses when they take a shower. First, you have to locate your water meter. It is probably in your basement, although sometimes it is somewhere outside your house where the meter person can read it. It will probably measure in units of cubic feet of water. Note the meter reading before and after you take a shower. Make sure there is no other water running in the house (washing machine, sinks, etc.). To convert cubic feet to gallons, use the conversion factor

$$1 \text{ cubic ft water} = 7.5 \text{ gallons}$$

Compare the value of the energy used by the hair dryer with the energy used in heating of water for a shower in *Question 7* of the *Physics to Go*. Can you suggest a reasonable trade-off between taking a shower and using a hair dryer?

Section 9

Comparing Energy Consumption: More for Your Money

What Do You See?

Learning Outcomes

In this section, you will

- **Measure** and compare the energy consumed by appliances.

- **Compare** the costs of operating a variety of electrical appliances in terms of power ratings, amount of time each appliance is used, and billing rate.

- **Distinguish** among the three ways of heat transfer.

What Do You Think?

Some hot-water heaters and furnaces for homes are more than 90% efficient.

- **If high-efficiency appliances cost more, are they worth the added cost?**

Record your ideas about this question in your *Active Physics* log. Be prepared to discuss your responses with your small group and the class.

Investigate

You will be heating up water three different ways in this section and comparing the energy, time, and costs for each.

1. Place 250 mL of cold tap water in a beaker made of heat-resistant glass. Make sure the outside of the beaker is dry so it does not slip from your grasp. Measure the temperature of the water.

    a) Record the temperature of the water in your log.

    b) Record the quantity of water in milliliters and grams. (1 mL of water has a mass of 1 g.)

2. Place the beaker of water in a microwave oven of known power, in watts. Mark the time at which the oven is turned on at its highest power level. After two minutes, stop the time measurement. Carefully check that the beaker is not too hot to grasp and remove the beaker from the oven, stir the water, and check the water temperature, all as quickly as possible.

a) Record the power rating of the microwave, the amount of time it was on, and the final temperature of the water in your log.

b) Why is it important to complete the temperature measurement as quickly as possible?

3. Prepare an identical heat-resistant beaker containing the same amount of cold tap water, preferably at the same original temperature as the water used above.

a) Record the mass and temperature of the water in your log.

4. Have ready a hot plate that has not been turned on (a "cold" hot plate) and that has a known power rating, in watts. Also have ready a clock or stopwatch capable of measuring time, in seconds, for an interval of several minutes. Place the beaker of cold water on the hot plate, and mark the time at which the hot plate is turned on at its highest setting. Gently stir the water while it is heating and monitor the temperature of the water. When the temperature of the water has increased to the value of the water from the microwave, mark the time and shut the hot plate off.

a) Record the power of the hot plate, the time required to heat the water, and its final temperature in your log.

5. Repeat the process a third time with an immersion heating coil.

a) Record all your observations in your log.

6. Calculate the energy used by each appliance to cause equal temperature increases in equal amounts of water. Recall:

Energy (in joules) = power (in watts) × time (in sec

$$E = Pt$$

a) Show your calculations in your log.

b) Which appliance is the "winner"?

7. Choose a way to express a comparison of the performance of the three appliances.

a) Was the method used to compare the three appliances fair? How could the fairness be improved?

b) The beaker that served as the container for the water also was heated by the three appliances. How did the method you used affect the outcome of the comparison? Might another kind of container be more or less effective to use with either appliance; for example, might using a metal pan as the container on a hot plate make the hot plate perform more efficiently? Explain your answer.

8. You measured the time that each appliance was used and calculated the energy used. You can also calculate the expense of that energy. To calculate the expense of running an electrical appliance you can use the following equation.

Cost = energy × price per unit of energy

Energy can be expressed in joules, which are equivalent to watt-seconds. However, electricity is usually priced by the kilowatt-hour. Converting from watt-seconds to kilowatt-hours (kW•h) will require you to convert the time to hours and the watts to kilowatts.

$$kW•h = 1000 \text{ W} \times 3600 \text{ s} = 3{,}600{,}000 \text{ W•s}$$

a) Calculate the cost of using each appliance to heat the water.

Assume that the cost of electricity is 10.40 cents per kilowatt-hour.

b) Does the cost difference seem significant? Explain your answer.

9. In a previous section, you estimated the time that an appliance is used, and the amount of energy required to use it for one month. Now you will calculate the expense of that energy. Combine the lists from the group members and calculate the expense of running the electrical appliances.

a) Record your calculations in your log.

b) Does the cost of running the appliances seem significant? Explain your answer.

Physics Talk

DETERMINING ENERGY CONSUMPTION

The electrical energy consumed by appliances can be determined in different ways. If the power rating of an appliance is known, and if the power remains at a steady value while the appliance is in use (for example, a light bulb will use electricity at a constant rate), the energy, in kW • h, can be calculated by multiplying the power of the appliance, in kilowatts, by the time, in hours, for which the appliance is used.

Determining the energy consumed by some appliances, however, is tricky, because the appliances vary in power while they are in use. For example, a refrigerator may cycle on and off under the control of a thermostat. Therefore, it is not operating during all of the time it is "plugged in" and the calculation described above would lead to a misleadingly high value for the refrigerator's energy consumption. For such appliances whose power varies throughout time, a kilowatt-hour meter is used to measure the total energy consumed, with variations in power throughout time taken into account. The same kind of meter, a kilowatt-hour meter, is used by the power company to measure the total electrical energy used in your home. The meter is mounted somewhere at your home (usually on an outside wall) so that it can be read by the power company's "meter reader," or electronically.

Active Physics

JONES ENERGY

Jones Energy Account: 3 544 943 - 0
Page 1 of 5

Billing Date: Nov 01, 2008

Current due date does not extend date due for previous amount due.

Date Due	Amount Due	Amount Due After Due Date
11/10/2008	$ 400.13	$ 410.47

Account Information

Account #: 3 496 917 - 0
Invoice #: 177001109843

Customer Name:

Account Name:

Account Summary

Previous Amount Due	$184.52
Payment	0.00
Balance Forward	184.52
Late Charge	8.90
Total Current Charges	206.71
Total Due	**$400.13**

Questions or Comments

Customer Service
www.jones.com/myaccount
Email us at: service@jones.com

713-207-7777   24-hours a day
1-866-222-7100   24-hours a day
TDD Device for Hearing Impaired
1-888-467-3542

Jones Energy Residential Services
Certificate: 10007

Jones Energy
PO Box 55959
Archer, TX 55959-4433

Payment Address
JONES ENERGY
PO BOX 55959
ARCHER, TX 99595-4433

Electricity Usage Summary

Billing Period	10/01/2008 - 10/31/2008	08/31/2008 - 10/01/2008	08/01/2008 - 08/31/2008
Billing Days	29	33	29
Electricity Used (kWh)	1242	1130	789
Avg. High Temperature*	87	84	75
Avg. Daily Usage (kWh)	43	34	27

*Temperature Source: National Weather Service Region: Houston, Texas

Important Message: Thinking about moving in Texas? Transferring your service with Jones Energy is easy. Jones Energy can provide you electric service at both residences during your move. Before it's time to move call 1-866-222-7100.

Please mail this portion with your payment. Make check payable to: Jones Energy

JONES ENERGY

Account: 3 544 943 - 0

C.A.R.E. Donation* $1, $5 or $10 $ ____ . ____   Amount Enclosed $ ____ . ____

P09GGH 1 2 5 6   349 2 AC 0.527 3   348 T203REI00101.RTP 348/665

3601 ALLEN PKWY #336
HOUSTON TX 77019-1647

Date Due	11/10/2008
Amount Due	$ 400.13
After Due Date	$ 410.47

Mail payment to:

JONES ENERGY
PO BOX 55959
ARCHER, TX 99595-4433

08000   74638   0121000003496   703000000400130000041047

Another way to determine the energy used by electrical appliances is to use the experience of power companies or corporations that sell electrical supplies. Extensive lists of appliances, their power ratings, and each appliance's average energy use per month by a typical family are available free from such sources.

The cost of operating an electrical appliance can be calculated using the following equation:

Cost = energy × price per unit of energy

where energy is in kilowatt-hours
$(1000 \text{ W} \cdot \text{h} = 1 \text{ kW} \cdot \text{h})$.

Sample Problem

An electric coffee maker uses an average of 22.5 kW • h of energy each month. If the family is charged $0.12/kW • h for electricity, what is the average monthly cost of operating the coffee maker?

Strategy: Use the equation for cost.

Given:

Energy $= 22.5 \text{ kW} \cdot \text{h}$

Price $= \$0.12 / \text{kW} \cdot \text{h}$

Solution:

Cost $=$ energy $\times$ price per unit of energy

$= 22.5 \text{ kW} \cdot \text{h} \times \$0.12/\text{kW} \cdot \text{h}$

$= \$2.70$

In this *Investigate*, you heated the same amount of water using an immersion heating coil, a microwave oven, and a hot plate. Although the water gained the same amount of energy in all three methods, the amount of electrical energy was different, as was the time required and the cost. The cost difference for the time you heated the water in the *Investigate* may have appeared insignificant. However, over long periods of time the differences in the energy used and the cost becomes evident.

Heat Transfer

Physics Words

heat transfer: the transmission of heat energy from a warmer substance to a cooler substance.

In this chapter, you have been looking at **heat transfer**. You saw that when there is a difference in temperature between two substances that are in contact, heat is always transferred between them. You also read that the second law of thermodynamics states that the transfer will always take place from the warmer body to the cooler one.

Active Physics

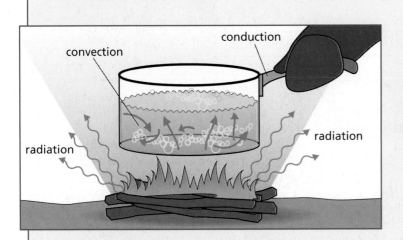

You may have studied in previous science classes the three ways that heat can be transferred: **conduction**, **convection**, and **radiation**.

In the case of conduction, the thermal energy of a material is transferred to another material by direct contact of the materials with one another. In your investigation, the rapidly moving (and hence high energy) atoms in the heating coil came in direct contact with the cold water. The thermal energy of the coil's atoms was conducted by physical contact directly to the water molecules. In turn, energy from these molecules was transferred to adjacent molecules, and so on. In this way, the heat was dissipated throughout the water, warming it in the process. Conduction always requires direct contact.

Once the water near the coil became hotter than the other water, the water began circulating. The hot water moved up and away from the coil and cold water came in contact with the coil. These are convection currents in the water. Convection is another means of transmitting thermal energy. In convection, the molecules or atoms of a fluid (a liquid or a gas) that have more thermal energy will move faster than the surrounding molecules of that material. As a result, they will move farther apart and, therefore, become pushed by the colder, more closely packed molecules or atoms. As the hotter molecules spread out through the colder surrounding material, they carry their thermal energy (motion) with them, losing it along their path to other colder molecules by conduction. Convection then, is the transmission of heat from one place to another due to physical movement of a warmer fluid through a colder fluid.

When heating the water in the microwave oven, microwaves moved through the oven and were absorbed by the water molecules. This increase in kinetic energy of the water molecules resulted in an increased temperature of the water. Some people make sun-tea by placing cold water in a glass jar with tea bags. Placing the jar in direct sunlight for a few hours will make the tea. The radiation from the Sun is used to heat the water. Radiation is the third form of energy transmission. In radiation, the electromagnetic radiation given off by high-energy (hot) materials can be transmitted through objects, or even a vacuum, at the speed of light. When this energy strikes a material that can absorb it, the radiant energy causes the atoms or molecules of the material it strikes to move faster and the molecules now have more heat.

Physics Words

conduction: the transfer of heat energy from particle to particle between substances through contact or within a substance.

convection: the transfer of heat energy through the movement of air or liquid currents.

radiation: the transfer of heat energy by emission of electromagnetic radiation in all directions.

Checking Up

1. What unit does the power company use to charge consumers for energy?

2. If a student leaves a 100-W light bulb on in his room for 1 h, how many kilowatt-hours of electricity does the bulb use? If the power company charges $0.18 per kilowatt-hour, how much will it cost to leave the light bulb on for this amount of time?

3. List two places where you could look to see how much electrical energy your family has used in the previous month.

4. What is the name given to heat transfer when objects are heated by direct contact? By currents flowing through a fluid? By electromagnetic waves?

5. When objects are heated by contact, what happens to the kinetic energy of the cold molecules in contact with the hot heating coil?

6. What happens to the distance between molecules in a fluid as their temperature increases?

Active Physics

+Math	+Depth	+Concepts	+Exploration
◆	◆		◆

Active Physics

Plus

Finding the "Best" Method of Cooking

What is the best way to cook a hot dog? Do you fry it in a pan? Cook it in the microwave? Boil it in water? What do you think "the best way to cook a hot dog" means? Does "best" mean the least energy, the least cost, the least time, the least cleanup? Or does "best" mean the best tasting or the best appearance? Or is "best" a combination of these?

Design an experiment that can compare all of these factors for cooking hot dogs. Once you get all the data, you will then have to weigh each criterion. For example, what is the most important factor to you – cost, taste, appearance, or clean-up? Once you place a weighting on each criterion (0 = don't care, 10 = extremely important), you can then multiply the

relative values for each method (3 = highest, 1 = lowest) by the weightings to have a better sense of how you will arrive at "best."

The following table may help you in your analysis. You do not need to limit yourself to these criteria. You may have other criteria that you consider important.

The "Best" Way to Cook a Hot Dog			
	Fry	**Boil**	**Microwave**
Cost (cents)			
Energy (joules)			
Time (seconds)			
Appearance			
Taste			
Ease of cleanup			

What Do You Think Now?

At the beginning of this section, you were asked:

• **If high-efficiency appliances cost more, are they worth the added cost?**

Now that you have completed this section, how would you figure out if an energy-efficient appliance is really worth the added cost? Looking back to your initial ideas recorded in your log, how did your thinking about this question change? Is there anything besides the physics you learned that you would consider when answering this question?

Essential Questions

What does it mean?

What is a kilowatt-hour and how is it related to the unit of energy used more commonly in physics—the joule?

How do you know?

How does the electric company compute your monthly electric bill?

Why do you believe?

Connects with Other Physics Content	Fits with Big Ideas in Science	Meets Physics Requirements
Electricity and magnetism	✳ Interaction of matter, energy, and fields	Good, clear, explanation, no more complex than necessary.

✳ How are electric energy, thermal energy, and mechanical energy related?

Why should you care?

Physics allows you to calculate energy use, but does not limit the amount of energy you use. The wind generator supplying electricity limits you to 2400 W and 3 kW • h per day. How will this impact your choice of appliances?

Reflecting on the Section and the Challenge

You know that the electrical appliances used in the universal dwelling cannot exceed 90 kW • h per month of energy consumption. In this section, you discovered that some appliances are more efficient than others. That is, a highly efficient appliance can accomplish a task while using less electrical energy than a low-efficiency appliance for the same task. Obviously you will want to make a careful selection for each kind of appliance based on efficiency so that Homes For Everyone (HFE) inhabitants can have the greatest possible benefit from the electrical system.

The *Chapter Challenge* requires that you need to be thinking about two things at the same time as you select appliances for the universal dwelling: the power consumed by each appliance and the amount of time for which each appliance is used. Both need to be taken into account to stay within the power and energy limits of the HFE electrical system.

Physics to Go

1. Calculate the energy used, in joules, by each of the following:

   a) a 1500-W hair dryer operating for 3 min

   b) a 1200-W hair dryer operating for 4 min

2. If both situations described in *Question 1* result in the same dryness of hair, which hair dryer is more efficient?

3. A 1200-W hair dryer is used by several members of a family for a total of 30 min per day during a 30-day month. How much electrical energy is consumed by the hair dryer during the month? Give your answer in:

   a) watt-hours

   b) kilowatt-hours

4. If the power company charges $0.15 per kW•h for electrical energy, what is the cost of using the hair dryer in *Question 3* during the month? What is the cost for a year?

5. Not enough heat from the furnace reaches one bedroom in a home. The homeowner uses a portable 1350-W electric heater 24 h per day to keep the bedroom warm during four cold winter months. At $0.12 per kilowatt-hour, how much does it cost to operate the heater for the four months? (Assume two 30-day and two 31-day months.)

6. A portable CD player is rated at approximately 20 W and uses 4 AA batteries.

   a) Estimate the number of hours that you can listen to the music on a CD player before the batteries need replacing.

   b) Calculate the energy requirements of the CD player.

   c) Estimate the cost of 4 AA batteries.

   d) Calculate the cost per kilowatt-hour of a battery.

   e) Compare battery costs with the cost of electricity from the utilities (use approximately $0.10 per kilowatt-hour).

7. Are some cooking utensils (pots, pans, etc.) better than others for certain purposes? Write what you think about the effectiveness of different cooking utensils, and what you could do to find out about their comparative effects on efficiency.

8. Does either the hot plate or the microwave oven seem to be a good choice to include in the HFE appliance package? Why, or why not?

9. You probably have concluded that the most efficient appliance of the three tested is the one that used the least energy. Explain how you could calculate the actual efficiencies.

10. *Preparing for the Chapter Challenge*

Prepare your personal list of electrical appliances to recommend to your group to be included in the HFE appliance package. Remember that you will have to justify why you chose a certain appliance. Be prepared to contribute your ideas to your group's decision-making process when completing the challenge.

Inquiring Further

Your electric bill

If possible, also obtain a copy of the monthly electric bill for your home or that of an acquaintance. Compare the electric bill to the ones from the homes of individuals in your group. What factors might account for differences among electric bills within your group? Identify as many factors as you can and explain what you think is the effect of each factor on the bill. What is the average monthly amount of electrical energy used in the homes represented in your group, and how does it compare to the 90 kW•h per month available to Homes For Everyone (HFE) dwellings? How might your consumption of electricity change if you had to pay for your own electrical bills? Be prepared to share your findings with the class.

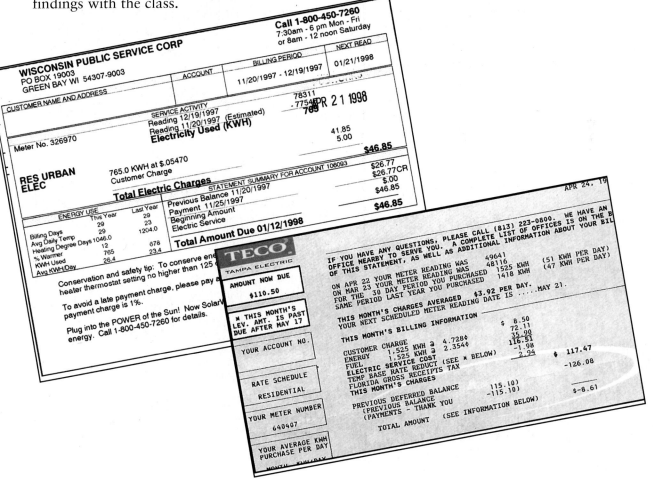

Active Physics

Physics
You Learned

Physics Concepts	Is There an Equation?
A closed circuit is required in order for electricity to flow. A closed circuit consists of a continuous loop that allows electricity to leave and return to the source without reversing direction.	
When an electric source, such as a generator, provides current to a circuit, work is being done.	
There are two types of **electric charge**—positive and negative, which are equal in magnitude. **Protons** carry the positive charge, while **electrons** carry the negative charge.	
A unit of charge is a **coulomb**, and is equal to 6.25×10^{18} electrons.	
The **current** (I) in any given point of a circuit equals the charge flowing past that point per second. When one coulomb of charge flows past the point each second, the current is one **ampere** (A).	
One **volt** equals one **joule** of energy for each coulomb of charge delivered a load in an electric circuit. Another term for **voltage** is potential difference.	
A **series circuit** consists of only one conducting path and all the current passes through each element in the circuit. The total current (I_T) provided by the battery is equal to the current $(I_1, I_2, ...)$ in the elements in the circuit.	$I_T = I_1 = I_2 = I_3$
In a series circuit, the total voltage (V_T) equals the sum of the voltage drops around the circuit $(V_1, V_2, ...)$. The battery voltage is shared among the elements in the circuit.	$V_T = V_1 + V_2 + V_3$
A **parallel circuit** consists of multiple current paths and the current provided by the battery is shared among them. The total current (I_T) is equal to the sum of the currents in the branches $(I_1, I_2, ...)$.	$I_T = I_1 + I_2 + I_3$
In a parallel circuit, the total voltage (V_T) is the same in all circuit branches connected in parallel.	$V_T = V_1 = V_2 = V_3$
The total current entering a junction in an electric circuit must equal the total current leaving the junction.	
Ohm's law states that the current in a circuit element (I) equals the voltage (V) across a circuit element divided by the element's resistance (R). Resistance is measured in **ohms** (Ω).	$I = \dfrac{V}{R}$
Electric power (P) supplied to a circuit element equals the product of the circuit current (I) times the voltage (V) across the circuit element. **Power** is measured in **watts** (W).	$P = VI$
In a properly operating circuit, when the circuit power exceeds the designed load limit, a **fuse** or **circuit breaker** will operate to interrupt the current flow.	
Active Physics Plus Electric power (P) equals the voltage squared (V^2) divided by the resistance (R), or the current squared (I^2) times the resistance. Both these relationships hold true for each element in a circuit.	$P = \dfrac{V^2}{R}$ $P = I^2 R$

An open switch will stop the flow of current in a circuit element when it is placed in series with that element.	
When measuring voltage in a circuit element, the voltmeter is always connected in parallel with that element.	
When measuring current in a circuit element, the ammeter is always placed in series with that circuit element.	
In a series circuit, the total resistance (R_T) for **resistors** connected in series is equal to the sum of the individual resistances $(R_1, R_2, ...)$. The more resistors added in series, the higher the total circuit resistance and the lower the total circuit current for a fixed voltage.	$R_T = R_1 + R_2 + R_3$
In a parallel circuit, the inverse of the total resistance $\left(\dfrac{1}{R_T}\right)$ is equal to the sum of the inverses of the individual resistances $\left(\dfrac{1}{R_1}, \dfrac{1}{R_2}, ...\right)$. The more resistors added in parallel, the lower the total circuit resistance and the higher the total circuit current for a fixed voltage.	$\dfrac{1}{R_T} = \dfrac{1}{R_1} + \dfrac{1}{R_2} + \dfrac{1}{R_3}$
The **heat** gained (Q_{gained}) by one object in a closed system is equal to the heat lost (Q_{lost}) by another object in a closed system. The **law of conservation of energy** states that for a closed system, no energy is lost or gained.	$Q_{gained} = Q_{lost}$
The **specific heat** of a material (c) is a measure of the amount of heat which must be added per gram to increase the temperature by one degree.	
The amount of heat gained or lost (ΔQ) by an object is equal to its mass (m) times its specific heat (c) times its change in temperature (ΔT).	$\Delta Q = mc\Delta T$
Temperature is a measure of the average random kinetic energy of a material's molecules.	
The **first law of thermodynamics** states that heat added to a system (ΔQ) is equal to the increase in the internal energy (ΔU) of the system plus any work (W) done by the system. When heat is added, it increases the system's temperature, does work, or both.	$\Delta Q = \Delta U + W$
The **second law of thermodynamics** states that systems naturally move toward increasing **entropy**, or greater disorder. The flow of time in the universe is in the direction of increasing entropy.	
Efficiency equals the useful energy output divided by the total energy input. Efficiency is a measure of how much useful output energy is obtained from the input energy required to make a system operate.	Efficiency = $\dfrac{\text{useful energy output}}{\text{total energy input}}$
Electric energy (E) equals electric power (P) multiplied by the operating time (t). Electric energy is measured in kilowatt-hours (kWh). One kilowatt hour is equal to 3,600,000 joules (J).	$E = Pt$ $E = (VI)t$
Heat may be transferred through three processes – convection, conduction and radiation. **Convection** transfers heat to surrounding molecules by flow in fluids. **Conduction** transfers heat through direct contact and **radiation** transfers heat via electromagnetic waves. Radiation does not require a medium for transmission and therefore can occur in a vacuum.	

Active Physics

Physics
Chapter Challenge

You will be completing a second phase of the *Engineering Design Cycle* as you prepare for the *Chapter Challenge*. The goals and criteria remain unchanged; however, your list of *Inputs* has grown.

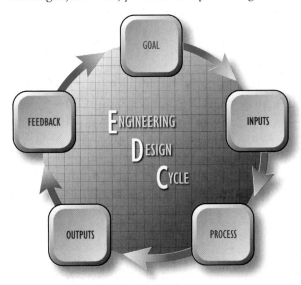

Goal

Your challenge for this chapter is to design an electrical appliance package and training manual to go with the 2400-watt wind generator system of the HFE dwelling. You will need to apply all that you have learned in this chapter to complete your design and convince the judges that your proposal most efficiently and effectively addresses the electrical needs of diverse families. Review the *Goal* as a class to make sure you are familiar with all the criteria and constraints.

Inputs

You now have additional physics information to help you identify and address the different physics concepts that apply to the design of an electrical appliance package. You have completed all the sections of this chapter and learned the content you will need

to select appliances that can be used within the power and energy limits of the HFE wind-generator package. Your group needs to apply these physics concepts to put together your design. You also have the additional *Input* of the feedback you received following your *Mini-Challenge* presentation.

Section 1 You generated electricity and developed a circuit that allowed you to light up a light bulb. The transformations of energy from your body to the wires, and then to the bulb, demonstrated the basics of electricity.

Section 2 You constructed a physical model for the flow of electricity in a circuit. By examining the different functions of the battery, the coulomb, and the bulb, you learned where energy goes when you use electricity.

Section 3 You explored two different types of electrical circuits and examined the similarities and differences. You also learned how to draw simple circuit diagrams for both types of circuit.

Section 4 You examined an electrical "black box" using tools to measure the voltage and current in a circuit. With this information, you learned about resistance in electrical circuits and how it affects the movement of coulombs, or electric currents. The relationship between resistance, voltage, and current in an electrical circuit is known as Ohm's law.

Section 5 You investigated load limits and electric power. Because the challenge requires that you stay within a 2400-W power limit at all times, this section provides critical information you will need.

Section 6 You explored the role of simple electrical switches. You also learned about the distribution of electricity and considered a wiring diagram to provide the best distribution in your electrical system design.

Section 7 You discovered how the law of conservation of energy applies to hot and cold objects. You also learned that every material, including water, has a specific heat, which dictates the amount of energy required to either heat or cool that material.

Active Physics

Section 8 You investigated the energy required to heat up a sample of water and investigated a method of converting electrical energy into heat by using a resistor. You also examined power ratings for various appliances.

Section 9 You calculated the energy used by an appliance based on the amount of time that it is operating. You also discovered that the energy available for your electrical system will be far below the average consumption of a typical household in the United States.

Process

In the *Process* phase, you need to decide what information you will use to meet the *Goal*. Defining your appliance package is a good way to start. Carefully select the appliances for your package that adequately provide for the needs of the family while operating within the constraints of the 2400-W wind-generator system. Remember to consider power ratings and total monthly energy consumption for each appliance. You will have to make difficult decisions about what services are absolutely essential for the family in your HFE dwelling. Your calculations will determine if you have the energy to run the appliances you've chosen and for how long. You may find that some appliances simply cannot operate on this electrical system and other appliances may be operated less frequently or for shorter periods of time.

It may be helpful to create a table to record your appliance list as well as the results of your time, power, and energy calculations. Each time you modify the appliance list, or the amount of time an appliance may operate, you have completed one iteration, and should create a new table. A computer spreadsheet could make this job easier to manage.

Once you have completed your appliance list and determined the range of operating times for each appliance, you will need to make sure that all of the necessary controls are on your circuit diagram. You may need to install switches or fuses that prevent too much power being used at one time. You will also need separate fuses or automatic switches to ensure that families don't run out of electricity or overload the system.

Develop an outline of the training manual for HFE volunteers. Your manual must explain the difference between 2400 W and 3 kWh. It should also give clear examples of how use of the appliances in the package can stay within the power and energy limits of the electrical system on both a daily and a long-term basis.

Outputs

Presenting your information to the class is your design-cycle *Output*. You should have a comprehensive appliance list, a complete circuit diagram, and the outline of your training manual. As you present each item to your class, you may be asked questions that will help you refine your design. Your presentation is also part of your design-cycle *Output*, so take the time to prepare your script and any posters, diagrams, or multimedia pieces you need to make your presentation effective and convincing.

Feedback

Your classmates will give you *Feedback* on the accuracy and the overall appeal of your presentation based on the criteria of the design challenge. This feedback will likely become part of your grade, but could also be useful for additional design iterations. From your experience with the *Mini-Challenge*, you should see how you could continuously rotate through the design process to refine almost any idea.

Physics
Connections to Other Sciences

Here are some examples of how the concepts you studied in this chapter relate to other sciences.

Electric Charges

Biology An isotonic solution contains a balance of charged particles identical to blood and therefore, can be safely used in the transfusions of liquid.

Chemistry The electrostatic forces between oppositely charged ions (cations and anions) bind crystals together, as in sodium chloride.

Earth Science Certain mineral crystals under pressure form an electric discharge.

Electric Energy

Biology Electric eels store energy in their organs in a configuration similar to an electric battery. This configuration allows larger eels to deliver powerful shocks of up to 600 volts, or five times the voltage of a wall socket.

Chemistry The electron affinity difference between two dissimilar metals in solution is the source of electric energy found in a cell or battery.

Earth Science The potential energy of the separated charges in a thunderstorm is the source of tremendous amounts of electric energy released in a lightning bolt.

Heat and Thermodynamics

Biology Life on Earth is water-based. The high specific heat of water is one factor that allows organisms to function in below-freezing temperatures for significant periods of time without damage.

Chemistry The position on the periodic table of an element is one factor that determines its specific heat. The specific heat is inversely proportional to an element's atomic mass: the higher the atomic mass, the lower the specific heat. This relationship for solids is known as the law of DuLong-Petit.

Earth Science The heat absorbed in the tropics is distributed to higher latitudes by convection of ocean and air currents. The high specific heat of the warm water from the Gulf Stream is responsible for the relatively mild climate of northern Europe.

Electric Currents

Biology A pacemaker is designed to analyze the function of the heart's own electrical system and when needed, to stimulate the heart by delivering small, precisely timed electric pulses via a current.

Chemistry The flow of electric charge through a solution is used to deposit a layer of material on a surface in a process called electroplating. The bright finish on car parts is produced by electroplating.

Earth Science A typical lightning bolt in a thunderstorm can transfer current at the rate of thousands of amperes with a potential difference of billions of volts.

Series and Parallel Connections

Biology When an electric pulse flows from one nerve to the next through a synapse along a long nerve fiber, the connection is analogous to a series circuit. The connections between nerve cells in the brain form a parallel connection.

Chemistry Monitoring systems for industrial chemical processes are connected either in series or in parallel. Pressure meters are connected in parallel to prevent interference with the process, while flow meters are connected in series.

Earth Science A river with only one channel transports water along a single path. A braided stream carries water in parallel channels. The water flowing in these various water courses follows the same patterns as series and parallel electric circuits.

Entropy

Biology Although entropy indicates that natural systems should always go to states of greater disorder, living organisms can violate this process locally with an input of energy, decreasing their entropy. This implies an increase in entropy in the systems that support life.

Chemistry Entropy dictates that naturally occurring chemical processes are not reversible without the input of energy.

Earth Science The erosion of landforms is a consequence of entropy, as differences in altitude are gradually reduced. The input of energy from inside Earth, evidenced by the creation of mountains, is necessary to reverse this process.

Debra Rucker Coleman

Architect; Citronelle, AL

Architect Debra Rucker Coleman is the owner of Sun Plans Inc., and has been designing passive solar homes for several years. She believes her love for the environment steered her toward solar energy. Growing up in Arizona with parents who loved the outdoors, Coleman was always fascinated by the Sun and the sky.

After graduating from the University of Arizona with a Bachelor of Architecture, she began working for an architecture firm. "I was appalled at their lack of sensitivity toward the environment," Coleman states. "I realized that in order to incorporate my design ideas, I had to work for myself."

Coleman opened her own business, Energetic Design, in North Carolina, and began designing for the local school district. She also became an energy consultant on residential development projects where she included passive solar energy. "At first, only 25 percent of my clients were interested in passive solar energy and I realized that the general public needed to be educated." Passive solar design revolves around one simple idea—to take advantage of the Sun's heat without the aid of any mechanical devices.

Passive solar energy is not all Coleman thinks about when she tackles energy efficiency: "I have to be aware of heat loss and heat gain. I have to understand that to let the Sun's energy in the house means putting the thinnest materials on the south side of the house," she explains. "A black roof will also absorb a lot more heat. For one climate you might want a black roof, and in another climate you might want a more reflective, or white roof."

Rochelle Boyl

**Music Teacher;
Covelo, CA**

Rochelle Boyl was introduced to living off-the-grid by her husband, a term which refers to living in a self-sufficient manner without reliance on one or more public utilities.

But it is the couple's ingenuity with their resources that is not only keeping their way-of-life exciting, but is also keeping Earth green. "We have gravity-fed spring water, hydro-electric power in the winter and solar in the summer. The Boyl's emphasize energy conservation, regardless of its source. "You have to have the desire to want to live this kind of lifestyle. I enjoy learning and want to keep living off-the-grid," pronounced Rochelle.

Craig Robinson

**Senior Composites Engineer,
Knight & Carver Wind
Group; National City, CA**

Craig Robinson has over 20 years experience designing products from composite materials, including tennis rackets, bike frames, and fiberglass replica cars. Currently, he is a Senior Composites Engineer at Knight & Carver Wind Group, a company that began as a yacht construction firm and today is recognized in the wind energy industry for repairing and building turbine blades.

Craig is optimistic about the wind energy industry. "It is great to be a part of a booming industry. Wind, solar and geothermal are going to be a big part of the future," predicts Craig.

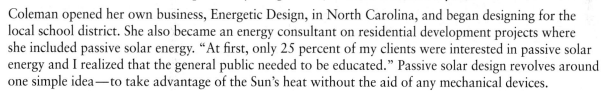

Physics

Practice Test

Before you try the Physics Practice Test, *you may want to review Sections 1–9, where you will find*
35 Checking Up *questions,* **14 What Do You Think Now?** *questions,* **36 Physics Essential Questions,**
94 Physics to Go *questions, and* **11 Inquiring Further** *questions.*

Content Review

1. A student is spinning an electric generator to power a circuit, as shown. When the switch is closed, which of the following occurs?

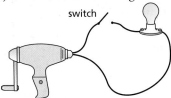

switch

   a) The generator gets easier to turn, and the light goes on.
   b) The generator gets harder to turn, and the light goes on.
   c) The generator gets harder to turn, and the light goes off.
   d) The generator gets easier to turn, and nothing happens to the light.

2. A series circuit delivers energy from the battery to the resistor. As the current flows around the circuit, which of the following does the resistor use up?
   a) charge only
   b) energy only
   c) both charge and energy
   d) neither charge nor energy

3. The circuit in the diagram shows a battery connected to a light bulb. If a second identical light bulb is added in series with the first, which of the following would occur?

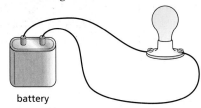

battery

   a) The first bulb would go out, and the second bulb would shine.
   b) The first bulb would stay bright, and the second bulb would be dimmer.
   c) Both bulbs would shine equally, but dimmer than the circuit with one bulb.
   d) Both bulbs would shine equally with the same brightness as the original.

4. Two light bulbs are connected in parallel to a powerful battery, as shown in the diagram. Compared to the energy used in one light bulb, the energy provided by the battery is

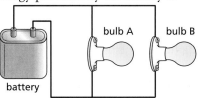

bulb A   bulb B

battery

   a) the same.   b) twice as much.
   c) half as much.   d) four times as much.

5. In the diagram in *Question 4*, if bulb A is removed from the circuit, bulb B will
   a) go out.   b) double in brightness.
   c) remain unchanged.   d) be half as bright.

6. In the diagram for *Question 4*, what happens if a third bulb is added in parallel to bulbs A and B?
   a) Bulbs A and B would both become dimmer.
   b) Bulbs A and B would both become brighter.
   c) Bulb A would remain the same, but bulb B would become much dimmer.
   d) Bulbs A and B would maintain the same brightness.

7. The diagram shows a circuit with a resistor, a battery, a voltmeter and an ammeter. Is this circuit connected correctly to measure the resistance of the resistor?

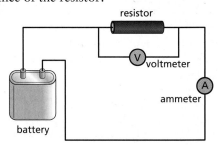

resistor

V voltmeter

A

ammeter

battery

   a) No, both the voltmeter and the ammeter should be connected in series.
   b) No, both the voltmeter and the ammeter should be connected in parallel.
   c) No, the voltmeter and ammeter should change places.
   d) Yes, it is connected correctly.

8. In the circuit shown in the diagram, what current is flowing through the resistor when the battery is connected?

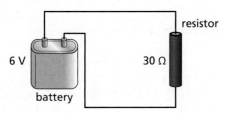

a) 5 A
b) 5 V
c) 0.2 A
d) 0.2 V

9. The graph shows the current through a resistor when different amounts of voltage are applied. The resistance of the resistor is closest to

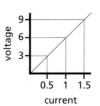

a) 1.5 Ω.
b) 18 Ω.
c) 6 Ω.
d) 4 Ω.

10. An electric clothes dryer requires 5000 W of power. Which combination of circuit voltage and maximum circuit current below would be sufficient to power the dryer?
a) 110 V and 30 A
b) 220 V and 20 A
c) 110 V and 40 A
d) 220 V and 30 A

11. A mass of 100 g of water at 80°C is added to 200 g of water at 50°C. Which of the statements below best describes the result of this process and the final temperature of the mixture?
a) The final temperature is 60°C and the entropy of the system increases.
b) The final temperature is 65°C and the entropy of the system increases.
c) The final temperature is 60°C and the entropy of the system decreases.
d) The final temperature is 65°C and the entropy of the system decreases.

12. Two identical batteries are each connected to identical light bulbs in two different circuits as shown in the diagram. Bulb A is connected in a series circuit, and bulb B is connected in a parallel circuit. Compared to the current flowing in bulb A, the current flowing in bulb B is

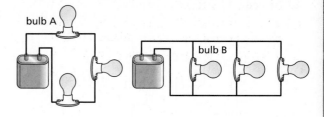

a) three times greater.
b) one third as great.
c) the same.
d) No current comparison can be made between two different circuit types.

13. In *Question 12*, if the resistance of each bulb is 6 Ω, what is the ratio of resistance in the series circuit to the resistance in the parallel circuit?
a) 1 : 1
b) 3 : 1
c) 6 : 1
d) 9 : 1

14. A heater that uses 120 V and 2 A is placed in a cup of water for 30 s. The temperature of the water rises 20°C during this process. How much electrical energy does the heater use in this time?
a) 7200 J
b) 240 J
c) 144,000 J
d) 360 J

15. A microwave oven that is rated at 1000 W increases the energy of 800 g of water by 24,000 J in 30 s. What is the efficiency of the oven?
a) 80%
b) 75%
c) 60%
d) 100%

Practice Test *(continued)*

Critical Thinking

16. Look at the following set of circuit diagrams – one has two equal batteries in series and the other has two equal batteries in parallel.

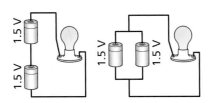

a) Compare the voltage each bulb receives.
b) Compare the current each bulb receives.
c) If the bulb has a resistance of 12 Ω, calculate the current in each bulb.

17. A 120-V circuit for the kitchen of a home is protected by a 20-A circuit breaker. The kitchen has the following appliances that may be plugged into the circuit:
    • 1000-W toaster   • 300-W blender
    • 1200-W frying pan • 600-W coffeemaker
    a) What current flows through the blender when it is plugged in?
    b) What is the resistance of the frying pan?
    c) What combinations of appliances can be used on the circuit at the same time without the circuit breaker shutting off the circuit?

18. In an experiment, 500 g of water at 60°C was cooled to 50°C by adding cold water.
    a) How much heat was lost by the hot water? (Use c = 4180 J/kg-°C for water)
    b) How much heat was gained by the cold water?
    c) The temperature of the cold water was 10°C. How much cold water was added to the hot water to bring the temperature down to 40°C?

19. A water immersion heater is rated at 600 W when plugged into a 120-V circuit. The heater is placed in a cup with 0.400 kg of water at an initial temperature of 10°C.
    a) How much current does the heater draw?
    b) What is the resistance of the heater?
    c) If the heater runs for 30 seconds, how much energy does it provide to the water?
    d) What is the final temperature of the water after 30 seconds? (Use c = 4180 J/kg-°C for water)

20. For the circuit shown in the diagram:

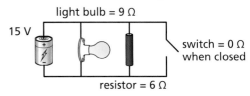

a) What is the voltage across the light bulb?
b) What is the current through the resistor?
c) What is the resistance of the circuit when the switch is open?
d) Describe what happens to the light bulb when the switch is closed.

Active Physics

Plus

21. A 60-W and a 100-W light bulb are both plugged into the same circuit. Using calculations, show which light bulb has the greater resistance.

22. A 100-kg mass is connected to a string that is attached to paddles in an insulated container of water, as shown. As the mass falls, the water is stirred, heating it.

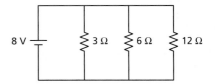

a) If the mass falls 5 m, how much gravitational potential energy does it lose?
b) If the container has 0.5-kg of water inside, what is the maximum temperature increase of the water due to the falling mass?

23. For the circuit shown in the diagram:

a) Find the total circuit resistance.
b) Find the current through the 6-Ω resistor.
c) Find the power used in the 3-Ω resistor.

Active Physics

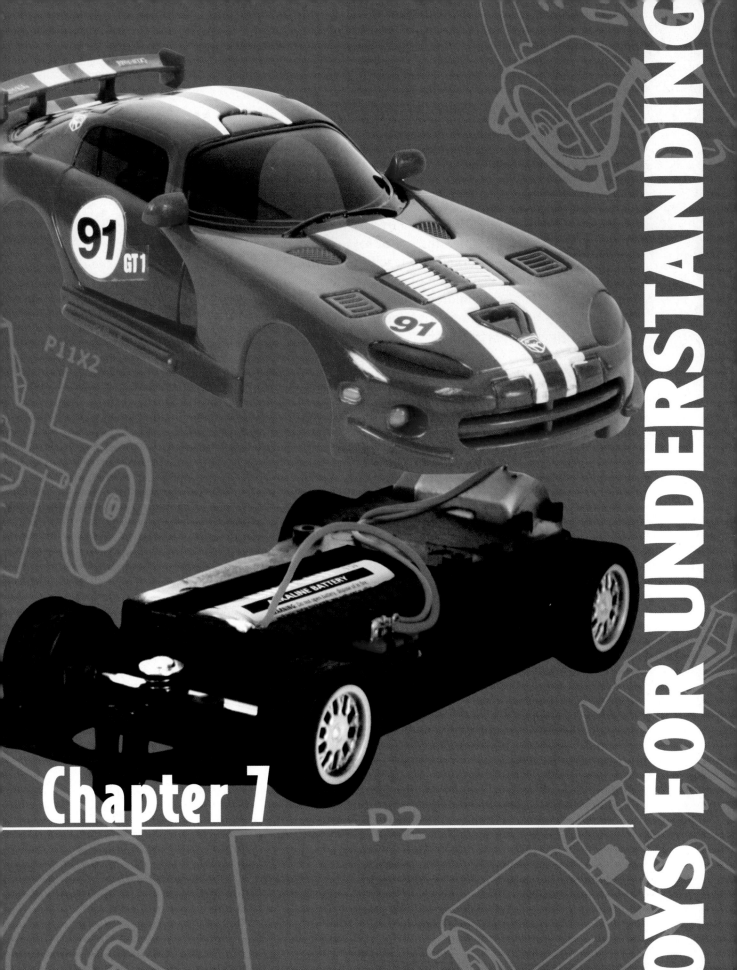

Chapter 7

Toys for Understanding

Scenario

In this *Active Physics* chapter, you will try to help educate children through the use of toys. The Homes For Everyone (HFE) organization would like to teach the children more about electricity and the generation of electricity. They hope that this may encourage interest in children to use electricity wisely, as well as encourage development of alternative sources for electrical energy by future generations.

The HFE organization will work with a toy company to provide kits and instructions for children to make toys that use electric motors and/or generators. These toys should illustrate how electric motors and generators work and capture the interest of the children.

Your Challenge

Your task is to design a toy that includes a motor, or generator, or both. You will prepare a list of materials and instructions for operating the toy. The toy will serve both as a fun device and as a way to illustrate how the electric motors in home appliances work. The toy will also illustrate how electricity can be produced from an energy source such as wind, moving water, a falling weight, or some other external source. The instructions for the children should explain not only how to assemble and operate the toy, but also how and why it works in terms of basic principles of physics. For safety considerations, the toy should not require more than 4 D-cell batteries.

Criteria for Success

Discuss the criteria for judging the value of each toy. How will each toy be graded? How much of the grade should depend on the quality of the toy or the instructions or the explanation of how the toy works? How many physics principles should be included in the explanation? Discuss the criteria and try to reach some consensus as a class.

You will have another opportunity to review and edit these criteria at the end of the chapter before you complete the challenge. After you have generated criteria, you may want to compare it with the suggested standards given on the next page.

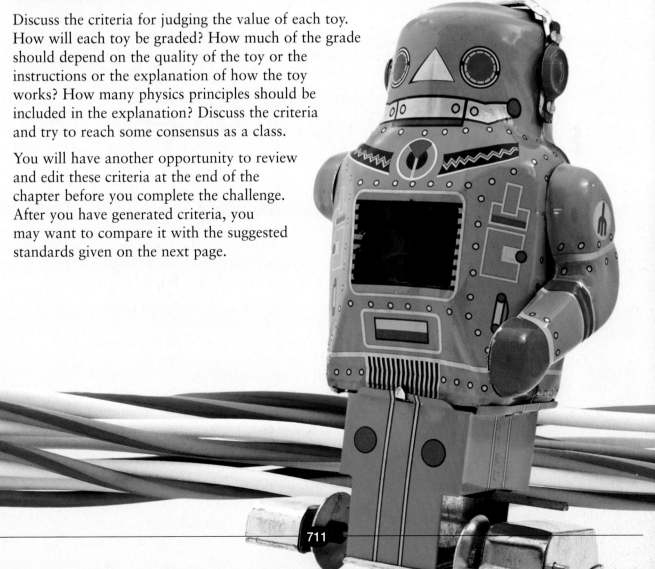

Standard for Excellence

1. The quality of the toy • the motor/generator is made from inexpensive, common materials • the working parts of the motor/generator are exposed • the toy is safe	**20 points**
2. Written instructions • the instructions are written in a way that a child will understand • the instructions clearly explain how to assemble the motor/generator • the instructions explain how and why the motor/generator works in terms of basic principles of physics • a number of different physics principles are accurately explained, including electricity, magnetism, and energy conversion	**50 points**
3. Entertainment value of the toy • the toy will capture a child's interest • the toy will keep a child amused for a length of time	**20 points**
4. Challenge completed on time	**10 points**

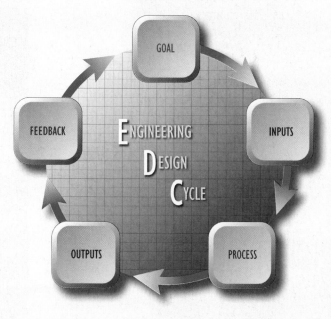

Engineering Design Cycle

You have now learned about your *Chapter Challenge* to design an electrical toy that will help HFE educate young children about electric generators and/or electric motors. You will use a simplified *Engineering Design Cycle* to help your group complete this design challenge. Defining the problem is the first step in the *Engineering Design Cycle*, so you have already begun.

As you experience each one of the chapter sections, you will be gaining *Inputs* to use in the design cycle. These *Inputs* will include new physics concepts, vocabulary, and even equations that will help you to build your electrical system. When your group prepares the *Mini-Challenge* presentation and the *Chapter Challenge,* you will be completing the *Process* step of the *Engineering Design Cycle*. During the *Process* step, you will evaluate ideas, consider criteria, compare and contrast potential solutions, and most importantly, make design decisions.

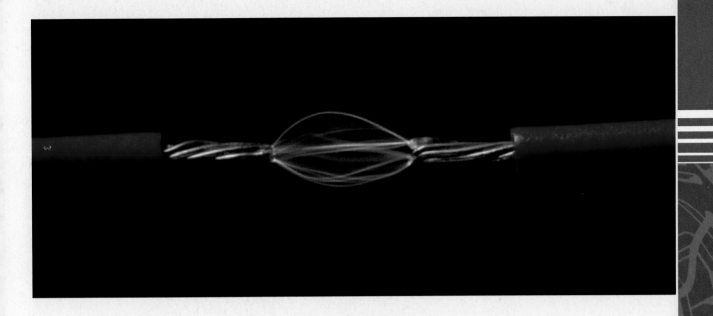

The *Outputs* of your design cycle will be the toy design that your group presents to the class, including any charts, diagrams, or calculations you may use to clarify the information you present. Finally, at the *Mini-Challenge*, you will receive *Feedback* from your classmates and your instructor about what parts of your presentation are good and what parts need to be refined. You will repeat the *Engineering Design Cycle* during the second half of the chapter when you gain more *Inputs*, refine your toy design, and make your final electrical toy package presentation in the *Chapter Challenge*.

Physics Corner

Physics in *Toys for Understanding*

- AC and DC
- Electricity
- Electromagnets
- Energy conservation
- Energy conversion
- Energy flow and power

- Energy transfer
- Galvanometers
- Induced current
- Magnetic fields
- Magnetism
- Solenoids

Section 1

The Electricity and Magnetism Connection

What Do You See?

Learning Outcomes

In this section, you will

- **Map** a magnetic field by using a magnetic compass.

- **Look** for a relationship between an electric current and a magnetic field.

What Do You Think?

A compass helps travelers determine which way is north.

- **How is a compass affected by a bar magnet?**

Write your answer to this question in your *Active Physics* log. Be prepared to discuss your ideas with your small group and other members of your class.

Investigate

In the first part of this *Investigate*, you will use a bar magnet to explore magnetic forces between magnets and magnetic materials. You will also use a compass to explore the shape of a magnetic field around a bar magnet. In the second part, you will investigate if a relationship exists between magnetism and electricity.

Part A: Mapping a Magnetic Field

1. You will be given two bar magnets. Note that each bar magnet is labeled N (north) on one end and S (south) on the other end.

   a) Explore whether there are attractive forces or repulsive forces when the magnets are placed near each other. Record your results in your log.

b) Determine the strength of one of the bar magnets by measuring how many paper clips the magnet can lift.

2. The needle of a compass is a small bar magnet that is placed on a point so that it can rotate easily. It can be used as a magnetic-field detector. Any magnet or magnetic material will affect the compass. When the compass is not near any magnet or magnetic material, it aligns itself with Earth's *magnetic field* and indicates which direction is north.

Note the direction of the compass needle. Rotate the casing.

a) Did the compass needle change direction?

3. Set the magnetic compass on the table and bring another type of magnet, such as a bar magnet, into the area near the compass needle. But do not get them too close because a strong magnet can ruin a compass needle if it gets too close.

a) Describe your observations.

b) What happens to the dependable north-pointing property of the compass?

c) How dependable is the compass at pointing north when it is placed in a region where there are other magnetic effects, in addition to Earth's magnetic field?

4. You will now make a map of the magnetic field of the rectangular bar magnet. Place the magnet on a piece of paper and trace its position. Label which end of the bar magnet is the N pole and which is the S pole. Keep the compass a centimeter or two away from the magnet to avoid ruining the compass. Place the compass at one location and mark the direction it points. Remove the compass.

Note: If the bar magnet is an extremely strong one, you should keep it close enough to the compass to see the effects, but not close enough to damage the compass.

a) Sketch a small arrow at the location from which you removed the compass to show the way it pointed. Pay attention to which end of the compass needle points to which pole of the magnet.

b) Place the compass at a second location near the tip of the first arrow you sketched. Remove the compass and sketch another small arrow in this location to show the way the compass pointed. See the diagram at the top of the following page.

c) Repeat the process at 10 or more locations to get a map of the magnetic field of a bar magnet. Tape or glue the map into your log.

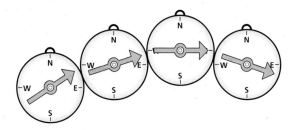

Part B: Electric Currents and Magnetic Fields

1. Wrap a wire around the magnetic compass a few times to form a coil. Wrap the wire across the north-south markings of the compass scale, as shown in the diagram below. Hold the turns of wire in place with tape, or use the method recommended by your teacher. Use sandpaper to remove the insulation from a short section of the wire ends.

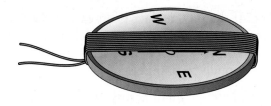

2. Connect a DC hand generator, a light bulb, and the compass/coil in a series circuit, as shown in the diagram at the bottom of the page. Rest the compass/coil so that the compass is horizontal, with the needle balanced, pointing north, and free to rotate. Also, turn the compass within, if necessary, so that the compass needle is parallel to the turns of wire. You might wedge some paper under the edges of the compass to make it rest level.

3. Crank the DC generator and observe the compass needle.

a) Record your observations.

4. Reverse the direction of the current in the wire by reversing the direction you crank the DC generator.

a) Describe the results in your log.

b) What evidence do you now have that electric currents can produce magnetic fields?

5. Notice that the compass does not need to be in contact with the wire to experience a force due to the current in the wire. This illustrates the general phenomenon of "action at a distance."

a) In your log, describe how this is similar to the force of gravity.

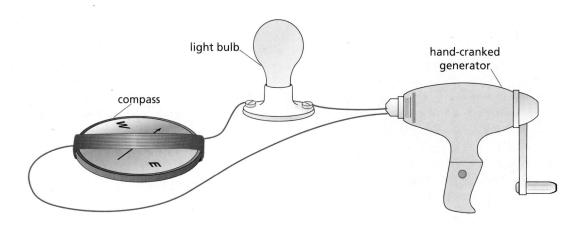

light bulb

hand-cranked generator

compass

6. The "action at a distance," of the magnetic field is used to bridge the "gap" between the wire and the compass. In short, the current running through the wire produces a magnetic field in the space surrounding it. When a compass is placed in a region of space where a magnetic field exists, it experiences a force. The magnetic field defines both the strength and the direction of the force.

a) Using a similar explanation, describe what a gravitational field of Earth may be like.

b) What is the direction of the gravitational force and how does its strength change as you move further from Earth?

7. The concept of a field is an example of a model used in physics to help you understand natural phenomena. Physicists use a ray model to describe how light travels. Chemists use balls and sticks as a model to represent molecules. Magnetic fields are depicted as lines surrounding the current-carrying wire or the magnet.

a) How does this model help you to understand or describe the properties of a bar magnet?

Physics Talk

MAGNETISM AND ELECTRICITY

Magnetic Fields

People have been fascinated by the invisible tug of one magnet on another magnet for hundreds of years. In the first part of the investigation, you found that when the north pole of one magnet is placed near the north pole of a second magnet, the two magnets repel. This can be summarized by stating that "like poles repel." In contrast, you found that when the north pole of one magnet is placed near the south pole of a second magnet, the two magnets attract. This can be summarized by stating that "unlike poles attract."

A compass is usually used to determine which way is north. The compass needle is actually a tiny bar magnet. Earth has the equivalent of a large magnet beneath its surface and the compass needle is attracted to Earth's interior magnet. How Earth's core can have the equivalent of a magnet given its extremely high temperature will be discussed in a later section.

The compass can be used as a magnetic-field detector. It can indicate if a magnet (in addition to Earth's magnet) is in the vicinity of the compass. You used the compass to map the **magnetic field** of a bar magnet. That field is sketched to the right.

Physics Words

magnetic field: a region of space where magnetic forces act on objects.

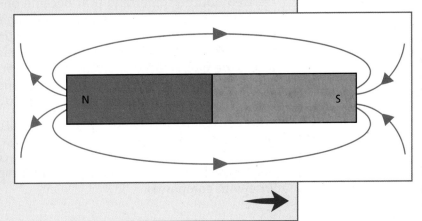

Active Physics

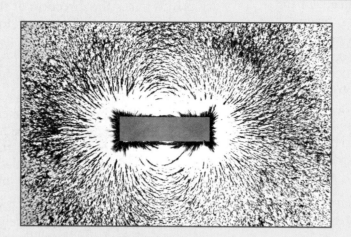

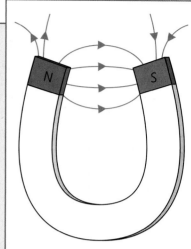

Notice that the north end of the compass points away from the north end of the bar magnet and toward the south end of the bar magnet. A magnetic field of a horseshoe magnet is drawn above. The field, once again, points away from the north end and toward the south end.

These magnetic field lines are a model to help describe the magnet and its effect on objects near it. The field is at all points near the magnet but only a few lines are drawn to show the shape of the field.

In the photographs, iron filings are placed near a bar magnet and a horseshoe magnet. The iron filings align themselves with the magnetic fields.

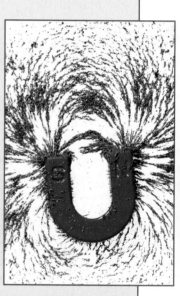

In 1820, the Danish physicist Hans Christian Oersted placed a long, straight, horizontal wire on top of a magnetic compass. Both the compass and the wire were resting on a horizontal surface. In order to create a demonstration for his students, Oersted then sent a current through the wire. No one knows for sure if he was doing this demonstration for the very first time, but when the current started, Oersted noticed something that became one of the greatest discoveries in physics. The compass needle moved. The discovery was that a current can produce a magnetic field. This connection between the apparently unrelated phenomena of electricity and magnetism resulted in changes across the globe. Motors, electricity for everyday use, communication through cellular phones, and the development of the Internet are all a result of Oersted's discovery that electric currents produce magnetic fields.

You reproduced this famous experiment using a hand generator, some wire and a compass needle. Rather than having a single wire near the compass, you wound the wire around the compass. A related experiment maps out the magnetic field by surrounding a single current-carrying wire with compasses.

In the diagram at the right, you can see that when no current is flowing in the wire, all the compass needles point north. When a current is flowing, the compass needles all point in different directions.

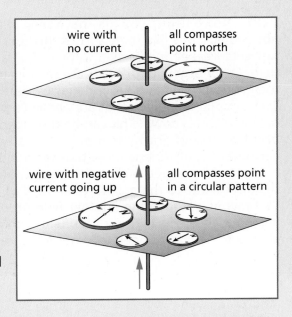

wire with
no current

all compasses
point north

wire with negative
current going up

all compasses point
in a circular pattern

The important concept is that the current-carrying wire can produce a magnetic field that can be detected with compasses. The magnetic field is circular about the wire. The direction of the magnetic field can be found experimentally with a compass. This direction can be recalled by using the left-hand rule. Point your left thumb in the direction of the current (the electron current travels from the negative terminal of a battery to the positive terminal). The direction of the curve of your fingers indicates the direction of the circular magnetic field.

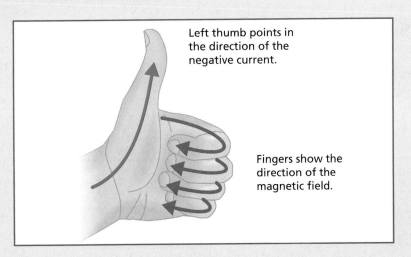

Left thumb points in
the direction of the
negative current.

Fingers show the
direction of the
magnetic field.

Notice that the compass does not need to be in contact with the wire to experience a force due to the current in the wire. This situation illustrates the general phenomenon of "action at a distance." In other words, the current produces a force (an action) without touching (at a distance). In order to better understand how this occurs, the concept of the magnetic field is introduced to describe the empty space between the wire and the compass. The current in the wire produces a magnetic field in the space surrounding it. When a compass is placed in a region of space where a magnetic field exists, it experiences a force.

Checking Up

1. Describe the direction of the magnetic field around a current-carrying wire.

2. Toward which pole of a magnet does the north end of a compass point?

3. Compare the magnetic field of a magnet with the gravitational field of Earth.

Unlike "force fields" you may have seen in a movie, a real field does not end abruptly like some sort of shield or invisible wall. Instead, it just gets weaker and weaker as you move away from the source of the field. Other examples of fields are the electric field around charges and the gravitational fields around masses. Earth has a gravitational field that can pull on objects that are above Earth. When you drop a ball, the ball accelerates down. This can be described by saying that there is an invisible force of gravity that pulls the ball down. You can also say that Earth has a gravitational field that surrounds it. When the ball is placed in that field, it experiences a downward force. You are very familiar with the effects due to the gravitational field of Earth. Now you are aware that magnets respond to another field produced by Earth, namely its magnetic field. The concept of a field is an example of a model used in physics to help you understand natural phenomena.

+Math	+Depth	+Concepts	+Exploration
◆◆	◆	◆	

Active Physics
Plus

Observing the Sum of Magnetic Fields

Another way of describing the attraction and repulsion of bar magnets is to notice the sum of the magnetic field lines between the magnets.

In the diagram below, note that when the bar magnets repel, the field lines from the two magnets are in the same direction. When the bar magnets attract, the field lines from the two magnets are in opposite directions.

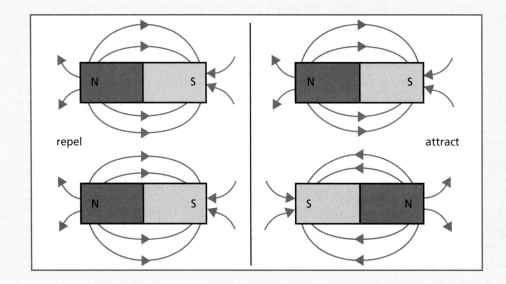

repel   attract

Below is a wire carrying a negative current, labeled *I*. Its magnetic field, labeled *B*, is shown as circles.

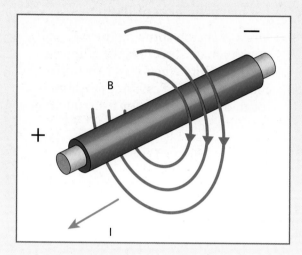

A useful convention for showing three dimensions on a sheet of paper is to draw the diagram in two dimensions. Then, use a dot in the circle representing the wire to denote "out of the page." A cross in the circle denotes "into the page."

If you think of an arrow piercing the page, this can help you remember the convention. If an arrow were coming out of the page, you would see its tip — a dot. If an arrow were going into the page, you would see the feathers — an X.

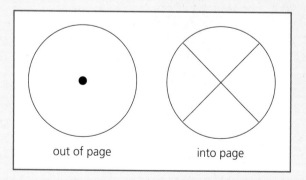

1. a) Draw a diagram that shows the magnetic-field lines for two parallel wires that are both carrying currents in the same direction.

   b) Compare the magnetic fields between the wires with the magnetic fields between the bar magnets above.

   c) On the basis of these diagrams, would you predict that these current-carrying wires attract or repel each other?

2. Repeat this exercise with parallel wires that are carrying currents in the opposite directions.

Is There an Equation for the Strength of a Magnetic Field?

When you investigated the magnetic field due to a current-carrying wire, you might have noticed that the field weakens as you move the compass away from the wire. An approximate formula for the magnetic field near a long current-carrying wire is

$$B = \frac{\mu_0 I}{2\pi d}$$

where *B* is the strength of the magnetic field measured in tesla,

   μ_0 is a constant equal to $4\pi \times 10^{-7}$ newton/ampere^2,

   I is the current in amperes, and

   d is the distance to the wire in meters.

From the equation, you can see one tesla is equal to one newton/(ampere × meter). A magnetic field of one tesla is a strong magnetic field.

Active Physics

The strength of the magnetic field of Earth at its surface is roughly 0.00005 T (tesla) or 5×10^{-5} T. On the other hand, magnetic resonance imaging (MRI) requires a magnetic field of about one tesla.

1. Calculate the strength of the magnetic field at three distances (0.5 cm, 1.0 cm, and 1.5 cm) from a straight vertical current-carrying wire with 3 A flowing through it. At approximately what distance does the magnetic field of the wire have the same strength as the magnetic field of Earth?

2. Draw a sketch showing the approximate direction the compass needle points when it is 1.0 cm from the straight wire carrying 3 A and located in four positions surrounding the wire.

What Do You Think Now?

At the beginning of this section, you were asked the following:

• **How is a compass affected by a bar magnet?**

Based on what you learned in your investigation, how would you answer this question now? Use what you learned in this section to describe how a compass is affected by a current-carrying wire.

Essential Questions

What does it mean?

Electricity is all about currents in wires. Magnetism is all about magnets. What is the connection between electricity and magnetism?

How do you know?

What did you observe that makes it clear that there is a connection between electricity and magnetism?

Why do you believe?

Connects with Other Physics Content	Fits with Big Ideas in Science	Meets Physics Requirements
Electricity and magnetism	Models	✳ Parsimonious - maximum of generality for minimum of primary concepts

✳ Physics helps make sense of the world by attempting to describe different phenomena with a single explanation. How does Oersted's discovery help make the explanation of the world "simpler"?

Why should you care?

A motor is useful because it can make things move. The electric current can make a compass needle move. A motor can make a clothes dryer or a mixing blade spin. How are these motors similar to and different from the compass needle near the current?

Reflecting on the Section and the Challenge

This section has provided you with knowledge about a critical link between electricity and magnetism, which is deeply involved in your challenge to make a working electric motor or generator. The response of the compass needle to a nearby electric current showed that an electric current itself has a magnetic effect that can cause a magnet, in this case a compass needle, to experience a force. You still have a way to go to understand and be able to be "in control" of electric motors and generators, but you have started along a path that will get you there.

Physics to Go

1. Sketch a bar magnet. Show the orientation of a compass placed at 10 different locations near the bar magnet.

2. Compare Oersted's experiment with a single wire and compass and your investigation with a wire and compass.

3. Suppose 100 compasses were placed on a horizontal surface to surround a vertical current-carrying wire. Describe the pattern of directions in which the 100 compasses would point in each of the following situations. (Pretend that one compass does not affect any other one.)

   a) No current is in the wire.

   b) A weak current is upwards in the wire.

   c) A strong current is upwards in the wire.

4. If a vertical wire carrying a strong current penetrated the floor of a room, and if you were using a compass to "navigate" in the room by always walking in the direction indicated by the north-seeking pole of the compass needle, describe the "walk" you would take.

5. Use the rule mentioned in the *Physics Talk* for the relationship between the direction of the current in a wire and the direction of the magnetic field near the wire to make a sketch showing the direction of the magnetic field near a wire which has a current:

   a) downward

   b) horizontally

6. **Active Physics** *Plus* Imagine that a second vertical wire is placed in the original apparatus used in this investigation, but not touching the first wire. There is room to place a magnetic compass between the wires without touching either wire. If a compass were placed between the wires, describe in what direction the compass would point if the wires carry equal currents:

   a) flowing in the same direction

   b) flowing in opposite directions

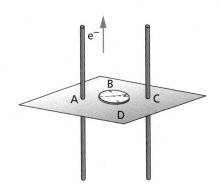

7. A hollow, transparent plastic tube is placed on a horizontal surface as shown in the diagram. A wire carrying a current is wound once around the tube to form a circular loop in the wire. In what direction would a compass placed inside the tube point? (Plastic does not affect a compass; only the current in the wire loop affects the compass.)

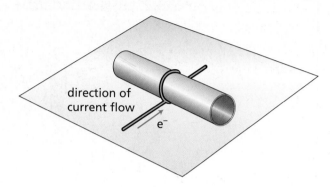

direction of
current flow

e⁻

8. *Preparing for the Chapter Challenge*

The challenge for you in this chapter is to develop a toy that contains either a motor or generator for a child. All motors and generators use either permanent magnets (like bar magnets) or electromagnets. All children find magnets fascinating. The instructions you include for assembling the toy may allow the students to explore the magnetic fields around any permanent magnets that you include in the kit. Write a brief description of at least three interesting things a child can do with the permanent magnets before assembling them to operate the toy.

Inquiring Further

Searching for magnetic fields

Use a compass to search for magnetic effects and magnetic "stuff." As you know, a compass needle usually aligns in a north-south direction. If a compass needle does not align north-south, a magnetic effect in addition to that of Earth is the cause, and the needle is responding to both Earth's magnetism and some other source of magnetism. Use a compass as a probe for magnetic effects. Try to find magnetic effects in a variety of places and near a variety of things where you suspect magnetism may be present. Try inside a car, bus, or subway. The structural steel in some buildings is magnetized and may cause a compass to give a "wrong" reading. Try near the speaker of a radio; try near electric motors, both operating and not operating.

Do not bring a strong magnet close to a compass, because the magnet may change the magnetic alignment of the compass needle, ruining the compass.

Make a list of the objects that are magnetic in nature and objects that affect a magnet that you find in your search.

Section 2

Electromagnets

Learning Outcomes

In this section, you will

- **Describe** the magnetic field of a current-carrying solenoid.
- **Compare** the magnetic field of a solenoid to the magnetic field of a bar magnet.
- **Identify** the variables that make an electromagnet strong or weak and explain the effects of each variable.

What Do You Think?

Large electromagnets are used to pick up cars in junkyards.

- **How does an electromagnet work?**
- **How could it be made stronger?**

Write your answer to these questions in your *Active Physics* log. Be prepared to discuss your ideas with your small group and other members of your class.

Investigate

In this *Investigate*, you will map the magnetic field of a current-carrying coil of wire (a *solenoid*) and compare it to that of a bar magnet. You will then determine how the number of turns, current size, and core material affect the strength of the magnetic field of a solenoid.

1. Wind 50 turns of wire on an end of a drinking straw to form a *solenoid* as shown in the diagram on the next page. It is better to put all of the turns at the same place on the straw rather than spread them out along the straw. Put some tape over the solenoid to keep the wires in place. Use sandpaper to clean the insulation from a short section of the wire ends down to bare metal.

2. Connect the wires from the DC generator to the wires of the solenoid. Bring one end of the solenoid near the magnetic compass and crank the generator to send a current through the solenoid. When current flows through the solenoid, you will have an *electromagnet*. Observe any effect on the compass needle. Try several orientations of the electromagnet to produce effects on the compass needle.

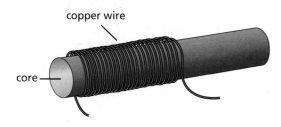

a) Record your observations in your log.

b) Compare your observations to those you made with the bar magnet.

c) How can you tell the "polarity" of an electromagnet? That is, how can you tell which end of an electromagnet behaves like the north pole of a bar magnet?

3. Predict what you can do to change the polarity of an electromagnet.

a) Write your prediction in your log.

b) Test your prediction. Record your results and compare them to your prediction.

4. Hang a paper clip or staple from a thread and see if your drinking-straw solenoid can pull it slightly to one side.

a) Record your observations in your log.

5. There are a number of variables that you can change to determine the effect on the strength of the electromagnet.

- You can replace the core of the straw from air to an iron nail.

- You can change the number of turns of wire.

- You can change the amount of current through the wire.

Decide which of these variable changes you will investigate.

a) Design an investigation of the effect of the variable on the strength of the electromagnet. Record the steps of your investigation.

b) After your teacher approves your procedure, carry out your investigation. Record the results in your log.

Physics Talk

ELECTROMAGNETS

A single current-carrying wire produces a magnetic field. In this section, you investigated what happens if the current-carrying wire is wrapped into a coil. You observed that this coil, also called a **solenoid**, behaved like a bar magnet. You had produced an **electromagnet**. (An electromagnet is any magnetic field created by a current. A solenoid is an electromagnet in the shape of a cylinder.) That is, it affected a compass in the same way that a bar magnet affects a compass. The diagrams on the following page show how the magnetic field consisting of loops of wire add up to make a stronger magnetic field than a single wire. →

Physics Words

solenoid: a coil of wire wrapped around a core of some material that provides a magnetic field when an electric current is passed through the coil.

electromagnet: any magnetic field created by a current.

Active Physics

By combining many loops, the total magnetic field of the solenoid resembles the magnetic field of the bar magnet.

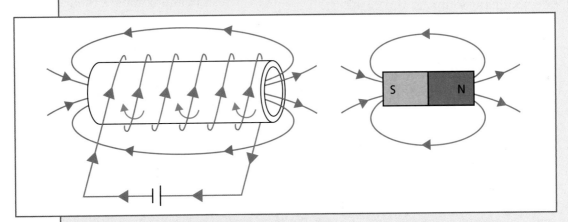

The magnetic field of the solenoid increases in strength when an iron nail is inserted into the core of the solenoid. One model that could explain this introduces the concept of magnetic domains. These domains are tiny bar magnets that exist within iron. At most times, these domains point every which way. The number of domains that point up is the same as the number that point sideways and down. The magnetic field of the solenoid causes these magnetic domains to align. When more and more of them align, the total strength of the solenoid increases. The magnetic field is no longer just due to the current-carrying solenoid but is also due to the sum of the strength of the aligned magnetic domains.

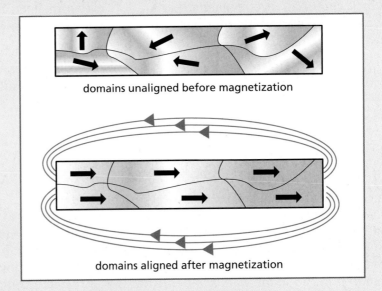

domains unaligned before magnetization

domains aligned after magnetization

"Soft iron" works well as the core of an electromagnet. Soft iron is a processing term. It means the iron that has not been "hardened" by heat treatments, added ingredients, or other processes.

It is not soft to the touch. Iron is a magnetic material, but in soft iron the material is made up of small domains, each with its magnetic field pointing in a different direction. So by itself, soft iron does not make a good permanent magnet, because the fields from all the differently oriented domains cancel each other out. But if soft iron is placed in the magnetic field produced by something else, the magnetic field causes many of the domains to line up in the same direction, with their north poles in the direction of the magnetic field. This causes the soft iron to be a strong magnet, but only as long as it is in the magnetic field of something else.

It does not take a strong magnetic field to line up most of the domains of soft iron. The magnetic field due to the lined-up domains can often be 1000 times larger than the magnetic field that caused most of the domains to line up.

This magnetic domain model also helps to explain where the magnetism of a bar magnet comes from. The bar magnet has aligned magnetic domains. Some magnets are more permanent than others. This depends on the ability of the domains to remain aligned. Dropping a magnet can rotate some of the domains, causing the magnet's strength to diminish. Heating a magnet can also cause the domains to rotate, also diminishing the magnet's strength.

Magnets (either permanent magnets or electromagnetic magnets) are found in all motors and generators. A motor converts electricity into movement such as a fan or a clothes dryer spinning. A generator converts motion into electricity. The knowledge about magnets from *Sections 1* and *2* will help you understand and explain how to build motors and generators.

Checking Up

1. What does the magnetic field of a solenoid most closely resemble?

2. Why does soft iron by itself not make a good magnetic material?

3. Why does adding an iron nail to a solenoid increase the strength of the magnetic field so dramatically?

Active Physics

+Math	+Depth	+Concepts	+Exploration
	◆	◆	◆

Active Physics

Plus

The Magnetic Field of Earth

The magnetic field of Earth is similar to the magnetic field of a huge bar magnet inside Earth with its south magnetic pole near the north geographic pole and its north magnetic pole near the south geographic pole.

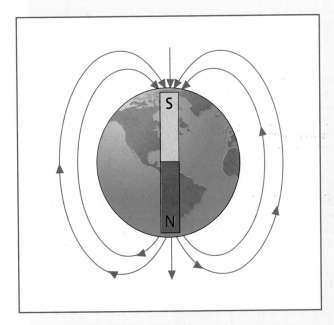

As shown in the diagram, at any point on the surface of Earth, the magnetic field is always directed toward the north geographic pole. Although the magnetic field resembles that of a bar magnet inside Earth, there is strong evidence that such a bar magnet does not exist.

First, all magnetic materials lose their ability to be permanent magnets at some high temperature. The temperatures deep inside Earth are much too high for any known material to be a permanent magnet.

Second, there is a huge amount of evidence pointing to the fact that the magnetic field of Earth has reversed its direction many times over the history of Earth. A permanent magnet cannot do this. Scientists' best hypothesis for the cause of Earth's magnetic field is that movement of material inside Earth, powered by Earth's rotation, generates currents that produce a magnetic field similar to an electromagnet.

1. Design and conduct an experiment to compare the strength of a bar magnet with the strength of Earth's magnetic field using only a compass and a ruler.

2. A dip needle is similar to a compass, but instead of being able to rotate in the horizontal plane, the needle is able to rotate in a vertical plane. Assuming you oriented the vertical plane of the dip needle along the north-south direction, what angle would you expect it to point if you were located at the north geographic pole? What if you were located at the Equator?

3. If you were doing this experiment in your classroom, in what direction (roughly) would the needle point?

What Do You Think Now?

At the beginning of this section, you were asked the following:

- **How does an electromagnet work?**

- **How could it be made stronger?**

How would you answer these questions now? Use your observations from the *Investigate* to explain how there are a number of variables of a solenoid that you can change to determine the effect on the strength of the magnetic field.

Physics
Essential Questions

What does it mean?
What is an electromagnet?

How do you know?
How can you increase the strength of an electromagnet?

Why do you believe?

Connects with Other Physics Content	Fits with Big Ideas in Science	Meets Physics Requirements
Electricity and magnetism	Models	✶ Experimental evidence is consistent with models and theories

✶ Imagine a bar magnet and current-carrying solenoid were put into identical boxes so you could not see what is inside. Describe an experiment you could conduct outside the boxes that would tell you which one is which.

Why should you care?

A motor requires a strong magnet. Strong permanent magnets can be quite large and heavy. What factors can be changed in an electromagnet to increase its strength?

Reflecting on the Section and the Challenge

An electromagnet, often constructed in the shape of a solenoid, and having an iron core, is the basic moving part of many electric motors. In this section, you learned how the amount of current and the number of turns of wire affect the strength of an electromagnet. You will be able to apply this knowledge to affect the speed and strength with which an electric motor of your own design rotates.

Physics to Go

1. Explain the differences between permanent magnets and electromagnets.

2. Which of the following will pick up more paper clips when the same electric current is sent through the wire:

   a) A coil of wire with 20 turns, or a coil of wire with 50 turns?

   b) Wire wound around a cardboard core, or wire wound around a steel core?

3. The diagram below shows an electromagnet with a compass at each end. Copy the diagram and indicate the direction in which the compass needles point when a current flows through the electromagnet in the direction shown in the diagram.

4. Explain the conditions necessary for two electromagnets to attract or repel one another, the way that permanent magnets do when they are brought near one another.

5. Explain what you think would happen if you made an electromagnet, with half of the turns of wire on the core going in one direction, and half in the opposite direction.

6. *Preparing for the Chapter Challenge*

   Your instructions for the toy a child will assemble may include making a solenoid by wrapping a hollow core with wire. What instructions would you give the child to ensure that the solenoid is strong enough to work as an electromagnet, strong enough to pick up pieces of iron and repel a permanent magnet?

Inquiring Further

1. Variables affecting the behavior of an electromagnet

Identify as many variables as you can that you think will affect the behavior of an electromagnet, and design an experiment to test the effect of each variable. Identify each variable, and describe what you would do to test its effects. After your teacher approves your procedures, do the experiments. Report your findings.

2. Use of permanent magnets and electromagnets

Find out how both permanent magnets and electromagnets are used. Do some library research to learn how electromagnets are used to lift steel in junkyards, make buzzers, or serve as parts of electrical switching devices called "relays." For other possibilities, find out how magnetism is used in microphones and speakers within sound systems, or how "super-strong" permanent magnets make the small, high-quality, headset speakers for today's portable MP3 players possible. Prepare a brief report on your findings.

3. Magnetic levitation

Do some research to find out about magnetic levitation. "Maglev" involves using super-conducting electromagnets to levitate, or suspend objects such as subway trains in air, thereby reducing friction and the "bumpiness" of the ride.

a) What possibilities do "maglev" trains, cars, or other transportation devices have for the future?

b) What advantages would such devices have?

c) What problems need to be solved? Prepare a brief report on your research.

Section 3

Building an Electric Motor

What Do You See?

Learning Outcomes

In this section, you will

- **Observe** the force on a current-carrying wire.

- **Build,** operate, and explain the operation of a motor.

- **Describe** the force on a current-carrying wire as the interaction between the magnetic fields of the wire and the external magnet.

What Do You Think?

You plug a mixer into the wall and turn a switch and the mixer spins and spins—a motor is operating.

- **How do you think the electricity makes the motor turn?**

Write your answer to this question in your *Active Physics* log. Be prepared to discuss your ideas with your small group and other members of your class.

Investigate

In this *Investigate*, you will explore the force of attraction between a permanent magnet and a current-carrying coil. You will then assemble a working model of a motor and investigate possible variations that will improve the motor's operation.

1. Take one meter of thin magnet wire. Wind the coil around a AA battery, then slip it off the battery and hold it in place with a piece of tape. Scrape or sand the insulating enamel off several centimeters of both ends of this wire. Connect the ends of this wire to the generator and dangle the coil so it swings easily.

Hold a magnet near the coil while another person cranks the generator and watch what happens. Is there a force on the coil when current flows through it?

a) Describe what you observe in your log.

b) Can you explain why this force occurs? (Hint: In *Section 2*, you experimented with a current-carrying coil and concluded that it acted similar to a bar magnet.)

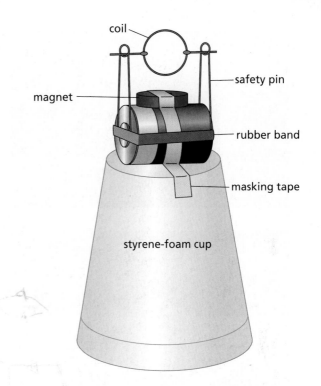

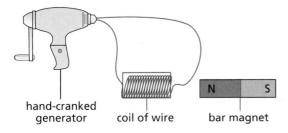

hand-cranked generator   coil of wire   bar magnet

2. Study the diagram of the motor closely, shown at the top right. Assemble the motor. Some of the steps for building the motor are shown in the photographs.

Use the same coil you just used, but wrap all the rest of the wire onto the coil, leaving only enough to stick out each side like in the diagram. Hold the coil together with small bits of tape if you like. Try to make the coil so that the two wires sticking out are directly across from each other. Make sure that the wires touching the safety pins are clean, bare metal so they can conduct electricity.

Assemble the other materials, as shown in the diagram, to build a basic electric motor. The best motors are those where the balance of the coil is "just right." This will take many small adjustments. If the rubber band is not strong enough, you may want to squeeze the safety pins against the battery for better contact. You may need to give the coil a slight spinning motion to get it started.

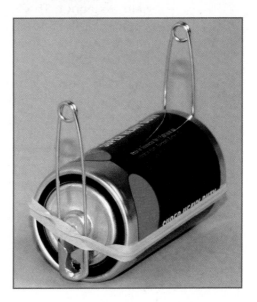

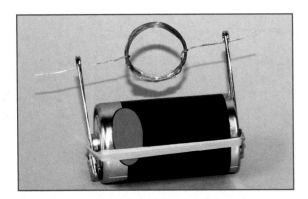

3. Your motor turns! Chemical energy in the battery was converted to electrical energy in the circuit. The electrical energy was then converted to mechanical energy in the motor.

a) List at least three appliances or devices where the motor spins.

b) List ways in which you could improve upon the performance of the motor. How might a change in magnet strength, coil, or distances affect the motor? Share this list with your teacher and get permission to explore one of these approaches.

Physics Talk

ELECTRIC MOTOR

In the *Investigate*, you first observed that a coil of wire with current would be attracted or repelled by a bar magnet. This was evidence that the current-carrying coil had properties similar to a bar magnet. You then shaped the wire into a loop, connected it to a battery, and placed it near a magnet. The loop spun. You had constructed a simple motor. The physics and technology illustrated in your investigation is responsible for all motors. These include motors in washing machines, blenders, and DVD players.

The basic physics of the motor is that a current-carrying wire creates a magnetic field. This magnetic field can then interact with the magnetic field of a permanent magnet or an electromagnet.

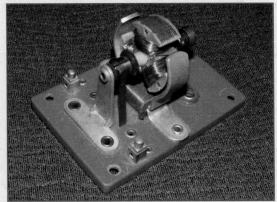

Active Physics

In the diagram at right, a current-carrying wire is placed between the poles of a horseshoe magnet. Notice that the current-carrying wire is perpendicular to the magnetic field lines of the horseshoe magnet. The magnetic force of the wire and the horseshoe's magnetic field create a

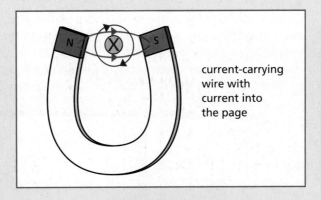

current-carrying wire with current into the page

force on the wire. A force on the wire pushes it up. If the current were to stop, the magnetic field of the wire no longer exists and the wire would drop due to gravity. If the current were to resume, the wire would jump up. Turning the current on and off repeatedly would cause the wire to jump up and fall down repeatedly. This illustrates the physics of the motor.

In *Technically Speaking: Why All Americans Need to Know More About Technology*, technology is defined as "the process by which humans modify nature to meet their needs and wants." Nature produces a force on a current-carrying wire in the presence of a magnetic field. Humans take this physics principle of nature and build motors to exploit the physics for their benefit.

Rather than having a single wire move up and down, a motor has a coil of wire that can spin. In the following diagrams, you can see how the coil spins.

Diagram 1: The current in the left-hand section of the loop creates an upward force. The current in the right-hand section of the loop creates a downward force. The part of the loop that is parallel to the field lines of the horseshoe magnet does not experience a force.

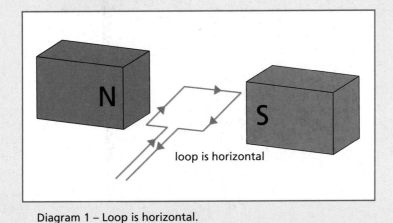

loop is horizontal

Diagram 1 – Loop is horizontal.

Diagram 2: The loop pivots to this position. The force is momentarily zero and the loop continues to pivot due to its momentum. The loop would then experience forces that would make it rotate in the opposite direction. A clever technology called a commutator switches the direction of the current in the coil. You will learn about commutators later.

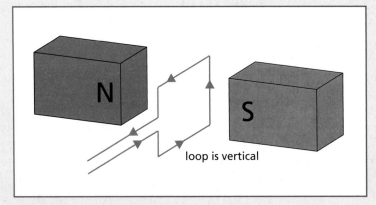

loop is vertical

Diagram 2 – Loop is vertical.

Diagram 3: Since the current has been reversed, once again, the current in the left-hand section of the loop creates an upward force. The current in the right-hand section of the loop creates a downward force. The motor continues to spin.

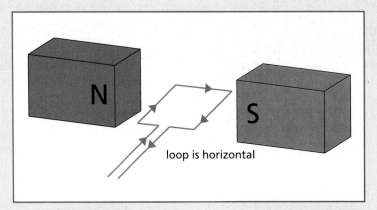

loop is horizontal

Diagram 3 – Loop is horizontal.

The force on a current-carrying wire in a magnetic field is actually a force on the moving electrons within the wire. This physics concept is not only used in motors. It can also explain how the images are created in some television sets and computer monitors.

A number of parts of the motor can be changed if a larger motor is needed. You can increase the current in the coil. You can also increase the number of turns of wire in the coil. In addition, a stronger permanent magnet or a stronger electromagnet can also be used. Increasing any one or all of these elements will increase the output of the motor.

The motor that you investigated in this section is referred to as a direct current motor or DC motor. That is because the battery providing the current had a steady current in one and only one direction (direct current).

Checking Up

1. What occurs when a wire that is perpendicular to the magnetic field lines has a DC current sent through it?

2. What is the basic physics of an electric motor?

3. When the wire loop is in the position shown in diagram 2 for the motor, why does the loop continue to rotate?

Active Physics

Plus

+Math	+Depth	+Concepts	+Exploration
◆◆	◆	◆	

An Equation for Magnetic Force

In this section, you observed the force on a current-carrying wire. In physics, students often ask, "Is there an equation that can describe this?" In this case, the equation is just what you would expect:

$$F = IlB$$

where F is the force,

I is the current,

l is the length of the wire, and

B is the magnetic field.

You can produce a larger force with:

• a larger magnetic field (by increasing the strength of the magnet)

• a larger current (by increasing the current in the wire)

• an increase in the length of the wire (more turns)

The force on the wire is due to movements of the electrons in the wire. As mentioned in the *Investigate*, beams of electrons also experience this force. You make use of this force and deflection of electrons every time you watch television (except flat-panel models) or look at a computer monitor. Once again, as student physicists, you may ask, "Is there an equation that can describe this?" and once again the answer is "Yes."

Charges moving perpendicular to a magnetic field experience a force that can be expressed by the following equation:

$$F = QvB$$

where Q is the charge,

v is the velocity, and

B is the strength of the magnetic field.

The unit of charge is the coulomb (C). When one coulomb passes a point in a wire each second, the wire is carrying a current of one ampere (A), or one coulomb per second. Notice that using this formula requires knowing that one tesla equals one newton second per coulomb meter, or one newton per ampere meter, since only then will the units for QvB equal units of force. A dimensional analysis of the units gives

$$\cancel{C} \times \frac{\cancel{m}}{\cancel{s}} \times \frac{N \cdot \cancel{s}}{\cancel{C} \cdot \cancel{m}} = N$$

The direction of the force on a current-carrying wire or a moving charge is given by another left-hand rule. Point your thumb in the direction that the negative charge or current is moving. Align all your fingers with the magnetic field lines. Your palm shows the direction of the force.

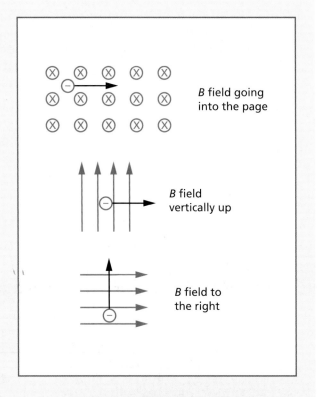

B field going into the page

B field vertically up

B field to the right

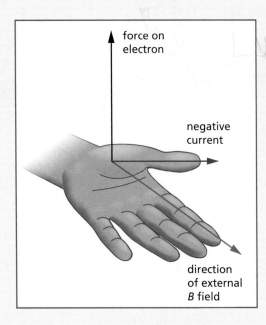

force on electron

negative current

direction of external B field

1. Using the left-hand rule, determine the direction of the force on negative charges moving in the following directions in magnetic fields.

2. Calculate the force on an electron (charge equals -1.6×10^{-19} C) in a wire moving 0.5 m/s in a magnetic field of 0.1 T (tesla).

When electrons experience a force and move along a wire that is not part of a closed circuit, charge builds up at the ends of the wire (or where the wire leaves the magnetic field). If the force on the electrons is removed, the electrons flow back to their original positions. This is just what happens when you compress a spring. It takes force to do so, and if you remove that force, the spring snaps back to its original position.

This is quite a general phenomenon in the natural world, and can be described in terms of energy. That is, the charges collected at the ends of the wire (or where the magnetic field ends) and the compressed spring represent situations in which the potential energy is higher.

When the force is removed in either of these situations, the potential energy is converted to kinetic energy as the electrons or the spring move. Because the situations are different, the potential energy of the charges is called electric potential energy, and the potential energy of the spring is called elastic potential energy.

(Voltage is the electric potential energy per unit charge.)

$$V = \frac{PE}{Q}$$

What Do You Think Now?

At the beginning of this section, you were asked the following:

• **How do you think the electricity makes the motor turn?**

Now that you have made an electric motor, how do you think an electric mixer works? Use evidence from your investigation to support your answer.

Physics
Essential Questions

What does it mean?

What are the essential parts of an electric motor? Describe the forces that make a motor turn.

How do you know?

Explain how the observations you made reveal the forces that make an electric motor turn.

Why do you believe?

Connects with Other Physics Content	Fits with Big Ideas in Science	Meets Physics Requirements
Electricity and magnetism	Models	✳ Experimental evidence is consistent with models and theories

✳ Physics looks for ways to explain observations. If these explanations are correct, then they can be used to build useful devices. How is a similar physics principle used to build an electric motor and a television?

Why should you care?

You have constructed an electrical motor that works. You also now understand the basic principles of all electric motors. List ten different technologies that use electric motors.

Reflecting on the Section and the Challenge

In this section, you built a very basic, working electric motor. This is an important part of the *Chapter Challenge*. However, knowing how to build an electric motor is only part of the challenge. Your toy must be fascinating to children. You must also be able to explain how it works.

Physics to Go

1. Describe the electric-motor effect in terms of energy transformations.

2. Some electric motors use electromagnets instead of permanent magnets to create the magnetic field in which the coil rotates. In such motors, part of the electrical energy fed to the motor is used to create and maintain the magnetic field. What advantages and disadvantages would result from using electromagnets instead of permanent magnets in a motor?

3. Design three possible toys that use a motor. One of these may be what you will use for your project.

4. The motor you submit for the *Chapter Challenge* must be built from inexpensive, common materials. Make a list of the materials that you used for the simple motor in this section.

5. *Preparing for the Chapter Challenge*

In the grading criteria for the *Chapter Challenge*, marks are assigned for clearly explaining how and why your motor works in terms of basic principles of physics. Explain how an electric motor operates.

6. *Preparing for the Chapter Challenge*

The motor you assembled in this section relied on the magnetic field of the coil forced to rotate in the same direction by the magnetic field. Write a brief description of what is needed to make the magnetic field always rotate a coil in the same direction so the motor toy will operate correctly.

Inquiring Further

Starting an electric motor

You may have noticed that a small push was required to get your motor spinning initially. Commercial motors obviously must start by themselves. See what you can discover about how a commercial motor may use a resistor or other electrical device to help it start without a beginning push.

When a large electric motor starts up (perhaps a large air conditioner), you may have noticed that the lights in the room dim momentarily. Look up motors and dimming lights to find out why this occurs.

Your challenge for this chapter is to create a new toy that will educate young children about the ways that electric motors or electric generators work. Your group will have to decide which technology they think will be more engaging for children and come up with a compelling toy design. Use the physics you have learned so far to explain in simple terms how the device actually functions. You might want to start by thinking about some of the electrical toys you have enjoyed playing with. What types of actions did your favorite toys perform?

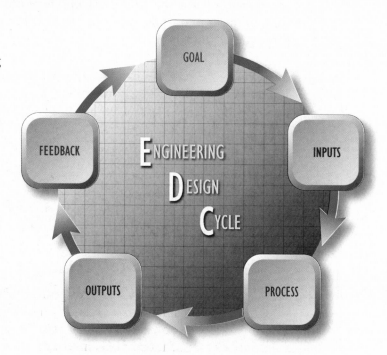

You still have more to learn before you can complete the challenge, but now is a good time to give the *Chapter Challenge* a first try. Having completed three sections, you have learned a lot about electric motors that will help you create your toy. At the very least you know you will need magnets and some wire. Your toy will also need some type of rotating shaft that will make some part of the toy move.

Your *Mini-Challenge* is to come up with a design idea and parts list for your toy to present to your class. Try to test out some of the design functions of your toy idea by making a model. The *Mini-Challenge* will provide you with valuable information for your final toy design with a motor or generator, as well as a good start on the instruction manual. Remember, at this time you do not have to create the actual toy, although a model will certainly be useful.

Go back and quickly read the *Goal* you established at the start of the chapter. As a class, review your *Goal* and all of the details for completing the entire *Chapter Challenge*. At this point, focus on the portions you can complete with the physics you have learned so far. You have been introduced to the physics principles that allow electric motors to function, even if you do not know all of the details.

In addition to the physics you have learned so far, you will be adding one of the most important *Inputs*. The type of toy you decide to make will have a large impact on the *Outputs* of your *Engineering Design Cycle*. Of course, the user's manual for whatever you create will require a similar explanation, because any motor will work on the same basic physics principles.

Your team should review the physics content from the first three sections to help you create your initial toy design.

Section 1: You mapped the magnetic field of a bar magnet and then compared these results to the effect of a wire carrying a DC current on a magnetic compass needle.

Section 2: You built and tested a solenoid that operates as an electromagnet. You also identified the variables that control the strength of the magnetic field a solenoid produces.

Section 3: You explored the force between a current-carrying wire and a nearby magnet. You also made use of that force to construct and operate a simple DC motor.

Once you have an idea of what type of toy you would like to create, making a model of the toy will be very useful. Creating the model will allow you to experiment with different readily available materials and determine how much force your motor can generate. Start by working with the materials that were made available for your class investigations.

By building onto experiments you have already done, you will have a better opportunity at troubleshooting problems. Start with a simple coil and one D-size battery. Remember that batteries added in series will add to the voltage, while batteries added in parallel will add to the total amount of current available at the voltage of only a single battery, 1.5 V.

Build a small model and test some of your design functions. For example, if you are creating a motor, is it strong enough to start the wheels rolling, or to turn a propeller? Remember some of the techniques you learned for increasing the size of an electromagnetic response. Do you need a stronger magnetic field, more turns in your coil, or a higher rate of rotation to get the results you want?

The results of your model testing should help you determine the types of materials that will need to be included in your kit. Chances are a bicycle wheel would be too large for your motor to turn, but a simple test would confirm that. You will have a much better idea of the scale of materials you should be working with following your tests. You may find that toothpicks and cardstock paper are closer to the types of materials of construction you should consider instead of wooden dowels, CDs for wheels, and blocks of wood for parts. Without a model, this distinction will be very difficult to make.

Presenting your information to the class are your design-process *Outputs*. For the *Mini-Challenge* you should have a design idea and parts list for your toy as well as a good start on the instruction manual. You will be able to explain why a magnet and a current-carrying wire can produce a force. You will also be able to explain how to create an electromagnet, if that is part of your toy design.

Your classmates will give you *Feedback* on the accuracy and overall appeal of your presentation based on the criteria of the design challenge. This *Feedback* will become an input for your final design in the *Chapter Challenge*. You will have enough time to make corrections and improvements, so you will want to pay attention to the valuable information they provide.

Remember to correct any parts of your design that didn't meet the design goals of the *Mini-Challenge*. It will be harder to remember what you need to change if you wait until the chapter is complete to go back and correct your mistakes. When you are finished revising, store all of your information in a safe place so that it will be ready to use in the *Chapter Challenge*.

Identify those goals that have not been addressed through research and were therefore not addressed in your *Mini-Challenge*. Look for additional information in the remaining chapter sections that will help you better understand the function of a generator.

Section 4

Detect and Induce Currents

What Do You See?

What Do You Think?

For 10 years after Hans Christian Oersted discovered that a current produces a magnetic field, scientists struggled to try to find out if a magnet could produce a current.

- **How would you explore whether a magnet could produce a current?**

- **What equipment will you need for your investigation?**

Write your answer to these questions in your *Active Physics* log. Be prepared to discuss your ideas with your small group and other members of your class.

Investigate

In this *Investigate*, you will use a *galvanometer* to determine if an electric current is generated when a bar magnet is inserted into a solenoid. You will explore how the relative magnet and coil speed determines the strength and direction of the current generated.

1. In a previous section, you saw that a small loop of a current-carrying wire experienced a force and rotated when placed near a magnet.

If a needle is attached to the small loop to show the amount of rotation, you have a meter that can measure very small currents. This is called a galvanometer. It is similar to the way in which a speedometer in a vehicle works. As the vehicle's tires turn, a small current goes through a coil and the speedometer needle rotates to show your vehicle's speed.

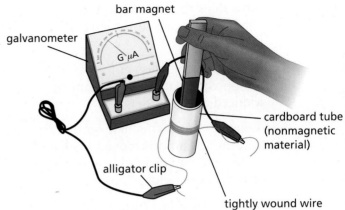

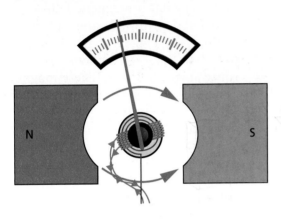

If a galvanometer is not available, you can make one as you did in *Section 1* by using a compass to detect the presence of a current. Instead of a needle showing the presence of the current, your compass needle will deflect in the presence of a current.

2. Connect a commercially made galvanometer or your homemade galvanometer to a solenoid wound on a hollow core of nonmagnetic material, such as a clear plastic or cardboard tube. For example, 25 turns of wire on a cardboard tube should work well. The cardboard tube must be big enough for a magnet to pass through. If you like, you can remove the coil from the cardboard tube, tape the wires together, and then tape the coil to a table so it sits on its edge (like a wheel, and the bar magnet will be in the position of the wheel's axle).

3. Hold a bar magnet in one hand and the solenoid steady in the other hand. Rapidly plunge one end of the bar magnet into the hollow core of the solenoid, stopping it inside. Another person should hold the galvanometer steady so that it will not be disturbed. Be sure to keep the galvanometer as far away from the magnet as possible. Watch the galvanometer during the sequence. You may need to practice this a few times.

  a) Write your observations in your log.

4. Remove the magnet from the solenoid with a quick motion, and watch the galvanometer during the action.

  a) Record your observations.

  b) A current is produced! Causing a current by moving a magnet near a coil is called inducing a current. What happens to the direction of the current compared to what you observed in *Step 3*?

5. Modify and repeat the last two steps to answer the following questions:

  a) What, if anything, about the induced current changes if the opposite end of the bar magnet is plunged in and out of the solenoid?

b) How does the induced current change if the speed of the magnet is changed?

c) When the magnet is not moving (stopped), what is the amount of induced current?

d) When the magnet is held stationary and the solenoid is moved back and forth over and around it, what is the effect on the induced current?

e) What is the effect of moving both the magnet and the solenoid simultaneously in opposite directions?

f) What is the effect of holding the magnet firmly inside the solenoid and moving both of them back and forth together?

6. Substitute an electromagnet for the permanent magnet. Place the electromagnet into the solenoid.

a) When the electromagnet is not moving, what is the amount of the induced current?

b) The current in the electromagnet is maintained by the battery or the rotation of the hand generator crank. While carefully watching the galvanometer, stop the current. Did you observe an induced current?

c) While carefully watching the galvanometer, create a current. Did you observe an induced current?

d) A current has a magnetic field associated with it. As the current is created, the magnetic field lines move out from the electromagnet to fill the space surrounding it. These magnetic field lines move past the wires in the solenoid. Even though there is no movement of the electromagnet, there is a movement of the field lines past the wires of the solenoid. Draw a series of sketches showing how field lines move past the wires.

Physics Talk

PRODUCING A CURRENT USING A MAGNET

Generating Electricity

In this *Investigate*, you were able to produce electricity by moving a magnet within a coil of wire. You created electrical energy by physically moving the bar magnet through the coil. When neither the magnet nor the coil moved relative to each other, no electricity was generated. A device that produces electricity is called a **generator**. When you produced electricity, you used the **galvanometer** as a detector.

Previously you have used a hand-cranked generator to produce electricity. A closer inspection of the hand-cranked generator shows that inside the generator, you either move a magnet through a coil or move the coil past the magnet. Inducing a current shows the conversion of mechanical energy to electrical energy to mechanical energy. The movement of the generator handle or magnet is an example of mechanical energy.

Physics Words

generator (electric): a device that produces electricity.

galvanomter: an instrument used to detect and measure an electric current.

In both cases electrical energy was produced. This electrical energy was converted to mechanical energy when the needle on the galvanometer moved.

A current is created or induced when a magnet is moved in and out of a solenoid. The current flows back and forth, changing direction with each reversal of the motion of the magnet. Such a current is called an **alternating current**, and you may recognize that name as the kind of current that flows in household circuits. It is frequently referred to by its abbreviated form, **AC**. It is the type of current that is used to run most electric motors in home appliances.

Physics Words

alternating current (AC): an electric current that changes direction cyclically.

When you observed the movement of the permanent magnet and solenoid, you noticed that some movements induced more current than other movements. It is easier to understand the creation of a current if you think of a set of invisible threads made of wax to signify the magnetic field produced by permanent magnets. The very thin wax threads fill the space and connect the north pole of one magnet with the south pole of the other magnet. If the moving wire is imagined to be very thin and very hot, the question you must ask is whether the hot wire melts through the wax threads as it moves. If the wire moves in such a way that it melts through the field lines, then a current is generated. If the wire moves in such a way that it does not melt through the field lines, but instead slides along between the threads, then no current is generated.

Look at the diagrams at the right of the magnetic fields and moving wires. In all three cases, the magnetic field lines are vertical and point from the north pole of the upper magnet to the south pole of the lower magnet. In case A, the wire is moving up and down. Since it does not cut through and "melt" the magnetic field lines, no current is induced in the wire.

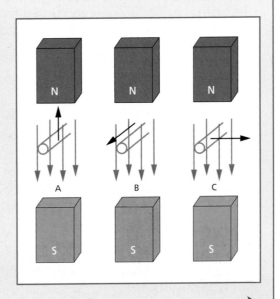

In case B, the wire is moving in and out along the direction of the wire itself. Again, since it does not cut through and "melt" the magnetic field lines, no current is induced in the wire. In case C, the wire is moving horizontally. When it does this, it cuts through and "melts" the magnetic field lines, so current is induced in the wire. There's one more detail that is very important. If the wire is moving to the right as in case C, the negative current flows along the wire out of the page. If the wire is moving to the left in case C, the negative current flows along into the page. In other words, when the wire moves so as to cut through or "melt" the magnetic field lines, the direction of the induced current in the wire reverses if the direction the wire is moving reverses.

Accidental Discoveries and the History of Physics

The history of science is filled with discoveries that have led to leaps of progress in knowledge and applications. This is certainly true of physics and, in particular, electricity and magnetism. These discoveries "favor" the prepared mind. Oersted's discovery in 1820 of the magnetic field surrounding a current-carrying wire already has been mentioned. Similarly, Michael Faraday discovered electromagnetic induction in 1831. Faraday was seeking a way to induce electricity using currents and magnets. He noticed that a brief induced current happened in one circuit when a nearby circuit was switched on and off. This is similar to your investigation of the current induced when you turned the electromagnet on and off. One story is that Faraday turned the circuit on expecting a continuous effect. Instead there was a very short current in the second circuit that stopped almost immediately. After waiting for some time while nothing happened, he disappointedly turned the main circuit off only to be surprised by another brief flow of current in the second circuit. After a flash of thought he excitedly turned the switch on and off repeatedly and found that as long as he kept switching the main circuit, then the second circuit's current continued to flow. Both Oersted and Faraday are credited for taking advantage of the events that happened before their eyes, and pursuing them.

About one-half century after Faraday's discovery of electromagnetic induction, which immediately led to the development of the generator, another event occurred. In 1873, a Belgian engineer, Zénobe Gramme, set up a demonstration of DC generators at an exposition (a forerunner of a world's fair) in Vienna, Austria.

Zénobe Gramme (1826 – 1901) was a Belgian engineer.

Steam engines were to be used to power the generators, and the electrical output of the generators would be demonstrated. While one DC generator was operating, Gramme connected its output to the output of another generator that was not operating. The shaft of the inactive generator began to rotate—because it was acting as an electric motor! Although Michael Faraday had shown as early as 1821 that rotary motion could be produced using currents and magnets, in other words a "motor effect," nothing useful resulted from it. Gramme's discovery, however, immediately showed that electric motors could be useful. In fact, the electric motor was demonstrated at the same Vienna exposition where Gramme's discovery was made. A fake waterfall was set up to drive a DC generator using a paddle wheel arrangement, and the electrical output of the generator was fed to a "motor" (a generator running "backward"). The motor was shown to be capable of doing useful work.

Zénobe Gramme invented the first useful electrical motor.

A motor converts electrical energy into mechanical energy. You used an electric current (electrical energy) to turn a loop of wire (mechanical energy). A generator converts mechanical energy into electrical energy. You pushed a magnet (mechanical energy) through a coil and produced an electric current (electrical energy.)

Checking Up

1. When a magnet is moved into and out of a coil of wire, what happens to the direction of the electric current produced?

2. In order to generate an electric current by moving a wire through a magnetic field, which way must the wire be moved?

3. What did Zenobe Gramme do to make the first practical DC motor start working?

Active Physics

+Math	+Depth	+Concepts	+Exploration
	◆◆	◆◆	◆◆

Plus

Investigating Factors that Affect the Strength of the Current Induced

In your investigation, you examined the current induced in a coil from a moving magnet. Two aspects of the motion varied: the direction and speed of the magnet.

It is interesting to examine how other factors affect the induced current.

a) Design an experiment that keeps all factors the same except the number of turns in the coil. It is best to test coils with a very different number of turns.

Active Physics

The goal is to find a quantitative relationship between the size of the induced current and the number of turns in the coil.

b) Design an experiment that keeps all factors the same except the strength of the magnet. It might be difficult to know how the strengths of magnets compare, but you might use the number of staples or paper clips it can pick up as a guide.

c) Design an experiment that keeps all factors the same expect the orientation of the magnet relative to the coil. You have already examined what happens when the positions of the poles of the magnet are reversed. In this experiment, examine what happens when the magnet is oriented at several different angles.

Lenz's Law

A current-carrying wire in a magnetic field experiences a force that moves the wire. This is the basis of the electric motor. A moving wire cutting across magnetic field lines induces a current. This is the basis of the electric generator. It seems that it may be possible to give a wire a tiny push and have the wire move. The wire's movement would then cause a current. The current would then make the wire move some more. More movement induces more current and then more movement and more current forever.

Conservation of energy implies that this cannot happen. You cannot get more and more energy out of a system without putting more and more energy into it.

The dilemma is solved by considering the directions of the force and the direction of the induced current. The left-hand rule for determining the direction of

the force is to place your thumb in the direction of the electron current and your outstretched fingers in the direction of the magnetic field. The force on the wire is perpendicular to your palm.

As the wire in the diagram is moved to the right, a current is created. For the sake of argument, imagine that the current could be into the page or out of the page. If the current were into the page, the force on the wire would be to the right. This would then move the wire more to the right and produce more current into the page. This is the "lots of energy for nothing" scenario described earlier.

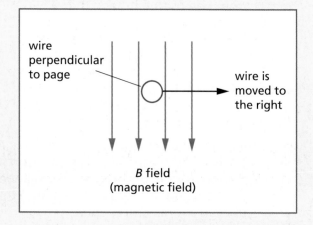

B field
(magnetic field)

The alternative is what really happens. As the wire in the diagram is moved to the right, a current is created. This current is out of the page. If the current is out of the page, the force on the wire would be to the left. This would then stop the wire's movement and no more current would be created. If you did want to create more current, you would have to push harder to the right to overcome the force due to the current in the magnetic field. More current requires more force and more electrical energy requires more mechanical energy. This is consistent with the principle of conservation of energy.

Active Physics

The principle of conservation of energy is implied in Lenz's law, which describes the direction of the induced current: When a current is induced in a wire, the direction of the current must be such as to oppose the change that produced it.

Below are some diagrams where currents are induced in a wire. Determine the direction of the induced currents using Lenz's law and the left-hand rule.

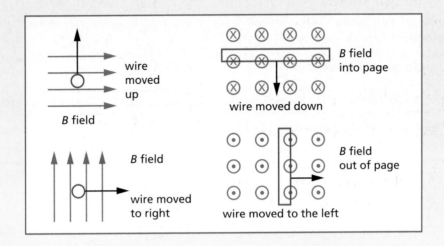

What Do You Think Now?

At the beginning of this section, you were asked

• **How would you explore whether a magnet could produce a current?**

• **What equipment will you need for your investigation?**

How would you answer these questions now? Michael Faraday was famous for his lectures for children at the Royal Academy. Imagine that you are Faraday and were about to show your students the surprising new fact that electricity can be created with magnetism. How would you set up the equipment for the experiment and what would you say as you performed the experiment?

Active Physics

Physics
Essential Questions

What does it mean?

How does the connection between electricity and magnetism allow you to make a motor out of a coil and a magnet? How do induced currents allow you to make a generator out of a coil and a magnet?

How do you know?

What did you observe that showed you a moving magnet can induce a current in a coil?

Why do you believe?

Connects with Other Physics Content	Fits with Big Ideas in Science	Meets Physics Requirements
Electricity and magnetism	Symmetry	✱ Parsimonious - maximum of generality for minimum of primary concepts

✱ Physics seeks to explain as many observations as possible with the same theory. What is it about a current causing a coil near a magnet to move and a moving magnet inducing a current that prompts you to think they might have the same explanation?

Why should you care?

You are going to construct a toy motor and/or generator. Why are you sure that what you observed in this section will be important when you do this?

Reflecting on the Section and the Challenge

In this section, you discovered that you can produce electricity. A current is produced or induced when a magnet is moved in and out of a solenoid. The mechanical energy of moving the magnet or the handle of the generator (which moves the coil) is converted into electrical energy. Part of your *Chapter Challenge* is to explain to the children how a motor operates in terms of basic principles of physics or to show how electricity can be produced from an external energy source. This section will help you with that part of the challenge.

Physics to Go

1. An electric motor takes electricity and converts it into movement. The movement can be a spinning fan, a washing machine, or a DVD player. The galvanometer may be thought of as a crude electric motor. Discuss that statement, using forms of energy as part of your discussion. Movement is one form of mechanical energy.

Active Physics

2. The galvanometer detects the amount and direction of the electric current. Explain how the galvanometer works.

3. How could the galvanometer be made more sensitive, so that it could detect very weak currents?

4. An electric generator takes motion and turns it into electricity. The electricity can then be used for many purposes. The solenoid and the bar magnet in this section could be thought of as a crude electric generator. Explain the truth of this last statement, referring to specific forms of energy in your explanation.

5. Imagine repeating the investigation in such a way that you would be able to see only the galvanometer and not the solenoid, the magnet, and the person moving the equipment. Would you be able to tell from the galvanometer whether the magnet is being moved, or the solenoid is being moved, or both are being moved? Explain your answer.

6. In generating electricity in this section, you moved the magnet or the coil. How can you use each of the following resources to move the magnet?

   a) wind

   b) water

   c) steam

7. *Preparing for the Chapter Challenge*

   If the toy you are going to have the child assemble has a generator as part of the design, it should not develop more than 10 V (volts) for safety reasons. Make a list of the things you should consider in the design of the generator that will determine the amount of voltage the generator can put out. What should you include in the kit list to allow the student to test the generator to see if it is working properly when it is assembled?

Inquiring Further

Household Currents

Find out about the 120 V (volt) AC used in United States home circuits. If household current alternates, at what rate does it surge back and forth? Write down any information about AC that you can find and bring it to class.

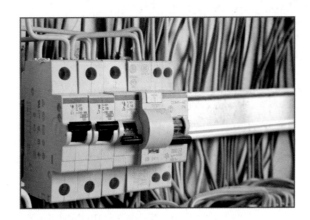

Section 5

AC and DC Currents

What Do You See?

Learning Outcomes

In this section, you will

- **Describe** the induced current when a wire moves around a square in a magnetic field.

- **Sketch** the current during a cycle for both an AC and DC generator.

- **Compare** AC and DC generators in terms of commutators.

What Do You Think?

Batteries produce direct current. The electricity from wall sockets is alternating current.

- **What is the difference between a direct current and an alternating current?**

Write your answer to this question in your *Active Physics* log. Be prepared to discuss your ideas with your small group and other members of your class.

Investigate

In this *Investigate*, you will observe a demonstration on the workings of AC and DC generators. By watching the motion of a galvanometer connected to the generators, you will be able to determine whether the generator is AC or DC. You will then try to design a device that extracts the current from these generators without tangled wires.

1. In the last section, you observed that a current was induced when a coil moved in the vicinity of a magnet. This effect is used in an electric generator. When you moved the magnet into the coil, the current was in one direction. When you moved it out of the coil, the current was in the opposite direction.

If you repeated this over and over again, your movements would be generating an alternating current. An *alternating current* is a current that changes directions. A *direct current* is a current that is in a single direction, like the current from a battery where the negative current always flows from the negative terminal to the positive terminal.

Your teacher will explain and demonstrate a hand-operated, alternating current (AC) generator. During the demonstration, make the observations necessary to answer these questions:

a) When the AC generator is used to light a bulb, describe the brightness of the bulb when the generator is cranked slowly, and then rapidly. Write your observations in your log.

b) When the AC generator is connected to a galvanometer, describe the action of the galvanometer needle when the generator is cranked slowly, and then when it is cranked rapidly.

2. The key to constructing an AC generator is to have the coil of wire rotate in a circle. You can see in the generator shown that the crank wheel has a belt that turns the coil in a circle. The coil has two ends that must supply the current to the light bulb.

If the ends of the wire were connected to any device, the wires would get tangled very quickly.

One solution is to have the wires touch "slip rings." Each end of the wire maintains contact with only one slip ring. The current can then travel from the slip rings to the bulb.

Below is a diagram of a single loop of wire rotating in a magnetic field.

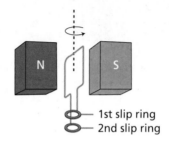

a) Try to design a device using pencils or straws and pieces of paper that demonstrates how the slip rings keep the wires from getting tangled while not losing electrical contact. Describe your design in your log.

3. In *Section 4*, you observed that when you moved the magnet into the coil, the current was in one direction. When you moved the magnet out of the coil, the current was in the opposite direction. This is similar to what is happening with the slip rings. The current leaves through the first slip ring during one part of the rotation, but enters through the first split ring during another part of the rotation. This is an alternating current.

4. To get a direct current from the rotating coil, it is necessary to have a different arrangement. Imagine the following: The current from one end of the wire exits the first slip ring. Connect the part of the wire where the current exited to the second slip ring during the part of the rotation when the current is entering the wire.

So, when the wires change sides, the current reverses, but the wire also changes slip rings at the same time, canceling the effect of the reverse current. This would provide a direct current. Changing the connection during every cycle can be done with a mechanical device called a commutator.

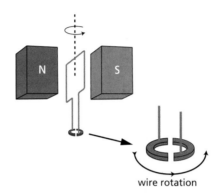

wire rotation

a) Try to design a device using pencils or straws and pieces of paper that demonstrates how the "split-ring"

commutator in the diagram keeps the wires from getting tangled while not losing electrical contact and changes the contact between the wires during each part of the cycle. Record your design in your *Active Physics* log.

5. Your teacher will demonstrate a hand-operated, direct current (DC) generator. During the demonstration, make the observations needed to answer these questions:

a) When the DC generator is used to light a bulb, describe the brightness of the bulb when the generator is cranked slowly, and rapidly. Write your observations in your log.

b) When the DC generator is connected to a galvanometer, describe the action of the galvanometer needle when the generator is cranked slowly, and rapidly.

Physics Talk

GENERATING ELECTRICITY

AC Generator

The key to constructing an AC generator is to make the wire go around in a circle so that it can keep moving while still between the two magnets. To make things easier, assume the wire is going around in a square instead of a circle. The diagrams show the wire moving in four directions as it goes around the square. The

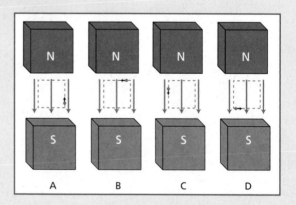

wire looks like a small circle in the diagrams because the view is along the wire (like looking at the eraser end of a pencil so all you see is the eraser).

Remembering that a current is induced when the moving wire cuts the magnetic field lines, a current is induced in diagrams B and D. These currents will be in opposite directions because the movements of the wire are reversed.

Active Physics

To better understand the current produced by a generator, it is useful to sketch a graph of the current as it varies during a cycle of the wiring going around the square. The vertical axis represents the current induced in the wire and the horizontal axis represents time during one cycle. The time from 0 to ¼ fraction of a cycle is shown in sketch A. The time from ¼ to ½ fraction of a cycle is shown in sketch B. The time for ½ to ¾ is shown in sketch C. The final time from ¾ to 1 is shown in sketch D.

If the wire moved around a circle instead of a square, the current would no longer jump from one value to another, but would vary smoothly for the entire cycle. There still would be times that the current would flow in one direction and other times that the current would flow in the other direction. There would also be two times during the cycle when the current would be zero.

An **alternating current** (AC) generator does not have a single wire but has a loop of wire. To keep the loop from getting tangled, a pair of slip rings provides an electrical contact as the wire spins. The diagram below shows one construction for a coil of wires and the slip rings.

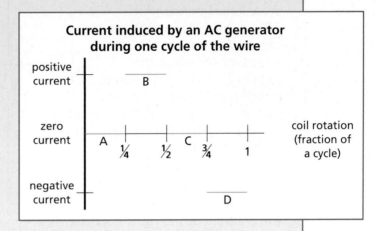

Current induced by an AC generator during one cycle of the wire

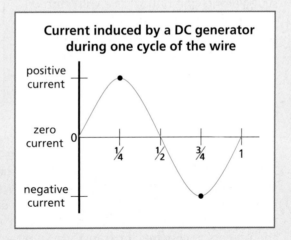

Current induced by a DC generator during one cycle of the wire

Physics Words

alternating current: an electric current that reverses in direction.

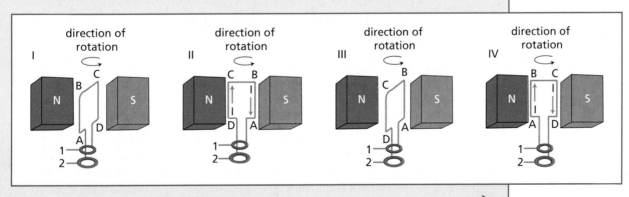

Active Physics

Physics Words

direct current: an electric current in only one direction.

transformer: a device that transfers electrical energy from one circuit to another through electromagnetic induction and, in the process, changes voltage from one value to another.

DC Generator

A **direct current** (DC) generator also has a loop of wire rotating in the magnetic field. A commutator switches the direction of the current during the cycle so that the current is always in the same direction. Although the current is always in the same direction, it is not a constant current. Half cycles of the induced current look like half cycles in the AC generator.

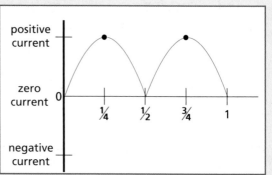

A split-ring commutator can reverse the current at the appropriate positions of the rotation. Notice in the diagram at the right how the wire slides along one half of the split ring. Just as the induced current changes the direction, the wire leaves that half of the split ring and begins contact with the other half of the split ring. This produces the DC current.

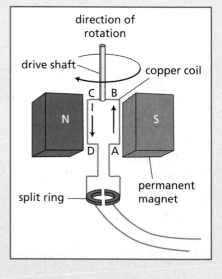

Power Transformers

Devices powered by electricity may use batteries, rechargeable batteries, or power cords. The voltage of the wall outlets in the United States is 120 V AC. However, many electrical devices, like audio players or radios, require 6 V. When these devices are powered by a wall outlet, a **transformer** must change the 120 V to 6 V. A transformer is a device that transfers electrical energy from one circuit to another through electromagnetic conduction. In the process, it changes (or transforms) voltage from one value to another.

A simple transformer consists of two coils of wire, separated from one another (electrically insulated). They are arranged so that a current in one coil (called the primary coil) will induce a current in the other coil (called the secondary coil). The diagram shows a step-down transformer. Notice that the wires in the primary coil do not touch the wires in the secondary coil. When the electrical current is generated in the primary coil, a magnetic field is created. These magnetic field lines expand around the primary coil. As they expand, their magnetic field lines pass through the secondary coil, producing the current there. The current is produced in the secondary coil because a changing magnetic field across a wire produces a current, as you observed in *Section 4*. When the current in the primary coil changes direction,

Active Physics

the magnetic field lines collapse and then expand with their north pole and south pole reversed.

A transformer can be a step down or step up transformer. The ratio of the number of turns in the primary coil to the secondary coil is equal to the ratio of voltages. By varying the number of coils in the primary and secondary coils, the transformer can step-down or step-up the voltage. The voltage can be stepped down by making the number of turns in the secondary coil less than the number of turns in the primary coil. The voltage can step up by making the number of turns in the secondary coil greater than the number of turns in the primary coil.

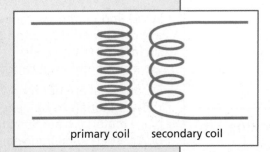

primary coil   secondary coil

It would appear that by merely making more turns of the wire, you can increase the electrical energy. This is not true. The increase in voltage is accompanied by a decrease in the current. Since electrical power is the product of voltage and current ($P = VI$), the power or electrical energy per second remains the same while the voltage changes.

Power transformers only work with alternating current. To induce the current in the secondary, the magnetic field must be in constant motion. This can only occur if the magnetic field expands and contracts in the primary coil. This can be accomplished with alternating current.

Generators for Cities

Most of the electrical energy in the United States is produced in large power plants. When Michael Faraday first discovered how to induce electricity in the 1830s, many people were skeptical about the value of electricity. Today it is hard to imagine a world without electricity.

Our society needs to create huge amounts of energy to satisfy our residential and industrial needs. Almost all our electrical energy is generated with giant coils of wire and giant electromagnets. The relative motion between the wires and magnets can be accomplished by water dropping over a natural waterfall (like Niagara Falls) or over a human-made dam. The motion can also be caused by the wind. More windmill farms are being built, and there is also talk about using the ocean tides to produce the required relative motion.

Most of the large power plants use steam to move the turbines. Water is converted to steam by burning coal, oil, natural gas or by the fission of nuclear materials. The steam from this boiling water is then used to turn the turbines. Each method of generating electricity has both positive and negative consequences.

Active Physics

Wind and water are renewable forms of energy. However, some people are concerned that wind generators may alter the velocities of global surface wind and cause temperature increases. Others worry about the environmental implications of building dams to use water energy.

Oil and coal are nonrenewable sources in that it takes too much time for these materials to be generated within Earth. Oil comes from the decay of plant material from 50 million years ago. Once the oil (or coal) is used, it will be another 50 million years to create new oil (and coal).

Some people are concerned that increased use of coal will increase our atmospheric carbon dioxide. Other people are concerned that dependence on foreign oil is politically dangerous. Nuclear energy raises concerns about safety, storage of used radioactive fuel, and nuclear proliferation by nations and terrorists. Solar energy requires photovoltaic cells to convert sunlight to electricity. If too much of the land surface is covered by farms of these cells, it is possible that Earth's temperature may increase, since most of the solar energy hitting photovoltaic cells eventually turns into heat.

Energy use is a major economic and political issue. As student physicists, you will be responsible for helping to find ways to use energy responsibly and to ensure that the economies of our country and the world can continue to grow.

Checking Up

1. How is the current produced by an AC generator different from the current produced by a DC generator?

2. Describe the operation of a split-ring commutator in a DC generator.

3. In an AC generator, how many times a cycle is the current zero?

Active Physics Plus

+Math	+Depth	+Concepts	+Exploration
	◆◆	◆◆	

Rotating Coils in Electrical Generators

1. Although the straight-wire electrical generators discussed in this section are useful in understanding how electrical generators work, they are not a practical design. It is much easier to construct an electrical generator with a rotating coil instead of a moving straight wire. The single rotating wire also had its limitations. The current varied from zero to a maximum value and then back to zero for a moment. If you had two coils that were oriented perpendicular to each other, one coil would be inducing a maximum current while the other would be momentarily inducing no current.

a) Create a graph showing the induced current from a pair of coils that are perpendicular to one another.

b) Try a similar exercise where you have three coils at angles of 60 degrees to each other.

c) Extend this exercise to additional coils.

d) What are the benefits of having multiple coils of wire rotating? What are the detriments of having multiple coils of wire?

What Do You Think Now?

At the beginning of this section, you were asked the following:

• **What is the difference between a direct current and an alternating current?**

How would you explain the difference now based on what you have learned in this section? How do the designs of AC and DC electrical generators differ?

Physics
Essential Questions

What does it mean?

What are the essential parts of a generator? How does an AC generator differ from a DC generator?

How do you know?

Describe the observations you made that contrasted the current from an AC and DC generator.

Why do you believe?

Connects with Other Physics Content	Fits with Big Ideas in Science	Meets Physics Requirements
Electricity and magnetism	Models	* Experimental evidence is consistent with models and theories

* Physics seeks to help you to understand how nature works. Once you understand how nature works, it is possible to use this understanding to design useful devices. What did you have to understand about electrical currents and magnets in order to design an electrical generator?

Why should you care?

You now can design your own electrical generator. What parts must every electrical generator have?

Reflecting on the Section and the Challenge

In the last section, you found that moving a wire past a magnet or moving a magnet past a wire could produce electricity. In this section, you refined that knowledge. By creating a loop that moves by a magnetic field, you created a constantly changing current. The current not only varied in magnitude, but also changed directions. This is called an alternating current. Through the use of a split-ring commutator, the alternating current could be turned into a direct current. Although the current still varied in magnitude, it did not reverse direction. Part of your challenge will be to explain the operation of your toy. This section should help you in that part of the challenge.

Physics to Go

1. What is the purpose of an electric generator?

2. How does a direct current differ from an alternating current? Use graphs to illustrate your answer.

3. In an electric generator, a wire is placed in a magnetic field. Under what conditions is a current generated?

4. Draw a graph of the induced current similar to the one you drew for an AC generator, but assume the coil is rotating in the opposite direction, starting at position I.

5. *Preparing for the Chapter Challenge*

   The toy you will be designing may have a generator as part of the kit. The child who will be using the kit will have to decide if the generator will operate as a DC or an AC generator. What extra parts should you include in the generator to allow the material you supply operate in either DC or AC mode? What instructions should you give to the recipient to explain the difference between AC and DC electricity to allow for the proper choice?

Inquiring Further

Investigating Hertz

Investigate the answers to these questions:

- What does it mean to say that household electricity has a frequency of 60 Hz?

- Heinrich Hertz was a nineteenth-century German physicist. Find out about the unit of measurement named after him, the hertz, abbreviated Hz. Write a brief report on what you find.

- Have you ever heard a sound caused by 60 Hz AC being emitted from a fluorescent light or a transformer? What does it sound like, and can you explain why it occurs?

- Look at a catalog or visit a store where sound equipment is sold, and check out the "frequency response" of speakers—what does it mean?

Section 6

Electromagnetic Spectrum: Maxwell's Great Synthesis

What Do You See?

Learning Outcomes

In this section, you will

- **Practice** discovering patterns to classify and make predictions.

- **Identify** the symmetry pattern between changing electric and magnetic fields that led to the discovery of electromagnetic waves.

- **Calculate** the distance traveled by electromagnetic waves during a time interval.

What Do You Think?

The fashion industry depends on creative designers producing patterns that can be used for this year's new clothing lines. When these patterns correctly predict the consumer's tastes, this is a billion-dollar industry. Scientists are also creative individuals who search for patterns in nature and in mathematics.

- **How do patterns in nature allow scientists to predict the existence of things not yet discovered?**

- **What do electric and magnetic field patterns have to do with how light travels through space?**

Write your answers in your *Active Physics* log. Be prepared to discuss your ideas with your small group and other members of your class.

Investigate

In this *Investigate*, you will first see how patterns in science and nature determine the decisions scientists make, and how they use patterns to make discoveries. Then, you will investigate the symmetry pattern of electric and magnetic fields.

Active Physics

Finally, you will explore how the speed of light was determined, and how to make calculations using the speed of light to determine travel times.

Part A: Patterns

Recognizing patterns is crucial to getting along in the world and in understanding nature. Even though chairs come in lots of different shapes and sizes, everyone knows what a chair looks like when they want to find a place to sit down.

1. The drawings below are of imagined alien life forms. Come up with a system to group them based on patterns you see.

   Example: Which of these are paynes?

   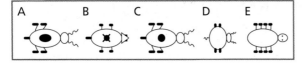

   Each of these answers would be acceptable.

   Paynes are creatures that have antennae; a, c, and d are paynes.

   Paynes are creatures that have tails; a, b, c, and d are paynes.

   Paynes are creatures that have a mark on their back; a, b, and c are paynes.

   Answer the following questions in your log. Be sure to write the reasons for your groupings.

   a) Which of these are chiavs?

   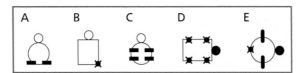

   b) Which of these are howes?

   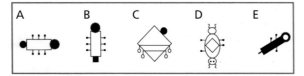

c) Which of these are stengels?

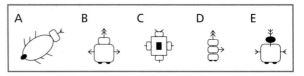

2. Patterns can help you predict the outcome of future events. A simple example of the use of patterns to predict future events can be seen in the game of Nim.

   Your teacher will supply you and your partner with 10 toothpicks. To play Nim, the students in a pair take turns picking up toothpicks. A student may pick up 1 or 2 toothpicks at each turn. The student who picks up the last toothpick wins the game.

   a) Play several games of Nim with your partner. Record the results of the games. Can you determine a rule that always lets you win? Does it matter who goes first?

   b) After playing a few games, you should begin to see the patterns. If there are three toothpicks and it is your turn, will you win or lose? What move will you make?

Active Physics

c) If there are four toothpicks and it is your turn, will you win or lose? What move will you make?

d) If there are five toothpicks and it is your turn, will you win or lose? What move will you make?

e) Figure out a strategy that will allow you to win when there are 10 toothpicks. Record your strategy in your log. When you know the strategy for winning at Nim, winning no longer seems like luck. Knowing the patterns of this game can help you win.

Part B: Electricity and Magnetism

You have learned about electricity and magnetism and the connection between them. By organizing that knowledge into a table, you may see a pattern emerge.

1. Construct the following table in your *Active Physics* log.

   a) Complete each element of the table.

   b) By using the pattern of this table, predict what might belong in the empty box. Discuss with your lab partners and record your prediction.

Electric fields (*E* fields)		Magnetic fields (*B* fields)	
A Draw the *E* field for a positive and negative charge.	**B** Draw the *E* field for a positive charge.	**C** Draw the *B* field for a bar magnet. N S	**D** There is no single north or south pole that scientists know of. Therefore, there is no way to draw a *B* field for a single pole.
Creating a *B* field from an *E* field		**Creating an *E* field from a *B* field**	
E	**F** If charges move, they create a current. A single charge can move and create a current.	**G** A current can be created when the magnetic field changes.	**H** There is no single north pole so you cannot have moving north poles without south poles.
	A current creates a *B* field.	Describe how an electromagnet can create current in a coil without any movement of the electromagnet.	
	Draw the *B* field for a negative current going into the page.	Show how the wire can move across the *B* field to produce a current. N S	
		Summary—If a current is created, there must be a force on the electrons to move them in the wire. A force on a charge is evidence of an electric field (*E* field). A changing *B* field has created a changing *E* field.	

Part C: The Speed of Light

The speed of light can be calculated by using the equation $v = d/t$. To make this calculation, you need a measurement of the time for light to travel a specific distance.

1. About 400 years ago, Italian scientist Galileo Galilei tried to measure the speed of light. He had no sophisticated instruments, not even a clock. Galileo stood on a hilltop in Italy, uncovered a lantern and began counting. When his assistant on a distant hilltop saw the light from Galileo's lantern, the assistant uncovered his lantern. When Galileo saw the assistant's lantern, he stopped counting. Galileo realized immediately that the speed of light was too fast to measure in this way.

   a) How does human reaction time affect Galileo's experiment?

2. Although Galileo's experiment was not successful, he recognized that light takes time to move from one place to another. This meant light has a speed. Galileo inspired others to try measuring the speed of light. Danish astronomer Ole Roemer succeeded about 70 years later by viewing Jupiter's moons. Roemer observed the moons at two different positions in Earth's orbit. This let him increase the total time the light traveled and allowed him to measure this longer time accurately. He then calculated a value for the speed of light. Because the distance of Jupiter to the two positions of Earth was so large, the time was long enough to be measured.

   a) In the motion equation $v = d/t$, which quantities did Roemer change to provide a more precise measurement of the speed of light?

   b) Roemer had measured the distance to be the diameter of Earth's orbit (3×10^{11} m or 186,000,000 mi) and the time difference for light to travel this distance was 22 min. Calculate the speed of light in meters per second and in miles per second.

   c) A better value for the time difference for light to travel that distance is 16 min. Calculate the speed of light in meters per second and in miles per second using this value for the time.

3. In the late 1800s, Albert Michelson, an American physicist, made a more accurate measurement of the speed of light with rotating mirrors. Instead of having humans on hills adjust the lanterns, Michelson used mirrors and a very precise timing mechanism. For his work, Michelson won the 1907 Nobel Prize, the first ever awarded to an American scientist.

   a) Michelson had measured the distance to be 0.7576 mi (1219 m), and the precise time he was able to measure for the light to travel that far was 4.065×10^{-6} s (0.000004065 s). Calculate the speed of light in meters per second and in miles per second using this value for the time.

Physics Talk

ELECTROMAGNETIC SPECTRUM

Isaac Newton said, "If I have seen further than others, it is because I have stood on the shoulders of giants." The same could have been said by James Clerk Maxwell, a Scottish physicist. Maxwell was able to take the contributions of Coulomb, Oersted, Ampere, and Faraday and create a pattern that mathematically predicted one of the greatest achievements in the understanding of the world. It also changed the world in ways that nobody imagined.

In this section, you completed a summary table for electricity and magnetism as well as electric fields and magnetic fields. This table is shown below with additional information about each of the people who contributed to the understanding of the phenomena.

Electric fields (*E* fields)		Magnetic fields (*B* fields)	
A The *E* field for a positive and negative charge. 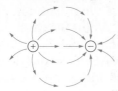 *Coulomb showed that there is a force between two charges.* $$F = k\frac{q_1 q_2}{d^2}$$ *Faraday showed that this force could be explained with the introduction of the concept of electric fields*	**B** The *E* field for a positive charge. 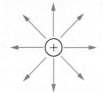 *Gauss derived an equation that could mathematically relate the electric field to the charge.*	**C** The *B* field for a bar magnet. 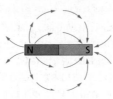 *Gilbert investigated the properties of magnets and found that like poles repel and unlike poles attract.*	**D** There is no single north pole that scientists know of. Therefore, there is no way to draw a *B* field for a north pole.
Creating a *B* field charges an *E* field		**Creating an *E* field from a *B* field**	
E	**F** If charges move, they create a current. A single charge can move and create a current. A current creates a *B* field. The *B* field for a negative current going into the page. *Oersted discovered that a current produces a magnetic field.* *Ampere derived an equation that could predict the strength of the magnetic field from the current.* *Faraday showed that charges had electric fields.*	**G** A current can be created when the magnetic field changes. The wire can move across the *B* field to produce a current.  An electromagnetic turning on and off can create a current in a neighboring wire. If a current is created, there must be a force on the electrons to move them in the wire. A force on a charge is evidence of an electric field (E field). A changing *B* field has created a changing *E* field. *Faraday found that a changing magnetic field can produce a current.*	**H** There is no single north pole so you cannot have moving north poles without south poles.

Active Physics

James Clerk Maxwell saw that there was a pattern in the mathematical equations that described these phenomena. In the table, A relates to B, C to D and A relates to C, B to D. Also, B relates to F, C to G, and D to H. The missing element in the pattern begged the question: If a changing magnetic field can create a changing electric field (that produces a current, G), can a changing electric field produce a changing magnetic field, E? If so, this would make the pattern of the mathematical equations much more symmetric and beautiful. (E would relate to G.)

Maxwell was not able to do any experiments to check his insight. He was, however, able to use mathematics to describe what Faraday had been talking about with his concept of "fields." When Maxwell developed the mathematics, he found that if a changing electric field produced a *changing* magnetic field, E, then that *changing* magnetic field would in turn create a *changing* electric field, G and so on. He also found that these electric and magnetic fields would move across the room. Maxwell used his equations to determine the speed at which the "electromagnetic fields" would move. The value he found was

$$3 \times 10^8 \text{ m/s} = 186{,}000 \text{ mi/s}$$

Maxwell recognized that this was the speed of light. Maxwell had discovered the essence of light. Light is an electromagnetic field. With Maxwell's four equations, physicists can now explain everything you know about electric charges, electric fields, electricity, magnetism, as well as everything that was known about light.

Maxwell's four equations are powerful stuff. But the story does not end there. Light has a very specific band of wavelengths. Blue light has a wavelength of 450 nm (nanometers) 450×10^{-9} m and red light has a wavelength of 700 nm. Maxwell tried to find out why light was restricted to this range of wavelengths and could not find a mathematical reason. That being the case, it was hypothesized that there were other **electromagnetic waves** of different wavelengths that had not yet been discovered and that the human eye could not see.

Maxwell's equations predicted the existence of gamma rays, X-rays, ultraviolet radiation, infrared radiation, microwaves, television waves, and radio waves. The first of these to be discovered were radio waves by the German physicist Heinrich Hertz a few years after Maxwell died. Each of these has since been discovered. In fact, people have invented all sorts of technologies that rely on this electromagnetic spectrum.

Most people delight in seeing a rainbow — a band of colors in the sky including red, orange, yellow, green, blue, and violet. The electromagnetic spectrum is Maxwell's rainbow. It shows a beauty and pattern in the world that nobody before Maxwell imagined.

Physics Words

electromagnetic waves: transverse waves that are composed of oscillating perpendicular electric and magnetic fields that travel at 3×10^8 m/s in a vacuum; examples of electromagnetic waves listed in order of increasing wavelength are gamma rays, X-rays, ultraviolet radiation, visible light, infrared radiation, microwaves, and radio waves.

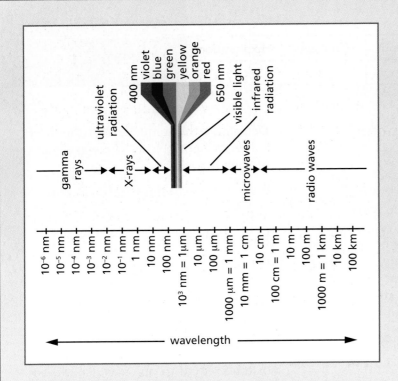

Electromagnetic waves share many properties.

- They can travel through a vacuum.

- They travel at the same incredible speed, 3.0×10^8 m/s (186,000 mi/s, in a vacuum). This is so fast that if you could set up mirrors in New York and Los Angeles, and bounce a light beam back and forth, it would make 30 round trips in just one second! (New York City to Los Angeles = 3000 miles.)

- They have wavelengths and frequencies that can be calculated using the equation: $v = f\lambda$ where v is the speed of all electromagnetic waves (3.0×10^8 m/s).

- Nothing travels faster than the speed of light. It can be considered a "speed limit" for the universe.

- Each of these electromagnetic waves can be used for technologies such as communication (radio waves), radar (microwaves) and medicine (X-rays). They also provide additional "views" of the cosmos. For example, telescopes are built for radio waves, infrared waves, and other electromagnetic waves.

Checking Up

1. At what speed do electromagnetic waves travel?

2. How did patterns play a role in Maxwell's equations?

3. Describe one thing that is the same and one thing that is different between infrared radiation and radio waves.

4. Approximately how long would it take light to travel from New York to Los Angeles?

5. What is the "speed limit" for the universe?

Active Physics

Active Physics

+Math	+Depth	+Concepts	+Exploration
◆◆	◆		◆

Plus

Relating Wavelength, Speed, and Frequency

There are three important characteristics of periodic waves—wave speed, wave frequency, and wavelength. The wave speed is how fast the wave moves. The wave frequency is the number of oscillations per second and the wavelength is the distance between adjacent crests of the wave. These quantities are related by the equation

speed = frequency × wavelength

In mathematical language,

$$v = f\lambda$$
where v = wave speed
f = frequency
λ = wavelength

All visible light travels at the same speed. Visible light has a range of wavelengths.

In order to find the frequency (f) for each of the different colors of light, you will need the speed of electromagnetic waves (also called the speed of light), $v = c = 3.0 \times 10^8$ m/s when the waves travel in a vacuum. All visible light travels at this same speed. When traveling through air, the light travels a bit slower, but for your purposes the speed is just about the same as that in a vacuum. The symbol c (from the Latin *celeritas*: speed, swiftness, rapidity, quickness) is used generally for the speed of light.

1. Determine the frequency for the three colors of light below. The wavelength of each is given.

Red: $\lambda = 650$ nm $= 650 \times 10^{-9}$ m

Yellow: $\lambda = 570$ nm $= 570 \times 10^{-9}$ m

Blue: $\lambda = 475$ nm $= 475 \times 10^{-9}$ m

2. Where does this expression $v = f\lambda$ come from? Here is a simple line of reasoning: The wavelength λ is the distance between adjacent crests of the wave. In one period T of the oscillating wave, the wave travels a distance equal to one wavelength. So the speed of the wave is given by

$$\text{Speed} = \frac{\text{distance traveled}}{\text{time elapsed}}$$

In mathematical symbols, this reads

$$v = \frac{\lambda}{T}$$

But the frequency f of the wave is the number of oscillations per second; so $f = 1/T$. Substituting that result in the previous equation to yield the equation:

$$v = f\lambda$$

Detail the logic of this reasoning with appropriate sequential mathematical statements in your log. If you wish, you may draw a concept map of the relationships.

Active Physics

Example:

An FM radio antenna on a car is approximately 1 m long. Since the lengths of the antennas are comparable to the wavelengths they radiate or receive, assume that FM radio waves have a wavelength of about 2 m. You can find the approximate frequency for FM radio from

$$f = \frac{v}{\lambda}$$

$$f = \frac{3 \times 10^8 \, \text{m/s}}{2 \text{m}}$$

$$f = 1.5 \times 10^8 \, / \, \text{s} = 1.5 \times 10^8 \, \text{Hz} = 150 \, \text{MHz}$$

Recall that 1 Hz = 1 oscillation/s. MHz means megahertz, which is the same as 10^6 oscillations per second. The actual FM broadcast band is from 88 to 108 MHz.

3. Look at the list below of electromagnetic waves and their frequencies:

Type of wave	Typical frequency
AM radio	1 MHz (10^6 Hz)
FM radio / commercial TV	100 MHz
radar	1 GHz (10^9 Hz)
microwave	10 GHz
infrared radiation	6×10^{12} Hz
light	10^{14} Hz
ultraviolet radiation	10^{16} Hz
X-rays	10^{18} Hz
gamma rays	10^{21} Hz

a) Calculate the wavelength of each type of wave.

b) Describe an object that is about the same size of each of those wavelengths. For the higher frequencies (shorter wavelengths), the objects will be small, perhaps bacteria, atoms, or nuclei.

4. Explore the wavelength of microwaves. You can measure the wavelength of microwaves in a microwave oven by placing a rectangular glass dish filled with marshmallows in the oven. Be sure that the dish will not rotate when you turn on the microwave. (You may have to remove the rotating glass dish from the microwave, but you want to make sure that the rectangular glass dish sits evenly on the bottom. Use waxed paper or pads of plastic wrap to make an even foundation for the glass dish.) Put the marshmallow dish in the microwave oven, and then turn on the microwaves for about 30 s. Take a look at the marshmallows. If you don't see any brown spots on the tops of the marshmallows, return the dish to the microwave oven in the same spot and turn on the microwave for another 30 s. As soon as the brown spots appear, carefully remove the glass dish and measure the distance between the brown spots on the marshmallows. This distance is about half the wavelength of the microwaves.

The pattern is due to wave interference within the microwave enclosure. The brown spots occur where the microwaves reinforce each other in what is called constructive interference. This creates areas where the microwaves are more intense, as shown by where the marshmallows were heated first.

What Do You Think Now?

At the beginning of this section, you were asked the following:

• How do patterns in nature allow scientists to predict the existence of things not yet discovered?

• What do electric and magnetic field patterns have to do with how light travels through space?

There are many patterns in nature, such as the changing of the seasons, the phases of the Moon, and the growth of a forest. In this section, you learned about two other patterns in nature. Describe the pattern between electric and magnetic fields. Describe the pattern that reveals similarities among X-rays, visible light, and radio waves.

Physics
Essential Questions

What does it mean?
X-rays, visible light, and radio waves are all electromagnetic. How are they all similar and how are they different?

How do you know?
Describe an experiment that can be used to measure the speed of light.

Why do you believe?

Connects with Other Physics Content	Fits with Big Ideas in Science	Meets Physics Requirements
Electricity and magnetism	Interaction of matter, energy, and fields	✱ Experimental evidence is consistent with models and theories

✱ Faraday created the concept of invisible field lines to help him understand the behavior of charges and magnets. Maxwell described the field model mathematically. This led to the discovery that light is an electromagnetic wave. Why does the discovery of X-rays and radio waves give us confidence that Maxwell was correct?

Why should you care?
A scientific discovery can make the world seem more beautiful. Rainbows have always been considered beautiful. How does Maxwell's electromagnetic spectrum add to this beauty?

Reflecting on the Section and the Challenge

In this section, you learned about the electromagnetic spectrum. The knowledge about the electromagnetic spectrum emerged from a better understanding of generating electricity. Visible light is one type of electromagnetic wave. Electromagnetic waves are used in all sorts of communications and medical technologies. As you develop your toy to demonstrate your understanding of motors and generators, you may also decide to mention how the toy uses electromagnetic waves or could be a part of other technologies that use electromagnetic waves.

Physics to Go

1. Think back to how Galileo attempted to measure the speed of light.

   a) How much time did it take the light to travel from one hilltop to the other? Assume that the hill was 5 km (5000 meters) away.

   b) Could Galileo have measured the speed of light with his method? Explain your answer.

2. Provide one use for each of the following electromagnetic waves:

   a) radio waves

   b) microwaves

   c) infrared rays

   d) visible light

   e) ultraviolet light

   f) X-rays

   g) gamma rays

3. Gamma rays can cause cancer, but they can also be used to treat cancer. How would you answer a sixth grader who asks you, "Is radiation good or bad?"

4. What strategy would you use for the game of Nim if you started with 15 toothpicks?

5. What strategy would you use for the game of Nim if each player were allowed to pick up one, two, or three toothpicks at a time?

6. For an optical system like your eye, the smallest spot size formed by the lens has a diameter about the same as a wavelength of the electromagnetic waves. The light-sensitive cells in the eye have a diameter of about 1.0×10^{-6} m.

   a) Assuming the size of the light-sensitive cells is the same as the smallest spot size the eye can form, use the diameter of the smallest spot to estimate the wavelength of visible light.

   b) From your answer to 6.a), estimate the frequency of visible light.

7. The table shows some astronomical distances in meters.

From—To	Distance (meters)
Earth to Moon	3.8×10^8
Earth to Sun	1.5×10^{11}
Sun to Pluto	5.9×10^{12}
Sun to nearest star	4.1×10^{16}

a) For each distance, calculate the time it takes light to travel that distance.

b) You can use the travel time of light as a unit of distance. For instance, the distance from Earth to its Moon is 1.3 light-seconds. Convert the distance from Earth to the Sun to light-minutes. To do this, find the number of minutes it takes light to reach Earth from the Sun. Or, you can use a conversion ratio given below:

$$\text{light-minute} = \left(3 \times 10^8 \, \text{m/s} = 300,000,000 \, \text{m/s}\right) \times 60 \, \text{s} = 18,000,000,000 \, \text{m} = 1.8 \times 10^{10} \, \text{m}$$

c) Convert the distance from the Sun to Pluto to light-hours. (Hint: You need to divide the time in your table by the number of seconds in an hour.)

8. The size of optical instruments is determined to a large degree by how big the wavelength of visible light is. Do you think that an extraterrestrial would be able to "see" with the same light that you do? If you learned that extraterrestrials could see microwaves, what might that tell you about their "eyes"? Draw an extraterrestrial that can see microwaves. Also draw one that can see radio waves.

9. When NASA has landed unmanned probes on Mars, the probes have always been self-guided during the landing, rather than controlled from Earth. Explain why the landings must be self-guided.

10. Energy rather than wavelength or frequency sometimes orders electromagnetic waves. Arrange the electromagnetic waves in the spectrum in the order you believe goes from highest energy to lowest. How does this order compare to the frequency of the waves?

11. **Active Physics** **Plus** A radio station emits radio waves by accelerating an electron up and down an antenna. If the radio station is operating at a frequency of 100 megahertz, how many times per second should the electrons in the antenna change direction?

12. *Preparing for the Chapter Challenge*

The toy motor or generator you will be designing for your challenge will have a spinning coil of wire that is carrying a current. Even small motors and generators will have areas where the electricity generates electromagnetic waves when sparks are generated. The electromagnetic waves from these sparks can be picked up by an AM radio. Write a brief paragraph explaining what electromagnetic waves are and why they may be heard on the radio when the children use their toy.

Inquiring Further

Speed of light

The speed of light is known to such accuracy that its value has been used to calculate the distance to Earth's Moon. A laser beam was sent to the Moon and it reflected off a mirror placed there and returned to Earth. By measuring the time of flight, and using the accepted value of the speed of light, the distance to the Moon was calculated.

a) Find a reference to this experiment and check the results.

b) Conduct a similar experiment of your own by listening to a tape recording of a conversation with an astronaut on the Moon. The time delay between a question asked at Mission Control and hearing the response is approximately equal to the time for the radio wave to travel to the Moon and back. Determine this value and use the speed of light (and radio waves) to calculate the distance to the Moon.

The speed of light is known to such accuracy that it is used to determine other constants. Find a reference that allows you to answer the following questions.

a) How is a meter defined?

b) How is a second defined?

Physics You Learned

Physics Concepts	Is there an Equation?
Magnets always have a north and a south pole. Like poles repel and opposite poles attract.	
Magnets attract iron and induce iron to act as a temporary magnet.	
A compass can be used to detect and map the presence and direction of a magnetic field.	
A **magnetic field** spreads throughout all of space but gets weaker with increasing distance from the magnet causing it.	
The "north seeking" (north) pole of a compass points toward Earth's geographic north pole, which is a south magnetic pole.	
The units for magnetic field strength are called teslas (T) or newtons per ampere-meter.	
Electric currents generate magnetic fields. A current-carrying wire is surrounded by a magnetic field. The magnetic field has a circular shape about the wire, and the direction of the field is determined by the direction of the current in the wire.	
Active Physics Plus Magnetic field strength (B) equals a constant (μ_0) times the current (I) divided by 2π times the distance (d). The strength of the magnetic field surrounding a current-carrying wire varies directly with the current flowing in the wire and inversely with the distance from the wire.	$B = \dfrac{\mu_0 I}{2\pi d}$
The magnetic field surrounding a current-carrying coil of wire (a **solenoid**) is very similar to that surrounding a bar magnet.	
The strength of a solenoid's magnetic field varies directly with the current in the coil, the number of turns comprising the coil, and the magnetic permeability of the core material.	
A wire carrying a current in a magnetic field experiences a force if the current is perpendicular to the magnetic field lines.	
Active Physics Plus The force (F) on a current-carrying wire in a magnetic field equals the current in the wire (I) times the length of the wire in the field (l) times the magnetic field strength (B) when the current is perpendicular to the field. The direction of the force on the charge is perpendicular to both the magnetic field and the current.	$F = IlB$
An electric motor consists of a rotating solenoid interacting with either a permanent magnet or an **electromagnet**.	
A DC motor uses a **commutator** to change current direction.	
Active Physics Plus The force on a charge moving perpendicular to a magnetic field is proportional to the velocity and magnitude of the charge, and the strength of the field. The direction of the force on the charge is perpendicular to both the magnetic field and the velocity of the charge.	$F = QvB$

When there is relative motion between a coil of wire and a magnetic field, a voltage is induced in the coil. The direction of the current in the coil depends upon the polarity of the magnetic field and the direction of its relative motion.	
A **generator** is a device that moves a coil of wire in a magnetic field to create a current. A generator induces maximum voltage when the coils of wire are moving perpendicular to the field lines, and zero voltage when the coil is moving parallel to the field lines.	
The voltage induced when a coil is moving in a magnetic field depends upon the length of the wire in the field, and the speed with which the coil is moved.	
A current induced by the relative motion between a magnet and a wire coil is always in a direction that sets up a magnetic field which exerts a force to oppose that motion. This is an example of the conservation of energy.	
When a coil of wire is rotated in a magnetic field, an **alternating current** is established, which changes direction each half cycle. This current can be changed by a commutator into a **direct current**, which travels only in one direction.	
Changes in magnetic fields cause changes in electric fields, and changes in electric fields induce changes in magnetic fields.	
Oscillating electric and magnetic fields which constitute electromagnetic waves propagate at the speed of light.	
The velocity (v) of an electromagnetic wave equals the wave's frequency (f) times its wavelength (λ). The electromagnetic spectrum is composed of waves formed by changing electric and magnetic fields. All these waves travel at the speed of light, but have different frequencies of vibration and wavelengths.	$v = f\lambda$
The speed of light in a vacuum is 3×10^8 m/s.	
Waves that compose the electromagnetic spectrum include radio waves, microwaves, infrared, visible light, and ultraviolet waves, x-rays and gamma rays.	
Transformers are used to raise or lower voltage. Transformers work only with AC electricity.	

Active Physics
Plus

Chapter Challenge

You will now be completing a second cycle of the *Engineering Design Cycle* as you prepare for the *Chapter Challenge*. The goals and criteria remain unchanged. However, your list of *Inputs* has grown.

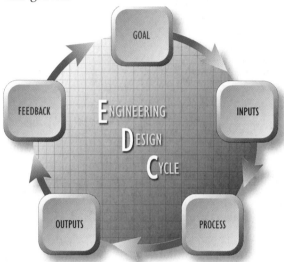

Goal

Your challenge for this chapter is to create a toy that converts the mechanical energy of motion into electricity, or electrical energy to mechanical motion with the purpose of educating children about the use of electricity to move things. Your toy can operate with a battery powered motor or a mechanically powered generator. Review the *Goal* as a class to make sure you are familiar with the criteria and constraints.

Inputs

You now have additional physics knowledge to help you identify and analyze the various physics concepts that apply to electric motors and generators. You have completed all the sections of this chapter and learned the physics content necessary to complete your challenge.

This is part of the *Inputs* phase of the *Engineering Design Cycle*. Your group needs to apply these physics concepts to put together your presentation. You also have the additional *Inputs* of your own personal experience with various toys, as well as the *Feedback* you received following your *Mini-Challenge* presentation.

Section 1 You mapped the magnetic field of a bar magnet and then compared the results to the effect of a wire carrying a direct current (DC) on a magnetic compass needle.

Section 2 You constructed a solenoid that operates as an electromagnet. You also identified the variables that control the strength of the magnetic field a solenoid produces.

Section 3 You explored the force between a current-carrying wire and a nearby magnet. You learned how to utilize that force to construct and operate a simple DC motor.

Section 4 You used a galvanometer, a device for measuring electric current. You explored the function of the galvanometer by moving a magnet in and out of an electric coil, and induced an alternating current (AC) by moving the magnet back and forth through the coil.

Section 5 You explored the technology behind AC and DC generators by considering the movement of a rotating coil in a magnetic field and the direction of the resulting induced current. You also examined the connections that are necessary to generate a direct current or an alternating current from a rotating electric generator.

Section 6 You observed how patterns in science and nature determine scientific discussions, and how patterns are used to make discoveries. You investigated the symmetry pattern of electric and magnetic fields. You also explored how the speed of light was determined, and calculated travel times using the speed of light.

Process

In the *Process* phase, you must decide what information you will use to help you meet the *Goal*. The first step is to select the physics principles you will use. Then you must decide what type of toy you will create to demonstrate those concepts. Your model from the *Mini-Challenge* should be very useful at this stage. Even if you change your design completely, the materials that you will need to create the motor or generator will probably be very similar.

Your toy can use a motor, a generator, or both. If you use a motor, you may use up to four D-sized batteries to power your toy. If you use a generator, you can turn almost any mechanical motion into electricity, but remember that you need constant motion to maintain a constant supply of electricity.

For your prototype to work properly, you may have to make many small adjustments. Remember that adding more batteries, more coils of wire, or more magnets may affect the output of your electric motor or generator. Also, if you are using a generator, you will want to include some description of how electricity is used in the toy design so children will be able to tell that it's working. Building a toy that "works" can be a lot of fun!

Your instruction manual should include all of the "how-to" steps for constructing and operating your toy, as well as information about the physics principles behind its mechanisms. Your manual should help children understand why a magnet is needed in your toy and why it has to be placed in a specific position. They should also understand the function of the wire coils and the reason connections are so important. You might also have to provide some basics about AC and DC currents to complete the explanations of your toy.

Remember, pictures and diagrams will help clarify your explanations and will increase the appeal of your manual.

Outputs

Presenting your information to the class are your design cycle *Outputs*. Create a presentation that highlights the main features of your design and demonstrates your new knowledge of electricity. Keep in mind that your audience may know as little about electric motors and generators as you did when you began this chapter, so be sure to explain everything in simple terms that listeners can understand.

You will present your toy design, the list of parts that the manufacturer will need, and the manual containing the instructions and explanations for how the toy works. As always, diagrams, charts, and drawings are helpful tools in a presentation—a sketch of your toy, with all of the significant parts clearly labeled, might be a good idea.

Feedback

Your classmates will give you *Feedback* on the accuracy and overall appeal of your presentation based on the criteria of the design challenge. Do not forget, your classmates' design solutions may present you with *Feedback* and alternative methods for solving the same problem. Remember, no design is perfect, and there is always room for optimization or improvement no matter how slight. From your experience with the *Mini-Challenge*, you should see how you could continuously rotate through the design cycle to refine your electrical-system design.

Active Physics

Physics
Physics
Connections to Other Sciences

Here are some examples of how the concepts you studied in this chapter relate to other sciences.

Magnetic Fields

Biology Magnetic bacteria are unique bacteria that respond to Earth's magnetic field by aligning along the field lines to safe areas in the mud of lakes and ponds where they propagate. Many bird species can also sense magnetic fields, and it is thought that this ability may be a significant aid in their yearly migrations.

Chemistry The magnetic field generated by electrons is responsible for one of the quantum numbers chemists use to classify and determine the states of electrons in atoms.

Earth Science Earth's magnetic field has left an imprint on the layers of rock that have extruded along the mid-ocean rift. This is the primary evidence of Earth's changing magnetic field, and supplementary evidence of continental drift.

Electromagnetism

Biology Powerful electromagnets are main components in the magnetic resonance imaging (MRI) devices that doctors use to diagnose a variety of medical conditions, including cancer.

Chemistry The configurations of spinning electrons in an atom determine its magnetic properties. When multiple electron spins are unpaired, atoms will exhibit magnetic properties.

Earth Science Earth's magnetic field is theorized to be the result of rotating currents of molten rock in Earth's core, triggered by the dynamo effect. The "dynamo effect" is believed to be responsible for Earth's magnetic field. The effect is a result of the rotation of the molten iron core of the planet.

Induced Voltage

Biology Experimental treatments for speeding the healing of complex bone fractures involve induced voltages from electrodes outside of the bone.

Chemistry The repulsion of atoms by an external magnetic field is the basis for the property known as diamagnetism. This form of magnetism results from the establishment of electron currents to oppose the external field.

Earth Science Solar flares on the Sun will often damage sensitive electronic equipment on satellites or on Earth due to induced voltages from the rapidly moving, charged solar particles.

EM Spectrum

Biology Certain snakes, known as "pit" vipers, can sense the presence of their prey by detecting the infrared or heat waves emitted by warm objects, and therefore are able to hunt easily at night. Although invisible, the ultraviolet light emitted by the Sun is responsible for tanning, and also causes skin cancer in humans.

Chemistry Ultraviolet light may be used in conjunction with some chemical compounds to initiate the reactions. Dentists use UV rays to set resins for dental repair more quickly. Atoms emit and absorb energy in many areas of the electromagnetic spectrum. In the infrared spectrum, these various energy signatures aid in compound identification and analysis.

Earth Science Much of the ultraviolet energy emitted by the Sun is absorbed by Earth's ozone layer. The infrared-absorbing characteristics of carbon dioxide and other "greenhouse gases" are thought to be responsible for much of Earth's recent temperature rise, since that energy is redirected back toward Earth, rather than lost to space.

Katie Broughton

Senior Project Manager, Wild Planet Toys; San Francisco, CA

Even though Katie Broughton grew up wanting to be an astronaut, her father, a professor and self-described "tinkerer" inspired her to tackle a career in toy design. After taking some design classes in college and then in graduate school at Stanford University, Katie realized that toy design no longer had to be just a hobby.

She has been working for Wild Planet Toys since 2005, a company that was founded in 1993 and is based in San Francisco, California. The company's mission is to create quality products that spark the imagination and provide positive play experiences for children. The company is best known for their high-tech *Spy Gear* and active learning games, including the popular brands *Hyper Games* and *Smart Step Games*.

According to Katie, the most exciting aspect of her job is making science look like magic. "One of my favorite ways to use magnets is to produce a hidden switch. You can bury a magnet inside one part of a teddy bear and hide another switch in a doll. Then, when the bear kisses the doll on the cheek, the hidden switch is flipped, causing the doll to giggle," said Katie.

Katie believes that an understanding of physics is essential in her field. "If you want a motor to move arms or wings on a robot, you need to understand that bigger wings are heavier and might require a stronger motor." But an artistic eye is just as valuable as her science background. "It is important to be able to draw. It is sometimes much more effective to be able to communicate my ideas in a sketch."

Even though she still thinks being an astronaut would be a lot of fun, she would not choose outer space over her toys. "If I didn't work for Wild Planet Toys, I would probably be designing toys somewhere else," she said.

Slater Harrison

Technology Teacher and Founder of Science Toy Maker Web Site; Jersey Shore, PA

Slater Harrison always had a fascination with science toys. His career was largely influenced by his volunteer work in the country of Bangladesh, where he went to aid in the country's technical development. The experience inspired him to create science toys that use everyday, recycled materials.

As a technology teacher with his own Web site, Harrison's ultimate goal is to make science fun and accessible. "The toys on my Web site are easy enough for young kids to make; others are more difficult." Harrison's latest project is an electrical engraver for metal that uses an electromagnet, powered by a 12-V car battery charger.

Karen Levitt

Director of the Leading Teacher Program, Duquesne University; Pittsburgh, PA

Karen Levitt has been teaching undergraduate and graduate courses in science method for elementary teachers at Duquesne University for 13 years. She also adapted the Teaching Science with Toys program, a workshop that began at Miami University (Ohio) and promotes using toys to teach physical science in elementary and middle school. "These workshops use simple explanations that will not intimidate the teachers and promote the need to start teaching science at a young age," she said.

Karen admits that toys are educational, but also a lot of fun. "I use them in my presentations and to engage my students, but they are fun for adults, too."

Physics

Practice Test

Before you try the Physics Practice Test, *you may want to review Sections 1-6, where you will find* **20 Checking Up** *questions,* **9 What Do You Think Now?** *questions,* **24 Physics Essential Questions,** **44 Physics to Go** *questions, and* **6 Inquiring Further** *questions.*

Content Review

1. The presence of a magnetic field may be detected by using a
   a) stationary charge.
   b) light bulb.
   c) small mass.
   d) compass.

2. A hand generator is connected to a coil of wire. A compass placed in the coil lines up with the axis of the coil when the generator handle is rotated. If the direction of the handle's rotation is reversed, what happens to the compass needle?
   a) The needle rotates 90°.
   b) The needle rotates 180°.
   c) The needle spins continuously.
   d) Nothing happens; the needle stays in place.

3. A current-carrying wire has electrons flowing downward, as shown in the diagram. Which compass is correctly pointing in the direction of the magnetic field around the wire?

   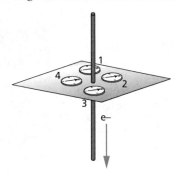

   a) 1
   b) 2
   c) 3
   d) 4

4. Which of the following has no effect on the strength of the magnetic field around a current-carrying coil of wire?
   a) the number of turns of wire in the coil
   b) the thickness of the wire
   c) the current flowing through the coil
   d) the material of the core placed in the coil

5. Which of the magnets below correctly shows the surrounding magnetic field lines?

   a)

   b)

   c)

   d)

6. The magnetic field of a solenoid is most like that of a
   a) horseshoe magnet.
   b) bar magnet.
   c) donut magnet.
   d) straight, current-carrying wire.

7. When soft iron is added as a core to a current-carrying solenoid, the magnetic field strength of the solenoid increases because
   a) soft iron is already magnetized.
   b) soft iron increases the current flowing around the coils of the solenoid.
   c) soft iron adds the strength of Earth's magnetic field to the solenoid.
   d) soft iron's magnetic domains align with the field due to the current.

8. Power plants send electricity at high voltages to local communities. To change this voltage to the 120 V used in residences, power companies use a device called a
   a) turbine.
   b) transmission tower.
   c) motor.
   d) transformer.

Active Physics

9. In which of the diagrams shown below will a current *not* be generated if the coil and magnet combinations are moved?

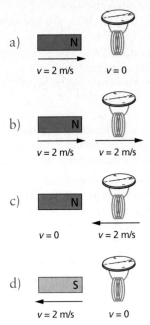

a)
N   v = 2 m/s   v = 0

b)
N   v = 2 m/s   v = 2 m/s

c)
N   v = 0   v = 2 m/s

d)
S   v = 2 m/s   v = 0

10. The diagram shows a loop of wire rotating in a magnetic field. Which statement below describes the current in section Y of the loop in the present position, and when the loop is rotated 180°?

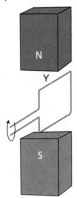

a) The current is at its maximum and at 180°, the current will be at its maximum in the opposite direction.

b) The current is zero and at 180°, the current will be at its maximum.

c) The current is at its maximum and at 180°, the current will be at its maximum in the same direction.

d) The current is at its maximum and at 180°, the current will be zero.

11. A wire is located in a section of a magnetic field as shown in the diagram. In which direction should the wire be moved to generate an induced voltage in the wire?

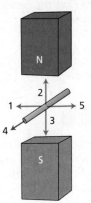

a) 1
b) 2
c) 3
d) 4

12. In the diagram above, if an electron current is flowing through the wire in the direction labeled 4, in which direction is the force acting on the wire due to the current flow?
a) 1
b) 2
c) 3
d) 5

13. Maxwell's equations demonstrate that
I   all electromagnetic waves travel at the speed of light in a vacuum.

II   electromagnetic waves are composed of changing electric and magnetic fields.

III   sound is an electromagnetic wave.

a) I only
b) I and II only
c) I and III only
d) I, II, and III

14. How long does it take a radio wave to travel from Philadelphia to Chicago, a distance of approximately 900 km? (The speed of light is 300,000 km/s).
a) 0.003 s
b) 0.3 s
c) 300 s
d) 3×10^8 s

Practice Test *(continued)*

15. The steam-powered device used by many power plants to spin the generators and to make electricity is called a
    a) turbine.
    b) transmission tower.
    c) motor.
    d) transformer.

Critical Thinking

16. Explain how an electrical current flows in the rotating loop of wire in an AC generator, and in the circuit to which the generator is connected as the loop rotates 360°. Use a voltage vs. time graph to help explain.

17. Explain how a galvanometer works. Include a diagram of a galvanometer.

18. A large electromagnet is often used in a junkyard to lift material.
    a) What specific types of material can an electromagnet lift?
    b) How does the electromagnet release the material once it has been moved?
    c) Explain why adding a soft iron core improves the electromagnetic power of a solenoid.

19. The distance to the nearest star is approximately 40,000,000,000,000 km and the speed of light is approximately 300,000 km/s. Use these two facts to explain why it would be extremely difficult to communicate with any "intelligent beings" on a planet circling that star.

20. Draw a transmission system for electricity powered by a wind generator and transmitted through an electric substation to your house.
    a) Assume the wind turbine generates electricity at 690 V. Include any steps up and down for the voltage that may be necessary as the electricity moves from the generator to your house.
    b) List all the energy changes that the system undergoes as wind energy is converted for use to heat water with an electric stove in your home.

Active Physics
Plus

21. A wire measuring 3.0 m in length is at rest in a magnetic field of 0.02 T. If the wire experiences a force of 12 N, what current must be flowing in the wire?

22. An electron (charge = 1.6×10^{-19} C) is moving at 4.0×10^5 m/s in a magnetic field of 0.0080 T. What is the size of the force acting on the electron?

Chapter 8

8

Atoms on Display

Scenario

High-school students in Oregon walk into a giant mouth and down a cavernous esophagus into a spherical and moist room filled with liquids and loud sounds. An elementary student in California melds a picture of his or her face with that of a friend to see how pretty or strange a composite face would be. Middle-school students in New York try to improve their "major-league" batting skills or their "professional" golf swing using computer video analysis. All of these students are visiting their science museums.

Science museums help to make learning memorable and fun. They feature hands-on exhibits that stimulate, educate, and entertain. They provide exciting experiences that help visitors develop an understanding of science.

The visitors at a science museum can come and go as they please. Research has shown that there are only 30 s (seconds) available at an exhibit to capture people's interest before they walk right by. Once they stop at the exhibit, you must get them involved. Often, this involvement includes some kind of interaction with the exhibit. Some of the exhibits are targeted for a specific age group. Other exhibits are for a broad audience.

If you have never been to a science museum, it's worth a visit. If you are not able to get to a city that has a museum, you may want to visit one of the many virtual science museums on the Internet.

Your Challenge

Your *Active Physics* class has been asked to develop an exhibit that will provide visitors to a science museum with an understanding of an atom.

The exhibit must

- *include* distinct features of the structure of an atom
- *communicate* the size and scale of the parts of an atom
- provide information on how an atom is held together
- explain the role of models in developing an understanding of an atom
- show your visitors the strengths and limitations of various atomic models
- educate visitors about the importance of indirect methods of measurement that scientists use to collect evidence about an atom
- capture the visitor's attention within 30 s
- include written matter that will further explain the concepts
- have a model, a T-shirt, a poster, a booklet, or a toy that can be sold at the museum store
- include safety features
- be interactive—visitors should not merely read
- include posters to provide an overview of what visitors are about to see and a review of what they witnessed.

Criteria for Success

You will be presenting your museum-exhibit plan to your class. As a class, decide how your work will be evaluated. Some required criteria are listed in the *Chapter Challenge*. Are there other criteria that you think are worth including?

How should each of the criteria be weighted? Should the written material be worth as many points as the item for the museum store? Should the 30-s criterion be worth more than anything else? Since the museum exhibit is supposed to educate the visitor, how much should the content be worth? Should all content criteria be equally weighted? Work with your class to agree on how many points should be assigned for each criterion. The total points should add up to 100.

Once you decide on the point allocation, you will have to decide how you can judge the assigned point value. For instance, assume that you chose the 30-s criterion to be worth 15 points. How will your class decide on whether your exhibit gets the full 15 points or only 10 points? It is worth knowing how each criterion will be judged so that you can ensure success and a good grade. You will probably want to assign some strict guidelines and also leave room for some extra points. Learning to judge the quality of your own work is a skill that all businesses expect to see in their professionals.

Standard for Excellence	
1. Quality of Exhibit • includes features of the structure of the atom • physics concepts from the chapter are integrated in the appropriate places • physics terminology and equations are used where appropriate • correct estimates of the magnitude of physical quantities are used • additional research, beyond the basic concepts presented in the chapter	**40 points**
2. Written matter	**25 points**
3. Entertainment value of the exhibit • capture visitor's attention in 30 s • interactive	**20 points**
4. Item sold at museum store	**10 points**
5. Challenge completed on time	**5 points**

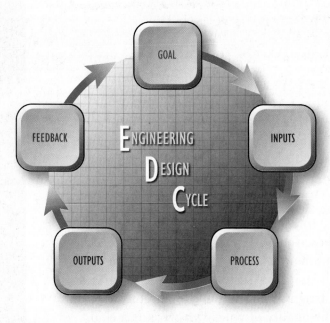

Engineering Design Cycle

You have now learned about your *Chapter Challenge* to develop an exhibit that will provide visitors to a science museum with an understanding of an atom. You will use a simplified *Engineering Design Cycle* to help your group complete this design challenge. Clearly your *Goal* is the first step in the *Engineering Design Cycle*, so you have already begun.

As you experience each one of the chapter sections you will be gaining *Inputs* to use in the design cycle. These *Inputs* will include new physics concepts, vocabulary, and even equations that you will need for your exhibit. When your group prepares the *Mini-Challenge* presentation and the *Chapter Challenge*, you will be completing the *Process* step of the design cycle. During the *Process* step you will evaluate ideas, consider criteria, compare and contrast potential solutions, and most importantly, make design decisions.

The first *Output* of your design cycle will be the *Mini-Challenge* where you present your design of a museum exhibit and your presentation to the class, including any models, diagrams, or calculations you may use to clarify the information you present.

Finally, you will receive *Feedback* from your classmates and your instructor about what parts of your design and presentation are good and which parts need to be refined. You will repeat the *Engineering Design Cycle* during the second half of the chapter, gaining more inputs, refining or changing your exhibit design, and making your final museum exhibit.

Physics Corner

Physics in *Atoms on Display*

- Binding energy
- Conservation of charge
- Conservation of energy
- Coulomb's law
- Diffraction of light
- Electron wavelength
- Feynman diagrams
- Interference of light
- Isotopes
- Light spectra
- Millikan's oil-drop experiment
- Models of the atom
- Neutron, proton, nucleon, electron
- Newton's law of universal gravitation
- Nuclear fission
- Nuclear forces
- Nuclear fusion
- Photoelectric effect
- Radioactive decay
- Rutherford's scattering experiment
- Size of nucleus

Section 1

Static Electricity and Coulomb's Law: Opposites Attract

What Do You See?

Learning Outcomes

In this section, you will

- **Produce** electrically charged objects.

- **Describe** the behavior of like charges, and the behavior of unlike charges.

- **Discover** the factors that determine the force between two charged objects.

- **Calculate** the electrical force using Coulomb's law.

- **Implement** the organizing principle of conservation of charge.

- **Recognize** the similarities and differences between Coulomb's law and Newton's law of gravitation.

- **Explain** how Coulomb was able to measure Coulomb's constant using a torsion balance.

What Do You Think?

Have you ever seen a tremendous lightning storm? Bolts of lightning ignite the sky as they streak toward and away from Earth. A tiny lightning storm also takes place when you get an electric shock. Think back to the last time you got a shock. Were you inside or outside? Was it winter or summer? What did you touch to get the shock?

- **What do you think caused the shock?**

Record your ideas about this question in your *Active Physics* log. Be prepared to discuss your responses with your small group and your class.

Investigate

The study of lightning, shocks, and static cling can reveal important physics. In this section, you will investigate what happens when two strips of matte-finish "invisible" tape are charged and brought near each other.

1. Cut two strips of invisible tape about 12 cm long. Fold over a 1-cm section on the end of each strip and press the sticky sides

How does a negatively charged rod pick up a neutral piece of paper? The rod is negatively charged. In the diagram to the right, there are more negatives than positives in the rod. The piece of paper is neutral. There are an equal number of positives and negatives. When the rod is brought close to the paper, the excess negatives on the rod repel

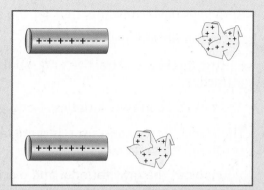

the negatives of the paper. The excess negatives of the rod are attracted to the positives in the paper and repelled by the negatives in the paper. Because the positives are closer, the force of attraction is larger. Coulomb's law informs you that the force gets weaker as the distance gets larger. With a stronger force of attraction on the positive charges and the weaker force of repulsion on the negative charges, the rod can pick up the paper.

Comparing Coulomb's Law and Newton's Law of Universal Gravitation

You found you could actually calculate the force of attraction or repulsion of charges by using Coulomb's law:

$$F = k \frac{q_1 q_2}{d^2}$$

Coulomb's law for electrostatic attraction and repulsion is very similar to **Newton's law of universal gravitation**. Newton's law gives the relationship among gravitational force, masses, and the distance between the masses. This relationship can be summarized by the following equation:

$$F = G \frac{m_1 m_2}{d^2}$$

Where F is the force in newtons (N),

m_1 and m_2 are masses in kilograms (kg),

d is the distance between the centers of the masses in meters (m),

and G is the gravitational constant, always equal to 6.67×10^{-11} N·m²/kg².

Look at the similarities:

• Both laws show forces that decrease in strength with the square of the distance between two objects.

• Both laws show forces that depend on the product of the masses or charges.

Physics Words

Newton's law of universal gravitation: the relationship among gravitational force, masses, and the distance between the masses.

Active Physics

- Both laws have constants that set the scale of their intrinsic strength.

Look at the differences:

- Electric forces are attractive and repulsive; gravitational forces are only attractive.

- Charges come in two varieties, + and −. Mass comes in one variety, +.

- The electric force constant k is quite large, while the gravitational force constant G is quite small.

If you look at the gravitational and electrical forces between two electrons, the gravitational force is much smaller. The force is so small that you don't need to take it into account when describing the electric forces between the charges.

The experimental techniques to find the value of k and G are quite similar. In Coulomb's experiment, two spheres were attached to the ends of a rod and the rod was suspended by a wire. These spheres were charged, and similarly charged spheres were brought near the ends of the rods. The repulsive force caused the wire to twist. The twist was a measure of the force, and Coulomb was able to verify his law.

The constant for the strength of the gravitational force was determined in an experiment by Henry Cavendish. Cavendish's setup was similar to Coulomb's, but the attraction between the pairs of spheres was due to their gravitational attraction. This tiny force was measured by the twist in the wire. The symmetry of what appears to be two unrelated forces provides a glimpse into the beauty of the world. Physicists remark on this beauty, which drives them to find out if there are other underlying understandings of the two forces because of that symmetry. This is what physicists are exploring when you hear about their work on unified theories.

Checking Up

1. If electrons are removed from a neutral object, what kind of charge will the object have? Explain.

2. What happens to the force of attraction between two charged objects as the distance between them increases? Explain using Coulomb's law.

3. When two charged objects are made to touch each other and then separated, what will be true about the net charge of the two objects after separation? Explain your answer.

The Cavendish Experiment

F

F

F

F

r

Active Physics

+Math	+Depth	+Concepts	+Exploration
◆◆			

Active Physics

Plus

Coulomb's Law

Coulomb's law describes the force between a pair of charged objects. You can also use Coulomb's law to find the force among a large number of charges.

Situation 1: Assume that you have three charged objects equally spaced along a line.

To find the net force on object B, you can immediately determine that the force will be toward A. This is because A attracts B (unlike charges attract) and B is repelled from C (like charges repel). Since both forces on B are to the left, B will accelerate toward the left.

You can find the value of the net force by calculating the forces using Coulomb's law and then adding.

Situation 2: Assume that you have three charged objects equally spaced along a line, as in Situation 1, but C has a positive charge.

To find the net force on object B, you can determine that the force will be toward C. A attracts B (unlike charges attract) and B is attracted to C (unlike charges attract).

The force of attraction to C is greater than the force of attraction to A because the charge on C is greater than the charge on A (and the distances are identical). You can find the value of the net force by calculating the forces using Coulomb's law and then adding the negative force (to the left) and the positive force (to the right).

Situation 3: Assume that you have three charged objects where C is twice as far from B as A is from B.

To find the net force on object B, you can immediately determine that the force will be toward A. A attracts B (unlike charges attract) and B is attracted to C (unlike charges attract). Because the force of attraction to A is greater (as it is closer), B will accelerate toward the left.

You can find the value of the net force by calculating the forces using Coulomb's law and then adding the negative force (to the left) and the positive force (to the right).

Situation 4: Assume that you have three charged objects where C is twice as far from B as A is from B.

Active Physics

For what charge of C would the net force on B be zero? Since C is twice as far from B, the charge would have to be four times as large to exert an equal force. That is because the force decreases by the square of the distance. Double the distance, and the force is $\left(\frac{1}{2}\right)^2$ or $\frac{1}{4}$ the strength; triple the distance, and the force is $\left(\frac{1}{3}\right)^2$ or $\frac{1}{9}$ the strength).

1. Find the direction of the net force on B in the following situations without any calculations.

   a) Assume that you have three charged objects equally spaced along a line.

   b) Assume that you have three charged objects equally spaced along a line.

   c) Assume that you have three charged objects, where C is three times as far from B as A is from B.

   d) Assume that you have three charged objects, where C is three times as far from B as A is from B.

   e) Assume that you have three charged objects, where C is three times as far from B as A is from B.

The charges do not have to be limited to positions along a line. If the charges are located in fixed positions on a plane, you can also determine the force by adding the forces. However, in this case, the vector addition of forces is a bit more complex than addition of forces along a line.

Situation 5: Assume that you have three charged objects equally spaced as shown in the diagram.

The force on B can be determined to be down and to the left. Object A will attract B to the left. Object C will attract B to the bottom of the page. Both forces will be equal since the charges and distances will be equal.

The vector sum of these forces can be determined by the vector addition in the diagram below.

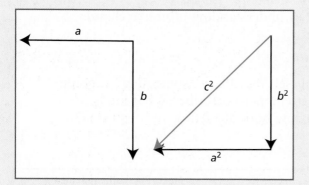

You can find the value of the force by calculating each force using Coulomb's law and then adding the forces using the Pythagorean theorem $\left(a^2 + b^2 = c^2\right)$.

The problems can get more complex if the charges and distances are no longer equal.

2. Determine the force (both magnitude and direction) on object B for each of the following charges and distances. Assume that the configuration is that A is to the left of B, and C is below B as shown in Situation 5.

Case Number	Charge on A	Charge on B	Charge on C	Distance Between A and B	Distance Between B and C
1	$+5 \times 10^{-6}\,C$	$+5 \times 10^{-6}\,C$	$+5 \times 10^{-6}\,C$	2 m	2 m
2	$+5 \times 10^{-6}\,C$	$+5 \times 10^{-6}\,C$	$-5 \times 10^{-6}\,C$	2 m	2 m
3	$+5 \times 10^{-6}\,C$	$+5 \times 10^{-6}\,C$	$-10 \times 10^{-6}\,C$	2 m	2 m
4	$-5 \times 10^{-6}\,C$	$-5 \times 10^{-6}\,C$	$-5 \times 10^{-6}\,C$	2 m	2 m
5	$+5 \times 10^{-6}\,C$	$+5 \times 10^{-6}\,C$	$-15 \times 10^{-6}\,C$	2 m	2 m

What Do You Think Now?

At the beginning of this section you were asked the following about getting a shock:

• **What do you think caused the shock?**

Now that you know about electrons, what happens when they are transferred from one object to another object? What is the law of conservation of charge? How is this law related to the transfer of charge between two objects?

Physics
Essential Questions

What does it mean?

How does Coulomb's law increase your understanding of unlike charges attracting and like charges repelling?

How do you know?

What experiments have you made yourself that show "something" is going on in the world that Coulomb's law attempts to describe? What kinds of measurements did you perform that show both attraction and repulsion?

Why do you believe?

Connects with Other Physics Content	Fits with Big Ideas in Science	Meets Physics Requirements
✳ Forces and motion	Models	Good, clear, explanation, no more complex than necessary

✳ The electrical force between charged objects is invisible. You can't see the charged particles and you can't see the force. In physics, scientists adopt models that can explain what they observe within nature. They try to derive equations that can accurately explain what they observe and can predict what they will observe in different situations. Forces and motion is one of physics' big ideas. Finding similarities (symmetries) between forces is one of the challenges of modern physics. Compare and contrast the electrostatic force with the gravitational force. A comparison between Coulomb's law for electrostatics and Newton's law of gravitational attraction would be helpful.

Why should you care?

You have seen that charged objects can attract or repel one another. These attractive and repulsive forces will help you create a model for how the atom is constructed and held together. Since your museum exhibit must include distinct features of the atom, you may decide to include something you learned about charges and forces from this section. Describe the aspects of electrical forces you might include in your exhibit and how you will make it engaging.

Reflecting on the Section and the Challenge

You are starting to provide evidence that atoms are composed of electrons and other particles. These particles have electric charge. You will need to provide a description of the interaction between the charges when you provide a description of the atom for your museum display. You may find a way to include in your exhibit the larger concepts of conservation of charge or the ability to actually calculate these forces of attraction and repulsion.

Physics to Go

1. Electrons are transferred from a rod to a piece of cloth.

   a) Which object will become negatively charged?

   b) Which object will become positively charged?

2. A rubber rod is negatively charged after being rubbed by wool. Explain how this happens.

3. Two identical spheres are mounted on insulated stands. The first sphere has a charge of –1. The second sphere has a charge of –3. After the spheres touch, what will the charge on each be?

4. One of two identical metal spheres has a charge of +1 and the other sphere has a charge of –5. Compare the total charge on the spheres before and after contact.

5. Charge A is $+2.0 \times 10^{-6} C$ and charge B is $+3 \times 10^{-6} C$. The charges are 3 m apart. What is the force between them? Is it attractive or repulsive?

6. Charge A is $-4.0 \times 10^{-6} C$ and charge B is $+2 \times 10^{-6} C$. The charges are 5 m apart. What is the force between them? Is it attractive or repulsive?

7. When the air is dry and you walk on a wool carpet with your shoes, you may experience a shock when you touch a doorknob. Explain what is happening in terms of electric charge. (Hint: Your shoes are similar to the rubber rod.)

8. Compare and contrast Coulomb's law and Newton's law of gravitational attraction. Provide at least one similarity and one difference.

9. Coulomb's law states that the electric force between two charged objects decreases with the square of the distance. Suppose the original force between two objects is 60 N, and the distance between them is tripled, the new force would be $\left(\frac{1}{3}\right)^2$, or nine times weaker. This new force would be $60 \text{ N} \times \frac{1}{9} = 6.7 \text{ N}$ or 7 N. Find the new forces if the original distance was

   a) doubled.

   b) quadrupled.

   c) halved.

   d) quartered.

10. Sketch a graph that shows how the electrostatic force defined by Coulomb's law varies with the distance.

11. A single electron has a charge of 1.6×10^{-19} C.

    a) Show why it takes 6.25×10^{18} electrons to equal 1 C.

    b) If you studied currents in *Electricity for Everyone*, solve this problem: Calculate how many electrons go by when 5 A of current exists for one minute.

12. Compare the gravitational force between two electrons to the electric force between them. Which force is stronger, and by how much? The mass of an electron is 9.1×10^{-31} kg.

13. How could you depict the invisible electrostatic force in a museum exhibit?

    For *Questions 14 to 19* choose the best answer from those given.

14. If the distance between two charged objects is halved, the force between them will

    a) double.

    b) be half as much.

    c) quadruple.

    d) stay the same.

15. Two charged identical spheres attract each other. If the charge on one is doubled, the force between them will

    a) double.

    b) be half as much.

    c) quadruple.

    d) stay the same.

16. The force between two charged objects A and B is determined to be − 47 N. Which of the following options is possible?

    I. The charge on A is positive and B is positive.
    II. The charge on A is negative and B is negative.
    III. The charge on A is positive and B is negative.
    IV. The charge on A is negative and B is positive.

    a) III and IV

    b) I and II

    c) III only

    d) II only

17. As two charged objects are brought closer together, the magnitude of the force between them will

a) increase.

b) decrease.

c) stay the same.

d) not enough information

18. To make a neutral object positively charged you should

a) add positives.

b) take away positives.

c) add negatives.

d) take away negatives.

19. An unknown object attracts both a "T" tape and a "B" tape. What kind of charge does the object have?

a) positive

b) negative

c) neutral

d) not enough information

20. *Preparing for the Chapter Challenge*

The Museum Director needs an update on your progress. Write a paragraph in your *Active Physics* log reassuring him/her that you are making progress. For example, the Director might walk in and ask, among other questions, "Are forces going to be a part of your exhibit? How could you depict the invisible electrostatic force in a museum exhibit?" What would be your answer?

Section 2

The Nature of Charge: Tiny and Indivisible

Learning Outcomes

In this section, you will

- **Detect** the number of hidden pennies in a container without opening the container.

- **Explain** why the masses of containers with pennies can only have certain values.

- **Describe** the Millikan oil-drop experiment.

- **Explain** the meaning of quantization of electric charge.

What Do You See?

What Do You Think?

It's easy to share a box of popcorn with a friend at the movies. It is a bit tougher to share a slice of pizza equally, but it can be done with a knife. You can keep cutting it but each piece will still be pizza. However, at some point, you will separate the cheese from the crust and the pieces will no longer be pizza.

- **Can you think of something that cannot be split into smaller pieces and retain its identity?**

Record your ideas about this question in your *Active Physics* log. Be prepared to discuss your responses with your small group and your class.

Investigate

In this *Investigate*, you will try to find the mass of a single penny in a closed container. The container may have one or more pennies but you will not have that information. You will find the mass of an empty container, using a balance, and the mass of the container with the pennies. You will then compare your results to those of the other groups.

1. Your teacher will provide you with a
set of film canisters or other containers
that contain pennies. Your goal is to
determine the mass of a single penny.

Do not open the containers. To develop
a strategy, assume that each container
has a mass of 5 g and each penny has a
mass of 2 g.

a) Make a list of possible masses of
containers that have 1 penny,
2 pennies, 5 pennies, etc. Make this
list for at least ten containers.

b) Suppose you were given only the
masses of the ten containers you
calculated in *Step 1.a*) and not the
mass of a penny. Describe how you
could find the mass of a single penny.

2. Now, measure the mass of an
empty container using a balance.
Then measure the mass of each
container, including the penny or
pennies inside.

a) Explain how you can find the
mass of one penny using the
measurements you are permitted
to make. It is very possible that no
container has only one penny. Write
down your strategy.

b) What do you determine the mass of a
penny to be?

c) Compare your value of the mass of
a penny with that of another group.
How does your confidence in your
value change as you compare it with
more and more groups? Scientists
use similar methods to share and
compare results with other scientists
to make scientific progress.

3. Suppose you obtain a new set of
containers with nickels in them.
Suppose that each container is 5 g and
each nickel is 5 g.

a) What are some possible masses
you would expect for four of
the containers?

b) A lab group stated that they
measured the mass of a container
of nickels and it was 23 g. Your lab
group thinks that they must have
made an error. Explain to the first
group in writing why you think that
there is a problem.

c) When your lab group measured
the mass of the container, you also
found it to be 23 g. You now have
a problem—a mystery—a puzzle.
It is this kind of puzzle where
calculations do not support the
actual measurements that challenges
and intrigues physicists. How could
this be? It would be great to open
up the container, but this may not be
possible. Can you solve the puzzle?
Suggest at least three different
solutions to this puzzle.

Physics Talk

QUANTIZATION OF CHARGE

Millikan's Oil-Drop Experiment

In 1910, Robert A. Millikan completed an experiment very similar in concept to the section you just completed. He did not measure containers of pennies. He measured the forces on charged oil drops. These measurements allowed him to calculate the charge on each drop. Millikan made hundreds of measurements. He always found that the oil drop had 1 charge, 2 charges, 5 charges, 17 charges, and other whole numbers of charges. He never found 3.5 charges or 4.7 charges or 11.2 charges. He showed that it was not possible to have a fraction of a charge, and concluded from his oil-drop experiment that there is a basic unit of charge.

Physics Words

quantum: smallest, indivisible unit of charge that cannot be further subdivided.

electron: a negatively charged particle with a charge of 1.6×10^{-19} C (coulombs) and a mass of 9.1×10^{-31} kg.

Millikan's experiment has been conducted many times. Nobody has found fractional charges. In other words, electric charge is quantized. Each **quantum** is the smallest, indivisible unit of charge that cannot be further subdivided. By way of analogy, consider United States money. There is a smallest unit of money, the penny. A dime is equal to ten pennies, a quarter, 25 pennies. In U.S. currency you cannot pull half a cent or 0.375 cents out of your pocket.

When the atom was discovered, scientists thought it was uncuttable. That is why they were called atoms from the Greek word *atomos*. The *a* means not and *tomos* means cut. Therefore, *atomos* means indivisible or not cuttable. But upon further investigation, it was realized that the atoms have internal parts.

In 1895, J.J. Thomson discovered one of these parts, the **electron**, a tiny negatively charged particle that is part of the atom. He did this by analyzing electron beams in a tube very similar to the tube where electrons travel in a picture-tube TV, not the flat-screen TV. (The flat-screen also uses electrons, but in a different way.) A television picture tube is a modern version of Thomson's apparatus. These electrons hit the screen and make the TV images.

Your penny lab was easy compared to Millikan's oil-drop experiment. The oil drops are so small that in Millikan's experiment he had to view them through a microscope. To find their mass required some ingenuity as well. Millikan sprayed the oil droplets between a positively charged plate and a negatively charged plate. If the oil drop had a negative charge, it would be repelled from the negative plate and attracted to the positive plate. If the positive plate were on top, the electric force would be pulling the drop up, while gravity would be pulling the drop down. If the two forces were equal, the drop would come to rest and remain suspended (or travel at a slow constant speed). By calculating the electrical force and the gravitational force, the charge on the oil drop (i.e., the charge of the electrons) could be found. Millikan won the Nobel Prize for this experiment.

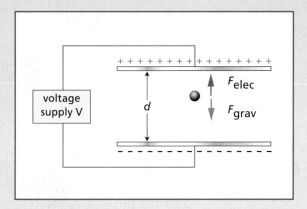

The diagram above shows the oil drop, the electrical plates, and the battery voltage that provides the charge on the plates. The voltage is adjusted so that the oil drop is suspended or moves with a constant speed (no acceleration).

The weight of the oil drop (*mg*) can be found by observing the oil drop as it falls because of air resistance. You can calculate the electrical force from the voltage, charge, and distance between the plates. You can calculate the gravitational force from the mass and the acceleration due to gravity. The voltage of the power supply and the distance between the plates can be measured. Using the equations below, you can find the charge on the oil drops.

$$F_{elec} = F_{grav}$$

$$\frac{qV}{d} = mg$$

$$q = \frac{mgd}{V}$$

Checking Up

1. What led to the discovery that charges are only present in whole numbers?

2. Explain the experiment Millikan used to determine the charge on an electron.

3. How would you calculate the weight of an oil drop?

From Millikan's and many additional experiments, the charge on an electron was determined to be 1.6×10^{-19} C (coulombs). You could expect to see twice this charge, three times this charge, nine times this charge, and any other whole number multiple of this charge. If you never see a fractional part of this charge, you assume that the charge is indivisible.

Current theories of physics state that a ⅓ charge and a ⅔ charge can exist. There is evidence for these fractional charges and the quarks (the tiniest known components from which matter is made) associated with them. The Millikan oil-drop results lead to the conclusion that these quarks always join up to make a total charge of +1 or −1.

Active Physics

Plus

+Math	+Depth	+Concepts	+Exploration
◆◆			◆◆

Calculations Involving Electric Charges

Sample Problem 1

Can an object have a charge of 9.6×10^{-19} C ?

Because each charge is 1.6×10^{-19} C , a charge of 9.6×10^{-19} C can be the sum of 6 charges.

$(6 \times 1.6 \times 10^{-19}$ C $= 9.6 \times 10^{-19}$ C)

Sample Problem 2

Can an object have a charge of 2.4×10^{-19} C ?

Because each charge is 1.6×10^{-19} C , a charge of 2.4×10^{-19} C can be the sum of 1.5 charges

$(1.5 \times 1.6 \times 10^{-19}$ C $= 2.4 \times 10^{-19}$ C) .

This value is impossible. Millikan's oil-drop experiment demonstrates that charge is quantized and you cannot have one and a half charges.

Determine whether objects can have the following charges:

1. 8.0×10^{-19} C
2. 4.2×10^{-19} C
3. 16×10^{-19} C
4. 24×10^{-19} C
5. 2.4×10^{-18} C

Simulating Millikan's Oil-Drop Experiment

The Millikan oil-drop experiment can be completed in a high-school lab. The experiment requires the use of a microscope, and incredible patience, to view the drops. Some computer simulations may be available on the Internet. You may decide to investigate using one of these or to design a computer simulation or game that works like the Millikan oil-drop experiment. Your created simulation should have the following features:

- The screen should look like the apparatus, with a variable power supply and oil drops between the plates.

- The drop should be able to get a new charge.

- The drop should be able to move.

- The voltage should be allowed to vary so that the net force on the drop is zero and the drop travels at constant velocity or is at rest.

- The velocity of the drop should be measurable to determine if it is traveling at a constant velocity.

- New drops should be able to be inserted between the plates.

Map out a design for this computer simulation and if you can, create the simulation and test it with other students.

What Do You Think Now?

At the beginning of the section you were asked the following:

- **Can you think of something that cannot be split into smaller pieces and retain its identity?**

Review what you have learned about Millikan's oil-drop experiment. How do you know that the charge on an electron is quantized?

An early example of Robert Millikan's setup for the oil drop experiment.

Physics
Essential Questions

What does it mean?

The electron's charge is said to be quantized. That charge has been measured to be 1.6×10^{-19} C. Is it possible to have 5.0×10^{-19} C of charge?

How do you know?

Describe Millikan's oil-drop experiment. What feature of Millikan's data shows that the electron charge is quantized, that is, it comes in discrete, indivisible units? Why would the use of a computer simulation of Millikan's oil-drop experiment not be considered evidence for the charge on an electron?

Why do you believe?

Connects with Other Physics Content	Fits with Big Ideas in Science	Meets Physics Requirements
Electricity and magnetism	Symmetry — laws of physics are the same everywhere	✳ Experimental evidence is consistent with models and theories

✳ When you measure the size of an object, you expect that any length is possible. You think that length is continuous. Similarly, you think that time can be broken into smaller and smaller intervals with no limit imposed by nature. (You may have limits due to the technologies available for measuring distance or time.) Charge is different.

You can have 1 charge, 2 charges, 35 charges, but you can't have parts of charges. The surprising experimental result that charge is quantized has led some physicists to wonder if length and time may also be quantized. Why would you believe that charge comes in small, indivisible units? Can you believe that time comes in small bits? Would this notion change the way you observe the world?

Why should you care?

If the negatively charged electrons come as quantized, whole-number units of electric charge, and if matter is normally electrically neutral, then should you expect the positive charge to also be quantized? What might be the consequence for the atom to be made of little blocks of positive and negative charges? How can you demonstrate the peculiar idea of charge in your museum display? How can you help people understand that you cannot find a half-charge?

Reflecting on the Section and the Challenge

When the atom was discovered, people originally thought the basic units of the elements such as hydrogen, carbon, and iron could not be further divided. But, upon further investigation, it was realized that the atoms have internal parts! One of them is the electron. As you can tell so far, the electrons are indivisible, having no internal parts.

Electrons are part of an atom. In your museum exhibit, you will have to include the charge on an electron. You may also find a way to tell how the Millikan oil-drop experiment helped scientists find out about the charge and its indivisibility. You may choose to make a part of the exhibit dealing with electrons and electric charge interesting by making it interactive.

Physics to Go

1. Two students are playing tug-of-war with a rope. How is this game similar to the two forces in the Millikan oil-drop experiment?

2. A doughnut can be split into two pieces. Does the result of Millikan's experiment suggest that the electric charge cannot be split into two pieces?

3. Assume that a container has a mass of 10 g and each penny has a mass of 3 g.

   a) Make a list of possible masses of five containers that have 1 penny, 2 pennies, 5 pennies, 10 pennies, and 12 pennies.

   b) List two masses you would not find for a container with pennies.

4. What is the net electric charge on a metal sphere having an excess of 3 elementary charges (electrons)?

5. How many coulombs are equivalent to the charge of 100 electrons?

6. How many electrons does it take to have a charge of −1 C?

7. **Active Physics** *Plus* Which electric charge is possible?

   a) $6.32 \times 10^{-18}\,\text{C}$ b) $3.2 \times 10^{-19}\,\text{C}$

   c) $8.0 \times 10^{-20}\,\text{C}$ d) $2.4 \times 10^{-19}\,\text{C}$

8. **Active Physics** *Plus* An oil drop has a charge of $-4.8 \times 10^{-19}\,\text{C}$. How many excess electrons does the oil drop have?

9. "Quarks" are particles that have charges $+\frac{1}{3}, -\frac{1}{3}, +\frac{2}{3}, -\frac{2}{3}$. They are important in subatomic physics.

   a) Show how three quarks can combine to create a particle with a total charge of +1.

   b) Show how three quarks can combine to create a particle with a total charge of 0.

   c) Show how three quarks can combine to create a particle with a total charge of −1.

10. Describe how you could make Millikan's oil-drop experiment into an exciting interactive display.

11. *Preparing for the Chapter Challenge*

J.J. Thomson, the discoverer of the electron, tried to describe the significance of the discovery of this tiny particle: "Could anything at first sight seem more impractical than a body which is so small that its mass is an insignificant fraction of the mass of an atom of hydrogen, which itself is so small that a crowd of these atoms equal in number to the population of the whole world would be too small to have been detected by any means then known to science?" Create a quote of your own that captures the significance of the discovery of the electron. Perhaps the quote could be displayed near the entrance to your proposed museum exhibit.

Inquiring Further

Estimating the size of an atom

At one time, the atom was thought to be uncuttable. It is now recognized that the atom has internal parts, one of which is the electron. The electron seems to be uncuttable, but forms a tiny fraction of the atom's mass. The size and mass of an electron raises an interesting question that will be examined in upcoming sections: How big is an atom?

Here is a way to obtain a rough estimate of the size of an atom. One cubic centimeter of olive oil is poured onto the surface of a large pond. The oil spreads out into an oil slick. When it stops spreading, the area of the oil slick is measured to be 100 square meters.

a) Assuming the oil layer is one atom thick, what is the size of the atom?

b) Perhaps the "smallest bit" of olive oil is not a single atom, but combinations of atoms, called molecules. If you are not sure whether the oil layer is one atom thick, then the answer you obtained estimates the size of a molecule. Would that be a maximum or a minimum size for an atom?

Section 3

The Size of a Nucleus: How Big Is Small?

What Do You See?

Learning Outcomes

In this section, you will

- **Calculate** the area of a penny using indirect measurement techniques.

- **Compare** statistical measurements to direct measurements.

- **Relate** the Rutherford scattering experiment to the penny simulation.

- **Describe** the relative scale of the nucleus to the atom.

What Do You Think?

Everyone has heard of atoms, but no one has ever seen an atom. Look at the sketch below of an atom that you often see in advertisements and some science books.

- **How would you describe what is shown in the sketch of an atom?**

- **Are there any problems with this depiction of the atom? Explain your answer.**

Record your ideas about these questions in your *Active Physics* log. Be prepared to discuss your responses with your small group and your class.

Investigate

You will use an indirect method to calculate the area of a penny by counting the number of times a pencil hits or misses a target. You will also apply a direct method to calculate the area of the penny and compare the results of the

Active Physics

two methods. You will then extend your reasoning in the *Investigate* to determine the size of an unknown object.

1. Suppose you randomly throw darts at a circular area of a dartboard that is partially shaded. After many trials, you count 50 hits in the shaded area of the 100 darts you threw in the dartboard.

🖊 a) Which of the dartboards below could you have been using? Explain your answer.

🖊 b) Would your answer change if the number of shaded hits were 25? Explain your answer.

2. Work with a partner. Use a ruler and a pencil to outline a square that is 10 cm × 10 cm on a card. Trace a penny as many times as you like within the square.

Draw the circles similar to the ones shown so that they do not touch each other. Make the circles as close to the actual size of the penny as you can. Note that the diagram is not drawn to scale.

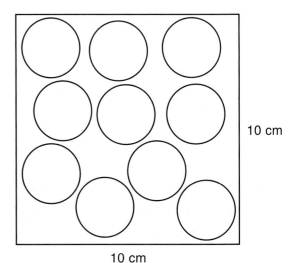

10 cm

10 cm

3. Place the card on the desk and stand beside it. Drop a pencil onto the card so that the point hits within the square. Do not aim the pencil. It is actually better if you don't look. You want the drops to be as random as possible. Your partner may actually shift the card after each drop so that there is less chance of you dropping the pencil in the same place.

Have your partner watch as you do your drops. If the pencil falls outside the square, ignore that drop. Make 50 "countable" drops. Switch roles with your partner, and continue until 100 drops are recorded.

Count the number of drops where the pencil landed inside circles. Call these drops "hits."

🖊 a) Record the number of hits.

🖊 b) Should the total number of hits be related to the area of the pennies? Explain your answer.

4. To test the hypothesis that the percentage of hits is related to the percentage of area occupied by the pennies, use the proportion given below to find the area of all the pennies.

$$\frac{\text{hits}}{\text{drops}} = \frac{\text{area of all pennies}}{\text{total area}}$$

a) Show your calculations in your log.

5. Find the area of one penny by dividing the area of all the pennies by the number of penny outlines on your card.

a) Record your calculation in your log.

b) Compare your value with that of other lab groups. How close are the values?

c) Why do you think this method of determining the area of a penny is an indirect method?

6. You can also find the area of one penny directly by using this equation:

$$\text{Area} = \pi r^2$$

where $\pi = 3.14$ and

$r = $ radius of the penny

a) Measure the diameter of a one-penny circle on your card with a ruler. Record your measurement. (The radius is one-half the diameter, the distance across.)

b) Calculate the area of a penny and record your calculation in your log.

c) To get a more accurate value of the diameter of a penny, you could line up 10 pennies before making the measurement with a ruler. Why would that give you a better result?

7. Compare the results you obtained using *indirect measurement* (dropping the pencil) and *direct measurement* (using a ruler).

a) How close are the results you got using the two different methods?

b) Compare your results with those of other lab groups. How do your results compare?

c) Which method is more accurate? Explain your answer.

d) Why is it important not to aim the pencil in the indirect measurement?

8. Average the results of the indirect measurements and direct measurements from the entire class.

a) How close are the results your class got using the indirect and direct methods?

9. Extend the experiment to an unknown object. Suppose a student conducts a similar experiment, but replaces the penny with a single unknown object. If that student got 50 hits out of 100 drops, then you would conclude that the unknown object's area was approximately 50%, or one half, of the total area of the 10 cm × 10 cm square. You don't know from the data the shape or the location of the object. All of the following are possible because one half of the total area of each square is shaded.

a) What might the unknown object look like if it was reported to have 75 hits out of 100 drops? Draw the outer square and the size of the unknown object inside.

b) What might the unknown object look like if it was reported to have 25 hits out of 100 drops? Draw the square and the unknown object's size.

Active Physics

✎ c) What might the unknown object look like if it was reported to have one hit out of 100 drops? Draw the square and the unknown object's size.

✎ d) What might the unknown object look like if it was reported to have one hit out of 10,000 drops? Draw the square and the unknown object's size.

Physics Talk

MEASURING THE SIZE OF THE NUCLEUS

Indirect Measurement

In this section, you used indirect measurement to find the area of a penny. **Indirect measurement** is a technique that uses proportions or probability to find a measurement when **direct measurement** is not possible, or measuring something by directly measuring something else. Finding the size of the penny without directly measuring it may seem like a good trick. However, you know that you can always verify the size by using direct measurement. You can measure a penny with a ruler. You may think that by using direct measurement you would obtain more accurate results. However, you found in the *Investigate* that both indirect and direct measurements gave very similar results.

Indirect measurement has been very useful in science. Quite often, indirect measurement is also necessary. The sizes and distances to the other planets in the Solar System, for example, have never been directly measured with a ruler or tape measure. The **atom** also cannot be measured with a ruler. Scientists must rely on an indirect method to obtain these measurements.

In this section, you probably concluded that if a single object was in a square and you only got 1 hit in 100 drops, the object would be small in comparison to the square's area. If you only got 1 hit in 1000 drops, the object would be very tiny indeed. And if you only got 1 hit in 10,000 drops, you probably recognize that you could not even draw such a small object in the square. This penny lab and these conclusions can be a model to help explain Rutherford's famous scattering experiment.

Rutherford's Experiment

A key scientific discovery, the discovery of an atom's **nucleus**, was made using a method similar to the one you used in this section. Ernest Rutherford and his colleagues, Hans Geiger and Ernst Marsden, made the discovery. In the lab, the team bombarded a piece of thin gold foil with a beam of positively charged particles called **alpha particles**. The alpha-particle beam was like your "dropping pencil." The foil was like your card. When they completed their experiment, they found that when they shot particles at an area of gold, they got one hit out of every 100,000 drops. Rutherford's conclusion was that there is a single object in each atom and that it must be extremely small. He called it the nucleus.

Of course, Rutherford's experiment was more complicated. As you learn the details, don't lose sight of the conclusion and its relation to the penny-lab simulation.

In Rutherford's experiment, most of the particles went straight through the gold foil. These were like the pencil drops that missed the circles. However, to the surprise of the team, Marsden saw that a very few of the alpha particles bounced back toward the source of the beam. This observation was similar to the pencil drops that hit the circles. When Marsden told Rutherford about the results, Rutherford was astonished. Rutherford said the actual result was as amazing "as if you fired an artillery shell at a piece of tissue paper and it bounced back and hit you!"

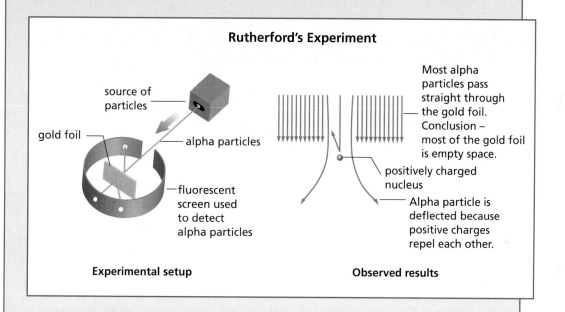

Rutherford's Experiment

source of particles

gold foil

alpha particles

fluorescent screen used to detect alpha particles

Experimental setup

Most alpha particles pass straight through the gold foil. Conclusion – most of the gold foil is empty space.

positively charged nucleus

Alpha particle is deflected because positive charges repel each other.

Observed results

Developing a Model of an Atom

Rutherford thought deeply about these observations. He also thought about all of the ideas that scientists had about what was in the atoms. The fact that most of the alpha particles went essentially straight through the foil suggested that most of them missed the atom's positive charge and mass entirely. He concluded that the positively charged alpha particles bounced back when they hit an area of concentrated positive charge and mass. This model was an improvement to the earlier model of the atom developed by Thomson. Thomson's model had positive and negative charges distributed evenly. Thomson said it was like plum pudding (a British dish). If he were American, he may have said it was like raisin bread with the negative charges (the raisins) spread evenly throughout the dough (the positive charges).

➡

Active Physics

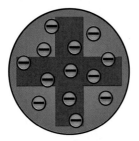

In the Thomson model of the atom,
the electrons are like raisins in the dough
of positive charge.

In the Rutherford model of the atom,
the electrons are moving around a very, very small,
tightly-packed sphere which contains all the
positive charge and most of the mass of the atom.

Rutherford's model had all the mass and positive charge in a tiny location that he called the nucleus. He used his results to calculate the size of the nucleus of these atoms. He could have compared the number of hits, particles that bounced back, with the total number of particles sent toward the foil. He could have used that information to determine the area of the foil where the atomic nuclei could be found. However, Rutherford's mathematics was a bit more complicated. In his situation, the hit was neither "yes" nor "no," but an angle of deflection that could range from 0° to 180°. In future courses, you may study the calculations in detail. Rutherford calculated the diameter of the atomic nucleus to be 10^{-15} m. The diameter of the atom is 10^{-10} m. The nucleus is only $\frac{1}{100,000}$ the size of the atom!

It would be great if it were possible to check Rutherford's indirect measurement. However, a direct measurement to measure the size of a nucleus is impossible because the nucleus is so small. In a direct measurement scientists use a measuring device to determine the size of an object. Because of the impossibility of using direct measurement, only the indirect measurement is available. This measurement is used as evidence of the existence of a nucleus and its size.

Rutherford's nucleus provides a view of matter as mostly empty space. In an atom, which is the smallest particle of an element, the electrons surround a tiny nucleus with nothing between the electrons and the nucleus. The nucleus has all the positive charge and almost all the mass of an atom. Why then do solids appear so solid? How can the empty space of your fist hurt so much when it hits the empty space of a table? Electrons whizzing around the nuclei of the atoms in your fist are repelled by the electrons whizzing around the nuclei of the atoms in the table. The closer you try to bring your fist to the table, the stronger the force of repulsion between the electrons. The force of repulsion can be greater than the force of attraction holding your fist together, and bones can break.

How can empty space exert such forces? Imagine a thin propeller blade. If the blade is still, it is surrounded by mostly empty space. When the blade rotates, it seems to fill that empty space and create a solid wall. The tiny electrons, in rapid motion, create a similar effect—as if the electrons are everywhere at once—and the empty space appears solid.

Your sense of touch is the repulsion of electrons. It follows Coulomb's law:

$$F = k\frac{q_1 q_2}{d^2}$$

Isn't it amazing that you are able to feel this force when it is as tiny as a kiss or as large as striking a table with your fist? The next time you kiss someone, remember that you are experiencing the repulsion of electrons!

Checking Up

1. Why would you rely on an indirect method to measure the size of an atom?

2. How was Rutherford able to determine the size of a nucleus?

3. How do electrons fill the empty space of matter?

Active Physics

+Math	+Depth	+Concepts	+Exploration
◆	◆		

Plus

Making a Model of an Atom

Rutherford's experiment is the only evidence that you have for the existence of the nucleus. In Rutherford's model of the atom, the nucleus takes up only $\frac{1}{100,000}$ of the atom's diameter. Drawing an atom with the nucleus to the proper scale requires ingenuity. The atom has a diameter of 10^{-10} m and the nucleus has a diameter of 10^{-15} m . If the nucleus were the size of a table-tennis ball, how large would a field have to be to represent the atom?

Use this model to create an illustration of a solid composed of a three-dimensional grid. Each atom would be represented by a field or stadium. Each nucleus would be represented by a table-tennis ball.

What Do You Think Now?

At the beginning of the section you were asked the following:

• **How would you describe what is shown in the sketch of an atom?**

• **Are there any problems with this depiction of the atom? Explain your answer.**

Now that you know Rutherford's model of an atom, you should be able to describe a nucleus and electrons in your sketch of an atom. Do the electrons have a fixed position in the atom, like the nucleus?

Physics
Essential Questions

What does it mean?

How can recording the number of "hits" and the number of "misses" tell you the size of targets? Why are such methods necessary for "seeing" the nucleus of an atom?

How do you know?

Compare and contrast your experiment determining the size of the penny with Rutherford's experiment determining the size (and existence) of the nucleus. Provide two similarities and two differences in the experiments.

Why do you believe?

Connects with Other Physics Content	Fits with Big Ideas in Science	Meets Physics Requirements
Atomic and nuclear	Models	* Experimental evidence is consistent with models and theories

* Physicists create models to provide a better understanding of the world. You know from observation that iron is different from water and you might wonder why. Unfortunately, you cannot see the tiniest structure of matter. Knowledge of that structure could provide insights into why materials are different and why they exhibit different properties. Physicists use a model to explain observations. They then conduct new experiments to test the model and amend that model to better accommodate new observations. Rutherford conducted his scattering experiment and concluded that his model of an atom would have a dense, tiny nucleus containing all the positive charge of the atom, and the rest of the atom would be mostly empty space. Rutherford could not "look up" in a book to see if his model of an atom was "right." Why do you believe in Rutherford's model of an atom?

Why should you care?

Knowing about the structure of matter allows scientists to create technologies that can alter the world. Understanding these technologies and their impact on society may depend on people understanding the structure of matter. How can you use your museum exhibit to help visitors understand Rutherford's model of an atom and the evidence you have for that model? How can you communicate to the visitors that this knowledge is important to them?

Reflecting on the Section and the Challenge

By shooting particles at thin foils and seeing how the particles scatter, you can investigate the structure of matter. Rutherford's scattering experiment revealed that a tiny nucleus contains all of the positive charge of the atom. This also implies that most of the atom is empty space. In your museum exhibit, you will certainly want to help visitors to get a sense of the structure of the atom with its tiny nucleus and orbiting electrons. Is there a way in which you can get visitors to your exhibit to explore the size of the nucleus? You may also want to help visitors understand how "mostly empty space" can make hard, solid objects.

Probability was important in this indirect method of measuring the size of a penny or the size of the nucleus. If you had aimed the pencil, the experiment would not have given good results. The use of probability and indirect measurements may be something you wish to include in your museum exhibit.

The museum exhibit must capture a visitor's attention within 30 s. How can you "grab" the visitor?

Physics to Go

1. Determine the size of a quarter indirectly by repeating the pencil-dropping experiment, substituting quarters for the pennies.

   a) Record your results.

   b) How close are the results you got using the direct and indirect method of measurement?

   c) Which method is more accurate? Explain your answer.

2. Repeat the quarter experiment, but this time aim at the card to get as many hits as possible.

   a) Record your results.

   b) How does aiming change the results?

3. Which is greater, 10^{-15} m or 10^{-10} m? How many times greater?

4. Find the areas of circles with the following diameters:

   a) 4 cm

   b) 7 cm

   c) 10 cm

5. Why do you get better results when you drop the pencil 1000 times instead of 10 times?

6. You drop a pencil 100 times and get 23 hits. There are seven coins on a card 10 cm × 10 cm. How large in area is each coin?

Active Physics

7. If the nucleus could be enlarged with a projector so that it was 1 cm in diameter, how far away would the next nucleus be? (Each nucleus is 10^{-15} m and each atom is 10^{-10} m.)

8. In the Rutherford scattering experiment, the alpha particles were deflected at different angles. It was not simply a hit or miss as it was in your penny simulation. How would you expect the angle of deflection to be affected as the positive alpha particles come closer to a positive nucleus?

9. Consider a square target foil of area A that has 10 atoms. If 999 out of 1000 alphas pass through undeflected, how big are the target positives as a fraction of A?

10. When Marsden told Rutherford about the results of the scattering experiment, Rutherford was astonished. Rutherford expected results predicted by Thomson's model of an atom. The Thomson "plum pudding" model (or raisin bread model) has a positive charge spread all through the atom like the raisins in raisin bread. Using this model, Rutherford expected the alpha particles would go straight through the foil but emerge with a smaller speed. Rutherford said the actual result was as amazing "as if you fired an artillery shell at a piece of tissue paper and it bounced back and hit you!" Explain what Rutherford meant with his artillery shell metaphor. When Rutherford adopts his new model of the atom, with all the positive charge residing in a tiny nucleus, how does the artillery shell metaphor now make sense to him?

11. Suppose two people are discussing how the electric charge is distributed in neutral atoms. Each draws a picture to help explain his or her idea.

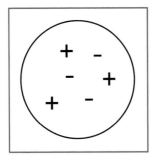 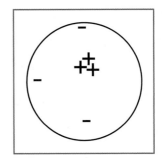

   a) Which person do you believe, and why?

   b) Are there problems with either of the models? Explain.

12. *Preparing for the Chapter Challenge*

How might you show the proper scale of the nucleus and the atom in your museum exhibit? In other words, if a model of the nucleus were the size of a grape, how large would the entire atom be (with its electrons)?

Section 4

Hydrogen Spectra and Bohr's Model of the Hydrogen Atom

What Do You See?

Learning Outcomes

In this section, you will

- **Observe** the spectrum of light emitted by energetic atoms, and describe differences in the spectra of different kinds of atoms.

- **Develop** the Bohr model of a hydrogen atom.

- **Calculate** the energy levels of the electron in the Bohr model of a hydrogen atom.

- **Describe** how the electrons jump from one orbit to another and give off light of a specific wavelength.

- **Cite** evidence for why scientists think the Sun is composed of hydrogen and helium gases.

- **Calculate** the wavelengths of light emitted from transitions of electrons in the Bohr atom.

What Do You Think?

You are very fortunate. With the invention of the electric light, you can engage in the same activities at night as you can during the day. You use fluorescent bulbs, incandescent bulbs, light-emitting diodes, and street lamps to produce light.

- **How is the light from different sources similar and how is it different?**

Record your ideas about this question in your *Active Physics* log. Be prepared to discuss your responses with your small group and your class.

Investigate

You are going to use your observation of colors to find information that will contain clues about the structure of an atom. Your teacher will set up tubes of hydrogen, helium, and neon gases and connect each to a high-voltage power supply. You will identify the gases in each tube by matching the colors you see to a specific set of wavelengths. Finally, you will explore Bohr's model of an atom and how light is emitted by electrons.

Active Physics

> ⚠ Only your teacher will handle the power supply and the tubes of gas. The power supply uses high voltage, which can be dangerous. The tubes of gas are glass and can be broken, leaving sharp edges. Do not look into bright lights (other than the sample of study) or the Sun with the spectrometer.

1. Observe the light of each tube with the naked eye. Then observe the same light with a spectrometer. A spectrometer is a device used to measure a wavelength of light. You teacher will explain how to use the spectrometer.

✎ a) Record your observations in your *Active Physics* log.

✎ b) The spectrometer has a scale and values within for measurement of the wavelengths of light. Record the wavelengths that correspond to each color of light that you are observing in each tube. The wavelengths are measured in nanometers (nm). The prefix *nano* means 10^{-9}. 1 nm = 10^{-9} m $\left(1 \text{ nm} = 0.000000001 \text{ m}\right)$. The wavelengths of visible light range from about 450 nm (violet) to about 700 nm (red).

2. The light emitted by each of the three tubes is comprised of a distinct pattern of colors. These colors correspond to specific wavelengths of light. Each gas has its own distinct set of wavelengths.

✎ a) Write down three wavelengths of light from one gas tube. Pass this list on to someone else in your group. Have that person identify the name of the gas you chose. Were you all successful?

Scientists try to determine characteristic properties of substances. A characteristic property of a substance is a unique attribute that can be used to identify that substance and distinguish it from other substances. Fingerprints or DNA patterns for humans are characteristic properties. No two people have been found who share an identical fingerprint or identical DNA (other than identical twins). The spectrum of light from a gas is a characteristic property of specific atoms in that gas.

3. When the spectrum of light from the Sun was analyzed, a set of observed wavelengths had the following values: 434 nm, 471 nm, 486 nm, 588 nm, 656 nm, and 668 nm.

✎ a) Which gas on Earth emits three of these wavelengths of light?

✎ b) Which gas on Earth emits the other three wavelengths?

✎ c) From these observations, what can you conclude about the gases that comprise the Sun?

4. In 1913 Niels Bohr, as a young physicist, constructed a model of the hydrogen atom that could account for the spectral lines of hydrogen. Bohr's model consists of only a few simple assumptions:

• A proton forms a nucleus and the single electron orbits the proton.

• The electron orbits in a circular path.

• The electron is held in orbit about the proton by Coulomb's law (unlike charges attract).

828

So far, the Bohr model is a replica of a tiny solar system, where the proton is like a little Sun, and the electron a planet. In this model, Coulomb's law plays the same role as Newton's law of universal gravitation. Bohr's model can be described by standard physics. However, Bohr made the following radical assumptions. He hypothesized that:

- the electron could only exist in specific orbits of specific radii. These specific radii corresponded to specific energies, and

- the radiation from the electron (the spectral lines) only occurs when the electron jumps from one orbit to another orbit.

From this model, Bohr derived an equation for the specific energies at different energy levels.

$$E_n = -13.6\left(\frac{1}{n^2}\right)eV$$

where $n = 1, 2, 3, 4...$

$$E_n = E_1, E_2, E_3, E_4...$$

eV = electron volt (a unit of energy, the amount of energy given an electron by a 1-V battery)

The energy of the electron's first orbit

$(n = 1)$ is $E_1 = -13.6\left(\frac{1}{1^2}\right)eV = -13.6\ eV.$

$E_1\ (n = 1)$ is also called the ground state.

The energy of the electron in the second orbit

$(n = 2)$ is $E_2 = -13.6\left(\frac{1}{2^2}\right)eV = -3.4\ eV.$

$E_2\ (n = 2)$ is also called the first excited state.

a) Calculate the energy of the electron in the 3rd, 4th, 5th, and 6th orbits.

5. When a particle is bound to another particle, the system is defined to have "negative" energy. To liberate one particle from the other, energy must be put into the system to raise the energy of an electron from a negative value up to zero. In hydrogen, an electron in orbit about the proton in the $n = 1$ orbit (the "ground state") has an energy of -13.6 eV. An electron in the ground state would have to be given 13.6 eV to free it.

a) Explain why an electron in the $n = 2$ orbit (the "first excited state," the state just above the ground state) would have to be given 3.4 eV to free it.

b) How much energy would have to be given to an electron in the $n = 3, 4, 5,$ and 6 states to free it?

6. The energy required to free an electron from a nucleus is called its ionization energy. The ionization energy of an electron in the ground state is 13.6 eV. The ionization energy of an electron in the $n = 2$ state is 3.4 eV.

a) What are the ionization energies of the electron in the $n = 3, 4, 5,$ and 6 states?

7. Niels Bohr explained why light was given off by the hydrogen atom. Light is emitted when the electron begins in one orbit and then jumps to a lower orbit. During that jump the electron loses energy. The energy lost by the electron in making the downward jump becomes the energy of light that is emitted. In this process, energy is conserved. If one object loses energy, something else must gain that same amount of energy for the total energy to remain the same.

Example:

Calculate the energy of light emitted by a hydrogen atom when the electron jumps from the $n = 3$ to the $n = 2$ state.

The energy of electron in $n = 3$ state $= -1.51$ eV

The energy of electron in $n = 2$ state $= -3.40$ eV

An electron jumping from $n = 3$ to $n = 2$ would have a change of energy.

$$\Delta E = E_{\text{final}} - E_{\text{initial}}$$
$$= E_2 - E_3$$
$$= -3.40 \text{ eV} - (-1.51 \text{ eV})$$
$$= -3.40 \text{ eV} + 1.51 \text{ eV}$$
$$= -1.89 \text{ eV}$$

The electron lost 1.89 eV of energy. Light was created with exactly this 1.89 eV of energy. Light of this energy leaves the atom, and can be observed by the spectrometer as red light. The wavelength of this light is a measure of its 1.89 eV of energy.

a) Calculate the change of energy ΔE when an electron jumps from E_4 to E_2.

b) Calculate the change of energy ΔE when an electron jumps from E_5 to E_2.

c) Calculate the change of energy ΔE when an electron jumps from E_6 to E_2.

Each of these energies corresponds to a specific wavelength of light. These were the colors of light that you observed in the spectrometer for hydrogen.

8. The success of Bohr's model was not limited to a way to calculate the light emitted from hydrogen that was observed with a spectrometer. Bohr also predicted that there would be light emitted from hydrogen that had never been observed.

a) The energy of this light would be due to electron jumps from $n = 2$ to $n = 1$, $n = 3$ to $n = 1$, $n = 4$ to $n = 1$.

Calculate the energies corresponding to these three transitions when the electron jumps from one energy level to another.

b) Other light emitted would be due to electron jumps to the $n = 3$ level. List three transitions to the $n = 3$ level and calculate the energies corresponding to these transitions.

c) Compare the energies of light emitted when electrons jump from higher levels to the $n = 2$ level, to the $n = 1$ level, and to the $n = 3$ level.

Physics Talk

BOHR'S MODEL OF AN ATOM

In the *Investigate*, you observed the **spectral lines** of several gases. These lines of different wavelengths tell you something about the structure of hydrogen, helium, neon, and the other elements as well. The lines are a means by which nature reveals its secrets.

Each element gives off only certain colors. The colors of each element are unique to that element. Niels Bohr began with the Rutherford model of the atom, which had a tiny nucleus in the center. From the Rutherford model he created a model of the hydrogen atom that was able to account for the specific colors of light given off by hydrogen. Hydrogen has only one proton and one electron.

In the Bohr model of an atom,

- the proton is the nucleus and the single electron orbits (revolves) around the nucleus in the same way that the planets orbit the Sun.

- the electron is able to move in a circle about the proton because of the attractive Coulomb force between the positively charged proton and the negatively charged electron.

- the electron can only be found in specific orbits with specific radii. Each orbit (path of an electron) has a specific energy associated with it. The energy levels of the orbits follow a simple pattern:

$$E_n = -13.6\left(\frac{1}{n^2}\right)\text{eV}$$

where n = 1,2,3,4...

$$E_n = E_1, E_2, E_3, E_4...$$

eV= electron volt (a unit of energy)

Physics Words

spectral lines: the lines of different colors that tell something about the structure of an element.

ionization energy: the energy required to free an electron from its energy level.

The negative sign in the equation indicates that the energy of the electron is negative. When a particle is bound to another particle, the system is said to have "negative" energy, because to free one particle from the other, and therefore raise its energy up to zero, energy must be put into the system. In hydrogen, an electron in orbit about the proton in the $n=1$ orbit (the "ground state") has an energy of -13.6 eV. An electron in the ground state would have to be given 13.6 eV to free it. The energy required to free an electron from a nucleus is called its ionization energy. The **ionization energy** of an electron in the ground state is 13.6 eV.

Active Physics

Using the equation,
$$E_n = -13.6\left(1/n^2\right)\text{eV with}$$
$n = 2, 3, 4, 5,$ and 6

yields the corresponding energies for excited states of the electron as shown in the sketch of the possible orbits for the hydrogen electron.

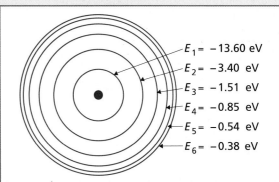

$E_1 = -13.60$ eV
$E_2 = -3.40$ eV
$E_3 = -1.51$ eV
$E_4 = -0.85$ eV
$E_5 = -0.54$ eV
$E_6 = -0.38$ eV

According to Bohr's model, these are the only allowable orbits for the electron. When the electron orbits the nucleus, it is restricted to these orbits and these energies. It cannot orbit at any distance from the nucleus, but only in these specific orbits.

The puzzle that Bohr was seeking to solve was finding the relationship between these energy levels and the wavelengths of light emitted in the hydrogen spectra. Bohr proposed that light is emitted when the electron jumps from a higher orbit to a lower orbit. For example, when the electron jumps from the $n = 3$ orbit to the $n = 2$ orbit, red light is emitted. The energy of the emitted red light is exactly equal to the change in energy of the electron. When the electron jumps from the $n = 4$ orbit to the $n = 2$ orbit, green light is emitted. The energy of the emitted green light is exactly equal to the change in energy of the electron.

Bohr's model and calculations correctly predicted the energy, wavelengths, and color of the light you observed from the hydrogen spectra with the transitions $E_3 \rightarrow E_2$, $E_4 \rightarrow E_2$, $E_5 \rightarrow E_2$, and $E_6 \rightarrow E_2$.

Bohr's model did more than this. Bohr also predicted that light would be emitted when the electron jumps from

$E_2 \rightarrow E_1$, $E_3 \rightarrow E_1$, $E_4 \rightarrow E_1$, $E_5 \rightarrow E_1$ and $E_6 \rightarrow E_1$.

Physics Words

Balmer series: the visible light rays of the hydrogen electromagnetic spectrum.

Lyman series: the ultraviolet light rays of the hydrogen electromagnetic spectrum.

Paschen series: the infrared light rays of the hydrogen electromagnetic spectrum.

His calculations indicated that these energies of light are not visible to the human eye. Visible light is only one part of the electromagnetic spectrum. If an ultraviolet detector is used, these exact wavelengths are observed. The visible light rays of the electromagnetic spectrum of hydrogen are called the **Balmer series**. The ultraviolet light of the electromagnetic spectrum rays are called the **Lyman series**.

Light should also be emitted when the electron drops from $E_4 \rightarrow E_3$, $E_5 \rightarrow E_3$, and $E_6 \rightarrow E_3$. These energies can also be calculated. The light with these energies is also not visible to the human eye. If an infrared detector is used, these additional wavelengths are observed. These infrared light rays are called the **Paschen series**.

Active Physics

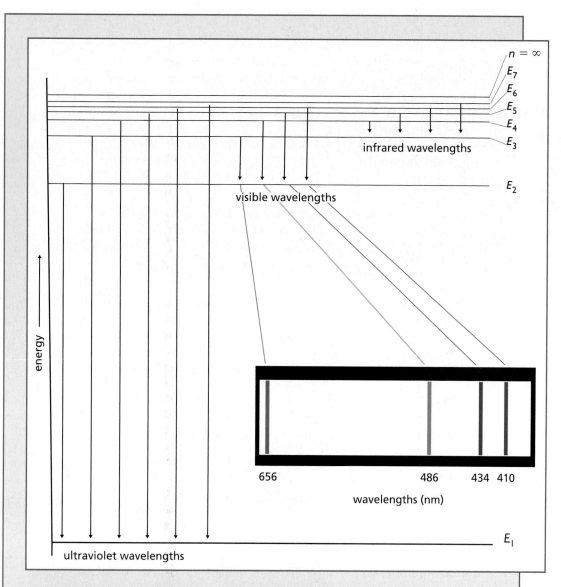

A good new theory should be able to explain whatever the old theory could explain. The new theory should also be able to explain something that the old theory could not explain. Finally, the new theory should be able to make a prediction of something that nobody had thought of previously. If that prediction turns out to be true, then you can sense the power of the theory. The Balmer and Paschen series had been observed before Bohr's theory. The Lyman series had never been observed. Bohr predicted the wavelengths of the Lyman series and then they were observed with the predicted wavelengths. Other spectra corresponding to transitions to the $n = 4$ state were also found later.

Energy can be provided to free an electron by having the electron absorb light. When the electron absorbs light, it jumps up to a higher energy state, the reverse of Bohr's downward transitions that emit light.

Active Physics

Unless the electron is completely removed from the atom, the only light that can be absorbed (or emitted) by the electron is the light that has just the right energy and just the right wavelength to get the electron to another fixed orbit. If the light has a little less energy or a bit more energy, it has no effect. If the electron absorbs enough light, it can be freed from the attractive force of the nucleus. So a neutral atom loses its electron to become a **positive ion**. This transition process is called **ionization**.

Discovery of Helium

When viewing the Sun, the following set of wavelengths can be observed: 410 nm, 434 nm, 471 nm, 486 nm, 588 nm, 656 nm, and 668 nm. From your observations in the *Investigate*, you concluded that these values match the wavelengths emitted by hydrogen and helium. This conclusion led you to the conclusion that the Sun is comprised of hydrogen and helium.

The history of these values, however, is a bit more interesting. The set of values corresponding to hydrogen (410, 434, 486, and 656 nm) were known from the lab. Nobody had ever observed other wavelengths (471, 588, 668 nm) in a lab. In 1868, Pierre Janssen observed one new yellow line from the Sun during a total eclipse in India. J. Norman Lockyear interpreted this yellow line as being evidence of a new element. This set of wavelengths did not correspond to any gas on Earth and so this unknown gas of the Sun was named "helium" after Helios, the Greek god of the Sun. Years later, in 1895, helium gas was discovered on Earth by William Ramsey of Scotland and independently by Per Cleve of Sweden.

Physics Words

positive ion: an ion created when a neutral atom loses its electron.

ionization: the process in which a neutral atom becomes an ion.

Checking Up

1. Using Bohr's model of an atom, explain why an electron remains in its orbit.

2. Why are different wavelengths of light found in a hydrogen spectrum?

3. If the energy of an electron in the ground state is -13.6 eV, would it able to jump to a higher orbit at -3.4 eV? Explain.

+Math	+Depth	+Concepts	+Exploration
◆◆		◆	

Calculations Involving the Hydrogen Atom

The Bohr model has a single electron of hydrogen orbiting a single proton nucleus of hydrogen. The force that holds an electron in orbit is the Coulomb electrostatic force between two unlike charged objects.

a) Using Coulomb's equation:

$$F = k \frac{q_1 q_2}{d^2}$$

calculate the force between the proton and electron (each has a charge of 1.6×10^{-19} C. The distance between them is 5×10^{-10} m.

As you will see in the next section, in 1905 Albert Einstein proposed the relationship between the energy of light and its frequency in the following equation:

$$E = hf$$

where E is the energy of light,
h is Planck's constant,
$\left(6.63 \times 10^{-34} \text{ J} \cdot \text{s}\right)$, and
f is the frequency of light.

To know the frequency is to know the wavelength. Wavelengths of light (λ) can be found from the wave equation

$$c = f\lambda$$

where c is the speed of light $(3.0 \times 10^8 \text{ m/s})$.

Einstein's proposed equation for the energy of light $E = hf$ can be combined with Bohr's calculation of the energy given to the light when the electron jumps from E_3 to E_2. You can use this combination to predict the spectrum of emitted light. You must also convert from the energy unit of electron volts to joules if you wish the wavelength to be in meters. To calculate the wavelength using the energy lost by the electron during the jump in electron volts requires using Planck's constant (h) in electron volts, or $h = 4.1 \times 10^{-15}$ eV.

Combining the two equations:
$\Delta E = hf$ and $c = f\lambda$ gives

$$\lambda = \frac{h \cdot c}{|\Delta E|}$$

where $h \cdot c$ is

$$(4.1 \times 10^{-15} \text{ eV} \cdot \text{s})(3 \times 10^8 \text{ m/s})$$

Therefore,

$$\lambda = \frac{1.24 \times 10^{-6} \text{ (m)(eV)}}{|\Delta E|}$$

ΔE is the energy change in electron volts (eV).

Example:

When the electron jumps from E_3 to E_2, the change in energy is 1.89 eV.

a) Calculate the corresponding wavelength of light.

$$\lambda = \frac{hc}{|\Delta E|}$$

$$\lambda = \frac{1.24 \times 10^{-6} \text{ (m)(eV)}}{|\Delta E|}$$

$$\lambda = \frac{1.24 \times 10^{-6} \text{ (m)(eV)}}{|1.89 \text{eV}|}$$

$$\lambda = 654 \text{ nm}$$

The wavelength determined by the above calculations equals the measured wavelength of the red line of hydrogen.

1. Calculate the wavelengths of light when the electron jumps from

   E_4 to E_2, E_5 to E_2, and E_6 to E_2.

2. How do these values compare with the ones you found in your observations of the hydrogen spectra?

What Do You Think Now?

At the beginning of this section you were asked the following:

• **How is the light from different sources similar and how is it different?**

You observed the difference in colors of light emitted by different gases. How does the wavelength of those colors relate to the structure of an atom?

Physics
Essential Questions

What does it mean?

The spectra of light for a given element (hydrogen, helium, neon) is said to be a fingerprint for that element. What is the spectra of hydrogen and why can the spectra be used as evidence that a gas is hydrogen, not neon?

How do you know?

What evidence do you have from the *Investigate* that the spectra of different gases are different?

Why do you believe?

Connects with Other Physics Content	Fits with Big Ideas in Science	Meets Physics Requirements
Optics	Symmetry – laws of physics are the same everywhere	✳ Good, clear, explanation, no more complex than necessary

✳ Physics tries to use the same explanation to explain observations anywhere on Earth and anywhere in the universe. You observe certain spectral lines from the Sun that are identical to the lines that are emitted from hydrogen and helium gas on Earth. Why do you believe that the Sun is composed of hydrogen and helium?

Why should you care?

The light from different gases has different colors and wavelengths. This light reveals something about the structure of the atom. How can you use this revelation to both generate interest in museum visitors and help them understand about Bohr's model of the atom?

Reflecting on the Section and the Challenge

The Bohr atom has electrons orbiting in "special" orbits surrounding the nucleus. Light is emitted when electrons jump from a higher-energy orbit to a lower orbit. An electron that absorbs energy can jump from a lower orbit to a higher-energy orbit. The wavelengths of light can be calculated, observed, and measured. The values from Bohr's theory and your observations from hydrogen are almost exactly equal. In your museum exhibit, you may try to show the Bohr model of the atom and the emission of light as electrons jump from one energy level to another.

You may also wish to show how an atom becomes ionized when the electron absorbs enough energy to free it. Finally, you may choose to show that invisible light in the ultraviolet and infrared regions is also emitted. Electron jumps and emitted light can be an interactive museum display. Will your display create an immediate interest? Provide a means by which the museum visitor will want to stop and see what is going on with hydrogen.

Physics to Go

1. Light of greater energy has a higher frequency. In the hydrogen spectrum, which visible line has the greatest energy? Which transition does this line correspond to?

2. Compare the energy of the light emitted from the electron jump from $n = 3$ to $n = 2$ to the light emitted from $n = 5$ to $n = 2$.

3. Given that the speed of light equals 3.0×10^8 m/s and the wavelength of light is 389 nm $(389 \times 10^{-9} \text{m})$, calculate the frequency of the light.

4. Calculate the energies of each Bohr orbit using the equation $E = -13.6 \text{ eV} (1/n^2)$ for $n = 1, 2, 3, 4,$ and 5.

5. Make a scale diagram showing the energies of each Bohr orbit as a vertical number line which goes from -13.6 eV to 0 eV.

6. The hydrogen spectrum is said to be a "fingerprint" for hydrogen. Explain why this is a useful metaphor (comparison).

7. Why can't light of 500 nm be given off from hydrogen?

8. Electrons can jump from the $n = 4$ state directly to the $n = 3$ or $n = 2$ or $n = 1$ states. Similarly, there are multiple jumps from $n = 3$. How many different wavelengths of light can be given off from electrons that begin in the $n = 4$ orbit?

9. Suppose you could build an atom with the following energy levels for its electron:

   a) $E = -(10\text{eV})(1/n)$ where $n = 1, 2, 3,$ and 4. Draw a diagram of the electron's energy levels. Describe the spectrum, that is, what are the energies of the spectral lines?

   b) Repeat 9.a) if $E = -(10 \text{ eV})(1/n)^2$.

10. A candle flame is mostly yellow; the flame from a welder's torch is bright blue. Why are these colors different?

11. *Preparing for the Chapter Challenge*

    How could the electron transitions be creatively displayed in a museum exhibit? Describe a way in which the display could be interactive.

Your challenge for this chapter is to create a new museum exhibit that will educate people about the atom. Your group will have many decisions to make regarding your exhibit. Use the physics from the sections you have completed so far to help you generate ideas for your exhibit. Remember, make it interactive and fun. You only have 30 seconds to get the audience's attention.

You still have more to learn before you can complete the challenge, but now is a good time to give the *Chapter Challenge* a first try. You are now halfway through the chapter and you have learned a lot about the structure of an atom. Your *Mini-Challenge* is to create an entrance poster, an exit poster, written text for education, a potential item for the gift shop, and at least a diagram of what you want your exhibit to look like to help it grab the audience's attention. Your group will then present your work to the class. Everything you create for your *Mini-Challenge* can be incorporated into your final museum exhibit design, so the more work you do now the better your final design will be.

You have a good understanding about the types of particles that are contained in an atom and you have learned a lot about the way those particles are arranged inside of the atom. The sections that you have completed so far may also help you think of hands-on ways to get museum visitors involved in your exhibit.

Go back and quickly read the *Goal* at the start of the chapter. There you will find all of the details for completing the entire challenge. At this point you will focus on the portions you can complete with the physics you have learned so far.

Each of the sections you have completed so far is rich with information you can use to create your museum exhibit. You have learned scientific measuring techniques, history content about the discovery of the atom, and detailed information about the structure of an atom. All you have to do is decide how to present that information in an exciting and interactive way.

Your team should review the physics content from the first four sections to help you create your initial toy design.

Section 1: You explored the nature of electrically charged objects. You also worked with a model for calculating the forces that charged objects exert on each other, Coulomb's law.

Section 2: You used deductive reasoning to examine the contents of a container without looking inside. This was one of the methods Millikan used to discover that electric charges come only in certain "quantized" amounts.

Section 3: You applied an indirect method to measure the area of a penny to simulate how Rutherford originally discovered and measured the size of an atomic nucleus. You then compared your results to the actual value for the area of a penny and explored the ratio of the size of a nucleus to the size of an atom.

Section 4: You examined the different colors of light that are emitted by a specific atom when it is energized. You also learned how each atom can be identified by the colors of light it gives off because the type of light depends on the arrangement of electrons in each particular atom.

 This challenge has a lot of products that you are responsible for creating. While you are not required to create the actual museum exhibit, models and diagrams will be very useful to help you explain your ideas. Models can also be very helpful in helping your design team decide on which design ideas you will actually include in your exhibit. For the *Mini-Challenge* as previously mentioned, you should create the entrance poster, the exit poster, written text for education, a potential item for the gift shop, and at least a diagram of what you want your exhibit to look like to help it grab the audience's attention. You might find it useful to assign one "product" to each member of your group to help ensure that each one gets completed. You can work together to develop the content, but having a product champion makes sure that someone is concentrating on each piece of the requirements.

During this challenge, time will be an important constraint for your team. It is difficult to complete so many different tasks in a short period of time. Communicating effectively with the members of your group will be essential. You may also find that in order to meet the presentation deadline you have to move forward with a design idea that is not perfect or completely thought out. The process will be stressful, so it is important to communicate often and as clearly as possible and to be accepting of others in your group. Collaboration on a project is difficult, collaboration on a short schedule is very difficult, and you will need the support of each one of your group members to be successful.

 Presenting your information to the class is your design cycle *Output*. For the *Mini-Challenge* you should have a lot of products to present. If you create a model of each product you will find it much easier to explain your ideas. Models will also make your presentation more interesting to watch. Don't forget that the accuracy and completeness of your written educational information is also an important output of your presentation.

 Your classmates will give you *Feedback* on the accuracy and the overall appeal of your exhibit idea and the different models you used to help present it. This *Feedback* will become an *Input* for your final design in the *Chapter Challenge*. You will have enough time to make corrections and improvements, so you will want to pay attention to the valuable information they provide.

Remember to correct any parts of your design that didn't meet the design goals of the *Mini-Challenge*. It will be harder to remember what you need to change if you wait until the chapter is complete to go back and correct your mistakes. When you are finished revising, store all of your information in a safe place so that it will be ready to use in the *Chapter Challenge*.

During the second half of the chapter you will learn more details about the structure of the atom and some of the methods scientists used to discover the properties of these "invisible" particles. As you complete the chapter, remember to add ideas to your entry and exit poster as well as to add educational materials to your exhibit. You may also use one of these new sections to inspire more interactive ideas for your exhibit.

Section 5

Wave-Particle Model of Light: Two Models Are Better Than One!

What Do You See?

Learning Outcomes

In this section, you will

- **Observe** the diffraction of light waves.

- **Observe** the interference of sound waves.

- **Observe** the interference of light waves.

- **Construct** a model of wave interference.

- **Solve** simple problems related to the photoelectric effect.

- **Describe** the wave-particle duality of light.

- **Describe** the wave-particle duality of electrons.

What Do You Think?

Light from the Sun takes eight minutes to reach Earth. Light from the nearest star takes years to reach Earth. Light from another galaxy takes millions of years to reach Earth.

- **When you turn on a lamp and the light travels from the bulb to your book, how long do you think it takes to get there?**

- **How does light travel from one place to another?**

Record your answers to these questions in your *Active Physics* log. Be prepared to discuss your responses with your small group and your class.

Investigate

In *Investigate*, you will observe the wave properties of light by simulating wave motion. You will observe constructive and destructive interference, and diffraction. By investigating Einstein's theory of the photoelectric effect you will learn about the nature of light. Finally, you will also compare the behavior of electrons to the behavior of light.

Part A: Does Light Behave as a Wave?

1. Physics is the art of creating *models* in terms of which scientists try to understand objects and processes in nature. Two important models are *particles* and *waves*. Particles are localized bits of matter, like a ball in flight. Waves spread out like ripples in a pond, even though the water does not move in bulk.

   a) If you write a letter, stuff it into an envelope and mail it to a friend, are you using particle motion or wave motion?

   b) When the crowd at a football game does a "wave" around the stadium, why is it called a "wave"?

   c) When you listen to music, does the sound travel from the band to your ears as a particle, or as a wave?

   d) In a hailstorm, does the hail come down as particles, or as waves?

   e) Does light from the Sun come to Earth as particles, or as waves?

   From the model of an atom, you have a good idea that most of the mass and all the positive charge are in a central nucleus, and the low-mass, negatively charged electrons orbit the nucleus. To better understand the behavior of the orbiting electrons, you must understand the contrasting properties of waves and particles.

2. The hallmark feature of wave motion is interference. When waves pass by each other, in some locations there are conditions where there is no motion of the medium, whatsoever. In the diagram, source 1 and source 2 interfere with each other and in some locations the waves cancel each other out. If these waves were in water, water waves + water waves would create still water.

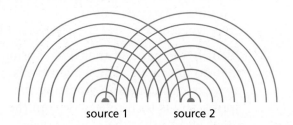

source 1   source 2

If sound were a wave, it would mean that sound + sound could equal silence. If light were a wave, it would mean that light + light could create dark.

Demonstrating interference is definitive evidence of wave phenomena.

   a) For the water waves shown above, the blue circles represent the crests of waves and the red circles represent the troughs of waves. Whenever a crest and a trough meet, the waves cancel. In your log, indicate where the waves would cancel to produce still water.

3. Consider a musical instrument, perhaps a guitar. When a string is plucked, the waves that travel up and down the string are some combination of standing waves that you will now simulate with a giant coiled spring.

   Stretch a coiled spring (or a rope) between you and your lab partner. While one of you holds one end fixed, the other will vibrate the spring. Adjust the *frequency* (number of times per second you shake the coiled spring) until you produce as many patterns as you can. In the diagrams below, *L* is the length of the coiled spring:

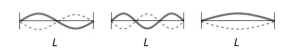

   L   *L*   *L*

a) In your *Active Physics* log, sketch the standing wave patterns that you were able to make.

b) Identify the parts of the coiled spring that do not move. The wave travels away from the person vibrating the spring and is then reflected from the other end so that the wave travels back toward that person. You have two waves interfering. The points where the spring does not move are called *nodes*. You conclude that the coiled spring waves are waves because they can interfere with one another and form nodes.

4. Hit a tuning fork gently against a rubber stand. Place the tuning fork near your ear. Slowly rotate the tuning fork so that one prong gets closer to the ear while the other gets further away. Listen carefully to the volume of the sound.

 Do not touch the vibrating tuning fork to your skin, especially near your ear.

a) Record your observations in your log.

A tuning fork produces identical sounds from each prong. At one orientation from the prongs to your eardrum, you heard a loud sound. This loud sound was *constructive interference*. When the orientation from the prongs to your ear was different, the sound diminished.

The interference of waves is another property of wave behavior. If you are unsure that you observed the interference of sound, listen to the tuning fork again. Because sound from one prong of the tuning fork can interfere with the prong of the other tuning fork and produce areas of very low sound (nodes), you conclude that sound is exhibiting a wave phenomenon.

5. Is light a wave? Two properties that define waves are interference and diffraction. The process of light bending and spreading out as it squeezes through a small opening is called *diffraction*. Light bending around an edge is also referred to as diffraction. Here you will use a laser. Shine a laser beam against a wall as shown on the next page.

 Never look directly at a laser beam or shine a laser beam into someone's eyes. Always work above the plane of the beam and beware of reflections from shiny surfaces.

a) Place a piece of paper on the wall, and trace the beam onto the piece of paper to measure its thickness. Record your measurement.

b) Place a single narrow slit in front of the beam. Measure and record the thickness of the beam again.

c) Place a thinner slit in front of the beam. Measure and record the thickness a final time.

d) What happens to the width of the laser beam as it passes through a smaller and smaller opening?

Diffraction is one of the properties that all waves exhibit, including water waves and sound waves. Diffraction of light seems to suggest that light is a wave.

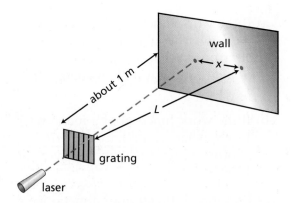

6. If you can find an instance where light plus light produces no light (a node), you will have evidence that light is a wave. Shine a laser beam through two slits or a diffraction grating made up of many slits. Direct the beam at a distant wall. Your teacher may do this as a demonstration. Observe the pattern of the light on the wall.

a) Record your observations in your log.

b) From your observations, what can you conclude about the ability of light to interfere? Are there places on the wall where there is no light? Explain.

On the distant wall, you will see places where the light from neighboring slits interferes constructively (there is maximum light) and places where the light interferes destructively (there is little or no light). These places of darkness are evidence of the interference of light and would seem to suggest that light behaves like a wave.

Part B: The Photoelectric Effect

Now that you have found that light behaves like a wave you can turn to the puzzle that Einstein solved. This puzzle, the *photoelectric effect*, has to do with the behavior of light shining on metal and freeing electrons from the metal. You make use of this effect in everyday life: solar-powered calculators, solar collectors, photogates for electronic timers, digital cameras, television remote controls, door-opener sensors, etc. This idea is illustrated with an analogy as follows:

1. A vending machine sells potato chips. The machine is not able to add coins.

Suppose a bag of potato chips costs 10¢.

- If you place 10¢ in the machine, a bag of potato chips comes out.

- If you place 5¢ in the machine, your 5¢ is returned.

- If you place 25¢ in the machine, a bag of potato chips comes out and you get 15¢ in change.

- If you place 2 nickels in the machine, the 2 nickels are returned (the machine cannot add coins).

a) What would happen if you placed a 50-cent piece in the machine?

b) What would happen if you placed 20 pennies in the machine?

c) What would happen if you placed a $1.00 coin in the machine?

d) An equation that could describe the behavior of the machine would be:

money inserted = returned money + cost of chips.

Does this equation work for the examples above?

This vending machine can be used to explain the photoelectric effect. In the photoelectric effect, light hits a metal surface and an electron may be freed. In the term photoelectric, "photo" is for the light and "electric" is for the freed electron.

In the photoelectric effect:

- The frequencies of light are like the coins placed in the chip machine. Some frequencies of light will never free electrons, regardless of how much light there is. This phenomenon is similar to having lots of pennies or nickels to place in the vending machine.

- Frequencies of light above a certain minimum frequency, called the threshold frequency, will free electrons. This phenomenon is similar to requiring at least a dime to get a bag of chips.

Active Physics

- Also, the brighter the light, above the threshold frequency, the more electrons freed. This phenomenon is similar to having lots of dimes to place in the chip machine and more than one bag of chips in the machine.

- Some frequencies of light will free electrons and give them lots of kinetic energy. This phenomenon is similar to quarters being placed in the chip machine. Each quarter gets a bag of chips and some change.

Einstein was able to explain the experimental observations of the photoelectric effect by assuming that light collided with the metal as particles of light. Each particle or *photon* of light would have a specific energy.

A metal may require a minimum energy of 10 eV to free a single electron. The minimum energy needed to remove an electron from an atom is called the *work function*. If each photon of light has less than 10 eV of energy, then no electrons will be freed, no matter how many photons are in the light beam. (This situation is similar to requiring 10¢ to get a bag of chips. No matter how many nickels or pennies you have, you will not be able to get chips.) If the photon of light has exactly 10 eV of energy, then one electron will be released. If the photon of light has 25 eV of energy, then one electron will be released and it will leave with 15 eV of kinetic energy.

2. This process can be written as an equation, very similar to the equation for the chips:

energy of light = (kinetic energy of freed electron) + (work function).

Or, in symbols,

$$E_{light} = KE_{electron} + w_o$$

a) If the work function of a metal were 7 eV, what would happen to the electrons in that metal if the photons of light hitting it had an energy of 12 eV?

b) If the work function of a metal were 12 eV, what would happen if the photons of light had an energy of 12 eV?

c) If the work function of a metal were 7 eV, what would happen if the photons of light had an energy of 18 eV?

d) If the work function of a metal were 9 eV, what would happen if the photons of light had an energy of 12 eV?

e) If the work function of a metal were 14 eV, what would happen if the photons of light had an energy of 12 eV?

3. The energy of light can be determined by its frequency, wavelength or color. Red light comes in low-energy packets of *photons*, violet light comes in high-energy packets and ultraviolet light comes in even higher-energy packets. The equation is

$$E = hf$$

where E is the energy of the photon of light,

h is a constant, called Planck's constant $\left(6.63 \times 10^{-34}\ J \cdot s\right)$, and

f is the frequency of light.

a) Explain why shining a very bright red light may not free an electron from a metal surface, while shining a very dim violet light may free many electrons.

Part C: Matter Waves – The Nature of Electrons

1. Recall that light shows both particle-like and wave-like behavior, and which one it shows depends on the experiment you are doing with light. Louis de Broglie, a French physicist, had a striking thought: Perhaps if two models are necessary for light, two models are also necessary for electrons. Electrons hit screens as if they are particles. Could they go through slits and exhibit interference?

If nature takes this suggestion seriously, then when you fire a beam of electrons through a double slit, you should see an interference pattern identical to that made by light of the same wavelength.

An experiment to test this idea with electron beams was first done in 1929 and confirmed the de Broglie hypothesis! The results are shown in the diagram.

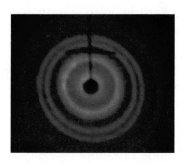

a) Sketch the diagram of the experimental result in your notebook. Indicate in your drawing that the dark positions are where no electrons hit the screen. These are nodes.

To create this experimental result, electrons traveled through a metal crystal of atoms. The spaces between the atoms served as "slits" for the electron beam. The electrons set up a diffraction/interference pattern on the screen. This is evidence that electrons can exhibit wave characteristics.

In summary, you have an astonishing result: For some situations, the electron can be described only in terms of waves; for others you have to describe it in terms of particles.

2. Consider, for example, an electron not in an atom, but just bouncing back and forth between the walls of a box. The electron's de Broglie waves in this situation look just like the standing waves on the coiled spring and like the standing waves on a guitar string.

a) Keeping in mind the guitar string concept, draw two additional waves that could fit in the box.

b) Identify where the nodes are for each of the standing waves.

3. The de Broglie wave determines the location of the electron in the box. If you imagine the standing wave in the box, the electron will most often be found where the peaks (*antinodes*) of the wave are located. The electron will never be found at the positions where the nodes are located.

a) In the first diagram on the next page, you expect that the electron will usually be found somewhere near the middle of the box because that is where the antinode is. The electron is never found at the edges of the box because there are nodes at both ends. Copy this diagram into your log and mark the spot where the electron is most likely to be found.

b) In the second diagram, you expect that the electron will usually be found on the left side of the box or on the right side of the box. The electron will never be found in the middle of the box because a node exists in the middle of the box. Copy this diagram into your log, and mark the spot where the electron is most likely to be found.

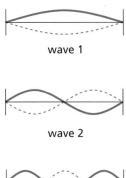

wave 1

wave 2

c) Indicate where it is likely to find the third electron, and where you would never find the third electron.

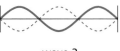

wave 3

Physics Talk

MODELS

The Dilemma of Light

Physics Words

wave: a model that describes transfer of energy without the transfer of matter.

photoelectric effect: the emission of electrons from certain metals when light (electromagnetic radiation) of certain frequencies shines on the metals.

particle: a model that describes localized bits of matter.

model: a conceptual representation of a process, system, or object.

diffraction: the ability of a wave to spread out as it emerges from an opening or moves beyond an obstruction.

The first set of experiments showed that light can diffract and can interfere. The experiments are evidence that light has **wave** characteristics. Einstein's explanation of the **photoelectric effect** also provides evidence that light behaves like a **particle**. In the photoelectric effect the emission of electrons from certain metals takes place when light (electromagnetic radiation) of certain frequencies shines on the metals.

You may want to ask, "What is light, wave or particle?" But that is not the question. Particles and waves are **models** that originated with the ways you think about things. Particles describe localized bits of matter and waves describe transfer of energy without the transfer of matter. These models are a conceptual representation of a process, system, or object. However, neither of these models alone can describe everything that light does. You need both models, using the one or using the other, depending on the situation, to describe all that light can do! For interference, a wave model of light makes sense of our experience; but for the photoelectric effect, a particle model is a better fit.

When you see light rays piercing through the clouds or a laser beam in a music show, you recognize that light travels in straight lines. In this section, you found out that light may also spread out as it squeezes through a small opening.

The process of light spreading out as it squeezes through a small opening is called **diffraction**. Light bending around an edge is also referred to as diffraction. Diffraction is one of the properties that water waves and sound waves exhibit. The phenomenon of diffraction leads toward the conclusion that light might also behave as a wave.

You also explored another property of water and sound waves. When water waves meet, they interfere with one another. **Constructive interference** occurs when the crests of a wave meet the crests of the second wave, and there is lots of movement of the water. **Destructive interference** occurs when the troughs of one wave meet the crests of the other wave and the water remains still.

You used a tuning fork to investigate if sound waves also interfere. A tuning fork produces identical sounds from each prong. At one orientation from the prongs to your eardrum, you heard a loud sound. This loud sound was constructive interference. When the orientation from the prongs to your ear was different, the sound diminished. The sound from one source can meet with the sound from another source and produce silence! The interference of waves is another property of wave behavior.

If light behaves like a wave, then it, too, must show interference. When you shone a laser beam through two slits onto a distant wall, you saw an interference pattern. There were places where the light from neighboring slits interfered constructively (there was maximum light) and places where the light interfered destructively (there was little or no light). Evidence of the interference of light would seem to prove that light behaves like a wave. The colors you see when light reflects off a CD or soap bubble are interference effects.

After you found that light behaves like a wave, you turned to the puzzle of the twentieth century that Einstein solved. The puzzle had to do with the behavior of light when it freed an electron from a metal. In the photoelectric effect, when beams of light shine on metals, some **wavelengths** (and **frequencies**) of light will always free electrons, while other wavelengths (and frequencies) will never free electrons. For some materials, light of high frequency (ultraviolet light) frees electrons and gives them kinetic energy. Light of low frequency (red light) is not able to free any electrons. Einstein developed a model of the process

Physics Words

constructive interference: the result of adding waves crest-to-crest to produce a wave with a greater amplitude.

destructive interference: the result of adding waves crest-to-trough to produce a wave with a decreased amplitude.

wavelength: crest-to-crest distance in a wave.

frequency: number of cycles per second in the wave's vibration.

as a collision between a particle of light (a photon) and an electron. By applying conservation of energy to that process, he derived the following equation for the photoelectric effect in 1905:

$$hf = KE_{electron} + w_o$$

The energy of the light-as-particle is equal to hf where h is Planck's constant $(6.63 \times 10^{-34} \text{J} \cdot \text{s})$ and f is the frequency of the corresponding light-as-wave. Einstein won the Nobel Prize in physics for his concept of photons (not his theory of relativity). A **photon** was described as a particle of electromagnetic radiation, a quantum of light energy.

Comparing the many behaviors of light, the extraordinary conclusion is that light sometimes behaves as a particle (the photoelectric effect) and sometimes behaves like a wave (diffraction and interference effects).

Developing the Wave-Particle Model of Electrons

Now consider the behavior of electrons. Electrons hit the front of your TV screen and make a temporary mark. Electrons have a mass $(9.1 \times 10^{-31} \text{kg})$ and a charge $(1.6 \times 10^{-19} \text{C})$. Electrons behave like particles. Electrons can also interfere! Clinton Davisson and Lester Germer demonstrated this by shooting electrons through a metal crystal foil. They observed some locations on a distant screen where many electrons landed and other locations where no electrons landed. This pattern of locations was identical to an interference pattern formed by light, and was explained as an interference effect of electrons. Electrons, like light, can sometimes behave like a particle and sometimes behave like a wave.

What are you to make of electrons as chunks of matter with a mass and charge, and electrons as standing waves? You need both the wave and particle languages to fully explain the electron. Whatever the electron is, neither a particle concept nor a wave concept can describe everything it does. However, the concept of **wave-particle duality** uses two models to describe the behavior of light—both as a particle and as a wave. A key to understanding wave-particle duality is to recognize that waves and particles are models. Particles and waves are conceptual representations of real things based on experience with familiar objects such as water and billiard balls. These models describe particles as localized bits of matter and waves as a transfer of energy but not matter. The real nature of an electron lies well beyond the range of immediate experience.

Electrons move about the nucleus and in the particle view they move in a restricted orbit. However, the models for the structure of the atom include a wave model. An electron may move about the nucleus, but it is not as simple as being restricted to precise orbits. An electron has wave properties. The best one can do is to describe the probability of where an electron can be found and where it cannot be found.

Physics Words

photon: a particle of electromagnetic radiation; a quantum of light energy.

wave-particle duality: the use of two models of light to explain the behavior of light—both as a particle and as a wave.

In wave language, Bohr's orbits correspond to locations where an electron in three dimensions is most likely to be found. Each orbit corresponds to the most probable location for an electron of specific energy. The equation that describes an electron wave and its corresponding probabilities is the Schrödinger equation. Erwin Schrödinger (1887–1961) was an Austrian physicist who shared a 1933 Nobel Prize for new formulations of the atomic theory.

Schrödinger's equation gives calculated results for the de Broglie waves that agree with experiment far more accurately than Bohr's. The subatomic world is not the like the everyday world you experience. The "everyday" view of the world makes common sense, but does not provide a complete picture of everything. The subatomic world lies far outside everyday experience and therefore appears to contradict common sense, but the models that have been developed of that subatomic world give correct answers. All the numerical results from predictions based on the Schrödinger model are more accurate than Bohr's. It is a dilemma. Do you go with the theory that gives right predictions but sometimes runs counter to common sense or go with common sense that does not give accurate experimental results? What do you think?

Erwin Schrödinger was a Nobel Prize winning physicist.

Checking Up

1. What is the dilemma of light? Explain why two models are used to explain the behavior of light.

2. Explain the difference between constructive and destructive interference.

3. How is an electron similar to light?

Active Physics
Plus

+Math	+Depth	+Concepts	+Exploration
◆			◆◆

The Wavelength of Light

1. If light behaves like a wave, then you can use the interference of light to measure the wavelength of light. Mount a diffraction grating in the path of a laser beam. Mount a screen at least one meter away from the grating as was shown on the next page. Observe the pattern of spots on the screen.

a) Measure and record the separation between one spot and the next, x.

b) Measure and record the perpendicular distance from the grating to the screen, L.

→

Active Physics

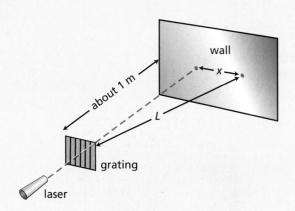

c) Record the spacing between the lines of the grating, *d*. You can use the spacing given by the manufacturer.

From your measurements, find the wavelength of the light. You will use the following equation:

$$\lambda = xd/L$$

where λ is the wavelength of laser light,

x is the separation between the spots,

d is the spacing between lines in the grating.

L is the perpendicular distance from the grating to the central spot on the screen,

Show your calculations in your log.

The Photoelectric Effect

1. In order to study the photoelectric effect, a student will vary the frequency of the light incident on a metal. For each frequency of light, the student recorded the kinetic energy (*KE*) of the ejected electron. The data in the chart below gives the result of one experiment.

a) Graph the results of the data set with the *KE* of the electron on the *y*-axis and the frequency of the incoming light on the *x*-axis.

Frequency of light (Hz) (x10¹⁴)	Maximum kinetic energy of the electron (eV)
6.32	0.15
6.67	0.30
7.06	0.45
7.50	0.65

b) By extending your graph, determine the threshold frequency of this material (i.e., the frequency of light that will free an electron with a *KE* of 0 eV).

c) What is the significance of the slope of the graph?

What Do You Think Now?

At the beginning of the section you were asked the following:

• **When you turn on a lamp and the light travels from the bulb to your book, how long do you think it takes to get there?**

• **How does light travel from one place to another?**

Now that you know more about light, how would you describe its nature? What evidence do you have that light behaves like a wave? How would you explain that light behaves like a particle?

Physics
Essential Questions

What does it mean?

Why can't you say that "the electron is a particle, at all times, and in all circumstances?"
Why can't you say "light is a wave, at all times, and in all circumstances?"

How do you know?

What evidence exists that sometimes light behaves like a wave, but sometimes light behaves like a particle?

Why do you believe?

Connects with Other Physics Content	Fits with Big Ideas in Science	Meets Physics Requirements
nature of matter	✳ Models	Experimental evidence is consistent with models and theories

✳ Physicists use models to explain observations of the world. The simple models of particle or wave were not sufficient to explain the behavior of light. What did physicists do when their models were not satisfactory?

Why should you care?

The structure of the atom includes an electron that exhibits both wave and particle characteristics. How can you incorporate the complex nature of electrons in your museum exhibit?

Reflecting on the Section and the Challenge

In this section, you found out that light behaves like a particle in the photoelectric effect and like a wave in diffraction and interference effects. Similarly, electrons behave like particles when they hit a screen and like waves when they move about the nucleus. The atomic model has grown more complex and because of that you have seen that the simple models have limitations. Your museum exhibit may require you to explain those limitations and why more than one model for light or electrons, and for the atom itself, is necessary. Creativity and your imagination will be required to make this part of your exhibit interactive and scientifically correct.

Physics to Go

1. Describe two differences between particles and waves.

2. Someone decides that a laser beam is not thin enough. They decide to pass the beam through a very thin slit to slim it down. Will this work? Explain.

3. What was the principal understanding that emerged from Einstein's explanation of the photoelectric effect?

4. Why don't you see in everyday life the "wave nature" of a baseball? The mass of a baseball is 0.145 kg. If the baseball moves at 30 m/s, compute its de Broglie wavelength ($\lambda = h/mv$). Since diffraction and interference, to be noticeable, requires slit dimensions that are roughly the same size as the wavelength, is "baseball diffraction" going to be observable?

5. In the photoelectric effect, a 10 eV photon of light frees an electron from a metal with a work function of 4.2 eV. What is the energy of the emitted electron?

6. The equation for the photoelectric effect is:

$$KE_{electron} = E_{light} - w_o$$

Explain what each of the terms in the equation represent.

7. In designing your museum exhibit, what might be a creative way to show the unusual behavior of an electron in an atom?

8. For your museum exhibit or perhaps a product for the museum store, can you invent a photoelectric-effect bank? How would it work?

9. The great physicist Niels Bohr once suggested that there are two kinds of truth: simple truth, and deep truth. The opposite of a simple truth is false, but the opposite of a deep truth is also true. Taking Bohr's definitions of simple and deep truth, is the wave model of light and the particle model of the electron, "simple" or "deep" truths?

10. In the *Physics Talk* section you were asked what you would do: Go with a theory that gives all the right predictions but runs counter to your common sense OR go with your common sense that does not yield accurate experimental results. Explain your answer to this question and the reasoning you used. (Consider that common sense is based on experience.)

11. **Active Physics** **Plus** A certain metal has a work function of 1.8 eV, and the wavelength of its threshold frequency is 700 nm. (A nanometer [nm] is 10^{-9} m.) Light shines on the metal, delivering energy at the rate of 0.01 eV/s.

a) Ignore for a moment the photoelectric effect. Supposing the electron could "soak up" and save all this energy until it could be liberated, how long would it take to liberate the electron?

b) Now recall the existence of the photoelectric effect. Will an electron be emitted if more energy per second is delivered to the metal but the light's wavelength is greater than 700 nm?

c) Will an electron be emitted if less energy per second is delivered to the metal but the light's wavelength is less than 700 nm?

d) Suppose you do the experiment with light at 690 nm, but with an energy delivery rate of 1.8 eV/s. If an electron is emitted in a millionth of a second, what does this mean for the "energy-soaking model" of *Step 11.a*)?

Section 6

The Strong Force: Inside the Nucleus

What Do You See?

Learning Outcomes

In this section, you will

- **Calculate** the number of protons, electrons, and neutrons in a neutral atom, given the atomic number and atomic mass.

- **Calculate** the Coulomb force of repulsion between protons in a nucleus.

- **Recognize** that the nucleus cannot be held together against the force of Coulomb repulsion unless there is another force, the strong force, that holds the particles together.

What Do You Think?

The alchemist's dream has always been to turn cheap lead into valuable gold.

- **What determines the difference between lead and gold?**

- **How can you distinguish one from the other?**

Record your ideas about these questions in your *Active Physics* log. Be prepared to discuss your responses with your small group and your class.

Investigate

In this *Investigate*, you will learn more about the different parts of an atom. You will draw models to understand the structure of a nucleus and what is meant by atomic mass. You will investigate the presence of atoms with the same atomic number but different atomic mass. The investigation will help you understand the forces holding the particles together in the nucleus.

1. Recall that the nucleus has all the positive charge, due to positively charged particles called protons, and almost all the mass of the atom. The simplest atom is an atom of the chemical element hydrogen. The hydrogen atom has one proton and one electron, which orbits the nucleus in the pattern you examined earlier.

The mass of a proton is 1.7×10^{-27} kg and the mass of an electron is 9.1×10^{-31} kg.

a) Calculate the ratio of the proton mass to the electron mass.

b) Does the value you calculated convince you that most of the mass is in the nucleus? Explain your answer.

2. A carbon atom is more complicated than a hydrogen atom. The mass of the 1 proton that is a hydrogen atom's nucleus is 1 AMU (atomic mass unit). Carbon has a mass of 12 AMU but has only 6 electrons surrounding the nucleus. One possibility for its nuclear structure is that there are 12 protons and 6 electrons within the nucleus, and 6 electrons orbiting the nucleus.

a) Explain how this structure of a carbon atom would account for a mass of about 12 AMU (atomic mass units).

b) Explain how this structure of a carbon atom would account for the atom having a net charge of zero.

3. The patterns of nuclear masses and charges started making sense when another type of particle, the *neutron*, that forms part of the nucleus, was discovered in 1932 by James Chadwick. The neutron has no charge, but does have about the same mass as the proton. Scientists determined that the carbon atom has 6 electrons, 6 protons, and 6 neutrons. The 6 protons and 6 neutrons are in the nucleus and the 6 electrons orbit the nucleus.

a) Explain how this model would account for a mass of about 12 AMU for the carbon atom.

b) Explain how this would account for the atom having a net charge of zero.

c) Draw a sketch of what you think an atom with a net charge of zero might look like.

4. All neutral atoms of carbon have 6 protons and 6 electrons and some neutrons. Most carbon atoms have 6 neutrons while some have 5, 7, or 8 neutrons. These atoms are all carbon because they each have 6 protons. It is the number of protons, not the number of neutrons that determines the element.

a) Sketch models of carbon atoms that have 5, 7, and 8 neutrons.

b) What will be the atomic mass and nucleus charge of each of the carbon atoms you sketched?

5. The neutral atom of chlorine has 17 electrons and 17 protons. One type of chlorine nucleus is described with the notation $^{35}_{17}$Cl. The lower number in $^{35}_{17}$Cl is the atomic number, which is the number of protons in the nucleus. The upper number is the sum of the number of protons and neutrons. This number is also approximately the mass of the nucleus (in units where the mass of the proton is about one unit).

a) Calculate how many neutrons are found in the nucleus of $^{35}_{17}$Cl.

b) Determine the number of protons, electrons, and neutrons in a neutral atom of gold $^{197}_{79}$Au.

c) Determine the number of protons, electrons, and neutrons in a neutral atom of potassium $^{39}_{19}$K.

6. Consider the two carbon atoms $^{12}_{6}$C and $^{14}_{6}$C. Atoms that have the same number of protons but different neutrons are called isotopes. Therefore, "carbon-12" and "carbon-14" are both isotopes of carbon.

a) Determine the number of protons, electrons, and neutrons in carbon $^{12}_{6}$C and $^{14}_{6}$C.

b) Hydrogen nuclei have 1 proton and come in 3 isotopes: no neutrons, 1 neutron, and 2 neutrons. Write the symbols for these isotopes of hydrogen, H, using the appropriate subscripts and superscripts. Incidentally, the no-neutron isotope of H is by far the most abundant; the 1-neutron isotope is rare, and the 2-neutron isotope is rarer still.

7. You have learned that protons repel other protons. The repulsive force between two protons can be calculated using Coulomb's law:

$$F = k\frac{q_1 q_2}{d^2}$$

The nucleus is very tiny and the protons must be extremely close. Such a small separation distance would make the repulsive force between the protons extraordinarily strong. This strong repulsive force should push the protons apart. If no other force acts between protons, besides the Coulomb force, then no nucleus other than hydrogen (a single proton) could exist! There must be another kind of force holding the nucleus together, that helps cancel out the Coulomb force. This nuclear force is called the *strong force* and has the following properties:

- The strong force acts equally between proton-to-proton, proton-to-neutron, and neutron-to-neutron. Electrons do not "feel" it at all.

- The protons or neutrons have to essentially touch or overlap one another before the strong force overcomes the repulsive Coulomb force. At these extremely small distances the attractive strong force is much stronger than the force of repulsion between adjacent protons.

- When protons or neutrons do not touch, then the strong force between them is zero.

a) Why is it important that the strong force be strong at short distances and weak at long distances? In other words, what would happen if the nuclear force were equally strong between protons or neutrons on opposite sides of the nucleus and between protons or neutrons that touch each other?

b) What would happen if the strong nuclear force extended beyond the nucleus to the next atom?

c) In your *Active Physics* log, sketch two circles of equal size to represent two protons. Let each circle or proton have radius R, the "radius of the proton." Let the center-to-center distance between your protons be called d. Draw a graph showing how the strength of the strong force depends on d.

d) What happens in the region where d is less than $2R$? What happens where d is greater than $2R$?

8. Neutrons and protons collectively are called *baryons*. The strong force acts between baryons.

a) Are electrons baryons?

b) The Coulomb force in the nucleus acts only between protons. Why do you suppose that there is no Coulomb force between neutrons?

You can describe the forces within the nucleus in the following way:

- The nucleus is a "contest" between two forces: the long-range repulsive Coulomb force between protons and the short-range strong force between the touching baryons (protons and neutrons). The Coulomb force tries to push apart the nucleus, while the strong force tries to hold the nucleus together.

- No super-heavy elements are stable, so far as is known, because the Coulomb repulsion between the huge number of proton pairs ultimately overwhelms the attraction of nearest-neighbor-baryon strong force binding the nucleus together.

- There is an upper limit to the number of protons that can exist in one nucleus. The element uranium with 92 protons in its nucleus is the heaviest nucleus that is stable for geologic time scales. (Here you have a clue of where the upper limit is.)

9. Think about how forces such as gravitation and the Coulomb force act at a distance.

   a) You hold out your hand and drop a penny. How does the penny "know" which way is down?

   b) How is the gravitational force between the penny and Earth communicated? Write down your thoughts on this question.

   c) You charge up a charged rod and attract a small styrene-foam ball. How does the ball know the direction to move? How is this electrostatic force different from the gravitational force? Write down your thoughts.

10. One way to describe forces is through an exchange of particles. For example, when an electron on the Sun's surface emits a photon, and that photon hits an electron in the retina of your eye, the two electrons—one on the Sun, the other in your eye—have exchanged a photon. However, interacting particles that are very close to one another exchange the particles so fast, and over such a short time, that the exchanged particles are not directly observable. But these particles are indirectly observable from the effects they produce.

These "indirectly observable" exchanged particles are called *virtual particles*. The exchange of virtual particles (virtual or otherwise) can be shown in a Feynman diagram, in the repulsion of two electrons, as follows:

- Time is on the *y*-axis. Position of the electron is on the *x*-axis.

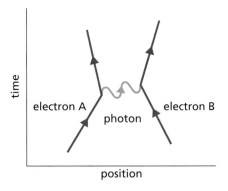

- Electron A is at first moving to the right as time progresses.

- Electron B is at first moving to the left.

- Electron A emits a virtual particle of light (a photon) and recoils to the left.

- Some time later, electron B absorbs the virtual photon of light and recoils to the right.

- The effect is that the electrons have repelled each other.

   a) Draw a Feynman diagram of an electron at rest.

   b) Draw a Feynman diagram of a proton and proton repelling.

   c) Draw a Feynman diagram of the attraction between a proton and an electron.

11. The strong force between baryons is caused by the exchange of another class of virtual particles called mesons. The mesons are to the strong force what the photon is to the electric force.

The protons and neutrons exchange mesons; the protons and protons exchange mesons; the neutrons and neutrons exchange mesons.

The diagram looks very similar to the exchange of virtual photons in the repulsion of two electrons. In this case, there is the attraction of two protons. The kinds of mesons exchanged between protons or neutrons are called pions. There are pions with a positive (+) charge, a negative (–) charge, and no (0) charge. The exchange of a pion is most important in the diagram, not the direction of motion of the particles. The attractive strong force is depicted here with a virtual pion, shown with a straight line.

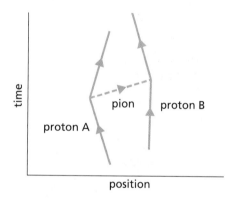

a) Draw the Feynman diagram for the attractive strong force between 2 neutrons.

12. In both of the previous Feynman diagrams, the exchanged particle was uncharged. The photon is always neutral. The pion comes in three varieties—the neutral, the positive, and the negative pions. The attractive strong nuclear force between a proton and a neutron can also be produced by a positive pion as shown in the diagram below.

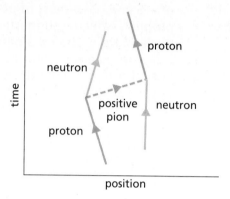

Notice that the proton emits a virtual positive pion. The pion carries the positive charge and the proton becomes a neutron. The neutron absorbs the virtual positive pion and becomes a proton. The strong nuclear force is still attractive. At every vertex of a Feynman diagram, the charge must be conserved.

a) Draw a Feynman diagram where a neutron emits a pion and becomes a proton. Note the charge of the pion on your diagram.

Richard Feynman, Nobel Laureate.

Physics Talk

NUCLEAR PARTICLES

Holding the Nucleus Together

Rutherford's scattering experiment provided evidence for a dense nucleus at the center of the atom. Early models of the nucleus included the **proton**, a positively charged particle with a charge of $+1.6 \times 10^{-19} C$. However, this model posed a problem because protons alone could not account for the mass of the nucleus. The carbon nucleus holds a charge of $+6$ and has a mass of about 12 protons. Rutherford addressed this problem when he suggested that another particle was present in the nucleus. He proposed a particle with about the same mass as the proton, but with no electric charge. He named this particle the "neutral proton," later shortened to **neutron**. In 1932, James Chadwick, a British physicist, discovered the neutron. This discovery added a great deal to the understanding of the nucleus of the atom, but the model of the nucleus was still a huge puzzle.

How could all of those protons and neutrons fit into a small space? Protons repel protons. Because the distance between protons in the nucleus is so small, the Coulomb repulsive force would be huge. If no other force were there to stop the protons from accelerating apart, the nucleus would explode. Another force must hold the nucleus together. This force must be very strong and limited to very small distances, affecting only nearest-neighbor nuclear particles. If this force were long-range, then all the nuclei would clump together. The force must be strong enough to hold all of the protons together but short-range, so that one nucleus does not affect the neighboring nucleus. Scientists found the presence of a force that holds the nucleus together. This force is called the **strong force**. The strong force is identical between neutrons and protons, protons and protons, and neutrons and neutrons. These particles are collectively called **baryons**. The Coulomb force acts only between protons and protons in the nucleus. Neutrons have no charge and do not "feel" the Coulomb force. Electrons do not feel the strong force.

Particle	Charge	Coulomb force?	Strong, nuclear force?
proton	positive	yes	yes
neutron	neutral	no	yes
electron	negative	yes	no

Physics Words

proton: a subatomic particle that is part of the structure of the atomic nucleus; a proton is positively charged with a charge of $+1.6 \times 10^{-19} C$.

neutron: a subatomic particle that is part of the structure of the atomic nucleus; a neutron is electrically neutral.

strong force: a strong nuclear force that holds neutrons and protons together in the nucleus of an atom; the force operates only over very short distances.

baryon: a group of elementary particles that are affected by the nuclear force; neutrons and protons belong to this group.

Checking Up

1. How did Chadwick's discovery of the neutron help explain the charge and mass of the nucleus?

2. What is the force in the nucleus that counteracts the repulsive force between protons?

3. What parts of the atom are affected by the strong force? What parts of the atom are not affected by the strong force?

+Math	+Depth	+Concepts	+Exploration
◆◆	◆		

Active Physics

Plus

More about the Nucleus

1. Protons repel other protons. The force can be calculated using Coulomb's law:

$$F = k \frac{q_1 q_2}{d^2}$$

   a) Calculate the force between two protons in the nucleus. The charge on each proton is 1.6×10^{-19} C. The distance between them on the average is the size of the nucleus 1.0×10^{-15} m. Coulomb's constant k equals 9×10^9 N·m²/C².

   b) Calculate the acceleration of a proton that would result from that force using Newton's second law, $F = ma$, if the proton were free to accelerate. The mass of a proton is 1.7×10^{-27} kg.

2. From a chart of the elements, write down the atomic numbers (for example, 6 for carbon, 26 for iron, 82 for lead) and, to the nearest integer, their atomic weights (for example, 12 for carbon, 56 for iron, 207 for lead) For at least ten different elements.

   a) Make a graph that plots the atomic number on the horizontal axis, and the number of neutrons plus protons on the vertical axis.

   b) What would be the number of neutrons plus protons in a nucleus with only one neutron for each proton? On the same axes for your graph in 2.a) plot 10 points for the isotopes of the 10 elements used to make the graph in 2.a) that would result if they contained only one neutron for each proton.

   c) Compare your graph of 2.a) to the line of 2.b) and discuss what happens to the ratio of neutrons to protons with increasing atomic numbers. What does this trend mean?

What Do You Think Now?

At the beginning of the section you were asked the following:

• **What determines the difference between lead and gold?**

• **How can you distinguish one from the other?**

Now that you have learned about the atomic structure and the difference between atomic number and atomic mass, how would you explain the presence of isotopes?

Active Physics

Physics
Essential Questions

What does it mean?

The nucleus has many protons in a tiny space. How is it that the repulsion between the positive charges does not cause the protons to move away from each other, thereby destroying the nucleus?

How do you know?

What evidence do you have that the electrostatic force between protons exists at very large distances, but the strong, nuclear force exists only at small distances?

Why do you believe?

Connects with Other Physics Content	Fits with Big Ideas in Science	Meets Physics Requirements
Force and motion	Change and constancy	✳ Good, clear, explanation, no more complex than necessary

✳ Physicists explain motion and stability in terms of forces. List five forces that you have encountered in your study of physics. Newton's second law states that accelerations are caused by forces. Why did physicists decide that it was preferable to invent a new force (the strong, nuclear force) than to say that Newton's second law does not work inside the nucleus?

Why should you care?

The nucleus is a "battle" of two forces—the repulsive Coulomb force between protons and the attractive strong, nuclear force, the strong force, between protons. How can you depict this battle in a museum display that will both capture people's attention and instruct them as well?

Reflecting on the Section and the Challenge

The nucleus is a crowded place. It contains all of the protons and neutrons of the atom. These protons and neutrons are held together by a strong, nuclear force, called the strong force. The strong force is short-range and very attractive. In a stable nucleus, the strong, nuclear force balances the Coulomb repulsive force between protons. Communicating the size of the nucleus and how it is held together will be quite a creative challenge.

Physics to Go

1. In the notation for a carbon nucleus $^{13}_{6}C$, what do each of the numbers represent?

2. In "nuclear notation" a proton is represented as $^{1}_{1}p$ and a neutron is represented as $^{1}_{0}n$.

   a) Why do they both have superscripts of one?

b) Why do they have different subscripts?

3. Isotopes are elements that have identical atomic numbers but different atomic masses. For the following sets of isotopes, list the number of protons, neutrons, and electrons:

a) $^{12}_{6}\text{C}$, $^{13}_{6}\text{C}$, $^{14}_{6}\text{C}$

b) $^{40}_{20}\text{Ca}$, $^{41}_{20}\text{Ca}$, $^{42}_{20}\text{Ca}$

c) $^{235}_{92}\text{U}$, $^{238}_{92}\text{U}$

4. Calculate the electrostatic force between two protons that are separated by $6\times10^{-14}\,\text{m}$ within the nucleus.

5. Calculate the electrostatic force between an electron and a proton that are separated by $8\times10^{-9}\,\text{m}$ in an atom.

6. Sketch a graph showing how the nuclear force between two protons varies over distance.

7. Sketch a graph showing how the electrostatic force between two protons varies over distance.

8. Complete a chart indicating if the following pairs of particles interact by the electrostatic force and/or the nuclear force: proton-proton; proton-electron; proton-neutron; neutron-electron; electron-electron; neutron-neutron.

9. Two protons are separated by $1\times10^{-15}\,\text{m}$ in a nucleus.

a) Calculate the gravitational force between them.

b) Calculate the electrostatic force between them.

c) Can the gravitational force be responsible for holding the nucleus together? Explain.

10. When your fingertips touch, your skin deforms. Explain why this happens and why the deformation increases when you press harder.

11. *Preparing for the Chapter Challenge*
Could a museum exhibit help visitors understand how the nuclear force is able to hold the nucleus together but not pull neighboring nuclei together? Could it be interactive? Could it capture people's attention within 30 s? Describe such an exhibit.

Inquiring Further

Chadwick's experiment

Prepare a research report and/or a simulation of the experiment that Chadwick performed to discover the neutron in 1932.

Section 7   Radioactive Decay and the Nucleus

What Do You See?

Learning Outcomes

In this section, you will

- **Construct** a graph representing radioactive decay.

- **Use** the concept of half-life to determine the age of an archaeological artifact.

- **Write** equations for alpha decay.

- **Write** equations for beta decay.

- **Write** equations for gamma decay.

What Do You Think?

Radiation is a big plus for medical procedures and a big hazard from nuclear bombs. Is nuclear radiation friend or foe?

- **What is radiation?**

- **Do scientists have any control over radiation?**

Record your ideas about these questions in your *Active Physics* log. Be prepared to discuss your responses with your small group and your class.

Investigate

In this *Investigate*, you will simulate the radioactive decay of atoms. You will use the concept of probability to understand how atoms go through changes.

1. Your teacher will give you 100 cubes. Mark one side of each of the 100 cubes with a dot. Place the cubes in a box. Now gently shake the cubes so that they can land randomly on any side. Remove the cubes that have the dot facing up and replace them with pennies.

   a) Record your result. Show the number of cubes left and total number of pennies added in a data table like the one drawn on the next page.

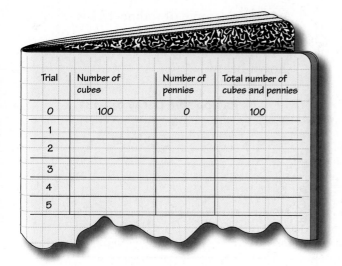

Trial	Number of cubes	Number of pennies	Total number of cubes and pennies
0	100	0	100
1			
2			
3			
4			
5			

2. Repeat *Step 1* with the remaining cubes. Continue with at least ten more trials.

a) Record your results each time.

b) Graph the information from the table. Place the number of trials on the *x*-axis, and the number of cubes left after each trial on the *y*-axis. Draw the best-fit smooth curve through most of the cube data points.

3. Use your graph to answer the following questions:

a) How many tosses did it take to remove half the cubes?

b) In this model, let each toss of the box represent a time interval of one hour. Change the "trials" label on your graph to "hours." How many hours did it take to remove half the cubes? This unit of time is the *half-life* of your sample, the amount of time it takes for half of the sample to change.

4. Compare your results with those of other groups.

a) Make a table and list the number of cubes remaining after each trial in adjacent vertical columns.

b) Graph the class data. How does the class data compare to your graph?

c) During each shake of the box, what was the probability, or chance, that a cube would land with the dot facing up?

5. Consider what would happen if the cube had a dot on two faces.

a) How would you expect the data to change?

b) During each shake of the box, what will be the *probability* that any one cube would land with a dot facing up?

c) Sketch a graph that you might expect to get.

d) What might be the value of the half-life for this new set of cubes with two dots?

6. Consider what would happen if the cube had a dot on three faces.

a) How would you expect the data to change?

b) During each shake of the box, what would be the probability that any one cube could land with a dot facing up?

c) Sketch a graph that you might expect to get.

d) What might be the value of the half-life for this new set of cubes with three dots?

7. Consider what would happen if the cube had a dot on five faces.

a) How would you expect the data to change?

b) During each shake of the box, what will be the probability that any one cube would land with a dot facing up?

c) Sketch a graph that you might expect to get.

d) What is the potential value of the half-life for this new set of cubes with five dots?

8. The half-life of an isotope of carbon-14 is 5730 years. That is, every 5730 years, half of the carbon-14 decays by emitting an electron and becomes nitrogen-14. By measuring the remaining carbon-14 in a long-dead organic sample, scientists can find out for how many half-lives the organism has been dead. If two half-lives have passed, one quarter (a half of one half) of the carbon-14 remains. If $\left(\frac{1}{16}\right)\left[\frac{1}{2} \text{ of } \frac{1}{2} \text{ of } \frac{1}{2} \text{ of } \frac{1}{2}\right]$ of the carbon-14 remains, then scientists know that four half-lives, or 22,900 years, have passed.

a) How many years have passed when the sample contains ⅛ of the carbon-14?

9. Here is a graph showing the *radioactive decay* of a 500-g sample of C-14.

Radioactive Decay of C-14

Use the graph to answer the following questions.

a) What is the half-life of the sample?

b) How many grams have undergone decay after 11,460 years?

c) The original sample had 500 g. The sample now has 100 g of C-14. How much time has elapsed?

10. A 1600-g sample of iodine-131 is observed to decay over the course of a few months. A graph of the decay is shown below.

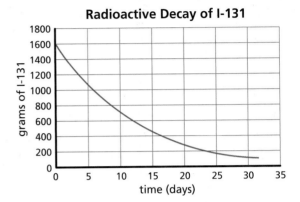

Radioactive Decay of I-131

a) What is the half-life of the sample?

b) How many grams have undergone decay after 25 days?

c) The original sample had 1600 g. The sample now has 1400 g. How much time has elapsed?

d) The original sample had 1600 g. The sample now has 600 g. How much time has elapsed?

11. In *Step 8*, carbon-14 (called the *parent nucleus*) decayed and became nitrogen-14 (called the *daughter nucleus*). In the last example, iodine-131 (parent nucleus) decayed and became xenon-131 (daughter nucleus). In the simulation using cubes, the cube (parent) "decayed" and became a penny (daughter). The total number of cubes plus pennies always remained at 100. In radioactive decay, the total number of parent and daughter nuclei must also remain the same.

a) Sketch a graph of the growth in pennies over time from your earlier data.

12. *Radioactive decay* can cause atoms of one element to become atoms of another element. Three different decay

processes can take place. In *alpha decay*, the nucleus emits an *alpha particle*. The alpha particle is a helium nucleus with two protons and two neutrons. The alpha particle is written as $_2^4\text{He}$. In all alpha decays, the number of protons must remain constant and the atomic mass (protons + neutrons) must remain constant. If an alpha particle is emitted from the parent nucleus, then the new daughter nucleus will have two fewer protons and two fewer neutrons. Writing the nuclear equation makes this process much simpler. If a uranium atom decays by emitting an alpha particle, the equation would be written as follows:

$$_{92}^{238}\text{U} \rightarrow \ _2^4\text{He} + \ _{90}^{234}\text{X}$$

where X is as yet unknown. Notice that the numbers of protons (the numbers on the bottom) remain constant:

$$92 = 2 + 90$$

The total mass of protons and neutrons (the top number) also remains constant:

$$238 = 4 + 234$$

The new daughter element has an atomic number of 90. Referring to the periodic table, the element is thorium and its chemical symbol is Th (X = Th):

$$_{92}^{238}\text{U} \rightarrow \ _2^4\text{He} + \ _{90}^{234}\text{Th}$$

Although the half-life of the element is not indicated in the decay scheme, the half-life of $_{92}^{238}\text{U}$ is 4.5 billion years.

Incidentally, the helium-4 *nucleus* emitted in reactions like this was the source of alpha particles that were the projectiles used by Rutherford to discover the nucleus. When this kind of radioactivity decay was discovered, there was no concept of a nucleus, so the first three kinds of decay products to be discovered were called *alpha*, *beta*, and *gamma* after the first three letters of the Greek alphabet. Only later, after the nucleus was discovered, could people realize that the alpha particle and the helium-4 nucleus are the same thing.

a) Write the decay scheme for $_{92}^{235}\text{U}$ emitting an alpha particle (half-life = 700 million years).

b) $_{92}^{238}\text{U}$ and $_{92}^{235}\text{U}$ are isotopes of uranium. They both have 92 protons in the nucleus. They have different numbers of neutrons. The half-lives are quite different. Calculate the number of neutrons in these isotopes of uranium.

c) Write the decay scheme for $_{90}^{232}\text{Th}$ emitting an alpha particle (half-life = 14 billion years).

13. A second possible nuclear decay occurs with the emission of a "beta particle" from the nucleus. A beta particle is a high-speed electron or a high-speed positron, which is identical to an electron except that it carries a positive charge. In this *Investigate*, you will learn about the negative beta particles (electrons). The symbol for an electron is $_{-1}^0\text{e}$ with the -1 subscript denoting the negative charge of the electron. (The positive subscripts for chemical symbols representing the number of protons also represent the positive charge on the nucleus.) When a neutron within a nucleus emits an electron it becomes a proton. Potassium-40 undergoes beta emission. The decay process known as *beta decay* is shown below:

$$_{19}^{40}\text{K} \rightarrow \ _{-1}^0\text{e} + \ _{20}^{40}\text{X}$$

where X is as yet unknown. Notice that the numbers of protons (the numbers on the bottom) and amount of electric charge remain constant:

$$19 = -1 + 20$$

(The number of protons in the nucleus has increased.)

The total mass of protons and neutrons (the top numbers) also remains constant:

$$40 = 0 + 40$$

Because the number of protons increased by one and the total mass remained the same, a neutron in the nucleus must have changed to a proton and an electron was emitted.

The negative beta-particle emission causes an increase in the number of protons (the neutron became a proton). There is little change in the atomic mass since the mass of a proton and neutron are almost identical. The new daughter element has an atomic number of 20. Referring to a periodic table, the element is calcium and its chemical symbol is Ca:

$$_{19}^{40}\text{K} \rightarrow \ _{-1}^{0}\text{e} + \ _{20}^{40}\text{Ca}$$

a) Write the decay scheme for $_{6}^{14}\text{C}$ emitting a negative beta particle (half-life = 5730 years).

b) Write the decay scheme for $_{38}^{90}\text{Sr}$ emitting a negative beta particle (half-life = 30 years).

14. A third type of radioactive decay is *gamma decay*. Here the energetic nucleus emits a high-energy photon, a "gamma ray." Because the gamma ray photon is pure electromagnetic radiation, like light, the number of baryons or the kinds of baryons do not change in gamma decay. Therefore, the nuclear identity of a gamma-emitter is preserved. The symbol for a gamma particle is $_{0}^{0}\gamma$.

Physics Talk

SCIENTIFIC MODELS

Probability and Atomic Structure

Lots of people go to Las Vegas or other gaming centers to gamble. They think that because dice are involved that it is all a matter of luck whether they win or lose. Have you ever looked at the size of the hotels in Las Vegas? From the size and numbers of these hotels, it is clear that the "house" almost always wins and there is less luck at the casinos than some people expect. Winning or losing depends more on **probability**, which measures how frequently an event occurs. Probability is not the same as luck. In this *Investigate* you studied probability as it relates to atomic structure.

Physics Words

probability: a measure of the likelihood of a given event occurring.

You modeled an event in the real world. Scientists make many kinds of models. Models are conceptual representations of real things. You are probably familiar with physical models of the planets, moons, and the Sun and their interactions in the Solar System. This type of model can help you "see" something too big to see all at once in nature. The model of the atom that you will create for your museum exhibit is another example of a model. The model is based on many observations and experimental results. Many models in science are complex mathematical models.

The radioactive model in the *Investigate* of this section used cubes to represent nuclei. When the cubes were tossed and a "dot" emerged face-up, the cube "decayed" and became a penny. In radioactive samples like carbon-14 or iodine-131, the nuclei are not being tossed. As time goes on, some parent nuclei become daughter nuclei. **Parent nuclei** are the original nuclei of the atoms before they undergo decay, while **daughter nuclei** are the nuclei of atoms that have undergone decay.

You had no idea which of the cubes were going to land with the dot face-up. You also had no idea which of the carbon-14 nuclei would decay. However, you did get a good sense of how many cubes would land with the dot face-up. You now have a very precise understanding of how many carbon-14 parent nuclei will decay in a given time.

Scientists use radioactive decay as precise clocks. **Radioactive decay** is a term applied to an atom that has an unstable nucleus and can spontaneously emit a particle and become the nucleus of another atom. Three different decay processes can take place.

In **alpha decay**, an unstable heavy nucleus "shakes off" some of its excess energy by emitting a helium-4 nucleus (alpha particle). In **beta decay**, the neutron in an unstable nucleus turns into a proton plus electron (beta particle). In **gamma decay** an excited nucleus emits some of its excess energy in the form of a high-energy photon (gamma particle).

Geologists want to know the age of rocks to provide an understanding of Earth. Paleontologists want to know the age of fossils to better understand life on Earth. Archaeologists want to know the age of tools to better understand humans. Scientists in each of these fields make use of their knowledge of a **half-life** of a radioactive element for dating purposes. Half-life is the amount of time it takes for half of the sample to change. One type of carbon atom, called carbon-14, is used in radioactive dating. As long as an organism lives, the ratio of carbon-14 to carbon-12 in the body stays the same. When organisms die, no new carbon-14 is added to their tissues. The decay of carbon-14 continues. If you know how much carbon-14 was in the organism when it lived, you can figure out how long ago the organism died by measuring the carbon-14 that remains.

Other elements are important tools in radioactive dating. Potassium-40 has a half-life of 1.3 billion years. Uranium-238 has a half-life of 4.47 billion years. Thorium-232 has a half-life of 14 billion years. These radioactive elements, as well as others, are found in rocks. Often, all three of these elements are used to date a specific rock. By comparing the radioactive decays, the age of a rock can be determined with more precision than if only one element was used. Rocks that are several billion years old have been discovered, indicating that Earth must be at least this old.

Physics Words

parent nuclei: the original nuclei of the atoms before they undergo decay.

daughter nuclei: the nuclei of atoms that have undergone decay.

radioactive decay: a term applied to an atom that has an unstable nucleus and can spontaneously emit a particle and become the nucleus of another atom.

alpha decay: electromagnetic decay process that occurs when an unstable heavy nucleus "shakes off" some of its excess energy by emitting a helium-4 nucleus (alpha particle).

beta decay: electromagnetic decay process that occurs when an unstable nucleus has one neutron that turns into a proton plus electron (beta particle).

gamma decay: electromagnetic decay process that occurs when an excited nucleus emits some of its excess energy in the form of a high-energy photon (gamma particle).

half- life: the amount of time it takes for half of the sample to change.

Checking Up

1. What are models? How did the model you designed in the *Investigate* explain the concept of radioactive decay?

2. Explain how scientists use their knowledge of half-life to determine the age of a fossil or rock.

3. Compare alpha and beta decay.

Active Physics

Plus

+Math	+Depth	+Concepts	+Exploration
◆◆	◆		

Equation for Radioactive Decay

In this section, you created a graph of radioactive decay to determine how many cubes will remain after a given time. You can also calculate the remaining number of radioactive particles when you apply the definition of half-life. If you began with 1000 particles, and a time equal to three half-lives has transpired, the number of particles remaining can be calculated as follows:

- **After the first half-life, $\frac{1}{2}$ of the 1000 original particles would remain, or 500 particles.**

- **After the second half-life, $\frac{1}{2}$ of the 500 particles would remain, or 250 particles.**

- **After the third half-life, $\frac{1}{2}$ of the 250 particles, or 125 particles, would remain.**

You can make the calculation immediately by recognizing that after three half-lives $\frac{1}{2}$ of $\frac{1}{2}$ of $\frac{1}{2}$ or $\frac{1}{8}$ of the original 1000 particles will remain, which equals 125 particles.

In physics, scientists always ask the question, "Is there an equation?" that can also describe the phenomenon. For the number of particles remaining, the equation for radioactive decay is

$$N = \frac{N_o}{2^n}$$

where N_o is the original number of particles; N is the number of particles that remain after a given amount of time; and n is the number of half-lives that have elapsed.

For example, if you began with 1000 particles, and a time equal to three half-lives has transpired, the number of particles remaining can be calculated:

$$N = \frac{N_o}{2^n}$$

$$N = \frac{1000}{2^3}$$

$$N = \frac{1000}{8} = 125 \text{ particles}$$

If 3.7 half-lives have transpired, you can calculate the remaining particles just as easily:

$$N = \frac{N_o}{2^n}$$

$$N = \frac{1000}{2^{3.7}}$$

$$N = \frac{1000}{13} = 77 \text{ particles}$$

This equation can also help you determine the number of half-lives that have transpired if you know how many particles remain. In the above example, if you knew that you began with 1000 particles and after a given time only 125 remained, you can find that a time equal to three half-lives has transpired.

$$N = \frac{N_o}{2^n}$$

$$\left(2^n\right) = \frac{N_o}{N}$$

$$2^n = \frac{1000}{125}$$

$$2^n = 8$$

$$n = 3$$

In another problem, if you found that you had 83 particles remaining, then $2^n = \left(\frac{1000}{83}\right) = 12$, you would have to try different values of n in your calculator until you found the value you needed with the precision that you wanted. For example, you know that $2^3 = 8$ and $2^4 = 16$. The value of n must be between 3 and 4. If you try 3.5, you find that $2^{3.5} = 11.3$. You might then try 3.6 and find that $2^{3.6} = 12.1$. You now know that it is between 3.5 and 3.6 half-lives. You can continue and get whatever precision you require through this hit-and-miss method.

Using logarithms, you can derive a new equation, as shown below.

$$N = \frac{N_o}{2^n}$$

$$\left(2^n\right) = \frac{N_o}{N}$$

$$n \log 2 = \log\left(\frac{N_o}{N}\right)$$

$$n = \left(\frac{\log\left(\dfrac{1000}{83}\right)}{\log 2}\right)$$

$$n = \frac{\left(\log 12\right)}{\log 2}$$

$$n = \left(\frac{\left(1.08\right)}{\left(0.3\right)}\right)$$

$$n = 3.6$$

1. Given the data in the following two tables, determine the number of particles remaining and the amount of time that has elapsed.

Original number of particles	Half-life	Time that has elapsed	Number of particles remaining
1000	2 days	8 days	
1000	500 years	3100 years	
100,000	5 minutes	17 minutes	
100,000	1 year	8 months	

Original number of particles	Half-life	Number of particles remaining	Time that has elapsed
1000	2 days	250	
1000	500 years	370	
100,000	5 minutes	80,000	
100,000	1 year	23,000	

What Do You Think Now?

At the beginning of the section you were asked the following:

• **What is radiation?**

• **Do scientists have any control over radiation?**

Now that you know about radioactive decay, how do radioactive elements emit some of their excess energy? How does the half-life of a radioactive element help scientists to determine the age of an organism that has not yet fossilized?

Physics
Essential Questions

What does it mean?

Uranium can become thorium through the emission of an alpha particle. This radioactive decay can be summarized as follows:

$$^{238}_{92}U \rightarrow \, ^{234}_{90}Th + \, ^{4}_{2}He$$

What does each of the symbols and numbers represent in this nuclear equation?

How do you know?

If you were to toss 100 dice, what evidence do you have that approximately $\frac{1}{6}$ of them will land with two dots on top? If you were to toss 10,000 dice, what evidence do you have that the fraction landing with two dots on top will be even closer to $\frac{1}{6}$?

Why do you believe?

Connects with Other Physics Content	Fits with Big Ideas in Science	Meets Physics Requirements
Atomic and nuclear	* Conservation laws	Experimental evidence is consistent with models and theories

* Physicists base theories on probability. Is probability the same as luck? In flipping 100,000 coins, you expect approximately $\frac{1}{2}$ to land heads and $\frac{1}{2}$ to land tails. Why do you believe this will happen even though you cannot know beforehand which coin will land which way?

Why should you care?

Your museum display has to grab someone's attention within 30 s. It must also be interactive. How can you fulfill both of these requirements and instruct visitors about the radioactive decay of nuclei?

Reflecting on the Section and the Challenge

Some nuclei are stable while some decay. The parent nuclei can decay through alpha, beta, or gamma emission. The decay process is random because you cannot tell which of the individual nuclei will decay. However, the number or fraction of nuclei that will decay is quite predictable. The decay rate is defined by the half-life of the element. The half-life is the time required for one-half of the parent nuclei to become daughter nuclei. You can show nuclei decaying as part of your museum exhibit. You may find it tricky to show the mechanism of decay and to adequately describe half-life, but these are both worthwhile topics to pursue.

Physics to Go

1. A box of 500 candies was dropped on a table. If the red side of the candy was facing up, the candy was eaten. The remaining candy was shaken and dropped on the table again. A data table was created.

Toss (every 10 minutes)	Candies with red face up and then eaten	Total candies eaten	Candies remaining
0		0	500
1	130	130	370
2	90	220	280
3	68	288	212
4	50	338	162
5	45	383	117
6	26	409	91
7	23	432	68
8	15	447	53

a) Construct three graphs of the data.

b) From the graph, determine the half-life of the candy in this tossing simulation.

c) From the percentage of candy that "decays" in each toss, determine the shape of the candy.

2. There are 600 g of radioactive iodine-133. The half-life of iodine-133 is 21 h. How much of this radioactive substance would exist after

a) 21 h?

b) 42 h?

c) 126 h?

3. The half-life for the radioactive gas radon-220 is 51.5 s. If a sealed bottle contains 100 g of radon-220. What mass of radon-220 will still be in the bottle after

a) 51.5 s?

b) 103 s?

c) 257.5 s?

4. Radioactive decay can be measured. One type of measuring tool gives a reading called a counting rate. A sample of radioactive material initially produces 2000 counts per second. Four hours later, the same sample produces 500 counts per second. What is the half-life of the sample?

5. Carbon-14 has a half-life of 5730 years. What fraction of the original amount of carbon-14 will remain after 23,000 years?

6. Suppose a sample of carbon is extracted from a partially burned log found in a prehistoric fire site. The sample is $\frac{1}{8}$ as radioactive as carbon extracted from a modern log. How old is the sample taken from the ancient log?

7. For what age materials is uranium dating more useful than carbon dating? Explain your reasoning.

8. Recall beta decay, $n \rightarrow p + e$ (neutron decays to proton plus electron). Verify that electric charge is conserved. What other kinds of decays can occur between these same particles (neutron, proton, electron) and/or their antiparticles? (An antiparticle has the same mass as the particle but an opposite charge.)

9. Radioactive uranium-238 decays by alpha emission. The decay product, thorium-234, then decays by beta emission. A table of the decay series is shown on the next page. The first line shows the decay of uranium-238. The thorium-234 is then placed on the next line. It then produces Pa-234 by beta emission. The Pa-234 is then placed on the next line and its decay is written.

Complete the chart on the next page. (The half-lives are given for interest and are not needed to complete the chart.) The periodic table will help you identify the element symbols from their atomic number. If the periodic table is not available, you can complete the chart with the atomic number and mass and leave a blank or X for the symbol.

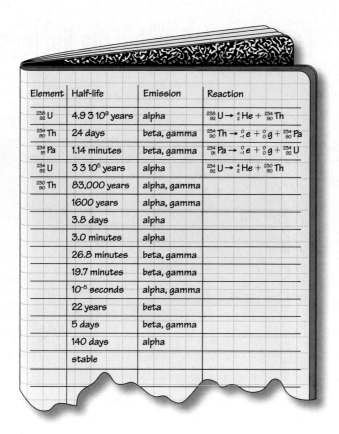

Element	Half-life	Emission	Reaction
$^{238}_{92}$U	4.9×10^9 years	alpha	$^{238}_{92}$U $\rightarrow$ $^{4}_{2}$He + $^{234}_{90}$Th
$^{234}_{90}$Th	24 days	beta, gamma	$^{234}_{90}$Th $\rightarrow$ $^{0}_{-1}$e + $^{0}_{0}$g + $^{234}_{90}$Pa
$^{234}_{91}$Pa	1.14 minutes	beta, gamma	$^{234}_{91}$Pa $\rightarrow$ $^{0}_{-1}$e + $^{0}_{0}$g + $^{234}_{92}$U
$^{234}_{92}$U	3×10^5 years	alpha	$^{234}_{92}$U $\rightarrow$ $^{4}_{2}$He + $^{230}_{90}$Th
$^{230}_{90}$Th	83,000 years	alpha, gamma	
	1600 years	alpha, gamma	
	3.8 days	alpha	
	3.0 minutes	alpha	
	26.8 minutes	beta, gamma	
	19.7 minutes	beta, gamma	
	10^{-5} seconds	alpha, gamma	
	22 years	beta	
	5 days	beta, gamma	
	140 days	alpha	
	stable		

Inquiring Further

1. Iodine-133 contamination

Iodine-133 a common byproduct of nuclear fission in electric power plants. You are given a sample of material contaminated by iodine-133. Find out how long you have to wait before you can dump the iodine into the environment. How do you know the iodine is safe to dump? Report your findings to the class.

2. Radon in homes

Find out about radon, a radioactive element found in some homes. Why is it considered a hazard? Report your findings to the class.

3. Radioactive materials in medicine

Medical doctors use radioactive materials in many ways. Research this and make a list of at least five uses for radiation in medicine. Create a poster of your findings.

Section 8

Energy Stored within the Nucleus

What Do You See?

Learning Outcomes

In this section, you will

• **Explain** the meaning of Einstein's equation: $E = mc^2$.

• **Calculate** the energy equivalent of different masses.

• **Discover** the relative stability of nuclei by calculating how much energy would be required to take the nucleus apart into individual protons and neutrons (the "binding energy").

• **Compare** the binding energy of the nucleus with the binding energy of electrons in the atom.

What Do You Think?

• **How are nuclear reactions different from chemical reactions?**

• **What does $E = mc^2$ really mean?**

Record your ideas about these questions in your *Active Physics* log. Be prepared to discuss your responses with your small group and your class.

Investigate

In this *Investigate*, you will calculate how much energy is released when mass is converted into energy. You will understand how the energy that holds the nucleus together is a result of lost mass.

1. Many people can recite Einstein's famous equation: $E = mc^2$ where E represents energy in joules (J), and m represents mass in kilograms (kg).

   In your log, write down the approximate mass in kilograms of the following objects:

   a) an eight-year-old child

   b) a bowling ball

✎ c) a box of spaghetti

✎ d) a compact car

2. The c in the equation $E = mc^2$ represents the speed of light, which is equal to 3.0×10^8 m/s. Use the equation:

$$d = vt$$

to calculate how long it takes light to travel:

✎ a) from one side of a football field to the other if the distance is approximately 100 m.

✎ b) from Atlanta to Miami (approximately 1000 km or 10^6 m)

✎ c) from the Moon to Earth (approximately 380,000 km or 3.8×10^8 m)

✎ d) from the Sun to Earth (approximately 150,000,000 km or 1.5×10^{11} m)

3. The mass of a pea is 1 g or 1×10^{-3} kg. Consider the energy equivalent of such a small mass.

The energy equivalent of an object at rest can be determined by $E = mc^2$.

✎ a) Calculate the energy equivalent in joules of a pea using $E = mc^2$. (Assume 100% conversion of mass into energy.)

4. There are many forms of energy. Kinetic energy, associated with moving cars, people, planets, and subatomic particles, can be calculated using the equation:

$$KE = \frac{1}{2}mv^2$$

where KE is kinetic energy in joules (J),

m is the mass in kilograms (kg), and

v is the velocity in meters per second (m/s).

✎ a) If a sprinter with a mass of 50 kg is running at 8 m/s, calculate the kinetic energy in joules.

✎ b) How fast would a sprinter have to be running to have the energy equivalent of converting the mass of one pea entirely into energy?

✎ c) What conclusion can be drawn about the amount of energy in an object even as small as a pea?

5. Gravitational potential energy is energy associated with position. It can be calculated using the equation:

$$GPE = mgh$$

where GPE is gravitational potential energy in joules (J),

m is the mass in kilograms (kg),

g is the acceleration due to gravity equal to about 9.8 m/s^2, and

h is the elevation in meters (m).

✎ a) How high would a bowling ball (mass = 6 kg) have to be elevated to have the same gravitational potential energy as the mass-energy equivalent of a pea?

6. In *Section 3*, you studied electrons in the atom. The *binding energy* of an electron in hydrogen is the energy that holds the electron to the nucleus. In other words, the binding energy is the amount of energy you would have to "spend" to remove the electron from the hydrogen atom. In the $n = 1$ (ground) state of hydrogen, the binding energy is −13.6 eV. The negative sign indicates to you that the electron is bound to the nucleus. That electron requires +13.6 eV in order for it to be pulled free of the nucleus with no kinetic energy left over.

Neutrons and protons are also bound to the nucleus, held there by the strong nuclear force. A nitrogen-15 ($^{15}_{7}\mathrm{N}$) nucleus has 7 protons and 8 neutrons. To free a baryon (proton or neutron) requires an addition of energy equal to the binding energy of the baryon. You can calculate that binding energy.

The *atomic mass unit* is used to compare the masses of atoms. It is defined in terms of the mass of carbon-12. The carbon-12 nucleus has a mass of exactly 12 atomic mass units, by definition of the atomic mass unit! The atomic mass unit is denoted by "u" so that the mass of carbon-12 is 12 u. Each atomic mass unit (u) is approximately equal to $1.7 \times 10^{-27}\,\mathrm{kg}$. (You can see from this value why scientists prefer to use atomic mass units instead of kilograms.)

Example:

Calculate the mass of all the protons and neutrons in a nitrogen-15 nucleus.

In atomic mass units, the proton's mass is 1.007825 u, and the neutron's mass is 1.008665 u. The mass of 7 separate protons, and 8 separate neutrons can, therefore, be found as follows:

Mass of 7 protons = 7 (1.007825 u)
            = 7.054775 u

Mass of 8 neutrons = 8 (1.008665 u)
            = 8.069320 u

Total mass of the separate (protons + neutrons) = 15.124095 u

---

- Compare this to the mass of the assembled nitrogen-15 nucleus. The mass of the nitrogen-15 nucleus (15.000108 u) can be found from a chart of the nuclides in a reference book. The nitrogen-15 mass is less than the total mass of the same number of separate protons and neutrons, which are also called *nucleons*.

Energy must be supplied to remove, say, a neutron from the assembled nucleus. This situation is analogous to pulling a rock out of a well—you have to use energy to raise the rock out of the well.

Total nucleon mass   = 15.124095 u

Mass of nucleus of $^{15}\mathrm{N}$ = 15.000108 u

Mass difference   = 0.123987 u

This difference in mass, known as the *mass defect*, is the binding energy of the nucleus.

Conversion factor between atomic mass units and energy (this comes from $E = mc^2$):

$$1\,\mathrm{u} = 931.5\,\mathrm{MeV}$$

$$1\,\mathrm{MeV} = 1{,}000{,}000\,\mathrm{eV}$$

(The derivation of 931.5 MeV is given in *Active Physics Plus*.)

- To calculate the total binding energy (*TBE*) of the nucleus,

$$TBE = 0.123987\,\mathrm{u} \times 931.5\,\frac{\mathrm{MeV}}{\mathrm{u}}$$

$$= 115.5\,\mathrm{MeV}$$

- To calculate the average binding energy per nucleon,

Total number of nucleons = 15
(7 protons and 8 neutrons)

Average binding energy/nucleon =
115.5 MeV/15 = 7.7 MeV

On average, it requires 7.7 MeV or 7.7 million eV to remove a proton or neutron from the nucleus of nitrogen-15 (The removal of the first baryon actually requires more energy than this—the 7.7 MeV is an average.) Recall that removing an electron from hydrogen required only 13.6 eV.

a) Calculate the average binding energy per baryon for chlorine-37, $^{37}_{17}\mathrm{Cl}$. The mass of chlorine-37 is equal to 36.965898 u. Use the masses of protons and neutrons given in the sample problem.

b) A neutron can be removed to create $^{14}_{7}N$ from $^{15}_{7}N$. Compare the mass of $^{15}_{7}N$ to the masses of $^{14}_{7}N$ plus one separate neutron to determine the energy required to free the neutron. The mass of nitrogen-14 equals 14.003074 u. The other values are given in previous text.

c) Compare this binding energy to remove the neutron with the average binding energy that you calculated in the sample problem.

Physics Talk

ENERGY AND MATTER

The speed of light is the "speed limit" of the universe. No material object can travel faster than this speed. In the *Investigate*, you examined Einstein's equation, $E = mc^2$, which gives the "exchange rate" between energy and mass and can be interpreted in several ways.

$$E = mc^2$$

• provides the energy equivalent of a piece of mass. (In the section, you found the equivalent energy of a pea.)

• tells you that energy and mass are equivalent entities, but one is given in joules and the other is given in kilograms.

• tells you that the conversion factor between energy and mass is the square of the speed of light (c^2). To change kilograms to joules, you have to multiply by c^2, equal to $9 \times 10^{16}\ m^2/s^2$.

• explains how much energy is produced when an electron (particle) and a **positron (antiparticle)** can annihilate each other and create light energy. A positron is identical to the electron but has a positive charge. When a particle and an antiparticle collide their mass is destroyed and the process is called **particle-antiparticle annihilation**.

In *Section 3*, you investigated the binding energy of electrons in an atom. In the $n = 1$ (ground) state of hydrogen, the binding energy was -13.6 eV. To pull the electron from the $n = 1$ state and take it completely out of the atom, it takes 13.6 eV of energy. The binding energy of the electron in the $n = 2$ state is -3.4 eV. You would have to give that electron $+3.4$ eV to free it from the $n = 2$ state. Similarly, if the nucleus of hydrogen captures an electron to make a hydrogen atom, and the electron drops into the $n = 1$ state, 13.6 eV is given off as a photon of light.

The conservation of energy requires that the energy of a system before an event must equal the energy after the event. In our examples of light and electrons in atoms, the system consists of the atom, its electron, and light. An electron absorbs a photon of light of $+13.6$ eV, bringing its total energy to 0 and it is free. Or, a free electron of 0 energy becomes bound to the proton nucleus with an energy of -13.6 eV and gives off a light photon with energy equal to $+13.6$ eV.

Physics Words

positron: a nuclear particle identical to the electron but with a positive charge.

particle-antiparticle annihilation: the process in which a particle and an antiparticle collide and their mass becomes energy.

Physics Words

nucleon: a nuclear particle that is either a neutron or a proton.

mass defect: the difference in mass between the nucleons inside the nucleus and nucleons as isolated particles.

atomic mass unit: the standard unit of atomic mass equal to $^1/_{12}$ the mass of the nucleus of ^{12}C.

binding energy: the energy required to remove an electron from an atom or a nucleon from a nucleus.

Checking Up

1. What is the energy equivalent of 6 kg in J?

2. Explain why nuclear binding energy is much stronger then an electron's binding energy.

3. Explain where the binding energy of a nucleus comes from.

In this section, you calculated the binding energy of a **nucleon**. A nucleon is either a proton or a neutron. To calculate the binding energy of a nucleon, you must know the difference in mass, which is the **mass defect**, between a nucleon inside the nucleus and a nucleon outside the nucleus. This difference is measured in **atomic mass units**. An atomic mass unit is the standard unit of atomic mass based on the nucleus of a carbon-12 atom.

Binding energy is the energy required to remove an electron from an atom or a nucleon from a nucleus. You found that to remove a proton or neutron from the nucleus of nitrogen-15 requires 7.7 MeV or 7.7 million eV. Compare that to the binding energy of an electron in hydrogen, which is 13.6 eV, and you can begin to appreciate the difference between chemical and nuclear reactions.

Chemical processes have to do with the exchange of electrons between atoms. Nuclear processes have to do with the exchange or transformation of nucleons. You can get a sense of the relative strength of these processes by comparing the binding energies. The nuclear binding energies are millions of times larger than the electron's binding energies. This is why nuclear reactions have so much more energy than chemical reactions.

Active Physics Plus

+Math	+Depth	+Concepts	+Exploration
♦♦		♦	

Converting Mass Units to Energy Units

1. The conversion of atomic mass units (u) to energy units in electron volts (eV) required the use of the equation $E = mc^2$ to find the corresponding energy from the mass difference or mass defect. This required certain conversions:

- The mass difference between the nucleus and constituent parts is called the mass difference or mass defect. It is given in atomic mass units (u).

- The mass units would have to be converted to kilograms ($1\ u = 1.7 \times 10^{-27}\ kg$).

- The energy would then be calculated in joules ($E = mc^2$).

- The joules could then be converted to electron volts ($1\ eV = 1.6 \times 10^{-19}\ J$).

Show how all of these steps can be combined into one step:

$1\ u = 931.5\ MeV$.

---

2. You can use the precisely measured nuclear masses to understand the decimal numbers that appear with each element on the periodic table. Consider, for example, uranium, element number 92 (which means it has 92 protons). The decimal number that appears with uranium says "238.029." This is an average mass of all the uranium isotopes. The isotopes of uranium include U-227, U-228, U-229, U-230, U-231, U-232, U-233, U-234, U-235, U-236, U-237, U-238, U-239, and U-240. The number of neutrons these nuclei have range from 135 for U-227 to 148 for U-240. Of these isotopes, only U-234, U-235, and U-238 are found in uranium ore. The others can be made in nuclear reactions but they are quite unstable and undergo radioactive decay in short periods of time that are very short compared to geologic processes. Of the naturally occurring isotopes, here are their masses and abundances:

Isotope	Mass (u)	Abundance (%)
U-234	234.0409	0.0056
U-235	235.04393	0.7205
U-238	238.0508	99.274

The number that appears as atomic mass in the periodic table is the average mass, allowing for relative abundances of the various isotopes: in the case of uranium, recalling that 0.7205%=0.007205,

average mass = $(0.000056)(234.0409 \text{ u})$ + $(0.007205)(235.04393 \text{ u})$ + $(.99274)$ $(238.0508 \text{ u}) = 238.029 \text{ u}$,

which is the mass shown on the periodic table for uranium. Find the average mass of the carbon and iron nuclei, given the masses and abundances of these isotopes in the table at the bottom of the page.

3. Compare your answers in *Question 2* to the masses shown on the periodic table for carbon and iron.

Atom name and atomic number	Isotope	Mass (u)	Abundance (%)
a) carbon, 6	C-12	12.000000	98.893
	C-12	13.003354	1.107
(Technically, the mass of carbon-12 is 12 u exactly because the definition of the atomic mass unit says that 1 u = one-twelfth the mass of C-12.)			
b) iron, 26	Fe-54	53.93962	5.82
	Fe-56	55.93493	91.66
	Fe-57	56.93539	2.19
	Fe-58	57.93327	0.33

What Do You Think Now?

At the beginning of the section you were asked the following:

• How are nuclear reactions different from chemical reactions?

• What does $E = mc^2$ really mean?

When you charge something electrically you always add or remove electrons. Now that you know the difference between an electron's binding energy and a proton's binding energy, how would you explain why only electrons are removed in charging an object?

Physics
Essential Questions

What does it mean?

It takes a trainload of coal every month to run a coal-fired power plant. When people first began to understand nuclear energy, it was suggested that, someday, the fuel required to run power plants for several months could be delivered in a teacup. Why were they able to suggest that? Use the equation $E = mc^2$ in your response.

How do you know?

What evidence exists to show that nuclear reactions have more energy than chemical reactions?

Why do you believe?

Connects with Other Physics Content	Fits with Big Ideas in Science	Meets Physics Requirements
Energy	* Conservation Laws	Good, clear, explanation, no more complex than necessary

* Conservation laws are organizing principles of physics. Prior to 1900, scientists had discovered the conservation of mass and the conservation of energy. How does $E = mc^2$ change the way they view the conservation laws?

Why should you care?

How can your museum display help visitors understand about the immense energy required to remove nucleons (protons and neutrons) from the nucleus? How can the energy stored in the nucleus be demonstrated through an exhibit about stars, nuclear reactors, or nuclear weapons?

Reflecting on the Section and the Challenge

Neutrons and protons are held tightly in a nucleus by the strong, nuclear force. You are now able to use the equation $E = mc^2$ to calculate the energy required to free one of them. The energy required is a million electron volts, while removing an electron requires only a few electron volts of energy. You might try to find a way to add numerical calculations to your atomic-structure museum exhibit. You may want to compare the binding energy of electrons to the binding energy of protons or neutrons. The nucleus is a wonderful place to introduce Einstein's famous $E = mc^2$ equation and its multiple interpretations.

Physics to Go

1. Calculate the energy equivalent in the mass of the following objects:

   a) an electron

   b) a pea

   c) a 50-kg student

   d) Lifting a 4-kg shovel full of snow 1 m requires 40 J of energy. How many shovels-full of snow could be lifted with the energies calculated in b)?

2. A direct observation of the equivalence of mass and energy occurs when an electron and a positron (same mass as an electron, but opposite charge) annihilate each other and create light.

   a) Calculate the total energy of the light produced. (The mass of both the electron and the positron is 9.1×10^{-31} kg.)

   b) Calculate the total energy of the light produced when a proton (mass of 1.7×10^{-27} kg) and an antiproton (same mass as a proton, but opposite charge) annihilate each other.

3. Any given quantity can be measured using various units. Length can be measured in meters, centimeters, and miles. Volume can be measured in liters, milliliters, gallons, meters cubed, and cubic feet. In a similar way, energy can be measured in kilograms or joules. How could this be depicted in a museum exhibit to make clear the notion that energy and mass can be converted back and forth into one another?

4. Calculate the total binding energy of phosphorus–31 with an atomic number of 15. The atomic mass is 30.973765 u.

   a) Calculate the binding energy per nucleon.

5. Describe binding energy in a way that a child visiting a science museum can understand. Is there a way that you can make the explanation visually appealing?

   a) Compare and contrast the binding energy of an electron in the atom to the binding energy of a proton with the nucleus.

6. In *Star Trek*, the television science-fiction series, the matter-antimatter energy source provides all the energy the spaceship needs to operate. How might a matter-antimatter energy source work?

7. Two energy units are commonly used in physics, the joule (J) and the electron volt (eV). One electron volt (eV) is equivalent to 1.6×10^{-19} J. If both of these units are energy, why are two different units useful?

8. Sketch a graph showing the relationship between energy and mass. What would be the slope of the graph?

9. The mass difference between the assembled nucleus and its separate constituent parts (also called the mass defect) is greater for nucleus A than nucleus B. Compare their binding energies.

10. The Sun emits energy at the rate of 4×10^{26} W (1 W = 1 J/s).

    a) At what rate is mass being converted into energy (kg/s)?

    b) In ten billion years (10^{10} yr), how much of the Sun's mass is converted into energy?

    c) The mass of the Sun now is about 2×10^{30} kg. In five billion more years of shining (assuming the rate of energy production stays constant), what percentage of the Sun's present mass will be converted into energy?

    d) How much mass will have been converted into energy over the Sun's entire 10-billion-year lifetime, assuming a constant energy production rate? How many Earth masses is that? The mass of Earth is about 6×10^{24} kg.

11. Complete this warning label that one might put on a cereal box (find the "net weight" of the cereal in a new box, as printed on the box): "Warning—this box contains enough mass that, if converted entirely into energy, it would lift a 10,000-lb truck _____ meters into the air." (Watch the units!)

Section 9

Nuclear Fission and Fusion: Breaking Up Is Hard to Do

What Do You See?

Learning Outcomes

In this section, you will

- **Construct** a graph of average binding energy per nucleon versus the number of nucleons.

- **Infer** the relative stability of different nuclear species by interpreting graphs.

- **Explain** how a fusion reaction can release energy.

- **Explain** how a fission reaction can release energy.

- **Describe** a mousetrap model for a fission chain reaction.

What Do You Think?

Nuclear energy powers the Sun and other stars, and is used for nuclear power plants and nuclear weapons.

- **How is nuclear energy created?**

- **Is all nuclear energy produced the same way?**

Record your ideas about these questions in your *Active Physics* log. Be prepared to discuss your responses with your small group and your class.

Investigate

In the previous section, you learned to calculate the binding energy of a nucleus. The greater the binding energy, the harder it is to take the nucleus apart.

In this *Investigate*, you will see if there is a pattern to binding energies and the related stability of nuclei. You will also calculate the binding energy per nucleon for all known elements and make a graph. To make the most efficient use of your time, you will limit your calculations to some specific elements.

1. To calculate the binding energy per nucleon of any element, you need to know the mass of the proton, neutron, and mass of that nucleus. The masses of a number of nuclei are given in the table below.

> **Example:**
>
> Calculate the binding energy per nucleon for phosphorus-31, $^{31}_{15}$P. (You will use the same method as you used in the previous section.)
>
> Number of protons (the "atomic number") = 15
>
> Number of neutrons = number of nucleons – number of protons = 31 – 15 = 16
>
> Mass of 15 protons = 15 (1.007825 u) = 15.117375 u
>
> Mass of 16 neutrons = 16 (1.008665 u) = 16.138640 u
>
> Total mass of separate nucleons = 15.117375 u + 16.138640 u = 31.256015 u

> Mass of nucleus of $^{31}_{15}$P = 30.973765 u
>
> Mass difference = 31.256015 u – 30.973765 u = 0.282250 u
>
> Total binding energy = 0.282250 u × 931.5 MeV/u = 262.9 MeV
>
> Total number of nuclei = 31 (15 protons + 16 neutrons).
>
> On average, it would require 8.48 MeV (million eV) to remove each proton or neutron from the nucleus of phosphorus-31.

a) Calculate the binding energies for the elements assigned to you by your teacher.

b) Use combined class data to plot a graph of the binding energy per nucleon versus the number of nucleons for each element on the periodic table.

Element	Atomic number	Mass number	Atomic mass (u)	Element	Atomic number	Mass number	Atomic mass (u)
neutron	0	1	1.008665	Co	27	59	58.933190
proton	1	1	1.007825	Zn	30	66	65.926052
H	1	1	1.007825	Br	35	79	78.918330
He	2	4	4.002603	Zr	40	91	90.905642
Li	3	7	7.016004	Rh	45	103	102.905511
Be	4	9	9.012186	Sn	50	119	118.903314
B	5	11	11.009305	Cs	55	133	132.905355
C	6	12	12.000000	Nd	60	145	144.912538
N	7	14	14.003074	Yb	70	173	172.938060
O	8	16	15.994915	Hg	80	200	199.968327
F	9	19	18.998405	Tl	81	205	204.974442
P	15	31	30.973765	Pb	82	207	206.975903
Ca	20	40	39.962589	Bi	83	209	208.981082
Mn	25	55	54.938051	Th	90	232	232.038124
Fe	26	57	56.935398	U	92	235	235.043915

2. If you made a graph of the binding energy per nucleon for all the elements, it would look like the following graph:

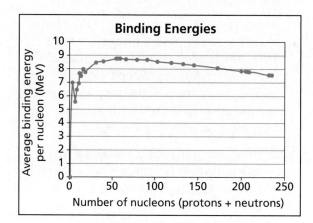

Binding Energies

a) Sketch this graph in your log.

b) Write down important features of the graph that describe the pattern of binding energy per nucleon as the atomic number increases. Describe three features of the graph that you took into account when you made your sketch.

3. Small nuclei can be put together to form larger nuclei.

Larger binding energy means that

• the nucleon is more tightly bound

• more energy is needed to free the nucleon

Use the graph of nuclear binding energy versus nucleon number to answer the following questions:

a) What is the nucleon number of the element that has the most tightly-bound nucleons?

b) Which element requires the most energy to free a nucleon?

c) Show evidence from your graph indicating how the binding energy per nucleon increases if two small nuclei are put together to form one larger nucleus.

For example, show that the average binding energy of phosphorus (atomic number 15) is greater than the average binding energy per nucleon of either nitrogen or oxygen.

4. If the nucleon becomes more tightly bound to the nucleus, additional energy is given off. It takes additional energy to free this nucleon. If nitrogen nuclei were to combine with oxygen nuclei to create phosphorus nuclei, energy would be released according to the calculations and the graph.

a) Suppose two atoms of a lighter element (e.g., atomic number 5) are fused together to create a larger nucleus (e.g., atomic number 10). This process is called *nuclear fusion*. How does the binding energy of the nucleons in the larger nuclei compare with that of the smaller nuclei? Will energy be emitted or absorbed during this transition?

b) If any two nuclei are slammed together hard enough, they may fuse. But not all elements can fuse and provide energy. In order to produce energy by nuclear fusion, the created nucleus must have a larger binding energy per nucleon than the incoming nuclei. Draw a sketch of the binding energy graph and indicate the portion of the graph where smaller nuclei can fuse and produce a larger nucleus with an increase in binding energy per nucleon. Label this portion—fusion.

5. There is another means by which it is possible to create nuclei with larger binding energy. If a very heavy element like uranium were to break apart, the two fragment nuclei would have a greater binding energy per nucleon than the original uranium nucleus. Such splitting of a large nucleus into smaller ones is called *fission*.

a) What is the average binding energy per nucleon for uranium-235?

b) From the graph, estimate the average binding energy per nucleon of barium-137.

c) From the graph, estimate the average binding energy per nucleon of krypton-84.

Because the fragment products, barium-137 and krypton-84, have more binding energy per nucleon than the parent uranium-235, energy is given off. This energy release is due to nuclear fission.

6. Only the heaviest elements can undergo fission and provide energy. In order to produce energy by nuclear fission, the products must have a larger binding energy per nucleon than the reactants. Refer to your sketch of the binding energy graph.

a) Indicate the portion of the graph where a larger nucleus can undergo fission and produce nuclei with an increase in binding energy per nucleon. Label this portion—fission.

7. Uranium-235 will become unstable and undergo fission when it absorbs a neutron. The reaction can be written as follows:

$$_{92}^{235}\text{U} + _0^1\text{n} \rightarrow _{56}^{144}\text{Ba} + _{36}^{89}\text{Kr} + 3_0^1\text{n}$$

a) Show that the number of protons are the same on both sides of the reaction.

b) Show that the total number of nucleons (the sum of protons and neutrons) is the same before and after the reaction (one says such a quantity is "conserved").

8. Notice that the fission of uranium-235 with the absorption of a neutron yields two additional neutrons. Those two neutrons are responsible for the ability to cause a chain reaction. The chain reaction permits two technologies – nuclear power and nuclear bombs.

In order to understand how the chain reaction takes place, imagine a set of 100,000 loaded mousetraps placed very close together. When a small marble is dropped onto any mousetrap, the mousetrap closes with a large snapping sound.

a) Imagine that each mousetrap now has a marble balanced on it. When that mousetrap snaps, its marble jumps in the air and can land on another mousetrap. What will happen if one marble is dropped and hits a trap, which results in its marble being flung into the air?

b) Imagine now that each mousetrap has two marbles balanced on it. When that mousetrap snaps, the two marbles jump in the air and can land on other mousetraps. What will happen if a marble is now dropped?

9. The mousetraps get out of control very rapidly. The first marble releases two marbles, then those two marbles hit two more mousetraps and release four marbles, and so forth.

a) Construct a chart to show how many marbles are released in the first 10 cycles.

b) Suppose you have an unlimited supply of mousetraps. Continue your chart to show how many marbles are released in the first 20 cycles. This enormous release of mousetraps is similar to the enormous release of energy in a nuclear chain reaction.

Physics Talk

BINDING ENERGY VS. ATOMIC NUMBER
Nuclear Fusion and Nuclear Fission

The structure of the atom has a nucleus made up of protons and neutrons. These nucleons are held together tightly with a specific binding energy per nucleon. To free a nucleon would require an input of energy equal to this binding energy per nucleon. In this *Investigate* you calculated the average binding energy per nucleon for various nuclei. The resulting calculations were plotted on a graph of binding energy versus atomic number. The graph revealed that iron has the highest average binding energy per nucleon and is therefore the most stable nucleus. The elements near iron, such as cobalt and nickel, are almost as stable as iron.

Nuclei of elements with smaller mass than iron have less binding energy per nucleon. This makes nuclear fusion as an energy source possible. In **nuclear fusion** two lighter nuclei fuse together to produce a larger nucleus. The larger nucleus has a greater average binding energy per nucleon than the original smaller nuclei. Energy is therefore released in the creation of the larger nucleus. This nuclear fusion is responsible for the Sun's energy. The Sun has provided Earth's energy for over five billion years. The Sun is expected to produce energy through the fusion of hydrogen into helium for another five billion years.

Nuclei of elements with larger mass than iron also have less binding energy per nucleon than iron. This makes **nuclear fission** as an energy source possible. In nuclear fission a heavy nucleus can break apart into two smaller nuclei. The smaller nuclei have a greater average binding energy per nucleon and energy is therefore released. You saw that the fission of uranium-235 with the absorption of a neutron yields two (sometimes three; the average is about 2.2) additional neutrons.

$$_{92}^{235}\text{U} + {}_0^1\text{n} \rightarrow {}_{56}^{144}\text{Ba} + {}_{36}^{89}\text{Kr} + 3{}_0^1\text{n}$$

Those three neutrons have changed the politics, the culture, and the lives of people around the world. Those three neutrons are responsible for the ability to cause a **chain reaction**. The chain reaction permits two technologies—nuclear power and nuclear bombs.

You compared the release of mousetraps to the enormous release of energy in a nuclear chain reaction. The uranium-235 nucleus absorbs one neutron, but gives off three neutrons. Each of those three neutrons can be absorbed and more uranium-235 can undergo fission. With each fission reaction, more energy is released. In a matter of a millionth of a second, a huge fission explosion can take place. The fission explosion can be a nuclear bomb. However, the fission chain reaction can also be controlled. By removing neutrons before another uranium nucleus absorbs them, a controlled reaction takes place. In a nuclear power plant, the control rods absorb these neutrons, and the uranium is more dispersed, so that the uncontrolled chain reaction that results in a nuclear explosion cannot take place.

Physics Words

nuclear fusion: a nuclear reaction in which nuclei combine to form more massive nuclei with the release of a large amount of energy.

nuclear fission: a nuclear reaction in which a massive, unstable nucleus splits into two or more smaller nuclei with the release of a large amount of energy.

chain reaction: one reaction causes two or more similar reactions, in a process that grows exponentially with a specific doubling time.

Checking Up

1. Explain why iron has the most stable nucleus.

2. How does the Sun produce energy?

3. Explain how nuclear reactions are controlled to produce nuclear power.

+Math	+Depth	+Concepts	+Exploration
◆			

Active Physics

Plus

Chain-Reaction Math

Imagine that you have an unlimited supply of mousetraps. Each mousetrap has two marbles balanced on it. When that mousetrap snaps, the two marbles jump in the air and can land on other mousetraps. What will happen if a marble is now dropped?

1. Suppose the time between one mousetrap snapping and the marble it released causing another mousetrap to release is $\frac{1}{10}$ s. The number of marbles released therefore doubles every 0.1 s. Complete the table below for $\frac{1}{10}$ s intervals, from $t = 0.1$ s to $t = 1.00$ s. Remember that each mousetrap that snaps releases two marbles which snap two more mousetraps. (This exercise is best done on a spreadsheet.)

   Continue the table for a few more $\frac{1}{10}$ s intervals as you wish.

2. How does the number of mousetraps snapped at each doubling time compare to the total number of traps snapped in the entire preceding history of the chain reaction?

3. Suppose each snapping of a mousetrap releases 200 MeV of energy. Make a fourth and fifth column in your table, showing the energy released in each doubling time, and the accumulated total energy released since $t = 0$.

4. In a chain reaction of uranium-235 that results in a nuclear explosion, several kilograms of U-235, or some 10^{23} nuclei are fissioned, and each fission releases about 200 MeV of energy. The doubling time, in other words the time between one fission and the next, is about 0.01 of a millionth of a second, or about 10^{-8} s. To fission, the entire sample of uranium takes about a hundred doublings, or about 10^{-6} s. Estimate the total amount of energy released, and express that figure in terms of the equivalent energy released in exploding dynamite. The explosion of a ton of dynamite releases about 4.184 GJ (4.184 billion joules = 4.184×10^9 J).

	A	B	C
	Times	**Number of mousetraps**	**Total number of mousetraps snapped that snap in next 0.01s since first marble thrown at a mousetrap at $t = 0$.**
1	$t = 0$		
2	$t = 0.1$ s	1	1
3	$t = 0.2$ s	2	3
4	$t = 0.3$ s	4	7
5	$t = 0.4$ s		
6	$t = 0.5$ s		
7	$t = 0.6$ s		
8	$t = 0.7$ s		
9	$t = 0.8$ s		
10	$t = 0.9$ s		
11	$t = 1.0$ s		

What Do You Think Now?

At the beginning of the section you were asked the following:

• **How is nuclear energy created?**

• **Is all nuclear energy produced the same way?**

Now that you know about the two different types of nuclear reactions, why are certain elements more likely to undergo nuclear fission, while others are more likely to undergo nuclear fusion?

Physics
Essential Questions

What does it mean?

Which is more stable, a nucleus with a large binding energy per nucleon, or a nucleus with a small binding energy per nucleon? Explain your reason for your answer.

How do you know?

What calculations have you completed that can explain why some elements can fuse together and release energy while other elements can break apart and release energy?

Why do you believe?

Connects with Other Physics Content	Fits with Big Ideas in Science	Meets Physics Requirements
Atomic and Nuclear	Interaction of matter, energy and fields	✳ Experimental evidence is consistent with models and theories

✳ Two atomic bombs were dropped on Hiroshima and Nagasaki, Japan, on August 6 and August 9, 1945 respectively. Their respective energy production yields were about 12.5 kilotons of TNT equivalent, and about 22 kilotons of TNT equivalent, respectively. The Hiroshima bomb used about 15 kilograms of uranium-235; the Nagasaki bomb about 5 kg of plutonium-239. Comment on whether, after such horrific events, there can be any doubt about the power packed into the nucleus.

Why should you care?

Given that life on Earth depends on energy from the Sun; and given that several nations of the world stockpile thousands of fission and fusion bombs, what should every citizen know about the nucleus and nuclear energy? Do you wish to limit your museum exhibit to the physics of fission and fusion or will you include the political aspects as well? How will you do this in a way that educates people and makes them think?

Active Physics

Reflecting on the Section and the Challenge

Both nuclear fusion and nuclear fission provide energy. Your museum exhibit on atomic structure can certainly include information about binding energy and nuclear fission and fusion. It will require some special insight to find ways to help museum visitors understand how breaking up a nucleus can provide energy while fusing together other nuclei can also produce energy. You may decide to draw people into your exhibit with something concerning fission or fusion, sunlight or bombs, solar energy sources, historical events, or political drama.

Physics to Go

1. Calculate and compare the binding energies per nucleon for these three elements:

    a) oxygen-16

    b) lithium-7

    c) calcium-40

    d) Which nucleus is most stable?

2. Sketch the general shape of the binding-energy curve where the number of nucleons is on the x-axis and the average binding energy per nucleon is on the y-axis.

    a) Label the peak of the graph as the most stable element. Identify that element.

    b) Label the part of the graph where fusion could occur.

    c) Label the part of the graph where fission could occur.

3. Should a single museum exhibit attempt to discuss both fusion and fission or should it focus on one? Discuss your reasons.

4. A simulation of a chain reaction can be constructed using dominoes.

    a) How would such a simulation be set up?

    b) Is there a way to set up such a simulation at a museum exhibit? You probably don't want everybody taking the time to set up the dominoes by hand. Is there a mechanical way of easing the setup time?

5. The Sun produces energy by the fusion of hydrogen into helium. Describe in detail (identifying reactions and their energy yields) how this energy can be created. How long do you think that the Sun could continue to produce energy in this way?

6. In a nuclear reactor, control rods (not made out of uranium!) absorb excess neutrons. Why would the absorption of neutrons slow the reaction?

7. Nuclear medicine, nuclear energy, nuclear bombs… some people have very strong opinions about these applications of the knowledge of the nucleus. Could a museum exhibit poll visitors to find their opinion? What would you like to know beyond their opinion? Describe an exhibit that could gather and display information.

8. What research is presently being investigated to provide fusion as an energy source?

9. What are the major advantages and disadvantages of fission as an energy source? How does one decide whether the advantages outweigh the disadvantages?

10. Why is Earth's interior still hot after some 4 billion years? In that time it should have cooled off and become solid to the core, unless there's a heat source. (The volcanoes are not the source of the heat; they exist because of the heat.)

11. Consider the nuclear fusion reaction that powers the Sun. Without worrying about particles such as electrons and photons, through a sequence of intermediate reactions the overall reaction is

$$4\,p \rightarrow {}^{4}_{2}He$$

What energy is released? How much energy is released per nucleon? Compare the energy released per nucleon to that of nuclear fission. Which is more efficient (which gives the most energy per nucleon), fusion or fission?

12. In your log, complete the steps of these sequences of nuclear reaction. This set of reactions powers the Sun and other stars:

$$p + p \rightarrow {}^{2}_{1}H + \underline{\quad}$$

$$ {}^{2}_{1}H + \underline{\quad} \rightarrow {}^{3}_{2}He$$

$$ {}^{3}_{2}He + {}^{3}_{2}He \rightarrow \underline{\quad} + 2\,p$$

Inquiring Further

1. **Positron emission tomography**

   Find out how doctors use the beta-decay of radioactive fluorine-18 in a clinical imaging procedure called positron emission tomography (PET).

2. **Where do elements come from?**

   Find out (perhaps by an Internet search for "supernovae") where the elements come from. How are elements heavier than iron possible in the first place, since, according to the curve of binding energy, making them requires energy?

Physics **You Learned**	
Physics Concepts	**Is There an Equation?**
There are two varieties of electric charges–positive and negative. Like electric charges repel, and unlike electric charges attract.	
For a macroscopic object, a positive charge is caused by a deficiency of **electrons** and a negative charge is caused by an excess of electrons.	
Grounding a charged object allows the excess charge to be sent to Earth, reducing the net charge on the object to zero.	
Charge is measured in coulombs. One coulomb (C) has a charge equal to 6.25×10^{18} electrons.	
The law of **conservation of charge** states that charge cannot be created or destroyed, but may be transferred, causing local imbalances.	
The force between two charges is proportional to the product of their magnitudes, and inversely proportional to the distance between them, squared.	$F_c = \dfrac{kq_1q_2}{d^2}$
Robert Millikan proved that the electron is the fundamental unit of charge and that the charge is quantized. The charge on the electron is equal and opposite to the charge on the **proton** with a value of 1.6×10^{-19} C.	
Indirect measurement and inference are often the only means to develop knowledge about the **atom**, since it is too small to be observed directly.	
The Rutherford experiment proved the existence of the atomic **nucleus** by bombarding atoms with positively charged **alpha particles**.	
Atoms may be identified by the radiation (spectrums) that they emit. The spectral signature of each atom is unique.	
The Bohr model of the atom assumes electrons revolve around the nucleus and may only exist in certain specified orbits.	
The energy of the **photon** of light emitted by an atom (E_p) equals the electron's initial energy state (E_i) minus the electron's final energy state (E_f). According to the Bohr model, light may only be emitted or absorbed by the atom in specified quanta equal to the difference in the atom's energy levels.	$E_p = E_i - E_f$
Active Physics *Plus* The energy of a photon (E_p) equals the photon's **frequency** (f) multiplied by Planck's constant (h). The speed c of the emitted photon equals the frequency times the wavelength.	$E_p = hf$ $c = f\lambda$
Photons of light and matter on the atomic scale have both wave and particle characteristics, although they only exhibit one behavior at a time. This is known as the wave-particle duality of light and matter.	
Interference of light demonstrates a photon's wave characteristics.	
The **photoelectric effect** demonstrates a photon's particle characteristics.	

Active Physics

In the photoelectric effect, the kinetic energy (KE) of an electron ejected from an atom by a photon equals the energy of the photon (E_p) minus the work function (w_o) of the atom where the energy of the photon is hf.	$KE = E_p - w_o$ $KE = hf - w_o$
The location of the electron in the atom is determined by the probabilities described in the Schroedinger wave equation.	
Active Physics *Plus* The wavelength of light or a particle passing through a **diffraction** grating may be calculated using Young's double-slit formula. The wavelength (λ) equals the distance between grating lines (d) times the distance from the central maximum to the first maximum, divided by the distance from the grating to the screen.	$\lambda = \dfrac{dx}{L}$
The nucleus has all the positive charge and almost all the mass of the atom. The nucleus is composed of protons and **neutrons** (collectively called **nucleons**).	
The **atomic number** (Z) of a nucleus is the proton number. The atomic mass number (A) is the sum of the protons and neutrons. The neutron number (N) in a nucleus is the atomic mass number minus the atomic number.	$N = A - Z$
The nucleus is held together by a **strong force** caused by the exchange of **virtual particles** called **mesons**.	
There are three main types of radioactive decay: alpha, beta, and gamma radiation, all of which carry energy away from the nucleus. Both charge and energy are conserved during radioactive decay.	
During **alpha decay**, the atomic number of the parent nucleus decreases by 2 while the atomic mass number decreases by 4.	
During **beta decay**, the parent nucleus atomic mass number remains the same, but the atomic number increases by 1 for negative beta decay.	
Gamma radiation does not change the atomic number or the atomic mass number.	
The half-life of a radioactive material is the time required for half of the non-disintegrated atoms to decay.	
Active Physics *Plus* Radioactive decay is governed by the rules of **probability**. The number of **particles** (N) remaining after a period of radioactive decay equals the original number (N_o) divided by the number 2 raised to the number of half-lives.	$N = \dfrac{N_o}{2^n}$
The nuclear **binding energy** holding the nucleus together comes from the mass converted into energy as the nucleus was assembled. Energy (E) equals mass (m) times the speed of light (c), squared.	$E = mc^2$
The mass converted into energy as the nucleus is assembled is called the **mass defect**, and is found by subtracting the mass of the nucleus from the mass of its individual components when they are not part of a nucleus.	
The greater the binding energy per nucleon, the more stable the nucleus is.	
Fission occurs when heavy nuclei, such as uranium, are split apart into light nuclei, liberating energy.	
Fusion occurs when lighter nuclei, such as hydrogen, are combined together, liberating energy.	

Physics
Chapter Challenge

You will be completing a second process of the *Engineering Design Cycle* as you prepare for the *Chapter Challenge*. The goals and criteria remain unchanged; however, your list of *Inputs* has grown.

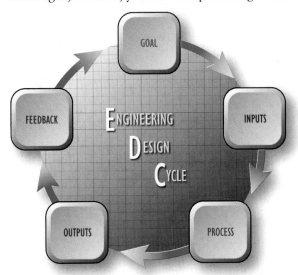

Goal

Your challenge for this chapter is to design an interactive museum exhibit that explains and demonstrates important facts about the atom and to create a novelty item related to the exhibit that might be sold in a museum gift shop. Review the *Goal* as a class to make sure you are familiar with all the criteria and constraints.

Inputs

You have completed all the sections of this chapter and now have more information about the atom to help you identify and address the different physics concepts that apply and that could best be demonstrated in an interactive museum exhibit. This is part of the *Input* phase of the *Engineering Design Cycle*. Your group's collective creativity will be a second major source of *Inputs*. You might visit some online science museums to get more ideas to engage your potential audience.

Section 1 In this section, you explored the nature of electrically charged objects. You also worked with a model for calculating the forces that charged objects exert on each other, demonstrating Coulomb's law.

Section 2 You applied deductive reasoning to examine the contents of a container without looking inside. This was one of the methods Millikan used to discover that electric charges only come in certain "quantized" amounts.

Section 3 You used an indirect method to measure the area of a penny to simulate how Rutherford originally measured the size of an atomic nucleus. You then compared your results to the actual value for the area of a penny and determined the ratio of the size of a nucleus to the size of an atom.

Section 4 You examined the different colors of light that are emitted by a specific atom when it is energized. You also learned how each atom can be identified by the color of light it gives off because the color, or type of light, depends on the arrangement of electrons in each particular atom.

Section 5 You explored different examples to investigate the wave behavior and particle behavior of light, including the photoelectric effect. You also learned that electrons behave like waves and particles.

Section 6 You investigated the organization of the atomic nucleus by building models. The models served to demonstrate the competing forces that must exist to hold protons together in a nucleus despite the Coulomb forces working to push them apart.

Section 7 You used cubes to simulate radioactive decay. You then combined your data from the cubes with your knowledge about the structure of the atomic nucleus to create a model of radioactive decay that demonstrates half-lives, a reliable tool for determining the age of certain archeological artifacts.

Section 8 You unlocked the secret of nuclear power and the meaning of Einstein's $E = mc^2$ equation by comparing the available nuclear energy in an object to other forms of energy you have studied in physics class. You learned that nuclear energy comes from the energy required to hold pieces of the atomic nucleus together and discovered the enormous magnitude of available nuclear energy.

Section 9 You calculated the average binding energy of a particle in a nucleus and explored the two nuclear events that can release energy—nuclear fission and nuclear fusion. Your understanding of these events contributes to your everyday knowledge about the benefits and dangers of nuclear power plants.

Process

In the *Process* phase, your group must decide what information you will use to meet the *Goal*. Your group will be restricted by time and you will need to be organized to complete all of the products for your presentation.

After deciding on the physics concepts you will address, think about how they can be adapted in an interactive display to catch attention—your museum exhibit needs to pull the audience into the exhibit in the first 30 seconds. You might consider turning one of your class investigations into a game or activity for museum visitors.

The challenge requirements also include entrance and exit posters. Your posters should outline the information available in your exhibit, but can also be designed to capture attention and tease viewers' curiosity. Add some thought-provoking questions or mind-boggling facts to spark interest in your exhibit. You will want to make viewers curious about what they can learn while entering your exhibit, and as they exit, help them connect the facts they have just learned with the world they know.

You will need to build a model that effectively communicates exactly how your exhibit might appear in a museum setting. Your model should demonstrate how people will move through the space, where the most captivating features will be located, and how people will be able to interact with the exhibit. Don't forget to include adequate safety features, as would be provided in a real museum.

The requirement to craft a novelty for the museum gift shop is another opportunity to be creative. Your exhibit souvenir could be a game, a toy, a T-shirt emblem, or anything that has a close connection with the information you present in your exhibit.

Outputs

Presenting your complete museum exhibit to the class is your design cycle *Output*. Organize your presentation to highlight the main features of your exhibit and to demonstrate your understanding of the physics concepts related to the atom. You will present your posters, your museum exhibit model, and the gift shop novelty that you created. If you made a model of your interactive idea, you might want to give a few students a chance to try it out. You should also present the facts about the atom that you will be teaching in your exhibit.

Feedback

Your classmates will give you *Feedback* on the accuracy and the overall appeal of your presentation based on the criteria of the design challenge. They will also decide whether they think your exhibit meets the 30-second challenge. Since your group will be creating a number of products for this challenge, it is likely that some of them will be more complete and accurate than others. No design is perfect; there is always room for optimization or improvement. From your experience with the *Mini-Challenge*, you should see how you could continuously rotate through the design cycle to refine your museum exhibit.

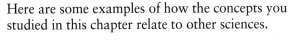

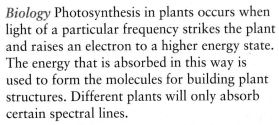

Physics
Connections to Other Sciences

Here are some examples of how the concepts you studied in this chapter relate to other sciences.

Atomic Spectrums

Biology Photosynthesis in plants occurs when light of a particular frequency strikes the plant and raises an electron to a higher energy state. The energy that is absorbed in this way is used to form the molecules for building plant structures. Different plants will only absorb certain spectral lines.

Chemistry Flame tests are used in chemistry to detect the presence of certain metal ions based on each element's characteristic emission spectrum. In principle, any element can be identified by its unique spectral signature.

Earth Science The presence of specific gases in the atmosphere of planets gives clues to their composition and nature. For example, the spectral signature of methane gas on Mars gives rise to speculation of life on that planet.

Duality of Nature

Biology Euglena, a common single cell organism, exhibits characteristics of both plants and animals. Like a plant, Euglena has chloroplasts for producing its own food, but like an animal, Euglena will also ingest food for energy.

Chemistry Chemists rely on both the wave and particle aspects of electrons to understand bonding between atoms. Ionic bonding seems to rely on the transfer of an electron as a particle to another atom, while covalent bonding seems to share the wave function of an electron between atoms.

Earth Science Volcanoes both raise and lower the global temperature by two different mechanisms. The large amount of ash and other aerosols ejected into the atmosphere serves to block incoming radiation from the Sun, which lowers temperatures. However, the ejection of carbon dioxide and water vapor contributes to greenhouse gases, which raise temperatures.

Electrostatics

Biology Static electric charges often build up on the fur of animals such as cats, when the fur is rubbed. It is speculated that the fibers of spider webs may also be electrically charged, helping them ensnare their prey.

Chemistry Ionic bonding between charged ions of salts is responsible for the formation of salt crystals. The electrostatic attraction between polarized water molecules explains much of the behavior of water on the macroscopic level.

Earth Science Volcanic eruptions are often accompanied by static electric discharges (lightning) in the clouds of ash caused by the interaction of ash particles that are ejected from the volcano.

Quantization or Fundamental Building Blocks

Biology The basis for life, DNA, is composed of the fundamental building blocks of the organic bases, guanine, cytosine, adenine and thymine, connected to a phosphate-sugar backbone.

Chemistry The quantization of the subatomic particles of an atom determines the chemical characteristics of that element, as well as how it interacts with other elements.

Earth Science The crystals that are the fundamental building blocks of igneous rock such as quartz and feldspar, are composed of repeating units locked into a specific pattern.

Nuclear Radiation

Biology Radioactive elements and nuclear (gamma) radiation are used to treat numerous diseases. Radiation from sources in the environment (for example, radon gas) may lead to genetic mutations.

Chemistry Using radioactive isotopes as tags to follow the steps in chemical reactions has proven to be a valuable tool, particularly in areas of biochemistry where the pathways can become extremely complex.

Earth Science The half-life of certain radioactive elements is the basis for one of the primary arguments establishing the age of Earth as approximately 4.5 billion years.

Dr. Linda Shore

Director of the Teacher Institute at the Exploratorium; San Francisco, CA

Dr. Linda Shore was intrigued by science growing up, and thought that one day she could turn her intrigue into a career. "I grew up watching Carl Sagan's television show, *Cosmos: A Personal Voyage*, and remember being fascinated by his ability to translate science and make it exciting," said Shore.

She earned her masters degree in physics from San Francisco State University and her doctorate in Science Education at Boston University. When she returned to San Francisco in 1993, she joined the Exploratorium, an interactive science and art museum, founded in 1969 by famed physicist and educator Dr. Frank Oppenheimer.

Dr. Shore wants to dispel the myth that the Exploratorium is merely a science museum. "That is just the tip of the iceberg." The museum houses teacher-education programs, exhibits for sale and for rent, along with over 700 hands-on exhibits.

As the director of the Teacher Institute, Dr. Shore fills her days helping science teachers teach better, assisting with a Web cast or the design of an exhibit, and traveling to other museums to design teacher programs. "Every day is a little bit of a surprise," she said.

But Dr. Shore said that the biggest surprise about her job is how much it still teaches her about science. "My job is to translate science to the public, teachers, and students, which is similar to receiving interesting homework assignments; I never know what the questions are going to be."

Roger Barrett

Exhibit Designer; Science Museum of Minnesota, Minneapolis, MN

Roger Barrett has been an exhibit designer for five years at the Science Museum of Minnesota, known for its traveling exhibit program, its innovative interactive exhibits, and their Exhibits-for-Sale program.

Recent exhibits that Barrett has been involved in are Robots, Race, BioMusic, Water, the Science of Fear, and Nanotechnology. During the fabrication portion of the project, Barrett will work with a scientist or Curator to develop exhibit content. Barrett also is involved in choosing building materials, which is not an easy decision. "Durability is a factor, as well as aesthetics, cost, ease of construction and green materials," said Barrett.

Patricia Rayner

Physical Science Teacher and Inventor of the All American Atom; Bethel, CT

Patricia Rayner has been teaching science for over 25 years, but it was early on in her career when she discovered that students learn better through hands-on activities. It was then that she developed the "All American Atom" that allows students to learn about the atom by making a model of it.

"Model-making is very important," says Patricia. "You can feel it, touch it, and see it to understand it, and it uses the creative part of the brain." Her students use the kit she developed, which involves building a plastic, three-dimensional nucleus with atoms spinning inside.

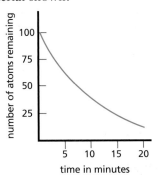

Physics

Practice Test

Before you try the Physics Practice Test, *you may want to review Sections 1–9, where you will find* **27 Checking Up** *questions,* **15 What Do You Think Now?** *questions,* **36 Physics Essential Questions,** **103 Physics to Go** *questions, and* **8 Inquiring Further** *questions.*

Content Review

1. Two small conducting spheres that are a fixed distance apart each carry an electric charge. If the charge on each of the spheres is doubled, the electric force between the two spheres will be
   a) doubled.
   b) quartered.
   c) halved.
   d) four times larger.

2. Two point charges, whose distance between centers is 10 m, repel one another with a force of 50 N. If the distance between their centers is now changed to 5 m, the force of repulsion will be

   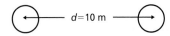
   $d = 10\ m$

   a) 25 N.
   b) 50 N.
   c) 100 N.
   d) 200 N.

3. The force that holds the nucleons of an atom together is
   a) weak and short-ranged.
   b) weak and long-ranged.
   c) strong and short-ranged.
   d) strong and long-ranged.

4. Atoms of different isotopes of the same element contain the same number of
   a) neutrons, but a different number of protons.
   b) neutrons, but a different number of electrons.
   c) electrons, but a different number of protons.
   d) protons, but a different number of neutrons.

5. According to the graph, what is the half-life of the material shown?

   a) 5 min
   b) 7 min
   c) 10 min
   d) 15 min

6. How many neutrons are in an atom of $^{222}_{86}\text{Rn}$?
   a) 84
   b) 86
   c) 136
   d) 222

7. What did Millikan conclude after performing his oil-drop experiment?
   a) The charge on an electron is 1.0 C.
   b) The mass of an electron is 1.7×10^{-27} kg.
   c) The charge on any oil drop is a whole number of electrons.
   d) The charge on an oil drop may have any value.

8. The equation $^3_1\text{H} + ^1_1\text{H} \rightarrow ^4_2\text{He} + \text{energy}$ is an example of
   a) fusion.
   b) fission.
   c) alpha decay.
   d) beta decay.

9. Which equation below is an example of nuclear fission?

a) $^{214}_{82}\text{Pb} \rightarrow ^{214}_{83}\text{Bi} + ^{0}_{-1}\text{e}$

b) $4\left(^{1}_{1}\text{H}\right) \rightarrow ^{4}_{2}\text{He} + 2^{0}_{+1}\text{e}$

c) $^{235}_{92}\text{U} + ^{1}_{0}\text{n} \rightarrow ^{138}_{56}\text{Ba} + ^{95}_{36}\text{Kr} + 3^{1}_{0}\text{n}$

d) $^{234}_{92}\text{U} \rightarrow ^{230}_{90}\text{Th} + ^{4}_{2}\text{He}$

10. After Rutherford bombarded gold foil with alpha particles, he concluded that the volume of an atom is mostly empty space. Which observation led Rutherford to this conclusion?
a) Some of the alpha particles were deflected 180°.
b) The paths of deflected alpha particles were hyperbolic.
c) Many alpha particles were absorbed by gold nuclei.
d) Most of the alpha particles were not deflected.

11. When a source of dim, orange light shines on a photo-sensitive metal, no photo-electrons are ejected from its surface. What can you do to increase the chances of producing photo-electrons?
a) Replace the orange light source with one of lower frequency.
b) Replace the orange light source with one of higher frequency.
c) Increase the brightness of the orange light.
d) Increase the angle at which the photons of orange light strike the metal.

12. The concept of the photon is best explained by assuming that light is
a) a wave.
b) a particle.
c) emitted by atoms.
d) without mass.

13. Which of the following is not a basic premise of the Bohr model of the atom?
a) An electron radiates energy as it moves about the nucleus.
b) An electron can only exist in certain specified orbits.
c) An electron emits energy as photons when it jumps from a higher energy level to a lower energy level.
d) The circumference of an electron's orbit is a whole number of electron waves.

14. Which phenomenon is evidence for the quantum nature of light?
a) interference
b) diffraction
c) reflection
d) photo-electric effect

15. The diagram shows some of the energy levels for a hydrogen atom. Which energy transition will result in the emission of a photon with the highest energy?

$n = 5$ ———— -0.54 eV

$n = 4$ ———— -0.85 eV

$n = 3$ ———— -1.51 eV

$n = 2$ ———— -3.4 eV

$n = 1$ ———— -13.6 eV

a) $n = 5 \rightarrow n = 4$
b) $n = 2 \rightarrow n = 1$
c) $n = 4 \rightarrow n = 2$
d) $n = 5 \rightarrow n = 3$

Critical Thinking

16. A beam of light composed of photons with energy of 8 eV strikes a metal with a work function of 4.3 eV.
a) What is the energy of the ejected electron?
b) If the intensity of the light falling on the metal is increased, what happens to the kinetic energy of the ejected electrons?

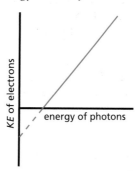

c) The graph shows the kinetic energy of the photoelectrons ejected from the metal versus the energy of the photons striking the metal. What does the x-intercept of the graph represent?
d) What does the y-intercept of the dotted line on the graph represent?

Practice Test *(continued)*

17. Two spheres have charges of +0.003 C and -0.005 C as shown in the diagram. The spheres are separated by a distance of 4 m.

+0.003 C   −0.005 C

4 m

   a) Calculate the electrostatic force between the spheres.
   b) On the diagram, indicate the direction of the force on the negatively charged sphere due to the positively charged sphere.

18. A lithium atom is composed of 3 protons and 4 neutrons, and has a nuclear mass of 7.0160 u. If the mass of a proton = 1.00728 u and the neutron mass = 1.00867 u, calculate the binding energy of lithium
   a) in atomic mass units.
   b) in MeV.

19. The diagram below shows some of the energy levels of hydrogen. An electron makes the transition from the $n = 3$ to the $n = 1$ level.

   $n = 5$ ———— -0.54 eV
   $n = 4$ ———— -0.85 eV
   $n = 3$ ———— -1.51 eV

   $n = 2$ ———— -3.4 eV

   $n = 1$ ———— -13.6 eV

   a) What is the energy of the photon emitted in eV?
   b) If 1 eV = 1.6×10^{-19} J, what is the photon energy in joules?
   c) What is the frequency of the emitted photon?
   d) What is the wavelength of the emitted photon?

20. For the following atoms and decay schemes, write down the equation for the decay of the parent nucleus into the daughter nucleus and all other decay products.

   a) $^{234}_{92}$U decays into thorium (symbol Th) by emitting an alpha particle.
   b) $^{34}_{15}$P decays into sulfur (symbol S) by emitting a negative electron.
   c) What effect does doubling the mass of the sample have on the half-life of the sample?

Active Physics
Plus

21. A sample of a radioactive element has a half-life of 22 days. If the sample of the original material consists of 1 g, how long will it take until 0.37 g remains?

22. A green laser ($\lambda = 532 \times 10^{-9}$ m) shines through a diffraction grating with a spacing between slits of 1.00×10^{-6} m onto a screen 1.25 m away. What is the distance between the central and first bright fringe?

23. A photon whose energy is 1.2×10^{-18} J strikes a metal with a works function of 4.7×10^{-19} J. If the mass of the ejected electron is 9.1×10^{-31} kg, what is the ejected electron's speed?

Chapter 9

9

Sports on the Moon

Scenario

One day, a colony will be set up on the Moon and families will live there for extended periods. Plans will have to be made for exercise and entertainment while people live on the Moon. Since sports on Earth satisfy both of these needs—exercise and entertainment—it is reasonable to assume that people in the Moon colony will also wish to participate in sports. It may even be possible that Moon sporting events could be television entertainment for the people back home on Earth.

Your Challenge

Your challenge is to identify, adapt, or invent a sport that people on the Moon will find interesting, exciting, and entertaining.

Write a proposal to NASA (National Aeronautics and Space Administration) that includes the following:

- a description of your sport and its rules and how it meets the basic requirements for a sport

- a comparison of factors affecting sports on Earth and on the Moon in general

- a comparison of the play of your sport on Earth and on the Moon, including any changes to the size of the field, alterations to the equipment, or changes in the rules

- a newspaper article for the sports section of your local paper back home describing a "championship" match of your Moon sport

Criteria for Success

The NASA proposal will be graded on the quality, creativity, and scientific accuracy of your invented sport as well as the description of your sport, the factors affecting sports on Earth and on the Moon, the comparison of play of your sport on Earth and on the Moon, and the newspaper article. One suggestion is that all of these will count for 80% of the grade; the quality and usefulness of charts, sketches, and other visual portions of the proposal count for another 20%. NASA proposals that include a mathematical analysis of the sport will be considered superior to those that describe the sport qualitatively (without numbers). In your pursuit of finding the "best" sport for the Moon, you may investigate sports that would not be suitable for the Moon. Descriptions of these rejected sports and the reasons that they were rejected would raise the quality of your proposal.

For each subject of the final proposal, your class should decide on what should be included and what point value each part should have. How many points should be allocated for creativity and how many should be allocated for mathematical analysis? How many points should be allocated for the comparison of the play on Earth and on the Moon, and how many points should be allocated for the newspaper article? When writing the newspaper article, should points be provided for the quality of the writing, for sketches or drawings that illustrate the article, and for reader interest? What are the attributes that make a superior newspaper article?

If a group is going to hand in one proposal, how will the individuals in the group get graded? How will the grading ensure that all members of the group complete their responsibilities as well as help the other members of the group? The grading criteria should satisfy every person's need for fairness and reward. Decide on the criteria that your class will use before comparing your class' standard with those on the next page.

Standard for Excellence	
1. Written proposal to NASA • a description of your sport and its rules and how it meets the basic requirements for a sport • a comparison of factors affecting sports on Earth and on the Moon in general • a comparison of the play of your sport on Earth and on the Moon, including any changes to the size of the field, alterations to the equipment, or changes in the rules	**60 points**
2. Newspaper article • a newspaper article for the sports section of your local paper back home describing a "championship" match of your Moon sport	**10 points**
3. Entertainment value of sport • the sport will capture the spectators' interest and be exciting and entertaining • the sport will be exciting and fun to play for participants	**20 points**
4. Challenge completed on time	**10 points**

Engineering Design Cycle

It's time to get started with your Moon design challenge. This new challenge requires you to submit a proposal to NASA for a new or modified sport to be played on the Moon. You will use a simplified *Engineering Design Cycle* to help your group complete this design challenge. Defining the *Goal* is the first step in the *Engineering Design Cycle*, so you have already begun.

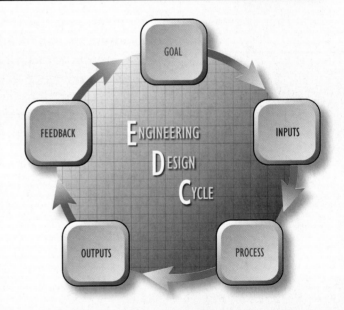

As you experience each one of the chapter sections, you will be gaining *Inputs* to use in the design cycle. These *Inputs* will include new physics concepts, vocabulary, and even equations that will help you to develop your modified sport. Even if you know nothing about the Moon at this point, each section of the chapter will provide you with new and useful information. When your group prepares the *Mini-Challenge* presentation and the *Chapter Challenge* you will be completing the *Process* step of the design cycle. During the *Process* step you will evaluate ideas, consider criteria, compare and contrast potential solutions, and most importantly make design decisions about the game play of your Moon sport.

The *Outputs* of your design cycle will include your written NASA proposal and your presentation of the Moon sport that you think Moon inhabitants will find interesting, exciting, and entertaining to play. Your *Outputs* may also include any charts, diagrams, or calculations you use to clarify the information you present.

Finally, you will receive *Feedback* from your classmates and your instructor about what parts of your presentation are good and which parts need to be refined. You will repeat the design cycle two times during the course of the chapter. First, as you complete the *Mini-Challenge* halfway through the chapter and then again during the second half of the chapter when you gain more *Inputs*, refine or change your game, and complete your final written proposal and class presentation.

Physics Corner

Physics in *Sports on the Moon*

- Acceleration due to gravity
- Air resistance
- Collisions
- Energy conservation
- Energy transformation
- Friction
- Gravitational mass
- Gravity
- Inertial mass
- Momentum
- Pendulums
- Projectile motion
- Proportions
- Scale models
- Trajectories

Section 1

Identifying and Classifying: What Is a Sport?

What Do You See?

Learning Outcomes

In this section, you will

• **Apply** brainstorming as a process for generating ideas.

• **Develop** a working definition of the term "sport."

What Do You Think?

A friend comes by and asks if you want to watch some sports on TV. You turn on the set and your friend says, "That's a movie." You try another station and your friend complains, "That's a soap opera." You try a third time and your friend says, "Stop, there's some sports."

• **How did your friend know what type of program was on after seeing the TV for only a few seconds?**

• **What did your friend observe on the screen that indicated that a sport was on TV?**

Record your ideas about these questions in your *Active Physics* log. Be prepared to discuss your responses with your small group and the class.

Investigate

1. Brainstorm a list of at least 10 words or phrases that identify attributes, or characteristics, of activities known as sports. (Example: team involved, individual involved, and/or score kept.)

In brainstorming, all ideas are accepted and no idea is evaluated or thrown out until brainstorming has been completed. During brainstorming, it is "okay" to ask for clarification of an idea, but the discussion of ideas should not occur until later. Continue brainstorming until your group identifies 10 or more attributes of sports or the group runs out of ideas.

a) A member of your group should volunteer to record the list of attributes of sports as the group is brainstorming them. Everyone, including the person serving as recorder, should participate in identifying attributes.

b) Discuss each attribute and decide on a final list of attributes that apply to many, but not necessarily all, sports. Each member of the group should copy the list in his or her notebook under the heading "Attributes Shared by Many Sports."

2. Brainstorm a list of names of at least 15 sports (examples: baseball, rock climbing). All sports should be accepted without discussion or evaluation. Continue identifying sports until the process either "slows down" after 15 sports are named or when the length of the list of sports reaches 30. Everyone should participate.

a) One member of your group should record the list of sports.

3. Decide which items on the list "Attributes Shared by Many Sports" apply to every one of the sports identified by the group. Consider the attributes one at a time and ask, "Does this attribute apply to every one of the sports on the list, or to only some of the sports?"

a) Mark with an asterisk (*) those attributes that apply to every one of the sports identified by the group.

b) In your log, make a new list with the heading, "Attributes That Apply to All Sports."

c) Discuss within your group whether any attributes that apply to all sports seem to have been left out; if the group finds any that seem appropriate or necessary, then add them to the list.

4. Define the term "sport."

a) Use the list "Attributes That Apply to All Sports" to construct a written definition of the term sport. Test the drafts of your definitions against the list of sports generated by the group—and other sports that may come to mind—until your group agrees upon a definition that seems to apply to all sports.

b) Write your group's definition of the term "sport" in your *Active Physics* log.

c) New sports are often considered for inclusion in future Olympic Games. Do the following sports meet your definition of a sport?
- karate
- squash
- roller sports

Physics Talk

THE LAWS OF PHYSICS

Everybody seems to recognize a sporting event when they pass by a field or see it on television. Defining the attributes of a sport can be a bit more difficult. In your group discussions on the nature of sports, you perhaps had disagreements as to which activities are sports. Is ballroom dancing a sport? Is ultimate disk throwing a sport? Is chess a sport? You have been asked to invent a sport that can be played on the Moon. Your discussion of sports from this section will aid you in developing that sport.

Trying to come up with a definition of a sport might have proven difficult, but most people would agree that a sport requires physical action. If a sport requires physical action, then it can be described by the appropriate physics – what scientists sometimes call the **laws of physics**.

Physics Words

Laws of physics: universal and invariable observations and relations of the physical world. The laws of physics may, however, be disproved if new facts or evidence contradict them.

The laws of physics are generalizations about relationships in the physical world based on universal and invariable observations. That means that if everywhere the observations of many people about the same event are always the same, scientists can use the observations to develop a law. Laws of physics are universal. They are true anywhere in the universe. They are also parsimonious, meaning that they are clear and concise, and they are no more complex than necessary. They follow "the simpler, the better," principle. You have already investigated a number of laws of physics. Newton's laws of motion are three well-known laws of physics you have studied. The law of conservation of energy is also a law with which you are familiar. The activities you see in sports can be explained using these and other laws of physics.

The laws of physics are not laws in the sense you usually think of them. They need no one to enforce them, since nature does the enforcing. If it is found that some event does not obey the laws of physics, the law of physics is amended so that the new law can explain that event as well as all the other events.

Checking Up

1. Explain why the laws of physics cannot be broken.

2. List two factors that would be radically different for an athlete playing a sport outdoors on the Moon when compared to Earth.

When a scientist tries to describe the action in a sport according to the laws of physics, the results may often be very complicated. A curve ball thrown by a pitcher in a baseball game, the spins, twists and turns of a diver, or the trajectory of a forward pass in football will all require complex physics to describe them adequately.

+Math	+Depth	+Concepts	+Exploration
	◆	◆	◆

Do Extreme Sports Require Extreme Physics?

Extreme sports take many forms, such as skydiving, hang gliding, and even "air surfing," where participants jump out of an airplane with a snowboard strapped to their feet. Similar to hang gliding, but with a smaller wing, these "air surfers" use a snowboard to control their descent to the ground.

The physics needed to explain sports of this nature is the same physics that is investigated in *Physics in Action*. For extreme sports like air surfing, scientists looking to explain just what is occurring must look deeply into these phenomena.

Equations for air resistance, or drag, like the one below, are used to help explain the motion of these falling air surfers.

$$D = \frac{1}{2}\rho A C_p v^2$$

This expression may appear extreme to you now, but you will soon learn more about drag in *Section 9* of this chapter, which will help give you a greater understanding of physics.

Motocross, another extreme sport, where people do stunts in midair while riding "dirt" motorcycles, requires understanding the physics of conservation of angular momentum, moment of inertia, and the gyroscopic principle.

All these concepts are part of the basic vocabulary of physics. They describe the real world and are only slightly more complex than the material you are studying in this book. In the future, you will continue to learn about physics and gain a better understanding about these marvelous sports.

To a physicist, physics occurs in even more extreme ways, like ultra-high energy particles, ultra-cold temperatures, and the ultra-strong gravity of black holes. All these exciting areas of study use even more complex and fascinating areas of physics.

1. Choose an extreme sport. Research one physics concept related to the sport that you have not learned about in class. For example, if you choose snowboarding, you may wish to find out what makes snow slippery. Be prepared to present your research to the class.

What Do You Think Now?

At the beginning of the section, you were asked the following:

• How did your friend know what type of program was on after seeing the TV for only a few seconds?

• What did your friend observe on the screen that indicated that a sport was on TV?

After your investigation of what makes a sport, is it possible to come up with a definition for a sport that includes all of the activities people would identify as requirements to be a sport? Explain your answer.

Physics
Essential Questions

What does it mean?
What does brainstorming reveal about the definition of a sport?

How do you know?
What convinced you that your definition of a sport was a good one?

Why do you believe?

Connects with Other Physics Content	Fits with Big Ideas in Science	Meets Physics Requirements
Forces and motion	Well-defined terms	✱ Agreement on the meaning of terminology and definitions

✱ Many groups considered the question of what is a sport. What convinced you that people agree or disagree on the definition of a sport?

Why should you care?
How will you convince NASA that the activity proposed by your group fits the definition of a sport?

Reflecting on the Section and the Challenge

The first item that you must address in your proposal to NASA is how your chosen sport for Moon dwellers meets the basic requirements for a sport. In order for you to convince NASA that you know what the requirements for a sport are, it seems necessary for you to include a fundamental definition of a sport as a basis of your proposal. You may wish to refine your definition later. The list of sports generated by your group during this activity is a good starting place for considering which sports could be adapted to the Moon. However, you probably need more information about the differences between Earth and the Moon before you can make a good decision about the particular sport to include in your proposal.

Physics to Go

1. You learned from this section that the term "sport" means different things to different people. Write a brief paragraph describing an occasion when someone asked you for the definition or the meaning of a term used in a conversation with you. (Example: A parent saying, "Don't get home too late.")

2. Look up the definition of "sport" in a dictionary. What do you think of the definition? Explain your answer. How did this definition of sport compare with the one you and your team proposed?

3. Outdoors on the Moon, astronauts must carry compressed air tanks for breathing (there is no air on the Moon). Astronauts must also wear pressurized suits. If the pressurized suit rips or the air tank malfunctions, the astronaut could die. How will this affect participation in sports played on the Moon?

4. List three sports that could be played outdoors on the Moon, taking into account the safety concerns listed in *Question 3*.

5. List three sports that could be played indoors in a stadium on the Moon.

6. Based only on what you know about the Moon so far, how would conditions on the Moon affect

   a) the sport you like playing the most?

   b) the sport that you like watching the most?

7. Do the following meet your definition of a sport? Explain.

   a) ballroom dancing   b) chess

   c) skateboarding   d) white-water canoeing

   e) beach volleyball   f) weightlifting

8. *Preparing for the Chapter Challenge*

   Part of the excitement of playing sports is having spectators. If the sport on the Moon is to be played on the surface, everyone (athletes and spectators) will require compressed air and pressurized suits. If a normal compressed air bottle holds enough air for 45 minutes, suggest a rules change for a softball game, since the game often lasts several hours.

Inquiring Further

Research the physics of a sport

Many books have been written about the physics of sports, and the Internet has dozens of sites devoted to the explanation of how physics describes a particular sport. Choose a sport that interests you and do an Internet search to find a site that deals with that sport. Summarize what the site says about the sport and the related physics, and give a brief report to the class.

Active Physics

Section 2

Acceleration Due to Gravity: Free Fall on the Moon

What Do You See?

Learning Outcomes

In this section, you will

- **Compare** the acceleration due to gravity on Earth and the Moon through a video analysis.

- **Apply** proportions to compare situations.

- **Apply** scale models for measurement and comparison.

What Do You Think?

The diameter of the Moon is only one fourth the diameter of Earth.

- **Compare and contrast the motion of a ball falling on the Moon with that of a ball falling on Earth.**

Record your response in your *Active Physics* log. Be prepared to discuss your response with your small group and the class.

Investigate

In this *Investigate*, you will first explore how objects fall on Earth under the influence of gravity and air resistance and then on the Moon. After watching a video of a hammer and a feather falling on the Moon, you will make measurements to determine the acceleration of gravity on the Moon.

1. Remember the last time you dropped your pencil on the floor? As student scientists, you will take a more careful look at dropped objects. For each of the following pairs of objects, hold one object in each hand and release both objects at the same instant from the same height:

- a single pencil/two pencils tied together with thread

- a closed book/an open sheet of paper

- a closed book/a tightly crumpled sheet of paper

- a hammer/a feather

a) Record which, if either, object hits the ground first, or if the objects strike the ground at the same instant. Try to explain each case in terms of what you know about *gravity* and air resistance.

2. Observe a video sequence of an astronaut, Commander David Scott, dropping a hammer and a feather while standing on the surface of the Moon. Answer the following questions in your log.

a) Why did the hammer and feather fall in the same way and hit the surface at the same time?

b) Explain why you do or why you do not think the Moon has a gaseous atmosphere similar to Earth's air.

c) Since the time it takes an object to fall is an indicator of the *acceleration* of the object, what would you conclude about the acceleration of a falling hammer on the Moon as compared to Earth? What evidence do you use to support your conclusion?

d) What information would you need to make a careful comparison of the acceleration of the falling hammer on Earth and on the Moon?

3. Examine the two "double exposure" diagrams below. They represent pictures taken with the same camera located the same distance away from the astronaut. On the left the astronaut is dropping a hammer while standing on the Moon. Two images of the hammer are visible. The first image was made at the instant he let go of the hammer. The second image was made 0.50 s after the hammer began to fall. On the right the astronaut is dropping the same hammer on Earth.

Active Physics

Again, one image was made at the instant of release, and another image was made after the hammer had fallen for 0.50 s.

a) The astronaut shown in the diagrams is known to have a real height of 2.1 m (210 cm) without his helmet. By placing a ruler on the diagram and measuring the height of the astronaut, see if you agree that the "scale factor" of the diagram is as follows: 33.3/1.0 = (cm in real life)/(cm in diagram).

b) Accurately measure for each diagram how far the hammer falls in 0.5 s. Use the same point on the two images of the hammer for your measurement. Record each distance, measured to the nearest millimeter, in your log book. (Example: 3.7 cm or 37 mm)

c) Multiply each of the fall distances from *Step 3.b*) by the scale factor of the diagram [(33.3 cm in real life)/ (1.0 cm in diagram)] to convert the distance the hammer falls on the diagram to real-world distances on the Moon and Earth. Refer to these distances as d_{Moon} and d_{Earth}.

d) In your *Active Physics* log, substitute the values of the distance, in meters, that the hammer falls on the Moon and on Earth in the equation below to find the ratio of the acceleration on the Moon $\left(g_{Moon}\right)$ to the acceleration on Earth $\left(g_{Earth}\right)$.

$$\frac{g_{Moon}}{g_{Earth}} = \frac{d_{Moon}}{d_{Earth}}$$

e) Record the answer for g_{Moon}/g_{Earth} in your log.

f) Is your answer about $\frac{1}{6} = 0.16$?

Do your calculations show that the acceleration due to gravity on the Moon is about $\frac{1}{6}$ of the value on Earth? Write about this in your log.

g) The acceleration due to gravity on Earth $\left(g_{Earth}\right)$ is 9.8 m/s^2 (meters per second every second). From your results for this investigation, what should be the value of the acceleration due to gravity, in m/s^2, on the Moon $\left(g_{Moon}\right)$? Show how you arrived at your answer in your log.

4. If you know the acceleration due to gravity on Earth, you can compute the distance an object falls by using the equation

$$d = \frac{1}{2}gt^2 ,$$

where d is the distance,
    t is the time, and
    g_{Earth} is the acceleration due to gravity on Earth
    ($g_{Earth} = 9.8$ m/s^2).

Similarly, you can calculate the distance an object falls on the Moon by using the same equation but substituting for the acceleration due to gravity on the Moon ($g_{Moon} = 1.6$ m/s^2).

Complete a chart that compares the distance an object falls on Earth and the Moon after 0.5 s, 1 s, 1.5 s, and 2.0 s.

5. The same equation

$$d = \frac{1}{2}gt^2$$

can be used to calculate the time it takes for an object to fall 5.0 m on Earth and the Moon.

- Method A: Use algebra and derive an equation for time. Solve for the time if the fallen distance is 5.0 m.
- Method B: Use the equation $d = \frac{1}{2}gt^2$ and, with your calculator, input different values of time, *t*, until you get a value close to 5.0 m for the distance. (A value of time to the nearest tenth of a second will be sufficient.)

Physics Talk

GRAVITY AND FREE FALL

When you watched the video of the astronaut dropping the hammer and the feather on the Moon, you were immediately exposed to two of the major differences between Earth and the Moon. The Moon's weaker gravity caused the hammer to fall much more slowly than it would on Earth. In addition, the feather, which normally would lag far behind the hammer on Earth due to air resistance, falls at the same rate as the hammer. These two factors by themselves may cause you to rethink many aspects of a sport you may be considering proposing to NASA.

You found that the acceleration due to gravity on the Moon is ⅙ the acceleration due to gravity on Earth. A diver will take much more time to get to the water than she would on Earth. In developing a sport for the Moon, you will have to always take into account how slowly objects accelerate on the Moon after being dropped.

All sports on Earth are affected by air resistance. It is air resistance that makes a curve ball curve. A wind can affect a runner's speed. On the Moon, you will have to make a decision about whether you want your sporting event to be outside or inside. Outside, there is no air and no air resistance. Athletes will have to wear spacesuits, which include air to breathe, if your sport is outside. Inside a stadium, you will have air and will have to be concerned with air resistance.

You may have been surprised that you were able to use the same equation for the distance covered by a falling object on the Moon,

$$d = \frac{1}{2}gt^2,$$

that is used to describe the motion on Earth. Falling objects on the Moon **accelerate** or increase speed the same way objects on Earth do, but at a different rate.

It was the work of Galileo and others, including Sir Isaac Newton, who showed that the rules of physics, which describe motion on Earth, apply to the Moon as well. It is a fundamental belief of scientists that the rules of physics are the same everywhere in the universe. Astronomers and other scientists are constantly testing the laws of physics to see if they need to be modified in any way to describe what they observe. If any changes are made to the laws of physics, they will also have to apply to how things behave on Earth and the Moon.

Physics Words

accelerate: to change the velocity per unit time.

Active Physics

Physics Words

gravity: the force of attraction between two bodies due to their masses.

Checking Up

1. How does the acceleration due to gravity compare on Earth and on the Moon?

2. What determines the force of gravity of a planet?

3. Why would the weight of an astronaut be different on different planets?

The rate at which all objects fall will vary from planet to planet, but their falling motion will always be described by the same equation. For example, on Mars, where **gravity** is approximately 40 percent as strong as that on Earth, the acceleration due to gravity is 4 m/s^2, so an object would fall 4 m for every 9.8 m an object falls on Earth. On Jupiter, where the acceleration due to gravity is approximately 26 m/s^2, in the time it takes an object to fall 26 m, an object on Earth would only fall 9.8 m. This ignores air resistance for both planets. The acceleration of gravity is directly related to the size and mass of the planet, which determines the gravitational force a planet is able to exert on a falling mass. This same force of gravity also determines the weight of the astronaut. Knowing a planet's mass and radius allows scientists to calculate the acceleration of gravity before an astronaut ever visits the planet. If NASA did not know what the acceleration of gravity for the planet was, landing on the planet could be dangerous to the spacecraft and astronauts.

Active Physics Plus

+Math	+Depth	+Concepts	+Exploration
◆◆			

Deriving a Useful Equation

Using the definitions of acceleration and velocity, you can derive an equation that relates the fallen distance to the elapsed time.

The distance an object falls can be found from the definition of velocity.

$$\text{Average velocity} = \frac{\text{change in distance}}{\text{change in time}}$$

$$v_{av} = \frac{\Delta d}{\Delta t}$$

Therefore: $d = v_{av}t$

For a constant acceleration, the average velocity can be found by calculating the average of the initial and final velocity.

$$v_{av} = \frac{v_f + v_i}{2}$$

Combining these two equations yields:

$$d = \left(\frac{v_f + v_i}{2}\right)t$$

If the object starts from rest, $v_i = 0$ and the equation simplifies:

$$d = \frac{v_f}{2}t$$

Acceleration, by definition, is equal to the change in velocity/change in time.

$$a = \frac{\Delta v}{\Delta t} = \frac{v_f - v_i}{\Delta t}$$

If the object starts from rest, then

$$a = \frac{v_f}{\Delta t}$$

This can be rewritten as $v_f = at$.

Returning to the distance equation,

$d = \dfrac{v_f}{2}t$, you now find that:

$$d = \left(\dfrac{at}{2}\right)t$$

$$d = \dfrac{1}{2}at^2$$

The equation

$$d = \dfrac{1}{2}at^2$$

was developed by combining equations already known. Physicists call this process "deriving" an equation. This new equation is very useful because it allows calculation of the distance an object falls when only the object's acceleration and time of fall are known if the initial velocity is zero. In addition, the equation works for falling objects on either Earth or the Moon. The symbol g is used for acceleration (a) due to gravity.

- Fall distance during time of fall t on the Moon is

$$d_{\text{Moon}} = \dfrac{1}{2}g_{\text{Moon}}t^2$$

- Fall distance during time of fall t on Earth is

$$d_{\text{Earth}} = \dfrac{1}{2}g_{\text{Earth}}t^2$$

Dividing the above equation for d_{Moon} by the above equation for d_{Earth}, with the condition that the times of fall t for objects on the Moon and Earth are equal yields:

$$\dfrac{d_{\text{Moon}}}{d_{\text{Earth}}} = \dfrac{\dfrac{1}{2}g_{\text{Moon}}t^2}{\dfrac{1}{2}g_{\text{Earth}}t^2}$$

$$\dfrac{d_{\text{Moon}}}{d_{\text{Earth}}} = \dfrac{g_{\text{Moon}}}{g_{\text{Earth}}}$$

The previous equation was simplified by canceling the equal "½" and "t^2" terms that appear in both the numerator and the denominator.

The equation

$$\dfrac{d_{\text{Moon}}}{d_{\text{Earth}}} = \dfrac{g_{\text{Moon}}}{g_{\text{Earth}}}$$

provides the answer, "Yes, the distances that objects fall from rest during equal time intervals on Earth and the Moon compare in the same way as the accelerations due to gravity on Earth and the Moon." Therefore, it is valid to compare the acceleration due to gravity on the Moon and on Earth by comparing the distances that the dropped hammer falls during equal time intervals on the Moon and Earth.

By comparing distances, you find that the ratio was 1:6. The acceleration due to gravity on the Moon is ⅙ the acceleration due to gravity on Earth.

What Do You Think Now?

At the beginning of this section you were asked the following:

- **Compare and contrast the motion of a ball falling on the Moon with that of a ball falling on Earth.**

Based on what you have learned in this section, how would you respond now?

917

Physics
Essential Questions

What does it mean?

The acceleration due to gravity on the Moon is ⅙ the acceleration due to gravity on Earth. What does this tell you about how things fall on the Moon compared to how things fall on Earth?

How do you know?

What observations or measurements did you make that allowed you to conclude that things fall differently on the Moon than they do on Earth?

Why do you believe?

Connects with Other Physics Content	Fits with Big Ideas in Science	Meets Physics Requirements
Forces and motion	✳ Symmetry — laws of physics are the same everywhere	Good, clear explanation, no more complex than necessary

✳ One of the grand insights of Galileo and Newton was that the laws of physics on Earth are identical to the laws of physics on the Moon. If falling objects on Earth and Moon both use the equation $d = \dfrac{1}{2}gt^2$, explain why objects fall so much slower on the Moon.

Why should you care?

What aspects of sports depend on how things fall while the sport is being played?

Reflecting on the Section and the Challenge

Objects take much longer to fall on the Moon than on Earth. A ball kicked straight up that requires only 2 s to return to the ground on Earth would take 12 s to return to the Moon (assuming it is kicked with the same initial velocity in each case). This is due to the acceleration due to the Moon's gravity being only ⅙ the acceleration due to the gravity on Earth. It is also due to the fact that the ball leaves the ground and returns to the ground along a straight vertical line.

Time and distance can be computed using $d = \frac{1}{2}gt^2$. It is important to understand that some properties of motion on Earth and the Moon do not have a ratio of 1:6. The rate of falling is an example. It takes an object on Earth 2 s to fall 20 m. On the Moon, an object takes 5 s to fall 20 m. The time is still longer on the Moon, but not six times longer. For falling objects, the Moon's time to fall is $\sqrt{6}$ or 2.45 times longer than that on Earth.

Now that you are equipped with a specific value for the acceleration due to gravity on the Moon, it is possible to make calculations to show exactly how anything in a sport that involves free fall would be affected if the sport were played on the Moon. This would include not only simple "up" and "down" cases of free fall—such as vertical jumps—but also all cases of projectile motion—such as the shot put or golf—in sports on the Moon. You will study these in a later section.

When developing a sport for the Moon, you will have to take time into account. How long an object is in the air is important since a sport can get boring if most of the time is spent waiting for a ball to drop or to return to the surface.

Physics to Go

1. Calculate the distance that an object falls after one second on the Moon and on Earth.

2. Calculate the distance that an object falls after three seconds on the Moon and on Earth.

3. Compare the sport of platform diving on Earth and on the Moon if both places use a 10-m high concrete platform.

4. Show that the equation $d = \frac{1}{2}gt^2$ can be rewritten as
$$g = \frac{2d}{t^2}$$

5. When exploring a planet, it was found that a rock dropped from 2.0 m above the planet's surface took 0.50 s to fall to the surface. What is the acceleration due to gravity on that planet? (Hint: Find the acceleration from the equation $d = \frac{1}{2}gt^2$.)

6. Show that the equation $d = \frac{1}{2}gt^2$ can be rewritten as
$$t = \sqrt{\frac{2d}{g}}$$

7. If a rock drops from 2.0 m above the surface of the Moon, how much time does it take to fall to the surface? (Hint: Find the time from the equation $d = \frac{1}{2}gt^2$.)

8. A baseball player on the Moon hits a fly ball straight up at an initial speed of 30 m/s.

   a) How much time does it take the ball to reach the highest point in its flight?
   b) How much time does the fielder have to prepare to catch the ball when it comes back down?

   c) What is the maximum height of the ball in its flight? Compare your answer to the length of a football field: 100 yards between goal lines equals about 91 m.

9. A group of physics students plans to adapt the soapbox derby to the Moon. The contestants' cars will start from rest and coast down a 160-m mountainside on the Moon. The mountain has a straight slope. The slope is great enough that a derby car that has low friction will accelerate at about ½ of the acceleration due to gravity on the Moon. Before each car's run, the race sponsors will place a high-tech instrument package on the car that will allow the driver to read the elapsed time, acceleration, speed, and distance traveled throughout the run. Copy and complete the table below to show the highest possible readings that the accelerometer, speedometer, and odometer could show at the end of each 2 s during an ideal, friction-free run. Be sure to fill in each empty cell in the table. You may want to use a spreadsheet.

Clock (s)	Accelerometer reading (m/s^2)	Speedometer reading (m/s)	Odometer reading (m)
0	0.8	0	0
2.0	0.8	1.6	
4.0	0.8		
6.0			
8.0			
10			
12			
14			
16			
18			
20			

10. How does the difference in time for the flight of a ball affect the game of basketball if played on the Moon with no modifications?

11. How does the difference in time for the flight of a gymnast in the air affect Earth gymnastics if done on the Moon with no modifications?

12. How does the difference in time for the flight of a projectile affect the throw of a javelin on the Moon?

13. Pretend that you are a sports commentator. Describe a home run in a baseball game on Earth. Take into account the time it takes for a ball to reach the seats. Now describe a home run in a baseball game on the Moon.

14. *Preparing for the Chapter Challenge*

The rate that objects fall on the Moon determines how long an object spends in the air. For the sport you propose to NASA, this may or may not be a factor in adapting the sport to be played on the Moon. Choose one sport where this increased time would make a difference in how the sport is played, and one sport where it would not make a difference, and explain why it would or would not affect the sport.

Inquiring Further

Landing probes on the Moon

When the Apollo 11 crew first landed on the Moon in 1969, they rode down to the surface in a Lunar Excursion Module (LEM), which had a rocket engine. When the astronauts decided on the exact spot to land, the engine was shut off and the rocket "dropped" a short distance to the surface. Prior to the first manned landing, many unmanned probes were launched and made a "hard" landing (a crash) on the planet's surface. These impact speeds are usually the same as the "escape velocity" for the body.

Look up some of the early unmanned probes sent to the Moon by various countries and record their impact speeds on the planet. Report on how they compare to the Moon's escape velocity, and how the probes were able to reduce their speeds.

Active Physics

Section 3   Mass, Weight, and Gravity

What Do You See?

Learning Outcomes

In this section, you will

• **Compare** the masses of objects using applied forces.

• **Measure** the weights of objects using a spring balance.

• **Understand** and apply Newton's universal law of gravitation to compare the acceleration due to gravity on Earth and the Moon.

What Do You Think?

The astronauts on the Moon carry instrument packages on their back that weigh 200 lb on Earth.

• **If an object has a mass of 1 kg on Earth, what is its mass on the Moon?**

• **If a 1-kg object weighs about 10 N on Earth, what is its weight on the Moon?**

Record your ideas about these questions in your *Active Physics* log. Be prepared to discuss your responses with your small group and the class.

Investigate

For this *Investigate,* you will compare the weight and mass of bottles as they would appear on Earth and on the Moon. You will use these measurements to decide if the lowered gravity of the Moon affects an object's mass, the object's weight, or if both are affected.

Part A: Comparing Mass

1. Your teacher has prepared a simulation that will allow you to compare the mass of an object on Earth to the mass that the same object would have on the Moon.

At the Mass Station you will find two bottles lying on a table, one labeled "1 kg, Earth" and another labeled "1 kg, Moon."

To keep the simulation accurate and realistic, follow the rules below:

- Keep the bottles lying on their sides on the table; do not stand the bottles upright.

- You may move the bottles only by poking and rolling them; do not lift the bottles.

2. Select the bottle labeled "1 kg, Earth" and use a push of your hand to start the bottle rolling freely across the table to a partner from your group. Your partner should use a push to stop the bottle and then push again to send it rolling back to you. Play roll the bottle-stop-return-roll until you and your partner have the "feel" of the pushing force needed to start (accelerate) and stop (oppositely accelerate) the 1 kg, Earth bottle.

3. Pretend that you and your partner are on the surface of the Moon, standing across a table from one another. Select the bottle labeled "1 kg, Moon." Play roll the bottle-stop-return-roll to compare the amount of pushing force needed to accelerate the 1 kg, Moon bottle to the force needed for the 1 kg, Earth bottle.

⚠️ Make sure you only use plastic bottles.

a) Record how the amount of force needed to accelerate a 1-kg mass on Earth compares to the amount of force needed to accelerate a 1-kg mass by the same amount on the Moon. Is the amount of force needed to produce equal accelerations in the two locations different? Is it about the same? If not, how is it different? How do you know?

b) Isaac Newton explained that an object's mass is a measure of its *inertia*. Inertia is the tendency of an object to resist a change in velocity. Newton also said that this is true no matter where the object is located. Using your observations, explain if Newton was correct.

c) Newton's second law says $F = ma$. Explain how if equal forces *(F)* applied to two objects produce equal accelerations *(a)* of the objects, then this means that the masses *(m)* of the two objects are equal.

Part B: Comparing Weight

1. Your teacher has prepared another simulation that allows you to compare the weight of an object on Earth to the weight of the same object on the Moon.

At the Weight Station, you will find two bottles resting upright on a surface, one labeled "1 kg, Earth" and another labeled "1 kg, Moon." To keep the simulation accurate and realistic, follow the steps described below.

2. Grasp the string attached to the bottle labeled 1 kg, Earth and lift the bottle vertically. Get the "feel" of Earth's downward gravitational pull on the bottle and then carefully lower it back to the surface to rest in an upright position. Attach a spring scale calibrated in newtons (N) to the string and measure the bottle's *weight*.

▷a) Record the weight in newtons of the 1 kg, Earth bottle in your log.

3. Pretend you have been transported to the Moon. Remember, this is only a simulation of what it would feel like to lift a kilogram mass on the Moon. Lift and weigh the bottle labeled 1 kg, Moon.

▷a) Record the weight in newtons of the 1 kg, Moon bottle in your log.

▷b) Divide the weight of 1 kg on Earth by the weight of 1 kg on the Moon and round off the answer to the nearest integer. Show your work and record your answer in your log.

▷c) If 2-kg masses instead of 1-kg masses had been used, what do you think would have been the individual weights of the bottles on Earth and the Moon? What would the ratio of the weights be? Write your answers in your log.

▷d) Why do you think the weights of equal masses, one on Earth and the other on the Moon, are different? Be as specific as you can. Use the values in your log to support your answer.

▷e) Your teacher knew the difference in weight of an object on Earth and the Moon to produce this simulation. How could you reproduce this simulation with two water bottles at home?

Physics Talk

GRAVITY ON THE PLANETS AND THE MOONS

In *Section 2*, you saw that the acceleration due to gravity on the Moon is $\frac{1}{6}$ of the acceleration due to gravity on Earth. Therefore, you probably were not surprised when the simulation in this *Investigate* showed that the weight of an object on the Moon is $\frac{1}{6}$ of the weight of the same object on Earth. Since, according to $F = ma$, the amount of acceleration of an object depends directly on the amount of applied force, the reduced rate of free-fall acceleration on the Moon must be caused by a gravitational pull that is smaller on the Moon than on Earth. On the Moon, both the free-fall acceleration and the force causing the acceleration are $\frac{1}{6}$ of the amounts on Earth, regardless of what object is compared at both locations. But why $\frac{1}{6}$ and not some other ratio? Isaac Newton answered that question.

Newton reasoned that any object with mass—a star, planet, moon, comet, or even a speck of dust—pulls other objects toward it with a force due to gravitation. This is often called the universal law of gravitation. Newton explained that the free-fall acceleration of a small object, such as a hammer, dropped near the surface of a huge object, such as a planet or a moon, depends on two factors: the mass of the planet and the size of the planet.

- If two planets are the same size, a more massive planet will have a greater acceleration due to gravity.

- If one planet is larger than the other, the distance between the small object and the center of the planet is larger. This will decrease the acceleration due to gravity by one over the distance squared. If two planets have the same mass, and one has 4 times the radius of the other, the acceleration on the larger planet will be 16 times less $\left(4^2 = 16\right)$.

Comparing Earth and the Moon requires taking into account the relative sizes and masses of each.

- Earth is approximately 100 times the mass of the Moon. The mass difference would make Earth's acceleration 100 times more than the Moon's.

- Earth is approximately 4 times as large as the Moon. The size difference would make Earth's acceleration 16 times less than the Moon's.

- Taking both into account, Earth's acceleration due to gravity will be $^{100}\!/_{16}$ or approximately 6 times as large as the Moon's.

It works! Isaac Newton's explanation, made more than 300 years before anyone went to the Moon, also relates to the Moon and can be verified. When Commander David Scott stood on the Moon and dropped a hammer, the free-fall acceleration was, according to Newton's prediction, $\frac{1}{6}$ of the free-fall acceleration due to gravity on Earth.

On the Moon, an athlete would find it easier to lift a shot-put ball from his equipment bag because it would weigh only $\frac{1}{6}$ as much as on Earth. When twirling and extending his throwing hand to accelerate the ball prior to launch, the athlete would find that the same amount of force is needed as "back home" on Earth. It is the same mass, and the force needed to accelerate it by the same amount as on Earth has not changed.

Active Physics

Physics Words

inertia: the natural tendency of objects to resist a change in velocity (acceleration).

weight: the vertical, downward force exerted on a mass as a result of gravity, measured in newtons in the SI system.

However, the athlete would be thrilled at the result. For an amount of muscular work done by the athlete equal to a shot-put effort on Earth, the shot put would fly six times further.

Mass is a measure of the **inertia** or resistance to acceleration of an object. Mass is measured in units of kilograms (1000 g). **Weight** is the force of gravity on an object near the surface of a planet, moon, asteroid, and so on. It depends on the object's mass and the amount of gravitational pull on the specific planet. The unit of force is the newton (N).

A surprising result occurs when you look at weight and mass for different objects on Earth.

- A heavy object has a large weight on Earth. This means that the force of gravity is large. It also has large mass and therefore, it has a large inertia and it is hard to get it moving. Large force of gravity and a large inertia gives the heavy object an acceleration of $9.8 \, \text{m/s}^2$ on Earth.

- A light object has a small weight on Earth. This means that the force of gravity is small. It also has a small mass and therefore, has a small inertia and it is easy to get it moving. Small force of gravity and a small inertia gives the light object an acceleration of $9.8 \, \text{m/s}^2$ on Earth.

- All objects have the same acceleration of $9.8 \, \text{m/s}^2$ on Earth. This is contrary to many people's "common sense." That is one reason many people did not believe Galileo when he tried to explain that all objects fall at the same rate.

The same thing happens on the Moon, where the acceleration of all objects is $1.6 \, \text{m/s}^2$. That is why the feather and hammer dropped on the Moon fell at the same rate. (Feathers and hammers do not fall at the same rate on Earth because the air alters the fall on Earth. Without air resistance, everything on the Moon falls identically.)

Mass is the same on Earth, the Moon, and any other place in the universe. Weight on Earth is six times as large as weight on the Moon. A 90-kg high school football player weighs approximately 900 N on Earth (approximately 210 lb). That same 90-kg player weighs only 150 N (approximately 33 lb) on the Moon.

At the end of the last Apollo 15 Moon walk in 1971, Commander David Scott performed a live demonstration for the television cameras. He held out a geologic hammer and a feather and dropped them at the same time. If you look carefully at the photo, you can see a hammer in his right hand and a feather in his left hand.

A game of football would be quite different on the Moon. It would be just as difficult to push somebody out of the way on the Moon because the mass (inertia) is identical as on Earth. However, it would be very easy to lift them in the air because they weigh so little on the Moon.

Newton's law of universal gravitation revealed much more about the world than the accelerations of objects on different planets or celestial bodies. Newton's law revealed that planets and moons were no different than any other objects. Newton's law describes a gravitational attractive force between any two objects. A table attracts a chair, a person attracts a person, and a house attracts a car. The forces between these objects is so small because of their small masses. Attractions between small masses are difficult to measure, but they can be measured and have been measured. Newton's equation does an exceptional job in predicting the force of attraction between masses.

Newton's law of universal gravitation can be expressed mathematically (as you can find in *Active Physics Plus*).

Checking Up

1. Two planets are of equal size but different masses. Which planet will have the greater acceleration of gravity?

2. Two planets are of equal mass but different sizes. Which planet will have the greater acceleration of gravity?

3. When a massive object is transferred from Earth to the Moon, what happens to the object's weight? What happens to the object's inertia?

4. Why is the force of gravity between two people so small?

Active Physics *Plus*

+Math	+Depth	+Concepts	+Exploration
◆◆	◆		

Gravitational Constant

Newton's law of universal gravitation states that every tiny bit of mass (physicists call these point masses) attracts every other point mass with a force proportional to the product of their masses and inversely proportional to the square of the distance between them. The proportionality constant is

$$G = 6.67 \times 10^{-11}\ \text{N} \cdot \text{m}^2 / \text{kg}^2$$

You often refer to this constant, G, as big G to distinguish it from the acceleration due to gravity, g (little g) for Earth, the Moon, and other planets. You call G the gravitational constant. Newton's law of universal gravitation is written as:

$$F = \frac{Gm_1 m_2}{r^2}$$

where m_1 and m_2 are the masses of the two objects and r is the distance between the centers of the masses (or planets).

Newton also showed that for spherical objects with real sizes, the law of universal gravitation still works as long as each spherical object is replaced with an imaginary point mass. This imaginary point mass must have a mass equal to the mass of the spherical object and must be located at the center of the spherical mass.

In the case of a large spherical object like a planet, an object placed on its surface experiences an attractive gravitational force as though all of the planet's mass were concentrated at its center. The distance from the object to the planet's center is the radius of the planet. So if the mass of the object on the surface is m, the mass of the planet is m_p, and the radius of the planet or moon is r_p, then the force on the object is given by:

$$F = \frac{Gm \cdot m_p}{r_p^2}$$

$$= m\left(\frac{Gm_p}{r_p^2}\right)$$

You already know that the gravitational force on an object on the surface of a planet is called its weight and is equal to the object's mass times a little g, a constant for that planet or moon. That constant equals the acceleration due to gravity on that planet, $F = mg$. Therefore, you now can calculate the acceleration due to gravity on a planet or moon, g_p, by rearranging the terms in the equations.

$$g_p = \frac{Gm_p}{r_p^2}$$

1. Now try this for Earth. The mass of Earth is 5.98×10^{24} kg and the radius of Earth is 6.38×10^6 m. Use these values to find g_E, the acceleration due to gravity on Earth.

2. The mass of the Moon is 7.36×10^{22} kg and the radius of the Moon is 1.74×10^6 m. Using these values, what is g_M, the acceleration due to gravity on the Moon?

3. What is the ratio of the acceleration due to gravity on Earth to the acceleration due to gravity on the Moon?

4. You can also take the two equations and form a ratio. Since the Moon's mass is $\frac{1}{100}$ of Earth's mass, and the Moon's radius is $\frac{1}{4}$ of Earth's radius, you can write Newton's law of universal gravitation in terms of Earth's mass and radius.

Earth: $F_E = \dfrac{GM_E m}{R_E^2}$

Moon: $F_M = \dfrac{G\left(\dfrac{1}{100}\right)M_E m}{\left(\dfrac{1}{4}R_E\right)^2}$

Create a ratio of Earth's force and the Moon's force to find that Earth's force would be approximately 6 times larger than the Moon's force for the same mass.

What Do You Think Now?

Mass is an attribute of objects; weight is a derived characteristic. In physics, it is often desirable to identify intrinsic attributes that depend on the object alone and not on other factors such as where the object is located or how fast it is going.

• If an object has a mass of 1 kg on Earth, what is its mass on the Moon?

• If a 1-kg object weighs about 10 N on Earth, what is its weight on the Moon?

Based on what you have learned about weight and mass on Earth and the Moon, how would you answer these questions now?

Physics
Essential Questions

What does it mean?

Is the mass of an object the same whether it is on Earth or on the Moon? Is the weight the same?

How do you know?

Physicists use models or simulations to help understand concepts. How did the simulation provide a sense of the comparison of weights on Earth and the Moon?

Why do you believe?

Connects with Other Physics Content	Fits with Big Ideas in Science	Meets Physics Requirements
Forces and motion	✳ Symmetry — laws of physics are the same everywhere	Good, clear explanation, no more complex than necessary

✳ An organizing principle of physics is that the same laws of physics are appropriate on Earth and the Moon. What does Newton's universal law of gravitation say about the weights of objects on Earth and on the Moon?

Why should you care?

How do the weights of objects affect the nature of a specific sport?

Reflecting on the Section and the Challenge

The facts that the weight of objects are different on the Moon but that the mass and inertial properties of objects remain unchanged on the Moon have great implications for sports on the Moon. Many sports involve lifting objects against the force of gravity and placing objects in a condition of free fall; these aspects of sports will be different in the "$\frac{1}{6}g$" condition on the Moon. Many sports involve applying forces to accelerate objects; these aspects of sports will be no different on the Moon than on Earth. In fact, many sports involve combinations of actions, some of which may be different on the Moon than on Earth, and some of which may be the same. It will be necessary for you to consider which parts of the sport that you choose to play on the Moon will be affected by reduced gravity and which parts will not be affected. Remember, lifting is six times easier on the Moon; pushing is just as difficult as it is on Earth.

Physics to Go

1. How would the sport of weight lifting be different on the Moon? If a person can lift 220 lb on Earth, what weight could that person lift on the Moon?

2. How would a baseball player's ability to swing (accelerate) a bat be affected on the Moon? Assume that a spacesuit does not inhibit the batter's movement.

3. For equal swings of the bat and equal speeds of the ball, how would the speed of a baseball when it leaves the bat compare on Earth and the Moon?

4. Imagine an outdoor game of baseball at Lunar Stadium.

   a) The center field wall is about 400 ft from home plate at a baseball park on Earth. Explain what the appropriate distance for the center field wall would be at Lunar Stadium. Use equations and numbers to explain your answers.

   b) Other aspects of baseball might be different on the Moon.

   • Should the pitcher's mound and the bases at Lunar Stadium be located at the same or different distances from home plate as on Earth? Explain your answer.

   • How fast would a major-league pitcher capable of a 100 mi/h "Earth pitch" be able to throw the ball on the Moon? Explain your answer.

   • How fast would players be able to run the bases on the Moon? Why?

   c) Describe the problems fans in the center field bleachers might have:

   • seeing a player slide into second base or home plate

   • watching a high fly ball

   • eating a hot dog

   • shouting at the umpire

5. Water would be very expensive on the Moon because it is unavailable.

   a) If you purchased a precious 1-L bottle of "Genuine Earth Water" at the Lunar Mall, what would be its mass, in kilograms? (Hint: On Earth, 1 L of water has a mass of 1 kg and a weight of 9.8 N.)

   b) What would be its weight, in newtons?

6. If you bought 10 kg of potatoes on the Moon, would they make as many servings as 10 kg of potatoes make on Earth?

7. Newton's law of gravity can explain why an object falls to Earth. Can Newton's law of gravity explain the attraction between people?

8. *Preparing for the Chapter Challenge*

The difference in someone's weight on Earth and the Moon will be a large factor in many sports that might be played on the Moon. NASA will be very interested on how the decreased gravity of the Moon will affect how the sport will be played and any additional dangers that might occur because of the change in gravity. Write a brief paragraph explaining how the Moon's low gravity will affect a sport that you choose. Explain why the sport might be more dangerous or less dangerous than when played on Earth.

Inquiring Further

Bone structure and gravity

When gravity is increased or decreased, an organism's weight will change accordingly. On Earth, big animals, such as elephants, have large weights, and small animals, such as mice, have small weights. Because of this, the bone structures of elephants and mice are very different. Research how the size of an animal's bones is related to the animal's weight. Use this knowledge to predict what the bones of an animal that evolved on a planet with a gravitational field stronger than the Earth might look like. What would the same animal that evolved on a planet with low gravity look like? Make a sketch of each animal, label one low gravity and the other high gravity, and present it to the class.

Active Physics

Section 4   Projectile Motion on the Moon

What Do You See?

Learning Outcomes

In this section, you will

• **Apply** the acceleration due to gravity on Earth to projectile motion on Earth.

• **Apply** this understanding to describe the acceleration due to gravity on the Moon to projectile motion on the Moon.

• **Design** a mathematical model and a physical model of the trajectory of a projectile on the Moon.

What Do You Think?

A baseball has ⅙ the weight on the Moon as on Earth, but a baseball's mass on the Moon is the same as on Earth.

• **Can a batter hit or a player throw a baseball faster on the Moon than on Earth?**

• **Can a batter hit or a player throw a baseball farther on the Moon than on Earth?**

• **If your answer to either question is yes, how much faster or farther?**

Record your ideas about these questions in your *Active Physics* log. Be prepared to discuss your responses with your small group and the class.

Investigate

In this *Investigate,* you will set up a scale drawing to calculate the range and maximum height achieved for a projectile launched with the same velocity when it is on Earth and on the Moon.

1. Use the following instructions to produce a ⅒ scale drawing, that is, a drawing ⅒ of the actual size, of a *trajectory* model of a *projectile* (the path an object you throw will take)

launched at a speed of 4.0 m/s. Work with members of your group.

a) On a standard-size sheet of paper (about 22 cm by 28 cm) as shown reduced in size below, mark a starting point 2 cm above and 2 cm to the right of the bottom-left corner of the paper. From the starting point, draw two straight lines entirely across the sheet, one horizontal and another inclined at an angle of 30°. Add the title shown in the sketch.

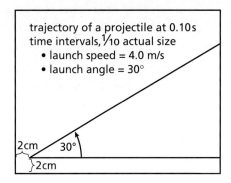

trajectory of a projectile at 0.10s
time intervals, 1/10 actual size
• launch speed = 4.0 m/s
• launch angle = 30°

2cm   30°

2cm

b) The horizontal line represents ground level, and the inclined line represents the path that a projectile launched from the starting point at a 30° angle would follow if there were no gravity. Measuring from the starting point, mark points at 4.0-cm intervals on the inclined line. Since the launch speed is 4.0 m/s (400 cm/s), the projectile would travel 40 cm every tenth of a second. This model is $\frac{1}{10}$ scale, so 4.0 cm is $\frac{1}{10}$ of the actual distance (40 cm) that the projectile would travel in 0.10 s. The marked points represent the position of the projectile every 0.10 s for a zero-gravity condition. Begin by labeling the starting point as 0.00 s, label successive points on the inclined line as 0.10 s, 0.20 s, 0.30 s, and so on.

c) Also mark points at 2.0-cm intervals on the horizontal line. Begin by labeling the starting point as 0.00 m.

Mark successive points on the horizontal line as 0.20 cm, 0.40 cm, 0.60 cm, and so on. These points represent distance along the ground, scaled, of course, by a factor of 10 from real-world distances.

d) Use the equation

$$d = \frac{1}{2}gt^2$$

(where $g = 980$ cm/s² instead of the usual 9.8 m/s²) to calculate the total distance an object on Earth would fall. Start from rest and then determine the distance fallen in 0.10 s, 0.20 s . . . 0.60 s. Draw three columns in your *Active Physics* log to make a table. Enter the time in seconds in the first column, the distance fallen in the second column, and then divide each fall distance by 10 to fit the $\frac{1}{10}$ scale of the drawing.

e) Next, draw a line vertically downward from each marked point on the inclined line to show the projectile's position at that time. For example, the line at the point labeled 0.10 s should extend 0.49 cm (or 4.9 mm) downward from the inclined line because 4.9 cm divided by 10 equals 0.49 cm.

f) The bottom ends of the vertical fall lines represent the projectile's position at 0.10 s intervals during its flight. Connect the bottom ends of the lines with a smooth curve to show the shape of the trajectory and label the curve "Trajectory on Earth."

g) Use the distance scale established on the horizontal line to measure, to the nearest 0.10 m, the projectile's real-world maximum height above ground level, and the horizontal range of the projectile before striking the ground. Record the maximum height and range on the drawing.

h) Use the time scale established on the inclined line to measure, to the nearest 0.010 s, the projectile's time of flight. Record the time of flight on the drawing.

2. You will now draw the trajectory that would result if the projectile were launched at the same speed and in the same direction on the Moon.

a) Use the same equation

$$d = \frac{1}{2} g t^2$$

to calculate the total distance an object on the Moon falls, starting from rest, in 0.10 s, 0.20 s, 0.30 s, and so on. The value of acceleration to use in the equation is the acceleration due to gravity on the Moon, 1.6 m/s², or 160 cm/s².

Prepare a table in your *Active Physics* log, making it similar to the table for Earth distances fallen, to show the calculated value of the total distance of fall at the end of each 0.10 s of flight on the Moon. Enter the time in seconds in the first column, the distance fallen in the second column, and then divide each fall distance by 10 to fit the ¹⁄₁₀ scale of the drawing. Draw the trajectory for the projectile on the Moon in a similar manner as the trajectory you drew on Earth.

b) Draw a vertical line downward from each marked point on the inclined line to show the projectile's position at that time on the Moon. For example, the line at the point labeled 0.30 s should extend 0.72 cm, or 7.2 mm, downward from the inclined line. This line, and others, will need to be drawn on top of or immediately next to the lines drawn earlier for fall distances on Earth.

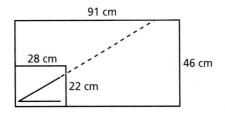

Extend the size of the paper to be able to show the entire trajectory on the Moon as shown in the sketch. Tape the sheet of paper containing your drawing to the lower left-hand corner of a sheet of wrapping paper approximately 46 cm high and 91 cm wide.

c) The bottom ends of the vertical fall lines represent the projectile's position at 0.10 s intervals during its flight on the Moon. Connect the bottom ends of the lines with a smooth curve to show the shape of the trajectory and label the curve "Trajectory on the Moon."

d) Use the distance and time scales on the drawing to measure the projectile's maximum height, range, and time of flight on the Moon. Record the values on the drawing. Fold and save your drawing.

3. Create a table to show the above measurements of the maximum heights, ranges, and times of flight of a projectile launched with equal initial velocities on Earth and the Moon to complete the calculations below.

a) Max height of projectile on Earth

Max height of projectile on the Moon

b) Range of projectile on Earth

Range of projectile on the Moon

c) Time of flight on Earth

Time of flight on the Moon

d) Show your work and discuss it in your *Active Physics* log.

4. Write a summary of the effects of the Moon's "$\frac{1}{6} g$" on the maximum height, range, and time of flight of a projectile launched on the Moon as compared to the same projectile launched at the same speed and angle of elevation on Earth.

a) Record your summary in your *Active Physics* log.

Physics Talk

PROJECTILES ON THE MOON

In the *Investigate* for this section, you drew a scaled-down version of an object's path, launched at an angle on the Moon. To do this, you assigned the **projectile** an initial speed of 4 m/s at an angle of 30° to the horizontal. To plot the object's trajectory, you calculated how far the object would fall from a line drawn at the 30° angle at one-tenth second intervals.

This plotting procedure relies on the principle that the motion of a projectile is composed of two independent motions: a constant-velocity portion and an accelerated-motion portion. The line ascending at 30° represents the path the projectile would take if there were no gravity to affect its path. Without gravity, the projectile would follow Newton's first law and continue in motion in a straight line with constant speed.

When gravity exists, it causes an object to accelerate toward the surface of the planet, and the distance the object would fall is given by the

equation $d = \frac{1}{2}gt^2$. For a planet that has an acceleration due to gravity of 2 m/s² (close to that of the Moon), the object would fall a distance of 1 m by the end of the first second, a total of 4 m by the end of second number two, a total of 9 m by the end of second three, and so on. When these two motions are combined, the **trajectory** or path of the projectile is established. The trajectory is a parabola because gravity's downward acceleration is constant.

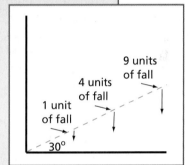

The operation described above can be used to find the position of a projectile at all points along its path at any time. To plot the trajectory in the more familiar x, y coordinates, only a slight modification of your procedure is required. If the velocity of the projectile at the launch angle is broken down into individual vertical and horizontal motions, each of these can be plotted separately. To find how high the object would travel during any time interval in the absence of gravity, you can just use the familiar equation

$$v_y = \frac{\Delta d_y}{\Delta t} \text{ or } d_y = v_y \, \Delta t$$

where v_y is the vertical component of the launch velocity, and d_y is the height at any time.

To find the height when gravity is included, add the vertical height without gravity to the calculated fall due to gravity for that time. When these two vertical motions are added, the vertical or "y" coordinate has been found.

$$d_y = \frac{1}{2}gt^2 + v_y t$$

The acceleration is negative because it is in the opposite direction of v_y.

Physics Words

projectile: an object traveling through the air with no power source of its own.

trajectory: the path followed by an object that is launched into the air.

The projectile's horizontal position at any time can be found from the equation

$$v_x = \frac{\Delta d_x}{\Delta t} \text{ or } d_x = v_x \Delta t$$

where v_x is the horizontal component of velocity and
d_x is the horizontal distance at any time.

Nothing needs to be added to the horizontal position, since the force of gravity works only in the vertical direction. The path of a projectile affected only by gravity (no air resistance) has a specific curved shape. This curve is referred to as a parabola. You drew a parabolic path on Earth and the Moon in the *Investigate*.

The vertical and horizontal components of the launch velocity can be found either by graphical methods (measuring) or by calculation. To find the velocities graphically, draw a right triangle with an angle to the horizontal the same as the launch velocity. Make the length of the hypotenuse equal to a scaled down version of the launch velocity. When you use a ruler to measure the size of the vertical and horizontal sides of the triangle, you have found the scaled down size of the vertical and horizontal launch velocities. You then scale the velocities up to the correct values.

To calculate the vertical and horizontal launch velocities, trigonometry can be used.

Knowing these velocities and using this method allows you to solve numerous problems in trajectories.

Sample Problem

A field-goal kicker in a football game on the Moon kicks the ball at an angle of 53° to the horizontal with a speed of 10.0 m/s. Will the football clear the crossbar 3.0 m above the ground if the goal post is 54 m away?

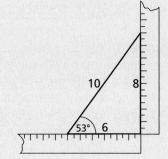

Strategy: First, measure the vertical and horizontal components of the velocity by setting up a scale diagram similar to the one on the right. The measured vertical and horizontal velocities then will be $v_y = 8$ m/s and $v_x = 6$ m/s, respectively.

Given: $a_g = 1.6 \text{ m/s}^2$ $v_y = 8$ m/s
                                              $v_x = 6$ m/s

Solution:

The time it takes the ball to travel the 54 m horizontally to the goal post is found using the horizontal velocity equation

$$v_x = \frac{\Delta d_x}{\Delta t}$$

Solving for t gives

$$\Delta t = \frac{\Delta d_x}{v_x}$$

$$= \frac{54 \; \cancel{m}}{6 \; \cancel{m}/s}$$

$$= 9 \; s$$

To find how high the ball is above the ground 9 s after being kicked, find the vertical distance the ball would travel without gravity and then subtract the fall due to gravity.

$$\Delta d_y = \left(\Delta v_y \right) \Delta t$$

$$= \left(8 \; m/\cancel{s} \right) \left(9 \; \cancel{s} \right)$$

$$= 72 \; m$$

The fall distance due to gravity is found from

$$d = \frac{1}{2} g t^2$$

$$= \frac{1}{2} \left(1.6 \; m/s^2 \right) \left(9 \; s \right)^2$$

$$= \frac{1}{2} \left(1.6 \; m/\cancel{s}^2 \right) \left(9 \; \cancel{s} \right) \left(9 \; \cancel{s} \right)$$

$$d = 65 \; m$$

Combining the two vertical distances gives 72 m of rise minus 65 m of fall or 7 m. The ball is 7 m above the ground, and easily clears the crossbar.

Checking Up

1. What is the path of a projectile without gravity? Why does it follow this path?

2. What is the shape of a projectile's path with gravity?

3. What two motions should be combined to find the vertical position of a projectile at any time?

4. What must be known to find the horizontal position of a projectile at any time during its flight?

5. How can you obtain the vertical and horizontal components of a projectile's velocity?

Active Physics

Plus

+Math	+Depth	+Concepts	+Exploration
◆◆	◆	◆	

Equations for Projectile Motion

If you have studied projectile motion prior to this section, you know some of the relationships between position, velocity, and acceleration. You may recall that the motion in the horizontal direction (x direction) is independent of the motion in the vertical direction (y direction). These relationships are summarized in equations for the horizontal and vertical motions on the following page.

All quantities are considered positive if they are directed upward. The object is assumed to have started at the position (0,0).

$$v_x = v_{x0} \qquad\qquad x = v_{x0}t$$

$$v_y = v_{y0} + gt \qquad y = v_{y0}t + \frac{1}{2}gt^2$$

In these equations, x and y are the horizontal and vertical positions, v_{x0} and v_{y0} are the horizontal and vertical components of the velocity at time $= 0$. Here, g is the acceleration due to gravity, and t is the time.

Notice that the horizontal component of the velocity is constant and equal to its value at time $= 0$. Finally, g is a negative number since the acceleration due to gravity is down ($-9.8\,\text{m/s}^2$ on Earth and $-1.6\,\text{m/s}^2$ on the Moon).

In analyzing projectile motion where the object starts at some height and returns to the same height, there is an easy way to use these relationships. Note that the motion from the start up to the point of maximum height is the same as the motion from the maximum height down to the finish except that one is the reverse of the other. The important point is that the time it takes for the projectile to reach its maximum height is the same as the time it takes for it to descend from its maximum height to the finish. Find the time it takes to reach its maximum height first, and use this result to find other quantities of interest.

As the projectile goes up, the vertical component of its velocity v_y decreases. At the same time the horizontal component of its velocity v_x remains constant. At some point in time v_y decreases to zero, then through zero, and finally becoming negative. When v_y is positive, the projectile is rising, and when v_y is negative, the projectile is falling. The point at which v_y is zero is the point of maximum height of the projectile. Setting $v_y = 0$ yields

$$0 = v_{y0} + gt_{max} \qquad \text{or} \qquad t_{max} = \frac{v_{y0}}{-g}.$$

The total time the projectile is in the air t_{total} is twice the time it takes to reach maximum height, so

$$t_{total} = 2t_{max} = \frac{2v_{y0}}{-g}.$$

From this result, it is easy to see that if two projectiles on Earth and on the Moon start off with the same value of v_{y0}, the time in flight is six times longer on the Moon because the value for the acceleration due to gravity g is one sixth as large on the Moon.

1. Did your results for the two trajectories you constructed in the *Investigate* agree with this?

Finding the maximum height is not difficult now that you know the time it takes the projectile to reach its maximum height. Simply substitute t_{max} into the equation for y (let $y_0 = 0$) and see if you can get the equation

$$y_{max} = \frac{v_{y0}^2}{-2g}$$

2. How should the maximum heights of a projectile launched with the same value of v_{y0} on Earth and the Moon compare? Compare this with your constructed trajectories.

The range of the projectile (denoted R or x_{max}) can be determined by finding the horizontal position x at time equal to t_{total}. Try this for yourself. The result is

$$R = x_{max} = \frac{2v_{x0}v_{y0}}{-g}$$

3. How should the ranges of projectiles on Earth and on the Moon compare if they start with the same values for both of the two components of the velocity? Is this what you found in the *Investigate*?

4. *Question 3* in *Physics to Go* states that if a projectile is launched at $45°$, the range is the velocity squared divided by the acceleration due to gravity (considered positive). See if you can derive this result starting with the more general equation for range given above.

What Do You Think Now?

At the beginning of this section you were asked the following questions:

- **Can a batter hit or a player throw a baseball faster on the Moon than on Earth?**

- **Can a batter hit or a player throw a baseball farther on the Moon than on Earth?**

- **If your answer to either question is yes, how much faster or farther?**

Based on what you have learned about projectile motion, how would you answer these questions now? Record your answers in your *Active Physics* log.

Essential Questions

What does it mean?

How do the trajectories of the same projectile launched identically on Earth and on the Moon differ?

How do you know?

What analysis did you perform that supports your previous answer? Be specific and use values in your answer.

Why do you believe?

Connects with Other Physics Content	Fits with Big Ideas in Science	Meets Physics Requirements
Forces and motion	Change and constancy	✱ Good, clear explanation, no more complex than necessary

✱ The laws of physics are identical on Earth and the Moon, but the acceleration due to gravity and the path of a baseball may not be. Explain how this can be so.

Why should you care?

Projectiles are a part of many sports. The human body is the projectile in some sports. What is going to be different for projectile sports when they are played on the Moon as compared to when they are played on Earth?

Reflecting on the Section and the Challenge

This section clearly demonstrates that some sports may be, quite literally, "out of sight" on the Moon. For example, a 300-m golf drive on Earth should translate into an 1800-m drive on the Moon. That is almost 2 km (over a mile). Could a golf ball be found after such a drive? Probably not. To a tall person on the Moon, the horizon is only about 2.5 km away because the Moon is much smaller than Earth. On Earth, that same person would be able to see the horizon about 5 km away.

Adapting "Earth sports" to the Moon is not as simple as you may have imagined initially. A proposal to play golf on the Moon with no adjustments would, without doubt, "not fly" with NASA.

Consider a baseball hit to the outfield in a Moon stadium. It might take so long for the ball to fall that everyone would be bored. Any sport involving projectile motion will need careful analysis to see if it is feasible to be used on the Moon. Adaptations of the sport may require you to speed up the game. How you do that will depend on your imagination and creativity.

Physics to Go

1. Due to the increased time and distance of travel of a projectile, discuss potential adjustments you need to make to play each of the following sports on the Moon:

   a) football

   b) gymnastics

   c) trapeze

   d) baseball

2. A typical sports arena on Earth has a playing field 120-m long and 100-m wide surrounded by tiered seats for spectators. World-class shot-put athletes throw the steel shot 23 m on Earth. Explain whether the spectators would be safe if a shot-put event were held in a stadium of similar size on the Moon.

3. The maximum range of a projectile launched at ground level occurs when the launch angle is $45°$. Physicists have shown that the range of a projectile launched at $45°$ is given by the equation $R = v^2/g$, where R is the range, v is the launch speed, and g is the acceleration due to gravity on the planet or moon where the projectile is launched. How would this equation be useful for estimating the size of facilities needed for sports on the Moon?

4. If a golf ball were hit at a speed of 40 m/s at a launch angle of $45°$ on the Moon, what would be its range? (Hint: Use the equation $R = v^2/g$, where R is the range, v is the launch speed, and g is the acceleration due to gravity on the Moon.)

5. Since the Moon's gravity is weaker than that on Earth, and since projectiles near the surface of the Moon do not experience air resistance, is it possible for an object thrown straight upward from the surface of the Moon to "escape" the Moon's gravity, never to fall back down to the surface of the Moon? Write a brief statement about your thoughts on this possibility.

6. You have found that the path of a trajectory from the ground to the ground requires six times the distance and six times the time. In basketball, the ball does not start at the ground and the hoop is not on the ground. You can, however, predict the trajectory in the following way:

   a) Draw a person 1.8 m tall and a hoop some distance away that is 3.5 m high.

   b) Draw a parabola that shows the ball moving from the player's head up and down through the hoop.

   c) On the same diagram, draw a horizontal line at the original location of the ball. Extend the basketball's path through the basket until it crosses this line.

d) The basketball on the Moon will travel six times higher from this line and six times further along this line. Approximate the high point of the ball and where it will hit this line. Draw the complete path on the Moon.

e) How will you adapt the game of basketball given this new insight into how the ball moves on the Moon?

7. *Preparing for the Chapter Challenge*

You have seen in this section that the range of a projectile on the Moon is greatly increased. Some of your classmates may suggest that the way to reduce the range of the projectiles is to increase their mass. Using what you know about how objects of different masses are affected by gravity, explain why this will not solve the problem once the projectiles are in the air with equal speeds. But use your knowledge of the principle of inertia to explain why increasing the mass might lead to projectiles with reduced velocity and thus, reduced range.

Inquiring Further

Orbital velocity

You have seen that as celestial bodies get smaller, their gravity becomes weaker, and this weaker gravity leads to increased range. During this investigation, it was assumed that gravity was acting straight down off a flat surface. Real planets are curved. When the curvature is taken into account, is it possible for the range of the projectile to increase so much that the object never comes down? Look up Newton's canon to investigate what happens when the speed of a projectile is increased on a spherical body. Find a reference for the term "orbital velocity" and relate that to the speed required for a projectile never to return to the surface once launched.

Section 5

Gravity, Work, and Energy: Jumping on the Moon

What Do You See?

What Do You Think?

Michael Jordan had a hang time of 1 s on Earth.

- **What would be a typical NBA star's hang time on the Moon?**

- **How high could the NBA star jump on the Moon? How high do you believe you could jump on the Moon?**

Record your ideas about these questions in your *Active Physics* log. Be prepared to discuss your responses with your small group and the class.

Investigate

In this *Investigate*, you will use the principles of conservation of energy and work to determine how high a person could jump on the Moon compared to that person's jump height on Earth.

1. In an area free of obstructions, crouch and jump straight up as high as you can. Next, crouch in the same way, as if you are ready to jump, but then rise without jumping. Discuss how to answer the following questions and be prepared to share your group's responses with the class.

a) What is the source of the energy used to push your body upward in each case?

b) Why does your body leave the floor in one case, but not in the other?

2. Stand with your shoulder near a wall on which a vertical strip of paper has been mounted. Hold a marker in your hand that is near the wall. Crouch in a deep knee bend as if you are ready to jump. While in this "ready" position, raise your arm straight up and make a mark on the paper.

a) Measure and record the distance from the floor to the mark to the nearest 0.01 m and label it the "ready height."

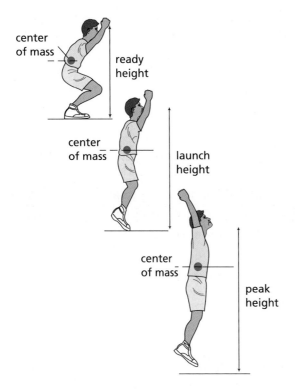

3. Rise to your tiptoes. While in this "launch" position, raise your arm straight up and make another mark.

a) Measure and record the distance from the floor to the mark as the "launch height."

4. Crouch to the ready position and jump straight up as high as you can. Make a mark as high as you can when you are at the peak of your jump.

a) Measure and record the distance from the floor to the mark as the "peak height."

b) By subtraction, calculate and record how high you can jump. Use the equation:

Jump height = (peak height) − (launch height)

c) By subtraction, calculate and record your total change in height using the ready position as a reference and using this equation:

Total change in height = (peak height) − (ready height)

5. On a piece of paper, draw three sketches (to scale) showing the jumper in the ready position, the launch position, and the peak position using the data from your jump. In the ready position, the sketch should show the legs bent. While in the launch and peak positions, the sketch should show the legs straight.

a) Tape the sketches into your *Active Physics* log.

6. On the Moon, one would expect that the jumper would be able to go six times as high because the acceleration due to gravity is only $\frac{1}{6}$ on the Moon. This is not what really happens. Analysis shows that this factor of 6 applies to the total change in height from the ready position to the peak position (see *Physics Talk*).

a) Calculate the total change in height on the Moon by multiplying the total change in height from *Step 4.c)* by 6.

b) From the total change in height, calculate the peak height on the Moon.

7. Using the same scale as you did for your Earth data, draw three sketches (to scale) showing the jumper in the ready position, the launch position, and the peak position. The ready position and the launch position should be identical to that on Earth. The peak position should use your calculated value for the Moon.

a) Tape the sketches into your *Active Physics* log.

Physics Talk

ANALYSIS OF JUMPING ON EARTH AND THE MOON

One of the most important ideas in physics is that under certain conditions, one form of energy can be transformed into the other form of energy, with no energy being gained or lost. An object can have **gravitational potential energy** due to its position above the surface of the planet. The object can have **kinetic energy** due to its velocity. The gravitational potential energy of the object can be transformed into kinetic energy as the object falls. The object loses gravitational potential energy (as it loses height) and gains kinetic energy (as it moves faster).

GPE represents gravitational potential energy.

$$GPE = mgh$$

where m = mass

g = acceleration due to gravity and

h = height above the ground.

since weight = mg

then GPE = (weight) × (height above the ground)

KE represents kinetic energy.

$$KE = \frac{1}{2}mv^2$$

where m = mass and

v = velocity

Hence, $KE = \frac{1}{2}$ (mass)(velocity squared)

Note that the units of energy are $\dfrac{(kg \cdot m^2)}{s^2}$. This unit is called a joule and its symbol is J.

You can analyze the jump on Earth by comparing the energy at the ready position, the launch position, and the peak position. Since the person is at rest in both the ready position and the peak position, she or he has no kinetic energy at either place. Chemical energy in your body is stored as leg muscle *PE*.

Physics Words

gravitational potential energy: the energy an object possesses as a result of its position near the surface of a planet or moon ($GPE = mgh$).

kinetic energy: the energy an object possesses because of its motion ($KE = \frac{1}{2}mv^2$).

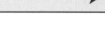

The ready position has only leg-muscle potential energy. The peak position has only gravitational potential energy. The launch position has both kinetic energy and gravitational potential energy.

	Ready position	Launch position	Peak position
Kinetic energy *KE*	0	✔	0
Gravitational potential energy *GPE*	0	✔	✔
Leg-muscle potential energy *LPE*	✔	0	0

This analysis uses sample data for the vertical jump of a person on Earth who has a mass of 44 kg:

- Body mass = 44 kg

- Body weight on Earth = mg = 44 kg x 9.8 m/s² = 430 N

- Ready height (from floor to ready mark) = 1.70 m

- Launch height (from floor to launch mark) = 2.05 m

- Peak height (from floor to peak mark) = 2.65 m

You may apply this analysis to your vertical jump by substituting your personal data for the sample data, or you can assign a mass to an "unknown" person if you wish.

The following table shows all of the results of the analysis. Exactly how each result is obtained is explained in the paragraphs after the table.

	Earth	Moon
Mass (kg)	44	44
Weight (N)	430	70
Ready height (m)	1.70	1.70
Launch height (m)	2.05	2.05
Peak height (m)	2.65	7.60
Jump height (m)	0.60	5.55
Total energy (J)	410	410

The total energy of the jump is equal to the overall gain in the jumper's gravitational potential energy from the ready position to the peak position:

$$\text{Total energy} = \text{change in gravitational potential energy}$$
$$= mg\left[(\text{peak height}) - (\text{ready height})\right]$$
$$= 430 \text{ N} \times (2.65 \text{ m} - 1.70 \text{ m})$$
$$= 430 \text{ N} \times 0.95 \text{ m}$$
$$= 410 \text{ J}$$

This 410 J of energy was produced by the legs of the jumper during the push phase, while the feet were in contact with the ground.

Assuming the leg muscles work the same on the Moon, you would expect an increase of gravitational potential energy of 410 J on the Moon as well. However, the acceleration due to gravity, g_M, on the Moon is only $\frac{1}{6}$ the acceleration due to gravity on Earth $(1.6 \text{ m/s}^2 \text{ compared to } 9.8 \text{ m/s}^2)$.

The Moon data would be:

• Body mass = 44 kg (identical to mass on Earth)

• Body weight = mg = 44 kg $\times$ 1.6 m/s^2 = 70 N ($\frac{1}{6}$ the value on Earth)

• Ready height (from floor to ready mark)
  = 1.70 m (identical to the value on Earth)

• Launch height (from floor to launch mark)
  = 2.05 m (identical to the value on Earth)

With these data, you can compute the peak height on the Moon.

$$\text{Total energy} = \text{change in gravitational potential energy}$$
$$= mg\left[(\text{peak height}) - (\text{ready height})\right]$$
$$410 \text{ J} = 70 \text{ N} \times \left[(\text{peak height}) - 1.70 \text{ m}\right]$$
$$5.9 \text{ m} = \left[(\text{peak height}) - 1.70 \text{ m}\right]$$
$$\text{Peak height} = 7.6 \text{ m}$$

The jump height on Earth and Moon is found by subtracting the launch height from the peak height:

on Earth   2.65 m – 2.05 m = 0.60 m

on Moon   7.6 m – 2.05 m = 5.55 m

$$\frac{5.55 \text{ m}}{0.60 \text{ m}} = 9.25$$

The ratio of these heights on the Moon and Earth is clearly more than six. A person can jump more than six times as high on the Moon as on Earth. The difference between the peak height and ready height is 0.95 m on Earth and 5.9 m on the Moon. As you can see, this is close to a factor of 6.

Checking Up

1. Before jumping, what type of energy is stored in your leg muscles when you are in the "ready" position?

2. While in the process of jumping, you go through the "ready," "launch," and "peak" positions. At which of these positions is your kinetic energy zero? At which position is it at the maximum?

3. How many times higher (greater) is the peak height of a jumper on the Moon compared to the same jumper on Earth?

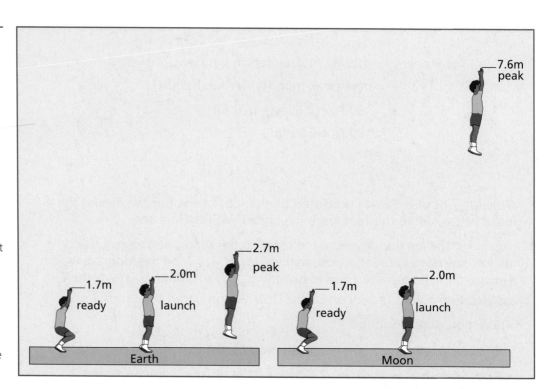

+Math	+Depth	+Concepts	+Exploration
◆	◆		

Active Physics

Plus

Kinetic Energy On The Moon

In the *Investigate*, you completed and compared the total energy of the launch position with the total energy at the peak position. Neither of these positions has kinetic energy. You can also look at the total energy of the launch position where the jumper has some gravitational potential energy and some kinetic energy. It is helpful to think about the energy during the push phase in two parts:

• The gain in gravitational potential energy of the body as it is lifted against gravity before it even leaves the ground.

• The gain in kinetic energy of the body as it is accelerated to a velocity high enough just to propel the body off of the ground.

The energy necessary to lift the body before leaving the ground (without acceleration) equals the gain in gravitational potential energy between ready distance and launch distance.

$$\text{Energy} = mg \ [(\text{launch ht.}) - (\text{ready ht.})]$$
$$= 430 \ \text{N} \times (2.05 \ \text{m} - 1.70 \ \text{m})$$
$$= 430 \ \text{N} \times 0.35 \ \text{m}$$
$$= 150 \ \text{J}$$

The kinetic energy needed to propel the body off the ground must be equal to any amount of the total energy that "remains" after subtracting the amount of energy needed to lift the body against gravity.

$$KE \text{ at launch} = (\text{total energy}) - (\text{energy to lift})$$
$$= 410 \text{ J} - 150 \text{ J}$$
$$= 260 \text{ J}$$

Of the 410 J of total energy that the muscles in the leg provide, 150 J are used to raise the body to the launch position and the remaining 260 J represents the kinetic energy for the jump.

What would happen if the person were to repeat the same jump on the Moon? What would be the person's jump height?

The person's mass, 44 kg, would remain the same on the Moon, but the person's weight would be less on the Moon:

$$\text{Weight on the Moon} = 44 \text{ kg} \times 1.6 \text{ m/s}^2$$
$$= 70 \text{ N}$$

The energy needed just to lift the body against gravity during the push phase on the Moon is equal to gain in gravitational potential energy between the ready height and the launch height.

$$\text{Energy} = mg \; [(\text{launch ht.}) - (\text{ready ht.})]$$
$$= 70 \text{ N} \times (2.05 \text{ m} - 170 \text{ m})$$
$$= 70 \text{ N} \times 0.35 \text{ m}$$

The kinetic energy needed to propel the body off of the ground on the Moon is equal to the total energy minus the energy needed just to lift the body against gravity:

$$KE \text{ at launch} = (\text{total energy}) - (\text{energy to lift})$$
$$= 410 \text{ J} - 25 \text{ J}$$
$$= 385 \text{ J}$$

Much more of the energy from the person's legs can go into propelling the body off of the ground. Although the leg muscles provided the same 410 J of energy as on Earth, only 25 J are required to lift the body on the Moon. More of the energy goes into kinetic energy allowing for a much higher jump.

The jump height can be predicted by assuming that the kinetic energy at launch is transformed into the gain in gravitational potential energy from launch to the peak of the jump. That is, at the launch position the person has some kinetic energy (385 J). But at the very top of the person's jump, the person's velocity is zero, so the person has no kinetic energy. The law of conservation of energy tells you that the 385 J of kinetic energy must be converted into 385 J of gravitational potential energy.

$$KE \text{ at launch} = PE \text{ gained from launch to peak}$$
$$385 \text{ J} = mg \; (\text{jump height})$$

Therefore:
$$\text{Jump height} = 5.47 \text{ m}$$

This height is almost identical to the height you found in the *Physics Talk* section. Rounding errors in the calculations produced the difference.

Notice that the jump height on the Moon (as measured from the launch position to the peak position) is 5.47 m as compared to 0.60 m on Earth. This is a factor of nine times higher on the Moon than on Earth.

It is tempting to arrive at the conclusion that jump heights on the Moon and Earth would compare in the same way—different by a factor of six—as the accelerations due to gravity on the Moon and Earth. This analysis shows that factor is only true when you compare the change in height from the ready position to the peak position.

The equations used for analyzing the vertical jump in the above analysis are based on the assumption that a jumper applies a downward force to the ground during the jump—and also that the ground pushes with an equal and opposite upward force on the jumper—during the pre-launch phase of jumping.

Research shows that the best jumpers are able to accelerate to high speeds in a very short amount of time and are able to maintain a fairly constant force while rising from a crouch to launch position.

Not enough is known about jumping on the Moon to be sure that a jumper there would have enough time before launch to build up the muscular force assumed in this example of a Moon jump. How do these physiological changes impact the analysis?

You can now work out the general equation for predicting the jump height and hang time for a person on the Moon knowing the data from the person's vertical jump on Earth. Let the mass of the person be denoted by m. Let the launch height minus the ready height be denoted by h_1, let the peak height minus the ready height be denoted by h_2, and let the acceleration due to gravity on Earth be denoted by g_E.

1. What is the expression for the total energy generated by the person's legs during a jump?

2. What is the expression for the energy required to raise the person from the ready height to the launch height on the Moon? Use g_M for the acceleration due to gravity on the Moon.

3. What is the expression for the kinetic energy of the person as he or she leaves the ground during a vertical jump on the Moon?

4. What is the expression for the person's jump height on the Moon? Test your expression by substituting the values from the example in *Physics Talk* or the values for your own vertical jump.

5. What is the expression for the person's hang time on the Moon?

What Do You Think Now?

Michael Jordan had a hang time of 1 s on Earth.

- **What would be a typical NBA star's hang time on the Moon?**
- **How high could the NBA star jump on the Moon? How high do you believe you could jump on the Moon?**

Based on what you have learned about kinetic energy and gravitational potential energy, how would you answer these questions now?

Physics
Essential Questions

What does it mean?

What is different when a person jumps on Earth compared to on the Moon?

How do you know?

What physics concepts and analysis did you use to compare jumping on Earth and on the Moon.

Why do you believe?

Connects with Other Physics Content	Fits with Big Ideas in Science	Meets Physics Requirements
Forces and motion	✳ Conservation of energy	Experimental evidence is consistent with models and theories

✳ Conservation of energy is a major organizing principle of physics and all science. How was the conservation of energy used in the analysis of the jump?

Why should you care?

Jumping is an integral part of many sports. For such a sport, what is going to change if it is played on the Moon?

Reflecting on the Section and the Challenge

Reflecting on energy transformations and jump heights leads to the notion that sports involving jumping would be interesting on the Moon. A human who jumps vertically should fly much higher on the Moon than on Earth. Traveling to a much greater height and returning to the ground also takes a longer time.

In a sport like gymnastics, people propel themselves with their leg muscles. In basketball, leg muscles also determine jump height and hang time. "Flying higher" will make these sports very different on the Moon. Adjustments in rules may have to be made to keep these sports fun, challenging, and competitive.

Physics to Go

1. On Earth, the top edge of a volleyball net is placed 8 ft above the ground, and a basketball hoop is 10 ft above the ground. At what heights would they need to be placed on the Moon to keep the sports equivalent in difficulty?

2. A spacesuit and life-support backpack have a combined mass of 110 kg. Wearing these reduces the height of a person's vertical jump. Calculate the reductions in the vertical jump when

   a) on the Moon.

   b) on Earth.

   Use the sample data in *Physics Talk* (mass of the person = 44 kg) in calculating your answers. The total energy of the person remains at 410 J.

3. Would jumping on a trampoline be different on the Moon than on Earth? Why or why not? If so, how?

4. How would events in gymnastics be affected if performed on the Moon? Choose an event and describe how it would be different on the Moon. Use numbers as well as descriptions.

5. What do you think will be the winning height in the high jump during the first Olympiad held on the Moon?

6. A student riding in a chair moving at constant speed throws a ball into the air and catches it when it comes back down. What would be the same and what would be different if the activity were done in exactly the same way on the Moon?

7. *Preparing for the Chapter Challenge*

   In a basketball game, tall people have an advantage over shorter people when rebounding a missed shot because of their height. On the Moon however, basketball players would be able to jump much higher than they normally could on Earth. Could this affect the advantage taller people have when rebounding? How? Explain your reasoning using what you know about the relative jumping ability of basketball players and how their energy changes as they jump.

Inquiring Further

Acceleration due to gravity on Ceres

Some scientists have speculated that in the future, people will live on small, celestial bodies that orbit the Sun. One such body is the "dwarf planet" Ceres, which has a mass of approximately 9.5×10^{20} kg and a radius of 9.5×10^{5} m. Remembering that when gravity is reduced, your jumping ability is greatly enhanced, use what you have learned in this section to calculate the acceleration of gravity on Ceres. Determine how high you could jump if you were to live there.

Chapter Mini-Challenge

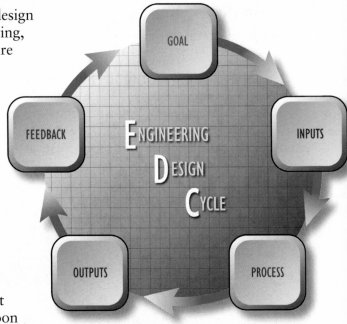

 Your challenge for this chapter is to design or modify a sport that will be interesting, exciting, and entertaining for the future inhabitants of the Moon to play and watch. The design of your game will be fully explained in a written proposal that you will submit to NASA. Your proposal will contain a complete comparison between playing your sport on Earth and the Moon and will also include a newspaper article covering a "championship" game to help describe how spectators will view the sport.

You still have more to learn before you can complete the challenge, but now is a good time to give the *Chapter Challenge* a first try. You are now halfway through the chapter and you have learned a lot about the different factors that will change the way sports are played on the Moon compared to on Earth.

For the *Mini-Challenge* you will complete three of the four parts of the *Chapter Challenge*. You will incorporate the physics you have learned so far to describe your sport, describe the factors you have learned about that will affect all sports, and describe any changes that need to be made to your sport to make it interesting, exciting, and entertaining on the Moon. You will use the simplified *Engineering Design Cycle* to help you work through this design challenge.

Go back and quickly review your *Goal* you established at the start of the chapter. You will find all of the details for completing the entire *Chapter Challenge*. At this point, you will focus on the portions you can complete with the physics you have learned so far.

This challenge will rely heavily on your knowledge of physics on the Moon as well as on Earth. Since you will be comparing how differences between the two locations will affect a sport of your choice, you will have to make sure you get the physics right. Your physics *Inputs* will come directly from the chapter sections that you have completed. The only constraints you have to consider are making sure that your sport retains its excitement and interesting characteristics when played on the Moon.

Your team should review the physics content from the first five sections to help you compose your NASA proposal.

Section 1: You practiced the creative process of brainstorming in an effort to create your own definition of the word "sport." You should now have a good understanding of all of the types of activities that your team would consider a sport.

Section 2: You examined falling objects and compared how quickly dropped objects will reach the ground on Earth to how fast they will reach the ground on the Moon. The difference is due to a different acceleration due to gravity at each location. You also learned how time, distance, and acceleration are related for falling objects.

Section 3: You explored the way a force causes a mass to react in order to compare the masses of different objects. You also explored how different gravitational forces are related to changes in weight for the same mass. (Pushing will be the same, but lifting will be different on the Moon.)

Section 4: You developed a model to compare the flight of a projectile on Earth to the flight of that same projectile on the Moon. During the construction of your model, you should have discovered some factors you could modify to make the projectile's path, or trajectory, on the Moon more similar to its typical trajectory on Earth.

Section 5: You used conservation of energy, work, and mass to analyze an athlete's vertical jump on Earth. You then used a similar analysis to estimate potential jumping heights for athletes on the Moon. Jumping is one area you will need to modify for your sport.

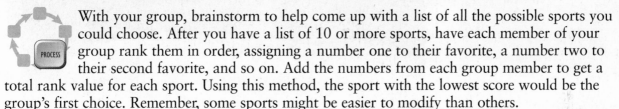 With your group, brainstorm to help come up with a list of all the possible sports you could choose. After you have a list of 10 or more sports, have each member of your group rank them in order, assigning a number one to their favorite, a number two to their second favorite, and so on. Add the numbers from each group member to get a total rank value for each sport. Using this method, the sport with the lowest score would be the group's first choice. Remember, some sports might be easier to modify than others.

Once you have selected a sport, make a list of all the physical actions that the sport requires. Activities like running, jumping, swinging a bat, pushing, throwing, and so on should be on your list. Put the list in the first column of a three-column table, labeled ACTIONS. Label the next column CHANGE. For each action on your list, put a mark in the second column if the action will change when played on the Moon based on what you have learned so far. Label the third column GAME PLAY. Look at your list of actions again, think about the changes you know will occur to that action on the Moon and decide if the game will require some type of modification to keep it exciting, interesting, and entertaining. Write MODIFY in the third column for any action that will have to be modified to keep the game interesting, exciting, or entertaining.

The decision table you have just constructed will help your group prepare the analysis you will need to help you design your Moon sport. Analysis is a key part of the engineering decision-making process. You will have to analyze jumps, throws, hits, and falling on the Moon to see how they will change your sport. Each time you analyze an action, you will also have to propose a modification. Then, you will have to analyze that modification to make sure it provides the change in action you were looking for. For example, making a basketball six times more massive might have unintended consequences.

 Presenting your information to the class are your design cycle *Outputs*. The *Outputs* should include a description of your sport, a discussion of the physics affecting sports on Earth as well as sports on the Moon, and a description of the changes you would make to your sport to keep it exciting, entertaining, and interesting. You might even try to create the newspaper article for a championship game based on what you know so far.

 Your classmates will give you *Feedback* on the accuracy and the overall appeal of the sport you have presented based on the criteria of the design challenge. This *Feedback* will become an *Input* for your final design in the *Chapter Challenge*. You will have enough time to make corrections and improvements, so you will want to pay attention to the valuable information your classmates provide.

Section 6 Momentum and Gravity: Golf on the Moon

What Do You See?

Learning Outcomes

In this section, you will

- **Compare** the bouncing qualities of balls made from a variety of materials.

- **Relate** bounce height to velocity immediately after impact.

- **Analyze** the required characteristics of a replacement for a standard golf ball that would limit the range of a ball hit on the Moon to the typical range of a golf ball hit on Earth.

- **Analyze** how a golf club would need to be modified to limit the range of standard golf balls hit on the Moon to the typical range of a golf ball hit on Earth.

- **Discover** collision and rebound difference when masses of the objects are not the same.

What Do You Think?

Astronaut Alan Shepard accomplished two firsts. He was the first American to ride a rocket into space (May 1961) and he was the first person to hit a golf ball on the Moon (February 1970).

- **How would the game of golf be different if it were played on the Moon?**

- **How could the game of golf be modified to be played on the Moon?**

Record your ideas about these questions in your *Active Physics* log. Be prepared to discuss your responses with your small group and the class.

Investigate

For this *Investigate*, you will first explore how balls of different construction respond when dropped on the floor and bounce. You will apply this information to the physics of golf to see how the game could be changed to make it playable on the Moon. Finally, you examine the physics of the interaction between a golf club and a golf ball to see if altering the ball, the club, or both would make golf an enjoyable sport for the Moon.

1. From your previous analysis, one would expect that the golf ball would travel six times as far on the Moon as on Earth. That may be much too far for players to walk.

a) List three ways in which you could limit the distance that the ball would travel.

2. You will explore one strategy to limit the distance — a golf ball that does not bounce well off the ground and/or off a golf club. A "dead" golf ball might reduce the flight distance on the Moon. Obtain a standard golf ball and several other balls of similar size, such as, a super ball and table-tennis ball that might be used for "Moon golf." Identify each ball in some way.

a) Make a descriptive list of the golf balls in your *Active Physics* log.

b) Decide whether or not you agree with the physicists who made the following statements:

   i) When different kinds of balls are dropped from equal heights, all of them hit the floor with the same speed if air resistance is small.

   ii) Each ball rebounds with its own particular speed relative to the floor.

   iii) The speed of each ball after impact would be the same if the balls remained still and the floor moved upward at impact speed and hit each ball from below.

c) Rank these in order of "ease of understanding."

3. Position a 2-m stick (or two ordinary meter sticks clamped end to end) vertically with the zero-end resting on the floor. Secure the 2-m stick to a wall or the edge of a table so that it will not move. Allow enough room to observe a falling ball with the stick in the near background.

4. Drop each ball from a height of 2 m so that it falls in front of the stick. One member of the group should be prepared to read the maximum height reached by the bottom edge of the ball when it bounces back up from the floor. Practice a few times before recording data. Decide how many trials for each ball you will perform and average the bounce heights.

a) Record the bounce height in your log next to the description of each ball.

b) Divide each bounce height by the bounce height of the standard golf ball. Record the answers in your log book.

c) One strategy for limiting the ball's traveling distance would be to alter the bounciness of the ball. Would a ball that bounces only $\frac{1}{6}$ as high as a golf ball "fly" only $\frac{1}{6}$ as far when hit by a golf club?

d) Do any of the balls bounce only $\frac{1}{6}$, or 0.167, as high as a golf ball? Which, if any of the balls, comes closest to bouncing $\frac{1}{6}$ as high?

Active Physics

5. Golfers on the Moon will want to swing their clubs at normal speed. Altering a traditional golf ball or using another type of ball could cause big problems. A second strategy is to change the mass of the head of the golf club as a way of reducing the range of a golf ball hit on the Moon. Use the apparatus shown in the diagram to simulate hitting a golf ball with the head of a golf club.

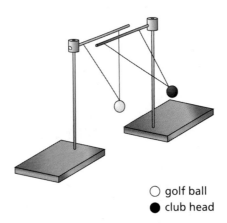

○ golf ball
● club head

One ball, representing the head of a golf club, is pulled back and released to collide with a stationary ball representing a golf ball.

Practice the collision a few times so that you can repeat it with precision.

6. On Earth, the launch speed of a golf ball is typically 1.5 times the speed of the club at impact. Perhaps the head of the golf club could be changed, so that the a golf ball's launch speed would be reduced to about 0.6 the speed of the golf club. Reducing the speed of the golf ball from 1.5 times to 0.6 times the speed of the golf club keeps the range of the golf ball about equal to a comparable *range* on Earth.

Try various combinations of masses representing the golf ball and the head of the golf club. Find a combination for which, as shown in the sketch, the ball moves away just after the collision at about 0.6 times the speed of the head

of the golf club just before the collision. Judging the speed of the "ball" after the collision to be 0.6 times the speed of "head of the golf club" is not easy. If the "ball" rises to about ⅓ the height the "head of the golf club" was dropped from, then the speed should be about right. (The *Physics Talk* discusses the energy transformations that show why this will work.)

a) What combination of masses for the golf ball and the head of the golf club most closely meet the above condition? For this case, which "representative ball" was more massive, "the one representing the golf ball" or the "one representing the head of the golf club"? What is the ratio of the masses, (mass of "golf ball")/(mass of "head of the golf club")? Write your answers in your log.

b) Describe how the "head of the golf club" moves after it hits the "golf ball." Do you think golfers would be able to accept that situation? What problems are apparent with this method of reducing the range of a golf ball on the Moon?

7. Discuss within your group whether it seems possible to use some combination of altering both the golf ball and the golf club to make the game of golf a viable sport on the Moon if the size of the golf course on the Moon is the same as that on Earth. Write the reactions of your group and your personal opinions concerning the following questions in your log:

a) Does playing golf on the Moon seem feasible? Explain.

b) Would golfers on the Moon be likely to have complaints? Explain.

c) How else might you try to solve the problems with Moon golf?

8. Golf may not be your game. Lots of other sports involve hitting a ball with a bat, a foot, a hand, or a racquet. For each of these sports on the Moon, you may be bothered by how far the ball travels and you may want to "tame" the sport by altering the ball or the object that hits the ball. Choose two sports in which a ball gets hit and describe how you might alter the ball or the object that hits the ball to decrease the distance the ball travels.

a) Record your descriptions in your log.

Physics Talk

THE PHYSICS OF TAMING THE GOLF BALL

The conservation of energy informs you that the total energy of an object must remain constant unless it does work or work is done on it. A bouncing ball has gravitational potential energy GPE, then it gains kinetic energy KE as it falls, which then leads to a gain once again of GPE as it travels up followed by KE followed by GPE, and so on. It is as if the energy is "bouncing" between GPE and KE as the ball is bouncing up and down. Since each successive bounce is not as high as the previous bounce, there is a loss of energy. In this section, you measured the change in height of a golf ball and could calculate the loss in energy of each successive bounce. Where does the energy go? Since energy is conserved and you noted a loss in the gravitational potential energy after each bounce, you must look or listen for where this energy went. Some of the energy went into sound (each bounce made some sound) and into heat (the temperature of the ball probably increased a tiny bit, and into vibration of the floor (yes, the floor vibrates — if it were a bowling ball, you would notice it). If you were able to measure all these energies with precision, their sum would equal the energy loss in the height of each bounce.

By introducing a different ball, you can have a poorer bounce and a greater loss of energy during each bounce. This could limit the **range** of the golf ball so that the game of golf on the Moon does not send the ball so far away.

Physicists like to view the same phenomenon from different perspectives in order to better understand all that is happening. When a ball bounces, one perspective is that the ball and floor collided. The very massive floor appears to remain at rest after the collision, but could be moving a bit, and it would take some ingenuity to measure the vibration of the floor. By changing the floor, you could change the bounce. The floor's bounce properties could change with padding or by using a different floor material. It is difficult to change the mass of the floor.

A golf club and a golf ball also undergo a collision. You can change the mass of the golf club in order to change this collision with the golf ball. You investigated this change and the affect on the golf ball in this *Investigate*.

→

Physics Words

range: the total horizontal distance that a projectile travels.

Active Physics

It is true that a ball that bounces only ⅙ as high as a golf ball when dropped from the same height would have ⅙ of the range of a golf ball when hit by a golf club. Two equations help to show this.

The first equation is found by equating the kinetic energy of the bouncing ball at the instant it leaves the floor to the gravitational potential energy the ball has at the peak of its bounce:

$$\frac{1}{2}mv^2 = mgh$$

For a specific ball, the mass remains constant as does the acceleration due to gravity. If the height decreases by a factor of 6 (on the right side of the equation), then the v^2 must also decrease by a factor of 6 (on the left side of the equation).

This means that if the "take-off" speed squared of an object doubles, then the height it reaches doubles. Or if the "take-off" speed squared of an object decreases to half its value, then the height the object reaches decreases to half its value.

A second equation provides the range or total horizontal distance that a ball travels.

$$R = \frac{v^2}{g},$$

where R is the maximum range (horizontal travel distance) of a projectile that is launched with speed v at a 45° angle of elevation. (This equation is explained in *Active Physics Plus*, if you wish to see how it is derived.) Notice that this equation shows that the maximum range of a ball is related to the ball's launch speed squared v^2 in the same way the maximum height an object reaches is related to the ball's "take-off" speed squared.

Both the bounce height of a dropped ball and the range of a ball depend on the ball's speed squared in a similar way. Therefore, a ball that bounces ⅙ as high as a golf ball also would have ⅙ of the maximum range of a golf ball.

The data you have gathered about the bounce heights of balls can be used to infer how the speeds of various kinds of balls, when hit, compare to the speed of a golf ball after it gets hit. This will help you decide if any of the balls you have tested would be feasible substitutes for playing golf on the Moon with a traditional Earth golf ball.

Checking Up

1. A bouncing golf ball loses energy with each successive bounce. Where does this lost energy go?

2. How is energy conserved if a ball loses height with each successive bounce?

3. How does the range of a projectile depend upon its launch velocity?

4. If the height of a golf ball's bounce decreases by a factor of 6, how will the range of the golf ball change?

Active Physics

+Math	+Depth	+Concepts	+Exploration
◆◆◆	◆		

Plus

Horizontal and Vertical Projectile Motion

You can analyze the motion of any projectile launched over level ground. To make the analysis general, you must consider a projectile launched at any speed and at any angle. Let v_0 be the speed at launch and let θ be the launch angle. First, draw the horizontal (v_x) and vertical (v_y) components of v_0 by constructing the right triangle with sides v_x and v_y and hypotenuse v_0. From this triangle, you can see that

$$\cos\theta = \frac{v_{0x}}{v_0} \text{ and } \sin\theta = \frac{v_{0y}}{v_0}$$

Using algebra, then

$$v_{0x} = v_0 \cos\theta \text{ and } v_{0y} = v_0 \sin\theta$$

These two relationships will be useful later.

In analyzing this projectile motion, the horizontal and vertical motion are independent of each other.

Now consider only the vertical motion. The projectile starts out with a vertical velocity of v_{0y} and it has a vertical velocity of zero when it reaches it highest point (because at that point it is not moving up or down). Then it undergoes free fall, starting with a vertical velocity of zero and ending with a vertical velocity of $-v_{0y}$ when it strikes the ground. The vertical motion on the way down is the same as the vertical motion on the way up, only in the reverse direction. This means that it takes the same time for both parts of the motion. You can find the time for half the trip by remembering the definition of acceleration and the fact that for one half of the trip, the velocity was zero.

$$a = \frac{\Delta v}{\Delta t}$$

$$\Delta t = \frac{\Delta v}{g}$$

This is the time for one-half the trip and can be signified as:

$$t_{1/2} = \frac{v_{0y}}{g}$$

The time for the entire trip would be twice this value:

$$t = 2t_{1/2} = \frac{2v_{0y}}{g}$$

The horizontal motion is simply motion at a constant speed. Therefore, the range R of the projectile is given by

$$R = v_{0x}t = v_{0x}\left(\frac{2v_{0y}}{g}\right) = \frac{2v_{0x}v_{0y}}{g}$$

If you now substitute in your earlier expressions for v_{0x} and v_{0y}, you arrive at the general result:

$$R = \frac{2(v_0 \cos\theta)(v_0 \sin\theta)}{g}$$
$$= \frac{2v_0^2 \sin\theta \cos\theta}{g}$$

1. To find the launch angle that gives the maximum range, first note that v_0 and g do not depend on the launch angle and therefore do not vary. The maximum range results when the function $2\sin\theta\cos\theta$ has its maximum value. Graph the function $2\sin\theta\cos\theta$ for various values of θ to determine at what θ it is a maximum.

You should have found that the R is a maximum when $\theta = 45°$. At this value of θ,

$$\sin\theta = \cos\theta = \frac{1}{\sqrt{2}} = 0.707.$$

This means that $2\sin\theta\cos\theta = 1$ and that

$$R = \frac{v_0^2}{g} \text{ when } \theta = 45°.$$

2. From your plot of $2\sin\theta\cos\theta$ vs. θ, compare the range when $\theta = 40°$ and when $\theta = 50°$. What about when $\theta = 30°$ and $\theta = 60°$? Can you make a general statement about the range for angles less than 45° as compared to angles greater than 45°?

3. Another way of finding that the maximum range occurs at 45° is by using the trigonometric equation $2\sin\theta\cos\theta = \sin 2\theta$. If you maximize $\sin 2\theta$, then you will maximize the range. The $\sin 2\theta$ function is maximum when $2\theta = 90°$. Therefore, $\theta = 45°$ will produce the maximum range as shown by your graphical analysis.

What Do You Think Now?

At the beginning of this section you were asked:

• **How would the game of golf be different if it were played on the Moon?**

• **How could the game of golf be modified to be played on the Moon?**

How would you answer these questions now, based on what you have learned in this section? Record your answers in your *Active Physics* log.

Physics
Essential Questions

What does it mean?
The rebound height of a dropped ball depends on its "take-off" speed after hitting the floor. The maximum range of a ball depends on its launch speed. What is similar about how the rebound height and maximum range depend on these velocities?

How do you know?
What did you observe about the collision between an object of less mass striking a stationary object of more mass?

Why do you believe?

Connects with Other Physics Content	Fits with Big Ideas in Science	Meets Physics Requirements
Forces and motion	✳ Conservation of energy	Experimental evidence is consistent with models and theories

✳ The conservation of energy is a major organizing principle of physics. You analyzed the rebound height of a ball. You used the fact that in ideal situations where there is no friction or air resistance, energy is not lost or gained but transformed from kinetic energy to gravitational potential energy. Why do you believe that this principle of energy conservation accurately describes this situation?

Why should you care?
Reduced gravity increases the distance that objects travel. You must compensate for this to make almost any sport playable on the Moon. For the sport you select, what changes will you make for it to still have the attributes of a sport on the Moon?

Reflecting on the Section and the Challenge

The range of a golf ball on the Moon is too large. You have learned how to "tame" the sport and reduce the range of the ball by changing the bounciness of the ball or changing the mass of the golf club. These adaptations may be all that are needed to present golf as a Moon sport for your NASA proposal.

What you learned in this section would apply in similar ways to other sports in which a bat, racquet, paddle, club, or other hitting device is used to launch an object into a state of projectile motion. In your actions to "tame down" the motion of a golf ball, you learned that you can expect similar problems and use similar solutions in other sports.

Physics to Go

1. Describe briefly why you would have to change the racquet or ball in a game of tennis.

2. On Earth, golfers sometimes hit "divots," chunks of grass sod, when the club hits the ground in the process of hitting the ball. On the Moon, a divot would be a cloud of sand and dust from the lunar soil. With weak gravity and no wind due to the lack of air, would "Moon divots" present a problem for golfers on the Moon? What would a "dust divot" look like on the Moon?

3. Many golfers enjoy the social part of golf as much as the game. It's a good chance to talk or to conduct business with golfing partners. Would golfers be able to talk and conduct business as usual on the Moon? Also, golfers holler "Fore" to warn people in the fairway who might be in the way of a hit golf ball. Would that method of warning work on the Moon? Explain your answers.

4. Make a list of three reasons for

   a) being in favor of proposing golf to NASA as a sport for the Moon

   b) being against proposing golf to NASA as a sport for the Moon

5. Name three sports that use bats, clubs, or racquets. Describe the changes that you would make in the ball or hitting device to ensure that the sport is fun on the Moon.

6. *Preparing for the Chapter Challenge*

   Not all Earth sports could be played on the Moon, even if modified. Other than golf, suggest a sport that you think would not be suitable for the Moon and give your reasons why.

Inquiring Further

Coefficient of restitution

It has been suggested that one way to play golf on the Moon would be to use a ball that bounces one-sixth as high as a standard golf ball. For a physicist, this would be discussed in terms of a golf ball's "coefficient of restitution." Find out how the coefficient of restitution is determined for a golf ball, and if professional golf associations set any limits on the size of the coefficient for officially sanctioned golf balls.

Section 7

Friction: Sliding on the Moon

What Do You See?

Learning Outcomes

In this section, you will

- **Measure** forces of sliding friction using a spring scale.

- **Compare** frictional forces on Earth and the Moon by applying the definition of the coefficient of sliding friction.

What Do You Think?

The Lunar Rover proved that there is enough frictional force on the Moon to operate a passenger-carrying wheeled vehicle.

- **How and why are frictional forces on Earth and the Moon different?**

Record your ideas about this question in your *Active Physics* log. Be prepared to discuss your responses with your small group and the class.

Investigate

In this *Investigate*, you will determine the coefficient of sliding friction between two surfaces. You will find the force required to overcome friction for various weights as you pull a box across a level surface. By graphing the data, you will calculate the coefficient of sliding friction. You will then calculate the force of friction on the Moon and how it affects sports played there.

1. Walk forward for a few steps and then come to an abrupt stop. Make the observations needed to write answers to the following questions in your *Active Physics* log:

Active Physics

🔏 a) In what direction do you push your feet to make your body go forward?

🔏 b) What force pushes your body forward with each step?

🔏 c) In what direction do you push your feet to stop your body?

🔏 d) What force makes your body stop?

🔏 e) Explain in terms of forces why it is difficult to walk forward or to come to a quick stop on a slippery surface like ice.

2. The next few steps will help you explore how the frictional force between an object and a surface depends on the weight of the object. Use a box as the object, a surface for it to slide on, sand (or something else) to adjust the weight of the box, and a spring scale for measuring both the weight of the box and the frictional force.

🔏 a) Prepare a table in your *Active Physics* log like the one shown for recording data.

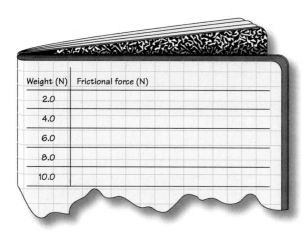

Weight (N)	Frictional force (N)
2.0	
4.0	
6.0	
8.0	
10.0	

3. Measure the weight of the box in newtons by suspending it from a newton spring scale. You might have to attach strings to the box to hold it horizontal when it gets heavy with sand. Add sand to adjust the weight of the box to 2 N.

4. Use the spring scale to pull horizontally on the box. Make sure that the spring scale is held parallel to the table surface and that you do not pull up at an angle. Measure the amount of force needed to cause the box to slide on the surface with a slow, constant speed. How will you know that the box is sliding with a constant speed?

🔏 a) Record the force measured by the newton spring scale in your table.

🔏 b) If the box is traveling at a constant speed in a straight line, what must be the net force acting on it?

🔏 c) In view of your answer to *4.b)*, how must the value of the frictional force pulling backward on the box be related to the value of the force with which you are pulling the box forward?

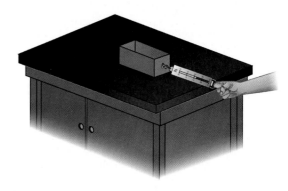

5. Continue adding sand to increase the weight of the box to 4.0, 6.0, 8.0, and 10.0 N, recording the newton force reading of the pull of the spring scale for each weight of the box.

a) Record the frictional force for each weight to complete your data table.

6. Plot a graph of frictional force versus weight. Frictional force is the vertical axis and weight is the horizontal axis.

a) Plot the points from the data table. Carefully consider whether the "best-fit" line should be straight or curved. Sketch a "best-fit" line representing the points. (This is a smooth line that has equal distribution of point differences above and below it.)

b) Based on the graph of the data, write a statement in your log that summarizes the relationship between frictional force and weight.

7. These steps will show you how to use the "best-fit" line on the graph of frictional force versus weight to determine what the force of *friction* would be if the same box is pulled on the same surface on the Moon when the box weighs 9 N on Earth.

a) From your graph, determine and record the frictional force on Earth for a box of weight 9 N on Earth.

b) From your graph, determine and record the frictional force on Earth for a box of weight 1.5 N on Earth.

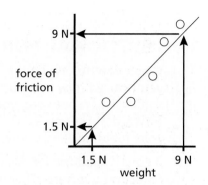

c) You learned in *Section 3* that the weight of an object on the Moon is $\frac{1}{6}$ of the object's weight on Earth. When the box used in this investigation weighs 9 N on Earth, what would the same box weigh on the Moon? Show your calculation in your log.

d) What would be the frictional force on the Moon for a box that weighs 9 N on Earth?

e) If all people and objects weigh $\frac{1}{6}$ on the Moon, what will happen to the friction on the Moon? How will this affect sports on the Moon?

8. Use what you have just learned about friction to ask yourself what walking and running on the Moon is like compared to doing so on Earth.

a) Write a statement in your log that explains how friction may affect a person's ability to walk and run on the Moon and thereby, how it will affect sports that involve walking and running.

967

Physics Talk

FRICTIONAL FORCE

When you observed your walk during the first part of the *Investigate*, you noticed how you push your feet back in order to move forward. The static friction between your shoe and ground is the force that pushes you forward. If there was no friction, you could not get the traction to push your feet back and you would slip in place.

A force called **friction** also arises when an attempt is made to slide an object on a surface. The amount of the force of friction between the object and the surface is equal in magnitude to the amount of horizontal force required to make the object move at constant speed. When the object moves at constant speed, the frictional force resisting the motion is equal in amount but opposite in direction to the applied force causing the motion. This is often shown in a force vector diagram.

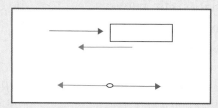

The red vector represents the applied force. The blue vector represents the frictional force. Since the two force vectors are equal, the object would have a net force of 0. Newton's second law $(F = ma)$ informs you that if there is no net force, there is no acceleration. Therefore, the object moves at a constant speed.

If the amount of the applied force is less than the maximum frictional force for that weight, the object does not slide at all on the surface; if the amount of the applied force is greater than the force of friction, the object accelerates as it slides across the surface. This occurs on ice where the friction is very small.

In the *Investigate*, you found that the force of friction increases if the weight of the pulled object increases. Since weight on the Moon is ⅙ the weight on Earth, you can therefore assume that friction on the Moon will be ⅙ the friction on Earth. That means everybody will be slipping and sliding on the Moon. In basketball, where you have to make a quick shift so you can go left instead of right, the decreased friction may cause you to slip and fall. When you slide into second base in baseball, you may slide right into the outfield.

Frictional forces also depend on surfaces. The lunar (Moon) surface is different than some Earth surfaces. You may be able to vary the surface of the playing field or the traction of the shoes to help players get more friction when they are engaged in a sport on the Moon.

Physics Words

friction: a force that acts to resist the relative motion or attempted motion of objects whose surfaces are in contact with each other.

Checking Up

1. When an object is moving at constant speed, how do the applied force and the frictional force compare in both magnitude and direction?

2. If you try to pull an object with a force less than the frictional force, what will happen?

3. What could be done to increase the friction of playing surfaces of a sport on the Moon?

+Math	+Depth	+Concepts	+Exploration
		◆	◆

Plus

The Coefficient of Sliding Friction

1. Astronauts on the Moon found that the soil at the surface is powdery but firm. Describe ways in which you could find out how the nature of the surface beneath an object affects the frictional force. Tell how this would affect the ability to walk or run on the Moon. Some characteristics of surfaces that you also should consider are smooth, rough, clean, dusty, wet, dry, slick, and sticky.

2. The force of sliding friction is proportional to the component of the force perpendicular to the surfaces between the sliding objects. The proportionality constant is called the coefficient of sliding friction and depends on the nature of the surfaces sliding by each other. When two variables are proportional to each other, the graph of one on the vertical axis with respect to the other on the horizontal axis is a straight line passing through the origin. Draw such a line on the graph you constructed in the *Investigate*, making sure it comes as close to your data points as possible. The slope of the line (how much it "rises upward" divided by how much it "runs sideways") is equal to the proportionality constant. Measure the slope of the line you drew.

   a) What is the coefficient of sliding friction for the two surfaces you used?

   b) What are the proper units for the coefficient of sliding friction?

   c) What might you do to change the coefficient of sliding friction between the box and the surface? Design and conduct an experiment.

What Do You Think Now?

At the beginning of this section, you were asked the following question:

• **How and why are frictional forces on Earth and the Moon different?**

Based on what you have learned about frictional forces, how would you answer this question now?

Essential Questions

What does it mean?

How is the frictional force on Earth related to the frictional force on the Moon for two identical objects moving along the same surfaces?

How do you know?

What observations did you make that support the conclusion that the frictional force on the Moon is $\frac{1}{6}$ the frictional force on Earth when all other conditions are the same?

Why do you believe?

Connects with Other Physics Content	Fits with Big Ideas in Science	Meets Physics Requirements
Forces and motion	Symmetry–laws of physics are the same everywhere	✱ Experimental evidence is consistent with models and theories

✱ Physicists assume that the physics on Earth and the Moon are identical. If you could travel to the Moon, how could you measure the frictional forces there?

Why should you care?

Is friction important to the sport you are proposing to NASA? If so, how is the sport going to be different due to the fact that the frictional force on the Moon is less? Does understanding what happens in sports when friction is reduced help you appreciate situations in your own life when friction is suddenly reduced? Some of these situations are potentially very dangerous. (For example, driving a vehicle.) Can you think of what you might do in advance to help with reduced friction situations?

Reflecting on the Section and the Challenge

Friction has some involvement in all sports. Any sport involving walking or running involves friction. Sliding friction is the basis for some sports, such as shuffleboard and curling. Most winter sports are based on sliding; since there is no water, snow, or ice on the Moon, are all winter sports "out," or could some winter sports equipment be adapted to slide on Moon soil? One thing is certain: your proposal to NASA will not "slide through" if you do not demonstrate that you understand frictional forces on the Moon.

Physics to Go

1. Based on what you have learned about friction, what difficulties do you envision for walking and running on the Moon? Explain your answer.

   a) What problems do you see for quick starts and quick stops for pedestrians, runners, or athletes on the Moon? Explain your answer.

2. How many 10-lb bags of potatoes (that is, a weight of 10 lb on Earth, or 4.5 kg of mass) would a 70-kg person need to carry on the Moon to have the person's combined weight on the Moon (body + potatoes) equal the person's weight on Earth (body only)? Show how you arrived at your answer.

3. Explain how carrying extra weight could create a frictional force that would allow for conventional walking or running on the Moon? Can you think of any problems associated with this?

4. Explain the problems that race cars or bikes would encounter going around curves on the Moon. How might they be solved?

5. Explain how sliding into second base would be different on the Moon and what modifications you might suggest to make the game work better.

6. Identify one sport upon which friction would have no effect as it exists on Earth and on the Moon. Explain why this is the case.

7. Imagine people on the Moon playing a game such as shuffleboard, in which disks are pushed along a surface, stopping at target locations that earn points for the person who pushed the disk. If you want the playing area to be the same size as it is on Earth, and if you want the players to push the disks with the same velocity as on Earth, what might you change about the disks to make playing shuffleboard work on the Moon? Explain what players would notice about your changed disks as they played shuffleboard on the Moon.

8. Will friction between your hand and a football or your hand and a bat be different on the Moon? Explain your answer.

9. If you were to give a shuffleboard disk a push on a shuffleboard court on the Moon, would it slow down just as it does on Earth, or would it take a longer or shorter distance to slow down? Assume that on Earth and on the Moon, the shuffleboard disk starts off with the same speed. Give reasons for your answer.

10. Basketball requires quick starts and stops and quick changes in direction.

    a) Describe how a basketball game will be affected by the decreased friction on the Moon.

    b) Describe a change you can make to basketball to allow the game to be played on the Moon.

11. *Preparing for the Chapter Challenge*

    Some sports can be improved by having lowered friction. Describe a sport that can be performed better on the Moon than on Earth due to lower friction. How could this sport be adapted to the Moon, either with less or more equipment than needed on Earth?

Inquiring Further

Friction vs. traction

The decreased gravity on the Moon leads to changes in friction. Athletes are more interested in their traction than the frictional force. Look up the difference between friction and traction and think of some ways to improve an athlete's traction on a surface, even in a low-friction environment.

Section 8

Modeling Human Motion: Bounding on the Moon

What Do You See?

Learning Outcomes

In this section, you will

- **Apply** a cylinder as a model of a human leg acting as a pendulum during walking.

- **Measure** the amount of time for a human leg to swing forward and back as a human walks on Earth.

- **Predict** the amount of time for a human leg to swing forward as a human walks on the Moon.

- **Explain** why it is not possible to walk unaffected on the Moon.

- **Discover** how the period of a pendulum depends on its length, mass, and angle of swing.

What Do You Think?

Neil Armstrong was the first human to set foot on the Moon.

- **Why do astronauts "bound" instead of walk or run on the Moon?**

- **Would running events in track and field be different if they were held on the Moon, even indoors?**

Record your ideas about these questions in your *Active Physics* log. Be prepared to discuss your responses with your small group and the class.

Investigate

1. Observe the *Active Physics* video of astronauts "walking" on the Moon. Record answers to the following in your log book:

   a) Compare how the astronauts use their legs and feet to move across the surface of the Moon to how legs and feet are used in habitual walking.

   b) Why do you think astronauts use their legs and feet that way to walk or run on the Moon?

2. Use a set of cylinders of various lengths as pendulums. Each cylinder has a hole at one end to allow it to be hung as shown in the diagram. The length of the string should be as short as possible while still allowing the cylinder to swing freely. If string is unavailable, you may choose to slip the drilled end of the cylinder directly on to the cross arm. This will allow the cylinder to swing freely. Measure the length of each cylinder in centimeters (to the nearest 0.1 cm) from the pivot point where the string is tied to the horizontal bar to the bottom edge of the cylinder.

a) Record the lengths of the cylinders (in centimeters) in a column in your *Active Physics* log. Leave room for several more columns of data to the right of this first one.

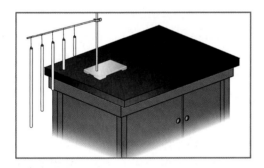

3. Choose one of the longer cylinders, pull it aside about ½ way up, and allow it to swing as a pendulum. Use a stopwatch to measure the *period* of this pendulum. (The period of a pendulum is the time, in seconds, for the pendulum to complete one full swing over and back. The symbol for period is "T" and it is capitalized to show that it is not the usual time, but the specific time for one full swing to take place.) A good way to measure the period accurately is to measure the time to complete 10 swings over and back and then divide the measurement by 10.

a) Record the measurement of this period in your *Active Physics* log in a separate column next to the length of the cylinder.

4. Using the same cylinder, pull it aside about ¼ of the way up, and allow it to swing. Measure the period of the pendulum.

a) Record it in your *Active Physics* log. Does it differ from the period measured in *Step 3*? If so, keep this in mind as you make measurements.

5. Measure the period of each of the cylinders using the method of *Step 3*.

a) Record the period of each cylinder, in seconds, in the column next to the lengths of the cylinders.

b) Plot a graph of period versus length for the cylindrical pendulums. Plot period, T, (in seconds) on the vertical axis, and length (in centimeters) on the horizontal axis. Mark the data points on your plot and sketch a smooth line that has an even distribution of data points around it. Observe carefully to decide whether the line should be straight or curved.

6. Now you will examine two types of walking, stiff-legged and the more usual style.

Observe a member of your group as he or she walks stiff-legged (without bending the knees). This can look pretty funny. Notice how after one foot hits the ground, that the opposite leg, trailing behind, swings forward as a pendulum before it is used for the next step. Also notice that a human leg is similar in shape to a cylinder. It is suspended at the top from the hip joint. The person does not use much muscular force to swing the leg forward because the force of gravity helps swing the leg forward. Therefore, the forward swing of a stiff human leg can be modeled by the cylinders used above.

Observe a member of the group walking more normally. Notice that the leg bends at the knee, making the motion more complicated. Now observe a group member walking again, focusing on the lower leg, from the center of the knee down. Maybe this part of the leg can be modeled by a swinging cylinder.

7. Measure the length of the lower leg (in centimeters), from the knee to the bottom of the foot, for each member of your group.

   a) Create a table in your *Active Physics* log to record the names and lengths.

   b) As each member of your group walks in a normal way, other members should use stopwatches to measure the time for the person's lower leg to swing forward during one stride. For accuracy, take the average of several measurements. Since the forward swing of the lower leg is only ½ of its period, double the measurement and record that as the period of each person's lower leg in the table in your *Active Physics* log.

   c) Create a graph of period versus length to find out how well a cylindrical pendulum models the forward swing of your lower leg. Explain whether a cylindrical pendulum is a reasonably good model of a person's lower leg while walking.

8. Use the following equation to calculate the predicted periods of each cylindrical pendulum for which you made measurements (see *Physics Talk* for the source of this equation):

$$T = 5.1\sqrt{\frac{L}{g}}$$

Here L is the length of the cylinder (in centimeters) and g is the acceleration due to gravity ($9.8 \text{ m/s}^2 = 980 \text{ cm/s}^2$). Include units of measurement when you do the calculations to be sure that the answer is in seconds. Divide the work among members of your group and then share the results.

   a) Add a column to the data table in your *Active Physics* log, and record the values predicted by the equation. Write a comment comparing the measured and predicted periods.

   b) Use the same equation to calculate the period of your lower leg. Share results within your group, enter the data in your log, and compare the predicted results to the measured values. Write a comment in your log comparing them.

9. Since acceleration due to gravity on the Moon is ⅙ the acceleration due to the gravity on Earth, the pendulum and your lower leg will require more time to swing. You might expect that the leg would take 6 times longer to swing since gravity is 6 times smaller on the Moon. Notice that the "g" in the equation for the period is within the square root sign. This informs you that the leg will not take 6 times as long to swing but $\sqrt{6}$ or 2.5 times as long.

   a) Multiply the time for the forward swing of your lower leg (half of the period) by 2.5 to find how much time it would take your lower leg to swing forward on the Moon. Try to walk with the "swing time" that your lower leg would have when powered by the Moon's gravity. You could ask a group member to give you time signals to help you get it right.

Physics Talk

PENDULUMS AND GRAVITY

Your leg swings back and forth as you walk. If your leg had one long bone, you could model this with a long rod swinging. The leg is more complicated. Analyzing your walking requires you to carefully observe the motion of your foot, ankle, lower leg, knee, and upper leg as you walk. In this section, you tried to find a model that is simpler to analyze and may provide insights into why your leg moves the way it does. In the investigation, a solid pendulum was used as a model. You found that the **period** of this pendulum varies with the length of the pendulum. This variation is similar to the variation with a simple pendulum — a mass hanging from a string.

Physicists have developed equations to predict the period of many kinds of pendulums. The "simple pendulum" (a ball hanging on a string) has a period:

$$T = 2\pi\sqrt{\frac{L}{g}}$$

where T is the period,
   L is the distance from the point of suspension to the center of
       the ball, and
   g is the acceleration due to gravity.

The equation for the period of a cylindrical pendulum of the kind you have been using in the *Investigate* is

$$T = 2\pi\sqrt{\frac{2L}{3g}}$$

$$\text{or } T = 5.1\sqrt{\frac{L}{g}}$$

Notice that the equations show that the periods of both kinds of pendulums are directly proportional to the square root of the length and are inversely proportional to the square root of the acceleration due to gravity. This explains why, for example, small children with short legs have such quick strides. The equations also predict that pendula and human legs swinging as pendula would behave differently on the Moon than on Earth due to the reduced effect of gravity on the Moon. Since the Moon's gravity is known to be $\frac{1}{6}$ of Earth's gravity, the equations can be adjusted to predict the periods of pendulums on the Moon by substituting $\frac{g}{6}$ for g. Therefore, the period of a cylindrical pendulum on the Moon should be not 6 times longer but $\sqrt{6}$ or 2.5 times longer.

Physics Words

period: the time required to complete one cycle (usual symbol is T).

Active Physics

$$T = 5.1\sqrt{\frac{L}{\left(\frac{g}{6}\right)}}$$

$$\text{or } T = 2.5\left(5.1\sqrt{\frac{L}{g}}\right)$$

The above equation shows that the period of a cylindrical pendulum is about 2.5 times greater on the Moon than on Earth. Perhaps astronauts do not walk normally on the Moon because they cannot. The Moon's gravity does not assist the swing of the leg enough to allow normal walking with normal rhythm on the Moon.

As you swing your legs in this investigation, gravity assists the movement. As the astronaut swings his leg, gravity does not assist nearly as much. The leg moves forward at a much slower rate and the astronaut walks in a different way than on Earth. Many astronauts, while traveling on the Moon, decide not to move by walking and swinging their legs but by jumping from one location to another.

Checking Up

1. What factors determine the period of a cylindrical pendulum?

2. Why do children seem to have such quick strides?

3. Why do humans walking on the Moon seem to have a much slower stride than humans walking on Earth?

4. What do astronauts do on the Moon to overcome the slow stride that the Moon induces?

Active Physics Plus

+Math	+Depth	+Concepts	+Exploration
◆◆◆		◆	◆

The Period of a Pendulum

The period of a simple pendulum (a mass hanging from a long string) is

$$T = 2\pi\sqrt{\frac{L}{g}}$$

where T is the period (time) for one complete motion back and forth, L is the length of the pendulum and g is the acceleration due to gravity — $9.8\,\text{m/s}^2$ on Earth and $1.6\,\text{m/s}^2$ on the Moon.

The period of a compound pendulum (a cylindrical mass hanging from a tiny hook) is

$$T = 2\pi\sqrt{\left(\frac{2}{3}\right)\frac{L}{g}}$$

where T is the period (time) for one complete motion back and forth, L is the length of the pendulum and g is the acceleration due to gravity ($9.8\,\text{m/s}^2$ on Earth and $1.6\,\text{m/s}^2$ on the Moon).

1. Determine mathematically what length rod and what length of simple pendulum will have the same period. Check the result experimentally by placing the two pendulums side by side and swinging them.

The motion of a pendulum can be simplified if you approximate it as a back-and-forth horizontal motion rather than the arc of a circle. This is the case when the amplitude of the motion is very small. This idealized motion is called simple harmonic motion, and occurs when the force on the object is always proportional to the distance the object is from its equilibrium position and always directed toward the equilibrium position. This means the force switches direction when it passes through the equilibrium position.

This relationship between force and distance is represented by the equation $F = -kx$, where k is the proportionality constant. If the force $-kx$ is set equal to the mass m times the acceleration, a (Newton's second law), then it follows that the ratio of the acceleration to the distance for simple harmonic motion is a negative constant equal to $-k/m$, $ma = -kx$.

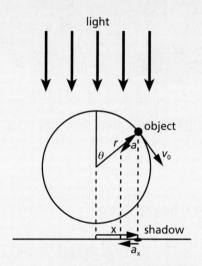

The motion of an object traveling around a circle of radius r with a constant velocity v_o (called uniform circular motion) is related to simple harmonic motion. Imagine that there is a light to one side of the circle and the shadow of the object falls on a screen as shown in the figure. The shadow moves back-and-forth as the object goes around the circle.

2. Compare the velocity of the shadow with the velocity of the pendulum bob (the mass).

   a) Where is the speed the greatest? Where is the speed equal to zero?

   b) How can you calculate the period of the shadow from the circular motion of the object?

3. Use a projector and a pendulum. As you rotate the pendulum in a horizontal circle, report on your observations of the motion of the shadow.

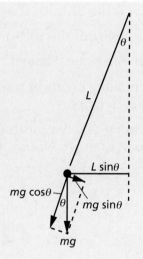

As seen above, the force on the mass when the string makes an angle θ with the vertical is equal to $mg \sin\theta$. This is because the force of gravity (weight) can be broken into two components, one along the line of the string and the other perpendicular to it. The component of the weight $mg \cos\theta$ is balanced by the force of the string on the mass. That's why the mass does not accelerate along the line of the string and instead only accelerates along the line perpendicular to the line of the string (the arc of the swing). If the angle θ is small, then the force $mg \sin\theta$ is nearly horizontal. The distance the mass is from the center position is approximately equal to $L \sin\theta$ and directly opposite to the force. Therefore, the spring constant is

$$k = \frac{-F}{x} = \frac{-(-mg \sin\theta)}{L \sin\theta} = \frac{mg}{L}$$

The period then is

$$T = 2\pi\sqrt{\frac{m}{k}} = 2\pi\sqrt{\frac{m}{mg/L}} = 2\pi\sqrt{\frac{L}{g}}$$

It is important to keep in mind that this relationship is approximate. The closer the pendulum is to a string of very low mass with a significant mass of very small physical size at its end, and the smaller the amplitude of the motion, the more accurate this relationship is.

What Do You Think Now?

At the beginning of this section, you were asked the following questions:

- **Why do astronauts "bound" instead of walk or run on the Moon?**

- **Would running events in track and field be different if they were held on the Moon, even indoors?**

Based on what you have learned in your investigation, how would you answer these questions now? Write your answers in your *Active Physics* log.

Essential Questions

What does it mean?

How does the period of a swinging cylinder or simple pendulum depend on its length? Does it depend on the acceleration due to gravity at its location? Can a pendulum be used to measure the acceleration due to gravity?

How do you know?

What did you observe about how the period of a swinging cylinder or simple pendulum depended on its length? What did you infer from the equation about how it is affected by the acceleration due to gravity?

Why do you believe?

Connects with Other Physics Content	Fits with Big Ideas in Science	Meets Physics Requirements
Forces and motion	*Models	Experimental evidence is consistent with models and theories

*Physicists use models to explain a wide variety of phenomenon. Why was a solid rod used as a model for the leg rather than a mass on a long string?

Why should you care?

Your model of the lower leg should have revealed that it swings on the Moon with a much longer period than it swings on Earth. Because of this, every sport in which people move using their legs is going to be drastically different on the Moon. For the sport you are proposing, how will it be affected?

Reflecting on the Section and the Challenge

There is a problem with walking on the Moon, and perhaps the same problem would extend to running on the Moon. Your legs will swing more slowly on the Moon. The period of the natural swing will be 2.5 times longer on the Moon. However, when running, does the runner simply allow the leg to swing forward? This swing delay, if it happens to runners also, could have serious implications for many sports on the Moon, unless "bounding" like astronauts is an acceptable substitute for walking or running. It probably can't even be said that a good runner on Earth would necessarily be a good "bounder" on the Moon because different muscles and skills are used. Maybe an Olympic champion who finished first in the 100-m dash would finish last in the "100-m bound" on the Moon! The time is nearing to write your proposal, so it's time to sort out the possibilities for sports on the Moon.

Physics to Go

1. The period of a "simple pendulum," a small massive object hanging from a string, is given by the equation $T = 2\pi\sqrt{(L/g)}$, where T is the time for the pendulum to swing once over and back, L is the distance from the point of suspension of the string to the center of mass of the object, and g is the acceleration due to gravity. Make a simple pendulum, let it swing, and see if the equation works. In using the equation, make sure the distance units of L and g are both measured in meters and m/s^2.

2. Describe how difficulty with walking or running on the Moon would affect at least one sport of your choice.

3. How would walking and running be affected on a planet that has an acceleration due to gravity greater than g on Earth?

4. How long would a simple pendulum need to be to have a period of 1.0 s ? Make one and see if it works. (Hint: Solve for L in the equation $T = 2\pi\sqrt{(L/g)}$ or try different values of L and calculate T.)

5. Pendulums were used as the mechanical basis for making the first accurate clocks. What is it about the period of pendulums, even as they swing less and less, that makes them good for clocks?

6. You also use your arms as pendulums when you walk. Do you think you use your arms for a reason? Why or why not?

7. Why do you "shorten" the length of your arms by bending at the elbows when you are running?

8. Obtain data for a small child's leg swing. Does it fit the data on your graph?

Active Physics

9. Using the equation for a pendulum, answer the following questions:

a) How does the period of a swinging cylinder or simple pendulum depend on its length?

b) How does the period of a swinging cylinder or simple pendulum depend on its mass?

c) How does the period of a swinging cylinder or simple pendulum depend on the acceleration due to gravity?

d) Can a pendulum be used to measure the acceleration due to gravity?

10. *Preparing for the Chapter Challenge*

On Earth, many competitive sports consist of people running from one place to another while something else is occurring. A tennis player chases an opponent's shot, a baseball player runs the bases when the ball is hit, and so on. How could the game of tennis be modified so that an athlete playing on the Moon with a much slower stride could still return an opponent's shot in time?

Inquiring Further

Factors affecting the period of a pendulum

The equations for both simple and cylindrical pendulums presented in *Physics Talk* make no mention of mass or amplitude (swing distance) as variables that may affect the period. Do you think it is true that such characteristics do not affect the period? Design experiments to test the effects of these and other properties of pendulums on the period and report your procedures and results. If you measure data and graph it, be certain the scales for both axes start at the zero point.

Section 9

Air Resistance and Terminal Velocity: "Airy" Indoor Sports on the Moon

What Do You See?

Learning Outcomes

In this section, you will

- **Observe** how air resistance changes when the speed of objects moving in air increases.

- **Observe** the terminal speed of falling objects.

- **Apply** effects of air resistance to adapting sports to the Moon.

- **Consider** requirements for self-propelled human flight in an air-filled shelter on the Moon.

What Do You Think?

Even though there is gravity on the Moon, there is no atmosphere. Any gas that is released on the Moon escapes, therefore, no atmosphere forms.

- **How would the acceleration due to gravity on the Moon compare indoors with air and outdoors with no air?**

Record your ideas about these questions in your *Active Physics* log. Be prepared to discuss your responses with your small group and the class.

Investigate

1. Drop a pencil and describe its motion. Drop a feather and describe its motion.

   a) Record your observations in your log.

2. Arrange 21 basket-type paper coffee filters into a set of six objects: one filter by itself, two filters nested together, three nested together, four nested together, five nested together, and six nested together. The filters should be tightly nested together. The filters in the diagram are shown separated only for clarity.

Active Physics

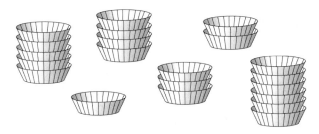

3. Have three members of your group stand side by side along a line, each person holding two of the objects, one in each hand, with the flat side facing down. Drop all six objects at the same instant from equal heights. Observe the order they hit the floor. Also measure the time it takes each object to fall to the floor. Finally, observe the kind of motion each object has as it falls. Repeat dropping the objects until you are able to make all of the observations.

a) Compare and contrast the motion of the coffee filters with that of the pencil.

b) Record your observations in your log. Record the mass of each object as "1," "2," "3," "4", "5" and "6," depending on how many filters make up the object. You can assume each filter has the same mass.

c) How are the times to fall to the floor related to the masses of the objects? Write your answer in your log.

d) Do any of the objects seem to fall at a constant speed instead of accelerating as they fall? If so, which ones, and why? Write your answers in your log.

e) Describe in your log what you think would happen if the coffee filters were dropped in the same way as above, but indoors, in air, on the Moon.

f) Describe how they would fall outdoors on the Moon, without air.

4. To find out what the game of badminton would be like on the Moon, observe as a member of your class or your teacher hits or tosses a badminton shuttlecock.

a) What is the range when the shuttlecock is hit very hard in a direction approximately parallel to the ground using a tennis-like overhand serve? Record the range in your log.

b) How is the range of the shuttlecock affected as the person "eases up" by hitting with less and less strength? Describe in your log how the range is affected.

c) The shuttlecock's speed changes a lot during the first one half of its flight. What is the difference in the way the speed changes when the hit is hard or soft? Write your response in your log.

d) Hitting a shuttlecock harder and harder does not result in proportionately greater and greater ranges. For example, hitting it five times harder probably did not make it go five times farther. Why not?

e) Imagine playing badminton on the Moon indoors with air. Including effects of $\frac{1}{6}g$, which aspects of the game would be the same as on Earth and which would be different? Would badminton be playable indoors on the Moon? Write your answers in your log.

f) Imagine playing badminton outdoors on the Moon. Including effects of $\frac{1}{6}g$, which aspects of the game of badminton would be the same as on Earth and which would be different? Would outdoor badminton be playable? Write your answers in your log.

5. To find out what the game of golf would be like on the Moon if regular golf balls were replaced by "whiffle" (perforated plastic) practice golf balls, toss a whiffle golf ball around.

a) Compare the range of the whiffle-type ball with that of a golf ball. Estimate the range of a whiffle ball in comparison to a regular golf ball. By what factor does using the practice ball reduce the usual range of the golfer's drive? Why? Write your responses in your log.

b) Since the acceleration due to gravity is ⅙ on the Moon what it is on Earth, would replacing regular golf balls with whiffle practice balls reduce the size of the golf course needed for outdoor golf, without air, on the Moon? What about indoor golf, in air, on the Moon?

Physics Talk

AIR RESISTANCE AND SPORTS ON THE MOON

You observed in the *Investigate* of *Section 2* that a hammer falls faster than a feather on Earth. In the video of Astronaut Commander Scott, you noticed that on the Moon, a feather and a hammer fall at the same rate. The feather falls differently because there is no air on the Moon to affect the downward motion of the feather. On Earth, the air provides a force on the feather opposing its downward motion. This can be shown with the following force diagrams:

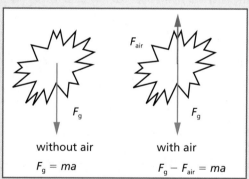

without air
$F_g = ma$

with air
$F_g - F_{air} = ma$

Notice that the acceleration with air will be smaller since the force due to **air resistance** opposes the gravitational force.

If the air-resistance force becomes equal to the gravitational force, there will be no acceleration. The object will float down with constant velocity. You observed this with the motion of the falling coffee filters. You can better understand this with the equation describing the motion:

If $F_{air} = F_g$ and

$F_g - F_{air} = ma$ then,

$0 = ma$

Physics Words

air resistance: a force exerted on a moving object by the air through which it moves; the force is dependent on the speed, volume, and mass of the object as well as on the properties of the air, like density.

Active Physics

Physics Words

terminal velocity: the speed reached by an object falling through air when the force of air resistance equals the force of gravity on the object.

Newton's second law of motion: if a body is acted upon by an external force, it will accelerate in the direction of the unbalanced force; the acceleration is proportional to the force and inversely proportional to the mass.

Newton's third law of motion: forces exist in pairs; the force of object A on object B is equal and opposite to the force of object B on object A.

A zero acceleration means that there is no change in velocity and the coffee filter moves at a constant velocity. This is called the **"terminal velocity."**

Air resistance could have important implications for adapting sports, or even for inventing new sports, that could be played in an air-filled indoor facility on the Moon.

Air resistance exists because, as an object moves through air, it collides with air molecules in its path. Each collision with an air molecule is governed by **Newton's third law** and the law of conservation of momentum. The air molecule is pushed in the direction of the object's motion, and, in reaction, the object experiences a tiny push by the air molecule in the direction opposite the object's motion. The result of steady collisions with many, many air molecules is that the object experiences a force due to the air and, therefore, an acceleration in the direction opposite to its motion. The amount of force due to air resistance depends on the object's speed, size, and shape.

According to **Newton's second law of motion**, $F = ma$, the effect of air resistance is to cause objects moving through air to slow down (negative acceleration).

Fly Like a Bird on the Moon?

Air resistance on a falling object causes the object's net downward acceleration to decrease. If the object reaches a great enough speed during its fall, it stops accelerating and continues its fall at a constant speed known as its "terminal speed" or "terminal velocity." This happens if and when the amount of the force of air resistance builds up enough to be equal and opposite to the object's weight.

Terminal speed is reached when

$$\text{Total force on object} = (\text{weight}) - (\text{force of air resistance}) = 0$$

When the total force acting on the object is zero, there no longer is any acceleration.

On Earth, a skydiver of average weight falling with an unopened parachute has a typical terminal speed of about 55 m/s (125 mi/h); with the parachute open, the terminal speed is reduced to a safe landing speed of about 11 m/s (25 mi/h). On the Moon, the skydiver's weight would be ⅙ as much as on Earth, and so the force of air resistance needed to balance the skydiver's weight would also be ⅙ of the amount on Earth. If an indoor stadium on the Moon had an atmosphere like Earth's, and since the force of air resistance depends on the speed, the skydiver's terminal speed falling without a parachute through a Moon atmosphere would be less.

This raises a possibility: people flying under their own power on the Moon. Does a pedal-powered helicopter seem out of the question for an indoor activity on the Moon? Could you equip people with gloves to create long, webbed fingers similar to a bat's wings so that strokes similar to those used for swimming underwater and the breast stroke might be tried for "swimming" through indoor air on the Moon?

A person who weighs 180 lbs on Earth weighs only 30 lbs on the Moon. If that person's arms can support this 30 lbs, it is possible to "float" in air during an indoor sport on the Moon.

Checking Up

1. As an object falls through the air at its terminal velocity, how does the force of gravity compare to the force of air resistance?

2. What causes air resistance?

3. What three factors determine the size of the force of air resistance?

Active Physics Plus

+Math	+Depth	+Concepts	+Exploration
	◆	◆	

Terminal Speed

1. When an object falls in a liquid, especially a "thick" or "viscous" liquid like honey, the force resisting the motion is roughly proportional to the speed of the object. This can be written $F_R = -bv$, where F_R is the resistive force, v is the object's speed, and b is a constant depending on the size and shape of the object and the properties of the liquid. The minus sign is necessary to remind you that the force is in the opposite direction to the motion.

a) A 10-g object falls through a liquid on Earth with a terminal speed of 1 cm/s. What is the value of b for this object and liquid?

b) If the same object and liquid are brought to the Moon, the value of b may be the same since the size and shape of the object and the properties of the liquid may not have changed. Assuming this is the case, if the object falls through the liquid on the Moon, what will its terminal speed be?

2. When an object falls through a gas such as air, the frictional force is roughly proportional to the square of the speed of the object. This can be written $F_A = -cv^2$, where F_A is the force of air resistance, v is the object's speed, and c is a constant depending on the size and shape of the object and the properties of the gas. The minus sign tells you that the force of air resistance and the direction of the motion are opposite to one another.

a) For a skydiver with a terminal speed of 55 m/s on Earth, what would her terminal speed be in an air-filled enclosure on the Moon (assuming the value of c is the same)?

b) If a skydiver's terminal speed on Earth with the parachute open is 11 m/s, what would her terminal speed be with the parachute open in an air-filled enclosure on the Moon (assuming the value of c is the same)?

What Do You Think Now?

Even though there is gravity on the Moon, there is no atmosphere. Any gas that is released on the Moon escapes, therefore no atmosphere forms.

- **How would the acceleration due to gravity on the Moon compare indoors with air and outdoors with no air?**

Based on what you have learned in this section, how would you answer this question now?

Physics
Essential Questions

What does it mean?

Why are the effects of air resistance different for various objects? Why do calculations that ignore air resistance often predict the trajectory of an object quite well?

How do you know?

What did you observe that helps to explain what determines the effects of air resistance on an object?

Why do you believe?

Connects with Other Physics Content	Fits with Big Ideas in Science	Meets Physics Requirements
Forces and motion	Symmetry—laws of physics are the same everywhere	✷ Optimal prediction and explanation

✷ Physics often predicts what will happen in circumstances where the experiment cannot be done. Why do you think you can believe a prediction of how air resistance will be different on the Moon compared to on Earth without doing the experiment on the Moon?

Why should you care?

Many sports involve objects moving through the air. Will the sport in your proposal be affected by air resistance?

Reflecting on the Section and the Challenge

This section has demonstrated that air resistance has profound effects on some sports on Earth and, if desired, could have profound effects on indoor sports in an air-filled sports facility on the Moon. Further, it seems possible that the eternal human quest of self-propelled flight could be realized in an Earth-like atmosphere combined with the Moon's reduced gravity.

Physics to Go

1. Invent a way for people to engage in self-propelled flight in air on the Moon.

2. A high-air-resistance replacement for a baseball might serve to reduce flight distances enough to allow baseball to be played as an indoor sport on the Moon. How would the ball need to be altered and what would happen when the ball is hit hard?

3. Many track and field events involve projectiles (for example, javelin, shot put, discus). How could these be "fitted with feathers" (or other air-resisting devices) to reduce indoor flight distances on the Moon?

4. How would table tennis (ping-pong) played outdoors be different on the Moon as compared to on Earth? How would it be similar?

5. If you already have chosen the sport for the Moon that you intend to propose to NASA, how will air resistance affect your sport? If you have not chosen a sport, use one you are considering to answer this question.

6. Take a piece of crumpled paper and throw it horizontally. Compare the distance it travels with your expectation of how a similarly thrown tennis ball would travel. Explain any differences.

7. Have someone throw the crumpled paper horizontally so that you can see and record the path of the paper. How is it different from the path you would expect a similarly thrown tennis ball to take?

8. *Preparing for the Chapter Challenge*
   Using the sport that you chose to be played on the Moon for your NASA presentation, write a brief paragraph explaining why air resistance will or will not be a critical factor affecting this sport.

Inquiring Further

Calculating air resistance

There are competing models for calculating the air resistance of an object based on the speed at which it falls. One model claims air resistance depends upon velocity, and another model on velocity squared. If the force of air resistance on the coffee filters depends upon the velocity, the time required for the filters to fall to the ground from a fixed height should vary inversely with the mass. If it depends upon the velocity squared, the fall time to the ground should vary as the inverse square root of the mass.

Design an experiment using the coffee filters from the *Investigate* to test these two models and determine which works best for the filters. To increase the mass, nest the filters inside one another.

Physics
You Learned

Physics Concepts	Is There an Equation?
The gravitational field strength and the **acceleration** due to gravity of the Moon is one-sixth that of Earth.	
Distance (d) equals one-half the acceleration due to **gravity** (g) times the fall time squared (t^2).	$d = \frac{1}{2}gt^2$
For an object falling identical time on Earth and the Moon, the ratio of distances fallen is equal to the ratio of acceleration due to gravity.	$\frac{g_M}{g_E} = \frac{d_M}{d_E}$
The mass of an object on the Moon is the same as the mass of the same object on Earth.	
Weight (F_w) equals an object's mass (m) times the acceleration of gravity (g). The weight of an object on the Moon is one-sixth the weight of the same object on Earth.	$F_w = mg$
The strength of a planet's gravitational field depends upon the planet's mass and inversely on the square of the distance from the center of the planet.	
All falling objects accelerate at the same rate because the ratio of the force of gravity to the mass of the object is the same for all masses.	
The law of gravitation applies to all masses in the universe.	
Active Physics Plus The force of gravity (F_g) equals the universal gravitational constant (G) times the product of the masses $(m_1$ and $m_2)$ divided by the square of the distance between their centers (r_p^2). The force of gravity between a planet and a mass depends upon the product of the mass of the planet and the mass being attracted, and is inversely proportional to the square of the distance to the planet's center.	$F_g = \frac{Gm_1m_2}{r_p^2}$
The **range** of a projectile launched horizontally on the Moon is $\sqrt{6}$ times its range on Earth. The horizontal range of a projectile launched upward at an angle is 6 times its range on Earth.	
The horizontal distance (d_x) covered by a projectile depends upon the time of flight (Δt) and the horizontal component of the launch velocity (v_x).	$d_x = v_x \Delta t$
The vertical position of a projectile (d_y) launched at an angle (v) equals the vertical component of the vertical velocity (v_y) times the time of flight (t) minus the distance the object would fall under the influence of gravity during the time of flight.	$d_y = v_y t - \frac{1}{2}gt^2$
Active Physics Plus Time of flight (t_{total}) equals twice the initial vertical launch velocity (v_{0y}) divided by the acceleration of gravity (g_y). The flight time of a projectile launched at an angle is twice the time to the peak of the **trajectory**.	$t_{total} = 2t_{max\,y} = \frac{2v_{0y}}{-g}$
Active Physics Plus The maximum **projectile** height is proportional to the initial vertical velocity squared and inversely proportional to the gravitational field strength.	$y_{max} = \frac{v_{y0}^2}{-2g}$

	Projectile range (R) equals twice the product of the initial vertical and horizontal velocities $(v_{x0})(v_{y0})$ divided by the gravitational field strength.	$R = x_{max} = \dfrac{2v_{x0}v_{y0}}{-g_y}$
	Maximum range equals twice the initial velocity squared divided by the acceleration due to gravity. The maximum range of a projectile occurs at a launch angle of 45°.	$R = \dfrac{v_0^2}{g}$ when $\theta = 45°$
	An object's **kinetic energy** (KE) is proportional to the object's mass (m) multiplied by its velocity squared (v^2). Kinetic energy is an object's energy of motion.	$KE = \dfrac{1}{2}mv^2$
	Gravitational potential energy (GPE) is proportional to an object's mass (m) multiplied by its vertical height above the surface (Δh) and the acceleration due to gravity (g). Gravitational potential energy is energy due to an object's vertical position.	$GPE = mg\Delta h$
	The law of conservation of energy states that energy may change forms, but is not lost during transformations. The total amount of energy remains the same during any changes in form.	$Energy_{before} = Energy_{after}$
	Friction is a force acting between bodies in contact that resists their relative motion. It always acts parallel to the surfaces in contact, and depends upon the force holding the bodies together.	
	The **period** (T) of a simple pendulum equals 2π times the square root of the pendulum's length (L) divided by the acceleration due to gravity (g). The period of a pendulum depends upon its length and is independent of its mass.	$T = 2\pi\sqrt{\dfrac{L}{g}}$
	The period (T) of a cylindrical pendulum equals 5.1 times the square root of the pendulum's length (L) divided by the acceleration due to gravity (g). A cylinder swinging from a pivot (like a leg) swings more slowly on the Moon than on Earth due to the decreased acceleration of gravity.	$T = 5.1\sqrt{\dfrac{L}{g}}$
	The acceleration of an object falling under the influence of gravity and **air resistance** depends upon the object's shape, mass, and speed.	
	An object falling with air resistance will reach a constant **terminal velocity** when its acceleration is zero. Terminal velocity is reached when the force of air resistance equals an object's weight.	
	Force of air resistance (F_a) equals a constant (b) times the velocity (v) squared.	$F_a = -bv^2$

Physics
Chapter Challenge

You will now be completing a second cycle of the *Engineering Design Cycle* as you prepare for the *Chapter Challenge*. The goals and criteria remain unchanged. However, your list of *Inputs* has grown.

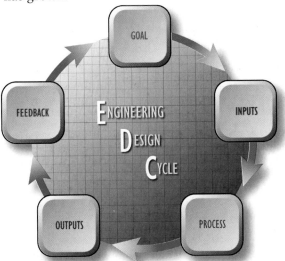

Goal

Your challenge for this chapter is to design or modify a sport so it can be played on the Moon. You must prepare a proposal to present to NASA explaining how the sport could take place on the Moon with clear descriptions of the adjustments and modifications that will need to be made to accommodate the different environment. At the same time, you must convince the NASA judges that your Moon sport will be interesting, exciting, and entertaining for participants and spectators.

Inputs

You have completed all the sections of this chapter and learned the physics content you need to complete this challenge. You now have additional physics information to help you identify and analyze the differences between actions that take place on Earth and the Moon and the physics concepts that apply to them. You also have the additional input of your own personal experiences in sports activities as well as the feedback you received following your *Mini-Challenge* presentation.

Section 1 You practiced the creative process of brainstorming in an effort to create your own definition of the word "sport." Your team should now have a good understanding of the type of activity that can be considered a sport.

Section 2 You examined falling objects and the effects of gravity. You compared the time it takes for a dropped object on Earth to touch ground with the time required for a similar object dropped on the Moon to hit the surface. You learned that the difference is caused by the acceleration due to gravity on each dropped object. You also learned about the relationship of time, distance, and acceleration for falling objects.

Section 3 In order to compare the masses of different objects, you explored the way a force causes a mass to react. You also learned how different gravitational forces are related to changes in weight for the same mass.

Section 4 You developed a model to compare the flight of a projectile on Earth to the flight of the same projectile on the Moon. While constructing your model, you took note of factors that could be modified to make the projectile's path, or trajectory, on the Moon similar to its typical trajectory on Earth.

Section 5 You applied conservation of energy, work, and mass to analyze an athlete's vertical jump on Earth. You then used a similar analysis to estimate potential jumping heights for athletes on the Moon. You recognized that jumping is an action you will need to modify for your sport.

Section 6 You explored two different methods that could be used to change the flight of a golf ball on the Moon. Changing the launch speed of the ball or the mass of the club could affect the total distance a ball will travel. You learned that this analysis also applies to other sports where a ball is hit with some type of stick or racquet.

Section 7 You learned the importance of friction in all sports and how friction on the Moon would be different for the same object on Earth. You recognized the need to perform a careful analysis to make sure athletes can handle the force of friction they will experience on the Moon.

Section 8 You discovered that walking is a more complex process than you may have previously thought. By examining a model of the human leg, a rod-shaped pendulum, you discovered that walking on the Moon would be different from walking on Earth. Would this also be the case for running?

Section 9 You explored the role of air resistance for moving and falling objects on Earth. You realized that whether your sport is an indoor sport with an atmosphere or an outdoor sport with no air resistance, the movement of athletes and other projectiles, such as balls, will be dramatically impacted.

Process

In the *Process* phase, your group must decide what information you will use to meet the *Goal*. You will need to confirm that the sport you have chosen to modify meets the basic requirements of a sport, and agrees with the definition of sport that your group decided upon. Have a brainstorming session to discuss and identify the rules for your sport, both original and modified for playing on the Moon. Remember, not only should the rules be modified for the Moon, they should also be crafted to keep the game exciting to play and watch. Do not forget to consider in your modifications the venue and equipment associated with your sport. It will be important to include the way any changes you have made to the field, equipment, and rules will affect the way the game is played. Be sure to explain how the game play will be different, but still exciting and interesting.

Prepare a list of factors affecting sports on Earth and on the Moon. Your presentation should include a comparison of these factors and how they affect the play of your sport. You will also need to compare the sport you envision for the Moon with the sport as it exists on Earth and highlight the ways it will be different. Identify the types of sports action that will be different for Earth and the Moon. You may also want to identify the parts that will not change to emphasize where the changes will be important.

The championship description that you will write for the newspaper should prove that your Moon sport is exciting. You might want to include a play-by-play of the home colony's winning score or the final stand of the defense. Do not forget to highlight the actions that are unique to playing your sport on the Moon.

Outputs

Presenting your information to the class are your design cycle *Outputs*. You should have a thorough description of your sport, a comparison of important physics concepts, and a description of changes you would make to the sport to maintain its integrity as a sport when played on the Moon. Your presentation is also part of your design cycle *Outputs*, so take the time to prepare your script and any posters, diagrams, or multimedia pieces you need to make your presentation effective and convincing.

Feedback

Your classmates will give you *Feedback* on the accuracy and the overall appeal of your NASA-sports presentation based on the criteria of the design challenge. This feedback will likely become part of your grade but could also be useful for additional design iterations. The different design solutions may represent *Feedback* in the form of alternative ways you might have solved the problem. From your experience with the *Mini-Challenge*, you should see how you could continuously rotate through the design cycle to refine your Moon sport.

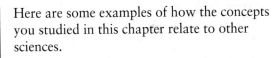

Physics

Connections to Other Sciences

Here are some examples of how the concepts you studied in this chapter relate to other sciences.

Mass, Weight, and Gravity

Biology Geotropic hormones regulate the growth of many plants. These hormones are produced in the growing tip of a plant, and when pulled downward by the force of gravity, cause the plant to grow upward, against the force. Plants that grow on a planet with a greater or lower level of gravity may not grow in a manner similar to those on Earth for this reason.

Chemistry The strength of the gravitational field of a planet determines what gases are trapped on the planet. Gas-giant planets retain large amounts of lighter gases such as hydrogen. This suggests a unique chemistry in the atmosphere of these planets that is very different from Earth's atmosphere.

Earth Science The gravity associated with a planet is significant in determining whether the planet is geologically active. Since smaller planets do not collect mass from material in space as quickly as larger planets, they may cool off more quickly and become inactive.

Oscillations

Biology The limbs of all animals have a natural oscillation rate. For this reason, animals with long legs tend to have relatively slow strides, while those with short legs have much quicker ones. A human sprinter can shorten her effective leg length by bending the leg at the knee to allow for quicker oscillation and greater speed.

Chemistry Oscillations of single atoms and atomic groups in molecular bonds are characteristic for different molecular groups. Infrared spectroscopy allows chemists to make determinations of the chemical composition and structure of molecules based on the oscillation rates of these molecular groups.

Earth Science Oscillations in Earth's orbit through many centuries are thought to be the cause of Earth's ice ages. The Milankovitch cycles that describe how Earth's orbit varies periodically are now thought to be responsible for Earth's periodic glacial-interglacial cycles.

Momentum and Energy Transfers

Biology On planets with increased gravity, the energy gained during a fall would be greater than on Earth. Since the velocity at impact would be higher, an astronaut falling to the surface of such a planet would more likely be injured due to the greater momentum and energy possessed during impact.

Chemistry The rate at which a chemical reaction occurs depends upon numerous factors in the environment. On a planet with a different gravitational force, the kinetic energy, density, and pressure of a gas may vary, leading to chemical reaction rates that are significantly different than what typically occurs on Earth.

Earth Science The erosive force of water or other liquids that might be flowing on other planets is largely determined by the work done by gravity on the liquid. Therefore, the geological features caused by water erosion on these planets may be correspondingly greater or less than an equivalent amount of water on Earth might cause.

Air (Fluid) Resistance

Biology Fluid resistance determines the rate at which unicellular animals that live in fluids can move. Most animals of this type use flagella to propel themselves, at the expense of a tremendous amount of energy.

Chemistry The dispersion rate of gases in an atmosphere is determined in part by the collision rate of the gas molecules with heavier molecules that provide the resistance to the spread of the gas.

Earth Science Air resistance determines the erosive power of air, and how the winds affect various features. Winds of sufficient strength can have a devastating effect. The winds on top of Mount Washington in New Hampshire, for example, are so strong that buildings must be staked to the ground by heavy cables.

Dr. Neil Tyson

**Director of New York's Hayden Planetarium;
New York, NY**

As a young boy, Dr. Neil Tyson would observe the night sky from his tarred rooftop apartment in the Bronx that was built on one of the highest hills in the borough. "Nothing I can write will capture the acute cosmic imprinting from my first view from the Bronx of the waxing crescent moon across the Hudson River," writes Dr. Tyson in his 2004 memoir titled *The Sky Is Not the Limit: Adventures of an Urban Astrophysicist.*

Dr. Tyson is currently the Director of New York's Hayden Planetarium at the American Museum of Natural History. He earned his B.A. in physics from Harvard University in Cambridge, Massachusetts, and his Ph.D. in astrophysics from Columbia University in New York City. To top that off, his contributions to helping the public understand and appreciate the cosmos have been recognized by the International Astronomical Union in their official naming of asteroid "13123 Tyson."

"At the moment, life on Earth is the only known life in the universe, but there are compelling arguments to suggest we are not alone," Dr. Tyson writes in the *Natural History* magazine. "On the chance that such a civilization exists, radio waves would be the communication band of choice because of their ability to traverse the galaxy unimpeded by interstellar gas and dust clouds."

Dr. Tyson believes physics helps him in his personal and professional life as well. "When used as a lens through which I observe life, it allows me to look at problems in a way that often gleans immediate insight into their solutions," he said. Dr. Tyson concluded by saying, "Being scientifically and mathematically literate is not about what you know, but how you think."

Dr. Michio Kaku

**Professor of Theoretical Physics;
New York, NY**

Dr. Michio Kaku, Professor of Theoretical Physics at City College in New York, believes a unified explanation of everything is attainable in his lifetime.

Currently, Dr. Kaku is absorbed in defining the "Theory of Everything," which begins with the four forces: electromagnetic, gravitational, and weak and strong nuclear forces. The Theory of Everything is a theory of abstract physics that attempts to fully explain and link together all known physical phenomena.

He anticipates that his research will open many doors regarding space and time. "In the future, when we unify the four forces, it will reveal the secrets of space and time."

Dr. Jill Tarter

**Head of the SETI Institute;
Mountain View, CA**

Even as a child, Jill Tarter dreamed big. "I decided to be an engineer because it was the most masculine thing I could think of." She was the only woman in her graduating class at Cornell University to earn an engineering degree, and she also earned advanced degrees in astronomy.

Dr. Tarter helped found the Search for Extraterrestrial Intelligence Institute (SETI), a private, nonprofit organization dedicated to scientific research, education, and public outreach. "We use radio telescopes to look for signals that only show up on one frequency. We are trying to find signals that cannot be generated by nature in terms of the physics we understand."

Physics

Practice Test

Before you try the Physics Practice Test, *you may want to review Sections 1–9, where you will find* **31 Checking Up** *questions,* **16 What Do You Think Now?** *questions,* **36 Physics Essential Questions,** **79 Physics to Go** *questions, and* **9 Inquiring Further** *questions.*

Content Review

Use the following information to answer *Questions 1-8.* The acceleration due to gravity on the Moon is 1.6 m/s^2.

1. An astronaut is assigned to lift a mass of 300 kg on the Moon. What would the mass weigh on the Moon and on Earth?
   a) The mass would weigh 3000 N on Earth and 500 N on the Moon.
   b) The mass would weigh 500 N on Earth and 3000 N on the Moon.
   c) The mass would weigh 500 N on both Earth and the Moon.
   d) The mass would weigh 3000 N on both Earth and the Moon.

2. An astronaut on the Moon pushes a cart on a horizontal, frictionless track while someone on Earth pushes a cart of equal mass on a similar track with the same force. Which statement best describes the motion of the two carts?
   a) The cart on the Moon accelerates faster than the cart on Earth because it weighs less.
   b) The cart on the Moon accelerates faster because it has less inertia.
   c) The cart on the Moon accelerates faster because it has less weight and less inertia.
   d) The two carts will accelerate equally.

3. A scientist on Earth drops a golf ball on a hard, metal surface from a height of 1.5 m and the ball rebounds to a height of 0.90 m. An astronaut on the Moon drops an identical ball onto an identical surface from the same height. The rebound height of the ball on the Moon would be
   a) 0.15 m
   b) 0.90 m
   c) 5.4 m
   d) 8.1 m

4. In a softball game on the Moon, the batter hits a "pop fly" with a vertical velocity of 16 m/s, as shown in the diagram. How long will it take for the softball to reach the peak of its rise, where its vertical velocity is zero?
   a) 1.6 s
   b) 3.2 s
   c) 5.0 s
   d) 10 s

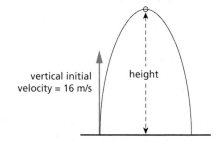

vertical initial velocity = 16 m/s   height

5. For *Question 4,* what would the height of the softball be at the peak of its rise?
   a) 26 m
   b) 16 m
   c) 80 m
   d) 160 m

6. During a basketball game on the Moon, a competitor jumps to block a shot and her center of mass reaches a height of 3.2 m above the surface. If she has a mass of 65 kg, what is her gravitational potential energy at the peak of the jump?
   a) 650 J
   b) 2100 J
   c) 100 J
   d) 330 J

7. A pendulum on the Moon has a period of 2.0 s. If the length of the pendulum is doubled, what is the pendulum's period?
   a) 1 s
   b) 2 s
   c) 2.8 s
   d) 4 s

8. In an indoor game of softball on the Moon, a ball is thrown upward fast enough that the force of air friction is equal to the ball's weight. What will the ball's downward acceleration be?
a) 0 m/s^2
b) 0.8 m/s^2
c) 1.6 m/s^2
d) 3.2 m/s^2

9. The acceleration due to gravity on the planet Mercury is 3.6 m/s^2. If an astronaut drops a hammer from a height of 1.8 m on Mercury, how long will it take the hammer to strike the ground?
a) 1 s
b) 2 s
c) 0.5 s
d) 0.25 s

10. Objects near the surface of the Moon fall slower than objects near Earth's surface. The reason for this difference is the
a) Moon has different laws of physics than Earth.
b) equations for free fall are different on the Moon.
c) acceleration due to gravity is less on the Moon, but the equations are the same.
d) different acceleration of gravity on the Moon means scientists must develop new laws of physics.

11. The person who first demonstrated that the laws of physics apply to the Moon as well as Earth was
a) Commander David Scott.
b) Sir Isaac Newton.
c) Galileo.
d) Albert Einstein.

12. The acceleration due to gravity of a planet depends upon the planet's
a) mass only.
b) radius only.
c) mass and radius.
d) mass, radius, and weight of the object accelerating.

13. Which of the following would have no effect on the range of a golf ball launched on the Moon?
a) the ball's velocity
b) the angle of launch
c) the ball's kinetic energy
d) the ball's mass

14. A student pulls a 10-kg box along a horizontal surface with a constant speed of 2 m/s by a force of 50 N. If the student stops and remains still, and then starts pulling the box with a force of 25 N in the same direction on the same surface, what is the box's speed?
a) 0 m/s
b) 1 m/s
c) 2 m/s
d) 0.5 m/s

15. A 50-kg skydiver falls toward Earth. If the force of air resistance on the skydiver is 150 N, what is the skydiver's acceleration?
a) 9.8 m/s^2
b) 7 m/s^2
c) 3 m/s^2
d) 1.6 m/s^2

Critical Thinking

Remember that the acceleration due to gravity on the Moon is 1.6 m/s^2. Use this information to answer *Questions 16-22*.

16. A softball player on the Moon hits the ball with a velocity off the bat of 25 m/s and a horizontal velocity of 15 m/s, as shown in the diagram.

a) What is the ball's vertical speed?
b) Calculate the ball's time of flight.
c) Calculate the horizontal distance the ball goes until it returns to the ground.

Practice Test (continued)

17. An 80-kg football player on the Moon jumps straight upward to a height of 5 m above surface to catch a pass.
    a) How much gravitational potential energy does he have at the peak of his jump?
    b) How much kinetic energy did he have as he left the ground?
    c) At what vertical speed did he leave the ground?
    d) How much time does it take for him to fall back to the ground?

18. A simple pendulum (a 0.200-kg mass on a string) is swinging on the Moon. The string length is 2 m.
    a) Calculate the period of the pendulum on the Moon.
    b) If the mass on the string were doubled to 0.400 kg, what would be the period of the pendulum?
    c) If the length of the string were reduced to 1 m, what would be the period of the pendulum?
    d) What length pendulum would be needed to have a period of 1 s on the Moon?

19. A 0.010-kg foam rubber ball is dropped inside a tower on the Moon. After a short while, the ball falls with a constant speed of 2 m/s due to the air resistance inside the tower.
    a) What is the force of air resistance on the ball?
    b) The foam rubber ball is now thrown downward with a speed of 4 m/s. Sketch a graph of the ball's velocity as a function of time as the ball falls.
    c) What happens to the ball's terminal velocity if its mass increases while all other factors remain the same?

20. An astronaut on the Moon is pulling a 300-kg crate across a horizontal floor with a force of 400 N.

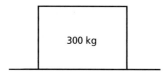

300 kg

   a) What is the weight of the box on the Moon?
   b) If the box is traveling with constant velocity across the floor, what is the force of friction between the box and the floor?
   c) Duplicate the diagram in your log and draw all the forces acting on the box, including correct size and direction.
   d) If the astronaut starts to pull with a force of 500 N, what is the box's acceleration?

Active Physics

Plus

21. An athlete on the Moon throws a shot-put with an initial velocity of 20 m/s at an angle of 37° to the horizontal. How far does the shot travel horizontally when it returns to the same height?

22. A mountain bike rider on the Moon is riding along a level surface at 10 m/s when he runs into a small hill and is launched upward. At the peak of his trajectory, he and the bike have a forward velocity of 8 m/s. How high above the surface are the bike and rider at the peak?

GLOSSARY/GLOSARIO

Glossary

A

acceleration: the change in velocity per unit time; acceleration is a vector quantity, it has magnitude (size) and direction.

accuracy: an indication of how close a series of measurements are to an accepted value.

additive color mixing: mixing colored lights on a screen or other object.

air resistance: a force exerted on a moving object by the air through which it moves; the force is dependent on the speed, volume, and mass of the object as well as on the properties of the air, like density.

alpha decay: the change that occurs when an unstable heavy nucleus that releases some of its excess energy by emitting a helium-4 nucleus (alpha particle).

alpha particle: a positively charged particle given off by certain radioactive nuclei, made up of two protons and two neutrons.

alternating current (AC): an electric current that reverses in direction.

ampere: the SI unit of current; one ampere is the flow of one coulomb/second (1 A = 1 C/s).

amplitude: the maximum displacement of a particle as a wave passes; the height of a wave crest; it is related to the wave's energy.

angle of incidence: the angle formed between an incident ray and the normal to the surface.

angle of reflection: the angle formed between a reflected ray and the normal to the surface.

antinode: a point on a standing wave where the displacement is the largest of the medium is at its maximum.

atom: the smallest particle of an element that has all the element's properties; it consists of a nucleus surrounded by electrons.

atomic mass unit: the standard unit of atomic mass based on the nucleus of a carbon-12 atom.

atomic number: the number of protons in the nucleus.

average speed: the distance traveled divided by the time it takes to travel that distance.

B

Balmer series: a sequence of emission lines in the visible part of the hydrogen electromagnetic spectrum.

baryon: a group of elementary particles that are affected by the nuclear force; neutrons and protons belong to this group.

battery: an electronic device that stores electric potential energy.

beta decay: the change that occurs when a neutron in an unstable nucleus turns into a proton plus electron (beta particle).

binding energy: the energy required to remove an electron or nucleon from an atom.

C

center of mass: the point at which all the mass of an object is considered to be concentrated.

centripetal acceleration: the acceleration of an object toward the center of a circle experienced by an object traveling in a circular path at constant speed.

centripetal force: a force directed toward the center that causes an object to follow a circular path at a constant speed.

chain reaction: a reaction that causes two or more similar reactions in a process that grows exponentially with a specific doubling time.

circuit breaker: an device placed in an electrical circuit that operates like an automatic switch that opens the circuit when too much current flows through.

coefficient of sliding friction: a dimensionless quantity symbolized by the Greek letter μ; its value depends on the properties of the two surfaces in contact and is used to calculate the force of friction.

concave mirror: a curved mirror in which the reflecting surface caves inward.

conduction: the transfer of heat energy from particle to particle between substances through contact or within a substance.

conductor: a material through which electric current can move easily; metals are good conductors.

conservation of charge: the total charge of an isolated system before an event equals the total electric charge after the event.

constant speed: speed that does not change over a period of time.

constructive interference: the result of adding waves crest-to-crest to produce a wave with a greater amplitude.

convection: the transfer of heat energy through the movement of air or liquid currents.

converging lens: a lens that is thicker in the middle and thinner toward the edge. Rays that enter the lens parallel to the axis of the lens will converge toward the axis and cross the axis on the far side of the lens at the focal point; a convex lens.

convex lens: a lens that is thicker in the middle and thinner toward the edge. Rays that enter the lens parallel to the axis of the lens will converge toward the axis and cross the axis on the far side of the lens at the focal point; a converging lens.

convex mirror: a curved mirror in which the reflecting surface is curved outward.

coulomb: the SI unit of charge; one coulomb (1 C) is approximately equal to the charge of a lightning bolt, the charge of 6.25×10^{18} electrons.

Coulomb's law of electrical attraction or repulsion: the force of attraction between two charges is directly proportional to the product of the charges and inversely proportional to the distance between them.

crest: the highest point of displacement of a wave.

critical angle: the angle of incidence, for a light ray passing from one medium to another, that has an angle of refraction of 90°.

current: the rate of flow of electric charge; the number of coulombs passing a point in one second.

D

daughter nuclei: the nuclei of atoms that have undergone decay.

destructive interference: the result of adding waves crest-to-trough to produce a wave with a decreased amplitude.

diffraction: the ability of a wave to spread out or change direction as it emerges from an opening or moves beyond an obstruction.

direct current: an electric current flowing in only one direction.

direct measurement: a method that uses a measuring device to determine the size of an object.

direct relationship: a relationship in which increasing one variable increases the other variable or decreasing one variable also decreases the other variable.

displacement: the difference in position between a final position and an initial position; it depends only on the endpoints, not the path; displacement is a vector quantity, it has magnitude (size) and direction.

Doppler effect: the change in the pitch, or frequency of a sound (or the frequency of a wave) for an observer that is moving relative to the source of the sound (or source of the wave).

E

elastic potential energy: the energy of a spring due to its compression or stretch; also see spring potential energy.

electric charge: a fundamental property of matter; charge is either negative or positive.

electric potential energy (electric potential): potential energy per unit of charge; voltage.

electrical circuit: a route along which electricity can flow.

electrical resistance: opposition of a material to the flow of electrical charge through it; it is the ratio of the voltage across a conductor divided by the current.

electromagnet: any magnetic field created by a current.

electromagnetic waves: transverse waves that are composed of oscillating perpendicular electric and magnetic fields that travel at 3×10^8 m/s in a vacuum; examples of electromagnetic waves listed in order of increasing wavelength are gamma rays, X–rays, ultraviolet radiation, visible light, infrared radiation, microwaves, and radio waves.

electron: a negatively charged sub atomic particle with a charge of 1.6×10^{-19} C (coulombs) and a mass of 9.1×10^{-31} kg.

entropy: a thermodynamic property of a substance associated with the degree of disorder in the substance; a substance is more ordered as a solid than a liquid, and a liquid is more ordered than a gas.

F

Feynman diagram: a diagram that shows the exchange of virtual particles.

first law of thermodynamics: the thermal energy added to a system is equal to the change in internal energy of the system plus the work done by the system on its surroundings.

focal length: the distance from the focal point to the mirror.

focal point: in a convex lens, the place where light rays that approach the lens parallel to the principal axis converge on the far side of the lens; in a concave lens, the place from which the rays that originated from rays that approach the lens parallel to the principal axis seem to diverge.

force: a push or a pull; an interaction between two objects that can result in an acceleration of either or both objects.

frame of reference: a vantage point with respect to which position and motion may be described.

free-body diagram: a diagram showing the forces acting on an object.

frequency: the number of waves produced per unit time; the frequency is the reciprocal of the amount of time it takes for a single wavelength to pass a point.

friction: a force that acts to resist the relative motion or attempted motion of objects whose surfaces are in contact with each other.

fuse: a device placed in an electrical circuit that melts when too much current flows through it, thereby breaking the circuit; it protects the other parts of the circuit from damage due to too much current.

G

galvanometer: an instrument used to detect and measure an electric current.

gamma decay: the change that occurs when an excited nucleus emits some of its excess energy in the form of a high-energy photon (gamma particle).

generator: a device that produces electricity.

gravitational field: the gravitational influence in the space around a massive object.

gravitational potential energy: the energy a body possesses as a result of its position in a gravitational field.

gravity: the force of attraction between two bodies due to their masses.

grounding: the process of adding or removing electrons to restore a charged object to neutral.

H

half–life: the amount of time it takes for half of the sample to change.

heat: energy transferred from one place to another by virtue of a temperature difference, resulting from the motion of atoms and molecules.

heat transfer: the transmission of heat energy from a warmer substance to a cooler substance.

Hooke's law: the restoring force exerted by a spring is directly proportional to the distance of stretch or compression of the spring.

I

impulse: a change in momentum of an object.

incident ray: the ray of light that strikes a surface.

index of refraction: a property of the materials at an interface that determine the relationship between the angle of incidence and the angle of refraction.

indirect measurement: a technique that uses proportions or probability to find a measurement when direct measurement is not possible.

inertia: the natural tendency of an object to remain at rest or to remain moving with constant speed in a straight line.

instantaneous speed: the speed measured during an instant: the speed as the time interval approaches, but does not become zero.

insulator: a material through which electric current cannot move easily; air, glass, plastic, rubber, and wood are examples of insulators.

inverse relationship: a relationship in which decreasing one variable increases the other variable or vice versa.

inverse-square relationship: the relationship between the magnitude of a gravitational force and the distance from the mass. This also describes how electrostatic forces depend on the distance from an electrical charge.

ionization energy: the energy required to free an electron from its energy level.

ionization: the process in which a neutral atom becomes an ion.

J

joule: the SI unit for all forms of energy.

K

kinetic energy: associated with motion; the energy an object possesses because of its speed.

L

law of conservation of energy: the law that states that energy in a closed system cannot be created or destroyed; it can be transformed from one form to another, but the total amount of energy remains constant.

law of conservation of momentum: the law that states that the total momentum before a collision is equal to the total momentum after the collision if no external forces act on the system.

law of reflection: a law for mirrors that states that the angle of incidence is equal to the angle of reflection.

laws of physics: the universal and invariable facts of the physical word; may be disproved if new facts or evidence contradicts them.

longitudinal wave: a wave in which the motion of the medium is parallel to the direction of the motion of the wave.

Lyman series: the ultraviolet light rays of the hydrogen electromagnetic spectrum that are not visible to the human eye.

M

magnetic field: a region of space where magnetic forces act on objects.

mass defect: the difference in mass between the nucleon inside the nucleus and a nucleon as isolated particles.

mass: the amount of matter in an object.

mechanical energy: the sum of kinetic energy and potential energy.

medium: the material through which a wave can travel.

meson: a virtual particle that produces the strong nuclear force of an atom; the protons and neutrons exchange mesons, the neutrons and neutrons exchange mesons.

model: a conceptual representation of a process, system, or object.

momentum: the product of the mass and the velocity of an object; momentum is a vector quantity.

N

negative acceleration: a change in the velocity with respect to time of an object by decreasing speed in the positive direction or increasing speed in the negative direction.

neutron: a subatomic particle that is part of the structure of the atomic nucleus; a neutron is electrically neutral.

Newton's first law of motion: in the absence of an unbalanced force, an object at rest remains at rest, and an object already in motion remains in motion with constant speed in a straight-line path.

Newton's law of universal gravitation: all bodies with mass attract all other bodies with mass; the force is proportional to the product of the two masses and gets stronger as either mass gets larger; the force decreases as the square of the distance between the two bodies increases.

Newton's second law of motion: the acceleration of an object is directly proportional to the unbalanced force acting on it and inversely proportional to the object's mass. The direction of the acceleration is the same as the direction of the unbalanced force.

Newton's third law of motion: forces come in pairs; the force of object A on object B is equal in strength and opposite in direction to the force of object B on object A.

node: region where the waves cancel each other out.

normal force: the force acting perpendicularly or at right angles to a surface.

nuclear fission: a nuclear reaction in which a massive, unstable nucleus splits into two or more smaller nuclei with the release of a large amount of energy.

nuclear fusion: a nuclear reaction in which nuclei combine to form more massive nuclei with the release of a large amount of energy.

nucleon: a nuclear particle that is either a neutron or a proton.

nucleus: the positively charged mass of an atom surrounded by electrons.

O

ohm: the SI unit of electrical resistance; the symbol for ohm is Ω.

Ohm's law: as the voltage increases at a fixed rate the current increases at the same rate.

P

parallel circuit: a circuit that provides separate paths for current to travel through each resistor; the same voltage is provided across each resistor.

parent nuclei: the original nuclei of atoms before they undergo decay.

particle: a model that describes localized bits of matter.

particle–antiparticle annihilation: the process in which a particle and an antiparticle collide and their mass becomes energy; a model that describes localized bits of matter.

Paschen series: the infrared red light rays of the hydrogen electromagnetic spectrum.

penumbra: the part of the shadow that gets partial light.

period: the time required to complete once cycle of a wave; usual symbol is T.

periodic wave: a repetitive series of pulses; a wave sequence in which the particles of the medium undergo periodic motion: that is, after a fixed amount of time, the medium returns to its starting point and then repeats oscillation.

photoelectric effect: the emission of electrons from certain metals when light (electromagnetic radiation) of certain frequencies shines on the metals.

photon: a particle of electromagnetic radiation; a quantum of light energy.

pion: a meson exchanged between protons or neutrons; a pion carries either a positive (+) charge, a negative (−) charge, or no (0) charge.

pitch: (in music) how high or low a note is.

positive acceleration: an increase in velocity with respect to time. The object can speed up (20 m/s to 30 m/s) or slow down (-20 m/s to -10 m/s).

positive ion: an ion created when a neutral atom loses its electron.

positron: a nuclear particle identical to the electron but with a positive charge.

potential energy: energy that is dependent on the position of an object.

power: the work done divided by the time elapsed; the speed at which work is done and energy is transferred.

precision: an indication of the frequency with which a measurement produces the same results.

pressure: force per area where the force is normal (perpendicular) to the surface; measured in N/m^2 (newtons per meter squared) or Pa (pascals).

probability: a measure of the likelihood of a given event occurring.

projectile: an object traveling through the air or other medium with no power source of its own.

proton: a subatomic particle that is part of the structure of the atomic nucleus; a proton is positively charged ($+1.6 \times 10^{-19}$ C) with a mass of 1.7×10^{-27} kg.

Q

quantum: smallest, indivisible unit of charge that cannot be further subdivided.

R

radiation: the transfer of heat energy by emission of electromagnetic radiation in all directions.

radioactive decay: a term applied to an atom that has an unstable nucleus and can spontaneously emit a particle and become the nucleus of another atom.

random error: an error that cannot be corrected by calculation.

range: the total horizontal distance that a projectile travels.

reaction distance: the distance that a vehicle travels in the time it takes the driver to react.

reaction time: the time it takes to respond to a situation.

real image: an image that can be projected on a screen or on the film of a camera. The rays of light actually pass through the image location.

reflected ray: the ray of light that reflects off a surface.

resistor: an electronic device that opposes (provides resistance to) an electric current.

S

scalar: a quantity that has magnitude (size/amount), but no direction.

second law of thermodynamics: thermal energy is transferred from hot objects to cold objects and never goes from cold to hot spontaneously.

series circuit: a circuit in which the current flows in a single line, so that all resistance in the circuit (light bulbs, and so on) has the same current flowing through them.

sink: (in physics) a place where things are stored.

Snell's law: the relationship between the index of refraction and the ratio of the sine of angle of incidence to the sine of angle of refraction at the boundary of the two media where refraction takes place.

solenoid: a coil of wire wrapped around a core of some material that provides a magnetic field when an electric current is passed through the coil.

specific heat: the heat energy required to raise the temperature of a mass of a substance a given temperature interval.

spectral lines: the lines of different colors that tell something about the structure of an element.

speed: the distance traveled divided by the time elapsed; speed is a scalar quantity, it has no direction.

spring potential energy: the energy stored in a spring due to its compression or stretch; also see elastic potential energy.

standing wave: a wave pattern that remains in a constant position; stationary wave.

stationary wave: a wave pattern that remains in a constant position; a stationary wave.

strong force: a strong nuclear force that hold neutrons and protons together in the nucleus of an atom; the force operates only over very short distances.

subtractive color mixing: mixing pigments or dyes that absorb light of different colors.

systematic error: an error produced by using the wrong tool or using the tool incorrectly for measurement and can be corrected by calculation.

T

tangent line: a straight line that touches a curve in only one point.

temperature: a measure of the average kinetic energy of the molecules of a material.

terminal velocity: the speed reached by an object falling through a viscous medium when the force of air resistance equals the force of gravity on the object.

thermal energy: a form of energy that results from the motions of atoms and molecules; the energy associated with the temperature of a substance.

thermodynamics: the study of the relationships between heat and other forms of energy and the transformation of one form into another.

threshold frequency: frequencies of light, above a minimum threshold frequency, that can free an electron.

total internal reflection: a phenomenon in which the refracting medium acts like a perfect mirror and the reflected light stays inside the medium.

trajectory: the path followed by an object that is launched into the air.

transformer: a device that transfers electrical energy from one circuit to another through electromagnetic induction and, in the process, changes voltage from one value to another.

transverse wave: a wave in which the motion of the medium is perpendicular to the motion of the wave.

trough: the lowest point of displacement of a wave.

U

umbra: the part of the shadow that gets no light.

V

variable: something that can change or vary during an investigation.

vector: a quantity that has both magnitude (size/amount) and direction.

velocity: the speed in a given direction; displacement divided by the time interval; velocity is a vector quantity, it has magnitude and direction.

vibrate: to produce a sound by an object moving back and forth rapidly.

virtual image: an apparent image from which light rays appear to diverge; it cannot be projected on a screen or on the film of a camera. Light rays do not actually converge at the virtual image location.

virtual particle: a particle exchanged between two interacting subatomic particles. The particles is exchanged so fast and at such a short distance that it can only be observed indirectly by its effects.

volt: the SI unit of electric voltage or potential; one volt is equal to one joule per coulomb (1 V = 1 J/C).

voltage: the energy (in joules) for each coulomb of charge.

W

watt: the SI unit of power; one watt is equal to one joule per second (1 W = 1 J/s).

wave: a transfer of energy with no net transfer of mass; a model that describes transfer of motion without the transfer of matter.

wavelength: the distance between two identical points in consecutive cycles of a wave.

wave-particle duality: the use of two models of light to explain the behavior of light — both as a particle and as a wave.

weight: the vertical, downward force exerted on a mass as a result of gravity.

whiplash: the common name for a type of neck injury to muscles of the neck.

work: the product of displacement and the force in the direction of the displacement the energy transferred to an object.

Z

zeroth law of thermodynamics: if two objects have the same temperature as a third object, then the two objects must also have the same temperature.

Glosario

A

aceleración/acceleration: el cambio en velocidad por unidad de tiempo; la aceleración es un vector de cantidad, tiene magnitud (tamaño) y dirección.

aceleración centrípeta/centripetal acceleration: la aceleración de un objeto hacia el centro de un círculo experimentado por un objeto viajando en una trayectoria circular a una velocidad constante.

aceleración negativa/negative acceleration: un cambio en la velocidad con respecto al tiempo de un objeto por medio de la disminución en velocidad en la dirección positiva o aumentando la velocidad en la dirección negativa.

aislador/insulator: un material a través del cual la corriente eléctrica no puede moverse fácilmente; el aire, vidrio, plástico, caucho, y madera son ejemplos de aisladores.

amperio/ampere: la unidad de corriente SI; un amperio es el flujo de corriente de un culombio/ segundo (1 A = 1 C/s).

amplitud/amplitude: el desplazamiento máximo de una partícula cuando está pasando una onda; la altitud de una cresta de onda; está relacionada con la energía de la onda.

ángulo crítico/critical angle: el ángulo de incidencia, para un rayo de luz pasando de un medio a otro, que tiene un ángulo de refracción de 90°.

ángulo de incidencia/angle of incidence: el ángulo formado entre un rayo incidente y la normal a la superficie.

ángulo de reflexión o reflectivo/angle of reflection: el ángulo formado entre un rayo reflejado y la normal a la superficie.

aniquilación partícula-antipartícula/ particle-antiparticle annihilation: el proceso en el cual una partícula y una antipartícula chocan y sus masas se convierten en energía; un modelo que describe pedazos pequeños de materia localizados.

antinodo/antinode: un punto en una onda estacionaria donde el desplazamiento es el mayor y el medio está en su máximo.

aceleración positiva/positive acceleration: un aumento en velocidad con respecto al tiempo. El objeto puede acelerar hasta (20 m/s a 30 m/s) o reducir (-20 m/s a -10 m/s).

átomo/atom: la partícula más pequeña de un elemento que tiene todas las propiedades de ese elemento; consiste de un núcleo rodeado por electrones.

B

barión/baryon: un grupo de partículas elementales que son afectadas por la fuerza nuclear; los neutrones y protones pertenecen a este grupo.

batería/battery: un artefacto electrónico que almacena energía eléctrica potencial.

C

calor/heat: energía transferida de un lugar a otro por virtud de una diferencia en temperatura, resultante del movimiento de átomos y moléculas.

calor específico/specific heat: la energía de calor requerida para aumentar la temperatura de una masa de una sustancia a un intervalo de temperatura dada.

campo gravitacional/gravitational field: la influencia gravitacional en el espacio alrededor de un objeto masivo.

campo magnético/magnetic field: una región del espacio donde las fuerzas magnéticas actúan sobre los objetos.

carga eléctrica/electric charge: una propiedad fundamental de la materia; la carga es o negativa o positiva.

centro de masa/center of mass: el punto en el cual se considera concentrada toda la masa de un objeto.

circuito eléctrico/electrical circuit: una ruta a lo largo de la cual la electricidad puede fluir.

circuito paralelo/parallel circuit: un circuito que provee rutas separadas para que la corriente viaje a través de cada resistor; el mismo voltaje es provisto a través de cada resistor.

circuito en serie/series circuit: un circuito en el cual la corriente fluye en una línea sencilla, de manera que toda la resistencia en el circuito (bombillas, etc.) tienen la misma corriente fluyendo a través de ellas.

coeficiente de fricción móvil/coefficient of sliding friction: una cantidad sin dimensión simbolizada por la letra griega μ; su valor depende de las propiedades de las dos superficies en contacto y se utiliza para calcular la fuerza de fricción.

conducción/conduction: la transferencia de energía térmica de partícula a partícula entre sustancias a través del contacto o dentro de una sustancia.

conductor/conductor: un material a través del cual la corriente eléctrica se puede mover fácilmente; los metales son buenos conductores.

conservación de carga/conservation of charge: la carga total de un sistema aislado antes de que un evento iguale la carga eléctrica total después del evento.

corriente alterna (CA)/alternating current (AC): una corriente eléctrica que cambia de dirección.

convección/convection: la transferencia de energía térmica a través del movimiento de corrientes de aire o líquidas.

corriente/current: el ritmo del flujo de carga eléctrica; la cantidad de culombios pasando un punto en un segundo.

corriente directa/direct current: una corriente eléctrica fluyendo en una sola dirección.

cortacircuito o interruptor de circuito/ circuit breaker: un artefacto colocado en un circuito eléctrico que opera como un interruptor automático que abre el circuito cuando fluye demasiada corriente a través de él.

cresta/crest: el punto más alto de desplazamiento de una onda.

culombio/coulomb: la unidad de carga SI; un culombio (1 C) es aproximadamente igual a la carga de un rayo, la carga de 6.25×10^{18} electrones.

D

defecto de masa/mass defect: la diferencia en masa entre el nucleón dentro del núcleo y un nucleón como partículas aisladas.

desintegración alfa/alpha decay: los cambios que ocurren cuando un núcleo pesado e inestable que libera parte de su exceso de energía emitiendo un núcleo de helio-4 (partícula alfa).

desintegración beta/beta decay: el cambio que ocurre cuando un neutrón en un núcleo inestable se convierte en un protón más electrón (partícula beta).

desintegración gamma/gamma decay: el cambio que ocurre cuando un núcleo excitado emite alguna de su energía en exceso en la forma de un fotón de alta energía (partícula gamma).

desintegración radioactiva/radioactive decay: un término aplicado a un átomo que tiene un núcleo inestable y puede emitir espontáneamente una partícula y convertirse en el núcleo de otro átomo.

desplazamiento/displacement: la diferencia en posición entre una posición final y una inicial; depende solamente de los extremos, no del trayecto; desplazamiento es un vector de cantidad, tiene magnitud (tamaño) y dirección.

diagrama de cuerpo libre/free-body diagram: un diagrama que muestra las fuerzas que actúan sobre un objeto.

diagrama de Feynman/Feynman diagram: un diagrama que muestra el intercambio de partículas virtuales.

difracción/diffraction: la capacidad de una onda para dispersarse o cambiar de dirección mientras emerge de una apertura o se mueve más allá de una obstrucción.

distancia de reacción/reaction distance: la distancia a la que viaja un vehículo en el tiempo que le toma al conductor reaccionar.

dualidad onda-partícula/wave-particle duality: el uso de dos modelos de luz para explicar el comportamiento de la luz –ambos como una partícula y como una onda.

E

efecto Doppler/Doppler effect: el cambio en el tono, o la frecuencia de un sonido (o la frecuencia de una onda) para un observador que se está moviendo con respecto a la fuente del sonido (o fuente de la onda).

efecto fotoeléctrico/photoelectric effect: la emisión de electrones de ciertos metales cuando la luz (radiación electromagnética) de ciertas frecuencias brilla en los metales.

electroimán/electromagnet: cualquier campo magnético creado por una corriente.

electrón/electron: una partícula subatómica de carga negativa con una carga de 1.6×10^{-19} C (culombios) y una masa de 9.1×10^{-31} kg.

energía cinética/kinetic energy: asociada con movimiento; la energía que un objeto posee debido a su velocidad.

energía de ionización/ionization energy: la energía requerida para liberar un electrón de su nivel de energía.

energía mecánica/mechanical energy: la suma de energía cinética y energía potencial.

energía potencial/potential energy: energía que es dependiente de la posición de un objeto.

energía potencial elástica/elastic potential energy: la energía de un resorte debido a su compresión o estiramiento; véase también energía potencial de resorte.

energía potencial eléctrica (potencial eléctric)/electric potential energy (electric potential): la energía potencial por unidad de carga; voltaje.

energía potencial gravitacional/ gravitational potential energy: la energía que un cuerpo posee como resultado de su posición en un campo gravitacional.

energía potencial de resorte/spring potential energy: la energía almacenada en un resorte debido a su compresión o estiramiento; véase además la energía potencial elástica.

energía térmica/thermal energy: una forma de energía que resulta del movimiento de átomos y moléculas; la energía asociada con la temperatura de una sustancia.

energía de enlace/binding energy: la energía requerida para remover un electrón o nucleón de un átomo.

entropía/entropy: una propiedad termodinámica de una sustancia asociada con el grado de desorden en la sustancia; una sustancia es más ordenada como un sólido que un líquido, y un líquido es más ordenado que un gas.

error al azar/random error: un error que no puede ser corregido por medio de los cálculos.

error sistemático/systematic error: un error producido usando la herramienta incorrecta o usando la herramienta incorrectamente para la medición y puede ser corregida por medio de cálculos.

escalar/scalar: una cantidad que tiene magnitud (tamaño/cantidad), pero sin dirección.

espejo cóncavo/concave mirror: un espejo curvo en el cual la superficie reflejada se hunde hacia adentro.

espejo convexo/convex mirror: un espejo curvo en el cual la superficie reflejada está arqueada hacia afuera.

exactitud/accuracy: una indicación de cuán cercanas están una serie de medidas al valor aceptado.

F

fisión nuclear/nuclear fission: una reacción nuclear en la cual un núcleo masivo e inestable se divide en dos o más núcleos pequeños similares con la liberación de una gran cantidad de energía.

fotón/photon: una partícula de radiación electromagnética; un quántum de energía de luz.

frecuencia/frequency: la cantidad de ondas producidas por unidad de tiempo; la frecuencia es el recíproco de la cantidad de tiempo que le toma a una longitud de onda sencilla pasar un punto.

frecuencia umbral/threshold frequency: frecuencias de luz, sobre una frecuencia umbral mínima, que puede liberar un electrón.

fricción/friction: una fuerza que actúa para resistir el movimiento relativo o intento de movimiento de objetos cuyas superficies están en contacto una con la otra.

fuerza/power: el trabajo hecho dividido por el tiempo transcurrido; la velocidad a la cual el trabajo se lleva a cabo y la energía es transferida.

fuerza/force: un empuje o un tirón; una interacción entre dos objetos que puede resultar en una aceleración de uno o ambos objetos.

fuerza centrípeta/centripetal force: una fuerza dirigida hacia el centro que causa que un objeto siga una trayectoria circular a una velocidad constante.

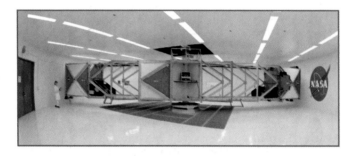

fuerza normal/normal force: la fuerza actuando perpendicularmente o en ángulos rectos a una superficie.

fusible/fuse: un artefacto colocado en un circuito eléctrico que se derrite cuando pasa demasiada corriente a través de él, por lo tanto rompiendo el circuito; éste protege de daño las otras partes del circuito debido al paso de demasiada corriente.

fusión nuclear/nuclear fusion: una reacción nuclear en la cual núcleos se combinan para formar núcleos más masivos con la liberación de una gran cantidad de energía.

G

galvanómetro/galvanometer: un instrumento utilizado para detectar y medir una corriente eléctrica.

generador/generator: un artefacto que produce electricidad.

gravedad/gravity: la fuerza de atracción entre dos cuerpos debido a sus masas.

I

imagen real/real image: una imagen que puede ser proyectada en una pantalla o en la película de una cámara fotográfica. Los rayos de luz pasan actualmente a través de donde está la localización de la imagen.

imagen virtual/virtual image: una imagen aparente de la cual los rayos de luz parecen divergir; no puede ser proyectada en una pantalla o la película de una cámara fotográfica. Los rayos de luz actualmente no se cruzan en el punto de la imagen virtual.

impulso/impulse: un cambio en momento de un objeto.

interacción fuerte/strong force: una fuerza nuclear fuerte que mantiene los neutrones y protones juntos en el núcleo de un átomo; la fuerza opera sólo sobre distancias muy cortas.

interferencia constructiva/constructive interference: el resultado de añadir ondas cresta-a-cresta para producir una onda con una mayor amplitud.

interferencia destructiva/destructive interference: el resultado de añadir ondas cresta-a-seno para producir una onda con una amplitud reducida.

índice de refracción/index of refraction: una propiedad de los materiales en un punto de contacto que determina la relación entre el ángulo de incidencia y el ángulo de refracción.

inercia/inertia: la tendencia natural de un objeto a mantenerse en reposo o mantenerse en movimiento con una velocidad constante en una línea recta.

ión positivo/positive ion: un ión creado cuando un átomo neutral pierde su electrón.

ionización/ionization: el proceso en el cual un átomo neutral se convierte en un ión.

J

julio/joule: la unidad SI para todas las formas de energía.

L

latigazo/whiplash: el nombre común para un tipo de lesión a los músculos del cuello.

lente convergente/converging lens: un lente que es más grueso en el centro y más delgado hacia el borde. Los rayos que entran al lente paralelos al eje del lente convergerán hacia el eje y cruzarán el eje en la parte más lejana del lente en el punto focal; un lente convexo.

lente convexo/convex lens: un lente que es más grueso en el centro y más delgado hacia el borde. Los rayos que entran al lente paralelos al eje del lente convergerán hacia el eje y cruzarán el eje en la parte más lejana del lente en el punto focal; un lente convergente.

Ley de Coulomb de atracción y repulsión eléctrica/Coulomb's law of electrical attraction or repulsion: La fuerza de atracción entre dos cargas es directamente proporcional al producto de las cargas e inversamente proporcional a la distancia entre ellas.

Ley de conservación de energía/law of conservation of energy: la ley que afirma que la energía en un sistema cerrado no puede ser creada o destruida; puede ser transformada de una forma a otra, pero el total de la cantidad de energía permanece constante.

Ley de conservación del momento/law of conservation of momentum: la ley que afirma que el momento total antes de un choque es igual al momento total después del choque si ninguna fuerza externa actúa en el sistema.

Ley de la gravitación universal de Newton/ Newton's law of universal gravitation: todos los cuerpos con masa atraen todos los otros cuerpos con masa; la fuerza es proporcional al producto de las dos masas y se vuelve más fuerte en la medida que cualquiera de ellas aumenta; la fuerza disminuye mientras el cuadrado de la distancia entre los dos cuerpos aumenta.

Ley de Hooke/Hooke's law: la fuerza restaurada ejercida por un resorte es directamente proporcional a la distancia del estiramiento o compresión del resorte.

Ley de Ohm/Ohm's law: mientras el voltaje aumenta a un ritmo fijo la corriente aumenta al mismo ritmo.

Ley de reflexión/law of reflection: una ley para los espejos que afirma que el ángulo de incidencia es igual al ángulo de reflexión.

Ley de Snell/Snell's law: la relación entre el índice de refracción y la proporción del seno del ángulo de incidencia al seno del ángulo de refracción en el límite de los dos medios donde ocurre la refracción.

leyes de la física/laws of physics: los hechos universales e invariables del mundo físico; pueden ser refutadas si evidencia o factores nuevos las contradicen.

líneas espectrales/spectral lines: las líneas de colores diferentes que dicen algo sobre la estructura de un elemento.

longitud de onda/wavelength: la distancia entre dos puntos idénticos en los ciclos consecutivos de una onda.

longitud focal/focal length: la distancia del punto focal al espejo.

M

marco de referencia/frame of reference: un punto de ventaja con respecto a cuál posición y movimiento puede ser descrito.

masa/mass: la cantidad de materia en un objeto.

media vida/half–life: la cantidad de tiempo que le toma a la mitad de la muestra cambiar.

medición directa/direct measurement: un método que utiliza un dispositivo de medición para determinar el tamaño de un objeto.

medida indirecta/indirect measurement: una técnica que utiliza proporciones o probabilidad para encontrar una medida cuando la medición directa no es posible

medio/medium: el material a través del cual puede viajar una onda.

mesón/meson: una partícula virtual que produce la fuerza nuclear fuerte de un átomo; los protones y neutrones intercambian mesones, los neutrones y neutrones intercambian mesones.

modelo/model: una representación conceptual de un proceso, sistema, u objeto.

momento/momentum: el producto de la masa y la velocidad de un objeto; el momento es un vector de cantidad.

N

neutrón/neutron: una partícula subatómica que es parte de la estructura del núcleo atómico; un neutrón es neutral eléctricamente.

nódulo/node: la región donde las ondas se cancelan las unas a las otras.

núcleo/nucleus: la masa con carga positiva de un átomo rodeada por electrones.

núcleo hija/daughter nuclei: el núcleo de átomos que han sufrido desintegración.

nucleón/nucleon: una partícula nuclear que es o un neutrón o un protón.

núcleo padre/parent nuclei: el núcleo original de átomos antes de que se desintegren.

número atómico/atomic number: la cantidad de protones en el núcleo.

O

ohmio o ohm/ohm: la unidad SI de resistencia eléctrica; el símbolo para ohm es Ω.

onda/wave: la transferencia de energía sin ninguna transferencia neta de masa; un modelo que describe la transferencia de movimiento sin la transferencia de materia.

onda longitudinal/longitudinal wave: una onda en la cual el movimiento del medio es paralelo a la dirección del movimiento de la onda.

onda periódica/periodic wave: una serie repetitiva de pulsos; una secuencia de onda en la cual las partículas del medio experimentan movimiento periódico; esto es, después de una cantidad fija de tiempo, el medio regresa a su punto de origen y repite entonces la oscilación.

ondas electromagnéticas/electromagnetic waves: ondas transversales que están compuestas de campos eléctricos y magnéticos de oscilación perpendicular que viaje en 3×10^8 m/s en un vacío; ejemplos de las ondas electromagnéticas enumerados en orden de longitud de onda son los rayos gamma, rayos-X, radiación ultravioleta, luz visible, radiación infrarroja, microondas, y ondas radiales.

onda estacionaria/standing wave: un patrón de onda que permanece en una posición constante; onda estacionaria.

onda estacionaria/stationary wave: un patrón de onda que permanece en una posición constante; una onda estacionaria.

onda transversal/transverse wave: una onda en la cual el movimiento del medio es perpendicular al movimiento de la onda.

P

partícula/particle: un modelo que describe pedazos pequeños de materia localizados.

partícula alfa/alpha particle: una partícula de carga positiva emitida por cierto núcleo radioactivo, compuesto de dos protones y dos neutrones.

partícula virtual/virtual particle: una partícula intercambiada entre dos partículas subatómicas interactuando. La partícula es intercambiada tan rápido y a tan corta distancia que sólo se puede observar indirectamente por sus efectos.

penumbra/penumbra: la parte de la sombra que obtiene luz parcial.

período/period: el tiempo requerido para completar un ciclo de una onda; el símbolo usual es T.

peso/weight: la fuerza vertical descendente ejercida sobre una masa como resultado de la gravedad.

pión/pion: un mesón intercambiado entre los protones o neutrones; un pión porta una carga positiva (+), una carga negativa (−), o ninguna carga (0).

positrón/positron: una partícula nuclear idéntica al electrón, pero con una carga positiva.

precisión/precision: una indicación de la frecuencia con la cual una medida produce los mismos resultados.

presión/pressure: fuerza por área donde la fuerza es normal (perpendicular) a la superficie; medida en N/m² (newtons [neutonios] por metro cuadrado) o Pa (pascales).

Primera ley de la termodinámica/first law of thermodynamics: la energía termal añadida a un sistema es igual al cambio en energía interna del sistema más el trabajo hecho por el sistema en su medio ambiente.

Primera ley del movimiento de Newton/Newton's first law of motion: en la ausencia de una fuerza desequilibrada, un objeto en reposo permanece en reposo, y un objeto que se encuentra ya en movimiento se mantiene en movimiento en una velocidad constante en un trayecto en línea recta.

probabilidad/probability: una medida de la posibilidad que ocurra un evento dado.

proyectil/projectile: un objeto viajando a través del aire u otro medio sin una fuente de energía propia.

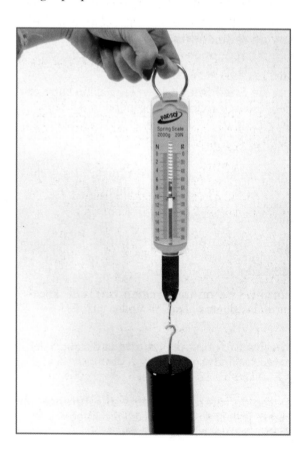

protón/proton: una partícula subatómica que es parte de la estructura del núcleo atómico; un protón tiene carga positiva ($+1.6 \times 10^{-19}$ C) con una masa de 1.7×10^{-27} kg.

puesta a tierra/grounding: el proceso de añadir o remover electrones para regresar a la neutralidad un objeto cargado.

punto focal/focal point: en un lente convexo, el lugar donde los rayos de luz que se acercan al lente paralelos al eje principal convergen en el lado lejano del lente; en un lente cóncavo, el lugar desde donde los rayos que se originaron de los rayos que se acercan al lente paralelo al eje principal parecen divergir.

Q

quántum/quantum: la unidad de carga más pequeña e indivisible que no puede ser dividida nuevamente.

R

radiación/radiation: la transferencia de energía térmica por medio de la emisión de radiación electromagnética en todas las direcciones.

rango, alcance/range: la distancia horizontal total a la que viaja un proyectil.

rayo incidente/incident ray: el rayo de luz que choca con una superficie.

rayo reflejado/reflected ray: el rayo de luz que se refleja de una superficie.

reacción en cadena/chain reaction: una reacción que causa dos o más reacciones similares en un proceso que crece exponencialmente con un tiempo específico duplicado.

reflexión total interna/total internal reflection: un fenómeno en el cual el medio refractor actúa como un espejo perfecto y la luz reflejada permanece dentro del medio.

relación del cuadrado inverso/inverse-square relationship: la relación entre la magnitud de una fuerza gravitacional y la distancia de la masa. Esto describe además cómo las fuerzas electroestáticas dependen de la distancia de una carga eléctrica.

relación directa/direct relationship: una relación en la que al aumentar una variable aumenta la otra variable o al disminuir una variable también disminuye la otra variable.

relación inversa/inverse relationship: una relación en la cual disminuyendo una variable aumenta la otra variable o viceversa.

resistencia del aire/air resistance: una fuerza ejercida en un objeto en movimiento por el aire a través del cual se mueve; la fuerza depende de la velocidad, volumen y masa del objeto así como en las propiedades del aire, tal como la intensidad.

resistencia eléctrica/electrical resistance: la objeción de un material a que una carga eléctrica fluya a través de éste; es la proporción del voltaje a través de un conductor dividido por la corriente.

resistencia/resistor: un dispositivo electrónico que opone (ofrece resistencia a) una corriente eléctrica.

S

Segunda ley de la termodinámica/second law of thermodynamics: la energía térmica es transferida de objetos calientes a objetos fríos y nunca pasa de frío a caliente espontáneamente.

Segunda ley del movimiento de Newton/Newton's second law of motion: la aceleración de un objeto es directamente proporcional a la fuerza desequilibrada actuando sobre ella e inversamente proporcional a la masa del objeto. La dirección de la aceleración es la misma que la dirección de la fuerza desequilibrada.

seno/trough: el punto más bajo del desplazamiento de una onda.

Serie de Balmer/Balmer series: una secuencia de emisión de líneas en la parte visible del espectro electromagnético del hidrógeno.

serie de Lyman/Lyman series: los rayos ultravioleta del espectro electromagnético del hidrógeno que no son visibles al ojo humano.

serie de Paschen/Paschen series: los rayos de luz infrarroja del espectro electromagnético del hidrógeno.

síntesis aditiva de color/additive color mixing: mezclar luces de colores en una pantalla u otro objeto.

solenoide/solenoid: un rollo de alambre envuelto alrededor de un núcleo de algún material que provee un campo magnético cuando una corriente eléctrica pasa a través del rollo.

sumidero/sink: (en física) un lugar donde las cosas son almacenadas.

síntesis sustractiva de color/subtractive color mixing: la mezcla de pigmentos o colorantes que absorben luz de colores diferentes.

T

tangente/tangent line: una línea recta que toca una curva solamente en un punto.

temperatura/temperature: una medida de la energía cinética promedio de las moléculas de un material.

Tercera ley del movimiento de Newton/ Newton's third law of motion: las fuerzas existen en pares; la fuerza del objeto A sobre el objeto B es igual en fuerza y opuesta en dirección a la fuerza del objeto B sobre el objeto A.

termodinámica/thermodynamics: el estudio de las relaciones entre el calor y otras formas de energía y la transformación de una forma a otra.

tiempo de reacción/reaction time: el tiempo que toma responder a una situación.

tono/pitch: (en música) cuán alta o baja es una nota.

trabajo/work: el producto del desplazamiento y la fuerza en la dirección del desplazamiento, la energía transferida a un objeto.

transferencia de calor/heat transfer: la transmisión de energía térmica (de calor) de una sustancia caliente a una sustancia más fría.

transformador/transformer: un artefacto que transfiere energía eléctrica de un circuito a otro a través de inducción electromagnética y, en el proceso, cambia el voltaje de un valor a otro.

trayectoria/trajectory: el curso seguido por un objeto que es lanzado al aire.

U

umbra o cono de sombra/umbra: la parte de la sombra que no recibe luz.

unidad de masa atómica/atomic mass unit: la unidad estándar de una masa atómica basada en el núcleo de un átomo de carbono-12.

V

variable/variable: algo que puede cambiar o variar durante una investigación.

vatio/watt: la unidad de fuerza SI; un vatio es igual a un julio por segundo (1 W = 1 J/s).

vector/vector: una cantidad que tiene ambas, magnitud (tamaño/cantidad) y dirección.

velocidad/speed: la distancia recorrida dividida por el tiempo transcurrido; la velocidad es una cantidad escalar, no tiene dirección.

velocidad/velocity: la velocidad en una dirección dada; desplazamiento dividido por el intervalo de tiempo; velocidad es un vector de cantidad, tiene magnitud y dirección.

velocidad constante/constant speed: la velocidad que no cambia a través de un período de tiempo.

velocidad instantánea/instantaneous speed: la velocidad medida durante un instante: la velocidad mientras se acerca el intervalo de tiempo, pero no se convierte en cero.

velocidad promedio/average speed: la distancia recorrida dividida por el tiempo que toma viajar esa distancia.

velocidad terminal/terminal velocity: la velocidad alcanzada por un objeto cayendo a través de un medio viscoso cuando la fuerza de la resistencia del aire es igual a la fuerza de gravedad en el objeto.

vibrar/vibrate: sonido producido por un objeto que se mueve hacia atrás y hacia adelante rápidamente.

voltaje/voltage: la energía (en julios) para cada culombio de carga.

voltio/volt: la unidad SI de voltaje eléctrico o potencial; un voltio es igual a un julio por culombio (1V = 1 J/C).

Z

Ley Zeroth de termodinámica/zeroth law of thermodynamics: si dos objetos tienen la misma temperatura que un tercer objeto, entonces, los dos objetos deben tener también la misma temperatura.

INDEX

Index

HERFF JONES EDUCATION DIVISION

84 Business Park Drive, Armonk, NY 10504
www.its-about-time.com

Publishing Team

President
Tom Laster

**Director of
Product Development**
Barbara Zahm, Ph.D.

Managing Editor
Maureen Grassi

Project Development Editor
Ruta Demery

Editors
Danielle K. Bouchat-Friedman
Julie Demery
Heidi Doss
Tamara Kathwari
Sampson Starkweather
Daniel M. Wolff

Writer – Physics At Work
Danielle K. Bouchat-Friedman

Editorial Coordinator
Susan Gibian

Equipment Kit Developers
Dana Turner
Joseph DeMarco
Henry Garcia

Indexer
Caryn Sobel

Creative Director
John Nordland

Assistant Art Director
Mauricio Gonzalez

Quality Control
Alexander Mari

Staff Photographer
Jason Harris

Creative Artwork
Thomas Bunk

Illustrators
Sean Campbell
Richard Ciotti
Doreen Flaherty
Fredy Fleck
Roberta Fox
Mark Hannon
Michael Hortens
Marie Killoran
Louise Landry
Scott Petrower
MaryBeth Schulze
Jason Skinner
Rick Wolff

**Production/Studio
Manager**
Robert Schwalb

**Production Studio
Coordinator**
Marie Killoran

Layout Artists
Robert Aleman
Sean Campbell
Richard Ciotti
Sharon Conway
Doreen Flaherty
Fredy Fleck
Mauricio Gomez
Mark Hannon
Marie Killoran
Louise Landry
Tom Lawrence
Scott Petrower
MaryBeth Schulze
Louis Suffredini
Marie Tischler
Stephanie Tothill